29ᵀᴴ EUROPEAN SYMPOSIUM ON COMPUTER AIDED PROCESS ENGINEERING

PART A

29ᵀᴴ EUROPEAN SYMPOSIUM ON COMPUTER AIDED PROCESS ENGINEERING

PART A

Edited by

Anton A. Kiss
The University of Manchester, United Kingdom
Manchester, M13 9PL

Edwin Zondervan
University of Bremen, Germany
D. Bremen, 28359

Richard Lakerveld
The Hong Kong University of Science and Technology
Clear Water Bay, Kowloon, Hong Kong

Leyla Özkan
Eindhoven University of Technology, The Netherlands
Postbus 513, 5600 MB

ELSEVIER

Amsterdam – Boston – Heidelberg – London – New York – Oxford
Paris – San Diego – San Francisco – Singapore – Sydney – Tokyo

Elsevier
Radarweg 29, PO Box 211, 1000 AE Amsterdam, Netherlands
The Boulevard, Langford Lane, Kidlington, Oxford OX5 1GB, UK
50 Hampshire Street, 5th Floor, Cambridge, MA 02139, USA

British Library Cataloguing in Publication Data
A catalogue record for this book is available from the British Library

Library of Congress Cataloging-in-Publication Data
A catalog record for this book is available from the Library of Congress

ISBN (Part A): 978-0-12-819939-8
ISBN (Set) :   978-0-12-818634-3
ISSN: 1570-7946

For information on all Elsevier publications visit our
website at https://www.elsevier.com/

Working together
to grow libraries in
developing countries

www.elsevier.com • www.bookaid.org

Publisher: Joe Hayton
Acquisition Editor: Kostas Marinakis
Editorial Project Manager: Kelsey Connors
Production Project Manager: Paul Prasad Chandramohan
Designer: Greg Harris

Typeset by SPi Global, India

Contents

Methods, models and computational tools for PSE

Preface

This volume of the Computer-Aided Chemical Engineering series puts together a selection of the contributions presented at the 29th European Symposium on Computer-Aided Process Engineering (ESCAPE), held in Eindhoven, The Netherlands, from June 16th to 19th, 2019.

This 29th event of the ESCAPE series is a continuation of the conferences under the auspices of the CAPE Working Party of the European Federation of Chemical Engineering (EFCE), Nederland Procestechnologie (NPT), and Process Systems Engineering NL (PSE-NL).

The conference has been organised since 1992, starting with two meetings in 1992 in Denmark and France, and since then having one event annually. Hosting countries to the conference have been Austria (1993, 2018), Ireland (1994), Slovenia (1995, 2016), Greece (1996, 2011), Norway (1997), Belgium (1998), Hungary (1999, 2014), Italy (2000, 2010), Denmark (1992, 2001, 2015), The Netherlands (2002), Finland (2003, 2013), Portugal (2004), Spain (2005, 2017), Germany (2006), Romania (2007), France (1992, 2008), Poland (2009), and the United Kingdom (2012). Having organised the event in 2002, The Netherlands takes on the torch of research and knowledge exchange with organising ESCAPE-29.

ESCAPE-29 is jointly organized by a team of skilled professionals from Eindhoven University of Technology, Delft University of Technology, University of Twente, and Upfield (The Netherlands), University of Bremen (Germany), The University of Manchester (UK), and The Hong Kong University of Science and Technology (Hong Kong). The main vision was to collaborate in organizing the event and coordinating the scientific program, such that besides traditional themes it offers a platform for additional topics covering a wide range of topics: *from molecule to enterprise*.

The themes of ESCAPE-29 have been selected after a comprehensive discussion with the CAPE Working Party members and the scientific community. The particular topics within these overarching themes have been formulated to allow researchers from CAPE-related sciences to present their results and exchange valuable knowledge and experience. The themes and topics include:

1. **Process-product synthesis, design and integration**: structured products, process integration, single- and multi-objective synthesis and design of processes, modular plants, integration of intensified process units, product-process design: property-prediction- based synthesis and design, synthesis of different supply-chains.
2. **Methods, models and computational tools for PSE**: generation and development of concepts for CAPE/PSE, advances in multi-scale modelling, modelling in different CAPE/PSE applications, numerical methods and tools, numerical analysis, process simulation, large-scale and multi-level optimization, process plant data analysis, agent based modelling.
3. **Process control and operations**: scheduling, operability, flexibility and optimization under uncertainty, supply-chains optimization and logistics,

cyber-physical structures, interaction and information infrastructure, off-line and on-line control, smart sensors, analysis of dynamic plant data, plant-wide control, remote plant control, operational excellence, real-time optimization, operator training.

4. **CAPE/PSE in sustainable development and food industry**: food & water issues, biorefineries, solar refineries, life cycle analysis, industrial infrastructures, infrastructures for sustainable production, sustainability indicators and footprints, risk assessment, safety, waste reduction and management, waste valorisation, waste-water treatment, conversions of fossil-free energy and materials.

5. **CAPE/PSE in energy transition**: heat and power integration, waste-to-energy applications, renewable resources in total-site integration, novel approaches to address the complex system integration challenges, electrification of chemical industry, integration of energy sources and sinks, reliable dynamic supply and demand.

6. **CAPE/PSE in hi-tech micro/nano-devices and processes**: frontiers at tiny scales: micro-, nano scale products & systems, micro- and nano-scale engineering, semi-conductors, solid state, advanced materials, self-assembly, energy storage.

7. **Education in CAPE/PSE & knowledge transfer**: best practices in academia, continued training in a changing professional practice, effective selling of top quality PSE solutions to industry, knowledge transfer hurdles and lessons, effective exploitation of CAPE/PSE tools.

ESCAPE-29 attracted over 300 contributions from five continents (Europe, Americas, Africa, Asia and Australia), and the International Scientific Committee (ISC) selected 120 oral presentations out of these contributions, the rest of them being presented as posters. The scientific program is rounded up by five plenary lectures given by renowned experts from academia and industry, as well as 24 keynotes given by academic and industrial leaders in their field. Putting together all this would have been impossible without the help of 8 topic coordinators, as well as the 86 members of the ISC. We are deeply thankful for timely and careful reviews by these committees, as well as their invaluable help in suggesting plenary and keynote speakers.

As editors of this special volume, we hope that the contributions in this edition of Computer Aided Process Engineering are excellent illustrations of the current state of the art in their respective field.

Anton A. Kiss
The University of Manchester | University of Twente

Edwin Zondervan
University of Bremen

Leyla Özkan
Eindhoven University of Technology

Richard Lakerveld
The Hong Kong University of Science and Technology

Organizing & Scientific committees

National Organizing Committee

Edwin Zondervan (Chair) – University of Bremen
Tony Kiss (Co-chair) – The University of Manchester / University of Twente
Leyla Özkan (Treasurer) – Eindhoven University of Technology
John Posada Duque (Secretary) – Delft University of Technology
Alex Kalbasenka (Infrastructure) – Upfield
Richard Lakerveld (ICT) – The Hong Kong University of Science and Technology

International Scientific Committee

Core members & Editors

Tony Kiss (Chair) – The University of Manchester / University of Twente
Edwin Zondervan (Co-chair) – University of Bremen
Richard Lakerveld – The Hong Kong University of Science and Technology
Leyla Özkan – Eindhoven University of Technology

Topic coordinators

Mariano Martin – University of Salamanca
Alexander Mitsos – RWTH Aachen
Paul van den Hof – Eindhoven University of Technology
Albert van der Padt – Wageningen University / FrieslandCampina
Antonis Kokossis – National Technical University of Athens
Stratos Pistikopoulos – Texas A&M Energy Institute
Ruud van Ommen – Delft University of Technology
Antonio Espuña – Universitat Politecnica de Catalunya

ISC members & reviewers

Jens Abildskov, Technical University of Denmark
Elvis Ahmetovic, University of Tuzla
Cristhian Almeida-Rivera, Organization for the Prohibition of Chemical Weapons
Norbert Asprion, BASF
Ana Paula Barbosa-Povoa, University of Lisbon
Andre Bardow, RWTH Aachen
Sorin Costin Bildea, Politehnica University of Bucharest
David Bogle, University College London
Heiko Briesen, Technical University of Munich
Jose Antonio Caballero, University of Alicante
Kyle Camarda, The University of Kansas
Ana Carvalho, Technical University of Lisbon
Benoit Chachuat, Imperial College London
Xi Chen, Zhejiang University
Calin Cormos, Babes-Bolyai University of Cluj-Napoca
Mircea Cristea, Babes-Bolyai University of Cluj-Napoca
Mario Eden, Auburn University

Sebastian Engell, Technical University of Dortmund
Erik Esche, Technical University of Berlin
Michael Fairweather, University of Leeds
Ferenc Friedler, Pazmany Peter Catholic University
Rafiqul Gani, PSE for Speed
Michael Georgiadis, Aristotle University of Thessaloniki
Krist V. Gernaey Technical University of Denmark
Moises Graells, Universitat Politecnica de Catalunya
Gonzalo Guillén-Gosálbez, Imperial College London
Iiro Harjunkoski, ABB Corporate Research
Christoph Herwig, Vienna University of Technology
Rene Hofmann, Vienna University of Technology
Radu Ignat, GTC Technology
Megan Jobson, The University of Manchester
Xavier Joulia, Laboratoire de Genie Chimique Toulouse
Eugeny Kenig, University of Paderborn
Achim Kienle, Otto von Guericke University Magdeburg
Jiri Klemes, Brno University of Technology
Emilia Kondili, Technological Educational Institute of Piraeus
Andrzej Kraslawski, Lappeenranta University of Technology
Zdravko Kravanja, University of Maribor
Gregoire Leonard, University of Liege
Filip Logist, BASF
Sandro Macchietto, Imperial College London
Davide Manca, Politecnico Milano
Christos Maravelias, University of Wisconsin-Madison
François Maréchal, Ecole Polytechnique Federale de Lausanne
Emanuele Martelli, Politecnico Milano
Peter Mizsey, Budapest University of Technology and Economics
Ludovic Montastruc, INP ENSIACET
Iqbal Mujtaba, The University of Bradford
Zoltan Nagy, Purdue University
Nikola Nikacevic, University of Belgrade
Nuno de Oliveira, University of Coimbra
Athanasios Papadopoulos, Centre for Research and Technology Hellas
Valentin Plesu, Politehnica University of Bucharest
Luis Puigjaner, Universitat Politecnica de Catalunya
Stefan Radl, Graz University of Technology
Marco dos Reis, University of Coimbra
Panos Seferlis, Aristotle University of Thessaloniki
Juan Gabriel Segovia-Hernandez, Universidad de Guanajuato
Levente Simon, Syngenta Crop Protection
Mirko Skiborowski, Technical University of Dortmund
Sigurd Skogestad, Norwegian University of Science and Technology
Robin Smith, The University of Manchester
Babji Srinivasan, Indian Institute of Technology Gandhinagar

Hirokazu Sugiyama, The University of Tokyo
Constantinos Theodoropoulos, The University of Manchester
Louis van der Ham, University of Twente
Franz Winter, Vienna University of Technology
Yoshiyuki Yamashita, Tokyo University of Agriculture and Technology
Yuan Yao, National Tsing Hua University
Fengqi You, Cornell University
Zhihong Yuan, Tsjinghua University
Victor Zavala-Tejeda, University of Wisconsin-Madison
Lei Zhang, Dalian University of Technology
Jinsong Zhao, Tsjinghua University

Anton A. Kiss, Edwin Zondervan, Richard Lakerveld, Leyla Özkan (Eds.)
Proceedings of the 29th European Symposium on Computer Aided Process Engineering
June 16th to 19th, 2019, Eindhoven, The Netherlands. © 2019 Elsevier B.V. All rights reserved.
http://dx.doi.org/10.1016/B978-0-128-18634-3.50001-1

Economic Nonlinear Model Predictive Control of Multi-Product Air Separation Processes

A. Caspari[a], Y. Martin Pérez[a], Chr. Offermanns[a], P. Schäfer[a], A.-M. Ecker[b], A. Peschel[b], F. Schliebitz[b], G. Zapp[b], A. Mhamdi[a], and A. Mitsos[a,*]

[a]*AVT Process Systems Engineering, RWTH Aachen University, 52056 Aachen, Germany*
[b]*Linde plc, Engineering Division, 82049 Pullach, Germany*
amitsos@alum.mit.edu

Abstract

Multi-product air separation units produce important gases such as nitrogen and oxygen from ambient air. Their high electricity demand suggests an economic advantage of flexible operation depending on fluctuating electricity prices. Flexible operation can be achieved using economic model predictive control by solving an economic dynamic optimization directly on the process controller level. The goal of the controller is to operate economically optimal with respect to operational cost while satisfying product purities and other operational constraints in the presence of disturbances, such as varying feed air temperatures. We solve the resulting large-scale dynamic online optimization problem using a suboptimal method based on direct single-shooting. The results show that economic model predictive control is viable for the optimal operation of air separation units in real-time. We demonstrate that it improves the process economics by around 4% compared to the stationary benchmark operation while satisfying all operational constraints. The control strategy is implemented in Python using a Modelica model and our dynamic optimization framework DyOS.

Keywords: economic model predictive control, demand side management, air separation process

1. Introduction

The integration of renewable energy sources into the electricity grid leads to fluctuating energy prices and promises an economic advantage of flexible process operation and demand side management (e.g., Daryanian et al. (1989); Ghobeity and Mitsos (2010)). This advantage is significant in the case of energy-intensive processes, like cryogenic air separation units (ASUs). Since the dominant time constants of the ASU are in the same range as the electricity price fluctuations, the process dynamics have to be taken into account by the process operation strategy.

Economic nonlinear model predictive control (eNMPC) (e.g., Engell (2007); Amrit et al. (2013) can be used for flexible and economically optimal process operation. To reduce the solution times of the dynamic optimizations required for eNMPC, fast-update methods (cf. Wolf and Marquardt (2016)) have been proposed, which approximate the optimal solution. In the considered suboptimal fast-update methods the iteration number of sequential quadratic programming (SQP) algorithms used for dynamic optimization are restricted (e.g., Diehl et al. (2005)).

The application of eNMPC to an ASU has been in the focus of research recently. Huang and Biegler (2012) used an advanced-step model predictive controller for the rectification column section of a multi-product ASU. However, the heat exchanger and compressor were not considered, although they are main parts of an ASU. Pattison et al. (2016) applied a combined dynamic scheduling and tracking controller approach to a liquid nitrogen ASU. Caspari et al. (2018) applied a suboptimal method to an ASU for liquid nitrogen production based on direct single-shooting.

The application of eNMPC to a complete multi-product ASU comprising a heat exchanger, two columns, a feed air compressor, and additional utilities has not yet been focused on. We show that eNMPC can be applied to realize demand side management without using a scheduling layer for a large-scale process in real-time.

The article is structured as follows: Section 2 describes the process, and process model and the eNMPC framework. Section 3 discusses the closed-loop case-study results before the work is finally concluded in Section 4.

2. Air Separation Process and Economic Model Predictive Control Method

We consider a multi-product ASU producing both liquid and gaseous oxygen and gaseous nitrogen. The flowsheet of the process, shown in Fig. 1, is similar to the one presented by Miller et al. (2008). However, the argon part of the ASU and the nitrogen product liquefier are not considered here. We add an oxygen storage tank to buffer the product to improve the process flexibility. Ambient air enters the process and is compressed at the beginning to 58 bar before one part of the stream is expanded to 5.5 bar and enters the high pressure column (HPC). The other part is cooled down further in the heat exchanger and is fed to the HPC and to the low pressure column (LPC) at a pressure of 1.424 bar.

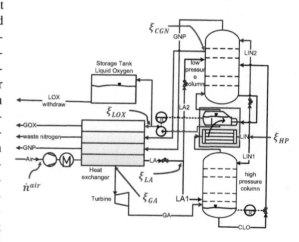

Figure 1: Process flowsheet of the multi-product ASU. The control variables for the eNMPC are illustrated in blue letters. $\dot{n}_{air}$ is the feed air stream entering the process, ξ_i are split factors for the respective streams.

The two columns are interconnected by the heat integrated condenser and reboiler. Gaseous and liquid oxygen product (GOX and LOX, respectively) is withdrawn from the reboiler. The gaseous nitrogen product (GNP) is taken from the LPC top. One part of the oxygen product stream is stored in the buffer tank, the other part is compressed to 5.5 bar and vaporized in the heat exchanger to cool down the feed air stream and exits the process as GOX. We developed a first-principle model of the ASU. The models used are similar to the models used by Huang and Biegler (2012) and Pattison et al. (2016). The main model assumptions are summarized in the following.

Thermodynamics: The vapor-liquid equilibrium is calculated using the isofugacity condition. The vapor pressure of the pure components are computed using the extended Antoine equation. The ideal gas law is used for the vapor phase. The liquid phase activity coefficient is calculated using the NRTL model. All parameter values for the thermodynamic models are retrieved from Aspen Plus version 8.8 (Aspen Technology, 2018).

<u>LPC/HPC:</u> The rectification columns are described by a stage-by-stage model. The column stages are modeled with dynamic MESH-equations using the following assumptions: (i) negligible vapor hold up, (ii) quasi-stationary energy balance, (iii) a constant pressure difference between neighboring stages and (iv) a linear relation for stage hydraulics. We modeled the LPC with 60 stages and the HPC with 30 stages.

<u>Heat exchanger:</u> The heat exchanger is described by a spatially-distributed model discretized using steady-state energy and mass balance equations for the fluid streams and dynamic energy balances for the heat exchanger wall elements. A discretization of 10 segments is used for each stream and the wall. The temperature profile has been regressed as function of enthalpy, pressure, and composition, allowing to handle phase transitions in the heat exchanger easily.

<u>Compressors/Turbine:</u> The compressors and the turbine are modeled using isentropic efficiencies of maximum 80% at steady-state operating point and quadratically decreasing in off-design operation.

The entire model results in a nonlinear index-1 differential-algebraic equation system (DAE) comprising of 300 differential and about 22500 algebraic equations.

2.1. eNMPC framework

In eNMPC, a dynamic optimization problem is solved repeatedly online during process operation on a moving horizon. An economic objective function is minimized subject to a DAE system defined by the model equations and further operational constraints, such as the product quality. As we use a large-scale nonlinear model, the high computational effort for solving the dynamic optimization problem impede real-time tractability and thus the application in process control. To overcome this issue, we use a suboptimal fast-update method (Diehl et al., 2005) to approximate the optimal solution of the dynamic optimization problem. We restrict iterations of the optimization algorithm, such that the optimization stops before the optimality conditions are satisfied. The optimization problems are solved using direct single-shooting (Brusch and Schapelle, 1973; Sargent and Sullivan, 1978), where a DAE integrator is used inside the optimization algorithm to solve the DAE. This guarantees the model equations to be solved exactly within the integrator tolerances at each iteration of the optimization algorithm and the NLP solver does not influence the physical reliability of the solution. In that sense, single-shooting is particularly suited for suboptimal fast-update methods. Moreover, delay compensation by prediction (Wolf and Marquardt, 2016) is used to improve the eNMPC performance; we use the control variable values from the last controller iteration to predict the system state over a time horizon that is defined by the computational time required to solve the eNMPC problem. This leads to a more aggressive controller reaction since the controller has less time to react to potential disturbance. The time delay is estimated a priori. All disturbances that may occur during operation are assumed to be time invariant over the complete control horizon.

2.2. Implementation

We implement the mechanistic model in Modelica (Modelica, 2018). We export it as functional mock-up unit (FMU) (FMI 2 standard, 2014) and use it in the dynamic optimization framework DyOS (DyOS, 2018). We apply the integrator NIXE (Hannemann et al., 2010) and the SQP optimization algorithm SNOPT (Gill et al., 2005). Integrator and optimizer are implemented in C++ and Fortran. Thus, the numerics are performed in those languages. We implement the overall eNMPC framework in Python (Python,

2018). We use a Windows 7 desktop computer equipped with an Intel Core(TM) i3-6100 processor running at 3.7 GHz and 8 GB RAM.

3. Closed-Loop Case-Study

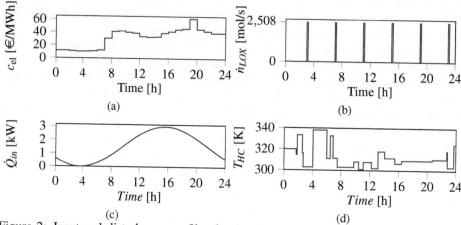

Figure 2: Input and disturbance profiles for the closed-loop case-study. (a) Electricity price of the day ahead auction for the 12th February, 2018 (Epexspot, 2018). (b) Liquid oxygen product rate withdrawn from the storage tank. (c) Heat transfer rate to each tray due to solar radiation. (d) Feed air temperature entering the heat exchanger.

3.1. Operational Scenario and eNMPC formulation

The goal of the eNMPC is to control the process economically optimal with respect to the electricity cost, satisfy the product demand, and reject disturbances. We compare the eN-MPC performance to a constant production rate as benchmark, i.e., time-invariant process input variables. The values of the input variables are the same as the initial input variable values of the eNMPC. We assume full state feedback and the electricity prices profile shown in Fig. 2a. Using the eNMPC problem formulation, we ensure that both the closed-loop process and the benchmark produce the same amount of product. We use an operation scenario where liquid oxygen product is withdrawn from the tank six times every day (cf. Fig. 2b) in an amount that corresponds to the oxygen produced by the benchmark production. This may correspond to product withdrawal and distribution by tank wagons. The eNMPC has to control the process such that the initial storage tank content is achieved again by the end of each control horizon. Additionally, the eNMPC has to guarantee the gaseous oxygen product amount to be the same as in the benchmark by using an end-point constraint. We constrain product purities by path-constraints in order to guarantee the required product quality during the complete time horizon. We bound column stage temperatures to additionally support the product purities. We assume two disturbances during operation: (i) the feed air temperature profile corresponding to temperature fluctuations and (ii) heat streams entering the columns (Fig. 2c and 2d). In the eNMPC, we minimize the economic objective function $\phi = \int_{t_0}^{t_0+\Delta t_c} c_{el}(t)(P_{com}(t) - P_{tur}(t))dt$, where t_0 is the initial time of the eNMPC controller, i.e., the current time on the moving horizon, Δt_c is the control horizon, i.e., the horizon over which the optimization problem is solved in the eNMPC controller, c_{el} is the fluctuating electricity price. P_{com} and P_{tur} are the compressor and turbine electricity demand, respectively. We bound control variables (cf. Fig. 1) by: $\dot{n}_{air} \in [1500, 2800]$ mol/s, $\xi_{GA} \in [0.31, 0.41]$, $\xi_{LA} \in [0.83, 0.9]$, $\xi_{LOX} \in [0.65, 0.84]$,

$\xi_{HP} \in [0.536, 0.579]$, and $\xi_{CGN} \in [0.56, 0.64]$. In order to compare the two operational modes we use the economic improvement measure $\eta = 1 - \frac{\Phi^*_{eNMPC}/n^*_{eNMPC}}{\Phi_{benchmark}/n_{benchmark}}$, where Φ^*_{eNMPC} and n^*_{eNMPC} is the objective function value and the total product amount resulting from the eNMPC controlled closed-loop simulation, respectively, and $\Phi_{benchmark}$ and $n_{benchmark}$ are the respective values corresponding to the constant benchmark operation. An eNMPC sampling time of 7.5 min and a control horizon of 8 h are used. We restrict the SQP algorithm to a single iteration. We assume full state feedback and no plant-model missmatch. Partial state feedback or plant-model missmatch would require the use of state estimation techniques. A PI controller is used for the HPC liquid tank holdup. We use absolute and relative integrator tolerances, and the optimality and feasibility tolerances of SNOPT of 10^{-3}. We select 0.1 as maximum major step length in SNOPT.

3.2. Results and Discussion:

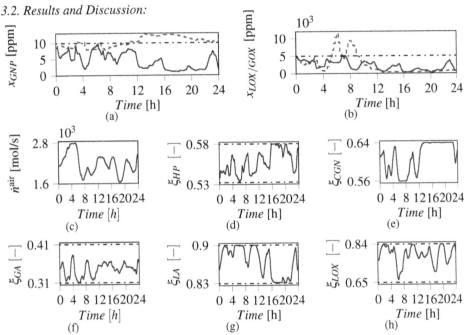

Figure 3: Top: Selected state profiles of benchmark operation (dashed red lines) and closed-loop (solid blue lines) simulation; dash-dotted lines the upper bounds. Rows 2 - 3: selected control profiles of the closed-loop simulation. (a) Impurities of the GNP product stream. (b) Impurities of the LOX and GOX product streams. (c) Feed air stream. (d)-(h) Split factors.

The eNMPC achieves an economic improvement of 3.7 % compared to the benchmark operation. The cost effectiveness can be expected to be further improved by using additional SQP iterations (Caspari et al., 2018). For comparison, we simulated the process benchmark operation, i.e., open-loop without eNMPC, using the same disturbance and electricity price profiles. From Fig. 3a and 3b, we see that the product quality constraints are violated in the benchmark operation due to the presence of the disturbances, as expected. The nitrogen product quality is violated especially in times of high heat streams after 16 h. The oxygen product impurity exceeds its upper bound in those times when the feed air temperature is higher. With eNMPC, the constraints are satisfied, as shown in Fig. 3a and 3b. The corresponding control variable profiles are depicted in Fig. 3c -

3h. We see, that the eNMPC varies the control variables in the whole range within the allowed bounds. The air feed stream (Fig. 3c) is low in times of low electricity prices (Fig. 2a). This is intuitive, since this stream directly corresponds to the electricity consumption of the main compressor. The split factor shown in Fig. 3d corresponds to the reflux ratio of the HP. A high split factor leads to a high reflux ratio and, thus, to higher purities. Increased reflux ratios are, hence, reasonable in times of high heat streams into the column in order to achieve the product purities. The average computational time for the suboptimal fast-update is about 50 s, i.e., about 18% of the control horizon.

4. Conclusion

We present a case study of eNMPC applied to a multi-product ASU based on direct single-shooting.We limit the number of SQP iterations of the NLP solver to reduce compuational time. We use a large-scale first principle model as controller model and considered disturbances in the closed-loop simulation. Using the eNMPC we improved the process operational cost by almost 4 % compared to stationary operation. The constraints that are violated in the benchmark operation are satisfied using the eNMPC operation. The computational times indicate that the method presented is applicable in real time. Further computational time reduction could be achieved using model reduction techniques or further algorithmic improvements, such as neighboring extremal updates (cf. Wolf and Marquardt (2016)), which however require the efficient computation of the second order sensitivities. SNOPT uses a BFGS approximation to calculate these starting with the unity matrix.. The use of exact second order sensitivities can improve both computational times and process economics (Würth et al., 2009).

Acknowledgments: The authors gratefully acknowledge the financial support of the Kopernikus project Syn-Ergie by the Federal Ministry of Education and Research (BMBF) and the project supervision by the project management organization Projektträger Jülich (PtJ). The authors thank J. Faust and F. Jung from AVT for fruitful discussions.

References

R. Amrit, J. B. Rawlings, L. T. Biegler, 2013. Comput. Chem. Eng. 58, 334–343.

I. Aspen Technology, 2018. https://www.aspentech.com/.

R. G. Brusch, R. H. Schapelle, 1973. AIAA Journal 11 (2), 135–136.

A. Caspari, J. M. M. Faust, P. Schäfer, A. Mhamdi, A. Mitsos, 2018. IFAC-PapersOnLine.

B. Daryanian, R. E. Bohn, R. D. Tabors, 1989. IEEE Power Engineering Review 4, 36–36.

M. Diehl, H. G. Bock, J. P. Schlöder, 2005. SIAM Journal on Control and Optimization 43, 1714–1736.

DyOS, 2018. http://permalink.avt.rwth-aachen.de/?id=295232.

S. Engell, 2007. J. Process Control 17, 203–219.

Epexspot, 2018. https://www.epexspot.com/de/marktdaten/dayaheadauktion.

FMI 2 standard, 2014. http://fmi-standard.org.

A. Ghobeity, A. Mitsos, 2010. Desalination 263, 76–88.

P. E. Gill, W. Murray, M. A. Saunders, 2005. SIAM Review 47, 99–131.

R. Hannemann, W. Marquardt, U. Naumann, B. Gendler, 2010. Procedia Comput. Sci. 1, 297–305.

R. Huang, L. T. Biegler, 2012. Comput. Aided Chem. Eng. 31, 1612–1616.

J. Miller, W. L. Luyben, P. Belanger, S. Blouin, L. Megan, 2008. Ind. Eng. Chem. Res. 47, 394–404.

Modelica, 2018. https://www.modelica.org/.

R. Pattison, C. R. Touretzky, T. Johansson, M. Baldea, I. Harjunkoski, 2016. IFAC-PapersOnLine 49, 681–686.

Python, 2018. https://www.python.org/.

R. W. H. Sargent, G. R. Sullivan, 1978. In: Optimization Techniques. Springer-Verlag, pp. 158–168.

I. J. Wolf, W. Marquardt, 2016. J. Process Control 44, 162–183.

L. Würth, R. Hannemann, W. Marquardt, 2009. J. Process Control 19, 1277–1288.

Anton A. Kiss, Edwin Zondervan, Richard Lakerveld, Leyla Özkan (Eds.)
Proceedings of the 29th European Symposium on Computer Aided Process Engineering
June 16th to 19th, 2019, Eindhoven, The Netherlands. © 2019 Elsevier B.V. All rights reserved.
http://dx.doi.org/10.1016/B978-0-128-18634-3.50002-3

From Single Process Simulation and Optimization to Decision Making Based on a Multitude of Solutions

Norbert Asprion,[a,*] Roger Böttcher,[a] Johannes Höller,[b] Patrick Schwartz,[b] Jan Schwientek,[b] Michael Bortz[b]

[a] BASF SE, Chemical Process Modeling, Carl-Bosch-Str. 38, 67056 Ludwigshafen, Germany

[b] Fraunhofer Institute for Industrial Mathematics ITWM, Fraunhofer Platz 1, 67663 Kaiserslautern, Germany

norbert.asprion@basf.com

Abstract

Quite often process simulation is only used as a representation of experimentally developed processes. With today's availability of computation power and advanced simulation and optimization methods much more than providing a closed heat and mass balance and some data for process unit design is possible. There is a need for a shift in paradigm to a model-centric process development. Supporting decision making to find out which design variables or model parameters are significant, which experiments should be done, how optimality could be reached, should be addressed in an iterative workflow and a supporting framework. This is discussed in the present contribution.

Keywords: process simulation, multi-criteria optimization, sensitivity analysis, surrogate modeling.

1. Introduction

Most common process simulation tools are focussing on generating and managing only a single process simulation. However, in process development, for rational decisions in general a broader and more transparent view on achievable simulation and optimization results is desirable. Parallelization reduces computation time to explore the solution space. Therefore, tools for a holistic view on several simulation and optimization runs and for decision support enabling efficient and fast access to large data bases including many simulations are needed. Furthermore, a workflow for an iterative modelling, simulation and optimization should be supported to improve models and results continuously with increasing information and knowledge. The paper is organized as follows: After a brief description of the workflow, examples of applications and visualizations using a multitude of solutions for different tasks within process development will be discussed before a conclusion is given.

2. Process Simulation and Optimization for Decision Making

In the present contribution a concept for an iterative use of process simulation and optimization (cf. Fig. 1) during different stages of process development will be discussed, which relies on comparisons and visualizations of a multitude of process simulations and optimization to support decision making. A more detailed discussion can be found in

Asprion and Bortz (2018). The novelty is the holistic approach to support the various workflow aspects of process development in one simulation environment.

In an early phase of process development, process simulation and optimization might help to identify and compare most promising process concepts. The comparison of Pareto sets (set of best compromises between competing objectives) in a decision support system helps to find sound decisions and allows to investigate trade-offs between the competing objectives. Furthermore, an investigation of the impact of uncertainties (sensitivity analysis) on simulation and optimization results helps to identify model parameters which have to be determined with decreased uncertainty or to minimize risk by a robust or stochastic optimization. This might be useful for the design of mini-plants since in this phase many relationships are rather unclear like for example the impact of impurities on catalyst behavior and expected yield. In a laboratory setup or in a mini-, pilot or production plant, model-based design of experiments enables an efficient (faster, less costly) and effective (doing the right experiments) investigation, which might be used for model discrimination, model parameter estimation or verification of optimization results. Independent of the type of process development – either for a new or an existing plant – in a certain stage there will be plant data available – either from a mini- or pilot plant or from the existing production plant. These data can and should be used for the validation and adjustment of the process model before an extensive simulation or optimization study starts. In case of missing models for specific units greybox modeling can be used to setup a model combining scientific models with data-driven parts (cf. Asprion et al., 2019). Finally, a multi-criteria optimization of the process model will identify Pareto sets for the design of a new plant or design modifications for existing plants. Here again a combination with sensitivity analysis helps to evaluate and/or minimize risks evoked by uncertainties. A framework supporting the workflow of Fig. 1 requires data management and visualization to support decision making and documentation (incl. versioning). Of course, in most cases there will be iteration loops. One such loop might, for example, include design of experiment, experiments in a plant for parameter estimation or for verifying optimization results and subsequent model adjustment until an acceptable parameter estimation or optimization result is obtained. A process simulator should support the different tasks shown in Fig. 1 for an efficient and effective decision making in process development.

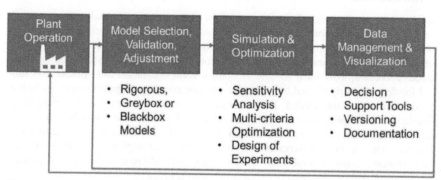

Figure 1: Workflow for an iterative use of process simulation and optimization to support decision making in process development

3. Examples

In the following examples for comparisons of a multitude of solutions including visualization for decision support in different phases of process development are presented.

3.1. Decision support for process concepts

In this example, four different concepts for the separation of three different mixtures of hexane, heptane and octane by distillation are compared based on Pareto sets (cf. Fig. 2). The optimization variables are summarized in Tab. 1. As objectives of the multi-criteria optimization the heptane product purity and the molar flow of heptane are maximized, whereas the total costs are minimized. As constraints the hexane and octane product streams should have a purity ≥ 99 mol%.

Table 1: Range of the optimization variables (N-number of stages, f-feed, sd-side draw, RR-reflux ratio, pf-pre-fractionator, ldw, hdw- lower and higher end of dividing wall, s-split) for the design of the column configurations for the separation of hexane, heptane, octane mixtures (600 kmol/h).

	N_1	$N_{f,1}$	RR_1	N_2	$N_{f,2}$	RR_2	n / kmol/h	n / kmol/h	
Indirect sequence	20-50	5-45	1-5	20-50	5-45	1-5	Hex:320-480; 160-260;60-140	Hep:60-140; 160-260;60-140	
Direct sequence	20-50	5-45	1-5	20-50	5-45	1-5	Oct:60-140; 160-260;320-480	Hep:60-140; 160-260;60-140	
	N_1	$N_{f,1}$	RR_1	N_{sd}			n / kmol/h	n / kmol/h	Constraint
Side-draw	20-50	5-45	1-20	10-40			Oct:60-140; 160-260;320-480	Hep:60-140; 160-260;60-140	$N_{sd} > N_{f,1}$
	N_{pf}	$N_{f,1}$	RR_1	N_1	N_{sd}	N_{ldw}	N_{hdw} S_{ldw} S_{hdw}	n / kmol/h	n / kmol/h
Dividing wall col.	5-41	5-45	1-20	20-50	10-40	1-40	10-50 0,2-0,9 0,1-0,9	Oct:60-140; 160-260;320-480	Hep:60-140; 160-260;60-140

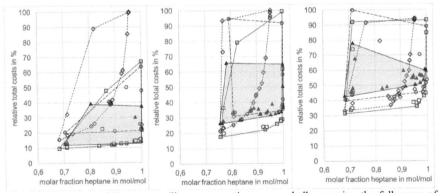

Fig. 2: Comparison of Pareto sets (lines representing convex hulls covering the full range of solutions also for the third objective, i.e. molar flow of heptane, gray area is only for better distinction) of 4 different concepts to separate mixtures of hexane, heptane and octane. ▲ direct sequence of 2 columns, ○ indirect sequence of 2 columns, ◇ side-draw column, □ dividing wall column. Left: light feed (molar fractions: 2/3 hex., 1/6 hep. and 1/6 oct.), middle: equimolar feed, right: heavy feed (molar fractions: 1/6 hex., 1/6 hep. and 2/3 oct.)

As can be seen for all three mixtures, the dividing wall column is the cheapest concept. The side-stream column is only feasible for heptane purities < 95 mol%. In terms of total costs at the same heptane purity, for the mixture with high light boiler (hexane) content, as expected, the direct sequence is more favorable as the indirect sequence, whereas for an equimolar feed both concepts are close to each other and for the mixture with large high boiler (octane) content the indirect sequence is more favorable than the direct one. Methods and further examples how to estimate Pareto sets and how a decision support system can be used to explore trade-offs are described in Bortz et al. (2014), Burger et al. (2014) and Hashem et al. (2017).

3.2. Sensitivity Analysis for Process Design

In this case the impact of uncertainties of an activity coefficient model on the design of a distillation column to separate a methanol-water mixture is considered (similar to Asprion et al. (2015), section 6.2 NQ Curve). In Fig. 3 on the left-hand side the impact of the uncertainties on the McCabe-Thiele can be seen, which look rather small, but since the purity specification of the product methanol is very high, there is a huge impact on the design. For the worst case this results in much higher number of stages required for a constant reboiler duty or significant higher reboiler duties at constant number of stages compared to the nominal model.

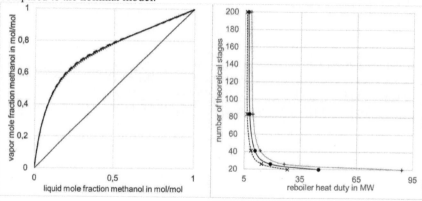

Fig. 3: Impact of uncertainties of a NRTL activity coefficient model for methanol-water on the design of distillation column with high purity of methanol. Left: McCabe-Thiele diagram at 1 bar and right part: N-Q curve for 3 different models: ●, ——: Nominal model, ✕, - - -: model with 10% higher limiting activity coefficient of water in methanol, ✚, ······ model with 10% lower limiting activity coefficient. Uncertainties effect the necessary number of stages and/or reboiler heat duty.

Further examples can be found in Chinen et al. (2018), Bortz et al. (2017), von Harbou et al. (2017) and Asprion et al. (2017), which partly also include examples for robust/stochastic optimization to minimize the impact of uncertainties.

3.3. Surrogate Modeling for Process Optimization

The next example demonstrates that tools originally developed for a different application as described in chapter 2 can be used in different contexts.

In this example for a process model of a cumene plant (for details see Asprion et al., 2017), the whole model is replaced by a surrogate model to be used for a multi-criteria optimization. These results will be compared with the results of the optimization (variables see Table 2) of the original, rigorous process model (cf. Asprion et al., 2017, Fig.7, VLE2; k1; k2) to demonstrate the feasibility of that approach.

In a first step, a sensitivity analysis of the rigorous process model is performed using a Quasi-Monte-Carlo sampling based on Sobol sequences. To start with, this was done in the range given in Table 2, leading however to a very high number (>70%) of infeasible, divergent simulation runs. Therefore, in a second step the range was reduced as given in Table 3. The number of samples (scenarios considered in the sensitivity analysis) was set to 10 per optimization variable yielding in this case 70 samples. From these a subset of 60 could be used to train surrogate models. The setup of the models was done using a functionality originally developed for greybox modeling (cf. Asprion et al., 2019).

Table 2: Range of the optimization variables for optimization of the rigorous process model: inlet temp. of the reactor T_{in}, propen to benzene ratio (p to b), reflux ratio (RR) and logarithmic cumene split ratio (ln(CR)) of column 1 and 2 (cf. Asprion et al., 2017 for details).

	$T_{in}/°C$	p to b	RR_1	$ln(CR_1)$	RR_2	$ln(CR_2)$	load
min	340	0.2	0.1	-12	0.1	-12	0.6
max	400	0.9	1	-1	1	-1	1.2

Table 3: Range of the variables for sampling of the rigorous model based on Sobol sequences (taken from Asprion et al., 2019, supplement, Table A1).

	$T_{in}/°C$	p to b	RR_1	$ln(CR_1)$	RR_2	$ln(CR_2)$	load
min	340	0.5	0.1188	-3.1	0.3	-10.5	0.6
max	345	0.6	0.4188	-2.5	0.4	-9	1.2

The objective *capacity* is proportional to the *load*, which was used directly in the surrogate model. For the objectives *OpEx* (operational expenditure discounted for 10 years per ton of cumene) and *GWP* (global warming potential) artificial neural networks with one hidden and one output layer with 7 neurons each (according to the 7 variables used as input, see Table 3) were trained (regression coefficients R^2=0.99 and 0.92). To account for the 21 constraints used in the original optimization problem, these corresponding functions have also been modeled using neural nets. 15 functions could be modeled without a hidden layer (R^2=0,87-1) and 6 have been modeled (R^2=0,98-1) with a net with the same structure as the net for the objectives *OpEx* and *GWP*. All nets use a α-sigmoid function with α=2. These models have been used in a multi-criteria optimization: minimizing *OpEx*, *GWP*, *load* and maximizing *capacity* as can be seen in Fig. 4.

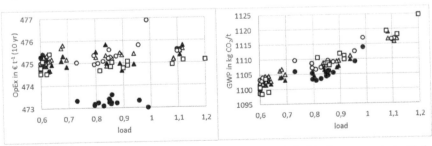

Fig. 4: Comparison of the results of a rigorous process model (□, O, △) of a cumene plant with the results of different versions of a surrogate model (●, ▲). First a surrogate model has been created using a quasi-Monte-Carlo sampling (Sobol sequences) of the rigorous model. This model has been used for multi-criteria optimization (●) and is compared with the optimization results of the original model (□). Verification with the rigorous model using the optimization variables of the surrogate (O) shows larger deviation. Therefore, this data has been added and used to retrain the surrogate. ▲, △ are representing the results of the optimization of the improved surrogate and the corresponding verification with the rigorous model.

The surrogate model (●) in general predicts too low values for the objectives and when using the estimated optimization variables as inputs of the rigorous model (○), the objectives are higher than the optimal values of the rigorous model (□). Therefore, in a second iteration the 22 verification runs together with the original samplings have been used to retrain the surrogate model. The optimization with this second surrogate model (▲) shows a good agreement with the objectives obtained from optimizing the rigorous model (□) and also the verification with the optimization variables (△) has only small deviations (mean absolute deviation OpEx < 0,067%; GWP < 0,13%). During the optimization the validity range of the models has been accounted for by using convex hulls, which were used to setup a constraint allowing for an extrapolation of 10% outside the validity range. This is the reason why the load range is not fully covered. One possibility would be to proceed with iterative retraining of the model and optimization until the full range is exploited. The agreement between the objectives of the surrogate and the verification can be used as a stopping criterion for an iterative optimization and retraining of surrogate models.

Further examples for surrogate modeling can be found in McBride and Sundmacher (2019).

4. Conclusions and Outlook

In process development many decisions have to be made concerning process concepts, experiments, models and model parameters, risk quantification and mitigation measures, which can be supported by process modeling, simulation and optimization. As was shown in the examples, it is essential that a process simulator supports methods like for example multi-criteria optimization, sensitivity analysis and surrogate modeling. Here an efficient data management for a multitude of solutions and helpful visualizations are required to enable comparisons, exploring the solution space and thus offering support to arrive at sound, documented decisions.

References

N. Asprion, M. Bortz, 2018, Chem. Ing. Tech., 90, No. 11, 1727–1738.

N. Asprion, R. Benfer, S. Blagov, R. Böttcher, M. Bortz, M. Berezhnyi, J. Burger, E. von Harbou, K.-H. Küfer, H. Hasse, 2015, Chem. Ing. Tech., 87 (12) 1810-1825.

N. Asprion, S. Blagov, R. Böttcher, J. Schwientek, J. Burger, E. von Harbou, M. Bortz, 2017, Chem. Ing. Tech., 89 (5) 665-674, DOI: 10.1002/cite.201600098

N. Asprion, R. Böttcher, R. Pack, M.-E. Stavrou, J. Höller, J. Schwientek, M. Bortz, 2019, Chem. Ing. Tech., 91 (3), DOI: 10.1002/cite.201800086

M. Bortz, J. Burger, N. Asprion, S. Blagov, R. Böttcher, U. Nowak, A. Scheithauer, R. Welke, K.-H. Küfer, and H. Hasse, 2014, Comp. Chem. Eng., 60, 354–363.

M. Bortz, J. Burger, E. von Harbou, M. Klein, J. Schwientek, N. Asprion, R. Böttcher, K.-H. Küfer, H. Hasse, Ind. Eng. Chem. Res. 2017, 56 (44), 12672 – 12681.

J. Burger, N. Asprion, S. Blagov, R. Böttcher, U. Nowak, M. Bortz, R. Welke, K.-H. Küfer, H. Hasse, Chem. Ing. Tech. 2014, 86 (7), 1065-1072.

A.S. Chinen, J.C. Morgan, B. Omell, D. Bhattacharyya, C. Tong, D.C. Miller, 2018, Ind. Eng. Chem. Res., 57 (31)10448-10463

E. von Harbou, O. Ryll, M. Schrabback, M. Bortz and H. Hasse, Chem. Ing. Tech. 2017, 89, No. 10, 1315-1324.

I. Hashem, D. Telen, P. Nimmegeers, F. Logist, J. Van Impe, 2017, Comp. Chem. Eng., 106, 544–558.

K. McBride, K. Sundmacher, 2019, Chem. Ing. Tech., 91, No. 3, DOI: 10.1002/cite.201800091

Anton A. Kiss, Edwin Zondervan, Richard Lakerveld, Leyla Özkan (Eds.)
Proceedings of the 29th European Symposium on Computer Aided Process Engineering
June 16th to 19th, 2019, Eindhoven, The Netherlands. © 2019 Elsevier B.V. All rights reserved.
http://dx.doi.org/10.1016/B978-0-128-18634-3.50003-5

A Framework for the Integration of Holistic Sustainability Assessment in Computer-Aided Molecular Design

Athanasios I. Papadopoulos[a*], Gulnara Shavalieva[b], Stavros Papadokonstantakis[b], Panos Seferlis[a,c]

[a]Chemical Process and Energy Resources Institute, Centre for Research and Technology-Hellas, 57001 Thermi, Greece
[b]Chalmers University of Technology, Department of Space, Earth and Environment, Division of Energy Technology, SE-412 96 Gothenburg, Sweden
[c]Department of Mechanical Engineering, Aristotle University of Thessaloniki, PO Box 454, Thessaloniki, Greedce
spapadopoulos@cperi.certh.gr

Abstract

We propose the integration of a holistic sustainability assessment framework in computer-aided molecular design (CAMD). The framework enables the assessment of life cycle (LCA) and safety, hazard and environmental (SHE) impacts from cradle-to-gate of chemicals designed through CAMD. It enables the calculation of an overall of 14 sustainability-related indices, with some of them aggregating several impact categories. Lack of models and data gaps in property prediction are addressed systematically through a data mining approach which exploits on-line similarity assessment with existing molecules for which data exist or can be predicted. The framework is implemented both simultaneously with CAMD or after CAMD to assess the designed solvents. A case study is presented on the design of phase-change solvents for chemisorption-based post-combustion CO_2 capture. Results indicate that the proposed approach enables the identification of verifiably useful phase-change solvents which exhibit favourable performance trade-offs compared to a reference CO_2 capture solvent.

Keywords: CAMD, Sustainability, LCA, SHE, Post-combustion CO_2 capture

1. Introduction

CAMD has been used widely in applications to design molecules of improved performance (Papadopoulos et al., 2018). The most common performance criteria include molecular or process properties pertaining to the thermodynamic and/or process performance of the evaluated molecular structures. While these are very important, the sustainability behavior of the evaluated molecules is also worth investigating; many chemicals exhibit significant environmental, health and safety impacts, rendering them undesired despite their otherwise favorable performance. Previous efforts incorporate sustainability-related considerations into CAMD, such as the work of Ten et. al (2016) where inherent safety and occupational health indices are considered and the work of Khor et. al (2017) which includes safety and health indices to select sustainable solvents for palm oil extraction. While these are among the few works which attempt to consider aspects of sustainability, in most publications the potential impact to the environment is either not assessed or considered to a limited extent through indices such as toxicity, flammability, emissions etc. Systematic sustainability assessment requires a holistic view of the chemical life-cycle, at least considering all the upstream processes employed for the chemical production together with the potential hazards associated with its use. Such an approach, and its incorporation in CAMD, calls for the use of much more comprehensive indices including resource depletion and requirements, energy demands, emissions etc., to achieve a reliable differentiation over a certain, typically large, number of molecules. However, due to data gaps, several of the necessary properties cannot be predicted using group contribution (GC) methods which are predominantly used in existing CAMD implementations. Data mining methods (Lu et al., 2014) can be used to analyse, interpret and exploit molecular similarities to supplement GC models to predict dangerous properties, to potentially improve their predictive capabilities and to expand the range of sustainability indicators that can be predicted. However, such approaches have not yet been investigated as part of sustainability-based CAMD implementations.

2. Proposed approach

2.1 Framework overview

Papadopoulos et al. (2016) proposed the integration of CAMD with sustainability assessment in an approach where the latter was considered as an afterthought to solvent design. We hereby propose for the first time an approach for simultaneous CAMD and sustainability assessment. Compared to Papadopoulos et al. (2016) we employ the same sustainability indicators, but here data gaps in sustainability property prediction are addressed through data mining, while the method may account for solvents exhibiting either vapour-liquid or vapour-liquid-liquid phase-changes.

The framework supports evaluation of two main categories: (1) the holistic environmental benefit at the cradle-to-process gate level and (2) the substance hazard identification for evaluation of the harm potential in accidental scenarios (Table 1). Category (1) is approached through a Life Cycle Assessment (LCA) methodology used to calculate indices such as cumulative energy demand, global warming potential and EI99, with the latter comprising impacts over 11 categories, defining human health, eco-system quality and resource depletion damages. The LCA metrics are predicted by "black box" type models in the form of neural networks based on the molecular structure of the studied compound (for details see Wernet et al., 2009). Category (2) includes safety, health and environmental hazard (SHE) assessment Predictions for the necessary properties are performed using GC models when available. Lack of models and data gaps are addressed systematically through a data mining approach which exploits on-line similarity assessment with existing molecules for which data exist or can be predicted. In SHE assessment, single S, H and E scores are calculated based on various dangerous property values, shown in Table 1. Dangerous property parameters are obtained from a database (if available), calculated by the GC+ method (Hukkerikar et al., 2012a) or estimated by a similarity approach based on the local lazy learning method (LLL). For a given compound with a missing experimental or GC+ method parameter, the LLL method identifies its nearest neighbours (the most structurally similar molecules) in a given dataset and then uses these molecules to predict the compound property as follows:

$$y_{pre} = \sum_{i=1}^{n} \frac{S_i}{\sum_{j=1}^{n} S_j} * y_{i,db} \tag{1}$$

where y_{pre} is the predicted value of the query compound, $y_{i,db}$ is the property value of the i-th nearest neighbour from the dataset, S_i is the Tanimoto coefficient indicating the similarity value between the compound and the i-th neighbour, and n is the optimized number of employed nearest neighbours. Details are reported in Shavalieva et al. (2018).

Table 1: Dangerous properties and estimation methods used for SHE assessment.

Dangerous Property	Parameter	Estimation method
Safety (*S*)		
Mobility	Difference between boiling point of the pure substance and highest process temperature	GC (Hukkerikar et al., 2012b)
Fire/ Explosion	Difference between flashpoint of the pure substance and highest process temperature	GC (Hukkerikar et al., 2012b)
Acute toxicity	$LD50_{oral}$ (rat) – the amount of orally ingested chemical that causes death to 50% of rats (mg/kg body weight)	GC+ (Hukkerikar et al., 2012a
Health (*H*)		
Chronic toxicity	Permissible exposure level (PEL) – a US legal exposure limit (mg/m^3) of an employee to a chemical, given as the average exposure concentration over 8 hours	GC+ (Hukkerikar et al., 2012a)
Environment (*E*)		
Water-mediated effects	Toxicity ($LC50/EC50_{aquatic}$) - concentration (mg/l) of a chemical in water causing death to 50% of most sensitive aquatic species	Similarity (Lu et al., 2014; Shavalieva et al., 2018)
Degradation in the environment	Persistency (days) - half-life of a chemical in the environment (water)	Similarity (Lu et al., 2014; Shavalieva et al., 2018)
Air-mediated effects	Chronic toxicity index	GC+ (Hukkerikar et al., 2012a)
Accumulation	Bioconcentration factor (BCF) assesses chemical accumulation in a living organism.	Similarity (Lu et al., 2014; Shavalieva et al., 2018)

2.2 Incorporation into CAMD

The framework obtains molecular structure information from CAMD and returns the values of the desired sustainability indices. It can be used either simultaneously with CAMD or after the molecules are obtained from CAMD, using criteria to evaluate their sustainability performance. The molecular structures in CAMD are represented by first order functional groups, hence they are compositions of the contained groups and their appearance frequency. For each structure the proposed implementation enables the generation of all potential isomers through RDKIt (Landrum, 2016) in the form of SMILES (Simplified Molecular Input Line Entry System). For each isomer, the corresponding SMILE is further used for the calculation of SHE and LCA scores. LCA values are computed and incorporated to FineChem models (Wernet et al., 2009). Dangerous properties required to compute *S* and *H* scores are generated by the GC+ method (Hukkerikar et al., 2012a). The dangerous property values required for *E* are computed by the similarity and GC+ methods. When the similarity approach is used, the numbers are calculated for each isomer and then averaged to give a single index to be used for *E* score calculation. The outcome of the calculation for *CED*, *GWP*, *EI99*, *S*, *H* and *E* values is returned back to CAMD to be used in the molecule selection process.

3. Case study details and mathematical problem formulation

The aim is to design solvents for chemisorption-based, post-combustion CO_2 capture. In this work we focus for the first time on phase-change solvents, exhibiting vapour-liquid-liquid phase changes, which hold great promise to reduce the regeneration energy requirements of CO_2 capture processes by over 50% (Zhang et al., 2012). Such solvents exhibit a liquid-liquid phase change upon reaction with CO_2 and increase of temperature. This enables mechanical solvent separation prior to introducing a reduced amount of CO_2-solvent product into the thermal regeneration step, which occurs at lower temperature than in conventional solvents, hence reducing regeneration energy. Results from the following cases are discussed:

1) Case A, where we use the proposed sustainability model simultaneously with CAMD.
2) Case B, where solvents are first designed using CAMD and their sustainability characteristics are calculated at a post-design step.

The implementation follows the multi-objective CAMD formulation of Papadopoulos et al. (2016), as shown in Table 2 for cases A (Eq. (2) and (4)) and B (Eq. (3) and (4)). In case B the sustainability properties are evaluated only for the solvents of the Pareto front obtained from CAMD.

Table 2: Mathematical formulation of Cases A and B

Case A		Case B	
$\max\limits_{G} \quad \rho$		$\max\limits_{G} \quad \rho$	
$\min\limits_{G} \quad P_{vp}, C_p, n, RED,$	(2)	$\min\limits_{G} \quad P_{vp}, C_p, n, RED$	(3)
$\quad\quad GWP, CED, EI99, S, H, E$			
s.t. $\quad T_m < T_{Abs}, T_{bp} > T_{Des}, \left\lvert \delta^s - \delta^{CO_2} \right\rvert_{T_{Abs}} < \varepsilon, \left\lvert \delta^s - \delta^{H_2O} \right\rvert_{T_{Des}} > \varepsilon$			(4)

Based on Papadopoulos et al. (2016) density (ρ) should be maximized, whereas vapour pressure (P_{vp}), heat capacity (C_p), viscosity (n) and relative energy difference (RED) should be minimized. RED is a scaled measure of CO_2 solubility in the solvent. Melting point temperature (T_m) should be less than absorption temperature (T_{Abs}) and boiling point temperature (T_{bp}) should be higher than desorption temperature (T_{Des}). The solubility parameter difference between solvent (δ^s) and CO_2 (δ^{CO2}) should be lower than a value ε to ensure solvent-CO_2 miscibility and the same difference between δ^s and δ^{H2O} should be higher than ε at T_{Des} to support liquid-liquid phase separation. We consider the following groups: CH_3-, -CH_2-, >CH-, >C<, -OH, -CH_2-NH_2, -CH_2-NH-, -CH_2-N<, >CH-NH_2, >CH-NH-, CH_3-NH-, CH_3-N<. The total number of groups allowed in each molecule range from 6 to 16, with up to 1 amine group. The latter allows for generation of simpler molecules, with fewer isomers, hence facilitating the use of the similarity approach in Case A. T_{Abs} is set to 40°C and T_{Des} to 90°C. The ε value is set to 7 $(MPa)^{0.5}$ (Papadopoulos et al., 2016). The sustainability indices are calculated as averages over all generated isomers for each molecule. Properties P_{vp}, ρ, δ^s and RED are calculated from Hukkerikar et al. (2012b), n from Conte et al. (2008) and C_p from Kolska et al. (2008).

Comparison between cases is facilitated by an aggregate index J_i to generate Pareto fronts between the index and each property. The latter indicates how the overall performance of each solvent (i.e. in all properties considered simultaneously) is affected by changes in each property separately (Papadopoulos et al., 2016). The resulting multi-criteria selection problem includes the identification of the Pareto structures by generation of a Pareto front per property $j \in Pr$, with $Pr = \{\rho, P_{vp}, C_p, n, RED, GWP, CED, EI99, S, H, E\}$, considering the index J for every molecule i against each one of the properties.

4. Results and discussion

Indicative results are shown in Figure 1 (left) as a Pareto front of RED vs. J, for Cases A and B. The ID numbers correspond to solvents numbered within an original, larger set obtained from CAMD. The Pareto front shows that the two cases include few similar and few different solvents. In the latter case their *RED* and *J* values are close. Due to space limitations the Pareto fronts of all properties against *J* are omitted. Observation of all other diagrams shows similar results to Figure 1 (left), except for properties P_{vp}, *S*, *H* and *E*. Consideration of the latter, results in molecules exhibiting better performance in Case A, compared to Case B. A similar trend also appears in Figure 1 (right). It shows the optimum value obtained for each property in Cases A and B (the values may correspond to a different solvent). Values for the 4 aforementioned properties are clearly different, whereas values for C_p, *n*, *RED*, V_m, *GWP*, *CED* and *EI99* are either the same or similar. A very intense difference appears in P_{vp}. This means that when sustainability is considered during CAMD the designed molecular structures exhibit lower P_{vp}. This indicates a reasonable correlation between high sustainability performance and P_{vp}. Solvents with lower P_{vp} exhibit lower emissions hence enhancing some sustainability indicators. Figure 1 (right) also compares the performance of the obtained molecules with MEA (monoethanolamine), which is the reference solvent in CO_2 capture. In several performance indicators the performance of the obtained molecules is better than MEA.

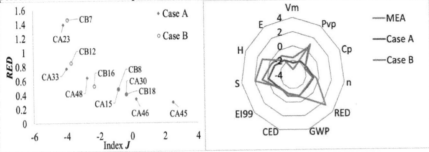

Figure 1: Pareto fronts between RED (sovent-CO_2 solubility) vs. index *J* (left), Optimum property values obtained by solvents in Cases A and B compared to MEA (right).

Table 3: Composition of selected, highly performing solvents from Cases A and B

ID	Groups	Frequency of appearance
CA23	[-CH₃,>CH₂,-OH,-CH₂-N<]	2,3,1,1
CA26	[-CH₃,>CH₂,-OH,>CH-NH-]	2,3,1,1
CA55	[-CH₃,>CH₂,-CH₂-NH-] (DBA)	2,5,1
CB7	[-CH₃,>CH₂,-OH,-CH₂-N<]	2,2,1,1
CB12	[-CH₃,>CH₂,-CH₂-NH₂] (HEXA)	1,4,1
CB16	[-CH₃,>CH₂,-CH₂-NH-] (DPA)	2,3,1

Table 3 shows molecular structures selected through observation of Pareto fronts for all properties vs. index *J*. It includes solvents such as Dibutylamine (DBA), Hexylamine (HEXA) and Dipropylamine (DPA) which are known phase-change solvents (Zhang et al., 2012). This indicates that CAMD identifies such solvents in both Cases A and B. Notice that some structures contain a OH group. In Case A they are 75% of all the designed solvents, whereas in Case B they are only 21% of the entire set. This is a clear indication that when sustainability is considered during CAMD it drives the search toward OH-containing structures. Such structures may not favor phase-change behavior because OH enhances solvent-water miscibility, whereas solvent-water immiscibility is desired. Figure 2 shows the performance of the structures in all properties, compared to MEA. The overall performance, expressed by *J*, is better than MEA for all solvents. In 7 of the 11 properties the performance is better or similar to MEA.

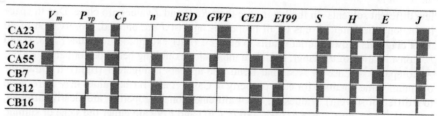

	V_m	P_{vp}	C_p	n	RED	GWP	CED	EI99	S	H	E	J
CA23												
CA26												
CA55												
CB7												
CB12												
CB16												

Figure 2: Performance of selected solvents compared to MEA, blue bars pointing right indicate better performance, red bars pointing left indicate worse performance

5. Conclusions

This work presents the integration into CAMD of a holistic sustainability assessment framework. The framework can used simultaneously with CAMD or after CAMD (sequentially) for the assessment of the designed molecular structures. Implementation shows that both the simultaneous and sequential approaches enable the identification of solvents which are verifiably good candidates for phase-change, CO_2 capture operations. The solvents obtained from the simultaneous approach exhibit a preference toward hydroxyl containing groups which may hinder the appearance of phase-change phenomena in this particular application. The overall performance of the proposed solvents, obtained with both approaches, is better than MEA.

Acknowledgements
This project has received funding from the EU's Horizon 2020 program under agreement 727503 - ROLINCAP – H2020-LCE-2016-2017/H2020-LCE-2016-RES-CCS-RIA.

References

1. Papadopoulos, A.I., Tsivintzelis, I., Linke, P., Seferlis, P., 2018, In: Reedijk, J. (Ed.) Reference Module in Chemistry, Molecular Sciences and Chemical Engineering. Waltham, MA: Elsevier. DOI:10.1016/B978-0-12-409547-2.14342-2
2. Ten, J. Y., Hassim, M. H., Chemmangattuvalappil, N., Ng, D. K. S., 2016, J. Loss Prev. Process Ind., 40, 67-80.
3. Khor, S. Y., Liam, K. Y., Loh, W. X., Tan, C. Y., Ng, L. Y., Hassim, M. H., Ng, D. K. S., Chemmangattuvalappil, N. G., 2017, Process Saf. Environ. Prot., 106, 211-23.
4. Lu, J., Peng, J., Wang, J., Shen, Q., Bi, Y., Gong, L., Zheng, M., Luo, X., Zhu, W., Jiang, H., Chen, K., 2014, J Cheminf., 6(1), 26.
5. Wernet, G., Papadokonstantakis, S., Hellweg, S. Hungerbühler, K., 2009, Green Chemistry, 11(11), 1826-31.
6. Hukkerikar, A. S., Kalakul, S., Sarup, B., Young, D.M., Sin,G., Gani, R., 2012a, J. Chem. Inf. Model., 52 (11), 2823-39.
7. Hukkerikar A.S., Sarup B., Ten Kate A., Abildskov J., Sin G., Gani R., 2012b, Fluid Phase Equilibria, 321, 25–43.
8. Shavalieva, G., Papadopoulos, A.I., Badr, S., Seferlis, P., Papadokonstantakis, S., 2018, Comput. Aided Chem. Eng., 44, 823-28.
9. Landrum, G., 2016. An overview of the RDKit — The RDKit 2018.03.1 documentation. Available at: http://www.rdkit.org/docs/Overview.html [Accessed 5 Nov. 2018].
10. Papadopoulos, A.I., Badr, S., Chremos, A., Forte, E.,Zarogiannis, T., Seferlis, P., Papadokonstantakis,S., Galindo,A., Jackson, G., Adjiman, C.S., 2016, Mol. Syst. Des. Eng.,1 (3), 313-34
11. Zhang, J., Qiao, Y., Agar, D.W., 2012, Energy Procedia, 23, 92-101.
12. Conte E., Martinho A., Matos H.A., Gani R., 2008, Ind. Eng. Chem. Res., 47, 7940-54.
13. Kolská, Z., Kukal, J., Zábranský, M., Růžička, V., 2008, Ind. Eng. Chem. Res., 47, 2075-85.

Anton A. Kiss, Edwin Zondervan, Richard Lakerveld, Leyla Özkan (Eds.)
Proceedings of the 29th European Symposium on Computer Aided Process Engineering
June 16th to 19th, 2019, Eindhoven, The Netherlands. © 2019 Elsevier B.V. All rights reserved.
http://dx.doi.org/10.1016/B978-0-128-18634-3.50004-7

Iterative Medium-Term Production Scheduling of an Industrial Formulation Plant

Vassilios Yfantis[a,*], Thomas Siwczyk[a], Matthias Lampe[b], Nicolai Kloye[b], Manuel Remelhe[b] and Sebastian Engell[a]

[a]*Process Dynamics and Operations Group, Department of Biochemical and Chemical Engineering, TU Dortmund University, Emil-Figge-Str. 70, 44227 Dortmund, Germany*
[b]*Bayer AG, Kaiser-Wilhelm-Allee 1, 51368 Leverkusen, Germany*
vassilios.yfantis@tu-dortmund.de

Abstract

In this contribution, a discrete-time medium-term production scheduling model of an industrial formulation plant for crop protection chemicals is presented. As the optimization model has to provide feasible solutions in a real-world environment, all relevant processing characteristics, as e. g. sequence- and unit-dependent changeovers, timing relations between different units and processing tasks or shift patterns must be represented in order to yield feasible and implementable schedules. In order to cope with the computational complexity of the problem, an iterative scheme is employed in which the production orders are scheduled in a sequential fashion. After each iteration a set reduction step is performed, removing all infeasible unit allocations from the feasible set of the next iteration. The proposed framework is tested on a realistic industrial case study.

Keywords: Production scheduling, MILP Model, Formulation Plants, Optimization

1. Introduction

Scheduling in the process industry describes the allocation of limited resources to manufacture several products over a given time horizon (Méndez et al., 2006). The increased global competition increases the need to generate good production schedules fast and efficiently. In order to satisfy varying customer demands, a key feature of the production systems is a high flexibility, e. g. by multipurpose lines and intermediate storage. This flexibility results in a high complexity of scheduling problems. Due to this inherent complexity, scheduling without optimization support is challenging (Harjunkoski et al., 2014). Rigorous mathematical programming-based solution approaches can find optimal schedules for suitably formulated models. However, for the use of optimization based scheduling algorithms in an industrial environment good schedules must be generated within reasonable response times, but the schedules do not necessarily have to be strictly optimal. A way to shorten the computation time is the combination of exact and heuristic methods. This contribution presents a hybrid approach combining a detailed MILP model and a sequential scheduling heuristic for the fast generation of (sub-) optimal schedules for a formulation plant.

2. Case Study

The formulation plant for the production of crop protection chemicals which is considered in this contribution is depicted in Fig. 1. After an initial raw material pre-processing step which mainly includes the preparation of the active ingredient (AI) and solvents, a standardization (mixing)

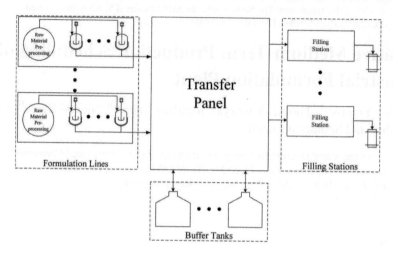

Figure 1: Schematic representation of an industrial formulation plant.

operation is performed in one of several identical standardization tanks within the formulation line, which process batches of a fixed and unit specific size. After a minimum standardization time has elapsed, the finished product can be sent to a filling station where it is filled with an order and unit specific flowrate, resulting in the final product. Since the plant includes fewer filling stations than standardization tanks and the filling stations operate on a shift system with two working and one non-working (night) shift, the filling step constitutes the bottleneck of the production. In order to utilize the full capacity of the plant, the formulation lines and filling stations are decoupled through the use of buffer tanks for finite intermediate storage. The transfer times between the standardization and buffer tanks can be neglected, while the transfer times between the different tanks and the filling stations depend on the flowrate of of the latter, since the tanks are gradually drained by the connected filling stations. The objective of the optimization is to satisfy all customer orders over a given time horizon, while minimizing the makespan. The due dates usually lie beyond the scheduling horizon and are considered here.

3. Solution Approach

In order to solve the scheduling problem, a hybrid approach is chosen in which an MILP optimization model is combined with a heuristic. Both elements of the scheduling framework are presented in the following sections.

3.1. MILP Model

The optimization model is based on a discrete representation of time (Méndez et al., 2006), in which a set of orders I are processed in the available units J over a scheduling horizon $T_H = \{1, \ldots, H, H+1\}$, while the makespan is to be minimized. The units can be split into three subsets, the standardization tanks of the formulation lines J^{FL}, the filling stations J^{FS} and the buffer tanks J^{ST}. The subset of units that can process order $i \in I$ is denoted by J_i. The same notation is used for the units of the subsets, except for the buffer tanks, for which $J_i^{\mathrm{ST}} = J^{\mathrm{ST}}, \forall i \in I$ holds. The set L denotes the formulation lines, each of which contains a set of standardization tanks $J_l^{\mathrm{FL}} \subset J^{\mathrm{FL}}, \forall l \in L$. The decisions taken during the optimization are the start times of processing or storage of material corresponding to order i in unit j (standardization and buffer tank respectively) at time t, expressed by the binary variable W_{ijt}. The release of material from a tank is similarly expressed through the binary variable W_{ijt}^R. The start of a filling process is expressed by the binary variable X_{ijkt}, where the index $k \in K$ contains information on the filling time (see constraints (5)-(7) below). The amount of material being sent to or being released from processing or storage is modeled through the continuous variables B_{ijt} and B_{ijt}^R. The amount of material stored in a buffer tank at each time point is tracked through the variable B_{ijt}^{ST}. The model contains a large number of constraints, only some of which can be discussed in this paper.

$$\sum_{\forall t \in T_H} \sum_{\forall j \in J_i^{FS}} B_{ijt} \geq D_i, \forall i \in I \tag{1}$$

$$B_{ij(t+1)}^{ST} = B_{ijt}^{ST} + B_{ijt} - B_{ijt}^R, \forall i \in I, j \in J^{ST}, t \in T_H \backslash \{H+1\} \tag{2}$$

$$\sum_{\forall j \in J_i^{FL}} W_{ijt}^R \cdot B_j + \sum_{\forall j' \in J^{ST}} B_{ij't}^R = \sum_{\forall j'' \in J_i^{FS} \cup J^{ST}} B_{ij''t}, \forall i \in I, t \in T_H \tag{3}$$

$$B_{ijt}^{ST} \leq V_j^{max}, \forall i \in I, j \in J^{ST}, t \in T_H \tag{4}$$

$$\frac{B_{ijt}}{F_{ij}} \leq Y_{ijt} < \frac{B_{ijt}}{F_{ij}} + 1, \forall i \in I, j \in J_i^{FS}, t \in T_H \tag{5}$$

$$\sum_{\forall k \in K} X_{ijkt} \cdot p_k = Y_{ijt}, \forall i \in I, j \in J_i^{FS}, t \in T_H \tag{6}$$

$$\sum_{\forall k \in K} X_{ijkt} \leq 1, \forall i \in I, j \in J_i^{FS}, t \in T_H \tag{7}$$

$$W_{ijt} + \sum_{t'=t}^{t+p_{ij}-1} W_{ijt'}^R \leq 1, \forall i \in I, j \in J_i^{FL}, t \in T_H \tag{8}$$

$$W_{ijt}^R + X_{ij'kt} + \sum_{\forall i' \in I} \sum_{t'=t}^{t+p_k+co_{ii'j}-1} W_{i'jt'} \leq 2, \tag{9}$$
$$\forall i \in I, j \in J_i^{FL} \cup J^{ST}, j' \in J_i^{FS}, k \in K, t \in T_H$$

$$W_{ijt}^R + W_{ij't} + \sum_{\forall i' \in I} \sum_{t'=t}^{t+co_{ii'j}-1} W_{i'jt'} \leq 2, \forall i \in I, j \in J_i^{FL}, j' \in J^{ST}, t \in T_H \tag{10}$$

$$W_{ijt} + \sum_{\forall i' \in I} \sum_{\forall j \in J_i^{FL} \backslash \{j\}} \sum_{t'=t}^{t+p_{ij}^c+co_{ii'l}-1} W_{i'j't'} \leq 1, \forall i \in I, l \in L_i, j \in J_i^{FL}, t \in T_H \tag{11}$$

$$W_{ijt}^R + X_{ij'kt} + \sum_{t'=t+1}^{t+p_k-1} W_{ijt'}^R \leq 2, \forall i \in I, j \in J^{ST}, j' \in J_i^{FS}, k \in K, t \in T_H \tag{12}$$

$$X_{ijkt} + \sum_{\forall i' \in I} \sum_{\forall k' \in K} \sum_{t'=t+1}^{t+p_k+co_{ii'j}-1} X_{i'jk't'} \leq 1, \forall i \in I, j \in J_i^{FS}, k \in K, t \in T_H \tag{13}$$

$$C_{max} \geq X_{ijkt} \cdot (t + p_k), \forall i \in I, j \in J_i^{FS}, k \in K, t \in T_H \tag{14}$$

Constraints (1) ensure that at least the ordered amount corresponding to order i, D_i is produced within the scheduling horizon. An inequality constraint is employed due to the fixed batch sizes B_j in the standardization tanks, which could lead to infeasibilities if the ordered amount had to be met exactly. Constraints (2)-(3) model the material balances around the buffer tanks and the transfer panel respectively. The amount stored in a buffer tank is limited by the maximum capacity V_j^{max} (4). A major challenge for the discrete-time formulation of the scheduling problem are the variable filling times which depend on the amount to be filled, B_{ijt}, and the order and unit specific flowrate F_{ij}. Constraints (5) emulate the ceiling function through the non-negative integer variable Y_{ijt} $(= \lceil B_{ijt}/F_{ij} \rceil)$. Constraints (6)-(7) capture the information on the filling time (in time intervals) through the binary variable X_{ijkt}, by selecting the corresponding filling time p_k, with $p_1 = 0$, $p_2 = 1, \ldots, p_{|K|} = 2 \cdot p^s$, where $2 \cdot p^s$ is the maximal duration of a filling process, corresponding to two consecutive shifts. The plant exhibits a complex timing behavior due to the interconnection of and the material transfer between the various units. These timing relations are modeled through the timing constraints (8)-(13). The formulation of Méndez et al. (2006) is used, which exhibits stronger relaxations than the commonly used big-M constraints. Constraints (8) enforce the minimum standardization time p_{ij}. If material is sent from a standardization or buffer tank to a filling station, the next standardization or storage can only start after the filling has been completed and an additional changeover time $co_{ii'j}$ between the two orders has elapsed (9). As material transfer between a standardization and a buffer tank is assumed to be instantaneous, only a changeover is required for the standardization tank, if such a material transfer is executed (10). Each formulation line contains multiple identical standardization tanks, but only one raw-material pre-processing line. Therefore processing can not start in all tanks of a line simultaneously. After one standardization has started, the charging time p_{ij}^c, during which the tank is filled and a line changeover time $co_{ii'l}$ have to elapse before a standardization can start in another tank of the same line (11). Two consecutive releases from a buffer tank are constrained by the filling time of the station to which material is sent (12). Lastly, the filling time and a changeover time have to elapse between two filling operations (13). The makespan of the schedule is used as the objective function. It is modeled by the constraints (14), where $C_{\max}$ is set to be larger than the end of all filling operations.

3.2. Iterative Scheduling and Set Reduction

Solving the optimization problem for a realistic set of orders simultaneously leads to a computationally intractable model size, even when using state-of-the-art MILP solvers. A way to deal with this limitation is to employ iterative scheduling (see e. g. Georgiadis et al. (2018)) in which the different orders are scheduled sequentially, while all decisions associated to previously scheduled orders are fixed. The main requirement for this approach is that the generated schedule represents a feasible solution of the original problem, i. e. that the constraints modeling the (timing) interactions of different orders in the model are satisfied. One way to ensure this feasibility is to include all variables and constraints of the model up to the order scheduled in the current iteration, while fixing all variables associated to the previous orders. In this way, each solution is guaranteed to be feasible together with the results of the previous iterations. However, a drawback of this approach is the increasing model size as the iteration progresses, since more variables and constraints are added to the model, resulting again in a computationally intractable approach. In order to maintain feasibility, we propose the implicit inclusion of the previously scheduled orders through a feasible set reduction. As the allocation and timing decisions of the preceding orders remain fixed, the time points can be identified which would result in an infeasible assignment in the current iteration. They can directly be derived from the timing constraints (8)-(13). The idea is demonstrated for constraints (13):

$$X_{i'jkt} = 1 \Rightarrow \{t - co_{ii'j+1} + 1, \ldots t, \ldots, t + p_k, \cdots t + p_k + co_{i'ij} - 1\} \subset T_{ij}^I.$$

If a filling process of a previously scheduled order i' started at time point t, the time points corresponding to the processing time in addition to the preceding and subsequent changeovers would lead to infeasible assignments of the current order i. The set T_{ij}^I includes all infeasible time points for order i in unit j. The infeasible time points for the other units are derived in a similar fashion from their respective timing constraints. For the scheduling of order i, all infeasible assignments due to previous allocations are eliminated through the constraints

$$\sum_{\forall t \in T_{ij}^I} W_{ijt} + W_{ijt}^R = 0, \ \forall j \in J_i^{FL} \cup J^{ST} \tag{15}$$

$$\sum_{\forall t \in T_{ij}^I} X_{ijkt} = 0, \ \forall j \in J_i^{FS}. \tag{16}$$

The time points corresponding to a non-working shift of the filling stations can also easily be added to the infeasible set. Due to the time consuming material transfer from the tanks and the variable filling time, the end of an operation is not solely determined by the variables associated to one unit. In order to still maintain feasibility, it must be guaranteed that each processing task finishes before the start of the next infeasible time points. This is achieved by identifying the feasible time points T_{ij}^F and splitting them into disjoint continuous sets $T_{ij}^{F,s} \subset T_{ij}^F$

$$T_{ij}^F = T_H \setminus T_{ij}^I = \bigcup_{\forall s} T_{ij}^{F,s}, \ T_{ij}^{F,s} \cap T_{ij}^{F,s'} = \emptyset, \ \forall s, s'. \tag{17}$$

It is ensured by additional constraints that an operation that starts within a feasible subset is finished until the end of that set.

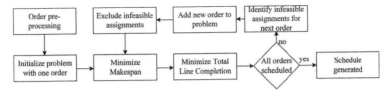

Figure 2: Algorithmic framework for the solution of the scheduling problem.

4. Computational Considerations and Results

Test runs showed a drawback associated to the minimization of the makespan. As only the maximum completion time affects the objective value of the optimization, standardizations that could finish earlier exhibit unnecessary waiting times. This leads to an underutilization of the available production capacity, as more time points are excluded from the feasible set of the next iteration. In order to resolve this limitation, the optimization is performed in two steps. In the first step the makespan C_{max} is minimized. In the second step the completion times of the formulation lines C_l are added to the model through constraints (18)

$$C_l \geq W_{ijt}^R \cdot t, \ \forall l \in L_i, \ j \in J_l^{FL}, \ t \in T_H. \tag{18}$$

The total line completion time is then minimized, while ensuring that the makespan stays below that of the first stage (C_{max}^*)

$$\min \sum_{\forall l \in L_i} C_l, \ C_{max} \leq C_{max}^*. \tag{19}$$

The test runs also showed that the computation time of each iteration strongly depends on the ordered amount D_i and the resulting number of batches that have to be scheduled. The computational effort can be decreased by splitting large orders into multiple artificial smaller orders, which are then also scheduled sequentially. The splitting can be performed in a pre-processing step according to a specified maximum number of standardizations that are allowed to be scheduled in each iteration. The complete proposed framework is illustrated in Fig. 2. It was tested for a plant consisting of 7 formulation lines, each with 3 standardization tanks, 8 filling stations and 5 buffer tanks. In total 20 different orders were scheduled over a one week horizon, with a time interval length of one hour. At most 5 standardizations were scheduled in each iteration. The framework was implemented in Julia 0.6.1.1 (Bezanson et al., 2017) with IBM ILOG CPLEX 12.7.1 as an MILP solver on a MS Windows 7 desktop PC (Intel Core i7-4790S CPU @ 3.20 GHz,

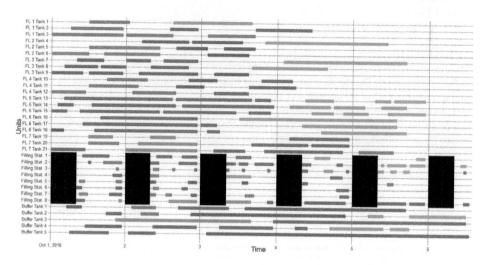

Figure 3: Gantt generated with the proposed scheduling framework.

16 GB RAM). Even for small instances, including just a few orders, no feasible solutions could be obtained due to the model size and complexity and the resulting failed model initialization due to memory limitations. Using the proposed approach the problem was solved in 38 minutes, where a relative gap tolerance of 5 % was used in each iteration. The generated Gantt-chart with a makespan of 133 h is shown in Fig. 3. The black regions in the charts of the filling stations represent non-working shifts. Although the schedule still exhibits unnecessary waiting times and release postponements in the standardization tanks, it finishes more than one day prior to the end of the scheduling horizon. It should also be noted that solving all iterations to global optimality (0 % gap) resulted in a nearly identical schedule, where the overall makespan was improved by only one hour, but the solution required 4.5 hours of computation time. This further underlines the good tradeoff between optimality and computation time that is achieved with the proposed framework.

5. Conclusion

In this contribution an approach for the fast generation of feasible and good schedules that includes an MILP model and a set reduction approach was proposed. The results show that good schedules can be found within relatively short computation times. This is preferable over the time consuming search for an optimal schedule in an industrial environment. Since the scheduling problem is solved in an iterative fashion, the quality of the schedule strongly depends on the sequence in which the orders are scheduled. Therefore further improvements can be achieved by employing a sorting of the orders in the pre-processing step, either through a prioritization of orders according to specified criteria, or based upon operational considerations provided by planners and operators.

References

J. Bezanson, A. Edelman, S. Karpinski, V. B. Shah, 2017. Julia: A fresh approach to numerical computing. SIAM Review 59 (1), 65–98.

G. P. Georgiadis, C. Ziogou, G. Kopanos, M. Garcia, D. Cabo, M. Lopez, M. C. Georgiadis, 2018. Production scheduling of multi-stage, multi-product food process industries. In: Computer Aided Chemical Engineering. Vol. 43. pp. 1075–1080.

I. Harjunkoski, C. T. Maravelias, P. Bongers, P. M. Castro, S. Engell, I. E. Grossmann, J. Hooker, C. Méndez, G. Sand, J. Wassick, 2014. Scope for industrial applications of production scheduling models and solution methods. Computers & Chemical Engineering 62, 161–193.

C. Méndez, J. Cerdá, I. E. Grossmann, I. Harjunkoski, M. Fahl, 2006. State-of-the-art review of optimization methods for short-term scheduling of batch processes. Computers & Chemical Engineering 30 (6-7), 913–946.

Anton A. Kiss, Edwin Zondervan, Richard Lakerveld, Leyla Özkan (Eds.)
Proceedings of the 29th European Symposium on Computer Aided Process Engineering
June 16th to 19th, 2019, Eindhoven, The Netherlands. © 2019 Elsevier B.V. All rights reserved.
http://dx.doi.org/10.1016/B978-0-128-18634-3.50005-9

Towards Model-Based Optimization for Quality by Design in Biotherapeutics Production

Alireza Ehsani[a], Chrysoula Dimitra Kappatou[b], Adel Mhamdi[b], Alexander Mitsos[b], Andreas Schuppert[a,c], Sebastian Niedenfuehr[a,*]

[a]*Bayer AG, 51368 Leverkusen, Germany*

[b]*RWTH Aachen University, AVT – Aachener Verfahrenstechnik, Process Systems Engineering, Forckenbeckstrasse 51, 52074 Aachen*

[c]*Joint Research Center for Computational Biomedicine; RWTH Aachen University, Pauwelsstrasse 19, 52074 Aachen, Germany*

sebastian.niedenfuehr@bayer.com

Abstract

Quality by Design (QbD) is the concept of designing a process by gathered knowledge to fulfill desired quality of the product. This requires monitoring and controlling product quality throughout process development. In biotherapeutics production, glycosylation is one of the major quality attributes. In general, the glycoform generated by the cell glycosylation machinery is highly dependent on the cell performance and the variations in its surrounding. Mathematical modelling of this machinery can facilitate process understanding, describe the complexity of different layers of cellular metabolism and enable model-based optimization of product formation.

In this work, we investigate possible feeding scenarios utilizing a calibrated model to help understanding the possible effects of process changes in the paradigm of QbD for biotherapeutics. Our QbD objective is to maximize product yield while satisfying product quality given by criteria on the protein glycosylation pattern. For this we use a mechanistic model comprised of three major layers (scales) including bioreactor dynamics, intracellular reaction network and kinetic reactions inside Golgi apparatus. We apply design of experiments method followed by *in silico* experiments using the mechanistic model to identify optimal feeding profiles and evaluate the respective formed glycopatterns. In a future step, these predictions can be experimentally tested. Thereby, in a series of steps, a model can be developed to be used for model-based optimization.

Keywords: Biotherapeutics, Quality by Design, Mathematical Modelling, Optimization

1. Introduction

Variations in product quality are generally caused by changes in the production process. In order to be able to ensure that the product quality variations lie within pre-defined ranges, a systematic approach is needed. This approach should be able to incorporate knowledge of the process and effects of critical factors on product quality. This is called QbD, where the key elements are the critical process parameters (CPPs), the critical quality attributes (CQAs), the design space, and the quality target product profile (QTPP) (ICH Q8). The implementation of QbD needs, first, a definition of the intended product properties to define QTPP. Through process knowledge, regulatory guidelines and literature, CQAs can be identified. To identify the sensitive parameters (i.e. CPPs) affecting the QTPP, often an initial experimental design for screening is conducted in the wet-lab. The CPPs should be monitored and controlled to ensure the process produces the desired quality.

In biotherapeutics production considered in this work, bioactivity, stability and *in vivo* circulatory half-life are examples for QTPP. One of the most important CQAs is the protein glycosylation pattern, since it highly affects the respective QTPPs. Human-like glycosylation is important for correct functionality of glycoproteins. Usually, well known CPPs for mAb CQAs include cultivation parameters (e.g., pH, dissolved oxygen, temperature) and medium composition (e.g., carbon and nitrogen sources, vitamins, trace elements).

An important step in the QbD process is to determine the design space for the CPPs. The design space as defined in (ICH Q8) is "*the multidimensional combination and interaction of input variables and process parameters that have been demonstrated to provide assurance of quality. Working within the design space is not considered as a change. Movement out of the design space is considered to be a change and would normally initiate a regulatory post-approval change process*". Description of the design space provides flexibility of the manufacturing process in the defined ranges.

To determine the design space, additional experiments are needed within the boundaries of the CPPs. Statistical design of experiments (DoE) helps in a systematic planning of such experiments in order to identify the effects of variations of CPPs on CQAs. In the paradigm of QbD, the traditional one-factor-at-a-time designs are no longer efficient since a holistic understanding of the system at hand is aimed for.

Combination of DoE methods for process development and model-based simulations within the QbD context can provide an estimate of the critical QbD elements before running time consuming and cost intensive experiments. In addition, it can help in assessing the points in parameter boundaries where performing real experiments face limitations.

As pursued in this work, model-based optimization for QbD in biotherapeutics production, the optimization of the cell culture process in regard to product quality requires systematic analysis of the glycosylation throughout the cell line and process development. The biosynthesis of glycans is a result of a complex network of metabolic and enzymatic reactions that are influenced by many factors, including the host cell line as well as the upstream and downstream bioprocesses (Sha et al. 2016). Mathematical modelling of the system provides better understanding on the product quality variations. Initial computational models (Umana and Baily 1997) approximated the Golgi apparatus as a series of continuously stirred tank reactors where reactions generate potential glycan structures. Hossler et al. (2007) started to adopt the Golgi maturation model and used plug flow reactors in series to mimic the change in enzyme concentrations along the Golgi apparatus. Follow-up models were developed to simulate antibody glycosylation specifically, and particular attention was paid to the nucleotide sugar donor level to link glycosylation to cellular metabolism (Jedrzejewski et al. 2014). The mechanistic models which link glycosylation to cellular metabolism are state of the art (Jedrzejewski et al. 2014, Sou et al., 2017).

In this work, we utilize the current state-of-the-art modelling approach in combination with DoE methods to assess and understand the process response. This is done as a first step towards a model-based approach of a QbD workflow. Before performing the experiments in wet-lab, the resulting responses are checked against observations taken from literature. The results of these *in silico* studies give first insights about the system's outcome and need to be later tested experimentally. Finally, the predictive nature of mechanistic models can be used for control of the glycosylation process and pave the way towards quality-based optimization of therapeutic production bioprocesses.

2. Modelling and Identification Approach

2.1. Mathematical Model of Cell Culture and Protein Glycosylation

We use our previous mechanistic model (Ehsani et al. 2017). It includes three layers (i) extracellular, (ii) intracellular dynamics coupled with (iii) glycosylation reactions inside Golgi apparatus. The model equations are solved using ODE15s in MATLAB R2017b. We perform a global sensitivity analysis (Wang et al. 2003) by evaluating 105 samples in the range of 50%-200% of the nominal values of the parameters nominal values. By calculating first order global sensitivity indices, we can fix 97 parameters, out of 133, to their nominal values. We use a scatter search optimization algorithm (Egea et al. 2009) to estimate the remaining parameter values and fit model outputs with experimental data of hybridoma batch culture taken from Jedrzejewski et al. (2014).

2.2. Design of Experiments

We conduct two rounds of design of experiments using Box-Behnken design (MATLAB Statistics Toolbox) as a response surface method, each one followed by *in silico* experiments. The design goals are, first, finding the strategy to maximize protein titer and second taking this strategy as starting point to adjust glycosylation pattern.

In the first DoE round, three factors (decision variables), namely glucose and glutamine feeding concentrations and the number of feed boluses are incorporated. Three levels of each factor are considered, which corresponds to low, middle, and high for the concentrations and one, two or three number of boluses. The boundaries of 5-15 mM and 2-6 mM are used for glucose (Glc) and glutamine (Gln) respectively, according to the feeding strategies reported for hybridoma cell by Pörtner et al. (2004). With this input, a set of 15 experiments are designed that are then performed *in silico* to examine the effects of different feeding strategies on process performance.

The values for the fed-batch process that results in the maximum value of response (protein titer) are selected as starting point to perform the second round of DoE. In this case, four factors, namely N-acetylglucosamine, fucose, galactose and sialic acid, in three levels within the boundaries of 1-10 mM, 1-8 mM, 5-20 mM and 1-5 mM are assessed using Box-Behnken design followed again by *in silico* experiments.

2.3. Identify Feeding Strategies by Optimization of Response Surface Function

We use the outcomes of the designed set of experiments in previous section to fit a second-order function as response surface (R). This function (Eq. (1)) is composed of intercept (β_0), linear terms (β_1, β_2, β_3), cross product terms (β_{12}, β_{13}, β_{23}) and squared terms (β_{11}, β_{22}, β_{33}).

$$R = \beta_0 + \sum \beta_1 Glc + \sum \beta_2 Gln + \sum \beta_3 No.Feed\,\beta_3 + \sum \beta_{12} Glc\,Gln + \sum \beta_{13} Glc\,No.Feed +$$
$$\sum \beta_{23} Gln\,No.Feed + \sum \beta_{11} Glc^2 + \sum \beta_{22} Gln^2 + \sum \beta_{33} No.Feed^2 \qquad (1)$$

We use numerical optimization function *fmincon* (MATLAB Optimization Toolbox) to calculate the optimum point of the response function (Eq. 1) within the boundaries of its variables as mentioned in previous section.

After performing two DoE rounds and *in silico* experiments, we find the optimal values for supplementation of both nucleotide sugars and nutrients for maximizing the response function. This approach can be extended in our future research using dynamic optimization in the whole space of decision variables.

3. Results and Discussion

In this section, we briefly present the results obtained in the considered case study.

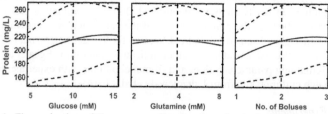

Figure 1. The projection of the response function (protein titer) with respect to the different levels of glucose and glutamine concentration and number of bolus feeds. Dashed lines show the protein titer in min/max levels; solid line shows the protein for medium values of the other factors.

We show the changes in response function (protein titer) in different levels of decision variables from the first DoE round in Figure 1. The toxic effect of ammonia in the culture is assumed to be the limiting factor when overfeeding occurs. In order to avoid overfeeding, the simulated culture stops, when ammonia accumulation reaches 4 mM.

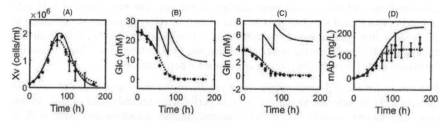

Figure 2. Batch (dashed line) and fed-batch (solid line) simulation results of (A) cell density, (B) glucose and (C) glutamine dynamics and (D) protein titer. Experimental data are shown with solid circles.

As shown in Figure 1 the optimum feeding strategy is two feeds with 13.4 mM glucose and 3.9 mM glutamine concentration. This fed-batch strategy results in a maximum cell density of 2e+6 cells/ml and 218.6 mg/L protein titer. Supplementing cell culture media by glucose and glutamine provides major nutrients and energy sources for growth and protein production. We show in Figure 2 the dynamics of cell density and the concentrations of glucose, glutamine and protein in batch and the selected fed-batch process with maximum protein titer in first round of *in silico* experiments.

Coupling glycosylation to the metabolic model provides the opportunity to assess the effects of supplementation on product quality and helps in making further improvements in the process. Figure 3 shows the differences between eight important glycosylation patterns in batch and fed-batch processes. Generally, there is a shift from accumulation of unmatured early structures (high mannoses like M5) to more complex structures: The glycosylation pattern of batch culture shows the presence of more than 10% Mannose-5 glycans which in monoclonal antibodies should be normally less than 10% (Blondeel and Aucoin, 2018).

In the fed-batch culture providing enough glucose and glutamine caused conversion of this early structure to more complex glycans. M3Gn2F is the most popular structure in monoclonal antibodies with around 40% (Blondeel and Aucoin, 2018). The fraction of this structure in fed-batch compared to batch culture is about 2.5 fold higher. This results in improved quality, albeit not sufficiently. Further quality improvement could be achieved possibly through supplementing N-Acetylglucosamine. In average, the amount of galactosylation is between 10-40% depending on the glycoprotein (Blondeel and Aucoin, 2018). As shown in Figure 3 the galactosylated (M3Gn2FG /M3Gn2FG2) content is also increased in fed batch but not in the same rate as M3Gn2F increased. This arises from the fact that the cell is producing more glycosylated protein having enough glucose available, while the intracellular biosynthesis rate of galactose is limited by the cell`s capacity. Therefore, Galactose supplementation can increase the galactosylated content.

In the second DoE round, we assessed further supplementation of nucleotide sugars using Box-Behnken design in 46 *in silico* experiments. According to the results the optimum glycosylation pattern can be achieved by adding 15 mM Galactose and 6 mM N-acetylglucosamine in 3 boluses. These predictions are in well agreement with literature reports where the most effective and popular supplementation strategy to increase galactosylated content is to feed N- acetylglucosamine 7-10 mM and galactose 10-20 mM (Blondeel and Aucoin, 2018). This feeding strategy also increased the sialylated content to about 2% which improves plasma half-life of the glycoprotein (Sha et al., 2016).

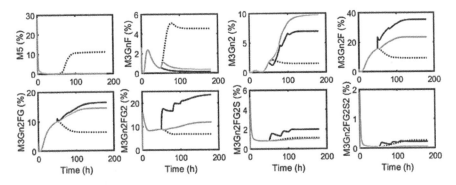

Figure 3. Batch (dashed line), fed-batch with (dark solid line)/ without (light solid line) nucleotide sugars supplementation, simulated dynamics of eight important glycan structures. M: mannose, Gn: N-acetylglucosamine, F: fucose, G: galactose, S: N-acetylsialic

4. Conclusions

Implementation of QbD requires detailed characterization of the process and thorough exploration of the various conditions that can affect the quality. In this work, we use a mechanistic model of cell culture and glycosylation to identify biological meaningful feeding strategies and pave the way towards quality-based optimization of glycoforms. We proposed adjustment of CQA (glycosylation) by supplementing nutrients (nucleotide sugars) and the qualitative behavior of our model showed agreement with reported literature data.

5. Acknowledgements

This work has received funding from the European Union's Horizon 2020 research and innovation program under the Marie Skłodowska-Curie grant agreement no.675251.

References

S. Sha, C. Agarabi, K. Brorson, D. Lee, S. Yoon, N-Glycosylation Design and Control of Therapeutic Monoclonal Antibodies, Trends Biotechnol., 34, 10, 835-846, 2016.

P. Umana, JE. Bailey, A mathematical model of N-linked glycoform biosynthesis, Biotechnol. Bioeng., 55, 890-908, 1997.

P. Hossler, BC. Mulukutla, WS. Hu, Systems analysis of N-glycan processing in mammalian cells, PLoS ONE, 2(8), e713, 2007.

PM. Jedrzejewski, IJ. del Val, A. Constantinou, A. Dell, SM. Haslam, KM. Polizzi, C. Kontoravdi, 2014, Towards controlling the glycoform: a model framework linking extracellular metabolites to antibody glycosylation, Int. J. Mol. Sci., 15, 4492-4522

A. Ehsani, S. Niedenfuehr, T. Eissing, S. Behnken, and A. Schuppert, How to Use Mechanistic Metabolic Modeling to Ensure High Quality Glycoprotein Production. Computer Aided Chemical Engineering, 40: 2839-284, 2017.

JA. Egea, E. Balsa-Canto, M. García, J. Banga, Dynamic Optimization of Nonlinear Processes with an Enhanced Scatter Search Method, Ind. Eng. Chem. Res., 48, 4388-4401, 2009.

SW. Wang, PG. Georgopoulos, G. Li , H. Rabitz, Random Sampling–High Dimensional Model Representation (RS–HDMR) with Nonuniformly Distributed Variables: Application to an Integrated Multimedia/Multipathway Exposure and Dose Model for Trichloroethylene, The J. Phys. Chem., 107, 23, 4707-4716, 2003.

R. Pörtner, JO. Schwabe, B. Frahm. Evaluation of selected strategies for fed-batch cultures of
    a hybridoma cell line. Biotechnology Appl Bioc. 40: 47–55, 2004.

E. Blondeel, M. Aucoin, Supplementing glycosylation: A review of applying nucleotide-sugar precursors to growth medium to affect therapeutic recombinant protein glycoform distributions, Biotechnology Advances, 36, 1505-1523, 2018.

ICH and FDA Guidance for Industry, Q8(R2) Pharmaceutical Development, November 2009. https://www.fda.gov/downloads/drugs/guidances/ucm073507.pdf

S. N. Sou, P. M. Jedrzejewski, K. Lee, C. Sellick, K. M. Polizzi, and C. Kontoravdi, Model-based investigation of intracellular processes determining antibody Fc-glycosylation under mild hypothermia, Biotechnol. Bioeng., 114: 1570-1582, 2017.

Anton A. Kiss, Edwin Zondervan, Richard Lakerveld, Leyla Özkan (Eds.)
Proceedings of the 29th European Symposium on Computer Aided Process Engineering
June 16th to 19th, 2019, Eindhoven, The Netherlands. © 2019 Elsevier B.V. All rights reserved.
http://dx.doi.org/10.1016/B978-0-128-18634-3.50006-0

Review of override control methods

Jan Schuurmans[a][*]

[a]DotX Control Solutions, Oudeweg 91, office B.1-1, Haarlem 2031CC, the Netherlands

j.schuurmans@dotxcontrol.com

Abstract

This paper focusses on potential issues with override control. We show that, in the presence of stochastic disturbances, the existing methods can fail due to frequent switching from one controller to the other. Based on the analysis of the cause of the problem, we propose a simple solution and demonstrate its applicability on a test setup involving a Siemens PLC and software.

Keywords: override control, PID, constrained output control, cascade control

1. Introduction

In some cases, the control must adjust a manipulated variable to control one process variable at setpoint while maintaining other process variable(s) within limits. In practice, this problem, sometimes referred to as the output constrained control problem, is often solved with the use of PID controllers. Scientific literature on this subject usually focusses on stability and performance in the presence of deterministic disturbances (Glattfelder 1988, Lopez 1996). To the knowledge of the author, the case of stochastic disturbances has not been considered so far. This paper analyses two common methods to handle output constraints and shows that they face potential problems in the presence of stochastic disturbances. Based on the analysis of the cause of the problem, we propose a simple solution and demonstrate its applicability on a test setup involving a standard Siemens PLC.

The paper is structured as follows. Section 2 defines the output constraint problem in full detail. Section 2 and 3 present two common solutions (override control and cascade control, respectively) to the output constraint problem, using PID controllers, and shows that these solutions may not work in the presence of stochastic disturbances. Section 4 analyses the problem and presents solutions. Finally, section 5 presents the conclusions.

2. Description of the output constraint problem

The main question of this paper, is: are the existing constraint handling methods (using PID controllers) capable of handling stochastic disturbances, and if not, can we fix the problem? This section describes this main question in more detail.

We assume that the process is described by the following model:

$$y_1 = G_1(s)\, m + d_1, \quad y_2 = G_2(s)\, m + d_2 \tag{1}$$

with m the manipulated variable, y_i (i = 1 or 2) process variable, d_i disturbance variable, $G_i(s)$ a transfer function as a function of the Laplace variable s.

This paper considers both deterministic and stochastic disturbances. The deterministic disturbances provide immediate insight in the dynamic behaviour, the stochastic disturbances are more common in practice.

The output constrained control challenge is defined in words as follows. Control y_1 as closely as possible to setpoint s_1, while the second process variable y_2 should not cross some limit (that we assume, without loss of generality, to be a high limit y_{2max}). When we are dealing with stochastic disturbances, it makes sense to try to ensure that the chance of exceeding the limit y_{2max} is less than some predefined percentage.

The controllers are assumed to be PID controllers equipped with a Tracking Mode option. Although the exact equations are usually not provided by commercial manufacturers, we shall assume, for clarity of the paper, that this means that the PID controllers can be represented by $m_i = C_i(s)e_i + b_i$, with $C_i(s)$ a PID controller in the Standard Form:

$$C_i(s) = K_{p,i}\left(1 + \frac{1}{T_{i,i}s} + T_{d,i}s\right)e_i \qquad (2)$$

Furthermore, $e_i = s_i - y_i$, and b_i is a bias term, defined by $b_i = \frac{1}{T_t s}(m - m_i)$ with m the manipulated input. If the i-th PID is active, i.e. if $m = m_i$, the bias term disappears. Otherwise, in Tracking mode, the controller's output can be written as:

$$m_i = \frac{T_t s}{T_t s + 1}C_i(s)e + \frac{1}{T_t s + 1}m \qquad (3)$$

and clearly, m_i tracks m for frequencies below $\omega < 1/T_t$

Basically, the Tracking mode ensures that the output of the controller that is not active 'tracks' the output of the controller that is active, to avoid a bump when switching. The exact equations for the Tracking mode method are not essential for the results in this paper.

In the next sections, we consider different control solutions. To simulate them, we shall simulate one specific process model, according to:

$$G_1(s) = \frac{1}{3s + 1}e^{-0.2s}, \qquad G_2(s) = \frac{2}{4s + 1}e^{-s}$$

The disturbances vary according to:

$$d_1(s) = w_1 + d_d, \qquad d_2(s) = w_2 + d_d$$

with w_1 and w_2 independent normally randomly distributed white noise, with variance 1, and d_d a deterministic disturbance component, starting at time t = 0.4 and changing stepwise to −2 at t = 100 s.

The setpoint for controller C_1 is $s_1 = -0.1$ and we assume that at t = 0, the system is in steady state. The maximum on output y_2 is $y_{2max} = 2$, and we wish to reduce the chance of y_2 exceeding y_{2max} to less than 2.5%. In order to allow comparison between different control options, we adopt the following control parameters for the controllers C_1 and C_2:

$K_{p1} = 5.25, \quad T_{i1} = 1.6, \quad T_{d1} = T_{d2} = 0, \quad K_{p2} = 0.7, \quad T_{i2} = 4$

These settings were chosen based on the tuning rules as presented in (Skogestad 2001) and results in well damped and fast response under normal conditions (i.e. no switching between controllers). We have chosen not to use D-action for reasons of simplicity.

Given these control parameter settings, and the stochastic disturbance w_2 as defined above, the standard deviation (σ_2) of y_2 will be close to $\sigma_2 = 1$, if C_2 is either active or not during the entire simulation period. This implies that if we choose the setpoint s_2 as 0 or slightly lower, we can expect that the output constraint on y_2 can be met in 'steady state conditions', i.e. at all times outside the transients caused by the deterministic variations in d_d. Therefore, we select setpoint $s_2 = y_{2max} - 2\sigma_2 = 2 - 2 = 0$, since the chance of exceeding $2\sigma_2$ is less than 2.5% for a normal distribution.

The override control solutions, as described in this paper, were tested on a hardware in the loop setup, as shown in Figure 1. In this setup, the process model was simulated using the PID Tuner software described in its manual (Schuurmans 2018). The control output (m) was calculated by the Siemens S7 1200 PLC, programmed with an override control solutions as described in the manual of the PLC (Simatic 2018). The controllers C_1 and C_2 were realised with the PID Compact blocks.

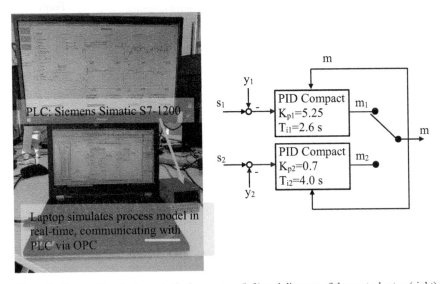

Figure 1   Photo of the Hardware in the Loop setup (left) and diagram of the control setup (right).

3. Override control

One method to handle the output constraint is Override control (Shinskey 2005) . In override control, the controller with minimal (or maximal) manipulated variable is selected, i.e. $m = \min(m_1, m_2)$. In other words, control switches to C_2 if (and only if) $m_2 < m_1$. For this method, it is clear how to set the control parameters. Indeed, the PID settings as presented in section 1 work well in the absence of stochastic disturbances, see Figure 2. This figure shows both the simulated response according to our assumed PID formulas (solid lines) and the actual PID Compact (dashed lines); the responses differ slightly, but in essence the behaviour agrees. Control switches correctly from C_1 to C_2 at t=100s.

However, in case of stochastic disturbances, frequent switching between controllers take place, and this results in a problematic performance (solid lines in Figure 3). The Mean Squared Error (MSE) of y_1, defined as $MSE_1 = \frac{1}{n}\sum_{i=0}^{n} e_1(t)^2$ increases to 9 (with n = number of samples), whereas MSE equals just 1.2 if C_1 is active all the time.

4. Cascade control

In case of cascade control, the PID controller C_1 adjusts the setpoint of the second PID controller (s_2). By constraining the setpoint of s_2, according to $s_2 \leq y_{2max}$, the output y_2 can be expected to satisfy the output constraint.

A disadvantage of this method is that the controller C_1 cannot be tuned optimally on the basis of the process model given by Eq. 1, but, instead, it must be tuned on the basis of the closed-loop dynamics given by $y_2 = \frac{G_2}{1+C_2G_2} s_2$. In many cases, these closed-loop dynamics are slower than the open-loop dynamics. This problem can be overcome using cleverly chosen filters, as was shown in (Lestage 1999). Nevertheless, this solution copes with the same issues as Override control, in the presence of stochastic noise, and similar results as shown in Figure 3 apply to this control solution.

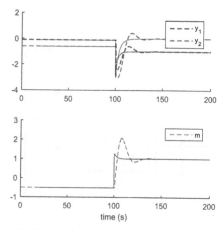

Figure 2   Simulated (solid) and measured response of the PID Compact (dashed).

5. Analysis of the problem and solutions

Override control and (cleverly chosen) cascade control boil down to the same solution, where control switches from C_1 to C_2 or vice versa. In case of stochastic disturbances, the switching may occur too frequently, resulting in lousy performance. We can analyse the switching conditions more closely. The controller that is not active, is in tracking mode. Let us, for example, assume that C_1 is active and C_2 is in tracking mode. In that case, the switching condition can be written as $C_1e_1 > C_2e_2$. The same condition applies when the second controller is active. Hence, the condition for switching from one controller to the other can be expressed in terms of a condition on controller deviations (e_i), weighed by the controller transfer function. Similar switching conditions, but with different 'weighting transfer functions' can be derived for cascade control, and in case of different PID implementations (such as the PID in velocity form). In the presence of noisy control deviation signals (e_i) with mean values that differ less than the variations, frequent switching will take place.

To resolve this issue, we can change the switching conditions such that switching takes only takes place when meaningful. Changing the switching conditions does not alter the stability (proofs) of the control systems, see for instance the stability proofs as presented in Glattfelder (1988, 2004) and Lopez (1996). We therefore defined a continuous 'switching' parameter α, according to

$$\frac{d\alpha}{dt} = K_{\alpha 1}(e_1 - e_2) - K_{\alpha 2}(\alpha - \alpha_c) \tag{4}$$

with $\alpha_c = \text{sat}(\alpha)$, i.e. $\alpha_c = \alpha$ if $\alpha_{min} < \alpha < \alpha_{max}$, $\alpha_c = \alpha_{min}$ if $\alpha \leq \alpha_{min}$ and $\alpha_c = \alpha_{max}$ if $\alpha \geq \alpha_{max}$.

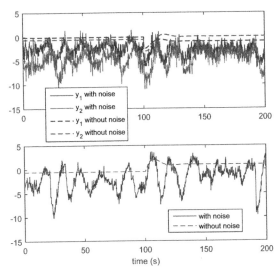

Figure 3 Measured response with stochastic disturbances (solid lines) and without (dashed) when using the Siemens PID Compact. In the case of stochastic disturbances, control switches frequently.

The parameter α is driven to 'one side' as long as there is a difference between e_1 and e_2. Control switches to C_1 if $\alpha_c > 0.45$. Control switches to C_2 if $\alpha_c < -0.45$.
For sufficiently small gain $K_{\alpha 1}$, it will not switch too frequently. The gain $K_{\alpha 2}$ feeds back on saturations of α, and basically provides anti-windup. The parameters were chosen as $\alpha_{min} = -0.5, \alpha_{max} = 0.5,\ K_{\alpha 1} = 3, K_{\alpha 2} = -3$.
     Figure 4 shows the results when we changed the switching conditions in the PLC to the conditions depending on α_c described here. Clearly, control switches only when it makes sense, from controller C_1 to C_2 at t =100 seconds in the simulation. As a result, the MSE of the deviations of y_1 from setpoint have reduced from 9 to 1.76 (compared to the results shown in Figure 3), while the percentage of y_2 samples crossing the limit y_{2max} is within specifications at 1.9% (outside the transients due to the deterministic disturbance change at $t = 100$, so outside the time span $t = 100$ to 130 s).

6. Conclusions

Returning to the main question posed in this paper, if the existing constraint handling methods (using PID controllers) are capable of handling stochastic disturbances, and if not, if we can fix the problem, the answer to the first question is 'no'. This answer was based on an analysis of the existing methods, both on paper and in experiments. Analysis showed that the problem was due to too frequent switching from one controller to the other. By changing the switching conditions this problem can be overcome though.

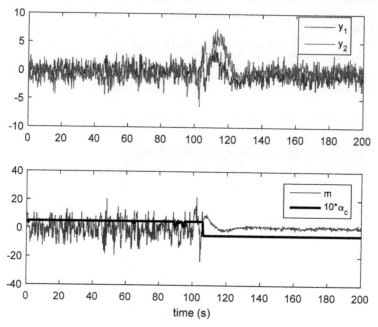

Figure 4 Results with override control with adjusted switching conditions applied to the Siemens PID Compact. Now, control switches from C_1 to C_2 at t=100s only.

References

A.H. Glattfelder and W. Schaufelberger, Stability of discrete override and cascadelimiter single loop control systems. IEEE Transactions on Automatic Control 33, 1988

A.H. Glattfelder,W. Schaufelberger, 'A path from antiwindup to override control, IFAC Nonlinear Control Systems, 2004

R. Lestage, Improved constrained cascade control for parallel processes, Control Engineering Practice, Volume 7, Issue 8, August 1999, Pages 969-974

A.A. Lopez, J.A. Joseph, 'On the stability of override control systems', LAAS-CNRS, Toulouse France, Rapport N° 98304, 1996

A.I. Ribic, M.R, Design and Tuning of PID Override Control System Based on Signal Filtering, International Symposium on Industrial Electronics INDEL 2014, 2014

J. Schuurmans, T.Zabel 'PID Tuner', manual, www.pid-tuner.com, 2018

F.G. Shinskey, J.P.Shunta, J.E. Jamison, chapter 2.28 Selective, Override, and Limit Controls, Instrument Engineers' Handbook, Volume Two: Process Control and Optimization, 4th edition, 2005

Simatic, S7-1200, S7-1500, PID Control, Function manual, Version 10, 2018

S. Skogestad, 'Probably the best simple PID tuning rules in the world', AIChE Annual meeting, 2001

Anton A. Kiss, Edwin Zondervan, Richard Lakerveld, Leyla Özkan (Eds.)
Proceedings of the 29th European Symposium on Computer Aided Process Engineering
June 16th to 19th, 2019, Eindhoven, The Netherlands. © 2019 Elsevier B.V. All rights reserved.
http://dx.doi.org/10.1016/B978-0-128-18634-3.50007-2

A comparison of the performance of multi-objective optimization methodologies for solvent design

Ye Seol Lee[a], Edward Graham[a], George Jackson[a], Amparo Galindo[a] and Claire S. Adjiman[a*]

[a]*Department of Chemical Engineering, Centre for Process Systems Engineering, Imperial College London, South Kensington Campus, London SW7 2AZ, United Kingdom*
c.adjiman@imperial.ac.uk

Abstract

In this work, we present a systematic comparison of the performance of five mixed-integer non-linear programming (MINLP) multiobjective optimisation algorithms on a computer-aided solvent design problem. The five methods are designed to address the nonconvexity of the problem, with the aim of generating an accurate and complete approximation of the Pareto front. The approaches includes: a weighted sum approach with simulated annealing (SA), a weighted sum approach with multi level single linkage (MLSL), the sandwich algorithm with SA, the sandwich algorithm with MLSL and the non dominated sorting genetic algorithm-II. These five combinations of optimisation techniques are applied to the design of a solvent for chemical absorption of carbon dioxide (CO_2). The results shows that the sandwich algorithm with MLSL can efficiently generate diverse Pareto points leading to a construction of more complete Pareto front.

Keywords: multiobjective optimisation, CAMD, MINLP, global search

1. Introduction

Computer-Aided Molecular Design (CAMD) is a promising technique that can accelerate the discovery of new molecules, such as solvents, refrigerants, and pharmaceutical products, by making it possible to explore *in silico* a very large space of possibilities. In the field of CAMD, numerous mathematical methods have been developed to handle the complexities that arise from the large number of molecules that can be formed from the combination of a given set of atom groups and from the inherent non-linearity and non-convexity of structure-property and process models. Many of the methods proposed to date have been based on an optimisation framework and have made use of single objective Mixed-Integer Non-Linear Programming (MINLP) to achieve better economic criteria or property targets. However, in many cases, it is beneficial to consider multiple conflicting objectives that cannot easily be combined together in a single metric. Multi-Objective Optimisation (MOO) is thus receiving increasing attention in the CAMD area. Papadopoulos and Linke (2006) proposed a multi-objective molecular design technique linked with a process synthesis framework, extending it (Papadopoulos et al., 2013) to the design of binary working fluid mixtures in organic Rankine cycles and (Papadopoulos et al., 2016) to the design of solvent for CO_2 capture. Burger et al. (2014) adapted the sandwich algorithm to the design of a solvent for a CO_2 physical absorption process. Herring and Eden (2015) also successfully introduced MOO with a genetic algorithm to the molecular design problem. Although the mixed-integer nature of molecular design MOO problems presents specific challenges, there has been no systematic analysis to compare the performance of MOO algorithms for CAMD applications.

In this work, we present a comparative analysis of the performance of three main MINLP MOO approaches, the weighted sum (WS), the sandwich algorithm (SD) (Rennen et al., 2011), and the non-dominated sorting algorithm-II (NSGA-II) (Deb et al., 2000). To increase the likelihood of identifying the globally optimal Pareto front, we make use of the simulated annealing version of WS (Marcoulaki and Kokossis, 2000), which has been previously applied to MOO CAMD (Papadopoulos et al., 2016). We also put forward a simulated annealing version of the sandwich algorithm, and multi-start approaches for the both WS and SD. This results in 5 combinations of algorithmic options, which are applied to the design of a solvent for the chemical absorption of CO_2. Algorithmic performance is compared based on reliability and efficiency criteria.

2. Optimisation methodology

In this section, we describe the methodologies for MINLP MOO that are used in this work. The WS and SD rely on on a scalarisation of the multiple objective functions as a single aggregated objective function. NSGA-II, on the other hand, falls into the category of 'evolutionary algorithms'. The NSGA-II can in principle solve a broader range of MOO problems as it is a derivative-free method, but the accuracy of the resulting approximation cannot be guaranteed.

2.1. Weighted sum method

WS is the most widely used scalarisation method in MOO . It is formulated as $\min \sum_{i=1}^{p} \lambda_i f_i$ (p : # of objectives) , where $\sum_{i=1}^{p} \lambda_i = 1$. The weights, λ_i are positive real values. The method is that it is easy to implement and the scalarised problem is of the same degree of difficulty as the original MOO problem. However, the weights have to be assigned beforehand and a large perturbation in weights does not always lead to a corresponding change in the objectives. As a result, the generated Pareto points are strongly dependent on expert knowledge and this might lead to points that are biased. Alternatively, weight vectors can be randomly generated to try and obtain a sufficient coverage of the Pareto front.

In our study, the weights are randomly chosen from the uniform distribution to achieve multiple search directions.

2.2. Sandwich algorithm

The basic idea behind the algorithm is that inner and outer approximations of the Pareto set are constructed iteratively until the difference (error) between the two approximations falls below a given tolerance. This approach can help to reduce the number of solutions of the scalarised problem that need to be obtained to construct a good approximation of the Pareto front (Rennen et al., 2011). In this study, the tolerance of error is taken as 10^{-3}.

2.3. Global phase for WS and SD

A challenge in applying WS and SD to nonconvex MOO problems is ensuring that the global solution of each scalarised problem is identified, as local solutions are dominated

Table 1: Algorithmic parameters for MLSL, GA, and NSGA-II

(a) Literature source of parameters			(b) Heuristic parameters	
Parameters		Source	Parameters	value
R_k	Critical distance	Kucherenko et al.,(2005)	Cooling parameter (SA)	0.8
Encoding	Tree-structure	Zhou et al. (2016)	No. of initial points (MLSL)	100
Fitness	Gaussian-like	Liu et al. (2018)	No. of population (NSGA-II)	150
Operators	Mutation, crossover	Zhou et al. (2016)	No. of generations (NSGA-II)	500
Selection	Tournament	Liu et al. (2018)	Mutation fraction (NSGA-II)	0.2
Stopping	No. of generations	Table (1b)	Crossover fraction (NSGA-II)	0.8

solutions of the MOO rather than Pareto-optimal points. In this work, Multi-Level Single Linkage (MLSL) (Kucherenko and Sytsko, 2005) and Simulated Annealing (SA) (Marcoulaki and Kokossis, 2000) are used. The MLSL method is based on the simple idea of enumerating all the local minima by starting a local minimization procedure at a set of starting points generated by a Sobol' sequence, combined with a clustering method in which the local search procedure is applied to a sample point, only if there is no other sample point within some critical distance (R_k) which has a lower objective function value. In the SA algorithm, the analogy of the heating and slow cooling of a metal so that a uniform crystalline state can be achieved is adopted to guide the search for an optimal point. The key algorithmic feature of SA is that it encourages a more extensive exploration of the search space, thereby increasing likelihood of global solution. The parameters were carefully chosen based on the statistical experiment and the values are listed in Table 1.

2.4. Non-dominated Sorting Genetic Algorithm-II (NSGA-II)

The NSGA-II algorithm (Deb et al., 2000) is a particular form of genetic algorithm (GA) and is one of the most widely-used MOO evolutionary algorithms. NSGA-II is directly applicable to MOO as it uses an explicit diversity-preserving mechanism based on a crowding distance metric to generate uniformly distributed Pareto points. Furthermore, it makes use of elite-preserving operators to give "elite genes" an opportunity to survive in the next generation. To implement the NSGA-II into a solvent design, one needs to specify a suitable set of heuristic parameters. These parameters are specified in Table 1.

3. Comparative methodology

A CAMD application based on the design of a solvent for the chemical absorption CO_2 is introduced in Section 3.1 as an example that can be used to evaluate the performance of each method. The formulation is based on the recent work of Papadopoulos et al. (2016), who considered an extensive list of property criteria for MOO. The performance of the selected algorithms is analysed based on the criteria, as discussed in Section 3.2.

3.1. Objectives and constraints

Four of solvent properties considered by Papadopoulos et al. (2016) are selected as objective functions in this study, namely, liquid density (ρ), heat capacity (C_p), saturated vapour pressure (P_{vap}), and relative energy difference (RED). Several other performance criteria are considered as constraints: a) the normal melting point (T_m), to ensure that the solvent is in the liquid phase at the lowest process operating temperature, b) the normal

Table 2: property constraints   Table 3: Solvent design space

Physical properties, **g(n)**	Bounds	Functional groups	Bounds
ρ (g/cm^3)	[0.6,1.5]	CH$_2$-N< ,-CH$_2$-N<,	
RED	(0, 6.5]	CH$_2$-NH-,-CH$_2$-NH-,	
T_b (K)	[393, 550]	>CH-NH-,-CH$_2$-NH$_2$,	$n_{total}=13$
T_m (K)	[273,313]	>CH-NH$_2$,$\geq$C-NH$_2$,	$n_{tot,amine}=5$
σ (dyn/cm) at 25°C	[25, 60]	CH$_3$-,-CH$_2$-,	
μ (cP) at 40°C	(0,60]	>CH-,> C< , -OH	

boiling point (T_b) to avoid excessive evaporation at absorber operating conditions, c) the viscosity (μ) to ensure ease of transport and d) the surface tension (σ), to promote mass transfer performance. The property targets and performance criteria are summarised in Table 2. The SAFT-γ Mie group contribution equation of state (Papaioannou et al., 2014) is used to predict ρ, C_p, P_{vap}, and T_b. The Group Contribution (GC) methods are used for T_m, σ, RED (Hukkerikar et al., 2012) and μ (Hsu et al., 2002). A set of 13 functional groups (n_i, $i=1,...,N$, $N=13$) shown in Table 3 including 8 amine molecular groups are selected as molecular building blocks based on the applicability of the in property prediction methods used and knowledge of the problem (Papadopoulos et al., 2016).The mathematical formulation of the solvent design problem for CO_2 capture by chemical absorption is described as follows:

$$\min_{\mathbf{n}} \quad C_p, P_{vap}, RED$$

$$\max_{\mathbf{n}} \quad \rho_{solvent}$$

$$\text{s.t.} \quad \mathbf{g(n)} \leq 0$$

$$\sum_{i=1}^{N}(2-v_i)n_i - 2m = 0, \tag{1}$$

$$\sum_{j\in G_a}^{N} n_j - n_{tot,amine} \leq 0, \ (G_a : \text{amine groups}), \quad \sum_{i=1}^{N} n_i - n_{total} \leq 0$$

where **g(n)**: inequality constraints of the physical properties, v_i: valence of each group, m: structural parameter ($m=1$ for acyclic)

3.2. Algorithmic performance measures

In this study, three measures for comparing the performance of the algorithms are used: 1) average CPU times (CPU_{avg}, seconds); 2) the number of Pareto points found (N_{Pareto}); 3) hypervolume indicator (HV) (Zitzler et al., 2003). The CPU_{avg} is calculated by averaging the time taken to generate one point on the Pareto front. An algorithm with a lower value of this criterion is preferable. The number of unique Pareto optimal solutions obtained by algorithm is also considered. The algorithm with the highest value of this metric provides a more complete and diverse representation of the Pareto front. The hypervolume indicator represents the volume in the objective space that is covered by a set of Pareto points and a corresponding reference point (Zitzler et al., 2003). The indicator can provide a measure of closeness to the real Pareto set as well as of the diversity of the points.

4. Results and Discussion

In this section, we compare the relative performance of five algorithms: the WS with MLSL (WSML), WS with SA (WSSA), SD with MLSL (SDML), SD with SA (SDSA), and non-dominated sorting genetic algorithm-II (NSGA-II). All algorithms under comparison were implemented in MATLAB 2017a and interfaced with gPROMS Model Builder, which provides a standard MINLP solver. All computations were run under 64-bit Windows 10 on a single Intel i7-6700 3.4GHz processor core and with 8 GB of memory.

Table 4 summarises the performance of the global search methods, SA and MLSL in combination with WS and SD method. WS combined with the local MINLP solver is are used as a base case. The simulation data correspond to a set of 100 different weight vectors: an identical set of weight vectors was assigned to each algorithmic options. The results in Table 4 demonstrate that the WSML outperforms the WSSA such that the higher hypervolume can be achieved within the same cost of CPU time. This clearly indicates that the MOO algorithm with MLSL is more efficient. However, for both WSML and WSSA, only a small number of chemical structures (Pareto points) has been identified. This confirms that different weight vectors do not always lead to different solutions. As can be seen in the results of SDML and SDSA, systematically assigned weights also cannot generates different Pareto points for each iteration although the methods result in a larger set of Pareto points than WS. This is mainly due to the fact that the mapping of the weights into objective space assume that the feasible region is continuous. As a result, the assigned weights may result in same Pareto point as the problem is MINLP.

Table 5 summarises simulation results under a fixed CPU time (48 h) with respect to the performance measures. In the comparison between five combinations of algorithmic options, SDML produces the best results for two criteria, hypervolume and the number of Pareto points. The reason is that the SDML can deterministically guide the direction of the weight vector in a sequence of iterations, which increases the possibility of finding different Pareto points. This results largely imply that more difference in molecular structures and physical properties can be seen in the Pareto optimal set generated by SDML. In Table 5, the NSGA-II exhibits a relatively lower hypervolume than other tested methods although it generated a larger number of Pareto points within the allowed CPU time. This implies the accuracy of the Pareto front generated is not satisfactory when using NSGA-II with the parameters in Table 1.

Table 4: Comparison of global search methods

Metric	Base	WSML	WSSA	SDML	SDSA
No. of iterations	100	100	100	100	100
N_{Pareto}	20	12	14	54	50
HV	3.436	3.689	3.539	4.891	4.724
CPU_{avg} (s)	23	809	22106	818	17837

Table 5: Comparison of WSML, SDML, and NSGA-II algorithms

Metric	WSML	SDML	NSGA-II
CPU time (fixed, h)	48	48	48
N_{Pareto}	26	74	100
HV	3.982	5.832	0.672

5. Conclusion

In this paper, five different MOO algorithms have been compared by assessing their specific performance on a solvent design problem. To increase the probability of finding the true Pareto front, two different global search algorithms were combined with two scalarisation based methods. The algorithms were tested using a solvent design problem with four objective functions. For the global search phase, comparative results have highlighted the efficiency of the MLSL algorithm. In comparison to WSML and NSGA-II, SDML been found to have the best performance as it can generate a better distributed Pareto fronts in a given time frame, as indicated by the number of Pareto points generated and the hypervolume achieved. In a future work, the application of the methodologies will be extended to different size of CAMD problems to generalised the performance of the methods beyond the solvent design for the CO_2 removal.

Acknowledgements

The authors gratefully acknowledge financial support from the Engineering and Physical Sciences Research Council (EPSRC) of the UK (grants EP/M507878/1, EP/J003840), innovation programme under Grant Agreement No.727503 (ROLINCAP), and Centre for Process Systems Engineering Research Committee of Imperial College London via Roger Sargent scholarship.

References

J. Burger, N. Asprion, S. Blagov, R. Böttcher, U. Nowak, M. Bortz, R. Welke, K.-H. Küfer, H. Hasse, 2014. Multi-Objective Optimization and Decision Support in Process Engineering - Implementation and Application. Chemie Ing. Tech. 86 (7), 1065–1072.

K. Deb, A. Pratab, S. Moitra, 2000. Mechanical Component Design for Multiple Objectives Using Elitist Non-dominated Sorting GA. Proc. Parallel Probl. Solving from Nat. VI Conf. (i), 859–868.

R. H. Herring, M. R. Eden, 2015. Evolutionary algorithm for de novo molecular design with multi-dimensional constraints. Comput. Chem. Eng. 83, 267–277.

H.-C. Hsu, Y.-W. Sheu, C.-H. Tu, 2002. Viscosity estimation at low temperatures (Tr<0.75) for organic liquids from group contributions. Chem. Eng. J. 88, 27–35.

A. S. Hukkerikar, B. Sarup, A. Ten Kate, J. Abildskov, G. Sin, R. Gani, 2012. Group-contribution+(GC+) based estimation of properties of pure components: Improved property estimation and uncertainty analysis. Fluid Phase Equilib. 321, 25–43.

S. Kucherenko, Y. Sytsko, 2005. Application of deterministic low-discrepancy sequences in global optimization. Comput. Optim. Appl. 30 (3), 297–318.

X. Liu, Y. Zhao, P. Ning, H. Cao, H. Wen, 2018. Modified Structural Constraints for Candidate Molecule Generation in Computer-Aided Molecular Design. Ind. Eng. Chem. Res. 57 (20), 6937–6946.

E. Marcoulaki, A. Kokossis, 2000. On the development of novel chemicals using a systematic optimisation approach. Part II. Solvent design. Chem. Eng. Sci. 55 (13), 2547–2561.

A. I. Papadopoulos, S. Badr, A. Chremos, E. Forte, T. Zarogiannis, P. Seferlis, S. Papadokonstantakis, A. Galindo, G. Jackson, C. S. Adjiman, 2016. Computer-aided molecular design and selection of CO_2 capture solvents based on thermodynamics, reactivity and sustainability. Mol. Syst. Des. Eng. 1 (3), 313–334.

A. I. Papadopoulos, P. Linke, 2006. Efficient integration of optimal solvent and process design using molecular clustering. Chem. Eng. Sci. 61 (19), 6316–6336.

A. I. Papadopoulos, M. Stijepovic, P. Linke, P. Seferlis, S. Voutetakis, 2013. Toward Optimum Working Fluid Mixtures for Organic Rankine Cycles using Molecular Design and Sensitivity Analysis. Ind. Eng. Chem. Res. 52 (34), 12116–12133.

V. Papaioannou, T. Lafitte, C. Avendaño, C. S. Adjiman, G. Jackson, E. A. Müller, A. Galindo, 2014. Group contribution methodology based on the statistical associating fluid theory for heteronuclear molecules formed from Mie segments. J. Chem. Phys. 140 (5).

G. Rennen, E. R. Van Dam, D. Den Hertog, 2011. Enhancement of sandwich algorithms for approximating higher-dimensional convex pareto sets. INFORMS J. Comput. 23 (4), 493–517.

T. Zhou, S. Engineering, M. Reviewers, K. S. Prof, R. G. Prof, Z. Qi, 2016. Systematic Methods for Reaction Solvent Design and Integrated Solvent and Process Design (August).

E. Zitzler, L. Thiele, M. Laumanns, C. M. Fonseca, V. G. Da Fonseca, 2003. Performance assessment of multiobjective optimizers: An analysis and review. IEEE Trans. Evol. Comput. 7 (2), 117–132.

Anton A. Kiss, Edwin Zondervan, Richard Lakerveld, Leyla Özkan (Eds.)
Proceedings of the 29th European Symposium on Computer Aided Process Engineering
June 16th to 19th, 2019, Eindhoven, The Netherlands. © 2019 Elsevier B.V. All rights reserved.
http://dx.doi.org/10.1016/B978-0-128-18634-3.50008-4

Automated open-loop control of directed self-assembly with multiple electrokinetic actuators in microfluidic devices

Yu Gao, Richard Lakerveld*

Department of Chemical and Biological Engineering, The Hong Kong University of Science and Technology, Clear Water Bay, Hong Kong S.A.R
kelakerveld@ust.hk

Abstract

Directed self-assembly provides a novel processing route for the manufacture of structured materials. Future processes based on self-assembly will need to be equipped with suitable automated process controls for improving performance. Closed-loop control has been applied to directed self-assembly with one or two actuators when real-time and non-invasive observation is feasible. However, such observation may be challenging in practice. Furthermore, multiple actuators may have to be used for the self-assembly of complicated structures. In this work, an automated open-loop control method for directed self-assembly using multiple actuators is developed and tested experimentally. The method relies on a novel design of microelectrodes to assemble a specific number of particles in a desired area in a microfluidic device. An empirical model is developed to determine an optimal sequence of control actions. The experimental results show that the number of particles after the implementation of the open-loop control is close to the targeted number.

Keywords: directed self-assembly, open-loop control, modelling, electrokinetics

1. Introduction

Self-assembly is the spontaneous association of small molecules or particles into structures, which provides a novel processing route for the manufacture of materials with structures at the micro/nano-scale. Future manufacturing processes based on self-assembly will need to be equipped with suitable automated process controls to compensate for design uncertainty and to reject disturbances. Local actuation is required to fabricate specific structural features or to heal defects, which can be enabled by the introduction of external fields to direct the self-assembly (Ulissi et al., 2013; Paulson et al., 2015). Electric fields are of particular interest for local actuation due to their noninvasiveness and flexibility in manipulating particles according to a diverse set of electrokinetic phenomena that can be induced (Oh et al., 2009). Feedback control has been implemented for directed self-assembly to effectively assemble colloidal structures using one or two electrokinetic actuators when real-time observation is feasible (Juárez et al., 2012; Tang et al., 2016; Gao and Lakerveld, 2018). However, to enhance control performance or to assemble more complicated and possibly non-periodic structures, multiple actuators have to be used systematically to direct the self-assembly process. Such control is challenged by the stochastic nature of self-assembly, nonlinear process behavior and also by the design of the actuators. In case a system would not allow for real-time and non-invasive observation, an open-loop strategy has to be considered based on a suitable mathematic model (Komaee and Barton, 2016). Model-based control methods are particularly interesting for nonlinear systems when multiple actuators are available. However, experimental studies on the performance of such control methods for directed self-assembly are limited.

In this work, a novel automated open-loop control method for directed self-assembly of colloidal particles using multiple actuators to induce various electrokinetic phenomena in a microfluidic device is developed and characterized experimentally. The control objective is to adjust the particle densities of two neighbouring regions. Firstly, a triple-parallel microelectrode is fabricated to provide multiple actuators in the microfluidic device for directing the self-assembly process over the two neighbouring regions. The multiple-electrode actuators can be manipulated flexibly to exhibit four types of system state. By engineering the different electrokinetic interactions within the four states, particles can either be transferred between two regions or be maintained in individual regions. Subsequently, an open-loop control strategy based on an input-output model is designed to transfer a specific number of particles from one region to the other. Finally, the open-loop control is implemented experimentally for performance assessment.

2. Microfluidic design and system characterization

The microfluidic cell and the microelectrode design are illustrated in Figure 1. A suspension of microspheres (radius $1\mu m$) is placed between two transparent ITO-coated glass slides that act as electrodes. After approximately 20 minutes, the particles settle to form a two-dimensional system on the bottom electrode, where the ITO is patterned such that three actuators are available. The space between the adjacent actuators is defined as the density control area (see Figure 1B). Each actuator is connected independently to a channel of a function generator (33500B, Keysight Technologies) to apply AC electric fields. An optical microscope (Nikon, Ni-U) equipped with a digital camera (Nikon Digital Slight Qi2) and automated image analysis (Matlab, The Mathworks) are used to observe the positions of all particles in real time with a typical image processing time of 1s.

Four types of system state form the basis of the process model (see Figure 2), which can be realized with different combinations of the electric fields parameters (i.e. voltage v, frequency f) applied to the three actuators. These states are referred to as stabilization, shifting, collection and transfer. The transitions between the four states enable the transfer of particles between regions, which are dynamically modelled (Gao and Lakerveld, 2018). During the stabilization step (see Figure 1(A)), negative dielectrophoresis (nDEP) at a high field frequency is induced, which directs the particles towards an electric field minimum (Gao and Lakerveld, 2018). The particles cannot cross the middle actuator, which can be understood from a COMSOL simulation of the field strength distribution (see Figure 1(A)). The particles all accumulate near the field minimum, which allows for easier transfer in the next step, as the distance towards the middle actuator is similar for all particles. Note that the particles form chains due to their induced dipoles at this frequency. In the shifting step (Figure 1(B)), the voltage on the left actuator is increased and the voltage on the right actuator is decreased, which shifts the electric field minima.

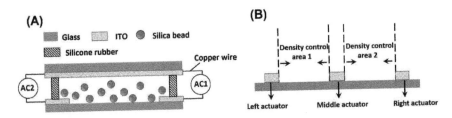

Figure 1. (A) Schematic design of the microfluidic device. (B) Illustration of the bottom electrode including density control areas and multiple actuators.

The shift causes the particles in the left control area to move closer to the middle actuator while the particles in the right control area move further away. In the collection step (Figure 1(C)), electroosmotic flow (EOF) at a low frequency is generated using only the middle actuator. The induced flow carries the particles from the left control area towards the middle actuator. Finally, in the transfer step (Figure 1(D)), the nDEP is induced again to transfer the particles collected at the middle actuator to the right control area. The electric field strength has been shaped such that only the particles on the middle actuator will be transferred to the right control area. The electric field parameters for each step are summarized in Table 1.

Table 1. Electric field parameters for the four types of state in Figure 2

	Left actuator		Middle actuator		Right actuator	
	f/kHz	v/volt	f/kHz	v/volt	f/kHz	v/volt
Stabilization	100	5	100	1	100	5
Shifting	100	8	100	1	100	1
Collection	-	-	5	0.5	-	-
Transfer	100	8	100	1	100	1

3. Model development and open-loop control design

To design an open-loop control strategy for transferring a specific number of particles from the left to the right control area, the dynamics of the collection step has to be modelled. To describe the dynamics of the collection step, two sets of experiments involving all four steps were conducted and the location of all particles as function of time were documented using optical microscopy and automated image analysis. Figure 3(A)-(B) shows the change in the number of particles that are present in the left control area during the collection step as function of time. The dynamic evolution of the change in the number of particles in the left control area with time can be modelled empirically using a fifth-order polynomial for both experiments. By taking the average of the two fifth-order polynomial models, the empirical model for simulating the collection dynamics is constructed as follows:

$$n(t) = 0.0000049t^5 - 0.00054t^4 + 0.02t^3 - 0.23t^2 + 0.81t + 0.057 \qquad (1)$$

where n represents the change of particle number in the left control area and t represents the implementation time of the collection step. Based on the four-step control framework and the empirical model for simulating the dynamics of the collection step, automated

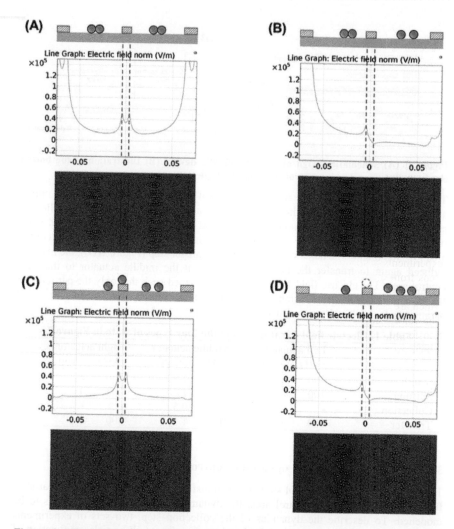

Figure 2. Illustration of the four types of system state with different electric field parameters. (A) Stabilization. (B) Shifting. (C) Collection. (D) Transfer. For each state, the top figure shows a schematic illustration of the locations of the particles. The middle figure shows the electric field strength distribution on the electrode surface from COMSOL simulation. The bottom figure shows a representative microscopy image.

open-loop control strategies can be designed to relocate a specific number of particles from the left density control area to the right density control area. The four steps are implemented sequentially and in an automated fashion using Matlab and an interface between Matlab and the function generator. To relocate a specific number of particles, the desired execution time for the collection step is estimated using the empirical model. Two open-loop strategies were designed and implemented for relocating 14 and 22 particles, corresponding to a transfer time of 21s and 25s, respectively.

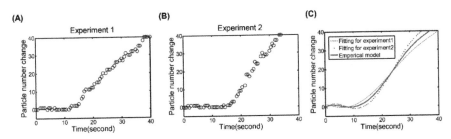

Figure 3. (A)-(B) The change in the number of particles in the left control area with respect to time during the collection step in an open-loop experiment. (C) Empirical model describing the dynamics of the collection step.

4. Control strategy implementation and performance assessment

The dynamic development of the particle number on the middle actuator for the two experiments with open-loop control is illustrated in Figure 4. Note that the different steps from the four-step control framework are labelled differently. It can be seen that 11 and 21 particles are relocated from the left to the right control area, respectively, which are equal to number of particles collected on the middle actuator (see Figure 4). The relocated particle numbers are close to the intended number of particles to be transferred (14 and 22, respectively) set as objective for the open-loop control strategy, which demonstrates the effectiveness of the proposed open-loop control strategy. The small deviation in the number of relocated particles can be due to the stochastic nature of the self-assembly process, which cannot be avoided in this type of system, or due to the inaccuracy of the process model.

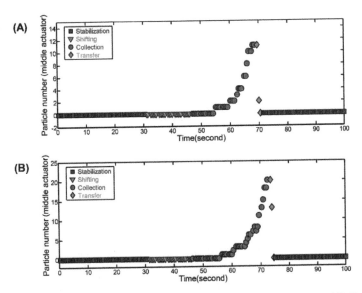

Figure 4. Dynamic change of the particle number on the middle actuator. (A) Open-loop control for relocating 15 particles. (B) Open-loop control for relocating 22 particles.

5. Conclusions and outlook

An automated open-loop control method for directed self-assembly using multiple actuators has been developed and experimentally validated in a microfluidic device. The method is illustrated with the control objective of transferring a specific number of particles from one control area to an adjacent control. The control approach has two main elements. First, a four-step framework can be utilized by engineering the different interactions between the particles and the electric fields. Second, an empirical model is used to describe the dynamics of the most critical step in that framework. The dynamic model is used to estimate the optimal actuation time for a given number of particles that need to be transferred to a different control area. The performance of two open-loop control experiments shows that the actually number of transferred particles is close to the targeted value. Since the involved interactions are generic, the approach can be applied to other small-scale objects such as nanoparticles or biological cells. Therefore, future work may focus on specific applications. The current framework may also provide a foundation for more comprehensive approaches to shape the particle density distributions over multiple control areas, which is needed for assembling complicated structures at the micro/nano-scale (Lakerveld et al., 2012; Solis et al., 2010). Finally, future work will involve using first principles for the development of the process model to improve the predictive capability of the model.

This work is financially supported by Hong Kong Research Grant Council No.16214617

References

Y. Gao, R. Lakerveld, 2018, Feedback control for defect-free alignment of colloidal particles, Lab on a Chip, 18, 2099-2110

Y. Gao, R. Lakerveld, 2018, Feedback control for shaping density distributions of colloidal particles in microfluidic devices, submitted

J. Juárez, P. Mathai, J. Liddle, M. Bevan, 2012, Multiple electrokinetic actuators for feedback control of colloidal size, Lab on a Chip, 12, 20, 4063-4070

A. Komaee, P. Barton, 2016, Directed self-assembly of linear nanostructures by optimal control of external electrical fields , arXiv preprint arXiv: 1603.00113

R. Lakerveld, G. Stephanopoulos, P. Barton, 2012, A master-equation approach to simulate kinetic traps during directed self-assembly, The Journal of chemical physics, 136, 18, 184109

J. Oh, R. Hart, J. Capurro, H.M. Noh, 2009, Comprehensive analysis of particle motion under non-uniform AC electric fields in a microchannel, Lab on a Chip, 9, 1, 62-78

J. Paulson, A. Mesbah, X. Zhu, M. Molaro, R. Braatz, 2015, Control of self-assembly in micro- and nano-scale systems, Journal of Process Control, 27, 38-39

E. Solis, P. Barton, G. Stephanopoulos, 2010, Controlled Formation of Nanostructures with Desired Geometries. 2. Robust dynamic paths, Industrial&Engineering Chemistry Research, 49, 17, 7746-7757

X. Tang, B. Rupp, Y. Yang, T. Edwards, M. Grover, M. Bevan, 2016, Optimial Feedback Controlled Assembly of Perfect Crystals, ACS nano, 10, 7, 6791-6798

Z. Ulissi, M. Strano, R. Braatz, 2013, Control of nano and microchemical systems, Computers and Chemical Engineering, 51, 149-156

Anton A. Kiss, Edwin Zondervan, Richard Lakerveld, Leyla Özkan (Eds.)
Proceedings of the 29th European Symposium on Computer Aided Process Engineering
June 16th to 19th, 2019, Eindhoven, The Netherlands. © 2019 Elsevier B.V. All rights reserved.
http://dx.doi.org/10.1016/B978-0-128-18634-3.50009-6

Automatic synthesis of distillation processes for the separation of azeotropic multi-component systems

Thulasi Sasi[a], Jonas Wesselmann[a], Hanns Kuhlmann[a] and Mirko Skiborowski[a,*]

[a]*TU Dortmund University, Department of Chemical and Biochemical Engineering, Laboratory of Fluid Separations, Emil-Figge-Strasse 70, D-44227 Dortmund, Germany*
mirko.skiborowski@tu-dortmund.de

Abstract

The synthesis of distillation processes for azeotropic systems is a complex task for which commercial simulation software mainly offers a graphical analysis of residue curve maps for ternary (sub)systems or an iterative evaluation based on tedious simulation studies. The current work presents a novel algorithmic approach that aims at an automatic synthesis of distillation-based separation processes for azeotropic systems. Building only on a thermodynamic model of the multi-component mixture, split feasibility at both limiting operating conditions of total reflux and reversible distillation are considered. Possible process variants including the integration of suitable recycle streams are automatically generated and stored in a tree structure and the incorporation of an efficient pinch-based shortcut method provides initial estimates of the required energy demand of the generated process variants. The application of the proposed method is illustrated for the separation of a four and five component azeotropic mixture, which allow comparison with previous publications.

Keywords: conceptual design, flowsheet optimization, azeotropic distillation

1. Introduction

Conceptual process design is of imminent importance in process development, since the choices made in this early stage account for about 80% of the final cost of the entire process (Biegler et al., 1997). Due to the reliability and robustness, distillation still represents the default choice in fluid separation processes. However, the evaluation of split feasibility and the synthesis of alternative separation processes presents a significant challenge for the separation of azeotropic multi-component mixtures. While finding the optimal process configuration for the separation of a zeotropic mixture is a combinatorial problem, for which all alternative sequences can be generated automatically and only the computational demand increases with an increasing number of components (Agrawal, 2003), the feasibility of certain splits for azeotropic mixtures is governed by the location of the azeotropes and the emanating distillation boundaries. Only few methods for the generation of a distillation-based separation of azeotropic mixtures have been proposed. None of them was designed to be fully automatic and none is available in a commercial software tool. Wahnschafft et al. (1993) have developed a synthesis tool called *Split*, which is based on a blackboard architectural model for developing separation processes. Although their work provides significant insight into the use of recycles for separation processes, its application for automatic sequencing is limited. A major simplification is the initial grouping of binary *separation tasks*, before selecting applicable separation methods. Rooks et al. (1998) have devised a generalized algorithm to synthesize separation sequences based on the creation of adjacency and reachability matrices, similar to the proximity and reachability matrix proposed by Poellmann and Blass

(1994). Feasible splits are further identified based on the so called *common saddle test*, which checks if the residue curves (RC) for the top and bottom products approach a common saddle. This feasibility check is fully algorithmic, very efficient and allows for the identification of feasible splits considering total reflux operation. However, as pointed out by Thong and Jobson (2001a), it excludes a lot of feasible splits especially for azeotropic mixtures. In a series of articles, Thong and Jobson (2001a,b,c) and Thong et al. (2004) developed an alternative approach, which builds on the evaluation of a linear approximation of the operating leaves/manifolds for rectifying and stripping section to determine split feasibility. Furthermore, the generation of sequences with the possibility of internal recycles is developed on the basis of the split feasibility test in combination with the topological analysis of distillation regions on the basis of the adjacency and reachability matrices. While the developed method is very sophisticated, the considered linear approximation of the operating manifolds is equivalent to the rectification bodies at total reflux (Bausa et al., 1998), such that feasibility is also determined primarily for total reflux operation. Another algorithmic approach was presented by Wasylkiewicz (2006) and was even available for some time in ASPEN *Distil*, which is however no longer part of the software. The tool was also based on the identification of the topological distillation regions in order to identify feasible products and propose potential recycle streams. The latest effort on an algorithmic feasibility test was proposed by Brüggemann and Marquardt (2011). Opposite to all previous approaches this test is based on the concept of pitchfork distillation boundaries (PDB), which represent the distillation boundaries for reversible, rather than total reflux distillation. It was not applied in the synthesis of alternative variants, but rather for the optimization of fixed process flowsheets with shortcut models (Brüggemann and Marquardt, 2011). While the test implements a sophisticated homotopy continuation algorithm and bifurcation analysis, the identification of valid solutions in case of intersecting branches presents a significant challenge.

While currently no tools exist that consider both limiting operating modes, reversible distillation and total reflux operation, several studies showed that a simultaneous consideration can extend the range of feasible splits for distillation (Wahnschafft et al., 1992; Krolikowski, 2006; Kraemer et al., 2009). The current article fills this gap by proposing such a feasibility test and illustrates how an automatic generation of process variants for the separation of azeotropic multi-component systems can be accomplished. Feasible splits are determined based on the highest purity products w.r.t. the different modes of operation and validated through application of the rectification body method (RBM) (Bausa et al., 1998), which does not only indicate the intersection of rectifying and stripping profiles, but also provides an estimate of the energy requirements for the single splits. The developed methodology is introduced in Section 2 and illustrated for two representative case studies in Section 3, before some conclusions and an outlook are presented in Section 4.

2. Methodology

The general concept of the developed methodology is illustrated in Figure 1 and is composed of three consecutive steps. First, a topological analysis of the given mixture is performed based on the thermodynamic property models. The computation of all azeotropes allows for a characterization of all singular points (SP) (Skiborowski et al., 2016), which present the basis for further computation of pinch lines (PL) as well as the adjacency and reachability matrices (Rooks et al., 1998). The latter is used for the computation of the topological distillation region (DR) and distillation boundaries (DB), as well as the compartments for each DR (Thong and Jobson, 2001a), which are stored as ordered subsets of the SP. The second step computes feasible splits based on the generated topological information in combination with the computation of RC and PL, as well as the RBM, and stores the resulting information in a tree structure. Different branches of the tree, which are generated sequentially, can finally be converted to respective column sequences. After specifying the initial feed stream, possible sequences are generated based on a recursive algorithm, which evaluates the products of each split as new feed streams on a subsequent layer, until the desired products are obtained or no further splits are feasible. The results are stored

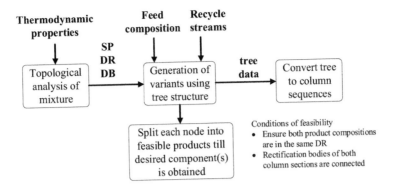

Figure 1: Schematic overview of the methodology for distillation process synthesis

in a tree-like structure, which links the feed and products via a number of nodes. These nodes represent the single splits that are located on different branches, which can subsequently be translated into corresponding column sequences. Figure 2 presents an exemplary illustration, which also indicates the consideration of a recycle stream and the translation of a branch (shaded) into the corresponding column sequence. Each layer of the tree is composed of alternative splits, for which distillate and bottom product result that each are potentially processed as feed streams on individual sub layers. For each feed stream that is to be separated, the topological DR is determined, by evaluating the terminals of the RC and PL passing through the feed composition. The RC is computed using the Runge-Kutta method and the PL is computed using continuation and bifurcation methods as described in more detail in the article of Skiborowski et al. (2016). Subsequently all SP of the feed DR are considered as possible products and a split feasibility test is performed in order to evaluate if a sharp split is feasible, or if a DB is limiting the separation. For the latter, the highest possible purity (HPP) of the opposing product on the DB is determined, based on a bisection along the mass balance line, monitoring the terminals of the RC and PL. As long as the terminals are equivalent for both products, they are located within the same DR, while the change of any terminal indicates the transition to another DR. The transition point for the PL marks a point on the PDB, while the transition of the RC marks the corresponding location of the simple distillation boundary (SDB). This test can be performed efficiently for any number of components, and directly provides information on differences between the feasibility at total reflux and reversible distillation thus circumventing the complexities of the pitchfork bifurcation analysis proposed by Brüggemann and Marquardt (2011). Starting the bisection based on the potential sharp separation, product compositions located in a different DR than the feed composition, so-called curved boundary processes, are automatically identified as feasible splits in case the terminals of the RC and PL through the products are equivalent.

The determination of HPP products is essential for the final step of the split evaluation, which is the computation of the minimum energy duty (MED) based on the RBM (Bausa et al., 1998). The general idea of the RBM is to check for the intersection of the tray-to-tray profiles of the stripping and the rectifying section, which is also considered as the sufficient criteria for split feasibility. In order to do this efficiently, the RBM uses linear approximations of the manifolds of possible tray-to-tray profiles based on respective pinch points for specific reflux and reboil ratios. The underlying assumption of an infinite number of equilibrium trays per section mandates the specification of HPP products. Therefore, the initial split feasibility test provides the necessary product specifications for a reliable application of the RBM that furthermore determines an MED estimate, which indicates if the column profiles of both sections intersect. The MED can further be used to rank the different sequences, which are generated by the algorithm.

In case the desired products are located outside the feed distillation region and curved boundary

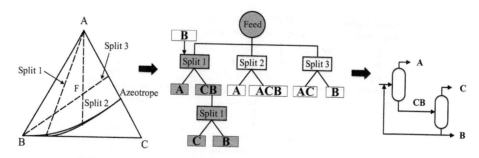

Figure 2: Exemplary illustration of the tree structure and a derived column sequence for the separation of an (A)cetone-(C)hloroform-(B)enzene mixture

splits are not feasible, recycle options can be included in the evaluation on demand. Hereby, the different SP are considered as internal recycle in order to reach the preferred DR, i.e. the DR with the desired product (Wasylkiewicz, 2006). In order to limit the number of options, potential recycle streams can be defined upfront. Necessary recycle ratios to shift the mixed feed to the preferred DR are again determined based on a bisection that aims at the maximization of the recovery of the desired product. After the variant generation, it needs to be checked if the necessary amount of the recycled stream is generated in the corresponding sequence. In the exemplary illustration of Figure 2, the possible recycle of benzene enables a full separation of acetone, as also demonstrated in the manual analysis of Wahnschafft et al. (1992). If only a fraction of a stream that is not a desired product is recycled, a post-processing step evaluates the feasibility of a full recycle, as will be illustrated in the subsequent case study. The methodology is implemented in a computer-based tool, which is primarily coded in Matlab and C-coded subroutines for thermodynamic property calculations and computation of all SP, RC and PL, which are available as open source code[1].

3. Case Studies

The application of the developed methodology is illustrated for the separation of a quaternary and a quinary mixture. The first case study considers the separation of an equimolar mixture of acetone, chloroform, benzene and toluene (ACBT). The mixture exhibits a maximum boiling azeotrope between acetone and chloroform and a respective DB, for which SDB and PDB deviate considerably, as illustrated in Figure 3. This mixture and possible separation sequences have been analysed in multiple studies (Thong and Jobson, 2001c; Kraemer et al., 2009) and the results of the proposed algorithm are further compared with the MED computations of Kraemer et al. (2009), who build up on the results of the process synthesis performed by Thong and Jobson (2001c). Figure 4 illustrates a combination of the four configurations (a-d) that were considered by Kraemer et al. (2009) and the highest ranked three configurations (b,d,e) of the

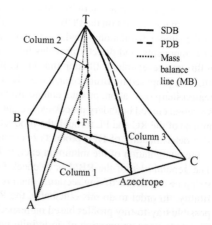

Figure 3: Illustration of the ACBT system and MB of variant (b) (cf. Fig. 4)

[1]Softwaresammlung Prozesssynthese (http://www.avt.rwth-aachen.de/cms/AVT/Forschung/Software/ iptu/Softwaresammlung-Prozesssynthese/)

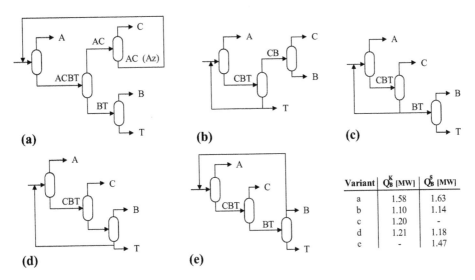

Figure 4: Alternative flowsheets for the separation of an equimolar mixture of acetone-chloroform-benzene-toluene (ACBT) alongwith their corresponding minimum reboiler duties

total 18 configurations, which are generated by the proposed synthesis method for the same feed and thermodynamic model as used by Kraemer et al. (2009). From the four variants considered by Kraemer et al. (2009), only variant (c) is not generated by the proposed method, since at current state only SP are considered as valid recycle streams. However, comparing the results in the embedded table it becomes apparent that the remaining three variants are evaluated with comparable MED by the current method (Q_B^S) and the approach by Kraemer et al. (2009) (Q_B^K) and that variant (b) is considered as lowest MED variant in both evaluations. The differences can be explained by different recycle rates, as Kraemer et al. (2009) perform a minimization of the MED for each process, applying the PDB criteria of Brüggermann and Marquardt (2011). While they report computational times of ~ 1000 s for each variant, the synthesis and ranking of the 18 variants in the current method is performed in less than 60 s.

To further illustrate the applicability of the method, the separation of a 25 mol-% acetone, 40 mol-% chloroform, 25 mol-% methanol, 5 mol-% ethanol and 5 mol-% benzene (ACMEB) mixture, as analysed in the article of Wasylkiewicz (2006), is studied. The quinary mixture exhibits six binary, two ternary and a quaternary azeotrope. The topological analysis identifies four distillation regions, with each of them containing four to six compartments. As in the study of Wasylkiewicz (2006), purified ethanol and benzene are to be separated from the feed. While overall nine process variants are generated by the proposed synthesis method, only the variant illustrated in Figure 5 allows for a full recovery of both products in only three columns. Herein, methanol is used as internal recycle, which enables a full separation of ethanol in the second column. However, the post-processing step shows that the

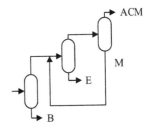

Figure 5: Process variant for ACMEB case study.

introduced methanol stream cannot be fully recovered from the third column. In fact, the generated process variant is equivalent to the one proposed by Wasylkiewicz (2006). However, Wasylkiewicz (2006) proposed operation of the third column at lower pressure, which then enables a closed methanol recycle. Thus, the case study illustrates the capability of the proposed method to automatically generate feasible process configuration for this complex multi-component system, but also illustrates that further extensions, e.g. for the consideration of pressure variations, are required to further extend the search space.

4. Conclusion and outlook

The current article introduces a fully automated method for the synthesis of distillation processes for the separation of homogeneous azeotropic mixtures. The method is not restricted to any number of components and incorporates a general feasibility test, which examines both limiting operational modes for distillation, total reflux as well as reversible distillation. The integration of the rectification body method further checks for an intersection of the rectifying and stripping profiles and provides an estimate of the minimum energy duty that is used for a direct ranking of the generated variants. The only requirements for the application of the method is a reliable thermodynamic model of the multi-component mixture. The current implementation further allows for an automatic consideration of the singular points as internal recycle streams. Future work will focus on the extension of the method towards alternative and more complex recycle options, pressure variations, as well as other process options, like extractive and heteroazeotropic distillation for heterogeneous mixtures. Furthermore, an automatic evaluation of different options for energy-integration, as proposed by Skiborowski (2018), is considered as future post-processing step.

References

Agrawal, R., 2003. Synthesis of multicomponent distillation column configurations. AIChE J. 49 (2), 379–401.

Bausa, J., Watzdorf, R. v., Marquardt, W., 1998. Shortcut methods for nonideal multicomponent distillation: I. simple columns. AIChE J. 44 (10), 2181–2198.

Biegler, L. T., Grossmann, I. E., Westerberg, A. W., 1997. Systematic methods for chemical process design. Prentice Hall, Old Tappan, NJ (United States).

Brüggemann, S., Marquardt, W., 2011. Conceptual design of distillation processes for mixtures with distillation boundaries: I. computational assessment of split feasibility. AIChE J. 57 (6), 1526–1539.

Brüggermann, S., Marquardt, W., 2011. Conceptual design of distillation processes for mixtures with distillation boundaries. ii. optimization of recycle policies. AIChE J. 57 (6), 1540–1556.

Kraemer, K., Kossack, S., Marquardt, W., 2009. Efficient optimization-based design of distillation processes for homogeneous azeotropic mixtures. Ind. Eng. Chem. Res. 48 (14), 6749–6764.

Krolikowski, L. J., 2006. Determination of distillation regions for non-ideal ternary mixtures. AIChE J. 52 (2), 532–544.

Poellmann, P., Blass, E., 1994. Best products of homogeneous azeotropic distillations. Gas Sep. Purif. 8 (4), 194–228.

Rooks, R. E., Julka, V., Doherty, M. F., Malone, M. F., 1998. Structure of distillation regions for multicomponent azeotropic mixtures. AIChE J. 44 (6), 1382–1391.

Skiborowski, M., 2018. Fast screening of energy and cost efficient intensified distillation processes. Chem. Eng. Trans. 69, 199–204.

Skiborowski, M., Bausa, J., Marquardt, W., 2016. A unifying approach for the calculation of azeotropes and pinch points in homogeneous and heterogeneous mixtures. Ind. Eng. Chem. Res. 55 (24), 6815–6834.

Thong, D. Y.-C., Jobson, M., 2001a. Multicomponent homogeneous azeotropic distillation 1. assessing product feasibility. Chem. Eng. Sci. 56 (14), 4369–4391.

Thong, D. Y.-C., Jobson, M., 2001b. Multicomponent homogeneous azeotropic distillation 2. column design. Chem. Eng. Sci. 56 (14), 4393–4416.

Thong, D. Y.-C., Jobson, M., 2001c. Multicomponent homogeneous azeotropic distillation 3. column sequence synthesis. Chem. Eng. Sci. 56 (14), 4417–4432.

Thong, D. Y.-C., Liu, G., Jobson, M., Smith, R., 2004. Synthesis of distillation sequences for separating multicomponent azeotropic mixtures. Chem. Eng. Process.: Process Intensification 43 (3), 239–250.

Wahnschafft, O. M., Koehler, J. W., Blass, E., Westerberg, A. W., 1992. The product composition regions of single-feed azeotropic distillation columns. Ind. Eng. Chem. Res. 31 (10), 2345–2362.

Wahnschafft, O. M., Le Rudulier, J. P., Westerberg, A. W., 1993. A problem decomposition approach for the synthesis of complex separation processes with recycles. Ind. Eng. Chem. Res. 32 (6), 1121–1141.

Wasylkiewicz, S. K., 2006. Synthesis of separation systems for azeotropic mixtures: Preferred distillation region. Comput.-Aided Chem. Eng. 21, 1033–1038.

Anton A. Kiss, Edwin Zondervan, Richard Lakerveld, Leyla Özkan (Eds.)
Proceedings of the 29th European Symposium on Computer Aided Process Engineering
June 16th to 19th, 2019, Eindhoven, The Netherlands. © 2019 Elsevier B.V. All rights reserved.
http://dx.doi.org/10.1016/B978-0-128-18634-3.50010-2

Design and Planning of Agri-Food Supply Chains

Lourenço Cruz[a], João Pires-Ribeiro[a] and Ana Barbosa-Póvoa[a,*]

[a]*CEG-IST, Universidade de Lisboa, Av. Rovisco Pais 1, 1049-001 Lisboa, Portugal*
apovoa@tecnico.ulisboa.pt

Abstract

This paper develops a mixed-integer linear programming (MILP) formulation to support the design and planning of agri-food supply chains (AFSC). The model focuses on the strategic-tactical decisions of capacity definition, selection of processing technologies, and the establishment of product flows to achieve expected net present value (ENPV) maximisation. Within the model, AFSC-specific characteristics are modelled as is the case of product perishability, flexible storage strategies, and reverse logistics operations. Supply and demand uncertainty is considered using a stochastic scenarios tree. The model is tested via the application of a case study from an existing sugar beet processing supply chain in The Netherlands.

Keywords: agri-food supply chain, perishability, reverse logistics, uncertainty

1. Introduction

With a growing world population and worldwide problems such as water scarcity and desertification, providing food on a global level will continue to be a challenge, one to which AFSC need to adapt to, cemented on solid drivers for change. Within the major drivers, sustainability concerns should be highlighted. Awareness for environmental impacts is currently on the rise, with a considerable portion of consumers beginning to adapt their consumption habits to reflect such concerns. Social concerns are also becoming generalised. These concerns, which span from supporting locally-grown products to investing in local job creation, lead customers to preferring a closer proximity to farms and markets, as well as paying more attention to the origin of their products. Naturally, this pushes supply chains (SC) towards a more local (decentralised) configuration and puts emphasis on product freshness and traceability. Finally, the access to ever-evolving technologies pushes changes and sector improvement at an increasing rate where uncertainty has to be dealt at both demand and supply sides.

This context creates a high level of complexity when designing and planning AFSC, that imply the development of decisions in tools, where AFSC characteristics are accounted for, so as to support the decisions makers in their decision making process.

In this paper we explore this need and a MILP modelling approach is proposed. This has a strategic-tactical breadth and focuses on defining technology and storage capacity for each AFSC facility, accounting for processing pathway selection, and definition of product flows between entities while considering the main ASFC characteristics as are product perishability, flexible storage strategies, reverse logistics operations, under a context where uncertainty on demand and supply exist.

The paper is structured as follows: Section 2 performs a literature review of papers addressing the design and planning of AFSC with quantitative methods. In Section 3, the major problem characteristics are introduced and briefly explained. In Section 4, the modelled objective is analysed, and novelties introduced explained. Section 5 highlights the details of the case study used to assess model performance. In Section 6, the results of the application of the case study are presented and discussed. Finally, Section 7 uses all previously gathered knowledge to arrive at conclusions and suggest future research directions.

2. Literature Review

The number of papers focusing on the design and planning of AFSC using quantitative models has been steadily increasing (Tsolakis et al., 2014), mostly due to the ever-increasing relevance of the topic on a worldwide scale. Sustainability is one of the most important current concerns. However, most authors still primarily address economic objectives, with just two publications addressing environmental sustainability without simultaneously pursuing economic goals (Banasik et al., 2017; Pipatprapa et al., 2016).

Among SC characteristics, a major focus is verified in centralised SC, against fewer which explicitly focus on decentralised configurations. This is particularly concerning, as decentralisation strategies may be a solution for current environmental and social challenges. In fact, decentralisation allows for the reduction of transportation costs and emissions, and supports local food production and job creation (Bosona and Gebresenbet, 2011; Accorsi et al., 2018). Apart from this, most studies have also addressed forward-oriented SC exclusively, in which reverse logistics are not considered. With current sustainability and waste reduction concerns on the rise, it is expected that the role of reverse and closed-loop SC will only increase (Barbosa-Póvoa et al., 2018). In light of this paradigm, the work of Banasik et al. (2017) must be highlighted, as it focuses on closing the loops in AFSC with the use of multi-objective optimisation.

In the literature is also clear that AFSC possess a series of characteristics which render them unlike any other, reason for which specific tools need to be devised for these SC. Among these, the high level of uncertainty verified in both supply and demand must be highlighted. Naturally, the inclusion of uncertainty modelling is an important trait when evaluating currently-proposed methodologies. Disregarding uncertainty drives models away from reality and, consequently, limits their applicability. When accounting for supply and demand uncertainty, it is clear that attention has been given to demand uncertainty. With fewer publications contributing with both demand and lead time uncertainty considerations (Galal and El-Kilany, 2016). Apart from recognising which authors address AFSC with uncertainty-encompassing approaches, the analysis of which methods have been used to model uncertainty is also interesting. Stochastic models are the more popular approach towards incorporating uncertainty in models.

To support solving some of the knowledge gaps identified throughout the literature review, this paper develops a generic model to assist decision makers on the design and planning of AFSC. The model achieves this goal by incorporating underexplored characteristics in the existing literature, such as reverse logistics, integration of both supply and demand uncertainty, as well as perishability and flexible storage strategies.

3. Problem Characteristics

A generic AFSC is here considered and it consists of five echelons: suppliers, which ensure the supply of raw materials; factories/processors, which use raw materials to manufacture products; warehouses/ distributors, which store products for posterior sale and distribute them to retailers; retailers, where products are sold to end consumers; and reprocessors, which receive wasted products from the remaining SC and produce other valuable products from them, which are then sold to end consumers. The different production processes are represented as technologies, which have associated production costs and bills of materials. To model supply and demand uncertainty, a stochastic scenario tree was established. Each tree node is associated to a randomised occurrence probability and has associated supply and demand variation rates. The problem can be described as follows:

Given: A set of products (raw materials, intermediate products, and final products); **a set of technologies**, which convert raw materials to intermediate and final products with associated operating costs, material inputs, and outputs; **a set of entities** (suppliers, processors, distributors, markets, and reprocessors) with associated locations and transportation costs, associated technology capacity, associated storage capacity, and associated demand.

Select the: Technology capacity to use in each entity in each time period; stored quantity in each entity in each time period; product flows between entities in each time period.

Subject to: Inventory/storage constraints; technology constraints; transportation constraints; demand constraints; supply constraints; reprocessing constraints; uncertainty-encompassing constraints.

4. Model Formulation

This section describes the modelled objective and puts emphasis on the differences operated from the modelling approach first proposed by Cardoso et al. (2013), which has been taken as basis for this work.

Equation 1 corresponds to the objective of ENPV maximisation, where the ENPV is expressed as a function of the cash flows $(CF_{s,t})$ of each time period (and scenario), corresponding interest rate (ir) and the probability of occurrence of each stochastic node.

$$maxENPV = \sum_{t \varepsilon T} prob_s \times \frac{CF_{s,t}}{(1+ir)^t} \tag{1}$$

Supply uncertainty has been pinpointed as one of the areas in which research is lacking. AFSC frequently show mismatches between supply and demand due to high lead times. To mimic this condition, the supply is a theoretical value (for instance, the total production from the arable land of a farm), which never truly corresponds to the effective supply that comes from it, due to inevitable loses. To mitigate such uncertainty, to the maximum expected production capabilities are then taken fractions corresponding to the various sources of loss and uncertainty that affect AFSC, Equation 2. This equation agglomerates all sources of waste in farms to obtain the total spoiled quantity in a given time period $(SQ_{p,v,t})$. The first element on the right hand side, takes into account what is produced $(W_{v,p,s,t}^{out1})$ and immediately spoiled $(imw f_{p,v})$ on each facility; the second element considers the mismatch between supply and demand and the spoilage created by excessive supply $(p_{p,v,t}^{farm})$; finally the third element considers the spoilage $(lostsf_{p,v,t})$ in inventory $(INV_{v,p,s,t})$ along the supply chain.

$$\sum_{p\varepsilon raw(p)} SQ_{p,v,t} = \sum_{p\varepsilon raw(p)} (W_{v,p,s,t}^{out1} \times imwf_{p,v}) + \sum_{p} p_{p,v,t}^{farm} + \tag{2}$$

$$\sum_{p\varepsilon raw(p)} (INV_{v,p,s,t} \times lostsf_{p,v,t}) \quad \forall v\varepsilon v_{sup} \wedge p\varepsilon P_{raw} \wedge (s,t)\varepsilon S \tag{3}$$

The inclusion of reverse logistics is also of extreme relevance since it is able to generate value with otherwise disposable products. The production of the reprocessors $(W_{i,v,p,s,t}^{out})$ is considered in Equation 4, as a function of the waste input $(W_{i,v,p,s,t}^{in})$ taking into account both the raw material requirements necessary to produce the new product $(qrmat_{p,p'})$ and what can be used from reprocessed products $(reprof_{p,v})$.

$$W_{i,v,u,s,t}^{in} \times reprof_{v,u} = \sum_{p\varepsilon raw(p)} (W_{i,v,p,s,t}^{out} \times qrmat_{u,p}) \tag{4}$$

5. Case Study and results

The case study here described is based on the work by Jonkman et al. (2018), a schematic of the SC in presented in Figure 1. The case study was divided in three different scenarios, all with specific changes meant to be addressed comparatively to assess the applicability of the model to a realistic context. The different scenarios are structured as follows: **Case A**: the expansion of an existing AFSC is considered, in which storage is allowed solely in warehouses, and under supply and demand uncertainty; **Case B**: the expansion of the same AFSC is considered, but storage is allowed in every echelon, and under supply and demand uncertainty; **Case C**: the expansion of the same AFSC is considered, in which storage is allowed in every echelon, under supply and demand uncertainty, and including a reprocessing echelon where reverse logistics operations are allowed.

The SC includes two processing facilities (factories), and two potential processing facilities, one equipped with conventional technology, and one with a small scale bio-refinery technology. The processing echelon is served by 43 suppliers. The distribution echelon includes 4 facilities, and serves a total of 17 markets. For the third scenario, the reprocessing echelon corresponds to facilities in which reprocessing technologies are installed.

As final results, an ENPV of €3074961.95, 3080248.23, and 4053404.26 were obtained for Cases A, B, and C, respectively. The economic performance between Cases A and B is not remarkably different, as the added storage capacity throughout the SC can help prevent product wastage, but only up to a certain level, as product perishability prevents keeping high inventory levels. Still, as can be seen, this added storage capacity does impact the economic performance positively, even if not in a striking manner. However, the same does not hold true for Case C, in which a considerably higher economic performance is

Table 1: Economic and service level results

	Case A	Case B	Case C
ENPV (€)	3074961.95	3080248.23	4053404.26
Unmet demand (%)	9.8	7.6	6.5

achieved due to the additional sales unlocked by the existence of reverse logistics, Table1.

In fact, the addition of reverse logistics does provide a very meaningful increase in the maximum registered ENPV, a finding which goes well in line with what is seen in the literature review. The appropriate response to the subsequent additions of AFSC characteristics also translates the correct behaviour of the model when addressing the AFSC context, one of the desired goals of this work.

It can also be seen that the capital investments increase from one case to the next, as the addition of flexible storage capacity and one entire reprocessing echelon do come at a cost (aprox. 1M€ from Cases A and B to C). However, and as previously mentioned, the additional investment does bear significant economic compensation.

Figure 1: Location of the facilities within the sugar beet SC. Suppliers are marked in blue, existing processors in red, the potential conventional processor in green, the potential bio-refinery processor in purple, warehouses/distributors in brown, and markets/retailers in orange.

It is interesting to note that the model behaves similarly for all three cases in terms of storage capacity. As far as technology is concerned, it should be highlighted that the model chooses to operate processing capacity increases in already-existing factories rather than opening a new facility. Contrasting, the alternative bio-refinery configuration is indeed installed, in all cases, to satisfy demand for products not generated by the standard technology alternative.

It is important to recognise how the improved economic performance of the model impacts customer service, with unmet demand being a good performance indicator. Before further analysis, it should be noted that a minimum percentage of demand satisfaction of 90% is imposed to the model. It can be seen that in Case A the minimum percentage is barely achieved (90.20% demand satisfaction). An increase in demand satisfaction is registered between Cases A and B, as the additional scattered storage capacity in Case B reduces waste cost, by 26%, and improves demand fulfilment, by 2%. Finally, an additional small increase in demand satisfaction (1%) is seen between Cases B and C, as the reverse logistics activities provide further waste reduction and generate resources that can be applied to other productive activities, thus positively impacting the available quantities for sale. Case C is also where waste costs are reduced to the maximum with reductions of 68% and 57% if compared with Case A and Case B, respectively.

6. Conclusions

In the present work a quantitative model is proposed to support the design and planning of AFSC via an optimisation approach, focused on the strategic and tactical decision levels.

The satisfactory performance of the model in an AFSC context solves a set of clearly identified knowledge gaps. Firstly, the model is an important step towards encompassing both supply and demand uncertainty in the AFSC sector, traits deemed essential for the appropriate applicability of the model to real-world cases. Secondly, the model incorporates reverse logistics, which have been identified as powerful tools in the optimisation of both the economic and environmental performance of AFSCs and that, so far, had been understudied. Finally, the model includes specific under-explored AFSC characteristics such as product heterogeneity and a flexible storage strategy.

Despite providing several improvements when compared to non AFSC-specific models, the current model can still be subject to several improvements. At first, it should be noted that the model here developed incorporates one single economic objective, a trait which fails to meet current Triple Bottom Line (TBL) optimisation concerns. Secondly, more attention can also be given to the stochastic scenarios tree used to model uncertainty. The proposed scenarios tree seems appropriate to the modelled context, but the application of a larger set of possible scenarios could help improve on the model's realism.

Acknowledgements: The authors acknowledge the support provided by FCT and P2020 under the project PTDC/EGE-OGE/28071/2017 e Lisboa - 01-0145-FEDER-28071

References

R. Accorsi, G. Baruffaldi, R. Manzini, A. Tufano, 2018. On the design of cooperative vendors' networks in retail food supply chains: a logistics-driven approach. International Journal of Logistics Research and Applications 21 (1), 35–52.

A. Banasik, A. Kanellopoulos, G. D. Claassen, J. M. Bloemhof-Ruwaard, J. G. van der Vorst, 2017. Assessing alternative production options for eco-efficient food supply chains using multi-objective optimization. Annals of Operations Research 250 (2), 341–362.

A. P. Barbosa-Póvoa, C. da Silva, A. Carvalho, 2018. Opportunities and challenges in sustainable supply chain: An operations research perspective. European Journal of Operational Research 268 (2), 399–431.

T. G. Bosona, G. Gebresenbet, 2011. Cluster building and logistics network integration of local food supply chain. Biosystems Engineering 108 (4), 293–302.

S. R. Cardoso, A. P. F. D. Barbosa-Póvoa, S. Relvas, 2013. Design and planning of supply chains with integration of reverse logistics activities under demand uncertainty. European Journal of Operational Research 226 (3), 436–451.

N. M. Galal, K. S. El-Kilany, 2016. Sustainable agri-food supply chain with uncertain demand and lead time. International Journal of Simulation Modelling 15 (3), 485–496.

J. Jonkman, A. P. Barbosa-povoa, J. M. Bloemhof, 2018. Integrating harvesting decisions in the design of agro-food supply chains, *under revision*.

A. Pipatprapa, H.-H. Huang, C.-H. Huang, 2016. A Novel Environmental Performance Evaluation of Thailand's Food Industry Using Structural Equation Modeling and Fuzzy Analytic Hierarchy Techniques. Sustainability 8 (3), 246.

N. K. Tsolakis, C. A. Keramydas, A. K. Toka, D. A. Aidonis, E. T. Iakovou, 2014. Agrifood supply chain management: A comprehensive hierarchical decision-making framework and a critical taxonomy. Biosystems Engineering 120, 47–64.

Anton A. Kiss, Edwin Zondervan, Richard Lakerveld, Leyla Özkan (Eds.)
Proceedings of the 29th European Symposium on Computer Aided Process Engineering
June 16th to 19th, 2019, Eindhoven, The Netherlands. © 2019 Elsevier B.V. All rights reserved.
http://dx.doi.org/10.1016/B978-0-128-18634-3.50011-4

An Explicit Online Resource-Task Network Scheduling Formulation to Avoid Scheduling Nervousness

Giancarlo Dalle Ave[a,b], Mert Alici[a], Iiro Harjunkoski[a,*] and Sebastian Engell[b]

[a]*ABB Corporate Research Center Germany*
[b]*Process Dynamics and Operations Group, Technische Universität Dortmund*
Iiro.Harjunkoski@de.abb.com

Abstract

Scheduling is a decision-making process that is often based on the assumption of nominal operating conditions. In reality, scheduling is a dynamic process and uncertainties often arise during the execution of a schedule. One way to handle uncertainty in schedule is via reactive scheduling, or rescheduling. Rescheduling accounts for uncertainty by revising the existing agenda in response to real-time events. The downside to frequent revisions of the schedule is that it often leads to scheduling nervousness. In this work, a novel set of constraints based on the Resource-Task Network (RTN), coupled with a region-based penalty approach is proposed to combat scheduling nervousness. Results show that the approach is able to produce more stable schedules, while still giving rescheduled agendas the flexibility needed to pursue the original scheduling objective.

Keywords: Resource-Task Network (RTN), Scheduling Nervousness, Rescheduling

1. Introduction

Scheduling is a decision-making process that plays a central role in almost any type of industrial production facility where tasks need to be processed on a set of resources. The production in these facilities needs to be appropriately planned in order to prioritize the tasks and to ensure that the equipment, material, utilities, personnel and other resources are available at the plant when they are needed (Harjunkoski et al., 2014). There exist several mathematical programming-based scheduling formulations that can be roughly divided into discrete- and continuous-time models, each of which have different strengths and weaknesses. One such mathematical programming-based scheduling formulation that has received significant attention is the the Resource-Task Network (RTN) model (Pantelides, 1994). The RTN model, particularly the discrete-time RTN model, is a generic scheduling framework that has been shown to be applicable to many different industries including stainless steelmaking (Castro et al., 2013), and petrochemical production (Wassick and Ferrio, 2011).

Most scheduling approaches are predictive techniques that deal with the generation of production plans while assuming a given set of tasks and resources. However, industrial environments are dynamic and unplanned events often disrupt the planned schedule. There are two main classes of approaches to accommodate these unplanned events, scheduling under uncertainty, and reactive/online scheduling. Scheduling under uncertainty aims at accounting for uncertain parameters *a priori* by building a production plan with some slack that is directly incorporated into the schedule (Gupta et al., 2016). Reactive or online scheduling on the other hand accounts for uncertainty by revising the existing agenda in response to real time events. Rescheduling approaches are the most common dynamic scheduling approaches in manufacturing (Ouelhadj and Petrovic, 2008).

The drawback to frequent revisions of the schedule is that they lead to what is known as scheduling nervousness. Scheduling nervousness is an important aspect of online scheduling and is one of the reasons scheduling is not as widespread in industry as it could be (Henning, 2016). In this direction, Méndez and Cerdá (2004) proposed an iterative MILP framework to repair schedules by limited reallocation and reordering of operations defined by user-controlled sets. Other work in the area includes that of Novas and Henning (2010) who propose a domain knowledge-based rescheduling framework using constraint programming.

In this work, a novel method is proposed to avoid scheduling nervousness with minimal domain-specific knowledge. This is accomplished by using a set of general constraints to compare subsequent rescheduling iterations. Zones are defined in which subsets of these constraints are enforced more or less strictly than in other zones. Deviations from the existing schedules are penalized between iterations in a multi-objective optimization approach. The goal of this approach is to provide the subsequent scheduling iteration flexibility to respond to a disturbance, but in a way that minimizes the impact to the shop floor.

2. Methodology

The proposed approach is based on the discrete-time RTN framework to make it generic and easy to adapt to various applications. The RTN model represents the entire schedule as a set of resources (R) and tasks (I). In this formulation, tasks represent operations that need to be performed, which consume and produce sets of resources. Examples of resources in this case include raw materials, final products, and processing units. In the discrete-time RTN, the scheduling horizon (H) is divided into a set of δ sized intervals (T). The resource availability over the time grid is controlled by the variable $R_{r,t}$ which is modified by the execution of a task ($i \in I$) with a duration of τ_i time slots. These tasks are characterized by two sets of variables, the binary variable $N_{i,t}$ and the continuous variable $\xi_{i,t}$. The binary variables couple the execution of the task i with time point $t \in T$ and are associated with the discrete-interaction of a resource ($\mu_{i,r,\theta}$). For example, the execution of a reaction task always consumes a reactor regardless of the amount of product reacted. Conversely, the continuous variable $\xi_{i,t}$ indicates the amount handled by the task and is not considered in this work as batching functions are often handled by higher level planning functions (Harjunkoski et al., 2014) and are treated as inputs to the problem. External interactions with the scheduling system are modeled using the variable $\pi_{r,t}$. Examples of external interactions include raw material deliveries, product shipments, or equipment breakdowns. The modified resource balance that is considered in this work can then be seen in Eq. (1), while Eq. (2) limits the excess capacity of a resource.

$$R_{r,t} = R_{r,t-1}^{t \neq 0} + \pi_{r,t} + \sum_i \sum_{\theta=0}^{\tau_i} \mu_{i,r,\theta} N_{i,t-\theta} \qquad \forall r \in R, t \in T \qquad (1)$$

$$R_{r,t}^{min} \leq R_{r,t} \leq R_{r,t}^{max} \qquad \forall r \in T, t \in T \qquad (2)$$

When using the RTN, tasks are often aggregated together into a single binary variable in order to reduce the problem size. For example, if five orders of a product have been requested, it is possible to treat each order as an individual task which will execute once, or to treat the orders as a single task which must execute five times. This aggregation however creates problems when accounting for scheduling nervousness as it is uncertain which specific order an active binary is referring to. Therefore, in this work, non-aggregated tasks are considered. The same logic applies to aggregated resources, especially to equipment resources.

2.1. Additional Model Constraints

In order to define the constraints necessary to combat scheduling nervousness some additional notation and sets will be used. When a reschedule is performed at time $t^{resched} < H$ the set of all tasks that have not yet been started is represented by $I^{resched}$. Additionally, tasks that have been assigned to a specific processing unit in the current iteration of the schedule will be denoted by I^u, where $u \in U$ represents a single unit in the set of all processing units. All units at a single production stage ($k \in K$) are referred to using U_k. The start time of a task ST_i^σ is given by Eq. (3), where the index σ is used to refer to a particular iteration of the schedule. Similarly, the end time of a task is given by Eq. (4). In the rescheduling problem, the new version of the agenda that is going to be calculated is given by σ while $\sigma - 1$ refers to the current in progress agenda. Lastly, each task that will be rescheduled ($i \in I^{resched}$) on a specific machine could potentially be directly preceded by a task ($i' \in I_i^{predecessor}$) and/or succeeded by a task ($i' \in I_i^{successor}$) both of which will have at most one member. Note that it is possible for the predecessor i' of a task to be already executed, or currently in progress, which implies it is not possible to reschedule this task ($i' \notin I^{resched}$). If a task has no direct predecessors or successors the corresponding sets will be empty. For example, tasks A, B and C are scheduled one after another on a specific machine. Task A has no predecessors but has task B as a successor. On the other hand, task B has task A as a predecessor and task C as a successor while task C has no successors but task B as a predecessor.

$$ST_i^\sigma = \sum_{t \in T} N_{i,t}^\sigma \cdot t \tag{3}$$

$$ET_i^\sigma = \sum_{t \in T} N_{i,t}^\sigma \cdot (t + \tau_i) \tag{4}$$

Scheduling nervousness is generally associated with three different components, the reallocation of tasks between units, the changing of task timings, and the reordering of tasks. Constraints (5) to (7) are proposed in order to account for these concerns:

$$1 - \sum_{t \in T} N_{i,t}^\sigma - S_i^{machine} = 0 \qquad\qquad \forall u \in U, i \in I^u \cap I^{resched} \tag{5}$$

$$ET_{i'}^{\sigma-1} - \sum_{u \in U_k} ST_i^\sigma + S_i^{backwards} \geq 0 \qquad\qquad \forall i \in I^{resched}, i' \in I_i^{predecessor} \tag{6}$$

$$\sum_{u \in U_k} ET_i^\sigma - ST_{i'}^{\sigma-1} + S_i^{forward} \geq 0 \qquad\qquad \forall i \in I^{resched}, i' \in I_i^{successors} \tag{7}$$

Eq. (5) penalizes the reallocation of tasks by summing up the binary variables corresponding to the execution of the task on the same machine as the previous scheduling iteration. If the task occurs on the same machine no value is assigned to the machine change slack variable ($S_i^{machine}$), else the slack takes a value of one. Constraints (6) and (7) together are then used to address the issues of task timing and sequencing. Each of these constraints penalizes changes in the timing of a task relative to the execution of either the tasks predecessor (Eq. (6)) or successor (Eq. (7)) in the previous iteration of the schedule. If a task should change places, large values of the slack variable will be needed to accommodate this. This also implicitly penalizes the deviations in the individual task timings within a certain range. This is because, if a task is planned to occur between two neighbouring tasks it can occur anytime in this range with the same total slack variable value. If a task is moved outside this range, a larger sum of slack variables will be incurred. It is worth mentioning at this point that these constraints will be penalized in the objective function according to the preferences of the scheduler. For example, if it is not a problem to move tasks forward from their planned time slot it may only be desirable to penalize backwards changes in the task timings. Some of these penalty function combinations may involve some additional constraints (for example, a penalty on the absolute value of a slack variable), however a detailed description of all these combinations is outside the scope of this paper. A general method to determine these penalties based on the timings of the tasks relative to the rescheduling point will be outlined below.

The objective function can be seen in in Eq. (8), where *OF* represents the original scheduling objective function, C_i^s represents the coefficient for the corresponding slack variable, and λ is a weight parameter to balance the two objectives. The set *Sl* refers to the set of the slack variables.

$$\min \quad \lambda OF + (1 - \lambda) \sum_{s \in Sl} C_i^s \cdot S_i^s \tag{8}$$

2.2. Overall Framework to Address Scheduling Nervousness

The goal of rescheduling is to restore feasibility to the schedule and to reduce the effect that a disturbance has on the quality of the scheduling solution. In the near future of a rescheduling point it is undesirable to have large changes. Due to interactions with the longer-term planning systems it is also desirable to minimize the propagation of a disturbance to the long-term result. A three time region approach is therefore proposed; in the short-term after a reschedule ($t^{reschedule} < t^{ShT}$) any changes to the schedule are very undesirable due to operational concerns. Changes in the medium-term ($t^{ShT} < t^{MedT}$) have the most freedom and should be utilized to restore optimality to the schedule and to ensure that disturbances do not propagate to the long-term. In order to prevent tasks switching from the medium-term into the short-term Eq. (9) will be used with the slack variable ($S^{regionChange}$) as an additional penalty being appropriately added to the objective function. Note that pushing tasks backwards from the medium-term to the long-term is sometimes necessary if a large scheduling disturbance occurs and therefore is not penalized. In the long-term, changes to the schedule are undesirable due to the need to meet planning targets. If a scheduling disturbance occurs it should ideally be dealt with before it propagates enough to impact long-term planning targets.

$$\sum_{u \in U_k} ST_i^\sigma + S^{regionChange} \geq t^{ShT} \tag{9}$$

Tasks in the three regions will each have a set of constraints and corresponding penalties applied to them. The pseudocode for how these penalties are applied can be seen in Figure 1.

Data: Update $I^{resched}$ based on $ST_i^{\sigma-1}$ and $t^{resched}$
foreach $i \in I^{resched}$ **do**
    if $ST_i^{\sigma-1} \leq t^{ShT}$ **then**
        Apply constraints (5) to (7)
        Set C_i^s to a high value
    else if $t^{ShT} < ST_i^{\sigma-1} \leq t^{MedT}$ **then**
        Apply constraints (5) to (7), and (9)
        Set C_i^s to a low value
    else
        Apply constraints (6) and (7)
        Set C_i^s to a medium value
    end
end

Figure 1: Pseudocode outlining the definition of the different regions.

Based on the soft nature of all the constraints, there still is the potential to switch sequence and machines, however, due to the nature of the penalty terms, tasks in the near term are less likely to switch than tasks in the medium-term. Comparing this algorithm and constraint setup to earlier work (Novas and Henning, 2010) this roughly corresponds to tasks in the near-term being only allowed to shift timing on the same machine (*Shift-JumpAT*), while tasks in the medium- and long-term can be more easily reordered and shifted to other machines (*ReassignAT*). The added benefit of this algorithm is that it is possible for any task to be moved, both in respect to time or to the resources used if this a large enough change in the original scheduling objective function, and

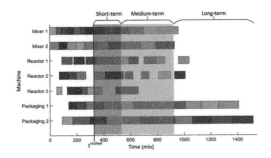

Figure 2: Initial schedule for the problem (objective = 39030 min).

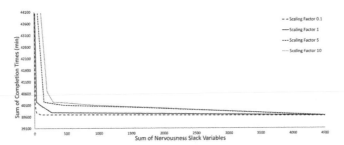

Figure 3: Pareto front illustrating the trade-off between scheduling stability and the original problem objective (sum of completion times).

that less expert knowledge is required as these regions need to be defined only on a time-basis, instead of a task-by-task basis.

3. Results

The aforementioned methodology is applied to the plant layout described in Harjunkoski and Bauer (2017). The first iteration of the schedule based on the minimization of the sum of completion times objective can be seen in Figure 2.

In this scenario, Reactor 2 needs to be maintained for two hours and rescheduling is performed at that point in time ($t^{resched} = 320min$). The length of the short- and medium-term regions are two and four hours respectively. The penalties (C_i^s) are 100 for the short-term region, 1 for the medium-term region, and 10 for the long-term region. There is a trade-off between the emphasis placed on scheduling stability versus the emphasis placed on the original scheduling objective. In order to analyze the effect of these parameters on the schedule a Pareto front is generated for a few scaling factors of these penalties. This can be viewed in Figure 3. Logically, the Pareto front shows that the more emphasis that is placed on scheduling stability, the larger the loss of optimality from the original scheduling objective. It is interesting that the lines seem to be very region-based, with nervousness dominating in one area and the original objective dominating in the other with little room in between. This indicates that several tasks need to be rearranged before a sufficiently large improvement in the original objective function is obtained.

Lastly a qualitative analysis of the results is performed. The Gantt charts for a complete reschedule ($\lambda = 1$) are compared with the values for a reschedule with large emphasis placed on nervousness ($\lambda = 0.1$), which can be seen in Figure 4. From the left Gantt chart it can be seen that the complete reschedule produces a vastly different result from the first iteration, with many changes being made in all three regions of the schedule. On the other hand, the reschedule with emphasis on stability produces a schedule with very similar sequence to the first iteration, but with a few modification

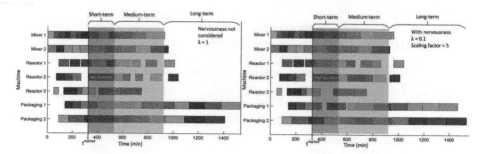

Figure 4: Gantt charts for the complete reschedule (left) compared to a reschedule with a large emphasis placed on nervousness (right).

being made in the medium-term region of the schedule. The more emphasis that is placed on the original scheduling objective, the more the resulting optimal solution reflects the solution obtained from the complete reschedule.

4. Conclusions and Future Work

In this work, a novel set of constraints and a corresponding region-based penalty method was proposed in order to combat scheduling nervousness. Results showed that the proposed method is able to produce the desired stability between scheduling iterations while still providing for sufficient flexibility to restore the quality of the resulting schedule. Additionally the trade-off between the original scheduling objective and the stability of the solution was explored. Results show that the stability of the solution is maintained for many different penalty values until the inertia to overcome these changes is surpassed by a sufficient improvement in the objective function. Future work will investigate the affect of the sizes of the regions on the optimal solution and stability as well as test the overall closed-loop performance of such an approach. Additionally, the constraints proposed focus on the stability between two subsequent iterations. It would be interesting to also investigate the effect of a bigger look-back period.

Acknowledgments: Financial support is gratefully acknowledged from the Marie Skłodowska Curie Horizon 2020 EID-ITN project "PRONTO" (Grant agreement No 675215).

References

P. M. Castro, L. Sun, I. Harjunkoski, 2013. Resourcetask network formulations for industrial demand side management of a steel plant. Industrial and Engineering Chemistry Research 52 (36), 13046–13058.

D. Gupta, C. T. Maravelias, J. M. Wassick, 2016. From rescheduling to online scheduling. Chemical Engineering Research and Design 116, 83 – 97.

I. Harjunkoski, R. Bauer, 2017. Industrial scheduling solution based on flexible heuristics. Computers and Chemical Engineering 106, 883 – 891.

I. Harjunkoski, C. T. Maravelias, P. Bongers, P. M. Castro, S. Engell, I. E. Grossmann, J. Hooker, C. Méndez, G. Sand, J. Wassick, 2014. Scope for industrial applications of production scheduling models and solution methods. Computers and Chemical Engineering 62, 161 – 193.

G. P. Henning, 2016. Realistic rescheduling: is it achievable? FOCAPO 2016.

C. A. Méndez, J. Cerdá, 2004. An milp framework for batch reactive scheduling with limited discrete resources. Computers and Chemical Engineering 28 (6), 1059 – 1068.

J. M. Novas, G. P. Henning, 2010. Reactive scheduling framework based on domain knowledge and constraint programming. Computers and Chemical Engineering 34 (12), 2129 – 2148.

D. Ouelhadj, S. Petrovic, Oct 2008. A survey of dynamic scheduling in manufacturing systems. Journal of Scheduling 12 (4), 417.

C. Pantelides, 1994. Unified frameworks for the optimal process planning and scheduling. In: Proceedings of the Second Conference on Foundations of Computer Aided Operations.

J. M. Wassick, J. Ferrio, 2011. Extending the resource task network for industrial applications. Computers and Chemical Engineering 35 (10), 2124 – 2140.

Anton A. Kiss, Edwin Zondervan, Richard Lakerveld, Leyla Özkan (Eds.)
Proceedings of the 29th European Symposium on Computer Aided Process Engineering
June 16th to 19th, 2019, Eindhoven, The Netherlands. © 2019 Elsevier B.V. All rights reserved.
http://dx.doi.org/10.1016/B978-0-128-18634-3.50012-6

Optimizing Return on Investment in Biomass Conversion Networks under Uncertainty Using Data-Driven Adaptive Robust Optimization

Jack Nicoletti, Chao Ning, Fengqi You

Cornell University, Ithaca, New York 14853, USA

Abstract

Bioconversion networks provide a means of turning raw biomass feedstock into useful biochemicals and fuels. These networks can display not only how crops and plants can be converted into bioproducts, but also how organic waste and other unconventional feedstocks can be used to create useful products as well. In order to determine the economic feasibility of the conversion pathways in these networks, an economic measure of design profitability such as return on investment must be used. Given a bioconversion network containing 216 technologies and 172 materials/compounds, we propose a two-stage adaptive robust mixed integer fractional programming model capable of measuring the economic success of bioconversion technology pathways. The proposed approach yields the processing pathways with optimal return on investment subject to minimum demand and maximum capacity constraints.

Keywords: adaptive robust optimization, return on investment, biomass conversion

1. Introduction

One of the primary goals of any business is to maximize the profit of their operations. In the context of bioconversion, if a plant cannot produce biofuels or industrial chemicals at a price even to or lower than the market price for that product, then the plant will not operate at a profit (Dodds et al., 20017; Yue et al. 2014; Gallezot, 2012). One way to measure the profitability and economic sustainability of any process is to calculate its return on investment (ROI), which is calculated in this work as the net yearly earnings of the process over the total capital investment. While work has been done to consider the cost of a bioconversion network under budgeted demand and price uncertainty (Garcia et al., 2015), in practice these facilities will only be built if they are proven to be profitable. A network that ignores the selling prices of the products that it creates could risk being economically infeasible (Sahinidis, 2004). It is necessary to ensure that a model is constructed such that the selling prices of the products are taken into consideration when deciding whether a bioconversion pathway is optimal (Lipinsky, 1981). Furthermore, with the increasing prevalence of historical data used in forecasting and planning decisions, it is quite useful to consider the uncertainty in feedstock price to be dependent on the historical price.

In this work, the biomass conversion network is optimized using a two-stage adaptive robust optimization method (Ben-Tal et al., 2009), with the first stage representing decisions made during the construction and planning phase and the second stage representing decisions made continuous during the day-to-day operation of the processing network (Ning and You, 2017). In this formulation, both the demand for products and price of biomass feedstocks are taken as uncertain parameters. Latent uncertainty realizations in collected data are identified using principal component analysis, and a kernel density estimator is used to form probability distributions of the projected uncertainty data given by principal component analysis like previous works (Ning and You, 2018). The resulting solution provided by this two-stage problem will be robust to worst-case instances of demand and price. Finally, the return on investment objective leads to an Adaptive Robust Mixed-Integer Fractional Program (ARMIFP) that can be solved using the Parametric Algorithm. This framework is then applied to an expanded bioconversion network, with the case study included in this work focusing on the upgrading and conversion of organic waste material to useful biomaterial.

2. Model Formulation

2.1. Return on Investment as an Objective

Return on Investment (ROI) is a key economic metric for measuring the payoffs of long-term investments (Gong et al., 2017). For the bioconversion network, return on investment was calculated as a ratio of the net revenue over the total capital cost of investment in the required processing and upgrading technologies. The net profit is expressed as the total revenue generated by selling units of bioproduct S_i, minus the cost of both the feedstock purchased P_i and the cost of operating the technology at a given operating level, W_j. The denominator is the total cost of building a plant of specified capacity Q_j. Overall, the objective function to be maximized is as follows:

$$\frac{\sum_{i \in I} c_{4,i} S_i - \sum_{i \in I} c_{3,i} P_i - \sum_{j \in J} c_{2,j} W_j}{\sum_{j \in J} c_{1,j} Q_j^{sf}} \tag{1}$$

where *sf* represents the scaling factor for technology j, $c_{4,i}$ represents the selling price of bioproduct i, and $c_{1,j}$, $c_{2,j}$, and $c_{3,i}$ represent parameters for economic evaluation as given in previous works (Gong et al., 2016). The first term of the numerator represents the profit from selling a specific quantity of bioproduct i at the market price. The second term represents the cost associated with buying a specific quantity of feedstock i. The last term in the numerator represents the cost associated with operating technology j. Upon inspection, it becomes clear that the decision variable for operating level W_j must be in the range of zero to the total capacity of the technology, Q_j. The denominator represents the cost associated with building technology j at a specific total capacity.

2.2. Two-Stage Adaptive Robust Optimization Formulation

Traditional robust optimization problems are static, meaning that all decisions are made at the same time and are final. However, in practice it is known that decision makers will make recourse decisions based on market conditions, risk tolerance, and many other factors. To ensure that the model accurately reflects the ability of a decision maker to act in real time, the model must allow for decisions to be made in multiple time frames. The solution is a two-stage adaptive robust optimization (ARO) formulation, which provides multiple advantages over static robust optimization (Shi et al., 2016). First, ARO leads to solutions that are less conservative that static robust solutions, as the solution can "adapt" to the uncertainty realizations. Additionally, ARO allows for "here and now" decisions to be made during the planning and construction of the bioconversion network as well as "wait and see" decisions to be made during the real-time operation of the facilities. In the bioconversion network, "here and now" decisions involve binary variables Y_j representing the decision to use technology j as well as continuous variables Q_j representing the capacity of technology j. Meanwhile, the "wait and see" variables that can be chosen in the second stage are the operating level of each technology W_j, the amount of feedstock purchased P_i, and the amount of product sold S_i.

The resulting two stage adaptive-robust optimization model considers uncertainty in both feedstock price and demand. Furthermore, the model allows for selection and capacity decisions to be made before uncertainty realization while also allowing for operational, purchasing, and sale decisions to be made after uncertainty has been realized. The model also employs nonlinear functions to evaluate the technology capital costs associated with the first-stage decisions. Furthermore, the model allows for the building of backup technologies that can sit idle and guard against uncertain demand fluctuations. The overall bioconversion optimization model is shown as follows:

$$\max_{Y,Q} \ \min_{c_3 \in U_2,\, d \in U_1} \ \max_{W,P,S} \ \frac{\sum_{i \in I} c_{4,i} S_i - \sum_{i \in I} c_{3,i} P_i - \sum_{j \in J} c_{2,j} W_j}{\sum_{j \in J} c_{1,j} Q_j^{sf}} \tag{2}$$

$$\text{s.t.} \quad a_{1,j} Y_j \le Q_j \le a_{2,j} Y_j, \quad \forall j \in J \tag{3}$$

$$W_j \le Q_j, \quad \forall j \in J \tag{4}$$

$$P_i - S_i + \sum_{j \in J} a_{3,i,j} W_j = 0, \quad \forall i \in I \tag{5}$$

$$P_i \le b_i, \quad \forall i \in I \tag{6}$$

$$S_i \ge d_i, \quad \forall i \in I \tag{7}$$

$$W_j, P_i, S_i \ge 0, \quad \forall i \in I, j \in J \tag{8}$$

$$Y_i \in \{0,1\}, \quad \forall i \in I \tag{9}$$

$$U_1 = \left\{ d_i \ \middle| \ \begin{array}{l} d_i = d_i^0 + \sum_k p_{ik} \left(\xi_k^L \cdot z_k^- + \xi_k^U \cdot z_k^+ \right), \ \forall i \\[4pt] \sum_k \left(z_k^- + z_k^+ \right) \le \Phi^{\text{dem}}, \ z_k^- + z_k^+ \le 1, \ 0 \le z_k^-, \ z_k^+ \le 1 \end{array} \right\} \tag{10}$$

$$U_2 = \left\{ c_{3,i} \ \middle| \ \begin{array}{l} c_{3,i} = c_{3,i}^0 + \sum_l r_{il} \left(\beta_l^L \cdot \delta_l^- + \beta_l^U \cdot \delta_l^+ \right), \ \forall i \\[4pt] \sum_l \left(\delta_l^- + \delta_l^+ \right) \le \Phi^{\text{pri}}, \ \delta_l^- + \delta_l^+ \le 1, \ 0 \le \delta_l^-, \ \delta_l^+ \le 1 \end{array} \right\} \tag{11}$$

where Eq. (2) represents the fractional objective, and Eq. (3) enforces first-stage capacity constraints. Eqs. (4), (5), and (7) enforce operational level, supply, and demand level constraints, respectively. Eq. (5) enforces a mass balance constraint, Eqs. (8) and (9) ensure non-negativity of continuous variable and range for binary variables, respectively. Eqs. (10) and (11) represent the data-driven uncertainty sets that are used in this work, with (10) representing the demand uncertainty set and (11) representing the feedstock price uncertainty set.

3. Solution Algorithm

The chosen approach for solving the computationally expensive ARMIFP is a combination of the parametric algorithm (Zhong et al. 2014) and a decomposition-based method. The parametric algorithm is first employed to handle the fractional term in the ARMIFP. We then break the MINLP into master problem and subproblem and solves these problems iteratively to obtain converging upper and lower bounds on the correct solution (Takeda et al. 2008). The proposed solution algorithm works as follows. First, the decomposition algorithm solves the master problem with feasibility cuts. The optimal value is used to update the lower bound on the optimal solution. Next, the subproblem is solved to obtain the optimal solution. This optimal value is then used to update the upper bound. The subproblem also generates cuts for the master problem, which are then added to the feasibility cut set. The uncertain demand and uncertain feedstock price are then changed to reflect the addition of the cuts in the set as well. The inner loop will terminate when the upper and lower bounds converge. The inner loop returns the current numerator and denominator to the outer loop. The outer loop will terminate when the numerator of the objective minus the denominator times the current multiplier value equals zero. When the outer loop does converge, the resulting multiplier value will be the optimal return on investment of the bioconversion system. Pseudocode for the algorithm is given in Fig. 1.

	Algorithm. Parametric algorithm and column-and-constraint algorithm
1:	Set $k \leftarrow 0$, $tol \leftarrow 10^{-3}$, $r \leftarrow 0$ and ζ ;
2:	**while** $N^* - r \cdot D^* \geq tol$
	$iter \leftarrow iter + 1$, $LB \leftarrow -\infty$, $UB \leftarrow +\infty$, $m \leftarrow 0$
3:	**while** $|UB - LB| > \zeta$ **do**
4:	$m \leftarrow m + 1$
5:	Solve **(MAS)** to obtain mo^*, N^*, D^* and Q^* ;
6:	Update $LB \leftarrow \max\{LB, mo^*\}$;
7:	Solve **(SUB)** to obtain so^*;
8:	Update $UB \leftarrow \min\left\{UB, -r \cdot \sum_j c_{1,j}(Q_j^*)^{sf} + so^*\right\}$;
9:	$M \leftarrow M \cup \{m\}$;
10:	$d_{i,m} = d_i^0 + \sum_k p_{ik}\left(\xi_k^L \cdot z_k^- + \xi_k^U \cdot z_k^+\right)$, $\forall i$
11:	$c_{3,i,m} = c_{3,i}^0 + \sum_l r_{il}\left(\beta_l^L \cdot \delta_l^- + \beta_l^U \cdot \delta_l^+\right)$, $\forall i$
12:	Create second-stage variables with respect to index m;
13:	**end**
14:	$r \leftarrow \dfrac{N^*}{D^*}$;
15:	**end**
16:	**return** UB ;

Figure 1. Pseudocode for the proposed nested solution algorithm

4. Case Study

In the case study, the demands for bioproducts were chosen to showcase the capabilities of some of the new bioconversion pathways. As explained in the introduction, one novel contribution of this work was the expansion of the bioconversion network to include organic and inorganic waste material as alternative potential feedstocks. In this example, the demands and uncertainty set for raw biogas, methane, and pectin were given.

When the solution algorithm presented in previous sections was executed, the processing network displayed in Fig. 2 was constructed. To make pectin, orange peel waste was treated using microwave hydrodiffusion. This process yields pectin as well as small amounts of essential oils (EO) and phenolic compounds (TPC). Meanwhile, to satisfy demand for methane, landfill methane extraction techniques can be used on various types

Optimizing Return on Investment in Biomass Conversion Networks under
Uncertainty Using Data-Driven Adaptive Robust Optimization

71

of municipal solid waste landfills. Finally, to satisfy the demand for biogas, multiple types of animal manure and anaerobic digestion (AD) methods were used.

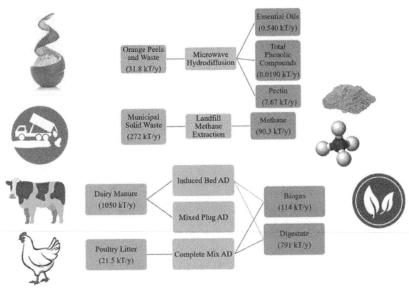

Figure 2. Process diagram displaying the conversion of waste materials to useful biofuels and other bioproducts. The amounts produced by each process vary widely based on average demand for each product.

For dairy manure, the best way to product biogas was through induced bed and mixed plug anaerobic digestion. To process poultry litter, however, the most efficient was to produce biogas was using a complete mix anaerobic digestion system. The other main by-product of anaerobic digestion, digestate, was also produced in large quantities along with the biogas. We also find that one of the processing pathways was built to operate at maximum capacity, while the others were built to ensure demand satisfaction. The biogas and methane production pathways are producing at demand-satisfying levels, while the orange peel processing pathway to produce pectin is operating at maximum capacity. Maximum pectin production implies that for the current input price, making pectin using microwave hydrodiffusion is profitable. In the aggregate processing network, the total cost was $277.6 M/y, with the cost being split between capital cost ($170.5 M/y) and operating cost ($107.1 M/y). The purchase cost for this case was assumed to be zero because the feedstocks for each pathway are waste products, which are assumed to have negligible or zero cost associated with obtaining them. The overall return on investment of the alternative feedstock processing pathway was 6.2%.

5. Conclusions

In this work, we developed a two-stage adaptive robust optimization model to maximize return on investment of a bioconversion network. We focused on uncertainty in feedstock price and bioproduct demand. Feedstock price was derived from historical data, leading to a data-driven uncertainty set for feedstock price that was constructed using the machine learning techniques. Furthermore, we also investigated the economic feasibility of using organic waste and other waste material as feedstock. The two-stage adaptive robust optimization problem with return on investment maximization is a MILFP which cannot be solved directly due to its multi-stage and fractional objective components. The case study focused on the production of useful chemicals from waste material. The result of the case study was a network that satisfied demand for all bioproducts and had a return on investment of 6.2%. Overall, the proposed solution method was able to quickly and efficiently identify optimal processing pathways for the bioconversion network.

References

Ben-Tal, A., El Ghaoui, L., Nemirovski, A. (2009). Robust optimization: Princeton University Press.

Ben-Tal, A., Nemirovski, A. (2002). Robust optimization - methodology and applications. Mathematical Programming, 92, 453-480.

Dodds, D. R., Gross, R. A. (2007). Chemcials from Biomass. Science, 318, 1250-1251.

Garcia, D. J., You, F. (2015). Multiobjective Optimization of Product and Process Networks: General Modeling Framework, Efficient Global Optimization Algorithm, and Case Studies on Bioconversion. AIChE Journal, 61, 530-551.

Garcia, D. J., You, F. (2015). Network-Based Life Cycle Optimization of the Net Atmospheric CO2-eq Ratio (NACR) of Fuels and Chemicals Production from Biomass. ACS Sustainable Chemistry & Engineering, 3, 1732-1744.

Gallezot, P. (2012). Conversion of biomass to selected chemical products. Chemical Society Reviews, 41, 1538-1558.

Gong, J., Garcia, D. J., You, F. (2016). Unraveling Optimal Biomass Processing Routes from Bioconversion Product and Process Networks under Uncertainty: An Adaptive Robust Optimization Approach. ACS Sustainable Chemistry & Engineering, 4, 3160-3173.

Gong, J., You, F. (2017). Optimal processing network design under uncertainty for producing fuels and value-added bioproducts from microalgae: Two-stage adaptive robust mixed integer fractional programming model and computationally efficient solution algorithm. AIChE Journal, 63, 582-600.

Lipinsky, E. S. (1981). Chemicals from biomass: petrochemical substitution options. Science, 212, 1465-1471.

Ning, C., You, F. (2017). Data-Driven Adaptive Nested Robust Optimization: General Modeling Framework and Efficient Computational Algorithm for Decision Making Under Uncertainty. AIChE Journal, 63, 3790-3817.

Ning, C., You, F. (2018). Data-driven decision making under uncertainty integrating robust optimization with principal component analysis and kernel smoothing methods. Computers & Chemical Engineering, 112, 190-210.

Ning, C., You, F. (2018). Data-driven stochastic robust optimization: General computational framework and algorithm leveraging machine learning for optimization under uncertainty in the big data era. Computers & Chemical Engineering, 111, 115-133.

Sahinidis, N. V. (2004). Optimization under uncertainty: state-of-the-art and opportunities. Computers & Chemical Engineering, 28, 971-983.

Shi, H., You, F. (2016). A computational framework and solution algorithms for two-stage adaptive robust scheduling of batch manufacturing processes under uncertainty. AIChE Journal, 62, 687-703.

Takeda, A., Taguchi, S., Tütüncü, R. H. (2008). Adjustable Robust Optimization Models for a Nonlinear Two-Period System. Journal of Optimization Theory and Applications, 136, 275-295.

Yue, D., You, F., Snyder, S. W. (2014). Biomass-to-bioenergy and biofuel supply chain optimization: Overview, key issues and challenges. Computers & Chemical Engineering, 66, 36-56.

Zhong, Z., You, F. (2014). Globally convergent exact and inexact parametric algorithms for solving large-scale mixed-integer fractional programs and applications in process systems engineering. Computers & Chemical Engineering, 61, 90-101.

Anton A. Kiss, Edwin Zondervan, Richard Lakerveld, Leyla Özkan (Eds.)
Proceedings of the 29th European Symposium on Computer Aided Process Engineering
June 16th to 19th, 2019, Eindhoven, The Netherlands. © 2019 Elsevier B.V. All rights reserved.
http://dx.doi.org/10.1016/B978-0-128-18634-3.50013-8

Towards a systematic framework for the synthesis of operable process intensification systems - application to reactive distillation systems

Yuhe Tian[a,b], Iosif S. Pappas [a,b], Baris Burnak [a,b], Justin Katz [a,b], Styliani Avraamidou[a,b], Nikolaos A. Diangelakis[a,b] and Efstratios N. Pistikopoulos[a,b,*]

[a]*Artie McFerrin Department of Chemical Engineering, Texas A&M University, College Station, TX 77843, United States*
[b]*Texas A&M Energy Institute, Texas A&M University, College Station, TX 77843, United States*
stratos@tamu.edu

Abstract

We present a systematic framework for the design and operability/safety optimization of process intensified systems, with specific focus on reactive distillation processes. This framework is based on a phenomenological process intensification/synthesis approach (i.e., Generalized Modular Representation Framework) which first identifies promising intensified tasks and then translates them to equipment-based flowsheet alternatives. Flexibility analysis is integrated with the synthesis model to ensure that resulting design configurations are operable under varying operating conditions. To systematically account for inherent safety performance, risk assessment criteria are included as process constraints involving failure frequency and consequence severity criteria. A case study on the production of methyl tertiary butyl ether is presented to highlight the potential of the proposed approach in deriving inherently operable and safe intensified reactive separation systems.

Keywords: Process intensification, Reactive distillation, Generalized Modular Representation Framework, Operability analysis, Risk assessment

1. Introduction

In recent years, process intensification (PI) has attracted burgeoning interest in the chemical engineering research community and the chemical/energy industry due to its potential for drastic improvements in process productivity, efficiency, and profitability (Tian et al., 2018). The integration of multiple processing tasks into a single unit (e.g., combined reaction/separation processes) is one of the major PI pathways towards the development of breakthrough technologies. Reactive distillation (RD), a classic intensified invention, is showing significant energy and cost savings over conventional reactor-distillation counterparts (between 15 and 80 %) (Harmsen, 2007). Recent works for the synthesis of reactive separation systems have been leveraging phenomenological representation methods to systematically generate intensified process options from a lower-aggregated level without the pre-postulation of plausible unit-operation-based flowsheets which may hinder the discovery of novel solutions (Tula et al., 2017; da Cruz and Manousiouthakis, 2017; Demirel et al., 2017). However, these efforts mainly focus on steady-state design at nominal operating conditions. The operational performances in these units under uncertainty and disturbances are mostly neglected, whereas their highly integrated schemes often decrease the degrees of freedom of the online decision maker, adversely affecting the process safety and limiting the operability of the systems (Baldea, 2015). Therefore, a holistic synthesis approach is required for the delivery of reactive distillation systems with guaranteed operability and safety performances at the early design stage.

In this work, we introduce a systematic framework for intensified process synthesis, which is based on the phenomenological Generalized Modular Representation Framework (GMF) with embedded process operability and safety assessment criteria. The rest of the paper is organized as follows. In Section 2, the proposed framework is presented in detail. Section 3 showcases this approach on a distillation-based reactive separation process for methyl tertiary butyl ether (MTBE) production. Finally, conclusions and directions for future work are discussed in Section 4.

2. Synthesis framework for Process Intensification

To address the synthesis of operable PI systems, we propose an integrated framework as depicted in Figure 1, with its stepwise procedure described in what follows:

Step 1: Process Intensification/Synthesis Representation via Generalized Modular Representation Framework – GMF, originally introduced by Papalexandri and Pistikopoulos (1996), represents chemical processes with two sets of phenomenological building blocks, namely the pure heat exchange module and the multifunctional mass/heat exchange module. Utilizing Gibbs free energy-based driving force constraints to characterize mass/heat transfer feasibility, GMF characterizes various (intensified) tasks (e.g., separation, reaction, combined separation/reaction) by optimizing physical and chemical driving forces to exploit the "ultimate" thermodynamic design space. The synergistic integration of multiple phenomena are automatically explored via superstructure optimization (Ismail et al., 2001) without a pre-postulation of plausible (and possibly myriad) tasks.

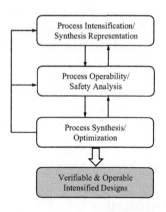

Figure 1: Proposed framework for the synthesis of operable process intensification systems (adapted from Tian et al. (2018)).

Step 2: Process Operability/Safety Analysis – Flexibility test is applied to identify the critical operating conditions when the resulting design configuration is operated under an expected range of the uncertainty. As for the consideration of inherent safety, risk assessment criteria (Nemet et al., 2017), which account for equipment failure frequency and consequence severity at the release of entire intrinsic hazards existing in the process, are included as constraints in the synthesis model to enable systematic generation of inherently safer design options instead of iterative evaluation in a posterior manner.

Step 3: Process Synthesis/Optimization – In this step, an integrated GMF-operability-safety synthesis strategy is developed in the formulation of a mixed integer nonlinear

Towards a systematic framework for the synthesis of operable process intensification systems - application to reactive distillation systems

75

programming (MINLP) problem, as shown in Table 1. The Generalized Benders Decomposition (GBD) method (Geoffrion, 1972) is utilized for the solution of this optimization problem and is implemented in the General Algebraic Modeling System (GAMS) (Rosenthal, 2016). The primal NLP subproblem is solved with solver CONOPT and the master MIP problem with CPLEX. The optimization results will deliver optimal GMF-based design configurations with desired operability and safety performances.

Step 4: Operable Intensified Designs Verified via Steady-State & Dynamic Simulation – The resulting GMF configurations are translated to corresponding equipment-based flowsheet alternatives and validated with steady-state simulation. To integrate steady-state and dynamic operation, "high-fidelity" dynamic models are developed to fully capture and analyze the system dynamics. This allows for further design and control optimization studies (Pistikopoulos et al., 2015; Diangelakis et al., 2017). Closed-loop validation is finally performed, with necessary iterations between different steps to ensure the delivery of consistent and verifiable operable intensification systems throughout the framework.

Table 1: Mathematical model for GMF-flexibility-safety synthesis – an indicative list.

GMF Synthesis Model	
Mass balance	$f^{LI}x_i^{LI} + f^{VI}x_i^{VI} - f^{LO}x_i^{LO} - f^{VO}x_i^{VO} + \sum v_i \times r \times M_{cat} = 0$
Energy balance	$f^{LI}h_i^{LI} + f^{VI}h_i^{VI} - f^{LO}h_i^{LO} - f^{VO}h_i^{VO} + \sum \triangle H_{reac} \times r \times M_{cat} = 0$
Driving force constraints	$G2_i = \ln\left[\frac{\gamma_i^L x_i^L P^{sat,L}}{\phi_i^V x_i^V P_{tot}}\right] + \sum_i \sum_k \left[\frac{v_{ik}\Delta G_k^f}{RT} + v_{ik}\ln(\phi_i^V x_i^V P_{tot})\right]\frac{\partial \varepsilon_k}{\partial n_i^L}$
Phase defining	liq: $\sum_i K_{eq,i}x_i \leq 1$, vap: $\sum_i x_i/K_{eq,i} \leq 1$
Kinetic model	$r = k[\prod a^\alpha - \frac{1}{K_a}\prod a^\beta]$, $k = A exp(-Ea/RT)$
Thermodynamic model	$\gamma_i = \gamma(x_i, T, P)$, $P_i^{sat} = P^{sat}(T)$
Structural interconnection	$y_{e+1} - y_e \leq 0$, $y_e - [\sum y_{ne}^{IL} + \sum y_{ee}^{LL} + \sum y_{ee}^{CL} \leq 0]$

Flexibility Analysis
$\max\limits_{V_\theta \in U(V_\theta)} \min\limits_{V_z} \max\limits_{j \in J_f} f_j(V_\theta, V_d, V_x, V_z) \leq 0$ s.t. $h(V_\theta, V_d, V_x, V_z) = 0$

Risk Assessment	
Consequence severity	$Severity_{i,e} = W_{i,e} \times O_e^1 \times O_e^2 \times O_e^3 / S_{risk}$
Risk evaluation	$Risk_{i,e} = freq_{e,fail} \times Severity_{i,e}$

Objective Function	
Total annualized cost	$Cost_{obj} = Cost_{cooling} + Cost_{heating} + Cost_{module}$

* Nomenclature: G = Gibbs free energy, O = factors accounting for process conditions, S = limit value for hazardous properties, W = quantity of hazardous substances present, y = binary variable, V_θ = uncertain parameters, V_d = design variables, V_x = state variables, V_z = control variables; Superscripts: LI = GMF module liquid inlet stream, VI = vapor inlet stream, LO = liquid outlet stream, VO = vapor outlet stream, LL = interconnecting liquid stream; Subscripts: e = module, i = component, k = reaction, n = feed stream.

3. Case study: MTBE production

In this section, the proposed framework is tested on a reactive separation system for the production of methyl tertiary butyl ether (MTBE) (Ismail et al., 2001). The case study aims to demonstrate the integration of operability/safety criteria at the early synthesis level as well as the potential of systematically deriving multiple intensified design options with different operational and cost performances for decision-making.

3.1. Problem statement

MTBE can be produced via the catalytic reaction of methanol (MeOH) and isobutylene (IB4) in the liquid phase using an ion-exchange resin as catalyst (e.g., Amberlyst 15 (Rehfinger and Hoffmann, 1990)). The production task is to obtain liquid MTBE at a rate of at least 197 mol/s with a purity higher than 98 mol%. Raw material availability (i.e., methanol and butene feed streams with given composition, flowrate, and temperature) is taken from Hauan et al. (1995). Additionally, an uncertainty range of ±10 mol/s is considered for the methanol feed flowrate. Given the hazardous properties of the substances in this process, manifold process risks (i.e., toxicity, flammability, explosiveness) need to be considered for a holistic evaluation of inherent safety performance. The synthesis objective is to identify a flowsheet alternative to meet the MTBE production specifications with minimum total annualized cost (TAC) and desired operability/safety performance.

3.2. Synthesis with operability and safety considerations

In this case study, a maximum of 10 GMF mass/heat exchange modules and 20 pure heat exchange modules are allowed for the representation/synthesis of this process. The separation and/or reaction task taking place in each mass/heat exchange module is not postulated *a priori*, but to be determined through the superstructure optimization driven by the minimization of total annualized cost.

A nominal GMF configuration without flexibility or safety considerations is first synthesized as a reference design. The resulting MINLP model has 14,594 constraints, 8,098 continuous variables, as well as 734 binary variables. The optimal solution, shown in Fig. 2, features reactive distillation column at a total annualized cost of 1.7×10^6/y. In this nominal design configuration, two pure heat exchange modules are selected as reboiler/condenser, while two reactive separation modules are used as reaction zone to produce MTBE, two separation modules as stripping section to separate unreacted methanol/isobutylene back to reaction zone, and another one as rectification section to transfer n-butene to distillate.

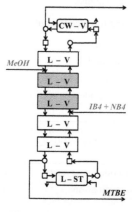

Figure 2: Nominal design.

Flexibility analysis is then applied to test if the nominal GMF configuration can be operated under the uncertainty of methanol feed flowrate, which identifies a critical point at the higher flowrate extreme value. On the other hand, inherent safety performance is improved by reducing the overall process risk by at least 20 % than that seen in the nominal design. The resulting design alternative, as shown in Fig. 3(a), utilizes four mass/heat exchange modules. Thus in this case, the enhancement of process safety is achieved by minimizing the unit size.

However, a comparatively more "risky" component is observed in Fig. 3(a) - i.e. the second reactive separation module (numbered from top to bottom) takes up more than 1/3 of overall process risk. To avoid the safety concerns resulting from a single module, the individual module risk is constrained to be less than 30 % of the overall process risk. The new optimal design configuration is illustrated in Fig. 3(b). The afore-mentioned module

Towards a systematic framework for the synthesis of operable process intensification systems - application to reactive distillation systems

77

is bypassed to alleviate its mass/heat transfer burden, thus introducing more degrees of freedom to enhance the system's flexibility and operability performances. The detailed design and operating parameters can be found in Table 2.

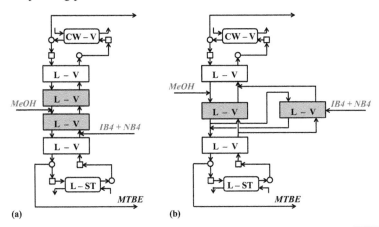

Figure 3: Flexible & inherently safer design configurations.
(a) Operable design I, (b) Operable design II

3.3. Steady-state & dynamic simulation and validation

Having generated the optimal and operable GMF configurations for the MTBE production (Fig. 3), in this step we identify and validate the corresponding equipment-based flow-sheet using steady-state simulation. Each GMF separation module is translated to two distillation trays in Aspen Plus® RADFRAC column (Aspen, 1981-2018), while each GMF reactive separation module to three reactive distillation trays. Therefore, the first operable design is verified as a 13-tray RD column, while the other one as a 10-tray RD column integrated with an additional 3-tray side-column. Table 2 provides a summary of quantitative validation between GMF and Aspen simulation on design/operating variables. "High-fidelity" dynamic models (Schenk et al., 1999) are also developed for the reactive distillation systems (Fig. 3) in gPROMS ModelBuilder® (PSE, 1997-2018), consisting of a system of differential and algebraic equations (DAE) for the description of component molar and energy balances for each tray, the partial reboiler and the total condenser, reaction kinetics, phase equilibrium, etc. The developed dynamic systems will be utilized for the derivation of receding horizon control policies (Pistikopoulos et al., 2015) to guarantee the optimal operation of the proposed designs.

Table 2: GMF quantitative validation with Aspen simulation.

	Nominal Design		Operable Design I		Operable Design II	
	GMF	Aspen	GMF	Aspen	GMF	Aspen
Column pressure (atm)	5.46	6.00	7.85	7.95	9.48	8.20
Reflux ratio	1.70	2.10	1.70	2.50	1.70	3.30
Reboiler duty (kW)	7.5×10^3	6.6×10^3	8.4×10^3	9.6×10^3	8.9×10^3	2×10^4
Condenser duty (kW)	2.3×10^4	2.2×10^4	2.3×10^4	2.4×10^4	2.3×10^4	3.4×10^4
Module/Tray Number	7	15	6	13	6	13
Bottom product flowrate (mol/s)	197.0	197.0	197.0	197.0	197.0	197.0
Product purity (MTBE mol/mol)	0.98	0.98	0.98	0.98	0.98	0.98
TAC ($\times 10^4$ \$/y)	171.1		182.4		190.2	

4. Conclusion

In this paper, we have presented a systematic framework to efficiently address the combinatorial PI design space and to integrate steady-state synthesis, dynamic analysis, and operability assessment to deliver validated operable intensification designs. It is shown, through an MTBE reactive separation example, that operability considerations may result in significant structural and operating changes of the process optimal solutions. Ongoing work addresses simultaneous design and control studies on the resulting MTBE reactive distillation configurations to close the loop under dynamic operating conditions.

5. Acknowledgement

We acknowledge the financial support from the Texas A&M Energy Institute, Shell Oil Company, RAPID SYNOPSIS Project (DE-EE0007888-09-03), and the NSF (Grant no. 1705423) under the project titled SusChEM: An integrated framework for process design, control and scheduling [PAROC].

References

Aspen, 1981-2018. Aspen technology, inc. https://www.aspentech.com/en/products/engineering/aspen-plus.

M. Baldea, 2015. From process integration to process intensification. Computers & Chemical Engineering 81, 104–114.

F. E. da Cruz, V. I. Manousiouthakis, 2017. Process intensification of reactive separator networks through the ideas conceptual framework. Computers & Chemical Engineering 105, 39–55.

S. E. Demirel, J. Li, M. F. Hasan, 2017. Systematic process intensification using building blocks. Computers & Chemical Engineering 105, 2–38.

N. A. Diangelakis, B. Burnak, J. Katz, E. N. Pistikopoulos, 2017. Process design and control optimization: A simultaneous approach by multi-parametric programming. AIChE Journal 63 (11), 4827–4846.

A. M. Geoffrion, 1972. Generalized benders decomposition. Journal of optimization theory and applications 10 (4), 237–260.

G. J. Harmsen, 2007. Reactive distillation: the front-runner of industrial process intensification: a full review of commercial applications, research, scale-up, design and operation. Chemical Engineering and Processing: Process Intensification 46 (9), 774–780.

S. R. Ismail, P. Proios, E. N. Pistikopoulos, 2001. Modular synthesis framework for combined separation/reaction systems. AIChE Journal 47 (3), 629–649.

A. Nemet, J. J. Klemeš, I. Moon, Z. Kravanja, 2017. Safety analysis embedded in heat exchanger network synthesis. Computers & Chemical Engineering 107, 357–380.

K. P. Papalexandri, E. N. Pistikopoulos, 1996. Generalized modular representation framework for process synthesis. AIChE Journal 42 (4), 1010–1032.

E. N. Pistikopoulos, N. A. Diangelakis, R. Oberdieck, M. M. Papathanasiou, I. Nascu, M. Sun, 2015. PAROC – an integrated framework and software platform for the optimisation and advanced model-based control of process systems. Chemical Engineering Science 136, 115–138.

PSE, 1997-2018. Process systems enterprise. gproms. https://www.psenterprise.com/products/gproms.

A. Rehfinger, U. Hoffmann, 1990. Kinetics of methyl tertiary butyl ether liquid phase synthesis catalyzed by ion exchange resin – i. intrinsic rate expression in liquid phase activities. Chemical Engineering Science 45 (6), 1605–1617.

R. E. Rosenthal, 2016. GAMS: A user's guide.

M. Schenk, R. Gani, D. Bogle, E. Pistikopoulos, 1999. A hybrid modelling approach for separation systems involving distillation. Chemical Engineering Research and Design 77 (6), 519–534.

Y. Tian, S. E. Demirel, M. F. Hasan, E. N. Pistikopoulos, 2018. An overview of process systems engineering approaches for process intensification: State of the art. Chemical Engineering and Processing-Process Intensification 133, 160–210.

A. K. Tula, D. K. Babi, J. Bottlaender, M. R. Eden, R. Gani, 2017. A computer-aided software-tool for sustainable process synthesis-intensification. Computers & Chemical Engineering 105, 74–95.

Anton A. Kiss, Edwin Zondervan, Richard Lakerveld, Leyla Özkan (Eds.)
Proceedings of the 29th European Symposium on Computer Aided Process Engineering
June 16th to 19th, 2019, Eindhoven, The Netherlands. © 2019 Elsevier B.V. All rights reserved.
http://dx.doi.org/10.1016/B978-0-128-18634-3.50014-X

Optimisation and control of a distributed energy resource network using Internet-of-Things technologies

Evgenia Mechleri[*a], Tim Sidnell[a], Bogdan Dorneanu[a], Harvey Arellano-Garcia[a,b]

aDepartment of Chemical & Process Engineering, University of Surrey, Guildford, United Kingdom

bLS Prozess- und Anlagentechnik, Brandenburgische Technische Universität Cottbus-Senftenberg, Cottbus, Germany

e.mechleri@surrey.ac.uk

Abstract

This work investigates the use of variable pricing to control electricity imported and exported to and from both fixed and unfixed distributed energy resource network designs within the UK residential sector. It was proven that networks which utilise much of their own energy and import little from the national grid are barely affected by variable import pricing, but are encouraged to export more energy to the grid by dynamic export pricing. Dynamic import and export pricing increased CO_2 emissions due to feed-in tariffs which encourages CHP generation over lower-carbon technologies such as solar panels or wind turbines.

Keywords: Internet-of-Things, Distribution Energy Resource, Mixed-Integer Linear Programming.

1. Introduction

Most electricity on the UK grid comes from large producers based far from customers, e.g. large offshore wind farms or isolated nuclear plans, leading to enormous volumes of electricity being wasted through transmission losses and step-up/step-down transformers [1]. Distributed Energy Resource (DER) networks have the potential to provide buildings capabilities for self-generation from renewable or low carbon assets and reduce both emissions and energy bills through mitigation of much of these losses [2]. Government incentives make a good case for investing in DER technologies, however large-scale investment into domestic DERs without sensible controls would destabilize the national grid [3]. Internet of Things (IoT) technologies have the potential to better control and optimize DERs, in conjunction with the needs of national electricity grids. This can be done through internet connected controllers which utilize live data on energy prices, generation, consumption, and asset failures, in a way which is aligned with national grid strategies. It also presents the capability to optimize the design and operation of local renewable resources, to cope with predicted changes in weather or disruptive events. The work presented in the following sections focuses on the use of IoT-type integration and communication strategies for the control of residential DERs, as opposed to the control of entire grids, as presented by [4]. With respect to dynamic pricing, the paper is unique from [5] in that it investigates both demand- and supply-side control. Finally the model builds on the models presented in [6] and [7]. The novelty is in the investigation of the effect of dynamic pricing on the demand- and supply-side control in residential housing scenarios. Section 2 presents the methodology, Section 3 the mathematical formulation, while Section 4 the results and discussion.

2. Methodology

A case study is used to illustrate the approach: a residential house arrangement based on streets in Guildford, Surrey, UK, with 5 houses (Fig.1). The demand profiles for this arrangement are presented in Fig.2

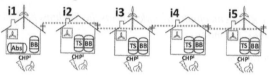

Fig 1. Design of the baseline scenario network

A baseline scenario with a set, pre-designed DER network is used to investigate the effect of dynamic pricing. A simulation is run to optimize the design of the network without IoT control, based on a number of available renewable technologies. The set of technologies installed in the network (*Tech*) could include: absorption chillers (*Abs*), air conditioning units (*AC*), biomass boilers (*BB*), gas boilers (*GB*), combined heat and power generators (*CHPs*), which are fuel cells, internal combustion engines or Sterling engines, gas heaters (*GH*), heating/cooling pipelines, microgrid controllers (*MGCC*), photovoltaic cells (*PV*), thermal storage (*TS*) and wind turbines (*WT*). A second scenario is investigated, where the design of the network is completed with IoT dynamic pricing control strategies. This is done to compare the design and operation of DER networks which have been designed and are yet to be designed.

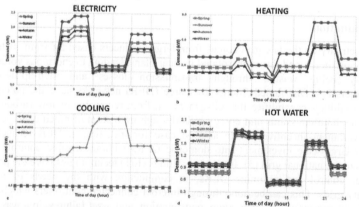

Fig 2. Demand profiles for the network for electricity, heating, cooling and hot water

Real seasonal and hourly variations in supply and demand of the various energy requirements and renewable generating assets are considered for the models. Weather and demand data is split into four seasons (*m1* – spring, *m2* – summer, *m3* – autumn and *m4* – winter), which each lasts for three months (Mar-May, Jun-Aug, Sep-Nov, Dec-Feb). Every day is split into six periods (*p1* – *p6*) in which demand, weather operation and thus energy supply are constant. The concept of dynamic pricing is investigated through the use of Equations (1) and (2), which calculate the price (in British pence per kWh) of electricity from the DER network purchased $(P_{Elec,mp})$ and sold $(P_{SalElec,mp})$ to the grid, respectively. The price is scaled against the average electricity price $(P_{Elec,Avg}$ and $P_{SalElec,Avg}$, for the purchased and sold price, respectively) for the UK residential sector, by dividing the national demand $(NatDemand_{m,p})$ at time of day, p, and season, m, by the yearly average national demand $(NatDemand_{Avg})$.

$$P_{Elec,mp} = P_{Elec,Avg} \cdot NatDemand_{m,p} / NatDemand_{Avg} \tag{1}$$

$$P_{SalElec,mp} = P_{SalElec,Avg} \cdot NatDemand_{m,p} / NatDemand_{Avg} \tag{2}$$

Table1. Cost of imported and exported electricity, per time of day and year

Time period (p)	p1	p2	p3	p4	p5	p6
Time of day	07:00-09:00	09:00-12:00	12:00-13:00	13:00-18:00	18:00-22:00	22:00-07:00
Season, m	Price purchased electricity, $P_{Elec,m,p}$ (pence/KWh)					
Spring, m1	31.120	33.660	8.290	10.110	24.870	8.787
Summer, m2	25.370	28.350	6.964	8.290	19.900	7.295
Autumn, m3	28.190	31.500	7.793	9.285	21.550	8.124
Winter, m4	36.480	39.790	9.948	11.610	29.840	9.948
Season, m	Price exported electricity, $P_{SalElec,m,p}$ (pence/KWh)					
Spring, m1	9.625	10.390	2.560	3.123	7.680	2.713
Summer, m2	7.833	8.755	2.150	2.560	6.144	2.253
Autumn, m3	8.703	9.727	2.406	2.867	6.655	2.509
Winter, m4	11.260	12.290	3.072	3.584	9.215	3.072

Overall the price of purchased electricity, taken as a time average, is $P_{Elec,Avg} = 16.29$ pence/kWh, while the price of exported electricity is that given by the government incentives, $P_{SalElec,Avg} = 5.03$ pence/kWh. Table 1 shows the calculated values for the imported and exported electricity, for each time period throughout the year.

3. Mathematical model

The model's objective function minimises the total cost of the network, C_{Total}, which is calculated as the sum, for all technologies, of the investment costs, C_{Inv}, annualised over the project lifetime, n (years), and the annual operating and maintenance costs, $C_{O\&M}$, the annual cost of carbon emission taxation, C_{Tax}, the annual cost of imported energy and fuel, C_{Fuel}, minus the annual income, C_{Inc} made from exporting the electricity to the grid, feed in tariffs (FITs) and renewable energy heat incentives (RHIs):

$$C_{Total} = \sum_{Tech}(C_{Inv} + C_{O\&M}) + C_{Tax} + C_{Fuel} - C_{Inc} \tag{3}$$

The annualized investment costs are calculated using a capital recovery factor, *CRF* based on an interest rate, r (%), and project lifetime, n:

$$CRF = r(1+r)^n / [(1+r)^n - 1] \tag{4}$$

A cost per kW of installed capacity, or cost per meter of piping and wiring was found, for each technology, from literature based on UK case studies and industrial sources, and used to calculate the annualised cost for each technology:

$$C_{Inv,tech} = \Sigma_i(CRF \times C_{InvTech} \times Max_{Tech,i}) \tag{5}$$

Here, the $Max_{Tech,I}$ is the maximum power generated by the technology in a house i, in a year, and represents the required capacity. The installed capacity must also fall between upper and lower bounds of available technology units. Binary variables are used to decide whether or not a technology is installed in a home.

O&M costs of the technologies are calculated using fixed costs, C_{Fixed} and variable costs, C_{Var}. The costs are defined in £/kWh.

$$C_{O\&M,tech} = \Sigma_i[(C_{Fixed} \times Max_{Tech,i}) + (C_{Var} \times \Sigma_{m,p} Gen_{Tech,i,m,p})] \tag{6}$$

C_{Tax} is calculated from the government tax per kg of CO_2 emitted, P_{CO2}, the carbon intensity of electricity purchased from the grid, CI_{grid}, and carbon intensities of emitting technologies, namely: *GB*, *CHP* and *CH*. All these units consume natural gas, so their intensities are calculated as the carbon intensity of grid gas CI_{Gas} divided by the technology efficiency, η_{Tech}. The intensities are defined in kg CO_2/kWh. The cost of fuel, C_{Fuel} is equal to the volume of gas and electricity purchased multiplied by the respective cost of each technology. The income, C_{Inc} is calculated from FITs per kWh of low carbon heat or electricity generated, $P_{FIT,Tech}$, electricity sales to the grid, $ESal_{Tech,i,m,p}$, and the annual payment for the utilization of a *BB* under the RHI, P_{RHI}. For pipelines and microgrid (*MG*) cables, binary variables are used to indicate connections between homes. An *MG* controller binary, Z_i, is introduced and its existence is decided by the *MG* cable existence. The demands for the house are met with balance equations that match demand with appropriate technologies:

$$Load_{i,m,p} + Additional\ Demand - \Sigma_j(\beta_{i,j}Q_{j,i,m,p} - Q_{i,j,m,p}) = E_{Grid,i,m,p} + \Sigma_{tech} Self_{i,m,p} + StorOut_{i,m,p} \tag{7}$$

$Load_{i,m,p}$ represents a generic demand, while *Additional Demand* can come from a unit (e.g., *AC* electricity) which, when installed, adds extra demand. $E_{Grid,i,m,p}$ represents electrical energy imported from the grid, while $Self_{i,m,p}$ is energy generated for self-use by the installed units. *StorOut* is the power available from storage facilities. Q is the power transferred via the *MG* or pipelines from house j to i. This value is subtracted from the demand and vice versa for *QE*. The left side of the equation is the net demand, met by technologies and imports on the right side. β is a loss coefficient, dependent on the cable or pipe lengths between 2 homes. Looped networks are mitigated by the following equation where E is a numerical position of a connected home. A higher order home cannot give energy to lower order homes, only import it from them, while *card* is the value of i.

$$E_j \geq E_i + 1 - [card_i \times (1 - YMG_{i,j})] \tag{8}$$

Moreover, energy flows in one direction along connections, and the energy transferred must be equal to the sum of energies from contributing technologies within the house i. Finally, the *MG* controller itself uses electricity and therefore has an O&M cost.

The electricity generated in the network which exceeds demand can be sold to the national grid. *CSalGRID* represents the annual income from electricity sales for the network and is calculated as the volume of electricity sold for a given technology and time period multiplied by the length of that time period, the number of days in which in that time period appears, and the number of months in which those days appear. This is summed for all time periods, houses and technologies. To ensure that homes do not become power plants, and are only selling electricity and not generating it for profit, a rule is put in place that states that the total energy sold from all technologies cannot exceed that generated by all units, minus the demand of the home. The annual electricity cost for energy purchase from the grid, *CPurGrid*, is calculated as the sum for all houses and time periods, of the volume purchased in any given period multiplied by the length of time period and the number of days and months. At any time, a house either buys or sells electricity, not both.

$$PurGRID = \sum_{i,m,p} EGRID_{i,m,p} \times PElec \times day(m) \times hours(p) \times season(m) \qquad (9)$$

According to legislation, *BB* units are not allowed to provide heat to more than one home, and there is also a limitation on the annual heat produced from *BB* which receive RHI payments. The capacity of the generating units is based on the demands which can come from self-provisions, sales to the grid, storage and transfer to other homes:

$$Self_{tech,i,m,p} + Sal_{tech,i,m,p} + Stor_{tech,i,m,p} + \sum_j Q_{tech,i,j,m,p} = Gen_{tech,i,m,p} \qquad (10)$$

Power generation from a unit cannot occur in a house unless the unit is installed. The money earned through FITs is calculated from the FIT price or electricity generated, *PFIT_{Tech}*.

$$FITPay = \sum_{i,m,p,tech} (EGen_{tech,i,m,p} \times PFITCHP \times day(m) \times hours(p) \times season(m))$$

For the sake of space, only one *CHP* is permitted in which dwelling. Electricity generation from *PV* cells is a function of solar irradiance, which varies with the time of day and seasons, the surface area installed (a variable which the model optimizes) and the panel efficiency, a set parameter. The volume of energy in the *TS* is a function of the volume in the unit in the previous time period, what is sent to the unit, what is withdrawn from the unit for heating and *DHW* demand, as well as the static loss. A balance is needed to calculate how much energy can be withdrawn and is based on energy provided in the previous time period. It is impractical to have *WT* in adjacent houses, hence a rule is put in place that there must be at least one house gap between *WT* installations. Power generated by *WTs* is not a continuous function of the available wind resource but is instead, a piecewise function dependent on the "rated", "cut in" and "cut-out" speed for the units available. Finally, a tax is imposed for electricity taken from the grid, which has its own carbon intensity.

4. Results and conclusions

The model is formulated as a MILP and solved using the GAMS CPLEX solver [8]. A summary of models' statistics and solution times is shown in Table 2. The combined variable import and export pricing increase charges both from and to the grid but, overall, profitability is increased. This is due to the extreme differences in volumes of imported and exported energy. While the relative increase in charges from purchased electricity is much higher than the relative increase in sales, the absolute increase in charges is slightly smaller than absolute increase in sales. This is due to the network generating much of its own energy. Carbon emissions per kWh are increased due to increased sales from *CHP* units which are more economically incentivised by the FIT payments than generation from *WT*. In the variable network design case study, variable pricing greatly affects the installations made and the operation of the DER network. The network becomes much less dependent on thermal storage (*TS*) capabilities and a pipeline connection is installed between houses *i4* and *i5*. The network also becomes less dependent on *AC* units for cooling demands and the number of absorption chillers (*Abs*) is increased. This is due to increased *CHP* sizes which allow *Abs* to be added and also the ability to share cold loads through the pipelines. Fig. 3 shows the layout of the newly designed network. In terms of operational effects, dynamic pricing increases environmental impacts, as for the fixed network, due to UK FIT payments encouraging electricity generation from *CHPs* over other renewable assets. Profitability increases more than for the fixed network because the model is able to adjust to the changes in pricing and take advantage of a more economical trading scenario.

Table2. Economic and environmental results of the different case studies

Pricing	Constant	Dynamic	Dynamic
Scenario	Baseline	Fixed	Unfixed
CO_2 emissions (kg / kWh)	0.0856	+ 1.17 %	+ 25.00 %
Profitability (£ / year)	1,535.81	1,550.80	1,620.83
Investment cost (£)	51,178.72	+ 0.00 %	+ 12.30 %
Sales to grid (£ / year)	1,106.57	+ 2.00 %	+ 47.30 %
Grid purchases (£ / year)	9.85	+ 143 %	- 100 %
Equations	3,810	3,810	10,397
Variables	4,475	4,475	14,983
Binaries	120	120	226
CPU Time (s)	0.14	0.11	160.22

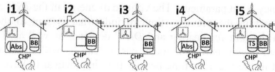

Fig 3. Layout of the newly designed DER network for dynamic import and export pricing

Furthermore, the short times for solving the models is encouraging as it demonstrates that optimization using dynamic pricing control is achievable and the network should be able to respond rapidly and reliably to incoming demand and pricing data, even for time periods in the distant future.

References

[1] L.B. Nikonowicz, J. Milewski, Virtual Power Plants – general review: structure, application and optimization, *Journal of Power Technologies 92*, 135, 2012;

[2] S. Acha, A. Mariaud, N. Shah, C.N. Markides, Optimal design of distributed low-carbon energy technologies in commercial buildings, *Energy 142*, 578, 2018;

[3] A.S. Hasan, L. Cipcigan, N. Jenkins, Optimal battery storage operation for PV systems with tariff incentives, *Applied Energy 203*, 422, 2017;

[4] B.L. Gowreesunker, S.A. Tassou, The impact of renewable policies on the adoption of anaerobic digesters with farm-fed wastes in Great Britain, *Energies 9*, 1038, 2016;

[5] G. Xu, W. Yu, D. Griffith, N. Golmie, P. Moulema, Toward integrating distributed energy resources and storage devices in Smart Grid, *IEEE Internet of Things Journal 4*, 192, 2017;

[6] E.D. Mehleri, H. Sarimveis, N.C. Markatos, L.G. Papageorgious, A mathematical programming approach for optimal design of distributed energy systems at the neighborhood level, *Energy 44*, 1, 2012

[7] C. Wouters, E.S. Fraga, A.M. James, An energy integrated, multi-grid, MILP (mixed-integer linear programming) approach for residential distributed energy system planning – A South Australian case-study, *Energy 85*, 30, 2015

Anton A. Kiss, Edwin Zondervan, Richard Lakerveld, Leyla Özkan (Eds.)
Proceedings of the 29th European Symposium on Computer Aided Process Engineering
June 16th to 19th, 2019, Eindhoven, The Netherlands. © 2019 Elsevier B.V. All rights reserved.
http://dx.doi.org/10.1016/B978-0-128-18634-3.50015-1

Engineering success: What does it take to get PSE technologies used?

Sandro Macchietto[*]

aImperial College London, South Kensingto Campus, London SW72AZ, UK

s.macchietto@imperial.ac.uk

Abstract

Over the years there have been many excellent contributions in the ESCAPE conferences to the R component of R&D, but less emphasis on the D element, and even less on the steps required for taking a piece of research to the final users in industry, that is, the technology transfer process itself.

These days, initiatives in tech transfer (variously called "third mission" or "translation" activities) are everywhere. A variety of supporting structures (Enterprise Launch Pads, Spinout Clinics, Tech Launch Prizes, Venture Competitions, Technology Parks, etc.) are implemented in most academic and research establishments. The enterprise climate is possibly at its hottest for many years, the message has been spreading widely, and there are a number of notable successes. However, in my experience, there is still a big gap between theory and practice, only a very small fraction of researchers are involved and there is an enormous untapped potential. Based on 30-year experience of "translation" activities, some more successful than others, a personal overview is presented of what it takes to go from novel research to final use of a technology. It briefly touches on things found working and not, essential and unnecessary (or counterproductive), drawing on the experience of launching and managing two companies in the PSE area (including Process Systems Limited), various interdisciplinary consortia and two applied research centres. Some final comments address how to tweak the odds towards "engineering success by design".

Keywords: technology transfer, R&D translation, industrial uptake.

1. The numbers

The ESCAPE Conference Series is 29 years old. Assuming ~350-400 papers accepted in each one, altogether over 10,000 papers have been produced and passed a peer review quality test, representing a huge collective investment in research time and resources. No doubt they include a good number of seminal papers presenting highly innovative ideas, results and applications. A quick scan indicates that most contributions address the R component of R&D (not surprisingly, given the nature of the conference), with less emphasis on the D element and even less on the steps required for taking a piece of research to the final users in industry, that is, the technology transfer process itself.

The longevity of the conference is a good indicator of its perceived usefulness to the community. It is however a legitimate question to ask how many of these ideas have actually found their way into industry and are productively used as methods, tools, or embedded in products. Some relevant related questions are: Does good research actually produce good impact? How many good ideas result in eventual industrial uptake and impact? Is academic recognition (e.g. publication in peer reviewed journals, number of citations) a good indicator of uptake and impact? How long does it take? And the more operative question, are there better mechanisms for "engineering" such success? These questions are complex and the subject of much research in the academic entrepreneurship community. Without pretence to provide a formal answer, some figures and considerations from personal experience are presented in the following.

The *inventive output* of an organisation is typically measured in terms of number of Disclosures (being considered for commercialisation) and Patents (filed and awarded), *technology transfer* performance in terms of Licensing and company Spinoff (formation plus various progress metrics e.g. survival rate, investment capital attracted, employment generated, turnover, growth, acquisition value, etc.). Other mechanism for transferring technology from academia include Consultancy, industrial projects and (in my experience, the main channel) "brain walks" (hiring of students and researchers).

Technology transfer is hard. US Venture capital funds invested $175bn in the two year technology boom period 1998-2000. Out the myriad companies started, Google, and Amazon are outstanding survivors, but most of the $175bn was wasted. The average rate of return of VC funds invested in the 2000-2004 period following the Dot.com bust was less than 2% (marginally less than ordinary bank savings). The concept of supporting the transfer of intellectual property (IP) and technologies from academic research into practical use was introduced in the UK in the 1980's Thatcher years. These days, initiatives in tech transfer (variously called "third mission" or "translation" activities) are everywhere. A variety of supporting structures (Enterprise Launch Pads, Spinout Clinics, Tech Launch Prizes, Venture Competitions, Technology Parks, etc.) are implemented in most academic and research establishments. The enterprise climate is possibly at its hottest for many years.

In the UK, Imperial College has a good reputation for being one of the most active and successful in technology transfer, and has created a quite variegated eco-system to nurture and support enterprise by student and staff along the long path from idea to Exit/IPO (Imperial College London, 2018, p.19). A summary of Imperial's tech transfer results for the 5 years to 2016-17 is given in Figure 1. A few things are worth noting. The number of yearly start-ups (5-9 per year) is relatively modest (those in the technology and industrial sectors based on IP produced by R&D are even fewer, 1-3 per year, most others being in health and medicine). Only about 20% of Disclosures results in a patent filing, with a conversion rate of ~50% to Patents granted. While a double digit number of new licences were signed each year and over 200 active ones are held, less than half of them (42% in 2016-17) actually generate income, on average of £33K each. Even a cursory thought to patenting, legal, commercial and administrative costs indicated there are no great returns here! Some data on generation rate and cost efficiency are also given in Fig. 1 in the form of ratios. On this basis, in 2016-17 £100m of research generated 92 Disclosures, 19 Patent filed and 11 granted, 2.5 IP based start-up and 4.4 student start-ups. The income from licensing and realisation of participated companies is 2.6% of the research income, a rate of return comparable to keeping the money in the bank. Actually, this performance is pretty good, as most societal and commercial gains do not accrue to the universities. A comparative analysis (Autio and Webb, 2015) of the ability of universities to spin out new ventures and their subsequent growth, found that while the UK entrepreneurial culture is weaker than in the US, after adjusting for population size and economic activity, UK universities are more efficient

Figure 1. Imperial College Inventive Output Scorecard YE 2016-2017 (extracts from Imperial College London, 2018, p. 20)

Metric	2012-13	2013-14	2014-15	2015-16	2016-17
Inventive Output					
Inventions disclosed	306	323	296	310	332
Patent applications filed	43	57	66	73	68
Patents issued	78	98	47	59	40
Active inventions in portfolio	832	977	1,007	1,021	1,009
Active patents in portfolio	325	373	394	404	429
Licensing Performance					
New licenses signed	29	27	39	39	46
Active licenses held	170	175	193	202	217
Licenses generating income in the period	48	71	74	70	91
Royalty and fee income generated in the period (£m)	£1.3	£1.6	£2.8	£2.1	£3.0
Startup Formation					
IP-based startups formed	5	7	8	6	9
Student-based startups formed	6	8	18	16	16
Ratios					
Research income (£m)	£330	£351	£436	£351	£361
Invention disclosures per £100m of research income	93	92	68	88	92
Patents filed per £100m research income	13	16	15	21	19
Patents issued per £100m research income	24	28	11	17	11
Licensing and realisation income : research income (%)	0.5%	0.4%	1.1%	1.1%	2.6%
IP startups per £100m research income	1.5	2.0	1.8	1.7	2.5
Student startups per £100m research income	1.8	2.3	4.1	4.3	4.4

than German and US ones in generating new ventures (576 spinouts in UK vs. 428 in US per $ trillion GDP, and 48 vs.16 per $ billion of tertiary education spending). The UK however was found to lag the US in scale-up performance, due to lower funding (US spinout raised on average 50% more equity) and lower entrepreneurial aspirations, including a number which are good indicators of scalability (Risc Capital, Internationalisation, High Growth and Product and Process Innovation aspirations). Their analysis focused on low-carbon technologies, but also gives useful general data. They identify the ecosystem in Figure 2 as enabling enterprise.

The fraction of academics involved in impact-related activities even in a relatively enterprising place like Imperial is small, with 26%, of total academic staff involved in collaboration with industry, 41% in consulting, 13% in patent ownership and just 4% in IP commercialization (Gann et al, 2016). Patents and IP commercialisation are the least preferred ways by academics to generate impact. Recent emphasis has been more on unleashing students' enterprise juices, with excellent response and good success. This is particularly important. While universities still largely train students for big company employment, they increasingly like to start their own. It is useful to remember that Apple, Facebook, Microsoft, Uber, Spotify and Tesla were all started by university dropouts. Perversely, some universities that have encouraged student enterprise activities in the early years have found that significant numbers do not return to their books, and (in the UK) risk being penalised due to high drop-out rate (e.g. Sheffield University, article in The Times, 14 Nov 2018). Data on UK university technology transfer is provided by the Higher Education Statistical Agency (HESA, 2018), while R&D data by OECD countries are in (OECD, 2018).

Figure 2. Structures and ecosystem which enable enterprise in the UK (Autio and Webb, 2018, p. 4)

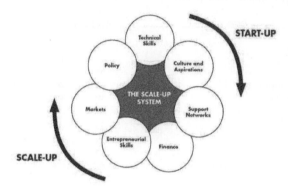

2. The practical experience

So much for statistics. If one follows the recommended path, first carries out fundamental research, then does a first prototype and product development, followed by trials, market research and business development. If/when this works, one may address commercialisation. This is often formalised into several sequential "technology readiness levels" (TRLs). In my experience, this has two main pitfalls. First, it may take years. Second, the best people at each stage are often not available for or interested in the next. A Phd or Post-doc who has demonstrated the superior convergence of a new algorithm is usually not interested in (or does not have the skills for) re-implementing it in professional code, with documentation, interfaces, testing, validation, versioning, customisation, applications support, etc. While continuity of funding across the TRLs is always a problem (some agencies fund research, other commercialisation, few the hard bit in between), in my experience a bigger challenge is ensuring continuity in technical expertise and injecting management, financial, commercial expertise at the right time.

Solving many problems: One way to address this is to pursue many related ideas in parallel, in larger projects with a broad research programme, with people of different competences, all at the same time. A multidisciplinary team ensures that each idea is explored from multiple angles and that many other unexpected ideas are generated, especially when industry is also closely involved. An example is represented by the Centre for Process Systems Engineering at Imperial, where from the inception PhDs and MSc researchers worked alongside "development" teams (full time programmers, project managers and industry visitors) on so-called "major projects", tasked with implementation, consolidation and early validation of the research. Notable outcomes of two of these projects were several "industry-tested" technologies that went into the Process System Enterprise spinoff, and the company formation itself.

Solving the right problem: In the PSE approach, a problem is conceptualised, formulated, analysed and solved. We typically seek an exact (rigorous) solution, using the best solvers, for a complete formulation. However, we often need to make simplifying formulation assumptions (e.g. on size, detail, constraints, nonlinearities) in order to use a solution technique. An alternative approach is to use an approximate solution of a more complete problem formulation. Failure to consider all relevant problem features is in my experience a key reason limiting the credibility and acceptability of a new method in industry, where "better but feasible" always trumps "optimal but not quite feasible". Understanding the problems in their full detail and complexity, ideally in the plant or design office, can be a humbling experience! An example from my own research include Batch Processing (Crooks et al., 1992) in the food industry. Key features include multipurpose recipes, multiples sources for the same material that must remain segregated, vessels coupling through shared piping, condition-based cleaning, multi-layered product packaging, and a myriad of other subtle but essential elements. Much of the published work in this area considers such simplified views of the process that make the methods not applicable, whatever the elegance of the combinatorial solution. A more heuristic solution which however captured all required features was successfully applied industrially to scheduling and design of very complex, large scale food productions (e.g. Figure 3, Macchietto, 2005). Similarly, much elegant heat exchanger network (HEN) optimisation work in the literature cannot deal with fouling, very often present. This requires much more detailed, representative models and sophisticated solutions (e.g. Diaz et al., 2016).

Figure 3. Scheduling of beer production in one of the largest UK breweries (26 beer families, 140 pieces of equipment) (Macchietto, 2005)

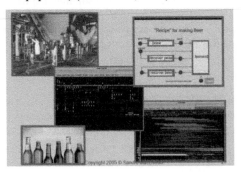

Solving the problem right: A 90% success rate for a new optimisation method is a very good improvement over methods that only solve 80% of the problems. However, it is not good enough for practical everyday use in industry, as users will spend 90% of their time in dealing with the 10% of failures, and will soon give up. Achieving a 100% rate is not easy, maybe impossible, so should we park the method? A common R&D failure is that too much emphasis is put on performance, and too little on usability. To address this requires analysing, understanding and facilitating user's workflows, and where benefits and losses (for them) really lie. Not easy without close contact with target users in their environment. For example, Dr. Chen, a brilliant student of mine produced a new, 90% good, nonlinear optimisation algorithm (SRQP, for successive reduced quadratic programming) for his PhD thesis. We spent the next 18 months with BP to make it industry-usable, including adding some obvious (but not easy) items such as meaningful error messages, a range of fail-safe, gently-degrading features, a guide to options and reverse communication for ease of embedding in third party software. As a result, the now robust software was licensed to and used in 4 different commercial simulators, in various on-line control applications, and has been for 20 years, with hardly any modifications, the optimisation workhorse within gPROMS.

Changing the odds: An example combining many of the above features is the UNIHEAT project, a £9.3m collaboration between Imperial College, the Boreskov

Institute of Catalysis in Novosibirsk, Russia, BP, the University of Novosibirsk, UNICAT, a Russian company, and the Russian Skolkovo Foundation (Macchietto and Coletti, 2015). It featured large multidisciplinary research teams with adjacent expertise; a dedicated knowledge and technology transfer team; several related projects in parallel; concurrent research, demonstration/prototype development and proof of concept; significant, integrated industrial involvement; very early IP identification and development alongside the research. This turbocharged the whole process. Results obtained in three years, described in the reference, include, in addition to the expected large number of publications in scientific journals, 3 spinoffs and 22 patents filed, Expectations based on the ratios in Fig. 1 would be 0.23 spinoffs (at 2.5/£100m), and 1.9 patent filed (at 20/£100m). Results achieved represents a x10 improvement in R&D productivity, even for a difficult multi-partner project across 7 time zones.

3. Conclusions

Technology transfer is not easy, but a few mechanisms have proved useful to boost it. These include shortening the timescales by working on multiple related developments in multidisciplinary teams, industrial involvement from the beginning, making sure we address the right problems by understanding the solution end use and users, addressing usability as well as performance from the outset, and integrating knowledge and technology transfer professionals and activities with the R&D team. Results on a recent project thus configured show that a large increase in R&D productivity can be achieved.

References

Autio E and R. Webb, 2015. Engineering Growth: enabling world-class UK entrepreneurship in the low-carbon economy. Imperial College Business School Report for Shell Springboard Awards 2015. http://www.shellspringboard.org/shell-springboard-imperial-college-study/

Crooks, C.A, K Kuriyan and S Macchietto, 1992. "Integration of batch plant design, automation, and operation software tools". Proceedings, ESCAPE I Conference, Elsinore, Denmark, May 24-28.

Diaz - Bejarano, E., Coletti, F. and Macchietto, S., 2016, A new dynamic model of crude oil fouling deposits and its application to the simulation of fouling - cleaning cycles. *AIChE J.* 62 (1), 90-107.

HESA, 2018. https://www.hesa.ac.uk/data-and-analysis/providers/business-community

Imperial College London, 2018. Review of Enterprising Activity 2016-17, http://www.imperial.ac.uk/enterprise/publications/enterprising-activity-2017/ accessed 10.10.2018

Gann, G., M. Tackett, C. Thorne, 2016. Pathways to Societal Impact, Report, Imperial College London.

Macchietto, S., 2005. Integrated Batch Processing: A model for advanced manufacturing. Proceedings, APACT 05 Conference, Birmingham,UK, 20-22 April 2005

Macchietto S. and Coletti F., 2015. Innovation: better together. *The Chemical Engineer*, 893 24-27. (Cover article)

OECD, 2018. http://www.oecd.org/innovation/inno/researchanddevelopmentstatisticsrds.htm

Anton A. Kiss, Edwin Zondervan, Richard Lakerveld, Leyla Özkan (Eds.)
Proceedings of the 29th European Symposium on Computer Aided Process Engineering
June 16th to 19th, 2019, Eindhoven, The Netherlands. © 2019 Elsevier B.V. All rights reserved.
http://dx.doi.org/10.1016/B978-0-128-18634-3.50016-3

Component based development of computer-aided tools for different applications

Anjan K.Tula[a], Mario R. Eden[a], Rafiqul Gani[b*]

[a]*Department of Chemical Engineering, Auburn University, Auburn, AL 36849, USA*
[b]*PSE for SPEED, Skyttemosen 6, Allerød, DK-3450, Denmark*

rgani2018@gmail.com

Abstract

Computer-aided methods and tools are used at different stages of chemical process development. However new tools are needed to meet the current and future challenges through innovative and more sustainable solutions that the currently available tools may not be able to provide. This work focuses on component-based software architecture for development of tailor-made computer-aided tools for specific application objectives. The architecture is based on "components", which can be model-objects that are stored in a library; collection of property models; databases; numerical solvers; design-algorithms (work-flows) etc. The main idea of these components is to incorporate a plug & play framework, where for a specific purpose, after the work-flow and associated data-flow are established, a specific computer-aided tool can be configured through a library of software components. Also, through the use of software components that are based on predictive model-based solution techniques, the final software can be reliably used to provide innovative and more sustainable solutions over a wide range of problems.

Keywords: component-based, tailormade tools, software architecture.

1. Introduction

Chemical engineering is in constant evolution and access to computational resources are changing the way chemical engineering problems are addressed. Process simulation, which emerged in the 1960s, has become one of the great success stories in the use of computing in the chemical industry. Process simulators are used today in most of the chemical engineering disciplines ranging from process design, research and development, production planning, optimization to training and education making it one of the most sought-after software. Some well-known process flowsheet simulators are Aspen Plus, ChemCad and PRO/II. This success, however, has led to a negative trend, that is, replacement of the trial and error experiment-based solution approach to a trial and error simulator-based solution approach, which is a faster and less expensive option. However, does it lead to the innovative and significantly better solutions which are required to deal the grand challenges of health, food, water, energy and environment (Negro et al., 2018)? The current unit-operation based process simulators, although having great success and wide applications, are not able to satisfy the demands for the new technologies (multiscale, multipurpose, new concepts leading to new algorithms, visualization, etc.). For example, process simulators can only be used indirectly for synthesis, control, analysis, etc., purposes through iterative approach. In this approach, the simulator is in the inner loop generating the simulation data for each trail while the outer loop has the techniques for synthesis, design and control. This is not the best way moving forward to solve where innovative and significantly better solutions are need of the hour. Clearly, a new class of methods and associated model-based computer aided tools are needed, and most importantly a structured approach in development of these software. This new software development approaches have to be modular, which can be described as component-based modeling that are flexible and easy to integrate with other components (pieces) of software. In this way one can easily design and develop smaller and flexible tailormade problem specific tools configured from a library of different software components (databases, models, design work-flows, analysis tools, solvers, etc.) according to the needs of the user. Modular based strategies have been proposed in different application areas ranging from modular modeling and simulation of chemical flowsheets to cellular systems however they failed to explain how a common interface can be used to develop software for different applications. This capability is important in industrial research and development where tools are developed for different applications. In this work a standard framework for software development based on components is proposed along with several illustrative examples of new tools that are able to achieve significant improvements through innovative, new and more sustainable solutions. This work also highlights the development of the component library and the common framework (standard interface) for the handling these components.

2. Overview for component-based software development

The main features of this new class of computer-aided tools are that they are based on software components that are taken from a database of components and are assembled through a standard interface (software framework) according to the needs of the user. This modular framework emphasizes separating the functionality of a software into independent, interchangeable components, such that each contains everything necessary to execute only one aspect of the desired functionality. Figure 1 shows the general framework for component-based software development, where it's possible to develop user specific tools by adding the necessary software components from the database. Figure 1 shows how 3 different problem specific software can be developed using components repository.

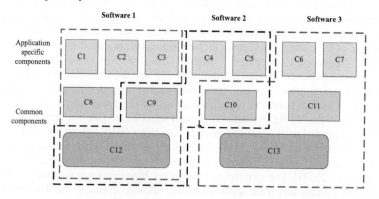

Figure 1: Framework for software component-based software development

Here components C1-C7 represents application specific components while C8-C12 represents common components. Compared to the classic development of large and complex generic software, modular approaches break down the complexity into smaller building blocks, making it easier to modify, maintain and most importantly reuse. This type of modular framework will be beneficial to research centers to reduce the software development times considerably and reuse components effectively. Here the software components can be databases, property models, process models of different types, and method-templates (for example, synthesis, design, analysis, control) with their specific work-flows (for example, step by step algorithms), the associated data-flows and computer-aided tools. Figure 2 shows the example of data and workflow of an integrated system, where in a template for process synthesis-design using superstructure-based optimization is shown. A software component is obtained through a collection of basic-tools and associated methods. A collection of components leads to a computer-aided tool. For example, a simulator for wastewater treatment industry can be constructed through the following software components: databases, membrane library, solver library, chemical dosing models, scaling models, flowsheet representation system. These software components define the application range and predictive capability of the software, so it is very important to select appropriate components keeping in mind the needs of the final software. With regard to system-wide co-ordination, these software components communicate with each other via the main interface.

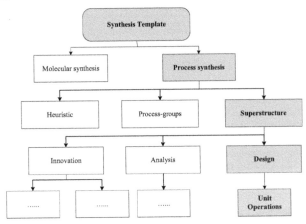

Figure 2 : Template example for Process Synthesis-Design

3. Application examples

3.1. Computer-aided tools for process-product synthesis, design, analysis

ProCAFD (Tula et al., 2017) is an integrated software component-based computer-aided tool that has been tailor-made for synthesis, design, analysis and optimization of chemical and related processes employing 12 hierarchical tasks based sustainable design methodology. It has only one design-template where the work-flow consists of 12 tasks organized into 3 stages. Each task has its associated list of software components, where the user has multiple options to carry out the task. For example, processing route generation may be performed based on well-known heuristics, group contribution based generate and test or superstructure optimization. Figure 3 illustrates the workflow and software components of ProCAFD, consisting of 12 tasks are performed in 3 stages. First define the problem; then solve the synthesis problem in stage-1; then perform design-analysis after process simulation in stage-2; finally, in the 3rd stage, apply process intensification, hybrid separations etc., to generate alternative more sustainable process designs. In stage 1, once the all the process alternatives are generated, the superstructure can be solved using mathematical optimization method or generate and test approach based on user choice. SUPER-O which is integrated with ProCAFD, can be used to automate the mathematical formulation of the generated superstructure and solve mathematically or the user can choose ProCAFD's built-in ranking algorithm based on generate and test approach to solve. In stage 2, ProCAFD is also integrated external simulation tools like Aspen, PROII, where the generated designs are automatically transferred, and a rigorous simulation model of the alternative is setup. Tula et al. (2015, 2017) illustrates the application of ProCAFD for sustainable chemical process synthesis and design where new innovative solutions have been found. In all the examples ProCAFD was able to quickly generate and evaluate numerous process alternatives that are truly innovative and better than the designs published in literature.

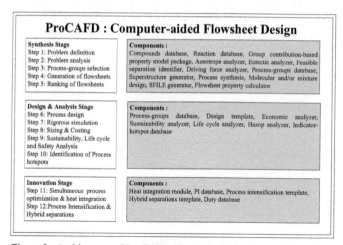

Figure 3 : Architecture of ProCAFD (Computer-aided Flowsheet Design)

ProCAPD (Kalakul et al. 2017) is an integrated tool for computer aided product design. This is analogous to process simulator, that is, it helps make the product design and development easier and faster and provides for a unified and consistent product documentation. However, unlike process simulators, ProCAPD can also be used directly for design of chemicals-based products, such as, single molecule products, formulations, blends, emulsions and devices (using different in-house synthesis design templates). It also has property-process modelling options, a large collection of databases for different classes of chemicals and properties and an interactive design template developer for new products and/or design methods. Figure 4 highlights the architecture and workflow of ProCAPD, where the main interface is at the inner core, then the method-template, then the associated software components and finally, the basic-tools. To design this chemical product simulator (ProCAPD), the components that must be selected are databases (chemicals, solvents, active ingredients, aroma, color-agents etc.); model objects (properties, product performance, etc.); solvers (product attributes, blend compositions, environmental impact, etc.); design algorithms (single molecules, blends, formulations, emulsions, devices). ProCAPD has been applied to design solvents & refrigerants (Kalakul et al., 2018), surrogate fuel blends (Choudhury et al., 2017) and formulated liquid products (Conte et al., 2011). Note, however, the objective of ProCAPD is not to provide the final design of a chemical product but to quickly screen-out inappropriate alternatives so that focused experiments could be performed on a small set of promising candidates, thereby saving resources by reducing the product development time.

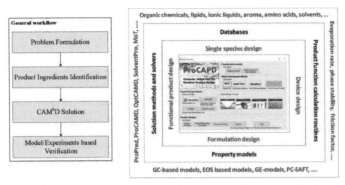

Figure 4 : Architecture of ProCAPD (Computer-aided Product Design)

3.2. ProCAPE: Computer aided property estimation

ProCAPE is a computer-aided property estimation tool consisting of chemicals database, pure component property models, mixture property models & phase equilibrium-based property calculation modules. It has the database for pure component, mixture properties of chemical species. To expand the capability and predictive nature of the software, software components related to property prediction models based on group contribution are also selected.

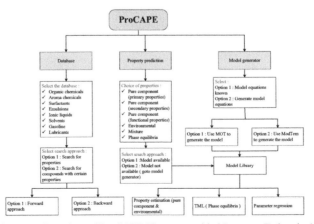

Figure 5 : Overview of ProCAPE (Computer-aided Property Estimation)

ProCAPE has different method templates like thermodynamic model selection guide, equilibrium analysis, parameter fitting for thermodynamic modes and simulation design calculations, etc. ProCAPE also has user model software component, where user can introduce his own models which can be used in performing different calculations. ProCAPE has models to predict 55 pure component properties (such as critical properties, acentric factor and solubility parameter) and 10 functional (temperature dependent) properties (such as vapor pressure, liquid viscosity, and surface tension) and collected measured data in database-tools covering 42,970 compounds. Also, ProCAPE has models (such as SRK, PR, UNIQUAC, UNIFAC, NRTL, PC-SAFT, etc.) for phase equilibrium calculations (vapor–liquid, liquid–liquid or solid–liquid) as well as mixture stability predictions.

4. Conclusions

Process systems engineering can play a leading role to address the current and future challenges of energy, water, food and health. Inorder to achieve innovative and sustainable solution we need to have access to next generation tools that can handle large datasets, models from different disciplines, establish solution strategies for multidisciplinary nature of problems. The key to these next generation tools would be software component-based computer-aided tools that has the flexibility to handle large and complex problems by breaking them down into smaller solvable problems (as in the case of 12 tasks based sustainable process design) while at the same time, designing different chemicals-based products through similar design templates but having different software components (for example, database and property models). The developed component-based software architecture has been successfully implemented in developing user specific tools ranging from property prediction to sustainable process-product design and analysis.

References

H.A. Choudhury, S. Intikhab, S. Kalakul, M. Khan, R. Tafreshi, R. Gani, N. Elbashir, 2017, Designing a Surrogate Fuel for Gas-to-Liquipd (GTL) Derived Diesel. Energy & Fuels, 31, 11266-11279.

E. Conte E, R. Gani, K.M Ng, 2011, Design of formulated products: a systematic methodology, AIChE Journal, 57(9), 2431-2449

S. Kalakul, M.R. Eden, R. Gani, 2017, The Chemical Product Simulator – ProCAPD, Computer Aided Chemical Engineering, 40, 979-984.

S. Kalakul, L. Zhang, Z. Fang, H.A. Choudhury, S. Intikhab, N. Elbashir, M.R. Eden, R. Gani, 2018, Computer aided chemical product design – ProCAPD & tailor-made blended products, Computers & Chemical Engineering, 116, 37-55.

C. Negro, F. Garcia-Ochoa, P. Tanguy, G. Ferreira, J. Thibault, S. Yamamoto, R. Gani, 2018, Barcelona Declaration – 10th World Congress of Chemical Engineering, 1–5 October 2017, Chemical Engineering Research & Design, 129, A1-A2

A.K. Tula, M.R. Eden, R. Gani, 2015, Process synthesis, design and analysis using a process-group contribution method, Computers Chem Eng, 81, 245-259

A.K. Tula, J. Bottlaender, M.R. Eden, R. Gani, 2017, A computer-aided software-tool for sustainable process synthesis-intensification, Computers Chem Eng, 105, 74-95.

Anton A. Kiss, Edwin Zondervan, Richard Lakerveld, Leyla Özkan (Eds.)
Proceedings of the 29th European Symposium on Computer Aided Process Engineering
June 16th to 19th, 2019, Eindhoven, The Netherlands. © 2019 Elsevier B.V. All rights reserved.
http://dx.doi.org/10.1016/B978-0-128-18634-3.50017-5

Predictive LCA - a systems approach to integrate LCA decisions ahead of design

Paraskevi Karka[a], Stavros Papadokonstantakis[b], Antonis Kokossis[a,*]

[a] *School of Chemical Engineering, National Technical University of Athens, Iroon Polytechneiou 9, 15780 Zografou, Athens, Greece*
[b] *Department of Space, Earth and Environment, Division of Energy Technology, Chalmers University of Technology, Hörsalsvägen 7B, 41296 Gothenburg, Sweden*

*Corresponding author: akokossis@mail.ntua.gr

Abstract

Bio-refineries are promising production options of chemicals production, capable to produce a wide range of fuels and chemicals equivalent to the conventional fossil-based products. To establish bio-refineries as mature choices and achieve the commercialization of their technologies, the application of sustainable solutions during the design and development stages are crucial. The innovative character of bio-based production and therefore data availability and access on process modelling details, is a challenging point for decision makers to move towards this direction.

Considering the environmental dimension out of the three aspects of sustainability, Life Cycle Assessment (LCA) is a suitable methodology for the evaluation of environmental impacts of bio-based processes because it highlights the stages with the greatest impact along a production chain. LCA studies require large amount of information, usually extracted from detailed flowsheets or from already completed pilot plants, making this procedure, costly, time consuming and not practical to act as a decision- support tool for the development of a bio-refinery.

The aim of this study is to develop predictive models for the assessment of LCA metrics and use them to highlight sustainable design options for bio-refineries. Models require the least possible information, which can be obtained from chemistry - level data or early (conceptual) design stages.

The modelling techniques used in this study are decision trees and Artificial Neural Networks (ANN), due to their easily interpretable structure and high computational capabilities, respectively. Models are based on the extraction of knowledge from a wide dataset for bio-refineries (it refers to 32 products that is, platform chemicals (e.g., syngas, sugars and lignin) and biofuels (e.g., biodiesel, biogas, and alcohols), starting from diverse biomass sources (e.g., wood chips, wheat straw, vegetable oil)). Input parameters include descriptors of the molecular structure and process related data which describe the production path of a study product.

Models are able to predict LCA metrics which cover the most critical aspects of environmental sustainability such as cumulative energy demand (CED) and Climate Change (CC). The average classification errors for decision- tree models range between 17% ($\pm$10%) to 38% ($\pm$11%) whereas for ANN models the average R^2_{cv} values (coefficient of determination) range between 0.55 ($\pm$0.42%) to 0.87 ($\pm$0.07%).

Demonstration of models is provided using case studies found in literature. Models are used to rank options in various design problems and support decisions on the selection of the most profitable option. Examples of such cases are the selection of the appropriate technology or feedstock to produce a desired product or the preliminary design of a bio-refinery configuration.

The proposed approach provides a first generation of models that correlate available and easily accessed information to desirable output process parameters and assessment metrics and can be used as pre-screening tools in the development of innovative processes, ahead of detailed design, thus saving time and money.

Keywords: GWP, early stage process design

1. Introduction

Decision making in identifying and developing the most sustainable option among a range of alternatives from biorefinery configurations pre-supposes a great amount of knowledge that is hardly available at early stages of process development. On top of that bio-based processes, in their majority, are characterized by low technology readiness level. Furthermore, there is a strong need to configure sustainability criteria (energy and water consumption, toxicity) as early as possible and identify critical aspects and profitable solutions from the portfolio of possible options.

To give answers for the most profitable option, the commonly used methods such as LCA require data collection and analysis, a kind of information usually obtained from simulations or already existing infrastructures, e.g. pilot plants. In addition, detailed LCA as a standardized method is limited to the final judgment of design decisions, as it is placed at the end of process development steps (that is, conceptual design, mass and energy balances, process integration and optimization) (Fig. 1a). This procedure leads to the formation of economic and environmental data which feed inventory analysis and the assessment of environmental profiles.

This study aims at the development of a streamlined LCA methodology which predicts LCA metrics and it can be applied at early stages of process development of biorefineries using the minimum required information. The proposed method supports decisions towards sustainable design options, providing assessments which can be conducted "ahead of detailed design" and identifies critical parameters which affect LCA metrics, thus providing guidance for design choices (Figure 1b). The concept is based on the FineChem tool (Wernet et al. (2008), Wernet et al (2010)) which predicts LCA metrics for petrochemical industry using as input the molecular structure of the product and no prior knowledge of process flowsheets. The current method expands this concept for bio-based production and, although it adopts molecular descriptors proposed by FineChem, it is enriched with process related information, easily found from laboratory scale and early conceptual design stages.

The proposed method is data-driven and based on a range of biorefinery configurations including all the impacts generated along the production pathways. The predictive LCA models use machine learning techniques and adopt molecular descriptors of the products chemical structure and minimum process information, extracted from a large database of biorefinery case studies. These types of models can be a valuable tool in early design phases for screening alternative biorefinery layouts considering their environmental impact or to guide design considerations without detailed modelling requirements.

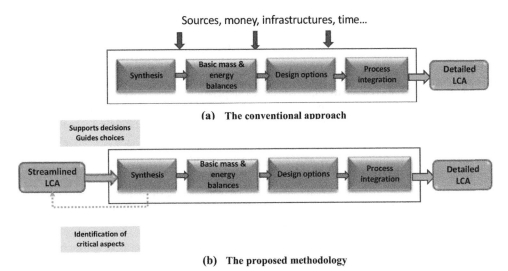

Fig. 1 (a, b) The research question

2. The methodological framework

The predictive models development procedure consists of 4 main steps that is:

- Step 1: Research question
- Step 2. Data collection and pre-processing
- Step 3. Use of data mining techniques to develop prediction models
- Step 4: Modelling performance-validation -demonstration in biorefinery cases

The research question addressed is the development of an amended version of LCA, able to predict LCA metrics for a wide range of environmental issues and guide design options at early design stages (Step 1).

The challenge to guide decisions "ahead of design" comes from the experience of machine learning to exploit data structures and identify patterns. The mathematical formulation aims at the development of functions $Y=f(X)$ which correlate Y, i.e. an LCA metric with a set of input variables $X=[X_1, X_2..X_n]$ easily available at early design stages. Thus, data for predictive model's training and development (Step 2) are collected from a wide range of biorefinery systems. The training dataset used in this study refers to thirty-two products produced from various synthesis paths which represent the most important groups found in literature (Karka et al. 2017). Training size refers to 91 study systems and data sources for the development of flowsheet models are pilot plant data, combined with literature sources and the knowledge acquired from industrial partners.

Two LCA metrics were selected as target attributes (one for each model), the Climate Change (CC) and the Cumulative Energy Demand (CED) which provide assessments for carbon dioxide emissions and the non-renewable fossil energy demand. Target attributes for the corresponding products were estimated using the LCA method according to the ISO 14040 for each study system as described in Karka et al. 2017. The functional unit is 1kg of product. Values of LCA metrics of each observation of the dataset are also provided for three allocation approaches (mass, market price, substitution).

Input (descriptor) variables refer to the molecular structure of the product of interest (e.g. molecular weight, number of oxygen atoms, number of hydrogen atoms etc.) and process-chain related variables corresponding to chemistry, complexity and generic process conditions (e.g. maximum temperature, efficiency factors, number of processing steps for the synthesis of the final product). Descriptor variables are arranged into two sets of 24 (reduced) and 30 (detailed) input variables depending on the level of access on early design stages, i.e. lab scale and conceptual design level, respectively. Thus, 12 datasets are developed which correspond to an equivalent number of models (2 metrics x 3 allocation approaches x 2 sets of predictor variables).

Data mining techniques used are decision trees which segregate the set of descriptor variables into classes of Low, Medium and High impacts in case of categorical prediction results, and RBF Artificial Neural Networks (ANN) in case of numerical result (Step 3). For the former technique all variables were discretized whereas for the latter they were normalized in the range [-1, 1] before entering the model.

Average modelling capabilities are obtained as a result of an iterative cross validation procedure in Step 4 using average classification error and coefficient of determination (R^2_{cv}). Classification error was defined as $\frac{\sum_{i=1}^{l} fp_i}{n}$, where fp is the number of wrong predicted class labels to the total number of observations, n, in the dataset and l is the number of class labels.

3. Results

Neural network models present a distinctive performance for both CC and CED metrics for the detailed set of predictor variables and especially for mass and economic allocation approaches. R^2_{cv} values result as an average of 500 cross-validation iterations, varying among 0.55 to 0.87 (Fig. 2).

Compared to the FineChem tool (Wernet et al., 2008) the respective performance ranges are about 0.3 for CC and 0.25-0.4 for CED depending on the number of predictor variables selected each time.

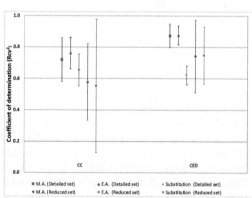

Fig. 2 Average and standard deviation values of R^2_{cv} for NN based models from 500 cross validation iterations (Values for substitution approach for the reduced sets are close to 0 and they are not shown)

The average prediction performance of the decision tree-based models results from a cross-validation procedure for 100 iterations (Table 1). The classification error values for CC and CED metrics (depending of the mass allocation approach and the set of predictor variables) range between 17% to 38%. These values can be acceptable for pre-screening models.

Table 1: Average classification error for CC and CED metrics and for all
allocation scenarios and input variables dataset

Predictor variables	Allocation approach	CC		CED	
		Avg.	St. Dev.	Avg.	St. Dev.
Detailed	Mass Allocation	22.2%	8.6%	21.6%	9.0%
	Economic Allocation	28.5%	9.1%	23.4%	9.1%
	Substitution	26.1%	10.2%	33.9%	10.8%
Reduced	Mass Allocation	19.6%	9.0%	17.3%	10.1%
	Economic Allocation	22.5%	8.7%	25.5%	10.7%
	Substitution	32.4%	12.2%	37.8%	11.0%

3.1 Models use in biorefinery processes

For demonstration purposes the graphical representation of the CC model (Fig. 3) for the mass allocation approach and the reduced set of predictor variables is used. Three paths of glucose production are tested, glucose through steam explosion (Option A), concentrated acid hydrolysis (Option B) and through biomass decomposition with organic acids, organosolv (Option C). Table 2, shows the minimum amount of information which is required to obtain an estimation whereas Table 3 summarizes the validation of prediction results using reported data for the options A, B and C.

Table 2: Input data for the assessment of CC metric
of glucose following the rules of the tree

	(A)	(B)	(Γ)
Feedstock	WChips	WChips	WStraw
Reacts	0	0	0
Steps	2	2	2
RME	Medium (0.211)	High (1)	
WAirReacts	100%	100%	
MaxT			Moder (100C)
Oxygen			=1

Table 3: Predictions using the CC metric tree, and
respective reported values

Production path	Estimation	Real class	Value	Source
Glucose (steam explosion) (A)	Low	Low	0.7	(Morales et al., 2017)
Glucose (acid hydrolysis) (B)	Low	Low	0.3	(Morales et al., 2017)
Glucose (organosolv) (C)	Medium	Medium	1.46	BIOCORE, 2010-2014, Karka et al. (2017)

✓ Correct ranking
✓ Correct class estimations

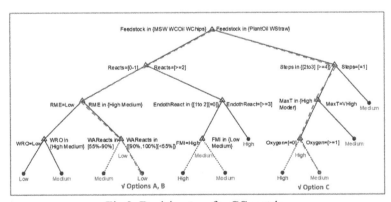

Fig 3. Decision tree for CC metric

Despite the practical use of decision trees, because of their interpretable format, we highlight below an example of using neural networks as a supportive tool to the categorical form of decision trees predictions.

Dihydroxyacetone-DHA (Morales et al., 2015; Lari et al., 2016), produced from biocatalytic processing of glycerine can be derived from plant oil based or waste cooking oil glycerine. The reported CC values per 1kg of DHA is 9.4 CO_2-eq and 6.4 CO_2-eq, respectively, which have been assessed following the steps of the ISO norm of LCA, both belong to the class of high impacts according to the categorization and classification of decision trees. A prediction like that would not support the designers towards the most profitable selection. Thus, the contribution of a numerical technique would enhance the capability of a classification model to rank the alternative options. In this case, neural networks can give a useful trend on the ranking of solutions even when their predicted values present high deviations from the reported values as shown in Table 4.

Table 4: Neural metrics predictions for CC, and respective reported values

	Production path	Reported value	30 predictor variables Estimation of NN	24 predictor variables Estimation of NN
1	DHA crude (biocatalytic), plant oil	9.4	6.28	4.84
2	DHA crude (biocatalytic), waste cooking oil	6.40	3.44	3.02

4. Conclusions

This study is a contribution towards estimating the environmental impacts of biorefinery products in early stages of process design, based on molecular descriptors of the bio-product and minimum process information. The resulting models for CED and CC show satisfactory accuracy in validation terms (e.g., coefficient of determination values around 0.6-0.85 and average relative errors of 17%-38%), similar to short-cut models previously developed for fossil-based production. The same modeling methodology (both classification trees and NN) was applied in LCA metrics provided by the ReCiPe method giving satisfactory results for other midpoint and endpoint LCA metrics such as Human Health, Ecosystems Quality, Marine Eutrophication etc. It is expected that an enrichment of the database and the appropriate selection of predictor variables will allow the development of a robust tool for predicting/benchmarking the cradle-to-gate environmental performance of the bio-based production.

References

Karka, P., Papadokonstantakis, S., & Kokossis, A. (2017). Cradle-to-gate assessment of environmental impacts for a broad set of biomass-to-product process chains. Int J Life Cycle Assess. doi:10.1007/s11367-017-1262-6

G. Wernet et al., 2008, Molecular-structure-based models of chemical inventories using neural networks, Environmental Science & Technology, 42, 6717-6722

G. Wernet et al., 2009, Bridging data gaps in environmental assessments: Modeling impacts of fine and basic chemical production, Green Chemistry, 11, 1826-1831

Lari GM, Mondelli C, Papadokonstantakis S, Morales M, Hungerbühler K, Pérez-Ramírez J (2016) Environmental and economic assessment of glycerol oxidation to dihydroxyacetone over technical iron zeolite catalysts. React Chem Eng 1:106–118

Morales M, Dapsens PY, Giovinazzo I, Witte J, Mondelli C, Papadokonstantakis S, Pérez-Ramírez J (2015) Environmental and economic assessment of lactic acid production from glycerol using cascade bio and chemocatalysis. Energy Environ Sci 8:558–567

Acknowledgements The authors would like to acknowledge financial support by FP7 KBBE Grant BIOCORE (FP7-241566), Marie-Curie Grant RENESENG (ITN-607415), the BAI4B: Accountable IT Infrastructures for Optimizing Supply Chains in Biomass Symbiotic Networks, General Secretariat for Research and Technology—Hellenic Ministry of Education and Religious Affairs, and Full material and chemical monitoring data and disclosure for the protection of the human health and environment LIFE MATHER (LIFE16 ENV/IT/000211)

Anton A. Kiss, Edwin Zondervan, Richard Lakerveld, Leyla Özkan (Eds.)
Proceedings of the 29th European Symposium on Computer Aided Process Engineering
June 16th to 19th, 2019, Eindhoven, The Netherlands. © 2019 Elsevier B.V. All rights reserved.
http://dx.doi.org/10.1016/B978-0-128-18634-3.50018-7

Energy System Modelling in support of the Energy Transition

Jan van Schijndel,[a*] Karin Griffioen,[b] Levi Ikele,[b] Andreas ten Cate[c]

[a]VSSC, Frederik Hendriklaan 2, Voorschoten, 2252 KJ, Netherlands

[b]ORTEC, Houtsingel 5, 2719 EA, Zoetermeer, Netherlands

[c]ISPT, Groen van Prinstererlaan 37, 3818 JN Amersfoort, Netherlands

jmg.vanschijndel@gmail.com

Abstract

The Dutch ISPT (Institute for Sustainable Process Technology) executes an innovation program that focusses on system integration and circularity. This program explores amongst others pathways for the re-use of CO contained in waste gases produced by steel making processes so to enable the circular use of carbon. ISPT commissioned an Energy System Modelling (ESM) project to demonstrate how ESM can be used to explore options for the upgrading of these CO-rich waste gas streams and to show which upgrade investments over time could meet CO_2 emission targets in the most cost-effective manner.

Keywords: Multi-Period Mixed Integer Linear Programming, monetisation waste gases from steel manufacturing, CO_2 abatement pathways, impact CO_2 taxation on CCS.

1. Introduction

Deep decarbonization of the energy system is required to mitigate climate change. ISPT executes an innovation program in the Netherlands that focusses on system integration and circularity to enable such a radical transformation. An example is the study on the re-use of CO from waste gases by steel making processes to enable circular use of carbon. Against this backdrop, ISPT commissioned a project to demonstrate how Energy System Modelling (ESM) could be used to explore a set of options for the most effective upgrading of CO-rich waste gas streams produced by a steel manufacturing complex.

2. Energy System Modelling

Energy System Modelling (ESM) is a dedicated application of the more generic network simulation and optimisation algorithm. It is based on a detailed techno-economic description of the conversion of energy flows. ESM systematically explores how to use over a given time horizon optionality in energy resource availability and conversion capacity in order to meet demand for heat, power, mobility and petrochemical products in the most cost-effective manner. An appropriately defined objective function that maximizes the net present value of the energy system whilst obeying CO_2 emission targets supports the evaluation of options how to be best structure the energy system. Scope and granularity for energy system modelling can vary widely: ESM can be applied at country level (Kejun and van der Made, 2014), but also at industrial cluster levels as shown by the example below for a steel manufacturing complex.

3. Mathematics

Energy System Modelling (ESM) is based on a mathematical optimization framework that uses a combination of the mathematical modelling system AIMMS and the mixed-integer solver CPLEX (Lasschuit and Thijssen, 2004). At the heart of ESM lies a Multi-Period Mixed Integer Linear Programming Model designed for strategic value chain studies and supply chain optimization purposes. ESM is a dedicated application of this generic framework with a focus on determining an economically optimal configuration of energy conversion systems such that it meets CO_2 emission targets and energy demand levels given available energy resources.

Mixed-integer Linear Programming (MILP) models have been successful in a vast range of applications. These algorithms evaluate the impact of integer decisions (on-off or 0-1) on the objective simultaneously with continuous variables subject to various constraints. ESM supports the selection and timing of conversion technology investments to meet CO_2 emission targets in the most cost-effective manner. The true value of the implemented mixed-integer linear programming model lies in its multi-period character. In particular, this means that multi-period mixed integer linear programming ensures that from a given set of potential technology investment options, those are selected and timed such that they minimize the total costs over the entire time horizon. This holistic approach avoids "technology lock-in situations" whereby technology options are selected with regrets later on leading to sub-optimal solutions over the time period considered. ESM adopts a complete end-to-end view both on a time-scale as on an infrastructure scale allowing for a fully integrated system optimisation from raw materials, to intermediates, to finished products that serve demand. ESM also allows to model non-linear 'economy of scale' features as multiple capacity choices aligned with relevant line-ups.

Figure 1 outlines the Energy System Modelling framework. Inputs define the structure of the energy system model and include data on various constraints and costs. The structure of the energy system may consist of various feedstock sourcing options, yields for conversion technology options and a distribution network to bring product to markets. Additional data are to be provided to define the optimisation space, such as product demand, CAPEX & OPEX for the conversion options and product distribution costs. Furthermore, the scope of the optimization space is defined by strategic input such as the time horizon considered and a set of scenarios to be evaluated. Simulation and Optimisation return a set of attractive energy system options for further analysis.

The model considers an annual planning horizon where t is the time period index, l the location index, p the conversion technology index, m the mode of operation index, s the stream index, i the investment index and r the investment effect time range index. The integer variable $\iota_{t,r,i}$ specifies the number of investments per investment option i, how many times it is active in period t and r periods after the start period of the investment. With r (relative to start) the aging of a conversion unit is tracked. The continuous variables $\sigma_{t,l,s}$, $\delta_{t,l,s}$, and $\pi_{t,l,p,m}$ denote supply, demand & processing variables for the infrastructure of the system. Processing optimizes the production yields per conversion technology per mode of operation per stream. Input and output yields for the production process are parameters denoted by $IY_{t,l,p,m,s}$ and $OY_{t,l,p,m,s}$. Mass balance constraints ensure that the total inflow equals the total outflow at each node.

$$\sigma_{t,l,s} + \sum_{(p,m)} \left(\pi_{t,l,p,m} * OY_{t,l,p,m,s} \right) = \sum_{(p,m)} \left(\pi_{t,l,p,m} * IY_{t,l,p,m,s} \right) + \delta_{t,l,s}$$
$$\forall t \in T, l \in L, s \in S$$

$PC_{i,r,l,p,m}$ denotes the processing capacity of a conversion unit with an age of r time periods. Cost minimization steers the investment in processing capacity for conversion technologies and determines the optimal set of conversion technologies.

$$\pi_{t,l,p,m} \leq \sum_{(i,r)} PC_{i,r,l,p,m} * \iota_{t,r,i} \ \forall t \in T, l \in L, p \in P, m \in M$$

The yield structure in the ESM denotes the amount of end products and by-products such as CO_2 generated at each production process in the energy system. A CO_2 abatement pathway can be modelled by assigning a cost per ton CO_2 leaving the energy system. Alternatively, direct emission targets can be defined to limit CO_2 emissions and set additional constraints that guide the model towards selection of the optimal energy system layout for the desired CO_2 abatement pathway. Let $MD_{t,l,s}$ be the maximum flow leaving the energy system, then the CO_2 emission limit is defined as follows.

$$\delta_{t,l,s} \leq MD_{t,l,s} \ \forall t \in T, l \in L, s \in S$$

From Figure 1 it can be inferred that the results of the optimised energy system depend on various input factors such as the layout of the system, conversion technology options, capital intensities & operating expenditures, feedstock availabilities & demand figures, which are deterministically modelled. In practice these input factors are of stochastic nature. This demands for sensitivity analyses to cope with the various types of uncertainties that affect the optimal results. Uncertainties emerge in different ways such as multiple scenarios for the outlook on energy supply and demand, technological developments affecting the capital intensities of conversion technologies or policy changes with regard to imposed CO_2 emission penalties. Therefore, the success of the decision-making process not only relies on the availability of a global optimal solution but also on sensitivity checks on the input data to address and confirm the robustness of the proposed optimal configuration of the energy system.

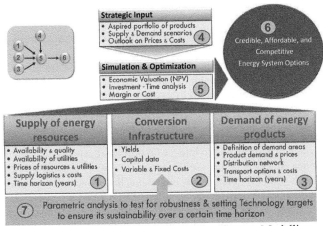

Figure 1: Generic framework for Energy System Modelling

4. Example

Europe produces some 170 million tonnes of steel per year. Significant volumes of waste gas are co-produced, like blast furnace gas (BF) and basic oxygen steel off-gas (BOS). Typically 1,7 tonnes of waste gases are produced per tonne of steel for a world scale plant producing 7 mln tonnes of steel per year. Apart from a high CO_2 content (40 wt%), waste gases contain high concentrations of valuable components, e.g. 23 wt% of carbon monoxide (CO). The remainder is predominantly N_2. Waste gases are burned to preheat enriched air for the blast furnaces. Waste gases are also used for steam and power generation. The resulting CO_2 footprint is some 1,3 tonnes CO_2 per ton of steel.

The combustion of CO contained in BF and BOS gas (see Figure 2) results in a major loss of potential value from a circular economy perspective. The recovery and conversion of CO into chemicals is therefore an alternative worthwhile pursuing. This has been studied by the CORESYM project (ISPT, 2017). This example builds on this project.

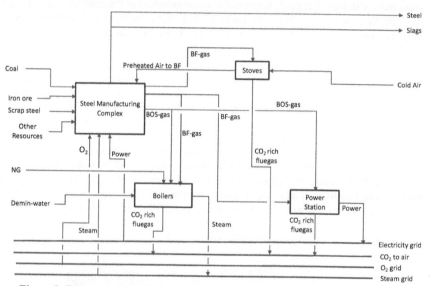

Figure 2: Base case upgrading waste gases from a steel manufacturing complex

Figure 3 below shows a superstructure of options for the upgrading of CO contained in BF and BOS waste gas into valuable products like Fisher-Tropsch (FT)-naphtha and methanol. The deficit in the amount of hydrogen to achieve this is by water electrolysis, steam methane reforming (SMR) and/or by shifting the H_2/CO content of the BOS gas in a dedicated water-gas shift reactor (WGS) or by buying H_2 from the grid. Furthermore, the superstructure shows a number of CO_2 capture units to ensure that remaining CO_2 volumes are captured and can be fed into a CO_2 grid for (deep-sea) storage. The purpose of this EMS pilot project is to analyse the attractiveness of recovery and conversion of CO into chemicals whilst simultaneously addressing the impact of CO_2-to-Air taxation in combination with a feed-in tariff of 50 $ per ton of CO_2 for a CCS system assumed to be in place. Another task set for the pilot is the development of a CO_2 abatement pathway to meet the 'Paris' goals set for 2030 and 2050 in the most cost-effective manner.

Figure 4 shows the relative attractiveness of the options studied. With CO_2-to-Air priced in accordance with a low ETS (Emission Trading System) price level of 4 $ per ton of CO_2, ESM identifies the recovery and conversion of CO into methanol (1350 ktpa methanol) with H_2 to be supplied through Steam Methane Reforming as most profitable (bar at the right).

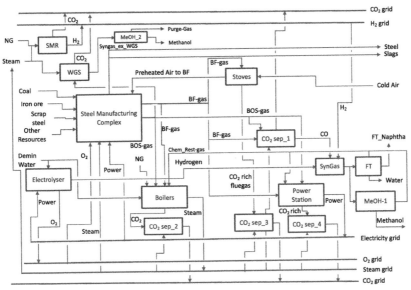

Figure 3: Options for the upgrading of waste gases steel manufacturing complex

Apart from a higher NPV, this option also lowers the CO_2 emission level of the reference case by some 12,5% from 9250 ktpa CO_2 to 8080 ktpa CO_2. This is due to the rerouting of the BOS and BF streams for methanol and hydrogen production and the elimination of NG imports to the boilers. This results in steam and power imports to meet all process requirements. Adjacent steam and power units allow for these imports. The resulting shift of CO_2 emissions to air to outside the complex is not accounted for.

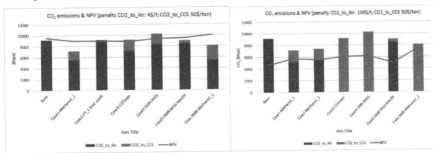

Figure 4: Relative attractiveness of CO monetisation options

Would CO_2 emissions to air be taxed at 100 $/ton, the most attractive CO-conversion option remains the methanol option. At this 100 $/ton CO_2 penalty, ESM concludes that it would be more cost-effective to invest in CCS facilities (and capture 50$ benefit per ton of CO_2) rather than enlarging methanol or FT-naphtha production (the amount of CO contained in the waste gases allows for the production of either 2500 ktpa methanol or 900 ktpa FT-naphtha). FT-naphtha and methanol are feedstocks for Base-Chemicals.

Figure 5 shows the CO_2 abatement profile with the CO_2-to-Air penalty set at 0 $/ton. In order to meet the 50% CO_2 reduction target in 2030 (50% relative to 2017, taken as Reference Year) investments are needed for the separation of CO_2 and CO from the BF and BOS waste gases, the production of Blue H_2 (e.g. through steam-methane-reforming while capturing and sequestering CO_2), the synthesis of methanol and treatment of flue gas ex boilers for CO_2 capture. Apart from the latter investment (taken in 2030), all other investments are advised to be taken in 2020. To meet the 95% reduction target in 2050 (again relative to 2017, taken as Reference Year), CCS investments are needed in 2050 for Power unit and Stoves. Timing of investments is optimal from an NPV perspective.

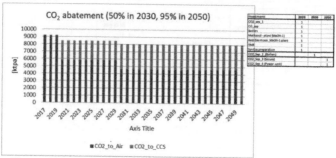

Figure 5: CO_2 abatement curve for steel manufacturing complex

5. Conclusions

ESM is a powerful decision support tool to assess the cost effectiveness of options for the upgrading of CO contained in waste gases from a steel manufacturing complex whilst simultaneously reducing its CO_2 emission footprint. Upgrading of CO into methanol is both economically attractive and it lowers CO_2 production by some 12,5%. This scenario assumes that CO_2-to-Air emissions are not subjected to any tax. In case 100 \$/ton tax would be levied on CO_2-to-Air emissions, methanol remains the preferred upgrading option. Assuming a CO_2 sequestration grid in place with a feed-in tariff of 50 \$/ton of CO_2, ESM shows that capturing and sequestering all CO_2 is economically preferred over increasing methanol production.

ESM supports the development of CO_2 abatement profiles defining which investments over time are needed to meet CO_2-to-Air emissions targets as set by the Paris agreement in the most cost-effective manner.

Acknowledgements

Authors acknowledge Shell Global Solutions International B.V. for making their Network Simulation and Optimisation tool available, TATA Steel for discussing decarbonisation options and Nort Thijssen for the modelling of the example discussed.

References

- ISPT, Report CORESYM study: CarbOn-monoxide RE-use through industrial SYMbiosis between steel and chemical industries; December 2017
- Jiang Kejun and Alexander van der Made: 'The greening and cleaning of China' in: The colours of energy: Essays on the future of our energy system by Kramer G.J. and Vermeer B. (Editors), Shell International B.V., Amsterdam, the Netherlands, ISBN: 978-90-9028343-2, July 2014
- Winston Lasschuit, Nort Thijssen: Supporting supply chain planning and scheduling decisions in the oil and chemical industry; Computers and Chemical Engineering, 28 (2004) 863-870

Anton A. Kiss, Edwin Zondervan, Richard Lakerveld, Leyla Özkan (Eds.)
Proceedings of the 29th European Symposium on Computer Aided Process Engineering
June 16th to 19th, 2019, Eindhoven, The Netherlands. © 2019 Elsevier B.V. All rights reserved.
http://dx.doi.org/10.1016/B978-0-128-18634-3.50019-9

Process Systems Engineering from an industrial and academic perspective

Anton A. Kiss,[a,b*] Johan Grievink [c]

[a]*School of Chemical Engineering & Analytical Science, The University of Manchester, Sackville St, Manchester, M13 9PL, United Kingdom*

[b]*Sustainable Process Technology, Faculty of Science and Technology, University of Twente, PO Box 217, 7500 AE Enschede, The Netherlands*

[c]*Delft University of Technology, van der Maasweg 9, 2629 HZ Delft, The Netherlands*

tony.kiss@manchester.ac.uk, a.a.kiss@utwente.nl

Abstract

Process Systems Engineering (PSE) deals with decision-making, at all levels and scales, by understanding complex process systems using a holistic view. Computer Aided Process Engineering (CAPE) is a complementary field that focuses on developing methods and providing solution through systematic computer aided techniques for problems related to the design, control and operation of chemical systems. The 'PSE' term suffers from a branding issue to the point that PSE does not get the recognition it deserves. This work aims to provide an informative industrial and academic perspective on PSE, arguing that the 'systems thinking' and 'systems problem solving' have to be prioritized ahead of just applications of computational problem solving methods. A multi-level view of the PSE field is provided within the academic and industrial context, and enhancements for PSE are suggested at their industrial and academic interfaces.

Keywords: PSE, industry, education, research, interface, perspectives

1. Introduction

Process Systems Engineering (PSE) is a discipline concerned with methods and tools to support decision-making for the creation and operation of chemical supply chains, including the discovery, design, manufacturing, processing, and distribution of chemical products (Grossmann and Westerberg, 2000; Stephanopoulos and Reklaitis, 2011). In other words, PSE is all about rational decision-making, at all levels and length / time scales, by understanding complex systems using a holistic view (Kiss et al., 2015). PSE is the wider field embracing Computer Aided Process Engineering (CAPE) as an important sub-domain where computing and information technologies play an essential role in finding solutions for problems of design, control and operation of chemical systems (Cameron and Lewin, 2009; Dimian et al., 2014).

This paper has several contributions: it defines PSE and CAPE areas and their mutual relationship; it questions what makes PSE less effective in chemical engineering (ChE) than it could potentially be; it shows that industrial as well as academic PSE have stronger & weaker points with known causes and amplified by deficient interactions with each other; it offers a model for enhanced PSE interactions between industry and academia covering key topics (e.g. sharing of industrial PSE problems with academia;

knowledge generation by research & know-how transfer by moving PSE professionals between academia and industry; start-ups of companies with deep PSE expertise and tools for industrial services), and it concludes there is ample potential for improvement of effectiveness of PSE by working better across industrial and academic interfaces.

2. Problem statement

The international PSE research community has successfully established a vital science of engineering. Yet, its accomplishments are unevenly absorbed by the process industry and in educational programs. Application potential is lost and locally even branding issues arise. The analysis of this paper is based on authors' experiences in the Dutch process industry and academia, but carries over well to other countries. There is a known divergence between academia and industry due to different focus: research (funding and output) vs economic profit (Klatt and Marquardt, 2009). A key consequence is that industry considers most important the core ChE disciplines, while academia (mainly driven by research funding / input) focuses on biotechnology, nanotechnology, or science-centred topics – as shown in Figure 1 left (Varma and Grossmann, 2014). Some barriers to more daring and effective use of PSE concepts, methods, models and tools (shown in Figure 1, right) include the following:

• The opportunities in making advancements in PSE seem to have moved from its interior (e.g. better models, faster computing) to external interfaces with other chemical engineering disciplines, such as process intensification (PI), product innovation and engineering for multi-phase products (Harmsen et al., 2018).

• The huge application success of CAPE tools has shifted barriers in process engineering projects. In the past doing process data handling and engineering computations fast and consistently was a key barrier. That kind of barrier has largely vanished, resulting in the emergence of other bottlenecks in: the human work processes; the knowledge levels of process engineers being incommensurate with the capabilities of the tools; at the interface of technology and society with societal acceptance of technology applications.

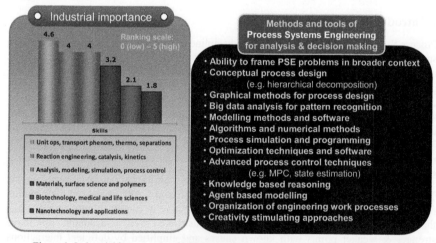

Figure 1. Industrial importance of PSE topics (left). Methods and tools for PSE (right).

3. PSE in industry

Research, development & innovation enable the introduction of new or improved products and processes, and reduce the uncertainty to acceptable levels. PSE supports such reductions: business risks, time, cost & profit, environment, safety, health, social. PSE is perceived as a service provider to "customers" in company applications, making it difficult to put a value (not a cost) on its activities or quantify their contribution.

Many industrial professionals have no idea about PSE, but they do know about process design, modelling, simulation, optimization, control, etc. This is likely due to the having these topics been taught at the university as separate topics without the interactions, but also due to the way in which the process design & engineering activities are compartmentalized in the engineering divisions of companies.

The industrial technology assessment models do take into account the probability of success when applying a new technology with a higher performance (or accounting for risk of failure), but it is rather unclear how does that tie in with PSE methods and tools for products and process innovations. Figure 2 shows a multi-level view of PSE positioning between the upper levels (determining the research directions) and the lower levels (tools and means to achieve the goals), with the "process" being seen as an optimized integrated production system, made up of one or more production plants.

Figure 3 shows that PSE has a key role in delivering more profit in shorter time, along all phases (e.g. research & development, engineering, process optimization, operation) taking into account all sustainability pillars (ten Kate, 2016). Of course, there is a trade-off between multiple criteria in Pareto type of optimization. Moreover, PSE reduces uncertainty along the way from idea to implementation, with the addition that there is also a reverse flow of information from an operational plant to the collection of process models. Plant data periodically collected in operational plants offer a rich base for "big data analysis": e.g. finding patterns of behaviour that can be exploited to improve process performances and be captured in updated models.

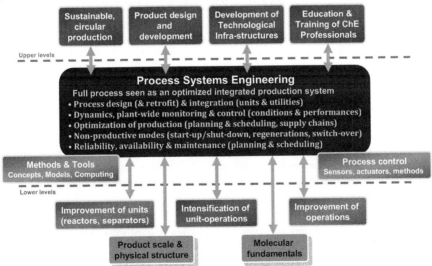

Figure 2. Multi-level view of PSE positioning

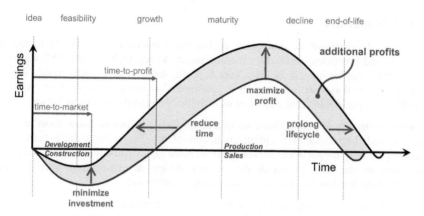

Figure 3. Role of PSE along all phases of plant development and exploitation

In PSE activities, the purpose shapes the models and these models have the role of transferable knowledge carriers (if the physical principles underlying the model are kept transparent in the structure of the equations). Setting up a model provides structured approach to understanding the system. However, a combined approach of experiments supported by modelling is the most effective. PSE offers a structured approach in process and product development: guiding the lab-scale experiments, interpreting the experimental observations, and translating the results into the desired outcome.

4. PSE in academia

Figure 4 illustrates the career span and life-long learning for PSE professionals at the interface of industry and academia, with a required exchange of professionals between academia & industry. But in the academic world, one must make a distinction between the academic research agenda for PSE, and the teaching / education in PSE topics.

PSE research includes: spanning a wider ranges of physical scales in processes & supply chains; broader range of feedstocks; integration of process intensification and PSE; circular systems: integration in design & operation of product manufacturing, product application, recovery and recycling, medical process systems; multi-scale modelling and computing; uncertainty in design & engineering. Major achievements of PSE include the development of methodologies and tools to support process modelling, simulation and optimization (MSO). But MSO technologies have become a commodity; they are not a distinguishing feature of the PSE field any more (Klatt and Marquardt, 2009). Hence PSE has to play a supportive role to the other engineering sub-disciplines that focus on smaller scales with specific objects. The proper integration of such objects in products and/or processes is certainly part of PSE area. Also, a large-scale energy transition with electrified processes and inherent dynamic operations offers challenges.

PSE education proved that one has to gradually build up the complexity, though the systems engineering aspects can be introduced from first year in BSc / BEng onwards. When teaching the PSE core elements in succession (e.g. process analysis, product & process synthesis and design, dynamics and control, optimization of process operations within supply chains, safety and reliability engineering) one could also emphasize the interdependencies between decisions made in these (PSE) activities.

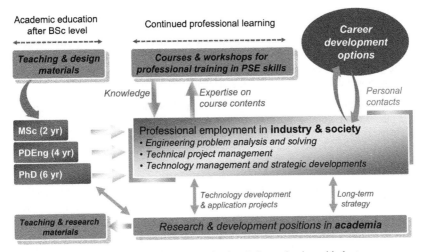

Figure 4. Career span for PSE professionals in academia and industry

5. PSE perspectives

Enhanced PSE interactions between industry and academia needs to cover: sharing of abstracted, generic industrial PSE problems with academia (education and research); knowledge generation by academic research with selective transfer to supportive industrial partners (see framework in Figure 5); as well as knowledge and know-how transfer by moving PSE professionals between academia & industry; and start-ups of small companies (providers) with deep PSE expertise and tools for industrial services.

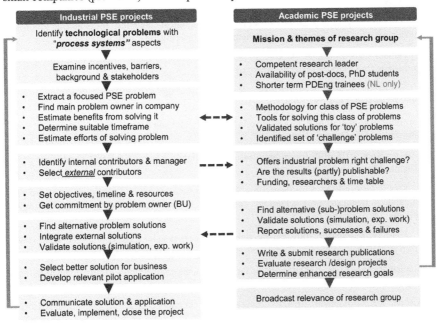

Figure 5. Industrial vs academic PSE projects

What needs to change for more enhanced interactions of both worlds includes:

• *Industry*: awareness from companies that the external development power is actually many times greater than internally in a company (although internally more focus on specific goals can be attained). Open innovation projects can accelerate the technology transfer of novel developments from the academic world into the industry.

• *Academia* needs to accept that the generation and use of engineering knowledge goes wider than writing good publications. The ultimate rationale for generating engineering knowledge is its application (potential) by joint projects & collaborations with industry.

6. Conclusions

PSE contributed significantly to chemical engineering, by providing MSO technology to address demanding and large-scale process problems in academia and industrial practice. Systems thinking and problem solving are indispensable in the academic education of chemical engineers and also in the industrial practice. Industry mainly focuses on profitability and sustainability, while academia aims at scientific progress, causing a potential gap between industrial practice and academic research. Sustainable success of PSE requires consistent co-operations between academia and industry. PSE is a key enabler for process and product innovation, and has a bright future with sustainable impact on the ChE sciences, and on industrial manufacturing processes.

Acknowledgements

AAK gratefully acknowledges the Royal Society Wolfson Research Merit Award.

References

I. T. Cameron, D. R. Lewin, 2009, Curricular and pedagogical challenges for enhanced graduate attributes in CAPE , Computers and Chemical Engineering, 33, 1781-1792.

A. C. Dimian, C. S. Bildea, A. A. Kiss, 2014, Integrated design and simulation of chemical processes, 2nd Edition, Elsevier, Amsterdam.

I. E. Grossmann, A. W. Westerberg, 2000, Research challenges in process systems engineering, AIChE Journal, 46, 1700-1703.

J. Harmsen, A. B. de Haan, P. L. J. Swinkels, 2018, Product and process design: Driving innovation, De Gruyter, Germany.

A. J. B. ten Kate, 2016, PSE for problem solving excellence in industrial R&D, Computers and Chemical Engineering, 89, 127-134.

A. A. Kiss, J. Grievink, M. Rito-Palomares, 2015, A systems engineering perspective on process integration in industrial biotechnology, Journal of Chemical Technology and Biotechnology, 90, 349-355.

K.-U. Klatt, W. Marquardt, 2009, Perspectives for process systems engineering – Personal views from academia and industry, Computers and Chemical Engineering, 33, 536-550.

G. Stephanopoulos, G. V. Reklaitis, 2011, Process systems engineering - From Solvay to modern bio and nanotechnology. Chemical Engineering Science, 66, 4272-4306.

A. Varma, I. E. Grossmann, 2014, Evolving trends in chemical engineering education, AIChE Journal, 60, 3692-3700.

Anton A. Kiss, Edwin Zondervan, Richard Lakerveld, Leyla Özkan (Eds.)
Proceedings of the 29th European Symposium on Computer Aided Process Engineering
June 16th to 19th, 2019, Eindhoven, The Netherlands. © 2019 Elsevier B.V. All rights reserved.
http://dx.doi.org/10.1016/B978-0-128-18634-3.50020-5

Process design meets sustainability: overview on the use of modelling tools for process design and sustainability assessment at Corbion

Van Bochove G., Cruz L., Morao A., Rugerio C.*

Process Modelling and Design, R&D, Arkelsedijk 46, 4206MD AC Gorinchem, The Netherlands

carlos.rugerio@corbion.com

Abstract

Bio-based companies must keep up with the needs of the consumers and the developments from their competitors. This needs to be done while managing the inherent risk of launching new products from new technologies to the market. To thrive it is essential to speed up research and development programs, to make the right choices for investment and to evaluate opportunities for reduction of production costs. Today's business ambitions incorporate not only economic growth but also sustainability targets. In this context, mathematical models are crucial to face these challenges. They are key to guarantee economy of scale whilst delivering on the commitments for sustainable development. In this work, the contribution of mathematical models in the process innovation funnel not only for process design but also for sustainability assessment within Corbion is presented. The methodology is illustrated with two case studies, in which it is shown how models help to find the optimal process in terms of economy and sustainability.

Keywords: process design, sustainability assessment, process modelling, bio-based economy

1. Introduction

Bio-based products are totally or partly derived from materials of biological origin, such as crops, plants or other renewable agricultural, marine or forestry materials. These products provide alternative material options to conventional petroleum-based materials by using renewable carbon as feedstock [1]. The use of renewable carbon feedstocks for chemical production has a clear link to reducing the risk of climate change and reduced dependency on fossil resources [2]. However, this is not sufficient to ensure the launching of these products. The newly introduced bio-based chemicals must compete with the well-established petro-based counterparts, in terms of cost and functionality, while outperforming in sustainability performance.

Corbion thrives to turn science into sustainable solutions based on renewable materials for applications in food, bio-chemicals and bio-based innovation products. This needs to be done while managing the inherent risk of launching new products from new technologies to the market. To thrive in this dynamic and challenging market it is essential to speed up research and development programs, to make the right choices for investment and to evaluate opportunities for reduction of production costs, at early stages of innovation.

A key success enabler is the use of mathematical models throughout the different stages of process design, from research to implementation/optimization of commercial processes. It guarantees the speed and the economy of scale whilst delivering on the commitments for sustainable development.

In this paper the applications of mathematical models within the innovation funnel of Corbion for process design and sustainability assessment is shown. Our methodology and achievements are illustrated with two case studies.

2. Process design and sustainability assessment in the innovation funnel of Corbion

To guide, direct and accelerate innovation efforts from idea to launch, Corbion uses the "stage gate pass" model [3]. Projects must pass through a gate to enter a new stage. Figure 1 shows a typical scheme of the development of the process from the feasibility phase to implementation in commercial scale. In each gate, decisions are taken about the continuity of the projects. This decision is based on the marketing perspective of the new product, technical aspects, economy of the process and a sustainability assessment. During all this path, models of different complexity levels are used to evaluate the health of the process.

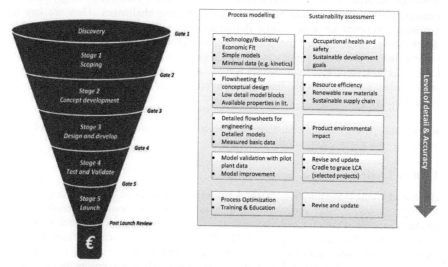

Figure 1. Stage gate pass model used by Corbion to evaluate new process and products.

In the early phase, screening of promising ideas is done. At this stage, typically few basic data are available, e.g. physical properties, and measuring them would be too expensive. Therefore, simple models are used to perform the techno-economical evaluation. Sustainability assessment in this stage consists in checking the safety of the chemicals (solvents, catalyst, etc.) used in the process and the impact of the project on the

Sustainable development goals (SDGs). This is a simple check but assesses safety risks. In case chemicals are found to be unsafe, they are replaced.

During Conceptual Design, different process alternatives are evaluated and the most promising is selected to move forward to the next stage. For this, models with a higher level of detail are developed. In this stage, physical properties available in literature or predicted by group contribution methods are used. Models based on short-cut methods are normally sufficient to achieve the goals of this stage. The aim of the sustainability assessment in this stage is to identify how the new process/product contribute to Corbion KPI's. Typical sustainability activities include comparing water and energy consumptions, waste and emissions to Corbion global average to create awareness of positive/negative impacts. The impact of the project on the SDGs is accessed at this stage.

Once that the project moves to the Design and Develop phase, detailed models of unit operations are used for flowsheeting. In this stage, missing basic data are measured, i.e. phase equilibrium diagrams, reaction kinetics, etc. Mass and energy balance are generated for engineering activities, such as equipment design, piping and pump sizing, etc. Also a more thorough sustainability assessment is made to quantify the environmental impact of the new process/product over its life cycle. This is done by comparing it with commercial benchmark in terms of biobased C-content and life cycle assessment (LCA). To evaluate LCA, an in-house excel based tool has been implemented, which is integrated with our process design software. As one of the inputs to the LCA tool, the mass and energy balance of the process is required [4]. Figure 2, shows a generic workflow followed by Corbion for sustainable process design

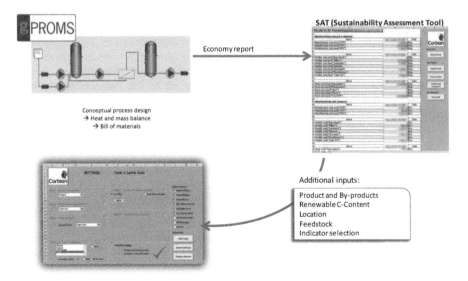

Figure 2. Workflow to reach sustainable process design.

In the next stage of the funnel, the new process/product is tested and validated by e.g. piloting, and experimental data are used to validate the model. Raw experimental data must first be processed before they are used. Methods, such as data reconciliation can be applied to force these data to fulfil the mass and energy balance. In case, important differences between the model and the experimental data are found, the assumptions and basic data are reviewed to improve the quality of the model. LCA is also revised and updated.

Finally, after successful validation of the process/product in pilot scale, the next stage is Launch.

3. Case studies

3.1 Conceptual design

Part of the mission of Corbion is to offer choices to customers to reduce their impact on environment. Bioplastics, such as polylactic acid (PLA) and polyethylene furanoate (PEF), can replace fossil based plastics, such as PET and offer the same or even better properties. Monomer for PEF is 2,5-furan dicarboxylic acid (FDCA). Since 2013, when Corbion acquired BIRD Engineering BV, Corbion has been working on a biotechnological route for production of FDCA, aiming to the lowest possible costs and lowest impact for environment. Like all projects at Corbion, the FDCA project is following the stage gate approach, which involves that economy and LCA are evaluated frequently and used to steer process development and optimization.

The role of process modelling started in 2013 when principles of key unit operations had already been proven on lab scale. A typical start for the *scoping phase* involves brainstorms for process concepts that fit within the boundaries of the project, like no use of toxic chemicals, low energy consumption and low waste production. Subsequently, in the *concept development stage*, process schemes are drafted for the highest ranking options. To generate the mass and energy balance, a flowsheet model of the complete processes from feedstock to FDCA was implemented in the commercial software gPROMS [5]. For this, we have developed an *inhouse model library and inhouse physical property databank*. Where needed new unit operation models were added to the model library, e.g. detailed fermentation models, and the physical property databases were extended with relevant lab data for FDCA and derivatives. Input parameters for the unit operation models were aligned with unit operation experts and are an educated guess representing the expectation of what research can bring to improve the current performance. The gPROMS flowsheet model will automatically produce the mass and energy balance and estimations for Bill of Materials, input for sizing of equipment and estimation of carbon footprint.

The results of the modelling activities were used to select the best feasible process concept. In the *design and develop phase*, sensitivity analysis was carried out to determine the areas that have the largest impact and/or uncertainty on costs and sustainability of the selected process. This is then used to determine further research and the possible need to make changes to the process concept.

In the *test and validate phase*, an iterative process where the model is being extended and validated with new experimental data, proposed changes are evaluated, lacks in our knowledge were identified and results of the model were used to steer further research.

At the stage gates a detailed LCA and economic evaluation is done, which can also lead to process changes, for example when a feedstock was found to have a higher than accepted impact on sustainability or when a solvent choice was not accepted a being sufficiently safe. The LCA and economy of FDCA is benchmarked against the LCA of terephthalic acid to ensure the bio-based alternative represents a large improvement towards to the fossil based alternative.

This process of combining and iterating process modelling, sustainability calculations and lab and pilot research ensured Corbion the process that was being developed for production of FDCA will meet Corbion's targets on sustainability and cost effectiveness, while using resources in the most time-effective way.

3.2 Revamping

To fulfil the higher demand of one of our products, revamping studies were done in one of our facilities. The aim was not only to increase capacity but also to decrease energy consumption and thus, CO_2 emissions. One way to achieve this was to increase the temperature of the feed to the unit using an available hot water stream in the plant. Therefore, the following three concepts were evaluated with help of models.

- Scenario 1: use of a network of heat exchangers to heat up the feed to the unit.
- Scenario 2: application of heat pumps
- Scenario 3: flashing the hot water stream and upgrading the flash vapour with an steam ejector.

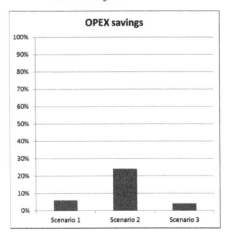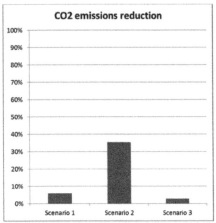

Figure 3. OPEX savings and reduction of CO2 emissions.

Figure 3 shows the reduction in OPEX for each concept with respect to the base case, and the reduction of CO_2 emissions are also presented. It can be noticed that scenario 2 is the case with both the largest OPEX savings and CO_2 emissions reductions. It is, however, the case with the highest investment, yet, the payback time is less than 3 years. The results of this study were presented during the stage gate assessment and allowed passing the Design and Develop phase.

4. Conclusions

In this paper, the contribution of mathematical models to steer research and development programs within Corbion was presented. By performing a techno-economical evaluation, sustainability assessment and lab/pilot research in each stage of the innovation funnel, Corbion ensures that the new process/product will meet sustainability and economic targets. Moreover, this approach also allows to identify changes needed in the processes and/or chemicals in the early stages of the process development, when this changes involves relatively low cost.

The methodology was illustrated with two different projects running at Corbion. One of them include the production of FDCA. For this case, the stage gate process starting from the scoping to the test and validate phase has been discussed. By process simulations, the most promising process, in terms of economy and sustainability has been determined. A second case study showed how models contributed to find the optimal solution in revamping studies.

References

[1] European commission. Growth – sectors: Biotechnology – bio-based products (online).   Visited: September   26,   2018. http://ec.europa.eu/growth/sectors/biotechnology/bio-based-products_en.

[2] Carus, Michael. Bio-based economy and climate change - Important links, pitfalls and opportunities. Hürth, Germany: Nova-Institut GmbH, 2017.

[3] Stage gate International (online), 2018. Visited: November 11, 2018. https://www.stage-gate.com/stage-gate-model

[4] Morao A., Dencic I., Visser D. 2017. Sustainability assessment in the innovation funnel. LCM Conference.

[5] Process System Enterprise. https://www.psenterprise.com/products/gproms

Anton A. Kiss, Edwin Zondervan, Richard Lakerveld, Leyla Özkan (Eds.)
Proceedings of the 29th European Symposium on Computer Aided Process Engineering
June 16th to 19th, 2019, Eindhoven, The Netherlands. © 2019 Elsevier B.V. All rights reserved.
http://dx.doi.org/10.1016/B978-0-128-18634-3.50021-7

New MINLP Formulations for Flexibility Analysis for Measured and Unmeasured Uncertain Parameters

Maria Paz Ochoa, Ignacio E. Grossmann[*]

Department of Chemical Engineering, Carnegie Mellon University, Pittsburgh, PA 15213, U.S.A.

grossmann@cmu.edu

Abstract

In this paper, we formulate the flexibility analysis with measured and unmeasured parameters as a rigorous multilevel optimization problem. First, we propose to recursively reformulate the inner optimization problems by the Karush-Kuhn-Tucker conditions and with a mixed-integer representation of the complementarity conditions to solve the resulting multilevel optimization problem. Three types of problems are addressed and solved with the proposed strategy: 1) linear programming problem, 2) nonlinear programming problem with monotonic variation of unmeasured uncertain, and finally 3) nonlinear programming problem. We illustrate the new formulation with a heat exchanger network problem with uncertain heat capacity flowrates.

Keywords: extended flexibility analysis, optimization under uncertainty, MINLP formulation.

1. Introduction

Traditionally, the approach to handle uncertainty in the parameters of a model is to consider nominal conditions in plant operation, and use overdesign to compensate for the potential impact of the uncertainty. In contrast, flexibility analysis addresses the guaranteed feasibility of operation of a plant over a range of conditions, with the ultimate goal being on how to design a process for guaranteed flexible operation (Grossmann *et al.*, 2014). The flexibility test problem only determines whether a design does or does not meet the flexibility target. To determine how much flexibility can be achieved in a given design, the flexibility index is defined as the largest value of δ such that the model inequalities hold over the uncertain parameter range (Swaney and Grossmann, 1985).

However, these formulations are based on the assumption that manipulated variables can compensate for any variation in the uncertain parameter set and that during operation stage uncertain parameters can be measured with precision to take the corrective action. Ostrovsky *et al.* (2003) and Rooney and Biegler (2003) extended the analysis by taking into account the level of parametric uncertainty in the mathematical models at the operation stage, by grouping the uncertain parameters, $\theta \in \Theta$, into two types, measured and unmeasured parameters. The flexibility constraint was then extended to account for model parameters, θ_u, that cannot be measured or estimated during the operation stage.

In this paper, we propose a new reformulation of the extended flexibility analysis where the innermost problems are recursively replaced by their optimality conditions and the complementarity conditions are expressed with a discrete representation.

2. Mathematical Model

The basic model for the flexibility analysis involves design variables, d, control variables, z, and uncertain parameters, θ. One of the main problems addressed in the flexibility analysis is the flexibility test problem. It consists in determining whether by proper adjustment of the control variables the process constraints $g_j(d,z,\theta) \leq 0$, $j \in J$, hold for any realization of uncertain parameters for a given design (Halemane and Grossmann, 1983). This statement can be expressed with the logic expression (1), and is reformulated by the use of min and max operators as shown in Eq. (2).

$$\forall \theta \in \Theta \{\exists z (\forall j \in J [g_j(d,z,\theta) \leq 0])\} \tag{1}$$

$$\leftrightarrow \chi(d) = \max_{\theta \in \Theta} \min_{z} \max_{j \in J} g_j(d,z,\theta) \tag{2}$$

The main difference between the design and control variables is that the design variables are fixed during the operation stage, while the control variables can be adjusted in order to satisfy process constraints. In fact, to solve the flexibility constraint it is required to have accurate estimation of the uncertain parameters. This can only be achieved if there is enough process data for precise determination of all uncertain parameter values. However, this assumption is restrictive, and is often not met in practice.

To address these limitations, two groups of uncertain parameters are identified. The first group of uncertain parameters contains parameters whose values can be determined to within any desired accuracy at the operation stage, namely the measured uncertain parameters, θ_m. Meaning that appropriate sensors are available to determine accurate values of all the uncertain parameters by direct measurement or by solving parameter estimation problems. Therefore, recourse action can be taken in order to compensate for their variation. Examples of this type of parameters include process conditions such as feed flowrates, pressures, temperatures, concentrations, and input variables such as product demands. The second group includes the unmeasured uncertain parameters, θ_u, whose estimation cannot be performed during the operation stage, consequently no control actions can be applied to them.

This distinction has been taken into account and the flexibility constraint was then extended to Eq. (3) and reformulated as the multilevel optimization problem described by Eq. (4) by Ostrovsky *et al.* (2003) and Rooney and Biegler (2003).

$$\forall \theta_m \in \Theta_m \{\exists z (\forall \theta_u \in \Theta_u, \forall j \in J [g_j(d,z,\theta_m,\theta_u) \leq 0])\} \tag{3}$$

$$\leftrightarrow \chi(d) = \max_{\theta_m \in \Theta_m} \min_{z} \max_{\theta_u \in \Theta_u} \max_{j \in J} g_j(d,z,\theta_m,\theta_u) \tag{4}$$

To solve the extended flexibility analysis, Ostrosvky *et al.* (2003) suggested an algorithm for the calculation of the flexibility function based on the branch and bound strategy, while partitioning the uncertain set into subregions. On the other hand, Rooney and Biegler (2003) proposed an extension to the approach presented by Raspanti *et al.*

(2000), which involved the use of the KS smooth function (Krelsselmeler and Steinhauser, 1983) that aggregated all of the model inequality constraints, and the KKT derivation together with a smooth approximation of the complementarity conditions for the inner optimization problems. Therefore, the extended flexibility constraint resulted in a nonlinear program.

In this work, we reformulate the extended flexibility constraint by developing the optimality conditions for each nested problems. In addition, in order to make the formulation tighter, the bounds of the nonnegative Lagrange multipliers related to the inequality constraints and the bounds on the slack variables are treated as constraints of the following level optimization problem. Finally, we express the complementarity conditions with a mixed-integer representation and assume that the Haar condition holds, which states that the number of active constraints is equal to the dimension of the control variables plus one. This condition holds true provided the Jacobian is full rank (Grossmann and Floudas, 1987).

In the following subsections, we derivate the formulation of three different cases, linear problem, nonlinear problem with monotonic variation of unmeasured parameters with respect to model constraints, and nonlinear problems.

2.1. Special Case 1: Linear Programming problem

The order of the inner max operators in Eq. (4), are interchangeable and can be equivalently expressed as follows.

$$\chi(d) = \max_{\theta_m \in \Theta_m} \psi(d, \theta_m)$$
$$s.t \;\; \psi(d, \theta_m) = \min_z \zeta(d, z, \theta_m) \qquad (5)$$
$$s.t: \;\; \zeta(d, z, \theta_m) = \max_{j \in J} \max_{\theta_u \in \Theta_u} g_j(d, z, \theta_m, \theta_u)$$

We consider that the inner problem is described by the linear inequality constraints:

$$g_j(d, z, \theta_m, \theta_u) = a_j \cdot d + b_j \cdot z + c_j \cdot \theta_u + d_j \cdot \theta_m \le 0, \forall j \in J \qquad (6)$$

Constraints g_j in Eq. (6) vary monotonically with respect to θ_u. Hence, the solution of the innermost problem must lie in one of the extreme points of its range of variation, depending on the sign of the derivative, $dg_j/d\theta_{j,u}$.

$$\max_{\theta_u \in \Theta_u} g_j(\theta_{j,u}) \to \theta^*_{j,u} \qquad (7)$$

The bilevel problem M1 described by Eq. (8) is obtained by replacing Eq. (7) in Eq. (5). To obtain a single level optimization problem, the innermost problem of Eq. (8) is replaced by its optimality conditions with a mixed-integer representation of the complementarity condition following the active constraint set strategy (Grossmann and Floudas, 1987). This yields the MILP problem:

$$M1 : \chi(d) = \max_{\theta_m \in \Theta_m} \psi(d, \theta_m)$$
$$s.t: \psi(d, \theta_m) = \min_{z, u}(u \,|\, g_j(d, z, \theta_m, \theta_u) = a_j \cdot d + b_j \cdot z + c_j \cdot \theta^*_{j,u} + d_j \cdot \theta_m \le u, \forall j \in J) \qquad (8)$$

Where u is a scalar variable that represents the worst constraint violation.

2.2. Special Case 2: Non-Linear Programming problem with monotonic variation of unmeasured uncertain parameters

If the set of functions $g_j(d,z,\theta_m,\theta_u)$ varies monotonically with respect to the unmeasured uncertain parameters, then the relationship expressed by Eq. (7) holds true. Therefore, the solution of the innermost problem lies at an extreme point of the range of variation of θ_u. Analogously, the following bilevel programming problem M2 is obtained and then reformulated in the same way as the previous case, but leading to the MINLP problem.

$$M2 : \chi(d) = \max_{\theta_m \in \Theta_m} \psi(d,\theta_m)$$

$$s.t: \psi(d,\theta_m) = \min_{z,u}(u | g_j(d,z,\theta_m,\theta_{j,u}^*) \le u, \forall j \in J) \tag{9}$$

2.3. General Case: Non-Linear Programming problem

The extended flexibility constraint can be equivalently expressed as the following multilevel optimization problem M3.

$$M3 : \chi(d) = \max_{\theta_m \in \Theta_m} \psi(d,\theta_m)$$

$$s.t \ \psi(d,\theta_m) = \min_z \zeta(d,z,\theta_m)$$

$$s.t: \zeta(d,z,\theta_m) = \max_{\theta_u \in \Theta_u} \varphi(d,z,\theta_m,\theta_u) \tag{10}$$

$$s.t: \varphi(d,z,\theta_m,\theta_u) = \min_u (u | g_j(d,z,\theta_m,\theta_u) \le u, \forall j \in J)$$

In order to solve Eq. (10), we propose to replace the inner problems by their optimality conditions in a recursive fashion. Due to space limitations, we cannot report the complete reformulation. To illustrate the solution strategy, we will replace the innermost problem of Eq. (10) by its KKT conditions (Eqns. (11) and (12)) and complementarity conditions (Eq. (13)). Bounds of the Lagrange multipliers, λ_j^0, and slack variables, s_j^0, are added as model constraints of the next level optimization problem, described by Eqns. (14) and (15), in order to tighten the formulation.

$$1 - \sum_j \lambda_j^0 = 0 \tag{11}$$

$$g_j(d,z,\theta_m,\theta_{j,u}^*) - u + s_j^0 = 0 \qquad\qquad \forall j \in J \tag{12}$$

$$\lambda_j^0 \cdot s_j^0 = 0 \qquad\qquad \forall j \in J \tag{13}$$

$$-\lambda_j^0 \le 0 \qquad\qquad \forall j \in J \tag{14}$$

$$-s_j^0 \le 0 \qquad\qquad \forall j \in J \tag{15}$$

Following this procedure, we obtain a single level optimization problem. The complementarity conditions are then expressed with a mixed-integer representation, the Haar conditions is assumed, leading to an MINLP problem.

3. Numerical Example

A well-known example in the flexibility analysis literature is the heat exchanger network shown in Figure 1. Grossmann and Floudas (1987) used this NLP example to introduce the active set strategy, which is able to find non-vertex solutions. After the elimination of the state variables, the reduced model consists of four constraints, and three variables: the cooling load (Q_c) is the control variable and the heat capacity flowrate of streams 1 and 2 (F_{H1} and F_{H2}) are the uncertain parameters. We solve a modified version the problem for three cases. First, considering both uncertain parameters as unmeasured, so no recourse actions can be taken, corresponding to one of the special cases of the traditional flexibility analysis. Second, considering θ_1 as a measured uncertain parameter and θ_2 as an unmeasured uncertain parameter, where control actions can only be adjusted to compensate for variations in θ_1, solved with the formulation proposed in Section 2.3. Finally, we consider both as measured uncertain parameters like in the traditional flexibility analysis following the active set strategy (Grossmann and Floudas, 1987).

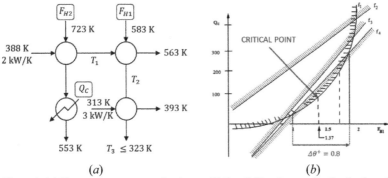

(a)   (b)

Figure 1. (*a*) Heat exchanger network scheme. (*b*) Feasibility diagram for fixed value of $F_{H2}=2$

Numerical results are summarized in Table 1Table 1. As we can see, we obtain positive values of u for all the cases, indicating an infeasible design. The worst constraint violation (u=138.5) is obtained for the case of no recourse actions. This value can be reduced up to certain degree (u=20) when control variables can compensate for the variations in θ_1. Furthermore, this can be reduced (u=7.08) when recourse actions can compensate for variation in both uncertain parameters. It is also important to note, that non-vertex critical points are obtained for the second and third cases. The different problems are implemented in GAMS 25.1.2 (GAMS Development Corporation, 2018) and solved with BARON 18.5.8 (Kilinc and Sahinidis, 2018) in an Intel i7 machine with 16 Gb of RAM. The tolerance of the solver is set to 0.01 and the big M value is 600.

Table 1. Worst constraint violation, critical parameters values for three examples and model size.

	Both unmeasured uncertain parameters[*] $\theta_u=\theta_1, \theta_2$	Combined type of uncertain Parameters $\theta_m=\theta_1, \theta_u=\theta_2$	Both measured uncertain Parameters $\theta_m=\theta_1, \theta_2$
u	138.5	20	7.08
$\theta_1= F_{H1}$	1	1.333	1.398
$\theta_2= F_{H2}$	1.95	2.041	2.034
#bin var	4	36	6
#cont. var	12	161	22
#constraints	13	163	21
CPU time	0.01	1.67	0.09

[*]For a fixed value of z.

4. Conclusion

In order to obtain more realistic results when dealing with operation under uncertainty, a distinction of the uncertain parameters can made between the measured and unmeasured uncertain parameters. Thus, the traditional flexibility constraint has been extended. In this work, we have proposed new reformulations of the resulting multilevel optimization problem, which involves the replacement the innermost problem by its optimality conditions in a recursive fashion and the introduction of a mixed-integer representation of the complementarity conditions, resulting in an MINLP problem.

We have developed the formulation of three different cases, linear problem, nonlinear problem with monotonic variation of unmeasured parameters with respect to model constraints, and nonlinear problems. A particular feature of the first two cases is that the worst constraint violation lies at a vertex of the unmeasured uncertain parameter set; where the formulation can be simplified, leading to a similar formulation as the one obtained by applying the active set constraint strategy, namely the traditional flexibility analysis (Grossmann and Floudas, 1987). An example of a heat exchanger network has been presented to illustrate the proposed reformulation of the general case and compared to cases with different degree of recourse actions.

Acknowledgements

The authors acknowledge the financial support from Eli Lilly and Company and the Center for Advanced Process Decision-making from Carnegie Mellon University.

References

GAMS Development Corporation, 2018, "General Algebraic Modeling System (GAMS) Release 25.1.2" Washington, DC, USA.

I.E. Grossmann, B. Calfa and P. Garcia-Herreros, 2014, "Evolution of concepts and models for quantifying resiliency and flexibility of chemical processes," Computers and Chemical Engineering, vol. 70, pp. 22-34.

I.E. Grossmann and C.A. Floudas, 1987, "Active Constraint strategy for flexibility analysis in chemical processes," Computers and Chemical Engineering, vol. 6, pp. 675-693.

K. Halemane and I.E. Grossmann, 1983, "Optimal Process Design under Uncertainty," AIChE Journal, vol. 29, no. 3, pp. 425-433.

M. Kilinc and N.V. Sahinidis, 2018, "Exploiting integrality in the global optimization of mixed-integer nonlinear programming problems in BARON", Optimization Methods and Software, vol 33, pp.540-562.

G. Kreisselmeier and R. Steinhauser, 1983, "Application of vector performance optimization to a robust control loop design for a fighter aircraft," International Journal of Control, vol. 37, pp. 251-284.

G. Ostrovsky, I. Datskov, L. Achenie and Y. Volin, 2003, "Process Uncertainty: Case of Insufficient Process Data at the Operation Stage," AIChE Journal, vol. 49, no. 5, pp. 1216-1232.

C. Raspanti, J. Bandoni and L. Biegler, 2000, "New Strategies for Flexibility Analysis and Design Under Uncertainty," Computers and Chemical Engineering, vol. 24, pp. 2193-2209.

W. Rooney and L. Biegler, 2003, "Optimal Process Design with Model Parameter Uncertainty and Process Variability," AIChE Journal, vol. 49, no. 2, pp. 438-449.

R. Swaney and I.E. Grossmann, 1985, "An index for operational flexibility in chemical process design. Part I. Formulation and Theory," AIChE Journal, vol. 31, pp. 621-630.

Anton A. Kiss, Edwin Zondervan, Richard Lakerveld, Leyla Özkan (Eds.)
Proceedings of the 29th European Symposium on Computer Aided Process Engineering
June 16th to 19th, 2019, Eindhoven, The Netherlands. © 2019 Elsevier B.V. All rights reserved.
http://dx.doi.org/10.1016/B978-0-128-18634-3.50022-9

Mathematical process modelling past, present and future – a personal perspective

J.P. Schmal

Process Systems Enterprise Inc., 4 Century Drive, Ste 130, Parsippany, NJ, 07054, USA[1]

p.schmal@psenterprise.com

Abstract

Progress in mathematical process modelling has been tied primarily to hardware developments and secondarily to better software, advanced algorithms and improved data availability. In this paper we review modelling history to extract some trends for the future. Modelling will play an increasingly important role in process industries. Historically separate techniques such as flowsheeting, custom modelling and CFD will likely merge as computational power increases. Initially parallel computing will give the needed additional computation power. Neural nets are expected to play a role in empirical models and analysis. We need to move from storing data to storing useful information.

Keywords: modelling, digitalization, big data, history.

1. Introduction

Mathematical process modelling has been around for many decades, but has evolved significantly with the advent of more powerful computers, better algorithms and the availability of more data. To help understand where mathematical process modelling may go in the future, we need to understand the past and the present. This paper represents a personal view and is based on historic events and personal experiences and beliefs. In a short paper, it is impossible to do justice to all people that contributed to these areas and to cover the history in the detail it deserves. The goal is to abstract general trends in the field and use them to look ahead.

Modelling technology encompasses four main elements: 1) modelling approaches, 2) software & algorithms, 3) hardware and 4) data. We will cover the status of each of these elements. For modelling approaches, we will cover custom modelling, flowsheeting, CFD and neural networks.

2. Past

2.1. Pre-1950

Process modelling has been around for a very long time. Initially the models needed to be solved analytically due to a lack of computers. The art of modelling was therefore to try and find a problem that was as close as possible to reality, yet could be solved analytically. As a consequence many simplifying assumptions were needed to make the

---

[1] Per May 1st 2019: ExxonMobil, 1545 US-22, Annandale, NJ 08801, USA

problem solvable. Several techniques were employed to get general solutions that could be used for different cases. For example, dimensionless numbers were extensively used to reduce the number of variables and allow for plotting solutions in 2-D. Dynamic behaviour was studied with the help of bifurcation studies, using the steady-state as a demarcation between regions of different dynamic behaviour (Aris, 1994). These general solutions or solutions to certain equations would often be published in books.

Process control was all manual and measurements were virtually non-existent. Chemical processes were run based on experience and by trial and error.

2.2. 1950-2018

With the advent of digital computers and the introduction of software, many areas such as modelling, control and neural networks evolved rapidly. Process modelling could relax some of the simplifying assumptions. One of the earliest industrial applications was by Sargent (1958) using a punch card computer to design a distillation column and a multi-stream heat-exchanger. Steady-state models were difficult to solve and dynamic models were used to find the steady-state as they were easier to initialise.

Initial computations could only use limited memory on what were slow computers, but memory, CPU clock speed and hard drive space grew rapidly. This allowed for ever more complex and realistic problems to be solved as demonstrated in Figure 1.

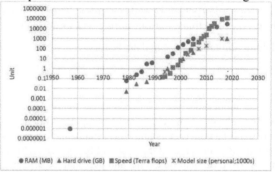

Figure 1: Historic size of RAM and hard drive (created with data from http://organdi.net/article.php3?id_article=82, https://en.wikipedia.org/wiki/History_of_supercomputing and personal experience)

Besides hardware improvements, advancements in several other areas were equally important to progress in modelling. New simulation-specific software, advanced algorithms and improved data availability all contributed to the development of more detailed and accurate models.

In 1957, Fortran (FORmula TRANslation) was developed and it allowed for easy implementation of equations. It is worth mentioning Matlab, whose first commercial version became available in 1985, Python, whose first version became available in 1980 and excel (1985; first spreadsheet was developed in 1969). Matlab, Python and excel have found wide spread use in the engineering community.

With regards to algorithms for sets of equations, broadly speaking two types of solutions were considered: sequential modular and simultaneous or equation-oriented. Sequential modular solvers were prominent in flowsheeting tools while simultaneous solvers were more often used in custom modelling tools. In the sequential modular approach the structure of the problem is exploited and each process unit is solved in turn. This requires the inputs to the units to be known or given. Back to front calculations or including recycles and/or heat-integration is difficult or requires intermediate steps and/or iterations through the loop. Equation-oriented solvers, solve all equations simultaneously, allowing for back to front calculations, easier solution of recycles and heat-integration. Because equation-oriented solvers are Newton-based solvers, good initial guesses are required. Process Systems Enterprise developed automated initialization procedures to get these good initial guesses. As all equations are solved simultaneously, debugging a problem is usually less straightforward than in sequential modular approaches.

Gear was one of the key pioneers in solving sets of Differential-Algebraic equations (DAEs). In 1971 he introduced a multi-step, backward difference formula (BDF) method. Petzold (1982) developed DASSL, which is at the basis of many of today's BDF solvers. In 1989 the semi-implicit Runge-Kutta method, a one-step method, was introduced and the rivalry between BDF and Runge-Kutta caused significant improvements in both solvers. The interest in partial differential equations bloomed in 1996. Although many algorithmic improvements have been made in linear algebra (e.g. MA28 in 1977 & MA48 in 1996), non-linear solvers and integration solvers, the next logical avenue for speed an capability improvements was the exploitation of parallelization.

With regards to software we will briefly consider Computational Fluid Dynamic (CFD), Flowsheeting, custom modelling and neural networks. 2-D CFD solutions were available as early as 1930 and the first CFD calculations using finite differences were done on ENIAC in 1940, one of the world's first computers. In 1957 Los Alamos solved the first 3D CFD calculations with first publications by Douglas aircraft and Boeing in 1967 and 1968 respectively. Unsteady aerodynamic flows were first successfully solved in the 1970's. Two-phase flow and reacting media were developed in the early 1990's until today.

The first flowsheeting tool was developed in 1959 by Monsanto and was called Flowtran. They later participated in the Aspen project with MIT and DOE, which led to first version of Aspen in 1981. Two other notable developments for flowsheeting tools are the development of PRO/II by SimSci which was established in 1967 and later became part of AVEVA and CHESS developed in 1968 at the University of Houston and the US Navy, which became Chemcad in 1985. In 1996 Hyprotech, a company spun out of the University of Calgary, developed HYSYS, which was sold to Aspen and then divested due to the fact it was anticompetitive and bought by Honeywell. Some of the developers of HYSYS also developed Unisim in 2005. Most flowsheeting tools are sequential modular, but Aspen EO, ROMeo, gPROMS ProcessBuilder and gPROMS FormulatedProducts are examples of equation-oriented flowsheeting tools.

Hundreds of tools were developed for custom modelling (able to solve general integral-partial-differential-algebraic equations, IPDAE), but two key developments were SPEEDUP in 1964 developed by Sargent and Westerberg. SPEEDUP was sold to Aspen and later became Aspen Custom Modeller. Pantelides and Barton developed gPROMS in 1993 and Process Systems Enterprise was set-up to commercialize gPROMS in 1997.

Neural networks (NN) were first developed in 1943 where electrical networks were used to represent the neural network. In 1950 IBM had its first successful neural network and in 1957 Cornell university developed percepton for pattern recognition. In 1959 Stanford used NN to remove echoes in telephone calls, but in 1969 a critical paper proved that percepton could not solve the "exclusive or" problem. As a consequence the interest in NN dissipated until 1982 when multi-layer NN were introduced. In 1989 feedforward was introduced, allowing for any function to be implemented in an NN. In 1995 another dead period started since people were unable to teach NN how to play chess. In 2006 the interest in NN rebounded by a rebranding to deep learning. Research led to a couple of key innovations with regards to initialization of the weights used to indicate the influence of each node in the previous layer on a node in the current layer. The weights traditionally were set randomly, requiring huge data sets to "train" the NN. The advent of big data and the use of GPUs (Graphical Processing Units) which sped up calculations drastically, allowed NN to become powerful (e.g. Watson, Google, Amazon etc.).

With the advent of computers and software to simulate complex models, the techniques of optimisation, parameter estimation and design of experiments became readily available. This in turn led to a need for data to estimate unknown or uncertain parameters and optimize the design or operation. In the early days measurements were analogue, often making use of pneumatic measurements, typically a pen moving up and down while a piece of paper was moving underneath it. This meant data had to be transcribed from the scrolls into usable forms. For example, the first electrical signal pressure measurements became available in the 1930's, but the first digital pressure sensor was developed by Honeywell in 1967 (http://www.sensorland.com/HowPage059.html). With the digitalization of operations more sensors were introduced in plants and the sensors were digital, meaning the data was easily accessible. The OPC, OLE (Microsoft Object Linking and Embedding) for Process Control) standard was introduced in 1995 and in 2001 the Historical Data Access (HDA) was introduced. As an example of this change, in 1994 during my internship at Hoechst, the unit I was modelling only had a few measurements (~25), while during my Ph.D. from 1999-2003, I modelled a large petrochemical plant from Shell and 2300 sensors were available, (350 used in the modelling).

3. Present

Present capabilities include among many others: Flowsheets of connected gas processing plants (Aluma et al., 2016), combined product and process design (Martin and Martinez, 2013), coupled DEM (discrete element models), custom multi-scale models of wet granulation (Barrasso et al. 2015), three-phase CFD simulations of units and neural nets that control more and more parts of our daily life.

Tsay et al. (2018) give an overview of optimal process design capabilities and practices. They interviewed 110 industrial people and found that there is limited adoption of optimization and modelling tools.

With regards to hardware there is a clear trend towards parallelization and cloud computing as the improvements of a single core seem to be flattening off. As an example we ran the same large model using the same software version on a high end i7 machine in 2012 taking 156 s CPU time, while on a high end Xeon machine in 2017 it took 105 s CPU time (~32% improvement). During this same time period we have achieved speed improvements of a factor of 3 for large models due to algorithmic improvements. With parallelization we have managed to achieve speed increases of close to a factor of 1000. The latter, is case dependent and not generally applicable however.

Data standards, integration and increased hard disc space have led to much wider availability of data for analysis and training of neural nets. The fact that chemical plants typically operate in a narrow operating window makes using neural nets both easier and harder: easier because it only needs to cover a limited number of possibilities and harder because it also means the information content in the data is limited and there is a danger of training the neural net how to predict noise.

On-line applications of models both linear and non-linear are common and models are used as soft sensors for unmeasurable quantities and phenomena such as coking and fouling. Advanced model-based control and optimization is applied in many different industries and on hundreds of plants world-wide.

4. Future

All we can do is consider different alternative scenarios and discuss their likelihood. It is clear from history (see Figure 2) that we have always tried to get the most out of the hardware and software. We always have been able to add complexity faster than hardware has been able to grow. The current digitalization trend is expected to increase the use of models both off-line and on-line. As such model-based engineering is expected to be a standard practice (e.g. see INCOSE vision 2025). In on-line models the use of more detailed models is now possible due to robust and fast solvers.

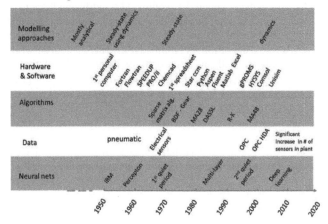

Figure 2: Summary of history

With regards to hardware, the trend we see towards cloud computing and parallelization most likely will continue and it seems it is the most secure way to get more computation power. There are still new developments in miniaturization allowing for more power. The development of the quantum computer is still progressing and has been for a long time (since 1982), chances of a major breakthrough in the next decade seem unlikely. Although progress is steady, the algorithms that can benefit from quantum computing are still limited. A breakthrough in quantum computing would be a disruptive event.

With the availability of more computational power, two trends most likely will continue: bigger envelops/systems and more detailed models. At the moment these bigger problems are solved using relatively simple models. Using more detailed models will require more computational power and bring additional benefits. The level of detail will also increase due to software like CFD, flowsheeting and custom modelling merging into a single tool.

Algorithms will keep on improving and there is still a lot of room for improvement in areas such as global mixed-integer non-linear programming. The application of neural nets will increase, but research interest (measured by hits in Google scholar) shows a decline in papers in this area. Neural nets can play an important role in cases where first-principles are not well-known or in areas such as data analytics.

Compared to nuclear physics, data analytics in chemical engineering can be improved upon. Also, techniques that combine information from signals to get a better overall picture (similar to PAT, Process Analytical Technology) can be improved. Finally, data is simply stored for a certain time and later simply deleted. With the increased availability of data it most likely will be necessary to extract useful information from the data to keep data storage requirements under control and the use of this data manageable.

5. Conclusions

Progress in hardware and software has driven mathematical process modelling and will continue to do so in the future. Single core hardware capabilities are flattening out, but parallelization and cloud-based solutions will allow us to keep expanding. A potentially disruptive technology of quantum computing is not expected to be available to engineers any time soon. Algorithm development has continued steadily and there is still room for improvements. With the availability of more data the application of neural nets will likely grow, but research interest seems to slow down. Neural nets will likely play a role in more traditional roles of pattern recognition for empirical elements of models, raw data analysis and generated data analysis. With the additional availability of data there is room for better analysis techniques such as PAT and a need for smarter storage, e.g. extracting the useful information before storing.

References

D.Aluma, N. Thijssen, K.M. Nauta, C.C. Pantelides, N.Shah, 2016, Optimize an integrated natural gas production and distribution network, Gas processing & LNG, October

D. Barrasso, T. Eppinger, F.E. Pereira, R. Algave, K. Debus, S.K. Bermingham and R. Ramachandran, 2015, A multi-scale, mechanistic model of a wet granulation process using a novel bi-directional PBM/DEM coupling algorithm, Chem. Eng. Sc., 123, 500-513

R. Aris, 1994, Mathematical modelling techniques, General Publishing Company Ltd.

INCOSE vision 2025, 2014, A world in motion- systemengineering vision 2025, https://www.incose.org/docs/default-source/aboutse/se-vision-2025.pdf?sfvrsn=b69eb4c6_4

M. Martin and A. Martinez, 2013, A methodology for simultaneous product and process design in the customer products industry: The case study of the laundry business, Comput.Chem. Engng., 32, 715-720

L. Petzold, 1982, A description of DASSL: A differential/algebraic system solver, IMACS World Congress, August 8-13, Montreal, Canada

R.W.H. Sargent, 1958, Applications of an electronic digital computer in the design of low temperature plant, Trans. Instit. Chem. Eng. 36, 201–214

C. Tsay, R.C. Pattison,M.R. Piana and M. Baldea, 2018, A survey of optimal process design capabilities and practices in the chemical and petrochemical industries, Comput. Chem. Engng. 112, 180-189.

Anton A. Kiss, Edwin Zondervan, Richard Lakerveld, Leyla Özkan (Eds.)
Proceedings of the 29th European Symposium on Computer Aided Process Engineering
June 16th to 19th, 2019, Eindhoven, The Netherlands. © 2019 Elsevier B.V. All rights reserved.
http://dx.doi.org/10.1016/B978-0-128-18634-3.50023-0

Simultaneous design and controllability optimization for the reaction zone for furfural bioproduction

A.G. Romero-García, [a] O.A. Prado-Rúbio,[b] G. Contreras-Zarazúa,[a] C.Ramírez-Márquez,[a] J.G. Segovia-Hernández,[a]

[a] *Universidad de Guanajuato, Campus Guanajuato, División de Ciencias Naturales y Exactas, Departamento de Ingeniería Química, Noria Alta S/N, Guanajuato, Gto., 36050, México*
[b]*Departamento de Ingeniería Química, Universidad Nacional de Colombia, Km 9 vía al Aeropuerto La Nubia, Campus La Nubia, Bloque L, Manizales, Caldas, Colombia. Corresponding author. Email:gsegovia@ugto.mx*

Abstract

In this work is presented the simultaneous optimization of design parameters and control properties, using a stochastic method named Differential Evolution with Tabu List Algorithm, as study case the reaction zone in the production process of furfural from biomass. In the objective function, the Total Annual Cost, eco-indicator 99 and condition number are combined as economic, environmental and control criteria respectively. From the multi-objective optimization, results show the direct influence that design parameters have over the control properties having an antagonist behaviour. As consequence, it is possible to see that to have the best control properties there is an increase in TAC and eco-indicator. Based on results, operating conditions founded allows having an acceptable furfural production of 2014.4 $^{kg}/_h$ by reducing costs in a 39% and environmental impact in a 42% in a system with good control properties in dynamic state.

Keywords: Furfural, Optimization, Total Annual Cost, Eco-Indicator99, Control Properties.

1. Introduction

Furfural is a chemical compound produced by biomass rich in pentoses content in the hemicellulose as raw material, in a reaction catalysed in presence of strong acids. Is used as a potential platform to produce biofuels. In recent years, furfural has received special attention as a potential platform to produce biofuels and biochemicals. In a study conducted by the Department of Renewable Energy of the United States, furfural was selected as one of the 30 main chemicals that can be manufactured from biomass (Cai et al., 2014). Industrially, it is a very versatile chemical because of its multiple applications: utilized as a raw material to produce phenol-furfural-resins (Brown, 1959), or can be converted furfuryl alcohol, tetrahydrofurfuryl alcohol, furan, tetrahydrofuran and diols (Bhogeswararao, 2015). The Quaker Oats process is the oldest commercial form of producing furfural industrially. This process was created by the Quaker Oat company using oat cereal waste as raw material, which is mixed with sulfuric acid. The process consists in two steps, first the reaction zone in which the biomass reacted with a solution of sulfuric acid to convert the xylan fraction into furfural, then high vapour stream is introducing to the reactor to remove the furfural as fast as possible in order to avoid furfural polimerization (Marcotullio, 2011). The vapor stream from the reactor is condensed to feed the azeotropic distillation sequences in order to remove the excess of water and some by-products such as methanol and acetic acid (Marcotullio, 2011).

Under the economy circle concept, the study of the reaction zone in the production of furfural is important because it allows to reduce the excessive use of water, high energy consumption and the formation of decomposition products by reducing the separation costs. In this work aims to present a novel proposal for the simultaneous optimization having as objective function TAC as economic criteria, Condition Number as a control indicator and EI99 as environmental conditions in order to improve reactor productivity in the reaction zone in the furfural production process. So far, there are no publications reported in the literature where the multi-objective optimization methodology for the furfural reaction zone is solved.

2. Methodology

In this work it is consider as raw material, stem of date-palm tree with a composition of: cellulose (glucan) 66.6 wt%, hemicellulose (xylan)14.52 wt%, lignin 13.72 wt% lignin. Experimental data are taken from Bamufleh et.al (2013) to propose a kinetic model and parameters. The model proposed, is analogous to the proposed by Saeman, (1945) on the hydrolysis of cellulose catalyzed by dilute sulfuric acid. In the proposed reaction, furfural is obtained from xylan and the furfural reacts to form the corresponding decomposition products such as methanol and acetic acid (Marcotullio, 2011). For simplicity, decomposition products are condensed in a unique expression as is shown in Eq. (1).

$$\text{Xylan} \xrightarrow{\text{r}_1} \text{Furfural} \xrightarrow{\text{r}_2} \text{Decomposition Product} \tag{1}$$

The r_i value it is expressed as Eq. (2). Kinetic parameters k_o, b and E were estimated with experimental data reported by Bamufleh using the Curve fitting tool from the software Matlab. From Eq. (1), it is reported two reaction rates, which kinetic parameters estimated are: k_{o1}=6.24x10^8 ± 2.28x10^9 (min^{-1}), b_1=1.20 ± 0.21, E_1=93.44 ± 11.16 (kJ/mol), k_{o2}=1.74 ± 7.33 (min^{-1}), b_2=2.06 ± 0.56 and E_2=33.63 ± 11.72 (kJ/mol). The adjustment has a correlation coefficient of 0.96447, indicating a good parameter fitting.

$$r = k_o C h^b \exp\left(\frac{-E}{RT}\right) \tag{2}$$

To produce furfural, a continuous CSTR reactor with continuous agitation is proposed. From a generalized balance the equations that describe the dynamic of the system are shown in Eq. (3), Eq. (4) and Eq. (5).

$$\frac{dC_{xylan}}{dt} = \frac{F_{in}}{V}\left(C_{in-xylan} - C_{xylan}\right) + r_{xylan} \tag{3}$$

$$\frac{dC_{Furfural}}{dt} = r_{Furfural} - C_{Furfural}\frac{F_{in}}{V} \tag{4}$$

$$\frac{dC_{D.P}}{dt} = r_{D.P} - C_{D.P}\frac{F_{in}}{V} \tag{5}$$

From Eq. (3), Eq. (4) and Eq. (5): the feed flow is represented by Fin [kg / h], the fraction of xylan at the entrance of the reactor $C_{in-xylan}$ [kg/L]. For this system, two other variables to consider are: temperature T [°K] and the concentration of the sulfuric acid Ch [% w], it is reported that the manipulation of acidic conditions and temperature play an important role in the reaction kinetics to produce furfural (Marcotullio, 2011). Within the reactor, it is of interest to study the behaviour that will have during the reaction time: first the degradation of the raw material C_{xylan} [kg/L], as well, the formation of furfural $C_{Furfural}$ [kg/L] and Decomposition Products $C_{D.P}$ [kg/L].

The reaction system presented, has significant number of variables to be optimized order to have an optimal design and operation conditions, by aiming a maximum production of furfural, the best control criteria, lowest environmental impact and lowest cost possible. In this context, the reaction system described as case study is a good model to be optimized simultaneous control and design parameters. Additional factors: the model proposed shows the dynamic behaviour of the system and there is no work in literature where the optimization of design parameters and simultaneous control for furfural reactor are reported. The design variables for the study case are shown in Table 1.

Table 1. Design variables for the multi-objective optimization

Variables	Type Variable	Symbol	Range	Units
Relation of solid (raw material) and water	Continue	LSR	1-15	ml/gr
Feed Flow	Continue	F_{in}	1×1010^3 - 6×10^6	kg/h
Temperature	Continue	T	373 - 413	K
Acid Concentration	Continue	Ch	5 - 15	% w
Volume	Continue	V_o	300 – 520000	L

A multi-objective optimization technique referred to as Differential Evolution with Tabu List (DETL) proposed by Srinivas and Rangaiah (2007) is employed. This technique works as a combined system between the biological evolution from Differential Evolution technique and the random search method from the Tabu search technique. The objective function involves three important axises to analyse: Total Annual Cost (TAC) as an indicator of the economy of the process by calculating the annualized cost of the process equipment and the operating cost, Condition Number (γ*) as an indicator of the dynamic behaviour of the process considering low condition number for systems with good controllability and Eco-indicator 99 (EI99) to quantify the environmental impact. Similar works have been reported by Sánchez-Ramírez et. al. (2017) applying this index for distillation columns. The objective function is expressed as Eq. (6).

$$min[TAC, \gamma^*, EI99] = f(LSR, F_{in}, T, Ch, Vo) \tag{6}$$

Subject to:
$$y_{i,F} \geq x_{i,F}$$
$$w_{i,F} \geq u_{i,F} \tag{7}$$

The objective functions are restricted to satisfy the mass flowrate ($u_{i,PC.}$) espeficfications of furfrual. The minimmum mass flowrate for furfural were fixed to 2000kg/ hr. The values of parameters required by DETL method are: Population size: 120 individuals, Generation number: 710, Tabu list size: 60, Tabu radius: 0.01, Crossover fractions: 0.8, Mutation fractions: 0.3.

3. Results

To represent the main results of the simultaneous optimization of the reactor for furfural bioproduction, Pareto charts are used to identify the best option to produce furfural satisficing in the multi-objective function. Pareto fronts of reactor for furfural bioproduction are presented: a) Condition Number vs Total Annual Cost, b) Total Annual Cost vs Eco-indicator 99 and c) Condition Number vs Eco-indicator 99, all of them comparing with the respective furfural yield %. (See Figure 1).

In Figure 1, each point represents a different design. The best design selected is marked as red square. It was selected according to utopian point methodology where two objectives cannot improve more, both are in equilibrium (Wang and Rangaiah, 2017). The red square corresponds to solutions closer to utopic point. Figure1.a, shows antagonist behaviour between condition number and total annual cost. To explain this trend variable such as temperature and volume, are related both to the costs and to the control properties. When temperature increase, energy consumption will increase having a direct increase in TAC. Referring to the volume, a bigger volume will require more building material and increment the feed flow having an increment in TAC, moreover, for control properties, having an increase in volume the disturbances have less influence on the system thus improving control properties.

Figure 1.b shows a relation between total annual cost vs eco-indicator 99, in this case both objectives presents the same behaviour strongly influenced by energy supply and cost of energy. To have a reactor of this magnitude it is necessary to increase the heat supply (this represent a direct increase in TAC) and to increase the steel used for the equipment, it is demonstrated that steel has a strong influence in EI99 (Sanchez-Ramirez et al., 2016). In this case is shown a unique minimum but it is not possible to choose it as the optimum because that minimum is an extreme when is evaluated in other index.   Figure1.c shows also an antagonist behaviour between control properties and eco-indicator 99, such as the presented in Figure 1.a, when volume is increased eco-points will increase because of the increment of steel used for equipment as well; and simultaneously when volume is increased perturbations has less influence in the system improving controllability. For all the designs the yield % is around 15-30% for an industrial production similar to the reported experimentally by Bamufleh, et al. (2013). The optimal design parameters are presented in Table 2.

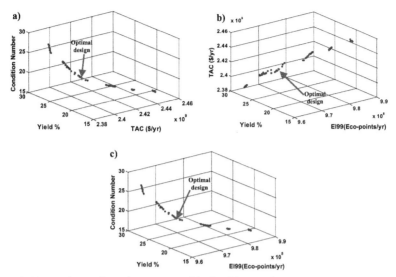

Figure 1. Pareto fronts from the reactor of furfural bioproduction.

Table 2. Optimal design parameters for the reactor.

Design Variables	Symbol	Value	Units
Reactor Volume	V_o	518880.77	L
Diameter	D	7.61	M
Height	H	11.41	M
Temperature	T	411.26	°K
Acid concentration	Ch	12.31	% w
Feed flow	F_{in}	728422.31	kg/h
Solid and water relation	LSR	10.497	ml/gr
Total energy Consumed (kJ/hr)	Q	5608969.50	kW
Furfural	Furf	2014.4	kg/h
Decomposition Product	D.P	1731.6	kg/h
Furfural yield	---	25.43	%
Utilities cost	---	2411.46	(millon\$/yr)
Equipment cost	---	0.322	(millon\$/yr)
TAC	TAC	2411.786	(millon\$/yr)
EI99	EI99	970.162	(millonEco-points/yr)
Condition Number	γ^*	18.55	------

4. Conclusions

In this work the reactor zone to produce furfural from palm-date has been optimized. Based on results, is possible to find many possible designs in which furfural yield is maximized as well cost and eco-points are minimizing in a controllable system. Optimal operation conditions found for the system, like temperature 411.26 °K and acid concentration 12.31%w have strong influence in reaction rate, this conditions allows to maximize furfural yield to 25.43% with a production of 2014.4 kg/h, this represents an improvement compering with the reported by Bamufleh et. al. (2013), with a furfural yield between 11-22% in non-optimal conditions of cost, environmental effects and control properties. As well, dimensions found for the reactor (volume of 518880.77 L) allows to minimize the TAC, eco-points and this size of reactor allows the system to have good control properties.

5. References

Bamufleh, H. S., Alhamed, Y. A., & Daous, M. A. (2013). Furfural from midribs of date-palm trees by sulfuric acid hydrolysis. Industrial Crops and Products, 42(1), 421–428.

Brown L. H., Watson D. D. (1959) ; Phenol-furfural resins. Industrial and Engineering Chemistry, , 51(5), 683-684

Bhogeswararao S., Srinivas D. (2015); Catalytic conversion of furfural to industrial chemicals over supported Pt and Pd catalysts. Journal of Catalysis, 327, 65-77.

Cai, C. M., Zhang, T., Kumar, R., & Wyman, C. E. (2014). Integrated furfural production as a renewable fuel and chemical platform from lignocellulosic biomass. Journal of Chemical Technology and Biotechnology, 89(1), 2-10.

Long, N. V. D., Kim, S., & Lee, M. (2016). Design and optimization of intensified biorefinery process for furfural production through a systematic procedure. Biochemical Engineering Journal.

Lu, Y., & Mosier, N. S. (2008). Kinetic modeling analysis of maleic acid-catalyzed hemicellulose hydrolysis in corn stover. Biotechnology and Bioengineering, 101(6), 1170–1181.

Marcotullio, G. (2011). The chemistry and technology of furfural production in modern lignocellulose feedstock biorefineries. TU Delft, Delft University of Technology.

Rijnsdorp JE, Bekkers P. (1992). Early integration of process and control design. IFAC Workshop on Interactions between Process Design and Process Control; London, UK; 17–22.

Saeman, J. F. (1945). "Kinetics of wood saccharification-hydrolysis of cellulose and decomposition of sugars in dilute acid at high temperature," Industrial & Engineering Chemistry Research 37(1), 43-52.

Sánchez-Ramírez, E., Quiroz-Ramírez, J. J., Segovia-Hernández, J. G., Hernández, S., Ponce-Ortega, J. M. (2016). Economic and environmental optimization of the biobutanol purification process. Clean Technologies and Environmental Policy, 18(2), 395-411.

Sánchez-ramírez, E., Quiroz-ramírez, J. J., Hernández, S., Segovia-hernández, J. G., & Kiss, A. A. (2017). Optimal hybrid separations for intensified downstream processing of biobutanol, 185, 149–159.

Srinivas M., Rangaiah G. P. (2007). Differential evolution with TL for solving nonlinear and mixed-integer nonlinear programming problems, Industrial & Engineering Chemistry Research, 46, 7126-7135.

Wang, Z., & Rangaiah, G. P. (2017) Application and analysis of methods for selecting an optimal solution from the Pareto-optimal front obtained by multiobjective optimization. Industrial & Engineering Chemistry Research, 56(2), 560-574.

Anton A. Kiss, Edwin Zondervan, Richard Lakerveld, Leyla Özkan (Eds.)
Proceedings of the 29th European Symposium on Computer Aided Process Engineering
June 16th to 19th, 2019, Eindhoven, The Netherlands. © 2019 Elsevier B.V. All rights reserved.
http://dx.doi.org/10.1016/B978-0-128-18634-3.50024-2

Design and Optimization of Azeotropic and Extractive Distillation to Purify Furfural Considering Safety, Environmental and Economic Issues.

G.Contreras-Zarazúa,[a] M.E. Jasso-Villegas,[a] E.Sanchez-Ramirez,[a] J.A. Vazquez-Castillo,[a] J.G. Segovia-Hernandez[a,*]

[a] *Deparment of Chemical Engineering University of Guanajuato, Noria Alta S/N, Guanajuato,Gto., 36000 , Mexico.*

[b] *Faculty of Chemical Sciences Autonomous University of Chihuahua, Circuito Universitario 8, Campus II, Chihuahua,Chih. 31125,*

g_segovia@hotmail.com

Abstract

In this work have been designed and optimized simultaneously three different process separations for purify furfural, using Differential Evolution with Tabu List Algorithm. The study cases are a conventional Quaker Oats process, a thermally coupled process and liquid-liquid extraction process. The objective of this work is select the best alternative to purify furfural taken into consideration economic, environmental and safety issues. The results show which the thermally coupled process has several improvements and reductions on the risk, similar cost and environmental impact compared with Quaker Oats process. While the liquid-liquid extraction process does not have any improvement in the objective function, these results are associated with the use of entrainer in this sequence with respect to Quaker Oats Process. Therefore, due to the important improvements in safety issues the TCP process is choosing as the best alternative.

Keywords: Furfural, Process Bio-Refinery, Safety, Optimization Processes.

1. Introduction

In the last years the furfural has aroused a special interest due to it is a chemical produced form biomass, which can compete with the petrochemicals. The US National Renewable Energy Laboratory (NREL) has listed the furfural as one of the 30 most important chemicals produced from biomass, due to their wide applications such as precursor in the production furfural-acetone polymers, extract agents, lubricant oils, nematocide and in the production of furfuryl alcohol which is used in the production of thermoset polymers (Niehn et al. 2016).

The furfural is produced from five carbon sugars as xylose and arabinose which are contained in the hemicellulose fraction of biomass. In an industrial scale the furfural is produced through Quaker Oats process, which is used since 1922. This process is based in two zones: a reaction and separation zones. In the reaction zone, the biomass is treated with sulphuric acid in order to release xylose and convert it into furfural, then a high pressure vapour stream is introduced to reactor in order to remove the furfural and avoid their resinification. During the purification stage, the vapour from the reactor which is rich in water, methanol, acetic acid and furfural is condensed and then it is feeding to a distillation sequence where the furfural is purified. This process has several disadvantages, one of the most important is the high separation cost due to large amount of water contained in the stream that is introduced to the purification zone. The presences of water imply the formation of azeotropes and therefore, is necessary the use of complex and expensive separation alternatives. However, despite the high separation costs of the Quaker Oats process has been used until now, because their easy implementation and lower cost compared with other alternatives (Zeitsch; 2000). Therefore, in this work are studied three different process separation alternatives for purify furfural. The total annual cost (TAC), eco-indicator (EI99) and the individual risk (IR) as economic, environmental and safety indexes respectively are used to evaluate. The novelty of this work since the point of view of circular economy is that, the optimization and identification of best process parameters allow for get a sustainable and profitable process for purify furfural with the less emissions and residues (Geissdoerfer et al. 2017). In the same time, the determination of best optimal parameters allows for the identification of safest process and operating conditions. In other hand the optimization of these 3 objective functions provide the generation of green and friendly process with the environment according with the reported by Jiménez-González and Constable, (2011).

2. Methodology

In this work three different processes distillation to purify furfural have been studied; the Quaker Oats process (QO), a thermally coupled process (TCP) and extractive distillation process (ED). The QO process consist in three distillation columns, the first equipment is an azeotropic distillation column (C1), wherein the mixture is concentrated until the heterogeneous azeotrope concentration. In the column C2 the methanol is recovered by the top if this equipment, and the column C3 where the furfural is purified in the bottoms column and the bottoms and the top products of columns C2 and C3 are sent to decanter. A side stream is withdrawn between the top and bottom of C1, this stream contains a mixture rich in water and furfural, which is sent to a decanter where the organic phase rich in furfural is purified in a third column (C3) (Zeitsch; 2000). In the case of TCP process is generated from the Quaker Oats process by the replacement of condenser associated to the first column, which was substituted by vapour and liquid streams that are linked in the last and penultimate stages of the rectification zone. The last scheme is the liquid-liquid extraction coupled with a distillation process (ED), which consist a liquid-liquid extractive column (E1) where the butyl-chloride is used as entrainer for separate the furfural from the water mixture according to reported by Nhien et al. 2016. Stream rich in solvent and furfural is obtained by the top of extractive column and subsequently the butyl-chloride and furfural are separated in a conventional distillation column (C1) whereas the C2 is used as a prefractionator and C3 is used for purify the methanol. This scheme was studied previously by Nhien et al. 2016. The Figure 1 shows the schemes of the study cases.

In order to perform this study, the most general and extendible possible to the majority of furfural plants, the average composition reported by Zeitsch has been considered. This composition consists in water 90 %wt, furfural 6 %wt, methanol 2 %wt, and acetic acid 2 %wt. The mass flow rate considered in this work is 105,000 kg/hr that corresponds to the estimated global furfural demand reported by Nhien et al 2016. The thermodynamic property model used to simulate the liquid-liquid-vapour equilibrium is Non-random Two-Liquids with Hayden-O'Connell equation of state (NRTL-HOC), which takes into account the two liquid phases and the dimerization and solvation characteristics of mixtures with carboxylic acids. All processes separations were simulated rigorously using the software Aspen Plus. The Total Annual Cost (TAC), Eco-Indicator 99 (EI99) and the individual risk (IR) as objective functions to be minimized.

The total annual cost has been computed using the Guthrie methodology, wherein the cost is calculated as the sum annualized of capital cost (cost of all equipments process) and the operating cost, which are associated with the use of steam, cooling water and electricity. All parameters used for calculated the TAC were taken from Turton et al. 2008. Ten years were assumed as payback period, whereas carbon steel is considered as construction material for the process equiments. The operating costs included cooling utilities, heating utilities and 8500 hours per year of operation for each alternative have been considered. Mathematically, the TAC can be defined according with Eq. (1).

$$TAC = \frac{Capital\ cost}{Payback\ period} + Operating\ cost \tag{1}$$

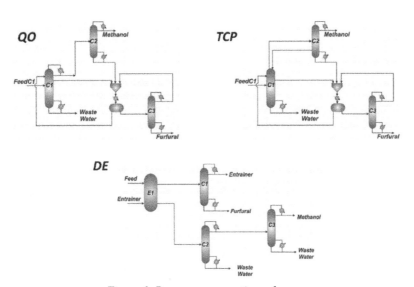

Figure 1. Processes separation schemes.

The EI99 is used to calculate the environmental impact that provokes of each case of study. This approach is based in the evaluation of three impact categories: human health, ecosystem quality, and resources depletion. This method has been successfully implemented in some previous works as the showed by Quiroz-Ramirez et al 2017. According to importance of three major impact categories the weighting for eco-indicator 99 was considered as follows: damages to human health and damage to ecosystem quality are of equal importance, thus these were equally weighted while the damage to the resources was considered to be half of importance weight. The EI99 can be expressed mathematically as:

$$EI99 = \sum_b \sum_d \sum_{k \in K} \delta_d \omega_d \beta_b \alpha_{b,k} \tag{2}$$

where β_b represents the total amount of chemical b released per unit of reference flow due to direct emissions, $\alpha_{b,k}$ is the damage caused in category k per unit of chemical b released to the environment, ω_d is a weighting factor for damage in category d, and δ_d is a normalization factor for damage of category d, respectively. the weights and the valus for the impact categories were taken from Quiroz-Ramirez et al 2017.

Finally, the individual risk is an index used to quantify the security of a process, it is calculated thought a quantitative risk analysis wherein the damage caused by accident is identified and quantified. For all the cases of study have been identified seven possible accidents divided in two categories. Instantaneous incidents: Boiling liquid expanding vapour explosion (BLEVE), unconfined vapour cloud explosion (UVCE), flash fire and toxic release, and whereas the continuous release incidents are: jet fire, flash fire and toxic release. For Calculate the individual risk a reference distance of 50m were chosen. The complete set equations for calculate the IR is showed by Medina-Herrera et al. 2014. The mathematical equation that describes the individual risk is the following:

$$IR = \sum_i f_i P_{x,y} \tag{3}$$

where f_i is the occurrence frequency of incident i, whereas $P_{x,y}$ is the probability of injury or decease caused by the incident i.

The multi-objective optimization problem was solved using the mathematic technique called differential evolution with tabu list (DETL.). The values of parameters requiered by DETL method are: Population size: 120 individuals, Generations Number: 710, Tabu List size: 60 individuals, Tabu Radius: 0.01, Crossover fractions: 0.8, Mutation fractions: 0.3. The DETL method and the objective functions were implemented in a hybrid platform, which link Aspen Plus™ and Microsoft Excel™ through Visual Basic. The design variables for the different study cases are showed in the Table 1.

Finally, the overall optimization problem can be mathematically expresed as in Eq. (4) and Eq. (5):

$$\min Z = \{TAC; Eco99; IR\} =$$

$$\left\{ \frac{Capital\,cost}{Payback\,period} + Operating\,cost\,;\, \sum_b \sum_d \sum_{k \in K} \delta_d \omega_d \beta_b \alpha_{b,k}\,;\, \sum_i f_i P_{x,y} \right\} \tag{4}$$

Subject to: $\quad y_{i,F} \geq x_{i,F}$

$$w_{i,F} \geq u_{i,F} \tag{5}$$

The objective functions are restricted to satisfy the purity ($x_{i,PC}$) and mass flowrate ($u_{i,PC}$) espeficfications of furfural. The minimmum purity of mass flowrate for furfural were fixed to 99.2%tw and 6200kg/ hr respectevely.

3. Results

In this section is showed the results obtained during the simultaneous design and optimization for the three alternatives. In order to simplify the results analysis, the Pareto graphs are studied. The Figure 2 shows a representative Pareto front for TCP scheme, wherein the QO and DE processes shows exactly the same behaviour. In the Figure 2, can be observed that Pareto front of total annual cost versus eco-indicator 99 have a linear dependency with an only one minimum to both objectives, while the other two charts show an opposite behaviour where the minimum TAC and EI corresponds to a design with highest risk and vice versa. The points selected as the best designs corresponds to black point, these were chosen, because are the points that provides an equilibrium between the three objectives. In the same way the designs for QO were chosen. The Table 1 shows the optimal design specifications for all separation schemes.

Table 1. Values of design variables for all process.

Design specifications	QO	TCP	DWC
Stages, C1	55	91	53
Stages, C2	12	40	50
Stages, C3	6	8	50
Stages E1	------	------	17
Feed stage recycle of C1	22	15	------
Feed stage, C1	27	55	35
Stage of side stream C1	16	39	------
Feed stage C2	8	16	27
Feed stage C3	3	2	9
Diameter of C1, m	.44	1.1	1
Diameter of C2, m	.42	.9	3.0
Diameter of C3, m	1.63	1.67	1.2
Diameter of E1, m	------	------	.58
Entrainer flowrate kg/hr			38945.2
Reflux ratio of C1	18.5	------	0.2
Reflux ratio of C2	0.21	25.45	18.5
Reflux ratio of C3	0.208	.353	5.1
Heat duty of C1, kW	19096.8	19357	5490.51
Heat duty of C2, kW	770.17	115.702	21912
Heat duty of C3, kW	456	1007.4	3030.4
Interlinking flow, kg h^{-1}	------	3649.2	------
Values of objective functions			
TAC ($/yr)x10^6	9.334	9.301	13.91
Eco99 (Eco-points) x10^6	4.335	4.3623	6.534
IR (1/yr) x10^5	18.674	13.548	36.00

Due to the large amount of water in the feed stream, the column C1 in the process QO and TCP has the greater contribution for energy, thus is the biggest equipment and it has more impact in the economic and environmental indexes. In the case of DE process, it does not have important reductions in the TAC and EI99 because the large amount of water is removed in the liquid-liquid extraction column, which need be purify in order to purify the methanol. In other hand, the DE process has not any saving or improves on TAC, EI99 and IR, which makes it the worst option. The results obtained in the DE process can be explained due to the addition of the solvent. The entrainer need be recovered in a distillation column, increasing the separation cost and the environmental impact caused by the use of energy. In the case of IR, an increment in the risk is observed because the C1 column contains mainly large amounts of solvent increasing the likelihood of releases and fires, and damage caused by a probable accident. TCP process is choosing as the best option of the three alternatives studied. The TCP process has similar EI99 and

TAC respect to Quaker Oats process, however the replacing of condenser in C1 column results in a shorter resident times and lower inventory inside of C1 reducing the risk.

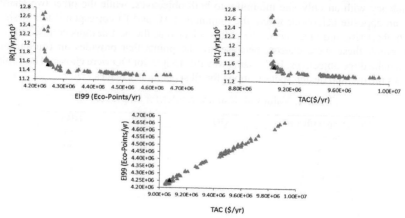

4. Conclusions

In this work three different process separation of furfural have been designed and optimized simultaneously, considering economic, environmental and safety issues, in order to find the most sustainable and safest process. The results indicate that ED process has not improvements with respect to any objective due to the addition of important amounts of solvent which need be separate. The entrainer used in ED process is an organic component, which is flammable and toxic and therefore its use affects the safety index. In other hand, the TCP do not have important savings in TAC and EI99 with respect to Quaker Oats process, but the interconnection flows between the top of C1 and the C2 promotes that the concentration of water inside of C2 be greater which causes a dilution of methanol and reduce the risk. The TCP process is chosen as the best alternative due to it has important improvements in security aspects.

References

Geissdoerfer, M., Savaget, P., Bocken, N. M., & Hultink, E. J. (2017). The Circular Economy–A new sustainability paradigm?. Journal of cleaner production, 143, 757-768.

Jiménez-González, C., & Constable, D. J. (2011). Green chemistry and engineering: a practical design approach. John Wiley & Sons.

Medina-Herrera, N., Jiménez-Gutiérrez, A., & Mannan, M. S.; Development of inherently safer distillation systems. Journal of Loss Prevention in the Process Industries, 2014, 29, 225-23

Nhien L. C., Van Duc Long N., Lee M.; (2017) Process design of hybrid extraction and distillation processes through a systematic solvent selection for furfural production. Energy Procedia, 105, 1084-1089

Quiroz-Ramírez, J. J., Sánchez-Ramírez, E., Hernández-Castro, S., Segovia-Hernández, J. G., Ponce-Ortega, J. M.; (2017). Optimal planning of feedstock for butanol production considering economic and environmental aspects, ACS Sustainable Chemistry & Engineering, 5(5), 4018-4030.

Turton, R., Bailie, R. C., Whiting, W. B., & Shaeiwitz, J. A. (2008). Analysis, synthesis and design of chemical processes. Pearson Education

Zeitsch, K. J. (2000). The chemistry and technology of furfural and its many by-products (Vol. 13). Elsevier.

Anton A. Kiss, Edwin Zondervan, Richard Lakerveld, Leyla Özkan (Eds.)
Proceedings of the 29th European Symposium on Computer Aided Process Engineering
June 16th to 19th, 2019, Eindhoven, The Netherlands. © 2019 Elsevier B.V. All rights reserved.
http://dx.doi.org/10.1016/B978-0-128-18634-3.50025-4

Revisiting Classic Acetic Acid Synthesis: Optimal Hydrogen Consumption and Carbon Dioxide Utilization

Juan D. Medrano-García,* Rubén Ruiz-Femenia, Jose A. Caballero

Institute of Chemical Process Engineering, University of Alicante, PO 99E-03080 Alicante, Spain

jd.medrano@ua.es

Abstract

Acetic acid is a bulk chemical with many applications in the manufacture of several important products. The carbon footprint of its classic synthesis process (methanol carbonylation) is around 1.3921 - 1.8746 kg CO_2-eq/kg, which adds up as the commodity is used in further syntheses. Hence, a reduction in the acetic acid synthesis Global Warming Potential (GWP) would impact in many end products GWP. We propose an acetic acid synthesis superstructure, including different syngas synthesis processes, gas separation technologies and methanol synthesis, which is aimed at reducing both the cost and GWP of the process. Results show that, integrating the methanol synthesis process provides the best results in both objectives. When minimizing the cost (classic synthesis) is best to use an Auto-thermal Reforming (ATR) and CO absorption configuration (0.388 $/kg, 1.832 kg$CO_2$-eq/kg). Adding a fuel cell and a Reverse Water Gas Shift (RWGS) reactor overall reduces both cost and emission (0.280 $/kg, 1.590 kg$CO_2$-eq/kg) of the synthesis and changes the configuration to Partial Oxidation (POX) and cryogenic distillation. Minimum emission (0.102 kgCO_2-eq/kg) can also be achieved with the fuel cell plus RWGS combo, POX and Pressure Swing Adsorption (PSA), although the cost is almost tripled (0.978 $/kg).

Keywords: CO_2 utilization, methane reforming, carbon monoxide separation, reverse water gas shift, acetic acid synthesis

1. Introduction

Acetic acid, with a high and ever-increasing annual production of more than 14 Mt (2017), is an important chemical used to synthesize vinyl acetate (vinyl acetate monomer, VAM), terephthalic acid (polyethylene terephthalate, PET) and acetate anhydride (cellulose flake) among others ("IHS Markit: Acetic Acid," 2018). However, the most extended process for acetic acid production, methanol carbonylation, whose two main raw materials are carbon monoxide and methanol, provokes an appreciable carbon footprint of 1.3921 - 1.8746 kg CO_2-eq/kg ("Ecoinvent Database 3.4," 2017). On the other hand, it is well-known that in methanol synthesis it is possible to consume CO_2. Furthermore, the main source of CO is syngas separation, hence CO_2 can also be used in syngas synthesis (Medrano-García et al., 2017) allowing for further consumption of the gas. Therefore, consuming CO_2 and decreasing the overall Global Warming Potential (GWP) in acetic acid synthesis would accomplish a significant reduction in global CO_2 emissions due to the relevance and high production of this commodity.

We propose a process superstructure in which carbon monoxide and methanol synthesis are integrated with the production of acetic acid. Seven different syngas synthesis processes, both classic and CO_2-consuming (Table 1) along with several gas separation technologies (adsorption, absorption and cryogenic distillation) for each gas component are considered. In addition, the hydrogen byproduct in the CO separation step can be used as fuel elsewhere in the process, as a methanol raw material or as reactant in the reverse water gas shift reactor (RWGS) to increase CO production while consuming additional CO_2. Additionally, heat integration is included across the whole model. We address the existence or non-existence of the units using the Generalized Disjunctive Programming (GDP) and then transforming the disjunctions into algebraic equations using the Hull reformulation (Lee and Grossmann, 2000). We perform multi-objective optimizations of the resulting MINLP model using the epsilon constraint method, minimizing the cost (\$/kg) (1) as our economic indicator and the Global Warming Potential (GWP) (kg CO_2-eq/kg) (2) as our environmental indicator:

$$cost = \frac{Annualized\ Capital\ Cost + Raw\ material\ Cost + Utility\ Cost}{Acetic\ acid\ production} \quad (1)$$

$$emission = \frac{Raw\ material\ GWP + Utility\ GWP + Outlet\ CO_2 - Inlet\ CO_2}{Acetic\ acid\ production} \quad (2)$$

Results show that the RWGS reactor acts as an important sink of CO_2 while reducing the raw materials needed in the syngas synthesis step, and therefore reducing the overall cost and emission of the process. Emissions can be reduced, approximately, 1 kg CO_2-eq per kg of acetic acid.

Table 1. Reforming agents used in methane reforming technologies.

	SMR	POX	ATR	CR	DMR	BR	TR
Steam	X		X	X		X	X
O_2		X	X	X			X
CO_2					X	X	X

SMR: Steam Methane Reforming; POX: Partial Oxidation; ATR: Auto-thermal Reforming; CR: Combined Reforming; DMR: Dry Methane Reforming; BR: Bi-Reforming; TR: Tri-Reforming.

2. Methodology

2.1. Superstructure overview

The aim of this work is the reduction of the GWP in the production of acetic acid using the methanol carbonylation classic process. This technology requires both a methanol and carbon monoxide feed. In the proposed superstructure, carbon monoxide is produced by separation of syngas. On the other hand, methanol is manufactured using a mixture of this syngas, H_2 separated as the result of purifying the CO, and a fraction of the CO itself, in addition to possibly being bought from an external source. Furthermore, removed H_2 can be used as fuel or as feedstock in a Reverse Water Gas Shift (RWGS) reactor that, while consuming CO_2, produces additional CO. In addition, depending on its purity, it can be used in a fuel cell that supplies the system electricity. The off-gas produced by the gas separation can also burn as fuel or be partially recycled in order to further remove valuable gases from it. The proposed superstructure is shown in Figure 1.

First, the raw materials, which include methane and a reforming agent (steam, oxygen, carbon dioxide or a combination), enter the syngas synthesis section of the superstructure. Here, the feedstock is compressed and heated up to the reaction pressure and temperature. Then, the mixture enters the reformer reactor where syngas is the product. Each syngas process operates at different feed ratios, pressures and temperatures, in addition to producing syngas with different compositions. These process variables are fixed to the most common values found in the bibliography for industrial operation. These values and employed models for the syngas synthesis section can be found in Medrano-García et al. (2017). The syngas stream is then headed to the gas separation section, where it first encounters a phase separator (40 °C) that removes all the water contained in the gas. The option of capturing CO_2 is given next in a diglycolamine (DGA) absorber. This CO_2 can be used as feedstock in the syngas synthesis step and RWGS reactor, or just be assigned for storage. The RWGS reactor works using an H_2/CO_2 inlet ratio fixed at seven, operating temperature of 300, 350, 400 or 450 °C and according CO_2 conversion of 11.6, 45.0, 77.6 or 85.9 % (Wolf et al., 2016). Next, a Pressure Swing Adsorption (PSA) unit targeting H_2 can be used to remove this gas from the syngas. This H_2, due to the purity a PSA separation can achieve, is a valid option for fuelling the fuel cell, in addition to be used as fuel or as feedstock in the methanol synthesis loop and/or RWGS reactor. After the H_2 removal option, a fraction of the syngas can be diverted in order to feed the methanol synthesis loop. The remaining syngas then arrives to the CO separation section of the superstructure, where cryogenic distillation, chemical absorption or a CO-targeting PSA can be chosen for the task. These technologies provide an off-gas in addition to the CO-rich product stream and, in the case of cryogenic distillation, also an H_2-rich stream. The off-gas can burn as fuel or be partially recycled back just before the H_2 PSA in order to further remove valuable gases from it. The H_2-rich stream can also be used as fuel or as a raw material for the RWGS reactor or the methanol synthesis loop. Note that the H_2-rich steam purity is insufficient for its use in the fuel cell, and hence this option is not considered. Finally, the CO-rich stream is given the possibility of removing any remaining CO_2 contained in it with a second ammine absorber. After this step, it can be split so that it can feed both the acetic acid synthesis process and the methanol synthesis loop if needed.

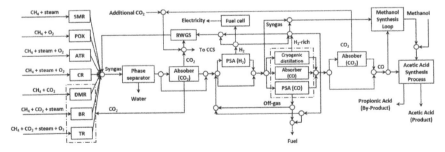

Figure 1. Proposed process superstructure for the integration, synthesis and separation of syngas, methanol and acetic acid.

2.2. Methanol synthesis loop

The methanol synthesis loop can be seen in Figure 2. The loop is modelled using linear equations derived from simulations studies in Aspen HYSYS v9.0 with the aim of achieving minimum cost and emission in the synthesis (Medrano et al., 2017). Syngas at 40 °C and 30 bar, with an $(H_2-CO_2)/(CO+CO_2)$ ratio of 2.00 (2.04 in the reactor inlet) and

5 % CO_2 content enters the loop and is compressed to 76.5 bar and heated up to 284.2 °C. The reaction takes place in a plug flow reactor modelled after (Bussche and Froment, 1996) kinetics. The resulting stream then gets depressurized and cooled down to 10 bar and 40 °C. In a phase separator, crude methanol (96.4 % wt. methanol content) is obtained and sent to the acetic acid synthesis process. The unreacted syngas stream is partially purged (5 %, to burn as fuel), recompressed and recycled back to the heating stage.

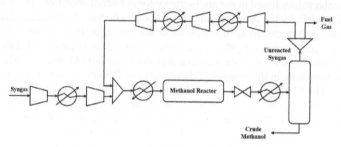

Figure 2. Proposed methanol synthesis loop embedded in the superstructure.

2.3. Acetic acid synthesis
The acetic acid synthesis process is shown in Figure 3 (Cheung et al., 2000):

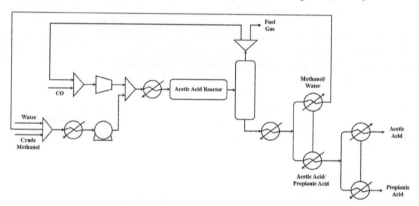

Figure 3. Proposed acetic acid synthesis process embedded in the superstructure.

Methanol, CO (40 °C, 1 and 30 bar respectively, 1:1 molar ratio) and water (40 °C, 1 bar), enter the process and are compressed and heated up to 30 bar and 175 °C. The catalyst needs water (4.0 - 4.5 % wt.) in order activate the carbonylation reaction, which allows the use of crude methanol as a feedstock for the process, hence resulting in the omission of the methanol purification column. Inside the reactor, the following reactions take place:

$$CH_3OH + CO \longrightarrow CH_3COOH \tag{3}$$

$$CH_3OH + CH_3COOH \longrightarrow CH_3CH_2COOH + H_2O \tag{4}$$

$$CO + H_2O \rightleftharpoons H_2 + CO_2 \tag{5}$$

For the main reaction, the synthesis of acetic acid (3), a CO conversion of 60 % is considered. The parallel reaction of the formation of propionic acid (4) as a byproduct transforms 1 % of the produced acetic acid in reaction (3). Lastly, the Water Gas Shift

(WGS) equilibrium reaction (5), is assumed to have a CO conversion of 10 %. After the reaction, the gaseous phase is recycled (50 % purged, to fuel gas) and the liquid phase is separated (86.25 °C, 1 bar, 62 stages) into a methanol-water stream, which is recycled, and an acetic acid-propionic acid stream which is further separated (116.97 °C, 1 bar, 62 stages) into the product (99.87 % wt. acetic acid) and byproduct (99.13 % wt. propionic acid).

3. Results and discussion

The resulting MINLP model consists of 2,029 equations and 1,587 variables, 25 of which are binary variables. The solving time was 1,667 s per case in an Intel Core 2 Quad with an 8GB RAM. The multi-objective optimization is performed applying the epsilon constraint method and using the solver ANTIGONE (Misener and Floudas, 2014) within GAMS (GAMS, 2018). The main results are shown in Figure 4. The use of specific syngas synthesis processes is separated into areas by dashed lines, while dotted lines split RWGS operating conditions and CO separation units. In addition, all solutions include the integrated methanol synthesis process.

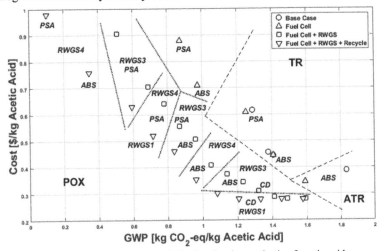

Figure 4. Results of the multi-objective optimization for the synthesis of acetic acid.

Results show that, minimizing the cost in classic (base case) acetic acid synthesis (0.388 $/kg, 1.832 kgCO$_2$-eq/kg) requires ATR as the syngas synthesis process and absorption of CO (ABS) as the CO separation technology. Including a fuel cell reduces overall cost and emission (0.345 $/kg, 1.587 kgCO$_2$-eq/kg) without changing the main configuration units. Adding the RWGS reactor provides a significant decrease in cost (0.280 $/kg, 1.590 kgCO$_2$-eq/kg) and changes the configuration into using POX and cryogenic distillation (CD). Allowing the partial recycle of off-gas streams (0.280 $/kg, 1.575 kgCO$_2$-eq/kg) barely reduces the emission maintaining cost invariable. On the other hand, when minimizing the emission, the addition of the fuel cell (0.873 $/kg, 0.879 kgCO$_2$-eq/kg) more than doubles the synthesis cost of the base case while reducing GWP value almost by 1 kgCO$_2$-eq/kg. The RWGS reactor inclusion (0.906 $/kg, 0.510 kgCO$_2$-eq/kg) further reduces emission and increases the cost. Finally, when off-gas streams are free to recycle (0.978 $/kg, 0.102 kgCO$_2$-eq/kg) the cost of the synthesis peaks, almost tripling the base case, while the emission reaches its minimum, reducing the base case emission by more than 1.7 kgCO$_2$-eq/kg; almost achieving carbon neutrality.

4. Conclusions

In this work, we propose an acetic acid synthesis superstructure in order to minimize both the cost and the emission of the production of this commodity. Integrating several methane reforming processes, gas separation technologies and methanol synthesis, we perform multi-objective optimizations of the resulting MINLP model in order to achieve the optimal configurations. Results show that for all cases, methanol should be produced simultaneously with acetic acid to minimize both cost and emissions.

Comparison with the minimum cost configuration (0.388 $/kg, 1.832 kgCO$_2$-eq/kg) states that the cost of the synthesis can be further reduced using a fuel cell and a RWGS reactor with POX and cryogenic distillation (0.280 $/kg, 1.590 kgCO$_2$-eq/kg), while recycling the process off-gases barely has an effect. On the other hand, emissions can be significantly decreased with the same configuration but using a PSA instead (0.906 $/kg, 0.510 kgCO$_2$-eq/kg), however, off-gas recycling does have an effect in further reducing the emission (0.978 $/kg, 0.102 kgCO$_2$-eq/kg), where the decrease surpasses 1.7 kgCO$_2$-eq/kg.

Acknowledgements

The authors gratefully acknowledge financial support to the Spanish «Ministerio de Economía, Industria y Competitividad» under project CTQ2016-77968-C3-2-P (AEI/FEDER, UE) and «Generalitat Valenciana: Consellería de Educación, Invenstigación, Cultura y Deporte» for the Ph.D. grant (ACIF/2016/062).

References

Bussche, K.M.V., Froment, G.F., 1996. A Steady-State Kinetic Model for Methanol Synthesis and the Water Gas Shift Reaction on a Commercial Cu/ZnO/Al2O3Catalyst. J. Catal. 161, 1–10.

Cheung, H., Tanke, R.S., Torrence, G.P., 2000. Acetic Acid, in: Ullmann's Encyclopedia of Industrial Chemistry. Wiley-VCH Verlag GmbH & Co. KGaA, Weinheim, Germany.

Ecoinvent Database 3.4 [WWW Document], 2017. URL https://www.ecoinvent.org/ (accessed 7.15.18).

GAMS Development Corporation. General Algebraic System (GAMS) Release 25.0.3. Washington, DC, USA, 2018, n.d.

IHS Markit: Acetic Acid [WWW Document], 2018. URL https://ihsmarkit.com/products/acetic-acid-chemical-economics-handbook.html (accessed 2.1.18).

Lee, S., Grossmann, I.E., 2000. New algorithms for nonlinear generalized disjunctive programming. Comput. Chem. Eng. 24, 2125–2141.

Medrano-García, J.D., Ruiz-Femenia, R., Caballero, J.A., 2017. Multi-objective optimization of combined synthesis gas reforming technologies. J. CO2 Util. 22, 355–373.

Medrano, J.D., Ruiz-Femenia, R., Caballero, J.A., 2017. Multi-objective Optimization of a Methanol Synthesis Process Superstructure with Two-step Carbon Dioxide Consumption. Comput. Aided Chem. Eng. 40, 721–726.

Misener, R., Floudas, C.A., 2014. ANTIGONE: Algorithms for coNTinuous / Integer Global Optimization of Nonlinear Equations. J. Glob. Optim. 59, 503–526.

Wolf, A., Jess, A., Kern, C., 2016. Syngas Production via Reverse Water-Gas Shift Reaction over a Ni-Al2O3 Catalyst: Catalyst Stability, Reaction Kinetics, and Modeling. Chem. Eng. Technol. 39, 1040–1048.

Anton A. Kiss, Edwin Zondervan, Richard Lakerveld, Leyla Özkan (Eds.)
Proceedings of the 29th European Symposium on Computer Aided Process Engineering
June 16th to 19th, 2019, Eindhoven, The Netherlands. © 2019 Elsevier B.V. All rights reserved.
http://dx.doi.org/10.1016/B978-0-128-18634-3.50026-6

Innovative application of statistical analysis for the optimization of CO_2 absorption from flue gas with ionic liquid

Grazia Leonzio,[a,*] Edwin Zondervan,[b]

[a]*Department of Industrial and Information Engineering and Economics, University of L'Aquila, Via Giovanni Gronchi 18, 67100 L'Aquila, Italy*
[b]*Laboratory of Process Systems Engineering, Department of Production Engineering, Universität Bremen, Leobener Str. 6, 28359 Bremen, Germany*

grazia.leonzio@graduate.univaq.it

Abstract

In this research, a model for the physical absorption of CO_2 from flue gas with [hmim][Tf2N] ionic liquid, an innovative solvent used in the last CO_2 absorption processes, is developed in Aspen Plus and optimized through a central composite design by using Minitab. Then a unique combination of simulation and statistical analysis is carried out for the process. The aim is to find the optimal operating conditions that can maximize the amount of captured CO_2 while minimizing the total costs. The study shows the percentage of CO_2 removal is 93.7%, operating costs are 0.279 trillion euro/a and capital costs are 21.9 million euro/year. The obtained results are in agreement with other works reported in literature, considering the high cost for ionic liquid.

Keywords: CO_2 capture, ionic liquid, process simulation, statistical analysis, optimization.

1. Introduction

From the combustion of natural gas, oil, fuels-coal, globally 30 gigatons (Gt) per year of carbon dioxide are emitted impacting the environment dramatically (Wilcox et al., 2014; Tlili et al., 2014). Reducing emissions is critical, but at this time it is also important to capture carbon dioxide efficiently from emission sources. Chemical absorption by with amines is a common technology to capture carbon dioxide from flue gases (Nittaya et al., 2014; Lin et al., 2011). High reactivity, low cost, good absorption capacity, high affinity to carbon dioxide are some positive aspects of this technology. However, there are also serious disadvantages such as tendency for corrosion, high energy demand for regeneration and loss of solvent. Ionic liquids (ILs) are a promising and green alternative due to their low volatility, good dissolution, high decomposition temperature and stability, excellent chemical tunabilities, that allow to reduce the losses of solvent and energy for regeneration (Luo and Wang, 2017; Ma et al., 2018). Using ionic liquids as a solvent for CO2 absorption is still a rather new carbon capture process. As an example: Valencia-Marquez et al. (2017) developed a mixed-integer nonlinear programming (MINLP) problem for absorption process to design the best ionic liquid that can ensure a recovery of CO_2 higher than 90% with a simultaneous optimal product and process design. Currently no study that employs ANOVA analysis, response surface methodology (RSM) by using central composite design has been used for optimizing the absorption process of CO_2 by using ionic liquid. In particular, a process for the physical absorption of carbon dioxide from flue gas (coming from power plant) with 1-n-hexyl-3-methylimidazolium bis(trifluoromethylsulfonyl)amide ([hmim][Tf2N]) ionic liquid is developed in Aspen Plus. A similar work is not present in literature. The model is used to carry out a face centered central composite design (FCCCD) according to the response surface methodology (RSM) by using Minitab software with the aim to find the optimal operating conditions. In this way c the factors (geometric and operating) and combination of factors that are significant can be identified. The aim is to improve the efficiency of the process reducing the costs. The inlet temperature of flue gas, absorption column pressure, the carbon dioxide composition of flue gas, the height of absorption column are the considered factors, while the percentage of carbon dioxide removal, operating costs (OPEX) and capital costs (CAPEX) are the analyzed responses.

2. Materials and methods

2.1 Description of the absorption process

A process for the absorption of CO_2 by flue gas of power plant is developed in Aspen Plus as in figure 1. In this process flue gas is composed by Ar, CH4, H2, N2, CO, CO2, H2O, NH3, H2S. Absorber (RADFRAC model) is a packed bed with plastic pall rings of 0.025 m and packing surface area of 205 m^2/m^3. The eight of each stage is 3 m. Compressed flue gas is fed at the bottom of the absorber, where IL contacts the flue gas, remove CO2 and discharges the clean gas to the air. The stream existing at the bottom of absorber is rich in IL so it is sent to a flash to recover it and to recirculate to the absorber. The stream gas existing at the top of flash is mainly composed by CO2 and water. Then it is cooled to 288 K in order to separate any water present, so that captured CO2 can be compressed up to 150 bar in the following refrigerated compressors.

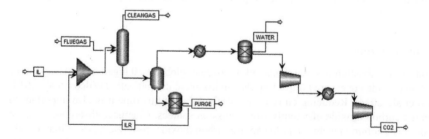

Figure 1 Process scheme of CO2 absorption process from flue gas with IL in Aspen Plus environmental

The IL [hmim][Tf2N] is characterized in Aspen Plus as new component by defining density, viscosity, surface tension, vapor pressure, heat capacity and critical properties as reported in Basha et al. (2013). The Peng Robinson Equation of State is chosen as thermodynamic model, by setting binary interaction parameter between each component via regression analysis (Basha et al., 2013). The amount of flue gas entering the column is 25.63 kg/s, while the amount of fed IL is 280 kg/s.

2.2 Response surface methodology

A face centered central composite design is setup for the absorption process using the response surface methodology principle (Montgomery, 2005). From this design, the surface plots of considered responses with respective second order polynomial models can be obtained. The flue gas inlet temperature, column pressure, CO_2 composition in flue gas and the height of absorber are the selected factors. It is evident as operating and design factors are selected for the optimization of the process. The percent of CO_2 removal from flue gas, operating (costs of raw material and utilities) and capital costs are the analyzed responses. These costs are evaluated by using Aspen Process Economic Analyzer (APEA), considering a price for IL of 20 €/kg over a period of 20 year (Ramdin et al., 2012). Table 1 shows the values set for each level of factor. As shown, three levels are considered for each factor. For the statistical analysis, 31 simulation tests are carried out including 16 cube points, 7 axial points, 7 central points and 1 replication. Star points are set on the centers of each factorial face: the value of α is 1. The significance of each term in the obtained model is validated by analysis of variance.

Table 1 Values of level for each factor in FCCCD analysis

Code	Factor	Level		
		(-1)	0	(+1)
A	Flue gas inlet temperature (K)	323	411.5	500
B	Column pressure (bar)	15	22.5	30
C	CO_2 composition in flue gas (mol%)	3	13.5	24
D	Height of absorber (m)	2	26	50

3. Results and discussions

The process scheme developed in Aspen Plus is used to carry out different simulations according to the face centered central composite design. From the parameters obtained from the simulation, a mathematical model is obtained for each analyzed response, as the capital costs, the operating costs, the percent of CO_2 removal from flue gas, respectively, as the following equations (Eqs 1-3):

$$CAPEX \ (euro) = 22370478 - 427029 \cdot A + 1076170 \cdot B + 1288803 \cdot D \qquad (1)$$

$$OPEX \left(\frac{euro}{year}\right) = 2.85 \cdot 10^{11} + 3.76 \cdot 10^9 \cdot DD \qquad (2)$$

$$CO_2 \ removal \ (\%)$$
$$= 72.42 + 23.59 \cdot B + 1.13 \cdot BC + 1.02 \cdot BD + 1.02 \cdot CD - 0.91$$
$$\cdot D - 3.36 \cdot BB \qquad (3)$$

where factor A is the flue gas inlet temperature, factor B is the column absorber pressure, factor C is the CO_2 composition in flue gas and factor D is the height of column absorber. Results show that factor B, interaction BC, BD, CD have a positive effect on the percentage of carbon dioxide removal, while factor D and interaction BB have a negative effect on this response. For the operating costs the interaction DD has a positive effect. In addition, for the capital costs factor D and B have a positive effect, while factor A has a negative effect. It is evident that factors B, C and D have an overall stronger influence on the process while factor A only influences the capital costs. Figures 2, 3, and 4 show the surface plots for CAPEX, OPEX and CO_2 removal respectively obtained by Minitlab as function of two factors, while the others are set to a value of 0 level. It is possible to see especially for the surface plots of CAPEX and OPEX, that even if interactions between factors are not significative, they are present.

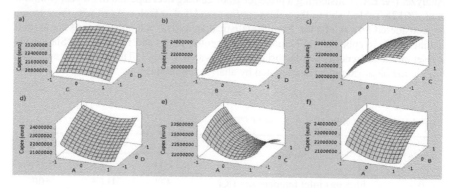

Figure 2 Response surface plots for CAPEX (euro): a) CAPEX (euro) as function of factor C and D; b) CAPEX (euro) as function of B and D; c) CAPEX (euro) as function of B and C; d) CAPEX (euro) as function of factor A and D; e) CAPEX (euro) as function of factor A and C; f) CAPEX (euro) as function of factor A and B. (Hold values: A=B=C=D=0).

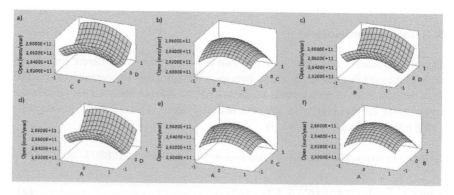

Figure 3 Response surface plots for OPEX (euro/year): a) OPEX (euro/year) as function of factor C and D; b) OPEX (euro/year) as function of factor B and C; c) OPEX (euro/year) as function of factor B and D; d) OPEX (euro/year) as function of factor A and D; e) OPEX (euro/year) as function of factor A and C; f) OPEX (euro/year) and function of factor A and B. (Hold values: A=B=C=D=0).

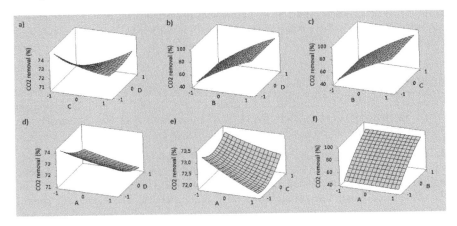

Figure 4 Response surface plots for CO2 removal (%): a) CO2 removal as function of factor C and D; b) CO2 removal as function of facto B and D; c) CO2 removal as function of factor C and B; d) CO2 removal as function of factor A and D; e) CO2 removal as function of factor A and C; f) CO2 removal as function of factor A and B. (Hold values: A=B=C=D=0).

The operating conditions that maximize the capture of carbon dioxide and minimize the costs using a desirability function are found: factor A, B, C and D should be respectively equal to 500 K, 30 bar, 24 mol% and 1.36 m. The percentage of carbon dioxide removal is equal to 93.7%, the operating costs are 0.279 trillion euro/year and the capital costs are 21.9 million euro. The obtained values rare supported by other studies. Significant reductions are made as compared to for example (Nguyen and Zondervan, 2018; de Riva et al., 2017). Capital and operating costs have not been reported for [himm][Tf2N] and comparison is not that easy. For other ionic liquids such as [Bmim][Ac], [bmim][BF4] and [bmim][PF6] economic data has been reported (Ma et al., 2017; Shiflett et al., 2010) but a straight comparison cannot be made. In the current study, the relation suggested by Nguyen and Zondervan (2018) for calculation of operating and capital costs in the case of [bmim][Ac] ionic liquid as function of flue gas flow rate and carbon dioxide composition is used. Results show that capital costs are in the same order, while a higher value for operating cost is obtained may be due to the high flow rate required and the cost of used IL.

4. Conclusions

In this research, an innovative optimization of physical absorption process to capture CO_2 from flue gas through ionic liquid ([hmim][Tf2N]) is developed and a similar work can not be found in literature. A new solution, as ionic liquid is considered due to its better properties compared to traditional ones. However, the high cost of this ionic liquid suggested to find the optimal operating conditions in order to maximize the amount of captured CO_2 and to reduce costs. A face centered central composite design is developed considering as factors flue gas inlet temperature, column absorber pressure, CO_2 composition in flue gas and the height of column absorber. Operating and capital costs and the amount of reduced CO_2 are considered as responses. Results show that to have an optimized process, flue gas inlet temperature, column absorber pressure, CO_2 composition in flue gas and the height of column absorber should be respectively equal to 500 K, 30 bar, 24 mol% and 1.36 m. In this way, operating costs, capital costs and the percent of CO_2 removal are respectively 0.279 trillion euro/year, 21.9 million euro and 93.7%.

References

Basha, O.M., Keller, M.J., Luebke, D.R., Resnik, K.P., Morsi, B.I., 2013. Development of a Conceptual Process for Selective CO2 Capture from Fuel Gas Streams Using [hmim][Tf2N] Ionic Liquid as a Physical Solvent, Energy Fuels, 2013, 27 (7) 3905–3917.

de Rivaa, J., Suarez-Reyesa, J., Morenoa, D., Díaz, I., Ferro, V., Palomara, J., 2017. Ionic liquids for post-combustion CO2 capture by physical absorption:Thermodynamic, kinetic and process analysis. International Journal of Greenhouse Gas Control 61, 61–70. Lin, Y.J., Pan, T.H., Wong, S.H., Jang, S.S., Chi, Y.W., Yeh, C.H., 2011. Plantwide control of CO2 capture by absorption and stripping using monoethanolamine solution. Am. Control Conf. 50 (3), 1338–1345.

Luo, X., Wang C., 2017. The development of carbon capture by functionalized ionic liquids, Current Opinion in Green and Sustainable Chemistry 3, 33-38.

Ma, Y., Gao, J., Wang, Y., Hu, J., Cui, P., 2018. Ionic liquid-based CO2 capture in power plants for low carbon emissions. International Journal of Greenhouse Gas Control 75, 134–139.

Ma, T., Wang, J., Du, Z., Abdeltawab, A., Al-Enizi, A.M., Chen, X., Yu, G., 2017. Process simulation study of CO2 capture by ionic liquids. International Journal of Greenhouse Gas Control, 58, 223-231.

Montgomery, D.C. 2005. Design and Analysis of Experiments; John Wiley & Sons: New York, NY, USA.

Nittaya, T., Douglas, P.L., Croise, E., Ricardez-Sandoval, L.A., 2014. Dynamic modelling and control of MEA absorption processes for CO2 capture from power plants. Fuel 116, 672–691.

Ramdin, M., de Loos, T.W., Vlugt, T.J.H., 2012. State-of-the-Art of CO2 Capture with Ionic Liquids. Ind. Eng. Chem. Res. 2012, 51, 8149–8177

Wilcox, J., Haghpanah, R., Rupp, E.C., He, J.J., Lee, K., 2014. Advancing Adsorption Membrane Separation Processes for the gigaton carbon capture challenge, Annu. Rev. Chem. Biomol. Eng. 5, 479-480.

Shiflett, M.B., Drew, D.W., Cantini, R.A., Yokozeki, A., 2010. Carbon Dioxide Capture Using Ionic Liquid 1-Butyl-3-Methylimidazolium Acetate. Energy Fuels, 24 (10) 5781-5789.

Tlili, A., Frogneux, X., Blondiaux, E., Cantat, T., 2014. Creating added value with a waste: methylation of amines with CO2 and H2, Angew. Chem. Int. Ed. 53, 2543-2545.

Valencia-Marquez, D., Flores-Tlacuahuac, A., Vasquez-Medrano, R., 2017. An optimization approach for CO2 capture using ionic liquids. Journal of Cleaner Production 168, 1652-1667

Anton A. Kiss, Edwin Zondervan, Richard Lakerveld, Leyla Özkan (Eds.)
Proceedings of the 29th European Symposium on Computer Aided Process Engineering
June 16th to 19th, 2019, Eindhoven, The Netherlands. © 2019 Elsevier B.V. All rights reserved.
http://dx.doi.org/10.1016/B978-0-128-18634-3.50027-8

Synthesis, Design and Optimization of Schemes to Produce 2, 3-Butanediol Considering Economic, Environmental and Safety issues

Eduardo Sánchez-Ramírez,[a*] Juan José Quiroz-Ramírez,[b] Juan Gabriel Segovia-Hernandez[a]

[a]*Universidad de Guanajuato, Noria Alta S/N, Guanajuato 36050, México*

[b] *CONACyT – CIATEC A.C. Centro de Innovación Aplicada en Tecnologías Competitivas, Omega 201 Col. Industrial Delta, León 37545, México*

eduardo.sanchez@ugto.mx

Abstract

2, 3-Butanediol is a very promising chemical due to its several applications and may be produced by microbial production. The recovery of 2, 3-Butanediol from the fermentation broth is yet a challenge due to its low concentration. Moreover, a broader point of view is also necessary since current needs require a process with low environmental impact and high inherent safety. In this work, the inherent risk will be approached at early-stages at the same time that economic and environmental issues. The aim of this paper is to synthesis, design and optimize some alternatives to purify 2,3-Butanediol based on distillation, those alternatives are synthesized in such way that is obtained as results thermally coupled, thermodynamically equivalent and intensified sequences. The alternatives were designed and optimized considering three objective functions: the total annual cost as an economic index, the eco-indicator 99 as an environmental index, and the inherent risk of the process (analyzed as individual risk). In general terms, the intensified alternative presented 15 % reduction of the TAC and 14% of the environmental impact. Moreover, the same alternative presented the lowest inherent risk with a reduction of about 50% in comparison with the reference alternative.

Keywords: 2,3-Butanediol, Multi-Objective Optimization, Downstream Process, Individual Risk.

1. Introduction

2,3-Butanediol (2,3-BD) is a renewable chemical if its production is based on biomass. Several reports pointed out 2,3-BD as a quite interesting bio-based compound since its application covers several industrial sectors. Currently, 2, 3-BD has shown its potential for being used in the manufacturing of printing inks, perfumes, explosives, etc. Moreover, an interesting consideration of this bio-based chemical is its use as potential liquid fuel with a heating value of 27.19 kJ/g; additionally, 2,3-BD is an intermediate to produce methyl-ethyl-ketone (MEK) a quire promising biofuel, using a dehydrogenation process. 2,3-Butanediol coming from fermentation comes with a high content of water, making its purification a challenge (Koutinas et al. 2016).

On the other hand, since the boiling point of 2,3-BD is about 180℃ at atmospheric pressure and it does not form an azeotrope with water, the use of conventional distillation seems a natural alternative. While this unit operation has many advantages, one drawback is its significant energy requirement. Therefore, energy consumption plays a major role in the operational costs of a process. Despite at first sight the use of distillation it might be not profitable, it is possible to implement several synthesis alternatives to reduce both capital and energy cost. Regarding the synthesis and design of separation process Errico et al. (2016) have presented an ordered and sequential methodology to generate subspaces of separation alternatives. This kind of methodologies jointly with optimization strategies have shown important improvements. Despite the usefulness of many synthesis and optimization approaches, they have focused mostly on the economic issue which is indeed a critical point. On the other hand, an important issue like inherent safety has been disregarded or considered as an afterthought following the design. So, do not include the risk involved in the downstream process can lead to misleading risk assessment. An effective alternative would be, to include inherent safety, economic and environmental issues on early design stages, guaranteeing in this way a process with low economic and environmental impact and also accounts the risk assessment on each alternative. In this manner, with all background mentioned, this work aims to synthesize, design and optimize some new alternatives to separate and purify an effluent of 2,3-Butanediol coming from fermentation. This approach proposes to produce purification alternatives which consider the balance among several targets, in other words, the optimization procedure will find separation alternatives which considers economic, environmental, and safety issues in order to accomplish the current industrial necessities.

2. Problem statement and methodology

Although 2,3-butanediol is a very useful chemical bio bulk, its microbial production involves a dilute broth which requires further purification. However, according to the state of the art of 2,3- butanediol, this downstream process is not well explored so far. Recently, Penner et al. (2017) proposed a conventional alternative for this task (see Figure 1a). However, it is clear the necessity for new alternatives which improve performance indexes. With this in mind, the schemes in Figure 1a)-b) will be considered as the references cases for further synthesis and design methodology. The complete methodology is described below.

Step 1: Identification of conventional distillation column: The schemes presented in Figure 1a)-b) were considered as reference cases. Initially, (Penner et al. 2017) proposed the direct sequence presented in Figure 1a), the natural complement for Figure 1a is the indirect sequence in Figure 1b).

Step 2: Generation of thermally coupled alternatives: having both cases of Figure 1 as a reference, it is possible to generate the subspace of the modified thermally coupled sequences by the substitution of heat exchangers (reboiler and condenser as appropriate) associated to no-product stream with a liquid/vapor interconnection (See Figure 2). In other words, where the streams of no-product are located, it is possible to set a thermally coupling if either a reboiler or condenser is eliminated, and a stream of steam and liquid is considered instead.

Step 3: Generation of thermodynamically equivalent alternatives. Now, with the thermal couplings already introduced, there are column sections where the condenser/reboiler provides a common reflux ratio/vapor boil-up between two consecutive columns. With this in mind, it is possible to move this section to generate thermodynamically equivalent alternatives in Figure 3. i. e. Figure 3a) is obtained if section 4 of Figure 2a) is moved below section 2 in Figure 3a).

Step 4 Generation of intensified alternatives: the following methodology is simple and consists of the elimination of the side columns which have only one column section (See Figure 4). i.e. Figure 4a) is obtained if section 3 in Figure 3a) is eliminated.

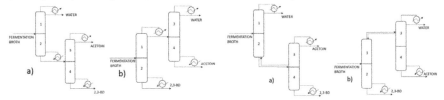

Fig. 1 Pure distillation schemes   Fig. 2 Thermally Coupled schemes

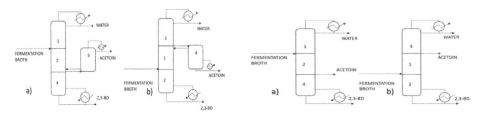

Fig. 3 Thermodynamic Equivalent schemes   Fig. 4 Intensified schemes

According to their result in fermentation, the Diol concentration is 150 g/L and 10 g/L of 2,3-Butanediol and Acetoin, respectively. In this work, we considered the same mass fractions and a mass flow of 73,170 kg h^{-1}. All alternatives were modeled using Aspen Plus modeler using the NRTL thermodynamic model, which according to Penner et al. (2017), it describes better the interactions among all components. The minimum purities were fixed on a mass base as 99.5% for 2,3-BD and water, and 99.0% for acetoin. The objective function and the optimization method are described below.

2.1 Multi-objective Optimization and Objective Functions

The objective function included the simultaneous minimization of the total annual cost (TAC), the eco-indicator 99 (EI99) and the Inherent Risk (IR) measured as individual risk. The minimization of these objectives was subject to the required recoveries and purities in each product stream (see Eq. 1).

$$Min(TAC, EI99, IR) = f(N_{tn}, N_{fn}, R_{rn}, F_{rn}, F_{vn}, D_{cn}, P_{cn}, FC_{cn}) \qquad (1)$$

Where N_{tn} are total number of column stages, N_{fn} is the feed stage in column, R_{rn} is the reflux ratio, F_{rn} is the distillate/bottoms flux, F_{rn} and F_{vn} are the interconnection liquid/vapor flow, D_{cn} is the column diameter, P_{cn} and F_{cn} are phisicochemical properties for IR calculation such as molecular weight, heat of combustion, LC50 and so on. This multi-objective minimization considered 25 continuous and discrete variables. TAC was calculated through the Guthrie method according to the equation TAC = (Capital Costs/Payback Period) + Operating Costs , all the parameters for the equipment were taken from (Turton R. 2001). The Eco-Indicator 99 (EI99) was used to evaluate the sustainability of the processes by means of the equation EI99 = $\sum\sum\sum$ (Amount of chemical x damage caused x weighting factor x normalization factor), this methodology is based on lifecycle analysis of different categories where individual scores are assigned depending on the category, three impact categories (steel, electricity, and vapor) were considered according to work presented by Errico et al. (2016) where this indicator has been utilized to quantify the environmental impact in some chemical processes. In the case of the safety, the individual risk was calculated through quantitative risk analysis technique, which is a methodology of inherent safety where the main objective is to evaluate the frequency and probability of decease or injury due to accidents like explosions or toxic release. The inherent risk is evaluated by the equation IR = $\sum$f*P, being f the frequency of accident and P the probability of affection. This methodology has been successfully used to evaluate the risk on the chemical process (Medina-Herrera, et al. 2014), the equations and procedure were realized to a distance of 50m from the equipment according to reported by American Institute of Chemical Engineers, 2000.

To optimize the process route for biobutanol production, a stochastic optimization method, Differential Evolution with Tabu List (DETL) was used, which have shown being robust to optimize intensified separation systems. Srinivas & Rangaiah, (2007) showed that the use of some concepts of the metaheuristic tabu could improve the performance of DE algorithm. The implementation of this optimization approach was made using a hybrid platform where the DETL method was coded using Microsoft Excel (ME). Initially, the method proposes a vector which is sent to Aspen Plus by means of dynamic data exchange (DDE). In there the separation process was rigorously simulated. For the optimization of process routes analyzed in this study, the following parameters for DETL method were used: 200 individuals, 500 generations, a tabu list of 50% of total individuals, a tabu radius of 0.0000025, 0.80 and 0.6 for crossover and mutation fractions, respectively.

3. Results

Although the three objective functions are evaluated, the obtained results are shown in Table 1. All Pareto fronts were obtained after 100,000 evaluations, as afterward, the vector of decision variables did not produce any meaningful improvement. Initially, note the pure distillation schemes present a difference of 32%. The high difference in TAC is high enough to select as the best option the direct sequence between both conventional alternatives. For such reason, since the direct alternative has been identified, only the schemes derived for that configuration are considered for optimization procedure. After the optimization process, some trends among objective function were observed. Note, in Figure 5, when the TAC is evaluated jointly IR, it is clear the competitive connection between both targets, as long as the TAC increase, the individual risk decreases and vice versa. Figure 5 also shows the antagonist behavior between the environmental impact and the individual risk associated with the conventional downstream process. It is possible to obtain process with low environmental impact, however, the probability of individual accident increase and vice versa.

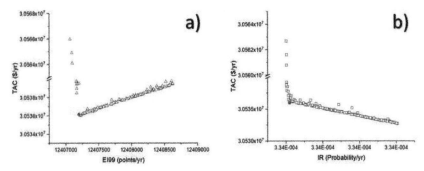

Fig. 5 Pareto fronts between EI99/TAC and TAC/IR for the intensified scheme

Table 1. Objective function values   **Table 2**. Intensified scheme 4a) parameters

Objective Function	TAC [$ y^{-1}]	EI99 [points y^{-1}]	IR [P Y^{-1}]		C1
Direct	35,032,419	14,328,558	0.0006686	Number of stages	87
Indirect	51,155,609	22,627,903	0.0006663	Reflux ratio	0.333
T Coupled	31,360,313	12,559,191	0.0006795	Feed-stage	42
T Equivalent	31,055,124	12,557,857	0.0006684	Column diameter (m)	0.675
Intensified	30,536,031	12,407,199	0.0003341	Distillate (kg h^{-1})	3,416.07
				Side stage	49
				Side flow (kmol h^{-1})	8.155
				Condenser duty (kW)	51,507
				Reboiler duty (kW)	61,457

Regarding the evaluation of TAC and IR, it is pretty interesting the reason for such reduction on this incident probability. Since IR calculation considers continuous and instantaneous chemical releases, it is clear that as long as internal flows increase, IR will increase because of the quantity of inventory inside the column increase, which it will provoke that if an accident happens the affectation and duration of the events or probability of death will be greater due to there is more mass that is source to fires, explosion, and toxic releases. This is the general tendency, however, note that for IR calculations several physicochemical properties are involved, such as heat of combustion, flammability limits and so on. With this in mind, note that the feed stream to be separated is mainly composed of water, which obviously for its physicochemical properties generates a contrary behavior. In other words, the IR increases with high internal flows (caused by high reflux o high diameters), however in this case of study for almost all sequences, the first columns separate mainly water, consequently, the internal flows are enriched with water. This amount of water solubilizes the other component to separates and its flammability and toxicity decrease.

Furthermore, at second column acetoin and 2,3-BD are separated, but at this instance, the internal flows follow the common IR behavior, because the quantity of water is fewer in comparison with the first column. In this manner, the IR calculation does not generate a proportional behavior with TAC because of this associated conflict. Finally, when is observed the tendency of EI99 evaluated jointly IR in Pareto front of Figure 5, similar behavior is observed. The internal flows play an interesting role already mentioned. However, those flows must be heated. So, in almost all alternatives, the first column separates the water and implies a significant amount of steam, impacting directly on EI99 value. However, the concentration of flammable compounds decreases. On the other hand, the last column to reduce both IR and TAC values is composed mainly by small columns, which indeed needs fewer services than the first column. Table 2 shows the main parameters of the intensified scheme.

4. Conclusions

This approach has been performed using a multi-objective optimization problem, finding through Pareto fronts the most balanced solution among all objective function, in other words, it was possible to find a solution where all objective functions reach its minimum values. Once the optimization test was applied to the proposed alternatives by a synthesis procedure, the initial results showed that between the two conventional alternatives the direct sequence is better than the indirect scheme. Derived from the direct sequence, the intensified alternatives, which separate and purify the feed stream in a single column, showed the best performance index (economic, environmental and safety) in comparison with all alternatives. It was possible to reach economic savings of about 15% in comparison with the direct sequences, a reduction of about 14% on the environmental impact and a reduction of about 50% regarding the IR. Regarding IR evaluation, it was clear the high dependence of this index with the size of the equipment, the amount of internal flows and the kind of chemical to be separated.

References

Koutinas, A. A., Yepez, B., Kopsahelis, N., Freire, D. M., de Castro, A. M., Papanikolaou, S., & Kookos, I. K. 2016. Techno-economic evaluation of a complete bioprocess for 2, 3-butanediol production from renewable resources. Bioresource technology, 204, 55-64.

Errico, M., Sanchez-Ramirez, E., Quiroz-Ramìrez, J. J., Segovia-Hernandez, J. G., & Rong, B. G. 2016. Synthesis and design of new hybrid configurations for biobutanol purification. Computers & Chemical Engineering, 84, 482-492.

Penner, D., Redepenning, C., Mitsos, A., & Viell, J. 2017. Conceptual Design of Methyl Ethyl Ketone Production via 2, 3-Butanediol for Fuels and Chemicals. Industrial & Engineering Chemistry Research, 56(14), 3947-3957.

Turton, R., Bailie, R. C., Whiting, W. B., & Shaeiwitz, J. A. 2008. Analysis, synthesis, and design of chemical processes. Pearson Education.

Medina-Herrera, N., Jiménez-Gutiérrez, A., & Mannan, M. S. 2014. Development of inherently safer distillation systems. Journal of Loss Prevention in the Process Industries, 29, 225-239.

Srinivas, M., & Rangaiah, G. P. 2007. Differential evolution with tabu list for solving nonlinear and mixed-integer nonlinear programming problems. Industrial & Engineering Chemistry Research, 46(22), 7126-7135.

Anton A. Kiss, Edwin Zondervan, Richard Lakerveld, Leyla Özkan (Eds.)
Proceedings of the 29th European Symposium on Computer Aided Process Engineering
June 16th to 19th, 2019, Eindhoven, The Netherlands. © 2019 Elsevier B.V. All rights reserved.
http://dx.doi.org/10.1016/B978-0-128-18634-3.50028-X

ORC on tour: Integrated design of dynamic ORC processes and working fluids for waste-heat recovery from heavy-duty vehicles

Dominik Tillmanns[a], Jonas Petzschmann[a], Johannes Schilling[a],
Christoph Gertig[a] and André Bardow[a,b*]

[a]*Institute of Technical Thermodynamics, Schinkelstraße 8, 52062 Aachen, Germany*

[b]*Institute of Energy and Climate Research – Energy Systems Engineering (IEK-10), Wilhelm-Johnen-Straße, 52425 Jülich, Germany*

andre.bardow@ltt.rwth-aachen.de

Abstract

Organic Rankine Cycles (ORC) convert low temperature heat into power. To maximize conversion efficiency, both ORC process and working fluid have to be tailored to the specific application. Common solution approaches for the resulting integrated design of ORC process and working fluid are limited to steady-state applications. However, for applications in dynamic settings, steady-state design approaches can lead to suboptimal solutions due to the neglect of the dynamic behavior. In this work, we present an approach for the integrated design of ORC process and working fluid considering the dynamics. The approach is based on the Continuous-Molecular Targeting–Computer-aided Molecular Design (CoMT-CAMD) framework. Herein, the physically based Perturbed-Chain Statistical Associating Fluid Theory (PC-SAFT) is used as thermodynamic model. To capture the ORC behavior under dynamic conditions, dynamic models for the ORC equipment are integrated into the process model. The result is an optimal control problem (OCP) yielding an optimal working fluid and the corresponding optimal process control for a given dynamic input. This so-called dynamic CoMT-CAMD approach is applied to an ORC for waste-heat recovery on a heavy-duty vehicle. Whereas steady-state design approaches fail, the presented approach identifies the optimal working fluid and the corresponding optimal control of the ORC process.

Keywords: CoMT-CAMD, integrated design, dynamic, PC-SAFT, Modelica

1. Introduction

Nearly 30 % of the on-road CO_2 emissions in 2014 were emitted by heavy-duty vehicles (HDV) in the European Union (Muncrief and Sharpe, 2015). CO_2 emissions of HDVs can be decreased by reducing their fuel consumption. To reduce the fuel consumption of HDVs, the exhaust gas waste heat of the engine can be transformed into mechanical power by an Organic Rankine Cycle (ORC). An ORC improves the compliance with future CO_2-regulations and the total cost of ownership (TCO) (Eichler et al., 2015). However, ORCs on HDVs have high investment costs and low power output due to low conversion efficiencies. To maximize conversion efficiency and thus render ORCs profitable, a tailor-made ORC is needed. To tailor an ORC, working fluid design has to be integrated into process optimization (Gani, 2004). To solve the resulting large-scale mixed-integer nonlinear program (MINLP), many solution approaches have been developed as recently reviewed by Papadopoulos et al. (2018). In our previous work, we developed the Continuous-Molecular Targeting – Computer-Aided Molecular Design (CoMT-CAMD) approach for the integrated design of processes and molecules (Bardow et al., 2010; Lampe et al., 2015). In CoMT-CAMD, the physically-based Perturbed-Chain Statistical Associating Fluid Theory (PC-SAFT) is used as thermodynamic model (Gross and Sadowski, 2001). In the first stage of CoMT-CAMD (CoMT stage), the discrete pure component parameters representing a working fluid in PC-SAFT are relaxed to identify a hypothetical optimal working fluid, the so-called target. In the second stage (Structure-Mapping stage), a second-order Taylor approximation around the target and a CAMD formulation are used to identify real working fluids in a mixed-integer quadratic program (MIQP).

So far, CoMT-CAMD and other integrated design approaches are limited to steady-state input. However, for ORCs on HDVs, the exhaust gas waste heat shows dynamic behavior resulting in transient temperature and mass flow rates of the ORC heat source. The design of ORC processes with dynamic heat sources leads to large-scale dynamic optimization problems (Huster et al., 2018). However, the optimal working fluid also depends on temperature and mass flow of the heat source (Colonna et al., 2015) as well as the control strategy for the ORC (Zarogiannis et al., 2017). Thus, a steady-state design point is not sufficient for working fluid design, and the process dynamics has to be considered within the integrated design to capture all process-related trade-offs.

In this work, we present the dynamic CoMT-CAMD approach for the integrated design of dynamic processes and fluids. For this purpose, dynamic models for the equipment are integrated into the process model of CoMT-CAMD leading to an optimal control problem (OCP). The solution of dynamic CoMT-CAMD is an optimal working fluid and the corresponding optimal process for a given dynamic input.

2. Dynamic CoMT-CAMD

The CoMT-CAMD approach was developed for the integrated design of steady-state applications (Bardow et al., 2010; Lampe et al., 2015). In this work, we extend the CoMT-CAMD approach to applications with dynamic inputs. For this purpose, dynamic models for the equipment are integrated into the process model to capture the dynamic behavior. Thereby, the original MINLP of the integrated design is transformed into a large-scale mixed–integer optimal control programming (MIOCP) problem. To efficiently solve this problem, we split the MIOCP into an optimal control problem (OCP) (CoMT stage, see section 2.1) and an MIQP (Structure-Mapping stage, see section 2.2) according to the idea of the original CoMT-CAMD approach (Figure 1). Finally, the identified working fluids are assessed by individual dynamic process optimizations (see section 2.3).

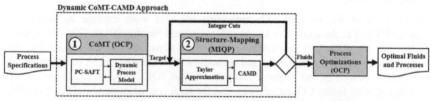

Figure 1: Workflow of the dynamic CoMT-CAMD approach

2.1. Continuous-molecular targeting (CoMT)

A working fluid is described by a set of pure component parameters in PC-SAFT. In the first stage, the CoMT stage, these discrete pure component parameters representing the working fluid are relaxed to transform the MIOCP into an OCP given by:

$$\max_{x(t),u(t),p_{pr},p_{wf}} \tilde{f} = \int_{t_0}^{t_1} f\big(x(t),u(t),p_{pr},\theta(t)\big)dt \qquad \text{objective}$$

$$s.t. \quad \dot{x}(t) = k(x(t),u(t),p_{pr},\theta(t))$$
$$g_1\big(x(t),u(t),p_{pr},\theta(t)\big) = 0$$
$$g_2\big(x(t),u(t),p_{pr},\theta(t)\big) \le 0 \qquad \left.\right\} \quad \text{DAE process model}$$
$$\theta(t) = h\big(x(t),u(t),p_{pr},p_{wf}\big) \qquad \text{PC-SAFT} \qquad (1)$$
$$x_{min} \le x(t) \le x_{max} \qquad \text{dynamic states}$$
$$u_{min} \le u(t) \le u_{max} \qquad \text{input signals}$$
$$p_{pr,min} \le p_{pr}(t) \le p_{pr,max} \qquad \text{process parameters}$$
$$p_{wf,min} \le p_{wf}(t) \le p_{wf,max} \qquad \text{working fluid}$$

Herein, the objective function $\tilde{f}$ (e.g., the mean net power output) depends on dynamic states $x(t)$ (e.g., time-dependent temperatures), input signals $u(t)$ (e.g., time-dependent control of the pump), process parameters p_{pr} (e.g., nominal pressure levels) and equilibrium properties of the working fluid $\theta(t)$ (e.g., enthalpies). The process model consists of a system of differential equations for the dynamic states $\dot{x}(t)$ (e.g. energy balances), equality constraints g_1 (e.g. isentropic efficiencies) and inequality constraints g_2 (e.g., pressure limits). The equilibrium properties of the working fluid $\theta(t)$ are calculated using the PC-SAFT equation of state h.

The result of the CoMT stage in problem 1 is a hypothetical optimal working fluid, the so-called target, and the corresponding optimal control of the process. The target is characterized by its optimal pure component parameters p_{wf}^*, the optimal objective function value $\tilde{f}^*$ and the derivatives of $\tilde{f}$ at the target.

To reduce the programming effort for the development of new processes, the process model is implemented in Modelica enabling easy drag-and-drop flowsheeting and the use of existing model libraries. The OCP in problem 1 is typically solved within hours using the multiple shooting algorithm MUSCOD-II (Leineweber et al., 2003).

2.2. Structure-Mapping using Computer-aided molecular design (CAMD)

In the second stage, the Structure-Mapping stage, a second-order Taylor-approximation around the target $\hat{f}$ is used to estimate the objective function value $\tilde{f}$ of real working fluids. To design molecular structures with a performance closest to the target in the resulting MIQP, a computer-aided molecular design (CAMD) formulation is used:

$$\max_n \hat{f}(p_{wf}) = \tilde{f}(p_{wf}^*) + \frac{\partial \tilde{f}}{\partial p_{wf}}\Big|_{p_{wf}=p_{wf}^*}(p_{wf}-p_{wf}^*) + \frac{1}{2}(p_{wf}-p_{wf}^*)^T \frac{\partial^2 \tilde{f}}{\partial p_{wf}^2}\Big|_{p_{wf}=p_{wf}^*}(p_{wf}-p_{wf}^*)$$

$$s.t. \quad k(n) = p_{wf} \qquad \text{group contribution method} \qquad (2)$$
$$n \in \mathbb{Z} \qquad \text{molecular structure}$$

Herein, the objective function $\hat{f}$ is the second-order Taylor approximation around the target $\tilde{f}^* = \tilde{f}(p_{wf}^*)$. The homosegmented group-contribution (GC) method for PC-SAFT (Sauer et al., 2014) is used to predict the pure component parameters of PC-SAFT p_{wf} from the molecular structure of the working fluid n. Here, the vector n contains the number of functional groups constituting the molecular structure of the working fluid. In this work, we consider the following non-polar, non-associating functional groups: -CH$_3$, -CH$_2$-, >CH-, >C< for alkanes, =CH$_2$, =CH-, >C= for alkenes, -C≡CH for 1-alkynes,

-CH^{Arom}=, >C^{Arom}= for aromatic compounds, -CH$_2$^{Hex}-, >CH^{Hex}- for branched cyclohexanes and -CH$_2$^{Pent}-, >CH^{Pent}- for branched cyclopentanes.

To overcome shortcomings of the Taylor approximation, a ranking of working fluids is calculated. For this purpose, the MIQP in problem 2 is solved repeatedly using integer cuts (Grossmann and Kravanja, 1995) to exclude previous solutions from the design space. The result of the Structure-Mapping stage is a ranking of optimal working fluids based on the Taylor approximation. The MIQP in problem 2 is typically solved within a few seconds using the software GAMS.

2.3. Final process optimization

Finally, to overcome shortcomings of the Taylor approximation, the working fluids identified in the Structure-Mapping stage are individually optimized using the dynamic process model of the CoMT stage. Thereby, we obtain a more accurate objective function value $\tilde{f}$ for the promising working fluids and the corresponding optimal control of the ORC process. The final optimal control problems are also solved with MUSCOD-II as for the CoMT stage.

3. Case study

3.1. Specifications

The presented dynamic CoMT-CAMD approach is applied to the integrated design of an ORC for waste heat recovery from heavy-duty vehicles based on Eichler et al. (2015) (see figure 2). The dynamic heat input of the ORC is characterized by time series for the temperature and mass flow of the exhaust gas after the exhaust gas after-treatment. We approximate these time series by sine waves with mean values and amplitudes based on time series from Dünnebeil et al. (2015). We assume cyclic steady-state constraints and thus only one sine wave of the slowest oscillating profile is needed to represent the full time series.

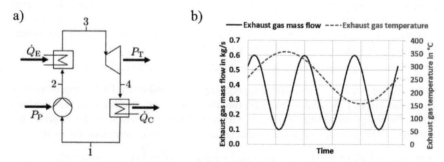

Figure 2: ORC process in (a) flowsheet and (b) temperature and mass flow of the exhaust gas after exhaust gas after-treatment.

The mean net power output of the ORC $\overline{P}$ is considered as objective $\tilde{f} = \overline{P} = \frac{1}{t_f - t_0} \int_{t_0}^{t_f} P(x(t), u(t), p_{Pr}, \theta(t)) \, dt$ in problem 1.

To react to the dynamic input of the ORC, the pump can be used to control the ORC process. For this purpose, the pump is modelled using affinity laws (Calise et al., 2015). The inertia of the pump is captured by a first-order lag element with a time constant $\tau_P = 1$ s (Esposito et al., 2015; Quoilin, 2011). An isentropic pump efficiency of $\eta_{P,s} = 0.5$ is assumed. For the evaporator, we use a 0-D model based on Peralez et al. (2015) that assumes a homogeneous temperature of the heat exchanger wall T_W. The mass of the heat exchanger wall mass is $m_W = 13$ kg. The expander is modelled by assuming a constant isentropic efficiency of $\eta_{E,s} = 0.7$. In the condenser, we assume a minimal approach temperature of $\Delta T_{min} = 20$ K and for the cooling water, an inlet temperature of $T_{CW,in} = 75\,°C$ and an outlet temperature of $T_{CW,out} = 80\,°C$. For this case study, the dynamic states $x(t) = (T_W, n_{rel})^T$ are the temperature of the evaporator heat exchanger wall T_W and the relative rotational speed of the pump n_{rel} calculated as the ratio of the rotational speed n and the nominal rotational speed n_N. The input signal $u(t)$ is the control variable of the nominal speed of the pump. The process parameters $p_{Pr} = (p_{l,N}^{red}, p_{u,N}^{red}, \dot{m}_N)^T$ are the nominal mass flow rate of the working fluid $\dot{m}_N$, the nominal lower reduced pressure level $p_{l,N}^{red}$ and the nominal upper reduced pressure level $p_{u,N}^{red}$. Additionally, limits on the absolute pressure levels $p_{min} = 1$ bar and $p_{max} = 35$ bar are assumed. Furthermore, a maximal number of functional groups per working fluid of $n_{max} = 25$ is considered in the CAMD problem.

3.2. Results

Dynamic CoMT-CAMD is applied to the integrated design of the described ORC. In this case study, the target has a mean net power output $\bar{P} = 3.20$ kW (see table 1).

All working fluids of the top 5 working fluids identified in the Structure-Mapping stage are short-chained alkanes, alkenes or alkynes. The best 2 working fluids consist of 5 carbon atoms and have an unstable triple bond. Thus, these working fluids would probably not be used in ORC applications. The following 3 working fluids consist of 4 carbon atoms and have just single or double bonds, which are more stable than triple bonds. The best identified working fluid without triple bond is isobutane with $\bar{P} = 1.77$ kW, which is 45 % lower than the mean net power output of the target and 37 % lower than the best working fluid with triple bond, 3-methyl-1-butyne. For isobutane, the net power varies between $P_{min} = 0.44$ kW and $P_{max} = 3.49$ kW during one cycle.

The results are compared to the integrated design based on a steady-state input calculated as the mean value of the temperature and mass flow of the dynamic heat source (cf. figure 2b). The steady-state design overestimates the mean net power output of isobutane by 20 %. For 1-butene and isobutene the net power output is overestimated by 23 % and 30 %, respectively. Thus, a steady-state design point is not sufficient for the selection of the optimal working fluid for dynamic ORC applications. Instead, the integrated design based on a dynamic process model is required, which is enabled by the presented dynamic CoMT-CAMD approach.

Table 1: The mean net power output of the target and top 5 identified working fluids.

Rank	Name	$\bar{P}$ / kW
Target	-	3.20
1	3-Methyl-1-butyne	2.79
2	1-Pentyne	2.66
3	Isobutane	1.77
4	1-Butene	1.66
5	Isobutene	1.54

4. Conclusions

The dynamic CoMT-CAMD approach is presented for the integrated design of molecules and processes with dynamic input such as ORCs for waste heat recovery on HDVs. The underlying CoMT-CAMD approach was limited to steady-state applications. This limitation is overcome in the presented dynamic CoMT-CAMD approach by using dynamic models for the ORC equipment in Modelica. MUSCOD-II is used in the CoMT stage to identify a hypothetical optimal working fluid in the resulting optimal control problem. Subsequently, a CAMD algorithm is used to identify real working fluids with a performance closest to the hypothetical optimum.

The resulting dynamic CoMT-CAMD approach is successfully applied to the design of an ORC for waste heat recovery on an HDV. Here, isobutane is identified as optimal stable working fluid for the dynamic application. In comparison, the integrated design based on a steady-state input calculated as the mean value of the temperature and mass flow of the dynamic heat source overestimates the mean net power output of the top 5 identified working fluids by up to 30 %. Therefore, the integrated design based on a dynamic process model is required, which is enabled by the presented dynamic CoMT-CAMD approach.

Acknowledgements

We thank the Deutsche Forschungsgemeinschaft (DFG) for funding this work (BA2884/4-2).

References

Bardow A, Steur K, Gross J. Continuous-Molecular Targeting for Integrated Solvent and Process Design. Ind. Eng. Chem. Res. 2010;49(6):2834–40.

Calise F, d'Accadia MD, Vicidomini M, Scarpellino M. Design and simulation of a prototype of a small-scale solar CHP system based on evacuated flat-plate solar collectors and Organic Rankine Cycle. Energy Conversion and Management 2015;90:347–63.

Colonna P, Casati E, Trapp C, Mathijssen T, Larjola J, Turunen-Saaresti T, et al. Organic Rankine Cycle Power Systems: From the Concept to Current Technology, Applications, and an Outlook to the Future. J. Eng. Gas Turbines Power 2015;137(10):100801.

Dünnebeil F, Reinhard C, Lambrecht U, Kies A, Hausberger S, Rexeis M. Future measures for fuel savings and GHG reduction of heavy-duty vehicles. Federal Environment Agency (Germany), Nr. 32; 2015.

Eichler K, Jeihouni Y, Ritterskamp C. Fuel Economy Benefits for Commercial Diesel Engines with Waste Heat Recovery. SAE Int. J. Commer. Veh. 2015;8(2):491–505.

Esposito MC, Pompini N, Gambarotta A, Chandrasekaran V, Zhou J, Canova M. Nonlinear Model Predictive Control of an Organic Rankine Cycle for Exhaust Waste Heat Recovery in Automotive Engines. IFAC-PapersOnLine 2015;48(15):411–8.

Gani R. Chemical product design: Challenges and opportunities. Comput. Chem. Eng. 2004;28(12):2441–57.

Gross J, Sadowski G. Perturbed-Chain SAFT: An Equation of State Based on a Perturbation Theory for Chain Molecules. Ind. Eng. Chem. Res. 2001;40(4):1244–60.

Huster WR, Vaupel Y, Mhamdi A, Mitsos A. Validated dynamic model of an organic Rankine cycle (ORC) for waste heat recovery in a diesel truck. Energy 2018;151:647–61.

Lampe M, Stavrou M, Schilling J, Sauer E, Gross J, Bardow A. Computer-aided molecular design in the continuous-molecular targeting framework using group-contribution PC-SAFT. Comput. Chem. Eng. 2015;81:278–87.

Leineweber DB, Schäfer A, Bock HG, Schlöder JP. An efficient multiple shooting based reduced SQP strategy for large-scale dynamic process optimization. Computers & Chemical Engineering 2003;27(2):167–74.

Muncrief R, Sharpe B. Overview of the heavy-duty vehicle market and CO2 emissions in the European Union. Washington, DC: The International Council on Clean Transportation 2015.

Papadopoulos AI, Tsivintzelis I, Linke P, Seferlis P. Computer-Aided Molecular Design: Fundamentals, Methods, and Applications. In: Reedijk J, editor. Reference module in chemistry, molecular sciences and chemical engineering: Elsevier; 2018.

Peralez J, Tona P, Nadri M, Dufour P, Sciarretta A. Optimal control for an organic rankine cycle on board a diesel-electric railcar. Journal of Process Control 2015;33:1–13.

Sauer E, Stavrou M, Gross J. Comparison between a Homo- and a Heterosegmented Group Contribution Approach Based on the Perturbed-Chain Polar Statistical Associating Fluid Theory Equation of State. Ind. Eng. Chem. Res. 2014;53(38):14854–64.

Zarogiannis T, Papadopoulos A, Seferlis P, Linke P. The Impact of Novel and Conventional Working Fluids on the Control Performance in Organic Rankine Cycles. Comput. Aided Chem. Eng. 2017;40:2443–48.

Anton A. Kiss, Edwin Zondervan, Richard Lakerveld, Leyla Özkan (Eds.)
Proceedings of the 29th European Symposium on Computer Aided Process Engineering
June 16th to 19th, 2019, Eindhoven, The Netherlands. © 2019 Elsevier B.V. All rights reserved.
http://dx.doi.org/10.1016/B978-0-128-18634-3.50029-1

Optimisation of multi effect distillation based desalination system for minimum production cost for freshwater

O.M.A.Al-hotmani[a], M. A. Al-Obaidi[a, b], G. Filippini[c], F. Manenti[c], R.Patel[a], and I. M. Mujtaba[a,*]

[a] Department of Chemical Engineering, Faculty of Engineering and Informatics. University of Bradford. Bradford, West Yorkshire BD7 1DP, UK

[b] Middle Technical University, Technical Institute of Baquba, Dayala – Iraq

c Chemical Engineering Department, Politecnico di Milano, Milan, Italy

I.M.Mujtaba@bradford.ac.uk

Abstract

The multi effect distillation (MED) process has been extensively used for seawater desalination as a prominent process to produce high quality freshwater. However, the impact of number of effects in the MED process-based seawater desalination on the fresh water production cost has not been critically evaluated in the literature. Therefore, the aim of this study is to resolve this particular challenge via the simulation for a given seawater concentration and temperature conditions. The simulation is carried out using a comprehensive MED process model coupled with appropriate cost functions within gPROMS model builder software. The simulation results show that selecting the optimal number of the MED effects as 17 is important to achieve the lowest fresh water production cost for a given seawater operating conditions.

Keywords: Seawater desalination, MED process, Simulation, Fresh water production cost.

1. Introduction

The Multi Effect Distillation (MED) process is the oldest technique for seawater desalination and was first reported back in the middle of the 19th century. Essentially, the thermal and membrane processes are considered as the main adopted technologies used for seawater desalination. These technologies are employed to overcome the scarcity of fresh water due to restricted available resources (Sadri et al., 2017). Specifically, the thermal process characterises by using heat to evaporate and distil the seawater. However, massive research efforts need to be paid to improve the system's efficiency and decrease the fresh water production cost. In this respect, the main concern of thermal process is to improve the steam economy and specifically the Gained Output Ratio GOR (defined as the ratio of the produced distilled water in kilograms to steam consumed in kilograms) (Darwish and AL-Juwayhel, 2006). Recently, MED process gained more attention than other thermal processes (such as Multi Stage Flash, MSF) due to its high effectiveness, straightforward operation and maintenance and feasible economic characteristics. Ettouney and El-Dessouky (1999) stated that the thermal desalination processes, in particular MED process is the more significant method for desalting seawater to obtain conductivity in very low level, which has a strong impact in power plant. More specifically, the MED process becomes a superior desalination processes due to its low specific energy consumption (Darwish and Abdulrahim, 2008) and low top brine temperature which ranges between 60 – 70 °C (Al-Sahali and Ettouney, 2007). Therefore, it is not surprised to notice that about 65% of the total capacity of production in the desalination industry is attributed to the thermal desalination including the MED process. Up to the authors' knowledge, the research on MED process is still required to alleviate the fresh water production cost by enhancing the performance efficiency besides keeping high-quality water. Specifically, the optimal number of effects in the MED process-based seawater desalination that attains the lowest fresh water production cost via model-based simulation has not been yet explored. Therefore, this research focuses on the implementation of an earlier model developed by the authors for MED process and an economic model gathered from the literature to investigate the optimal number of effects which can attain the lowest fresh water production cost for specified sweater operating conditions.

2. MED process model

Figure 1 shows the MED process that involves of a number of effects. External heat is used to rise the brine temperature within the first stage in order to evaporate the brine. The vapour from each stage supplies energies to the brine in subsequent stages. MED process is typically designed at different capacity that vary from 600 to 30,000 m³/day, and the design is made according to two main arrangements: (a) the seawater boils in a vertical tube in a thin film flowing within the tube and vapour condensate on the heat-transfer tubes (b) the horizontal tube where the seawater feed is sprayed onto the outside surface of the tubes and vapour flows inside the horizontal tubes, which is condensed to produce the water. Table 1 shows the process model taken from our earlier work (Filippini et al., 2018)

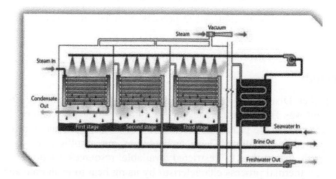

Figure 1. Schematic diagram of MED process (Adapted from Alkaraghouli, 2013)

3. Economic model of MED process

The economic model developed by Druetta et al. (2014) and given in Table 2 was used to calculate the total production cost for MED process. In this respect, Table 3 presents the parameters used in the economic model of MED process. In this respect, the fresh water production cost is the division of total annual production cost and the total annual productivity of MED process. Specifically, for any seawater thermal desalination process, the total annual cost (TAC) is the sum of the total capital cost (TCC) and annual operational cost (AOC). Principally, the total capital cost comprises the installation, equipment, and indirect costs. However, some other related costs such as the steam cost, chemicals cost, labour, etc. are listed in the operational and maintenance cost.

Table 1. The model equations of MED process (Filippini et at. 2018)

No.	Title	Unit	Equation
1	Temperature drop among effects first attempt	(°C)	$\Delta T = \frac{T1-Tb}{n-1}$ or $\Delta T = \frac{Ts-Tb}{n}$
2	Temperature drop among pre-heaters first attempt	(°C)	$\Delta T = \Delta t$
3	Mean temperature in the plant	(°C)	$T_{mean} = \frac{T1 + Tb}{2}$
4	Mean salinity	(ppm)	$x_{mean} = \frac{xf + xb}{2}$
5	Fraction of flashed distillate	(-)	$\propto = \frac{cp(T_{mean}, x_{mean})\Delta T}{\lambda(T_{mean})}$
6	Fraction of total distillate boiled in each evaporator	(-)	$\beta = \frac{\alpha[xb(1-\alpha)^n - xf]}{(xb - xf)[1-(1-\alpha)^n]}$
7	Heat load in i-th effect	(kJ/s)	$Qi = D_{boiled,i-1}\lambda(Tv_{i-1})$
8	Sensible heat used in first effect	(kJ/kg)	$Q_{sensible} = Mf \int_{t1}^{T1} cp(T1, x1)dT$
9	Feed flowrate	(kJ/s)	$Mf = \frac{Ms\,\lambda(Ts)}{Q_{sensible} + Q_{latent}}$
10	Latent heat in first effect	(kJ/s)	$Q_{latent} = D1\lambda(Tv1)$
11	Rejected brine flowrate	(kg/s)	$Mb = Mf - Md$
12	Feed flow rate	(kg/s)	$Mf = Md\frac{xb - xf}{xb}$
13	Distillate produced by boiling in i-th evaporator	(kg/s)	$D_{boiled,i} = \beta Md$
14	Total distillate produced in i-th effect	(kg/s)	$D_i = D_{boiled,i} + D_{flash,i}$
15	Brine rejected in the i-th effect	(kg/s)	$B_i = B_{i-1} - D_i$
16	Mean salinity in the plant	(ppm or w/w%)	$x_i = \frac{x_{i-1}B_{i-1}}{B_i}$
17	Feed temperature in first effect	(°C)	$t1 = tn + (n-1)\Delta t$
18	Temperature of the vapour phase in i-th effect	(°C)	$Tv = T - BPE(T, x)$
19	Driving force for heat exchange in i-th pre-heater	(°C)	$\Delta t_{log,i} = \frac{\Delta t}{\log(\frac{Tv_i - t_{i+1}}{Tv_i - t_i})}$
20	Gained Output Ratio	(-)	$GOR = \frac{Md}{Ms}$
21	Performance Ratio	(-)	$PR = GOR\frac{2330\ kJ/kg}{\lambda(Ts)}$
22	Specific total area	(m² s/kg)	$Atot_s = \frac{Atot}{Md}$
23	Specific seawater intake	(-)	$Mw_s = \frac{Mw}{Md}$
24	Area of i-th effect	(m²)	$A_{ev,mean} = \frac{Q_I}{U_{ev,i}\,\Delta T_{ex,i}}$

Table 2. The economic model of Druetta et al. (2014)

No.	Title	Unit	Equation
1	Total Capital cost	($)	$TCC = CAPEX_{dir} + CAPEX_{indir}$
2	Indirect CAPEX	($)	$CAPEX_{indir} = 025 CAPEX_{dir}$
3	Civil work cost	($)	$CAPEX_{civil\_work} = 0.15 CAPEX_{equipment}$
4	MED process cost	($)	$C_{med} = K_{MED} C_{mat\_MED} A_{MED}^{0.64}$
5	Fresh water production cost	($/m³)	$FWC_{MED} = \frac{TAC}{M_{fresh,MED} THY (3600)}$
6	Annual operating cost	($/yr)	$AOC = AOC_{chem} + AOC_{lab} AOC_{pow} + AOC_{man} + AOC_{steam}$
7	Seawater intake and pre-treatment cost	($)	$C_{intake} = \frac{K_{intake} 243600 M_{seawater,MED}}{2a}$
8	Capital recovery factor	(1/yr)	$CAF = \frac{Ir(1 + Ir)^{lift}}{(1 + Ir)^{lift}\_1}$
9	Cost of human labor	($/yr)	$AOC_{lab} = \frac{C_{lab} THY 3600 M_{fresh,MED}}{\rho}$
10	Cost of manutention	($/yr)	$AOC_{man} = 0.002 TCC$
11	Cost of external steam	($/yr)	$AOC_{steam} = \frac{C_{steam} THY (Ts-40) M_{steam}}{80} + 0.005 TCC$
12	Total Annual Cost	($/yr)	$TAC = AOC + CRF \times TCC$
13	Equipment cost	($)	$CAPEX_{equipment} = C_{intake} + C_{MED} + C_{cond}$
14	Direct CAPEX	($)	$CAPEX_{dir} = CAPEX_{equipment} + CAPEX_{civil\_work}$
15	Cost of power for pumps	$/yr	$AOC_{POW} = \frac{C_{pow} THY 100 M_{fresh,MED}}{\rho\mu} f(\Delta P)$
16	Final condenser cost	($)	$C_{cond} = K_{cond} C_{cond} C_{mat\_cond} A_{cond}^{0.8}$
17	Cost of chemical treatment	($/yr)	$AOC_{chem} = \frac{C_{chem} THY 3600 M_{seawater,MED}}{\rho}$

Table 3. Parameters used in the economic model of MED process (Al-Obaidi et al., 2019)

Parameter	Description	Value	Unit	Parameter	Description	Value	Unit
$C_{mat-MED}$	Material of MED process	3644	($/m²)	K_{MED}	Coeff. for MED process	1.4	-
Ir	Interest rate	0.07	(-)	C_{Lab}	Labour	0.05	($/m³)
$C_{mat-cond}$	Material of condenser	500	($/m²)	THY	Total hour per year	8760	(hr/yr)
$f(\Delta P)$	Pressure losses	3571	(-)	C_{chem}	Chemical treatment	0.024	($/m³)
μ	Efficiency of power generation	0.75	(-)	C_{pow}	Power	0.09	($/kWh)
life	Life of the plant	25	(year)	K_{intake}	Seawater intake	50	$ day/m³
C_{steam}	External steam	0.004	($/kg)	K_{cond}	Coeff. for condenser	2.8	-

4. Simulation of the MED Process

The simulation of the MED process is carried out at specified seawater conditions of feed concentration and temperature of 39000 ppm and 25 °C, respectively. Moreover, Steam flow rate Ms and steam temperature Ts are assumed to be known as 8 (kg/s) and 70 (°C), respectively. The case study analysed in this paper corresponds the desalination plants installed in Gulf regions with somehow high seawater salinity. Figure 2 (a) shows the fresh water production cost ($/m³) against the number of effects in MED process. This in turn showed that the optimum number of effects of 17 has entailed the lowest fresh water production cost for seawater desalination at the selected seawater operating conditions. Specifically, the lowest fresh water production cost is around 0.615 $/m³. Interestingly, the fresh water production cost exponentially decreases with number of effects below 17. However, a slow progress in the fresh water production cost is observed as a result to increasing number of effects up to 17. Also, the simulation results of the Figure 2 (b) shows that the total annual cost is increased with increasing the number of effects. Basically, this is attributed to increasing both capital costs (from 5118362.5 $ to 19055098 $) and operating costs (from 862693.1 $/yr to 1190574 $/yr) as a result to increasing the number of effects from 8 to 20 in the MED process. Therefore, the minimum fresh water production cost observed in Figure 2 (a) can be ascribed to the progress of distillate flow rate that rapidly increased as a result to increasing number of effects. This in turn causes a rapid decrease in fresh water production cost despite the increase of total annual cost (Eq. (5) presented in Table 2). However, the increase of distillate flow rate beyond 17 effects was insignificant compared to a continuous increase in the total annual cost, which in turn results in a slow increase in the fresh water production cost (Figure 2 (a)). Figure 2 (c) shows the improvement in Gained Output Ratio (GOR) due to increasing number of effects. GOR value raised to its optimum of 17.06 as the number of effects hits 20. However, GOR alone cannot be the unique tool to measure the performance of thermal process as it does not account the impact of capital and other operating costs (such as pumping etc.). More important, the minimum fresh water production cost corresponds to an optimum GOR of 14.5 at 17 effects.

5. Conclusions

In this paper, an earlier model developed by the authors for multi effects desalination MED process was coupled with cost model to estimate the fresh water production cost under different number of effects and fixed seawater operating conditions. The cost model accounts for both capital and operating costs (such as steam, pumping, etc). The optimum number of effects was investigated via repetitive simulation, which illustrates the lowest fresh water production cost for seawater desalination. In this research, the optimum number of effects was obtained to be 17 with the corresponding minimum cost of 0.614 $/m³. In this respect, the optimum GOR has been discovered for the optimum design. This current research can be used as a powerful tool to design the MED process and specially to address the optimum number of effects for any specified seawater operating conditions. It is fair to realise the insignificant implementation of the current methodology for an already instilled MED plant. Therefore, a comprehensive simulation-based optimisation methodology needs to be explored to investigate the optimal seawater operating conditions and steam flow rate that minimises the fresh water production cost for a fixed number of effects. This would be an interesting scope of the future research.

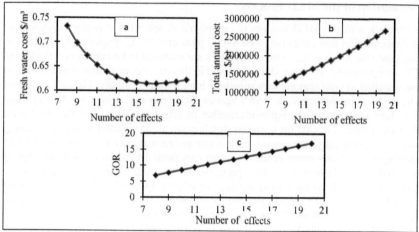

Figure 2. (a) Fresh water cost against number of effects (b) Total annual cost against number of effects (c) Gained output ratio against number of effects

References

Al-Sahali M., Ettouney H., 2007. Developments in thermal desalination processes: Design, energy, and costing aspects. Desalination, 214, 227–240.

Al-Obaidi M.A., Filippini G., Manenti F., Mujtaba I. M., 2019. Cost evaluation and optimisation of hybrid multi effect distillation and reverse osmosis system for seawater desalination. Desalination, 456, 136–149.

Al-Karaghouli, A. and Kazmerski, L.L., 2013. Energy consumption and water production cost of conventional and renewable-energy-powered desalination processes. Renewable and Sustainable Energy Reviews, 24, pp.343-356.

Darwish M.A., Al-Juwayhel F., Abdulraheim H.K., 2006. Multi-effect boiling systems from an energy viewpoint. Desalination, 194, 22–39

Darwish M.A., Abdulrahim H.K. 2008. Feed water arrangements in a multi-effect desalting system. Desalination, 228, 30–54.

Druetta P., Aguirre P., Mussati S., 2014. Minimizing the total cost of multi effect evaporation systems for seawater desalination. Desalination, 344, 431–445.

Ettouney H.M., El-Dessouky H., 1999. A simulator for thermal desalination process. Desalination, 125, 277–291.

Filipini G., Al-Obaidi M.A., Manenti F., Mujtaba I.M., 2018. Performance analysis of hybrid system of multi effect distillation and reverse osmosis for seawater desalination via modeling and simulation. Desalination, 448, 21–35.

Anton A. Kiss, Edwin Zondervan, Richard Lakerveld, Leyla Özkan (Eds.)
Proceedings of the 29th European Symposium on Computer Aided Process Engineering
June 16th to 19th, 2019, Eindhoven, The Netherlands. © 2019 Elsevier B.V. All rights reserved.
http://dx.doi.org/10.1016/B978-0-128-18634-3.50030-8

A model-based approach for optimizing petroleum refinery configuration for heavy oil processing

Cheng Seong Khor,[a*]Tareq A. Albahri,[b]Ali Elkamel[c,d]

[a]*Chemical Engineering Department, Universiti Teknologi PETRONAS, 32610 Seri Iskandar, Perak Darul Ridzuan, Malaysia*

[b]*Chemical Engineering Department, Kuwait University, P.O. Box 5969, Safat 13060, Kuwait*

[c]*Department of Chemical Engineering, University of Waterloo, Waterloo, ON N2L 3G1, Canada*

[d]*Department of Chemical Engineering, Khalifa University, The Petroleum Institute, Abu Dhabi United Arab Emirates*

chengseong.khor@utp.edu.my, khorchengseong@gmail.com

Abstract

This work presents a model-based optimization approach to determine the configuration of a petroleum refinery for a new (grassroots) or an existing site for heavy oil processing of atmospheric distillation unit residue. We develop a high-level superstructure representation for the refinery configuration that encompass many possible alternatives comprising the technologies and their interconnections. The superstructure is postulated by decomposing it to include representative heavy oil processing scheme alternatives that center on the technologies for atmospheric residual hydrodesulfurization (ARDS), vacuum residual hydrodesulfurization (VRDS), and residual fluid catalytic cracking (RFCC). We formulate a mixed-integer nonlinear optimization model (MINLP) appended with logic propositions devised from experience and heuristics to aid solution convergence. Implementation on a case study of Kuwaiti refineries demonstrate the applicability and practicality of the proposed approach when validated against existing real-world refinery configurations.

Keywords: petroleum refinery configuration, heavy oil, mixed-integer linear programming, superstructure; logic propositions

1. Introduction

An important aspect of process synthesis and design is to identify the best flowsheet structure that performs a specific task while achieving a set of objectives, which mainly involve maximizing profit or minimizing cost and/or environmental emissions. Within this scope, the task complexity entailed in determining an optimal refinery configuration requires developing systematic approaches that can rigorously consider the interactions among numerous process variables and tradeoffs involving multiple possibly conflicting design objectives. In the literature, three available approaches for process synthesis are heuristic methods, pinch analysis, and optimization for which optimization allows developing decision making tools that can handle the complexities mentioned (Khor and Elkamel, 2010).

In the last decade, the superstructure-based mixed-integer nonlinear programming (MINLP) optimization approach has been proposed for synthesizing biorefinery or biomass-based processes. Zondervan et al. (2011) presents an MINLP based on the transshipment model to determine optimal processing routes to produce fossil fuel substitute chemicals for gasoline blending. The model considers individual objectives for yield maximization and waste minimization besides conventional economic cost functions. Quaglia et al. (2015) extends the superstructure-based MINLP methodology with systematic data management. A simultaneous economic and environmental-based multiobjective MINLP model derived from a large scale superstructure is proposed by del Rio-Chanona et al. (2017). A recent review of this area is offered by Cremaschi (2015).

The present work attempts to contribute by demonstrating the applicability of a MINLP model for large scale grassroots refinery configuration synthesis using a common business tool (Excel). The formulation considers rigorous process models with nonlinearities representative of major commercial refining technologies in terms of material balances, product yields and qualities, and costs. The model is implemented on an industrial case study of Kuwaiti refineries with the results validated against existing real-world refinery configurations to elucidate the practicality of the approach.

2. Problem statement

We consider the structural optimization problem to devise a petroleum refinery configuration. Given the following data is available: amount, properties, and cost of a mixture of crude oils (petroleum) as raw materials; a set of refining process units with known processing or throughput capacities and capital and operating costs; and amount and properties or qualities of a set of refining products. Our goal is to determine an optimal configuration by computing the continuous variables on material stream component flowrates (denoted by F_i for each component i) and the binary variables on selecting and sequencing the process units that satisfy an objective to minimize the total refinery cost (denoted by U_k for each unit k).

3. Superstructure representation

In the superstructure representation in Figure 1, crude oil is separated by a crude oil distillation unit (CDU) into gases, naphtha, kerosene, diesel, and atmospheric residue. CDU products are usually high in sulfur (also called sour products) and require treatment. The sour gas is typically treated for sulfur removal using a gas treating unit (GAS) and amine treating unit (AMN). The recovered hydrogen sulfide gas is converted to sulfur in the sulfur recovery unit (SULF). Straight run naphtha, kerosene, and diesel are hydrotreated in separate catalytic hydrotreaters (NHT, DHT, and KHT, respectively) to lower the amount of sulfur and other objectionable materials to meet environmental regulations for sale. Hydrotreated naphtha is typically separated into light and heavy naphtha using naphtha splitter (NAPS). Heavy naphtha is upgraded in a catalytic reformer (REF) while that of light naphtha in a catalytic isomerizer (ISO) to produce high octane gasoline blending stock. Alkylation (ALK1–2) and polymerization (POLY) units produce alkylate and polymerate blending stocks to supplement gasoline production. The olefin gas feed to the alkylation and polymerization units are supplied by fluid catalytic cracker (FCC), residue fluid catalytic cracker (RFCC), and delayed coker (DCOK). Three main alternative processing schemes for heavy oil processing are incorporated in the superstructure. In the first alternative for atmospheric residual treating, high sulfur atmospheric residue is first processed in an atmospheric residue desulfurizer (ARDS) to produce low sulfur atmospheric residue that can be sold, or physically separated in a vacuum rerun unit (VRU) to produce low sulfur vacuum gas oil and low sulfur vacuum residue, or catalytically cracked in a residue fluid catalytic cracker (RFCC) to produce gasoline and other fuel types. In the second alternative of vacuum residual treating, the high sulfur atmospheric residue is physically separated in VRU into high sulfur vacuum gas oil and high sulfur vacuum residue. The latter (high sulfur vacuum residue) can be converted to low sulfur vacuum residue in vacuum residue desulfurizer (VRDS) to reduce the sulfur content and produce more valuable products such as transportation fuels. High sulfur vacuum gas oil is either sold after conversion to low sulfur vacuum gas oil in gas oil hydrotreater (GOHT) or converted to lighter products in hydrocracker (HCR) or fluid catalytic cracker (FCC1). We can sell low sulfur vacuum residue as fuel oil or further process it in DCOK or RFCC to produce lighter materials with or without prior visbreaking (VIS). In the third processing alternative called atmospheric residual cracking, the high sulfur atmospheric residue is first desulfurized in ARDS to produce low sulfur atmospheric residue that is either cracked in to produce lighter materials with or without a prior VIS. Typically, there is no vacuum pressure-operated unit in this configuration although some studies have shown the potential to process a feed from such units (Reynolds et al., 1992; Ancheyta, 2011).

4. Model formulation

The MINLP formulation for refinery configuration design is as follows:

$$F_i + \sum_k Q_{ik} X_k = P_i, \quad \forall i \in I \tag{1}$$

$$F_i \le S_i, \quad \forall i \tag{2}$$

$$X_k \le L_k B_k, \quad \forall k \tag{3}$$

$$FP_{i,k,p} = f(VS_{i,k}, VP_{i,k}), \quad \forall i, k, p \tag{4}$$

$$PP_{i,k,p} = f(FP_{i,k,p}, XU_k), \quad \forall i, k, p \tag{5}$$

$$F_k \le M_k U_k, \quad \forall k \tag{6}$$

Eq. (1) describes the material balances where F_i = feed amount of component i, Q_{ik} = yield coefficient of component i in process unit k, X_k = capacity of unit k, and P_i = total amount of component i. Eq. (2) imposes maximum feed supply S_i for each component i. Eq. (3) allows designing additional trains of the same unit as given by a multiple number L_k of the capacity B_k of a single unit k. Eq. (4) and (5) governs feed and product properties of the process units, respectively. The objective function as given by Eq. (7) maximizes product sales minus the associated costs of raw materials (cf), capital (CC), and operation (CR) including utilities, maintenance (CM), and payroll (CP).

$$\text{maximize} \sum_i \text{sp}_i P_i - \sum_j \text{cf}_j F_j - \sum_k \left(\text{CC}_k + \text{CR}_k \right) - \text{CM} - \text{CP} \tag{7}$$

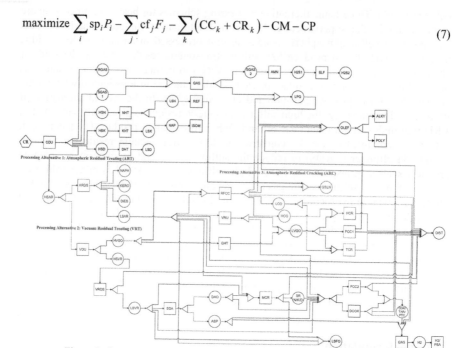

Figure 1. Superstructure representation of petroleum refinery configurations

5. Solution strategy

We develop a computational procedure that first generates and assigns a set of binary values (0–1) to the structural variables in generating a new refinery configuration at each iteration as based on the superstructure (Step 1). Then the procedure invokes a nonlinear optimizer to compute the unit conversions and product cuts in a corresponding configuration to maximize total profit-based objective function (Step 2). Figure 2 presents the described procedure flow.

The master module alternates the structural variable binary values U_k between 1 and 0 to indicate the selection or rejection, respectively of a process unit in an overall refinery scheme. Thus the algorithm can consider all possible alternatives within the superstructure that give rise to refinery configurations, which are given as inputs into the optimization submodule. The Excel submodule contains information on the superstructure element interconnections as well as their rigorous correlations for the material balances, product yields and qualities, utility requirements, feed and product prices, and associated running costs for all the units. The model accounts for all interconnections between the units and gathering pools for the intermediates and final products, and they involve both linear and nonlinear relations.

The submodule optimizes the unit conversions and product cuts in each configuration developed by the master module to determine the unit capacities and flow rates of intermediate and final product streams. By computing the capital and running costs, the submodule maximizes the objective function of total profit using the generalized reduced gradient-based method called GRG2 available in Excel Solver (Frontline

A model-based approach for optimizing petroleum refinery configuration
for heavy oil processing
179

Systems, 2018). The master module then reads the new configuration profit from the submodule results and compares it with the current value to decide in storing the binary variable and objective variable values associated with that of higher profit; otherwise, we retain that of the previous scheme.

This algorithm terminates when all possible configurations are considered to determine an optimal configuration. Thus, our algorithm is one of complete enumeration as different from a partial enumeration approach such as branch-and-bound. Expectedly, our method entails more iterations to converge to optimality, hence motivating us to incorporate use of 0–1-based logic propositions on design and structural specifications to reduce the computational time but without compromising the solution quality.

6. Results and discussion

The model solution indicates that a configuration resembling the residual fluid catalytic cracking (RFCC) route is more economical than to use a combined vacuum unit and delayed coker with or without visbreaker, which is consistent with the literature on refinery configurations (Khor et al., 2011; Meyers, 2016; Albahri et al., 2018). Using RFCC to process atmospheric residue is favored to physical separation combined with thermal cracking mainly because we can improve the selectivity and yield of the desired product flows. RFCC-based configuration also entails less process units than that of ARDS and VRDS, hence promotes lower capital and running costs.

Although a low sulfur vacuum residue can be produced from the vacuum unit which can then be processed in the RFCC unit, that route is not an optimal choice because it is less economical. Moreover, unless preceded by ARDS, RFCC removes only 30 to 50% of sulfur in the feed, and its products therefore require hydrotreating. The selected optimal technologies show that hydrotreating straight-run products is favored cost-wise and essential too. Hydrotreating straight-run distillates from crude distillation unit is more economic than selling them due to the lower price of high sulfur products. In our model runs over different price sets and scenarios, the solutions preferentially choose naphtha, kerosene, and diesel hydrotreaters as part of the configurations, hence we decide to include these units as fixed structures (i.e., they are not evaluated by means of the binary variables) to enhance convergence and reduce computational time.

The total capital investment estimated is US$2.1 billion, which is consistent with reported values for a refinery of this size (Maiti et al., 2001). Our optimal result run shows that a configuration that employs RFCC is the most profitable with a net profit of 8.40 US$/barrel (20 cent/gallon). While the computed values may differ for a specific case's cost values (e.g. for erection and running expenses) and sale prices, the relative trend and conclusion remain valid for a similar comparison made.

7. Conclusions

This work presents an approach to synthesize an optimal petroleum refinery configuration during the preliminary screening of design alternatives. The configuration determined shows good agreement with refinery configurations in practice. We obtain an optimal processing scheme for a specific crude oil mixture to be that of residual fluid catalytic cracking (RFCC) of desulfurized atmospheric residue, without a need for a vacuum distiller or vacuum residue desulfurizer (VRDS). The latter structure conventionally forms part of the former (as incorporated in our superstructure), but the MINLP approach applied finds such a configuration to be actually suboptimal.

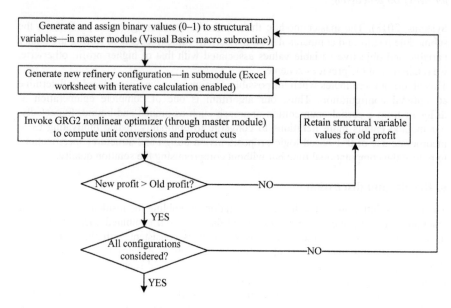

Figure 2. Flowchart on solution strategy used

References

T. A. Albahri, C. S. Khor, M. Elsholkami, and A. Elkamel, 2018, Optimal Design of Petroleum Refinery Configuration Using a Model-Based Mixed-Integer Programming Approach with Practical Approximation, Ind Eng Chem Res, 57, 7555-7565.

J. Ancheyta, 2011, Modeling and Simulation of Catalytic Reactors for Petroleum Refining, Wiley, p. 35.

S. Cremaschi, 2015, A Perspective on Process Synthesis: Challenges and Prospects, Comp Chem Eng, 81, 130-137.

E.A . del Rio-Chanona, D. Zhang, and N. Shah, 2018, Sustainable Biopolymer Synthesis via Superstructure and Multiobjective Optimization, AIChE J, 64, 91-103.

Frontline Systems, 2018, FrontlineSolvers, USA.

C. S. Khor and A. Elkamel, 2010, Superstructure Optimization for Oil Refinery Design, Petroleum Science & Technology, 28, 1457-1465.

C. S. Khor, X. Q. Yeoh, and N. Shah, 2011, Optimal Design of Petroleum Refinery Topology Using a Discrete Optimization Approach with Logical Constraints, J App Sci, 11, 3571-3578.

R. A. Meyers, 2016, Handbook of Petroleum Refining Processes, 4th ed., McGraw Hill.

A. Quaglia, C. L. Gargalo, S. Chairakwongsa, G. Sin, and R. Gani, 2015, Systematic Network Synthesis and Design: Problem Formulation, Superstructure Generation, Data Management and Solution, Comp Chem Eng, 72, 68-86.

B. E. Reynolds, E. C. Brown, and M. A. Silverman, 1992, Clean Gasoline via VRDS/RFCC, Hydrocarbon Processing, pp. 43–51.

E. Zondervan, M. Nawaz, A. B. de Haan, J. M. Woodley, and R. Gani, 2011, Optimal Design of a Multi-Product Biorefinery System, Comp Chem Eng, 35, 1752-1766.

Anton A. Kiss, Edwin Zondervan, Richard Lakerveld, Leyla Özkan (Eds.)
Proceedings of the 29th European Symposium on Computer Aided Process Engineering
June 16th to 19th, 2019, Eindhoven, The Netherlands. © 2019 Elsevier B.V. All rights reserved.
http://dx.doi.org/10.1016/B978-0-128-18634-3.50031-X

Performance Evaluation of Reverse Osmosis Brackish Water Desalination Plant with Different Recycled Ratios of Retentate

A. A. Alsarayreh [a], M. A. Al-Obaidi [a, b], A. M. Al-Hroub [c], R. Patel [a], and I. M. Mujtaba [a, *]

a School of Engineering, Faculty of Engineering and Informatics. University of Bradford. Bradford, West Yorkshire BD7 1DP, UK

b Middle Technical University, Iraq – Baghdad

c Senior Chemical Engineer, Energy and Water Directorate, Arab Potash Company, Jordan

I.M.Mujtaba@bradford.ac.uk

Abstract

Reverse Osmosis (RO) process can be considered as one of the most widely utilised technologies for brackish water desalination due to its capabilities of retaining salts and producing high-quality water. This paper focuses on the retentate recycle design of an industrial medium-sized spiral wound brackish water RO desalination plant (1200 m³/day) of Arab Potash Company (APC) located in Jordan. The plant is essentially designed as a multistage and multi pass RO system including a low salinity retentate recycle stream from the 2nd pass and a high salinity retentate disposal from the 1st pass. However, in this work, we have considered recycle of high salinity retentate stream from the 1st pass and explored the impact of different recycled ratio on the process performance indicators such as the fresh water salinity, overall recovery rate, and specific energy consumption. The simulation is carried out using the model developed earlier by us for the specified RO plant using gPROMS software. The results indicate the possibility of increasing the product capacity by around 3% with 100% retentate recycle ratio.

Keywords: Reverse Osmosis; Brackish Water Desalination, Simulation, Retentate Recycle, Energy Consumption.

1. Introduction

Broadly speaking, water scarcity is a major environmental challenge facing Jordan since the early 1960s until these days. Jordan occupies the 10th rank in the world in terms of the shortage and insufficient of water resources (Hadadin et al., 2010). Therefore, it is important to exploit the brackish water using desalination to be used as a main source of drinking water and industrial requirements. In this respect, the Arab Potash Company (APC) implemented a power plant including brackish water RO desalination plant capacity of 1200 m³/day to produce low-salinity water (i.e. conductivity of less than 0.641 ppm) to be used in the ion exchangers (Al-Obaidi et al., 2018).

The RO process has affirmed its robustness as a superior technology for brackish water desalination due to its high performance of salt rejection and water permeation

(Ghaffour et al., 2015). Moreover, the application of RO process is interestingly increased due to its low cost and energy consumption compared to other conventional thermal technologies (Al-Karaghouli and Kazmerski, 2013). The multistage RO process is originally designed in several configurations to satisfy the specifications of the produced water. Specifically, the permeate and retentate recycling designs were employed by several researchers and their impacts on the process performance were investigated. For instance, Al-Bastaki and Abbas (1999) used a small-scale spiral wound RO water desalination plant of water solution (with concentration of 10,000 mg NaCI/I) in a cyclic mode to study the performance of permeate flow rate and salt rejection. They confirmed a reduction in the concentration polarisation that increased the permeate flux as a result to applying the cyclic mode of operation. Al-Bastaki and Abbas (2003) studied the impact of permeate recycled design on the performance of a small-scale spiral wound RO desalination plant. The simulation results of permeate recycle ratios between 0% to 25% confirmed a reduction in the concentration polarisation which entirely improved the product quality despite a reduced production rate. Specifically, the product concentration is reduced by 15% at 25% of recycling ratio compared to the case of no recycle mode. Whereas, the production rate is reduced by 22% compared to the case of no recycle mode.

Al-Obaidi et al. (2018) have demonstrated an extensive study to evaluate the performance of brackish water desalination plant of APC located in Jordan and based on multistage RO process via modelling and simulation. The model developed is validated with an actual data collected from APC and then used to carry out a sensitivity analysis to predict the plant performance against the variation of operating conditions. However, up to the authors' knowledge, the influence of different ratios of retentate stream recycle (that combined with raw water stream) on the process performance indicators has not yet been explored. In this respect, the performance of RO process with 10% to 100% high salinity retentate stream of the 1st pass will be investigated. Then, the process performance would be compared against the original experimental data of no recycle mode that carried out at specified operating conditions.

2. Description of BWRO desalination plant of APC

Fig.1 depicts the configuration of BWRO plant which contains 120 membranes, 20 pressure vessels (6 membranes in each) and includes two passes with retentate reprocessing design. The 1st pass comprises 2 stages arranged in parallel of 6 pressure vessels with configuration (4:2) and the 2nd pass comprises 3 stages of 4 pressure vessels with configuration (2:1:1).

The low-pressure permeates of 1st pass (position 1) are combined and pumped to the 2nd pass. Therefore, two forwarding high pumps are used to drive the water through the membranes in the 2nd pass. However, the high salinity retentate from the 1st pass is discharged into drain system (position 4). The permeate streams of 2nd pass are gathered to form the plant product stream, which is collected in product tank with salinity around 2 ppm (position 3). However, the low salinity retentate stream from the 2nd pass (position 2) is recycled back to be coupled with the main stream of raw water (with salinity 1098.62 ppm).

Table.1 shows the transport parameters and membranes specification. Also, the operating parameters of BWRO plant of APC are listed in Al-Obaidi et al. (2018).

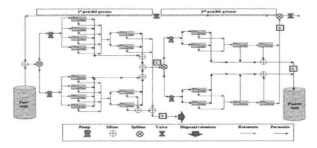

Figure 1. Schematic diagram of BWRO desalination plant of APC (Adapted from Al-Obaidi et al., 2018).

Table 1. Specifications of the spiral wound membrane element (Adapted from Al-Obaidi et al., 2018).

Parameter	Feed water salinity [ppm]	Feed water flow rate [m³/h]	Feed temperature [°C]	Daily production capacity [m³/day]	Average product salinity [ppm]	Total system rejection [%]
Value	(1098.62)	(74)	(25)	(1200)	(1.96)	(99.80)

3. RO process modelling

The steady state model for an individual spiral wound RO process is developed by Al-Obaidi et al. (2018) and successfully used to characterise the complete mathematical model of multistage brackish water RO plant of Arab Potash Company (APC). The complete mathematical model has been coded and solved within the gPROMS software suite. The model developed is validated with the actual data collected from APC and showed a good agreement.

4. Impact of recycling the retentate of 1ˢᵗ pass on process performance

The performance of the BWRO process of APC plant is investigated in this section by varying the 1st pass retentate stream recycle ratio from 10% to 100% in a step change of 10%. It is noteworthy to confirm that the RO plant is currently working at no recycle mode of 0% retentate recycle ratio. More importantly, this study is based on investigating the process performance against a step change of a spontaneous retentate recycle. The process performance indicators include the total plant recovery (Rec), total plant rejection (Rej), product flow rate and concentration (Qp, Cp), retentate flow rate and concentration (Qr, Cr), and energy consumption. Also, the current simulation is carried out at fixed values of 1098.62 ppm, 74 m3/h, 9.22 atm, and 25°C, of raw water concentration, feed flow rate, operating pressure, and temperature, respectively.

Fig. 2. shows insignificant variation of total plant rejection in an exponential relationship and a continuous drop in total plant recovery in a linear relationship against the increased retentate recycle ratio of 1st pass. In this respect, it can be said that 40% of recycled ratio has attained the optimal value of rejection. More importantly, the reduction of water recovery ratio can be attributed to an increase in the plant feed flow rate due to an increase in the retentate recycle ratio of 1ˢᵗ pass coupled with retentate stream from the 2nd pass and with the raw water stream. This in turn causes an increase in the bulk velocity of all the membrane stages that accompanied with a reduction in the residence time of solution inside the feed channel. Moreover, the continuous increase of feed concentration has passively impacted the concentration polarisation that entirely reduces the permeated water through the membranes. Therefore, the total permeate flow rate of 1st pass is decreased as a response to increasing retentate ratio. This in consequence had reduced the total water recovery as noticed in Fig. 2. Subsequently, it is fair to expect an increase of the energy consumption due to increasing the recycle ratio. It is worth noting that a decrease in total recovery means that the requirements for energy consumption will be higher. This is already highlighted in Table.3.

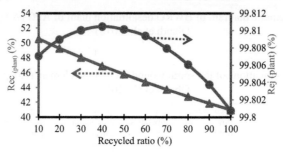

Figure 2. Impact of ratio variation on total plant recovery and rejection.

The influence of increasing the 1st pass recycle ratio of retentate on the product and retentate plant flow rates is shown in Fig. 3. It is clear that the product flow rate and retentate flow rate are significantly increased and decreased, respectively. The increasing of product flow rate is belonging to a lower velocity inside the module caused by decreasing the inlet feed flow rate of 2nd pass with increasing recycled ratio of retentate. It is important to realise that the total permeate of 1st pass is used as feed stream of 2nd pass. Up to this point, this would be associated with a lower residence time that reduced the retentate flow rate and increased water recovery of 2nd pass. However, the total water plant recovery keeps down due to a high progress of feed flow rate compared to a lower progress in product flow rate.

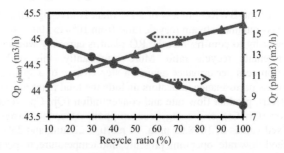

Figure 3. Impact of ratio variation on product and retentate plant flowrate.

The simulation results of Fig. 4 confirm that increasing of recycled retentate ratio causes a considerable increase in both product and retentate concentrations. This is ascribed to increasing the plant feed water concentration due to increasing the recycle ratio of high-

Performance Evaluation of Reverse Osmosis Brackish Water Desalination
Plant with Different Recycled Ratios of Retentate

185

salinity stream. Furthermore, these results support the findings of Fig. 2 that associated with a continuous reduction of total water recovery.

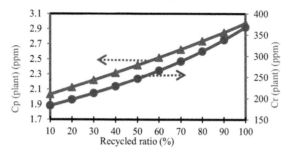

Figure 4. Impact of ratio variation on product and retentate plant concentration.

Table 3 presents the simulation results of energy consumption with the tested recycle ratios of the 1st pass retentate at fixed operating pressure and raw water concentration. Basically, the energy consumption is significantly increased by around (15%) as a response to this variation. This is might attributed to the progress of plant feed flow rate that dominated the energy consumption despite the noticeable improvement of product flow rate with increasing recycle ratio.

Table 3. The energy consumption simulation results with variation of recycled retentate.

Recycle ratio	10%	20%	30%	40%	50%
Power consumption [kWh/m^3]	0.860	0.873	0.887	0.900	0.914

Recycle ratio	60%	70%	80%	90%	100%
Power consumption [kWh/m^3]	0.929	0.944	0.959	0.975	0.992

To understand the performance of multistage RO process with no recycle mode (0% retentate ratio), Table. 4 presents the simulation results of several performance indicators with 40% and without recycle mode for comparison purposes. Specifically, it is noticed that no recycle mode can keep the process at the lowest product concentration and highest water recovery that commensurate with the lowest energy consumption.

However, the highest total product flow rate is achieved at 100% retentate recycle of the 1st pass which involved a slight increase of product concentration from 1.937 to 2.974 ppm at the same operating conditions. Therefore, this would enhance the productivity of fresh water which might be a possible negotiable point despite the necessity of increasing the requirements of energy consumption by around 17% within almost fixed solute rejection.

5. Conclusions

The performance of multistage and multi pass RO brackish water desalination plant of Arab Potash Company (APC) with different recycled ratios of 1st pass retentate is investigated via simulation. This is occurred in terms of several performance indicators. The simulation is carried out at fixed raw water flow rate, concentration, pressure, and temperature. This in turn explored that 100% retentate recycle can perform the highest production capacity with increased energy consumption.

This is originally compared to no recycle mode that currently used in the RO process of APC plant, and showed the lowest product concentration at the minimum product capacity.

Table 4. The simulation results of process performance indicators with 100%, 40%, and without recycle mode.

Indicators of process performance at recycle ratio from 1st pass = 0 % [APC plant]		Indicators of process performance at recycle ratio from 1st pass = 40 %		Indicators of process performance at recycle ratio from 1st pass = 100 %	
Rej_plant [%]	99.804	Rej_plant [%]	99.811	Rej_plant [%]	99.801
Rec_plant [%]	51.898	Rec_plant [%]	46.889	Rec_plant [%]	40.981
Qp_plant [m³/h]	43.991	Qp_plant [m3/h]	44.578	Qp_plant [m3/h]	45.297
Qr_recycle from 2nd pass [m³/h]	15.005	Qr_recycle from 2nd pass[m3/h]	12.095	Qr_recycle from 2nd pass[m3/h]	8.139
Cp_plant [ppm]	1.937	Cp_plant [ppm]	2.319	Cp_plant [ppm]	2.975
Cr_recycle [ppm]	169.159	Cr_recycle [ppm]	228.545	Cr_recycle [ppm]	368.465
power consumption pump [kWh/m³]	0.848	power consumption pump [kWh/m3]	0.900	power consumption pump [kWh/m3]	0.991

References

AL-Bastaki, N. & Abbas, A. 1999. Improving the permeate flux by unsteady operation of a RO desalination unit. Desalination, 123, 173-176.

AL-Bastaki, N. & Abbas, A. 2003. Permeate recycle to improve the performance of a spiral-wound RO plant. Desalination, 158, 119-126.

AL-Obaidi, M. A., Alsarayreh, A. A., AL-Hroub, A. M., Alsadaie, S. & Mujtaba, I. M. 2018. Performance analysis of a medium-sized industrial reverse osmosis brackish water desalination plant. Desalination, 443, 272-284.

Hadadin, N., Qaqish, M., Akawwi, E. & Bdour, A. 2010. Water shortage in Jordan Sustainable solutions. Desalination, 250, 197-202.

Sharma, A., Jelemensky, M., Paulen, R. & Fikar, M. 2017. Modeling and optimal operation of batch closed-loop diafiltration processes. Chemical Engineering Research and Design, 122, 198-210.

Toray membrane USA INC., M. T. S. O., Maintenance and handling manual, 2015. Available: http://www.toraywater.com/ [Accessed 10/3/2018].

Anton A. Kiss, Edwin Zondervan, Richard Lakerveld, Leyla Özkan (Eds.)
Proceedings of the 29th European Symposium on Computer Aided Process Engineering
June 16th to 19th, 2019, Eindhoven, The Netherlands. © 2019 Elsevier B.V. All rights reserved.
http://dx.doi.org/10.1016/B978-0-128-18634-3.50032-1

Globally Optimal Design of Double Pipe Heat Exchangers using Local Properties and Discretized Models

Alice Peccini[a], André Costa[b], Miguel Bagajewicz[c,*]

[a]*Federal University of Rio de Janeiro (UFRJ), Escola de Química CT, Bloco E, Ilha do Fundão, CEP 21949-900, Rio de Janeiro, RJ, Brazil*

[b]*Rio de Janeiro State University (UERJ), Rua São Francisco Xavier, 524, Maracanã, CEP 20550-900, Rio de Janeiro, RJ, Brazil*

[c]*School of Chemical, Biological and Materials Engineering, University of Oklahoma, Norman, Oklahoma, USA 73019*

bagajewicz@ou.edu

Abstract

The design of heat exchangers in general, including double pipe, is typically performed using methods based on simplifying assumptions (e.g. uniform overall heat transfer coefficient based on averaged physical properties, mostly). However, these assumptions may sometimes result in considerable under or oversizing, especially when ample variations of the physical properties with temperature take place. Aiming at circumventing this limitation, we present a novel MILP (globally optimal) formulation of the optimization of hairpin double-pipe heat exchangers using rigorous models and discretization. Numerical results illustrate the importance of the utilization of the proposed approach in relation to the traditional analytical models, showing to what extent one can undersize or oversize severely the heat exchanger.

Keywords: optimization, mathematical programming, linear programming, double pipe heat exchanger.

1. Introduction

Due to the importance of heat exchangers in chemical process plants, a large number of papers has focused on optimal design optimization procedures. Gonçalves et al. (2017) contains a brief overview of the main solution approaches. Independently of the approach, all of these papers rely on calculating the heat transfer coefficients using constant values of the physical properties.

This paper presents a novel mathematical programming formulation that is able to consider the variation of the overall heat transfer coefficient along the heat transfer surface. The resultant formulation, applied for hairpin double-pipe exchangers, is a mixed-integer linear programming problem (MILP), thus rendering globally optimum solutions.

2. Proposed Approach

The optimization problem corresponds to the minimization of a structure composed of a set of hairpin heat exchangers connected in series, as it is illustrated in Figure 1. One wants to find the inner tube diameter, the outer tube diameter, the length of each hairpin and the number of hairpins that minimize the heat transfer area. The model encompasses energy balances, heat transfer coefficient equations and flow velocity bounds. The flow is assumed to be turbulent, without phase change.

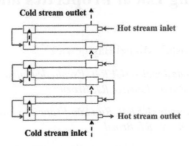

Figure 1: A set of three double pipe hairpins arranged in series.

Instead of modelling the heat exchanger using overall analytical descriptions, like the LMTD approach (i.e. $Q = U.A.\Delta T_{LM}$), which may involve large prediction errors, we propose to explore the original differential equations in the modelling:

$$\frac{dQ}{dz} = U \cdot (T_h - T_c) \cdot \pi \cdot dte \qquad (1)$$

When applying a discretization procedure, the value of the overall heat transfer coefficient at each point along the mesh depends on the stream temperatures. As a consequence, the resultant model would be nonlinear and therefore would present the usual numerical problems (need of good initial estimate and possible existence of multiple local optima).

Our proposal to circumvent this problem is to apply the discretization procedure to one of the streams temperature range (in this case the hot stream, as shown in Figure 2) rather than to the length of the equipment. This approach is used so that the temperatures in the discretization points become known parameters, while the distance between mesh points becomes the variable. In this way, the physical properties also become parameters, eliminating all nonlinearities in the model equations.

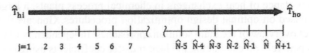

Figure 2: Hot stream discretization mesh.

For each adjacent pair of discrete temperature points, there is a corresponding length between them required for heat transfer. Thus, we rewrite Eq. (2), as follows:

$$\frac{dz}{dT_h} = \frac{\dot{m}_h \cdot Cp_h}{U \cdot (T_h - T_c) \cdot \pi \cdot dte} \qquad (2)$$

For the corresponding cold stream temperatures between both intervals, we have (the mark (^) above symbols represents known parameters):

$$\frac{dT_c}{dT_h} = \frac{\hat{m}_h \cdot Cp_h}{\hat{m}_c \cdot Cp_c} \tag{3}$$

We highlight that the uniform mesh in the hot stream temperature does not correspond to a uniform mesh in the length of the equipment. Figure 3 illustrates it by showing, in a generic temperature curve, the relation between both meshes:

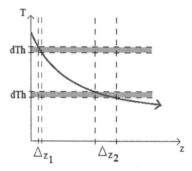

Figure 3: Discretization applied to the hot stream temperature curve.

For the discretization shown in Eq. (2), a second order central finite difference approximation for the intermediary points and a second-degree polynomial approximation for the last point, as well as a boundary condition for the first point are used, yielding, where $\Delta\hat{T}$ is the increment associated to the temperature mesh:

$$z_j = 0 \qquad \text{for } j = 1 \tag{4}$$

$$\frac{z_{j+1} - z_{j-1}}{2 \cdot \Delta\hat{T}} = \frac{-\hat{m}_h \cdot \hat{Cp}_{h,j}}{U_j \cdot \left(\hat{T}_{h,j} - \hat{T}_{h,j}\right) \cdot \pi \cdot dte} \qquad \text{for } j = 2,...,N \tag{5}$$

$$\frac{z_{j-2} - 4z_{j-1} + z_j}{2 \cdot \Delta\hat{T}} = \frac{-\hat{m}_h \cdot \hat{Cp}_{h,j}}{U_j \cdot \left(\hat{T}_{h,j} - \hat{T}_{h,j}\right) \cdot \pi \cdot dte} \qquad \text{for } j = N+1 \tag{6}$$

Knowing that tubes come in discrete options, we use discrete representations of the design variables. One of these, the one for inner tube diameter is shown in Eq. (7):

$$dte = \sum_{sd=1}^{sdmax} \hat{p}dte_{sd} \cdot yd_{sd} \tag{7}$$

$$\sum_{sd=1}^{sdmax} yd_{sd} = 1 \tag{8}$$

Similar equations are written for the other design variables. We now replace the design variables by the corresponding binaries and reformulate to obtain an equivalent linear formulation (no loss of rigor). Gonçalves et al., (2017) show specific details of this procedure. After such manipulations, Eq. (5) becomes:

$$\frac{z_{j+1}-z_{j-1}}{2\cdot\Delta\hat{T}}=\frac{-\hat{m}_h\cdot\hat{C}p_{h,j}}{(\hat{T}_{h,j}-\hat{T}_{h,j})\cdot\pi}\sum_{sd=1}^{sd\max}\sum_{sD=1}^{sD\max}\hat{X}_{j,sd,sD}\cdot wdD_{sd,sD}$$

(9)

where $\hat{X}_{j,sd,sD}$ is now a parameter representing the value of $\left[U_j dte\right]^{-1}$ written for each instance of yd_{sd} and yD_{sD}.

$$\hat{X}_{j,sd,sD}=\frac{\hat{p}dti_{sd}^{0.8}}{\hat{k}_{c,j}\cdot 0.023\cdot\hat{P}r_{c,j}^{0.4}\cdot\left(\frac{4\hat{m}_c}{\pi\hat{\mu}_{c,j}}\right)^{0.8}}+\frac{\hat{R}f_c}{\hat{p}dti_{sd}}+\frac{\ln\left(\hat{p}dte_{sd}\cdot\left[\hat{p}dti_{sd}\right]^{-1}\right)}{2\cdot\hat{k}_{tube}}+$$

$$+\frac{\hat{R}f_h}{\hat{p}dte_{sd}}+\frac{\hat{p}As_{sd,sD}^{0.8}\cdot\hat{p}dh_{sd,sD}^{0.2}}{\hat{k}_{h,j}\cdot 0.023\cdot\hat{P}r_{h,j}^{0.3}\cdot\left(\frac{\hat{m}_h}{\hat{\mu}_{h,j}}\right)^{0.8}\cdot\hat{p}dte_{sd}}$$

(10)

$$wdD_{sd,sD}\le yd_{sd}$$ (11)

$$wdD_{sd,sD}\le yD_{sD}$$ (12)

$$wdD_{sd,sD}\ge yd_{sd}+yD_{sD}-1$$ (13)

3. Results

The formulation proposed was applied to obtain the optimal design for the service described in Table 1. Polynomial fittings were applied to experimental data from Incropera et al (2011) to obtain the functions that describe the variation of the physical properties with the temperature. The sets of discrete options available for the optimization are depicted in Table 2.

Table 1: Stream data for the optimization problem.

Stream		Flow mass (kg/s)	Inlet Temperature (K)	Outlet Temperature (K)
Hot stream	Engine Oil	1.3	310	295
Cold stream	Cooling water	1.3	280	286

Table 2: Structural discrete options (pipe schedule 40).

Parameter	Discrete Options								
Number of hairpins	1	to	20						
Tube length (m)	3.048	6.096	9.144	12.192	15.240				
Inner tube OD (m)	0.021	0.027	0.033	0.042	0.048	0.060	0.073	0.089	0.102
Outer tube OD (m)	0.042	0.048	0.060	0.073	0.089	0.102	0.144	0.127	0.168

In order to illustrate the importance of accounting for the property's variations, four scenarios were considered. Scenario 1 shows the results using the proposed approach, taking into account the temperature influence on the physical properties. The other three scenarios explored consider the physical properties constant, which incidentally generates the same results as the usual analytical approaches. Scenario 2: properties calculated using a mean temperature for each stream; Scenario 3: properties calculated using the lowest temperature for each stream, a more conservative approach; and Scenario 4: the overall heat transfer coefficient is set to be the mean between its values calculated in the inlet and outlet temperatures. The results obtained are shown in Table 3.

Table 3: Optimal solutions obtained for the three different scenarios.

Scenario	Inner tube OD (m)	Outer tube OD (m)	Tube length (m)	Number of hairpins	Total heat exchanger area (m²)
1	0.042	0.060	15.24	15	30.28
2	0.042	0.060	15.24	14	28.26
3	0.042	0.060	15.24	20	40.37
4	0.042	0.060	9.144	20	24.22

For constant physical properties (Scenario 2) and using an average value of the overall heat transfer coefficient (Scenario 4), we obtain severe underestimation of the area. The conservative approach (Scenario 3) renders an area that is 32% higher.

These results point out the risk that a designer takes by using the simplified approach of adopting average or conservative temperatures, achieving a design that cannot fulfil the heat transfer task, or one that exceeds it, rendering a larger cost.

These disparities can be explained due to the nature of the hot stream. The example studied involves an engine oil stream with a large variation of the viscosity with the temperature. Such a large variation in viscosity affects the heat transfer coefficient on the oil side (from 144.7 W/(m²K) in the inlet to 57.7 W/(m²K) in the outlet).

4. Conclusions

We showed that modeling a double-pipe exchanger using the LMTD analytical method with uniform overall heat transfer coefficient can involve significant deviations from a more accurate solution obtained through discretization. When applied to a problem where physical properties vary substantially with temperature (the viscosity in our case), there is a significant risk of either obtaining an infeasible solution for the heat transfer task, or a significantly oversized exchanger. The implications for other cases (i.e. shell and tube exchangers) and other thermal tasks (i.e. condensers or vaporizers) is obvious. In addition, we also show that the spatial discretization, which leads to a nonlinear model, can be replaced by a temperature discretization, which generates a linear MILP, thus allowing globally optimal solutions.

5. Appendix

The symbols applied in this paper are shown in Table 4

Table 4: Stream data for the optimization problem.

Symbol	Description	Symbol	Description
ΔT	Temperature increment (K)	Pr	Prandtl number
Cp	Heat capacity (J/(kg.K))	Q	Heat load (W)
dte	Internal tube OD (m)	T	Stream temperature (K)
k	Thermal conductivity (W/(m.K))	U	Global heat transfer coefficient (W/(m².K))
m	Stream flow mass (kg/s)	wdPd	Substitution for binary product yd.yD.yP
pAs	Annular flow areas (m²)		
pdh	Hydraulic diameters (m)	yd	Binary for internal tube diameter selection
pdte	Internal tube ODs (m)	yD	Binary for external tube diameter selection
pdti	Internal tube ID (m)	z	Position (m)

Acknowledgments

Alice Peccini thanks the Coordination of Superior Level Staff Improvement (CAPES) for her scholarship. André L. H. Costa thanks the National Council for Scientific and Technological Development (CNPq) for the research productivity fellowship (Process 311225/2016-0) and the Rio de Janeiro State University through the Prociência Program.

References

C.O. Gonçalves, A.L.H. Costa, M.J. Bagajewicz, 2017, Shell and Tube Heat Exchanger Design Using Mixed-Integer Linear Programming, AIChE Journal, 63, 6, 1907-1922.

F.P. Incropera, D.P. Dewitt, T.L. Bergman, A.S. Lavine, 2011, Appendix A, Fundamentals of Heat and Mass Transfer, Seventh Edition, John Wiley & Sons, Hoboken, NJ.

Anton A. Kiss, Edwin Zondervan, Richard Lakerveld, Leyla Özkan (Eds.)
Proceedings of the 29th European Symposium on Computer Aided Process Engineering
June 16th to 19th, 2019, Eindhoven, The Netherlands. © 2019 Elsevier B.V. All rights reserved.
http://dx.doi.org/10.1016/B978-0-128-18634-3.50033-3

Optimization of Biogas to Syngas via Combined Super-Dry and Tri-Reforming. Analysis of Fischer-Tropsch Fuels Production

Borja Hernández,[a*] Mariano Martín,[a].

[a]*Departamento de Ingeniería Química. Universidad de Salamanca. Pza. Caídos 1-5, 37008 Salamanca, Spain.*

borjahb@usal.es

Abstract

This work presents an optimization approach to compare tri-reforming and super dry reforming for the production of syngas. Next, this section is integrated with the synthesis of Fischer-Tropsch liquids at low and high temperatures. The optimization of the tri-reforming technology is carried out introducing a parametric approach to evaluate different O_2:Biogas ratios. Tri-reforming is always selected to produce syngas. The biogas composition depends on the purpose of the syngas including ethanol, FT or methanol production. The large amount of hydrogen required in the last option is achieved introducing more steam in the WGS reactor in the tune-up section. In the second part of the work, the integration of previous reforming types with FT processes suggests that the operation in the LT mode is more profitable ($3.3/gal of diesel) than the HT ($5.4/gal). However, both are far from other production costs reported in literature that reach up to $0.34/gal.

Keywords: Biogas, CO_2, circular economy, reforming, optimization.

1. Introduction

Current developed societies generate large volumes of wastes. Waste needs to be treated before disposing them. Anaerobic digestion represents a technology that allows not only processing and stabilizing the waste, but that also generates additional value in the form of biogas and digestate. For decades, biogas was only used for the production of power and as a source of methane for natural gas networks (Wellinger et al., 2013). However, biogas is an interesting source of carbon not only because of the methane, but also due to its CO_2 content since it can be used for the production of chemicals via dry reforming (DR) (Hernández et al., 2017). The DR technology has been evaluated by integrating it with other reforming technologies such as in combined steam and dry reforming (Hernández and Martín, 2016) or in tri-reforming (TR) (Chein et al. 2017, Vita et al. 2018). Apart from its combination, another relevant technology has been recently developed by intensifying the process (Buelens et al., 2016). Super-dry reforming (SDR) has been created by intensifying DR with the objective of maximizing the conversion of CO_2. It is based on eliminating the reverse WGS reaction, obtaining the global reaction presented in Eq. (1).

$$CH_4 + 3CO_2 \leftrightarrow 4CO + 2H_2O \tag{1}$$

The optimization and comparison of TR with other reforming technologies was only recently addressed by Balasubramanian et al. (2018). They performed an MINLP optimization selecting the optimal reforming type for different H_2:CO syngas ratios and using natural gas as raw material. However, SDR was not taken into account. Thus, this work presents a comparison including the SDR technology within the superstructure and using biogas as raw material. Furthermore, the work is extended integrating the previous reformers with the production of Fischer-Tropsch (FT) fuels via low and high temperatures.

2. Modelling Issues.

The problem presented in this work is divided in two parts. First, in section 2.1 the superstructure for the production of syngas with different H_2:CO ratios using biogas as raw material and with parallel TR and SDR is presented. Next, the integration of TR and SDR for the optimal production of FT fuels is presented in section 2.2.

2.1 Tri-Reforming versus Super-Dry Reforming for Syngas Production.

The problem addressed in this section is presented in the superstructure given by Figure 1, where only the main operations of the process are defined. The modelling of these units is briefly defined in the following paragraphs. Other units such as heat exchangers and compressors are not included in Figure 1 but they are also modelled based on thermodynamics, mass and energy balances.

The biogas fed in the system is a mixture of gases whose optimal composition is also desired to be obtained. It is fed in the system, and split into three streams: one for processing and the other two ones used as fuel for heating up the reforming reactors. The biogas fed to the process section is initially sent to a bed for removing the ammonia and H_2S that would reduce the catalyst efficiency of the reformer in later stages.

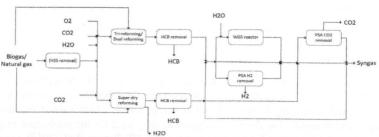

Figure 1. Superstructure of the Reforming Selection Problem for Syngas Production.

After cleaning the biogas, it is split in two streams. The first is sent to the TR reactor and the other one is sent to the SDR reactor. The TR is modelled dividing the reactor in two stages as presented by Hernández and Martín (2018). In the first stage, partial oxidation occurs and in the second stage the concentration of the components is computed based on chemical equilibrium. The oxygen required in this TR reactor is evaluated using different ratios by mean of a parametric optimization. The SDR reactor is modelled using a reduced order model, Eq. (2), that it is based on the thermodynamic results presented by Buelens et al. (2016). Two streams leave this SDR reactor: one for the water captured by the absorbent during regeneration and another one for the CO and unreacted gases produced.

$$X_{CH_4} = 8.13 + 0.76g\ln(\frac{molCO_2}{molCH_4}) - \frac{4746.4}{T(K)} - 2.6g10^{-3}gT(K) - 6.3g10^{-4}gT(K)g\ln(\frac{molCO_2}{molCH_4}) \qquad (2)$$

The syngas coming out from both reactors needs to be treated and its composition adjusted to ensure the H_2:CO ratio desired in the syngas. First, the traces of methane are removed in order to avoid carbon deposition on the catalyst of future synthesis or WGS reactors. The removal efficiency of the beds is assumed to be 100%. Then, the H_2:CO ratio is adjusted by considering three technologies: a WGS reactor to increase the concentration of H_2 (modeled as an equilibrium), a by-pass to keep constant the ratio and a hybrid membrane-PSA system to remove the H_2. The last stage assumed in the modelling of the tune-up section is the CO_2 removal since large concentrations of CO_2 promote the carbon deposition on the catalyst of synthesis reactors.

2.2 Super-dry and Tri-reforming for Fischer-Tropsch liquids production.

The previous syngas production can be integrated with the production of different chemicals and, among them, FT fuels. The superstructure for FT fuels production is presented in Figure 2. It considers two modes of operation depending on the reactor operating conditions: at high (HT), 590K-630K, and low temperatures (LT), 440K-530K. In both cases, the mass product distribution, w_i, follows the Anderson-Schulz-Flory distribution that depends on the number of carbons of the component, n_c, and the chain growth, α, as presented in Eq. (3). α is also dependent on the reactor temperature and molar fractions (Hernández and Martín, 2018).

$$w_i = \alpha^{n_c - 1}(1 - \alpha) \cdot n_c \qquad (3)$$

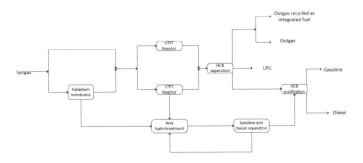

Figure 2. Superstructure for the Integration of FT-Fuels.

When the FT reactor operates at HT, light products are dominant and waxes only appear as traces. Thus, the product obtained from the reactor is sent to a separation stage composed by a flash separator to remove the unreacted gases of the syngas and fractions lighter than C_3. The products heavier than C_3 are expanded and separated in a tri-separator that has three outlets: a gas stream in the top that contains the LPG, a bottom stream with the water fraction and an intermediate stream with the organics with a chain larger than C_4. These organics are later separated in a distillation column in two fractions: gasoline and diesel.

The FT reactor operating at LT produces fuels with larger chain lengths, including waxes. In order to provide an added value to these waxes, an integrated recovering procedure based on hydrogenation is proposed. The hydrogenation reactor is modelled following a reduced model (Hernández and Martín, 2018), It requires H_2, which is separated from the syngas before the FT reactor, see Figure 2. After separating the H_2, the syngas is sent to the LT-FT reactor, whose products are separated as follows. First, the waxes are separated at the exit of the reactor as liquids. The rest of components are gases that are cooled down and sent to a flash separator. Second, the flash separator removes the unreacted syngas and hydrocarbons (HCB) with a chain length shorter than C_3. The hydrocarbons with a chain larger than C_3 and water are sent to a tri-separator that separates the fractions as in the previous HTFT process. Finally, the hydrocarbons with a chain larger than C_4 (gasoline and diesel) are separated in a distillation column together with the fractions recovered from the waxes hydrogenation.

3. Solution procedure.

3.1 Tri-Reforming versus Super-Dry Reforming for Syngas Production.

The first part of this work focuses on the optimization of the syngas production using two type of reformers: super-dry and tri-reforming. This problem is solved maximizing the profit obtained from the process. It is computed following Eq. (4) as function of the product costs ($\$_i$), the fluxes ($F_i$), power ($W_i$) and heat ($Q_i$) consumptions. This objective function completes the definition of the NLP optimization problem that is composed by 1,200 equations and 1,400 variables that are written in GAMS and solved using a multi-start approach with CONOPT 3.0.

$$profit = \$_{H_2} F_{H_2} - \$_{elec} \sum_{i \in Compressors} W_i - \$_{CH_4} \sum_{i \in CH_4 inlets} F_{CH_4} - \$_{CO_2} \sum_{i \in CO_2 inlets} F_{CO_2} - \$_{O_2} \sum_{i \in O_2 inlets} F_{O_2}$$

$$- \$_{H_2O} \sum_{i \in H_2O inlets} F_{H_2O} - \$_{steam} \sum_{j \in Q_{heat}} Q_j + \$_{H2Oref.} \sum_{k \in Q_{ref}} Q_j - \$_{H_2S} \sum_{i \in H_2S_{recovered}} F_{H_2S} \qquad (4)$$

3.2 Integrated Super-dry and Tri-reforming with Fischer-Tropsch processes.

The second part of this work focuses on the optimization of the integrated process that combines the reforming technology with the production of FT fuels. In this case, the integrated MINLP problem defined in the super-structures of Figure 1 and 2 is divided in two NLP sub-problems that are independently written in GAMS for the maximization of their profit. The problem involving the HT-FT reactor mode is composed over 2,100 equations and 2,500 variables, meanwhile the problem involving the LT-FT reactor model consists of 2,600 equations and 3,100 variables. Both cases are solved in GAMS using a multi-start approach with CONOPT 3.0.

4. Results

4.1 Syngas production from Tri-Reforming and Super-dry Reforming.

The optimization of the syngas production provides the optimal biogas composition for different products, the technologies selected and the operating conditions. The optimal composition of the biogas fed to the process is presented in Table 1. It can be seen that for ethanol production, the biogas composition required is approximately 48% of CO_2 and 52% of CH_4, while for FT and methanol production the methane content is to be at the upper bound. The large amount of hydrogen required to produce methanol is obtained by increasing the steam added in the WGS reactor of the tune-up stage.

After specifying the feed composition, the reforming technology selected is always the TR. Thus, oxygen is also needed in the process requiring 0.275 $molO_2$:mol Biogas for syngas used for methanol and FT, and 0.035 $molO_2$:mol Biogas ethanol. The temperature in this reactor is suggested to be 1273 K for methanol and FT production and 1231 K for ethanol production.

In the tune-up section, the production of a syngas with a H_2:CO ratio of 1:1 only requires to remove the unreacted HCB. The production of a syngas with a H_2:CO ratio of 1.7 requires the removal of HCB, the use of a WGS reactor and the addition of 0.06 mol of steam per mol of biogas fed in the process. Finally, the production of a syngas with a H_2:CO ratio of 2.5 requires all the units defined in the tune-up section: a silica bed to remove the unreacted HCB, a WGS reactor that needs 0.21 mol of steam per mol of biogas fed in the process and a PSA system that removes the excess of CO_2 and receives the 66% of the syngas produced.

Table 1- Optimal Compositions of Biogas an Boundaries (% vol.).

Comp.	Methanol (H_2:CO=2.5)	FT (H_2:CO=1.7)	Ethanol, DME (H_2:CO=1)	Minimum	Maximum
CO_2	0.25	0.25	0.479	0.37	0.75
CH_4	0.75	0.75	0.521	0.25	0.50
H_2O	$1 \cdot 10^{-10}$	$1 \cdot 10^{-10}$	$1 \cdot 10^{-10}$	$1 \cdot 10^{-10}$	0.17
N_2	$1 \cdot 10^{-4}$	$1 \cdot 10^{-4}$	$1 \cdot 10^{-4}$	$1 \cdot 10^{-4}$	$2 \cdot 10^{-3}$
H_2S	$2 \cdot 10^{-5}$	$2 \cdot 10^{-5}$	$2 \cdot 10^{-5}$	$2 \cdot 10^{-5}$	0.031
NH_3	$1 \cdot 10^{-6}$	$1 \cdot 10^{-6}$	$1 \cdot 10^{-6}$	$1 \cdot 10^{-6}$	$3.5 \cdot 10^{-6}$

4.2 Integrated Super-dry and Tri-reforming with Fischer-Tropsch processes.

The second part of the problem focuses on integrating the selection of the two previous technologies with the production of FT fuels from syngas. The problem has been divided in two parts according to the operating mode in the reactor.

On the one hand, if the FT reactor operates at HT, the process shows a profit of $7 \cdot 10^{-4}$ per mol of biogas fed in the process. This process produces a large amount of HCB with short chain length that are less valuable than other fractions. However, the reduced income is balanced with a lower consumption of utilities. According to the process operation, the suggested biogas composition is 62% of CH_4 and 38% of CO_2. This biogas is processed selecting a TR reactor and the PSA system for removing the CO_2 in the tune-up section. As a result, the syngas obtained to be fed in the FT reactor has a ratio of 1.2. On the other hand, when the FT reactor operates at LT the profitability of the process is improved up to $2.2 \cdot 10^{-2}$ per mol of biogas fed in the process. The products obtained from this process are mainly gasoline, diesel and LPG. Thus, in spite of the higher consumption of utilities, the income is larger than in the previous mode and the process profitability is improved. Apart from the utilities, another characteristic variable is the biogas composition in the feed, similar to the previous one, 69% CH_4 and 31% CO_2. In this case, the TR reactor and PSA system for the removal of CO_2 are also selected, obtaining a syngas with a H_2:CO ratio of 1.

The optimization of the process is completed with an economic evaluation. For a plant fed with 12Mm^3/y of biogas, the CAPEX is estimated to be $8 M for the HT-FT process and $19M for the LT-FT process. The production cost of the HT-FT process is estimated to be $610/ton for LPG, $2.57/gal for gasoline and $3.02/gal for diesel. For the LT-FT process this production cost is estimated to be $520/ton for LPG, $1.25/gal for gasoline and $1.67/gal for diesel. The production cost of the FT processes developed can be scaled-up to a facility that processes 3100 kt/y of manure and compared with a previous renewable process as it is presented in Table 2. As a result from this comparison, it can be seen that the HT-FT and LT-FT are less competitive than the previous work (Hernández and Martín, 2017).

Table 2- Production costs of different processes for the production of fuels.

Process	Production cost.
HT-FT	$5.4/gal
LT-FT	$3.3/gal
Hernández and Martín (2017)	$0.34/gal

5. Conclusions

This manuscript presents an optimization of biogas to syngas processes comparing super-dry and tri-reforming technologies. To optimize the TR process a parametric approach has been introduced since different O_2:biogas ratios are required. The results show that TR is always selected as the most profitable technology. However, SDR consumes more CO_2 in the reaction, being necessary further works to analyse its environmental impact. The different H_2:CO ratios are achieved by modifying the biogas compositions operating conditions and technologies in the tune-up section.

The work is completed integrating the syngas production section with two FT processes, at low and high temperature. The LT-FT shows to be more profitable than the HTFT process but none of the processes is not competitive with other renewable processes developed before.

References

P. Balasubramanian, I. Bajaj, M.M.F. Hasan, 2018, Simulation and optimization of reforming reactors for carbon dioxide utilization using both rigorous and reduced models. Journal of CO2 Utilization, 23, 80-104.

L.C. Buelens, V.V. Galvita, H. Poelman, C. Detavernier, G.B. Marin, 2016, Super-dry reforming of methane intensifies CO2 utilization via Le Chatelier's principle. Science, 354, 449-452.

R.Y. Chein, C.Y. Wang, C. Yu, 2017, Parametric study on catalytic tri-reforming of methane for syngas production. Energy, 118 , 1-17.

B. Hernández, E. León, M. Martín, 2017, Bio-waste selection and blending for the optimal production of power and fuels via anaerobic digestion. Chemical Engineering Research and Design. 121, May 2017, 163-172.

B. Hernández, M. Martín, 2016, Optimal process operation for biogas reforming to methanol: effects of dry reforming and biogas composition. Industrial and Engineering Chemistry Research, 55, 23, 6677-6685.

B. Hernández, M. Martín, 2017, Optimal Integrated Plant for Production of Biodiesel from Waste. ACS Sustainable Chemistry & Engineering, 5, 8, 6756-6567.

B. Hernández, M. Martín, 2018, Optimization for biogas to chemicals via tri-reforming. Analysis of Fischer-Tropsch fuels from biogas. Energy Conversion and Management, 174, 998-1013.

A. Vita, C. Italiano, D. Previtali, C. Fabiano, A. Palella, F. Freni, G. Bozzano, L. Pino, F. Manenti, 2018, Methanol synthesis from biogas: A thermodynamic analysis. Renewable Energy, 118, 673-684.

A. Wellinger, J. Murphy, D. Baxter, 2013, The biogas handbook: Science, production and applications. Woodhead, Publishing.

Anton A. Kiss, Edwin Zondervan, Richard Lakerveld, Leyla Özkan (Eds.)
Proceedings of the 29th European Symposium on Computer Aided Process Engineering
June 16th to 19th, 2019, Eindhoven, The Netherlands. © 2019 Elsevier B.V. All rights reserved.
http://dx.doi.org/10.1016/B978-0-128-18634-3.50034-5

Optimising European supply chains for carbon capture, transport and sequestration, including uncertainty on geological storage availability

Federico d'Amore[a], Nixon Sunny[b], Diana Iruretagoyena[b], Fabrizio Bezzo[a,*], Nilay Shah[b]

[a]*CAPE-Lab - Computer-Aided Process Engineering Laboratory, Department of Industrial Engineering, University of Padova, via Marzolo 9, Padova PD 35131, Italy*

[b]*CPSE - Centre for Process Systems Engineering, Chemical Engineering Department, Imperial College London; South Kensington Campus, London SW7 2AZ, United Kingdom*

fabrizio.bezzo@unipd.it

Abstract

Carbon capture and storage is considered a key option for decarbonising the energy sector. However, both the necessity of deploying large-scale infrastructures between the nodes of production and sequestration of CO_2, and the uncertainty related to the effective storage availability of sequestration basins still represent major challenges. Here, a mixed integer linear programming approach is proposed for the optimisation of a European supply chain model for carbon capture, transport, and storage. A quantitative assessment of storage uncertainty is incorporated to represent the volumetric capacity of basins to date considered capable of efficiently trapping the anthropogenic CO_2 emissions (i.e., deep saline aquifers, hydrocarbon fields and coal fields). The objective is to minimise the total expected cost required to install and operate, over a 10 years' time horizon, the overall network for carbon capture, transport and storage, while also taking into account the financial risk that is generated by uncertainty in geological capacity. The model defines economically optimal European supply chains, whilst simultaneously minimising the financial risk generated by uncertainty in local sequestration availability to ensure a robust design.

Keywords: Carbon capture transport and storage, European supply chain optimisation, Mixed integer linear programming, Uncertainty in storage capacity and risk.

1. Introduction

Addressing global warming through the reduction of CO_2 emissions is a crucial international goal. To constrain the mean global temperature rise below 2 °C by 2100, the planet must collectively keep the level of CO_2 equivalent below 550 ppm (Luderer et al., 2013). The power and industry sectors combined dominate current global CO_2 emissions, accounting for about 60 % of the total anthropogenic CO_2 generation, which must be drastically reduced by 2050 to meet COP21 targets (IPCC, 2018). Accordingly, carbon capture, transport, and storage (CCS) technologies have been highlighted as potential key players, considering their efficacy in delivering low carbon heat and despatchable power, decarbonising industry, and facilitating the net removal of CO_2 from the atmosphere. The feasibility of implementing a European CCS infrastructure has been investigated through a number of studies and demonstration plants in different countries, and this resulted in the development of a variety of technological and infrastructural options, whilst providing no clear consensus on which to deploy in any given context. To tackle this complexity, it is fundamental to establish engineering and cost analyses related to the whole CCS supply chain (SC), and in this sense, mathematical programming and optimisation techniques constitute the ideal methodological approach, in order to assess high-level, highly-combinatorial decisional problems, such as CCS. In particular, mixed integer linear programming (MILP) is frequently used in the modelling of large-scale energy systems, occasionally of continent-level CCS networks (Han and Lee, 2013; d'Amore and Bezzo, 2017; d'Amore et al., 2018). When designing CCS SCs, comparatively little attention has been paid to storage-related uncertainties such as geological volumes and long-term storage capacity, which are not usually known to a sufficient degree of accuracy before operation. As geological uncertainties may have a significant impact on overall sequestration costs, a more flexible pipeline network may be necessary rather than that designed using deterministic storage capacity data alone. Accordingly, the necessity of dealing with geological uncertainties in the planning and design of the infrastructure in terms of capacity must be highlighted as a primary action to improve the economic feasibility and manage the risks of large-scale CCS infrastructure. Amongst recent advances in the optimisation of process systems under uncertainty (Grossmann et al., 2016; Yue and You, 2016), several MILP models have been proposed for the optimisation of CCS networks under uncertainty, typically through either stochastic/probabilistic or robust techniques (e.g., Jin et al., 2017). Despite underlying the broad variety of investigated parameters (e.g., economics, storage injectivity, leakage, policy) and the abundancy of employed methodologies (e.g., multiple scenario realisation, inexact optimisation), none of the previous studies focused on the quantification of risk that may emerge as a consequence of uncertainty in the actual geological volume that is available for CO_2 sequestration. This paper proposes a novel adaptive methodology for the calculation of risk based on uncertainties in local storage capacities in the European context. A MILP methodology that optimises the SC in terms of resiliency on risk was developed and applied. The model defines economically optimal designs of European SCs, whilst simultaneously minimising the economic risk generated by uncertainties in local sequestration availability to ensure a robust design. Risk is quantified as additional infrastructure costs that may emerge from the rerouting of CO_2 flowrates, upon realisation of geological uncertainty. Therefore, monetary consequences can be interpreted as additional investment costs that may need to be incurred to improve the flexibility of a European CCS infrastructure.

2. Material and methods

This contribution proposes a MILP optimisation under uncertainty based on the deterministic CCS SC model described in d'Amore and Bezzo (2017). Here, we address uncertainty related to the effective volumetric efficacy of those European basins that are nowadays considered capable of efficiently trapping the anthropogenic CO_2 emissions for long-term storage. The objective is to minimise the total costs required to install and operate, along a 10 years' time horizon, the overall network for CCS, considering the financial risks that are generated by uncertainties in both onshore and offshore European sequestration basins. The 10 years' time horizon is discretised according to a set $t=\{1, ..., 10\}$. European large-stationary sources are described according to data retrieved from d'Amore and Bezzo (2017). The capture stage and associated constraints are implemented through a set of technological options $k=\{$*post-combustion from coal power plant, post-combustion from gas power plant, pre-comb from gas power plant, oxy-fuel combustion*$\}$. The transport set includes different options $l = \{$*onshore pipeline, offshore pipeline, ship*$\}$, each discretised through a set of possible flowrate capacities $p=\{1, ..., 7\}$ that ranges from a minimum of 1 Mt of CO_2/year to a maximum of 30 Mt of CO_2/year. The entire European area is discretised based on a grid of regions $g=\{1, ..., 134\}$. A terrain factor is implemented to consider local geomorphology. The sequestration basins are distinguished into different categories according to a set $s=\{$*deep saline aquifers, hydrocarbon fields, coal fields*$\}$ (EU GeoCapacity Project, 2009). Overall, the main inputs are: the spatial distribution of European upstream sources of CO_2; the techno-economic parameters of capture options k; the European carbon reduction target α to be pursued along the time horizon t; the techno-economic parameters of transport means l; the spatial distribution of deterministic minimum and maximum upper bounds of local geological potential of sequestration basins s; the random matrix (generated through Mersenne Twister algorithm) of uncertain minimum upper bounds of local geological potential of sequestration basins. The key variables to be optimised are: location, scale and cost of the capture system, of the transport infrastructure, and of the deterministic-driven sequestration system; the adaptive, uncertainty-dependent upper bound of local geological potential for storage; location, scale and consequent risk of the uncertainty-driven sequestration system; the differential flowrates that may be generated (i.e., surplus and deficit) between the deterministic and the uncertainty-driven sequestration stage; the total risk generated by uncertainty according to the planning features and the location of the sequestration infrastructure.

3. Mathematical formulation

The model addresses uncertainty through a unique objective function that aims to minimise the total cost TC [€] of CCS, including cost for capture TCC [€], transport TTC [€], sequestration TSC [€], and total financial *risk* [€] generated by the sequestration stage:

$$\forall it, loop\left[objective = \min(TC); TC = TCC + TTC + TSC + risk(it)\right] \qquad (1)$$

Quantities TCC, TTC, and TSC of Eq.(1) are evaluated as in d'Amore and Bezzo (2017). Uncertainty is here introduced through a novel approach that aims at evaluating adaptive regional sequestration potential and, therefore, minimising its associated *risk* through Eq.(1). The latter is given by the contribution on risk of both inter-connection between regions g and g' ($risk^{I}_{it,g,t}$ [€]), and intra-connection within region g ($risk^{II}_{it,g,t}$ [€]):

$$risk = \sum_{it,g,t}\left(risk^{I}_{it,g,t} + risk^{II}_{it,g,t}\right) / N_{it} \qquad (2)$$

Indeed, either inter-connection or intra-connection related risks can be defined, at each sample it in region g at time period t, as the additional costs (i.e., with respect to TTC) to install and operate further transport links between different regions or basins:

$$risk^{I}_{it,g,t} = \sum_{g'}\Delta Q_{it,g,g',t} \cdot c^{I} \cdot LD_{g,g'} \cdot \tau_{g} \qquad \forall it,g,t \qquad (3)$$

$$risk^{II}_{it,g,t} = \sum_{s}S^{deficit}_{it,s,g,t} \cdot c^{II} \cdot LD_{g} \cdot \tau_{g} \qquad \forall it,g,t \qquad (4)$$

In particular, c^I [€/t/km] and c^{II} [€/t/km] (i.e., the average inter- or intra-connection unitary costs, respectively), $LD_{g,g'}$ [km] and LD_g [km] (i.e., the linear distances between region g and g' and the size of region g, respectively) and the tortuosity factor τ_g, are retrieved from d'Amore and Bezzo (2017). Variable $\Delta Q_{it,g,g',t}$ [t/year] represents the flowrates of CO_2 that must be transported at sample it between regions g and g' at time period t according to sequestration discrepancies between the deterministic and the uncertain models, whereas $S_{it,s,g,t}^{deficit}$ (t/year), together with its specular $S_{it,s,g,t}^{surplus}$ (t/year), are variables that define the differences between the uncertain and the deterministic amounts of CO_2 that are stored on basin s in region g at time period t. Overall, the yearly deterministic $S_{s,g,t}^{D}$ (t/year) and uncertain $S_{it,s,g,t}^{U}$ (t/year) stored amounts, are compared with surpluses ($S_{it,s,g,t}^{surplus}$) and deficits ($S_{it,s,g,t}^{deficit}$) in local sequestration capacities and with potential additional flowrates ($\Delta Q_{it,g,g',t}$) through the following mass balances:

$$S_{it,s,g,t}^{U} = S_{s,g,t}^{D} - S_{it,s,g,t}^{deficit} + S_{it,s,g,t}^{surplus} \qquad \forall it,s,g,t \qquad (5)$$

$$\sum_{s} S_{it,s,g,t}^{deficit} + \sum_{g'} \Delta Q_{it,g',g,t} = \sum_{g'} \Delta Q_{it,g,g',t} + \sum_{s} S_{it,s,g,t}^{surplus} \qquad \forall it,g,t \qquad (6)$$

According to Eq.(5) for each sample it, if a basin s in region g presents at time period t a value of $S_{it,s,g,t}^{U} \geq S_{s,g,t}^{D}$, this implies that $S_{it,s,g,t}^{surplus} \geq 0$ is generated in g (which is capable at receiving a deficit from g'). Conversely, when $S_{it,s,g,t}^{U} \leq S_{s,g,t}^{D}$, then $S_{it,s,g,t}^{deficit} \geq 0$, implying that a deficit occurs in region g and must be transported either to a different basin s, or region g' according to Eq.(6). The overall uncertain stored amount $S_{it,s,g,t}^{U}$ is then constrained to be lower than the local adaptive sequestration capacity:

$$\sum_{t} S_{it,s,g,t}^{U} \leq \sum_{t} \left[S_{it,s,g}^{U,min} \cdot Y_{it,s,g,t}^{start} + 0.1 \cdot \left(S_{s,g}^{D,max} - S_{it,s,g}^{U,min} \right) \cdot Y_{it,s,g,t}^{keep} \right] \qquad \forall it,s,g \qquad (7)$$

In particular, $S_{it,s,g}^{U,min}$ [t] is the matrix of uncertain minimum upper bounds of local sequestration capacity, constituted by random values comprised within the deterministic range $\left[S_{s,g}^{D,min}, S_{s,g}^{D,max} \right]$ (EU GeoCapacity Project, 2009). Furthermore, $Y_{it,s,g,t}^{start}$ and $Y_{it,s,g,t}^{keep}$ are binary variables that define, respectively, when the injection starts and/or continues being performed at it on basin s in region g at time period t. Overall, Eq.(7) defines the uncertainty in sequestration according to two contributions: a precautionary base storage potential preventively defined at the beginning of the operations, and the possibility of a yearly rate of increase (fixed to 0.1 year^{-1} to exploit 10 years' simulation).

4. Results and discussion

Scenario A will be considered, in which the aim is to achieve a yearly European carbon reduction target α=50 % of CO_2 emissions from large stationary sources. Results are compared with those from Scenario 0 (a risk-neutral network in which risk is not included within the objective function). The model was implemented in GAMS and optimised using the CPLEX solver on a 24-Core cluster (96 GB RAM). The uncertainty in sequestration capacity is approximated by $10 \leq N_{it} \leq 400$ random samples in order to test the efficacy of the proposed methodology, and show that the model achieves reliable results for *it*=100 (Figure 1a). The design resulting from this sampling should constitute the initial design for future CCS optimisations.

Scenario A entails (Figure 1b) a *TC* for installing and operating the CCS system (including the contribution of financial risk) of 232.1 G€ (i.e., 38.302 €/t of sequestered CO_2), of which the major contribution is represented by *TCC* of 216.0 G€ (i.e., 35.637 €/t of sequestered CO_2). Interestingly, *TTC* (with 14.4 G€, i.e. 2.377 €/t of sequestered CO_2) and *TSC* (with 1.8 G€, i.e. 0.287 €/t of sequestered CO_2) constitute altogether only the 7 % of *TC*. With respect to *risk*, its final value is negligible, thus demonstrating the robustness of this solution on storage uncertainty. However, comparing the results with those from Scenario 0, despite having almost identical *TC* (+0.1 % with respect that of Scenario 0), the drawback of managing to keep such low values of risk is constituted by higher *TTC* (+11.2 % with respect to that of Scenario 0) and *TSC* (+5.5 % with respect to that of Scenario 0) costs. These additional infrastructural costs are a direct consequence of the choice of improving flexibility to nullify the contribution of risk to overall costs. In fact, regarding the SC configuration, under Scenario A (Figure 2a), the number of basins in which a deficit may occur is minimised and in general it is strategically chosen to exploit the sequestration potential of a larger number of regions (and basins) compared to Scenario 0 (Figure 2b), with the drawback of increasing transport costs. Accordingly, to distribute the investment for storage across different European regions, is an effective hedging strategy. In fact, the regions near the Baltics and Northern Poland are the only areas in which storage risk necessitates the balancing of deficits and surpluses, but these result in a range of $33 \leq \Delta Q_{g,g',i} \leq 720$ kt of CO_2/year, therefore minimal with respect to the CO_2 shipped between regions (up to 30 Mt/year). When some risk is unavoidable, slightly risky basins are chosen in areas in which nearby regions are likely to receive a surplus of CO_2, in order to minimise additional transport costs. In fact other deficits are scattered in Slovenia and near the Black Sea, but the CO_2 is diverted towards different basins within the same region and constitutes only a minor contribution to total economic risk, overall still negligible with respect to the total cost to install and operate the CCS network.

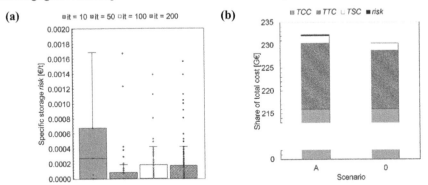

Figure 1. Scenario A, **(a)** dependency of *risk* [€/t] from *it*; and **(b)** share of costs [G€].

5. Conclusions

This contribution proposed a MILP modelling framework for the economic optimisation of a European CCS SC, with uncertainty in effective volume capacity of sequestration basins. The effects of uncertainty were quantified in terms of risk related to the necessity of installing further transport links with respect to the risk-neutral solution of the model, with the aim of improving the intrinsic flexibility of European CO_2 infrastructures in opposition to geological uncertainties. The proposed tool provides economically optimal network configurations resilient on risk and allows a decision-maker to understand the financial penalties associated with designing infrastructure in the absence of uncertainty. It was shown that only minor modifications and investments should be taken into account with respect to a European deterministic CO_2 network, in order to increase the level of flexibility of the transport infrastructure long enough to guarantee that uncertainty in storage capacity does not affect the final deployment of the overall system.

(a)   **(b)**

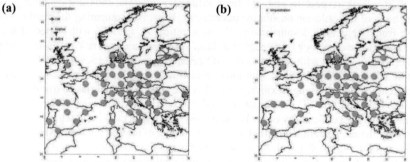

Figure 2. SC configuration for **(a)** Scenario A; and **(b)** Scenario 0.

References

F. d'Amore, F. Bezzo, 2017, Economic optimisation of European supply chains for CO_2 capture, transport and sequestration, Int. J. Greenh. Gas Control, 65, 99-116.

F. d'Amore, P. Mocellin, C. Vianello, G. Maschio, F. Bezzo, 2018, Economic optimisation of European supply chains for CO_2 capture, transport and sequestration, including societal risk analysis and risk mitigation measures, Appl. Energy, 223, 401-415.

EU GeoCapacity Project, 2009, Assessing European Capacity for Geological Storage of Carbon Dioxide.

I. E. Grossmann, et al., 2016, Recent advances in mathematical programming techniques for the optimization of process systems under uncertainty, Comput. Chem. Eng., 91, 3-14.

J. H. Han, I. B. Lee, 2013, A comprehensive infrastructure assessment model for carbon capture and storage responding to climate change under uncertainty, Ind. Eng. Chem. Res., 52, 3805-3815.

IPCC, 2018, Global warming of 1.5 °C. An IPCC special report on the impacts of global warming of 1.5 °C above pre-industrial levels and related global greenhouse gas emission pathways, in the context of strengthening the global response to the threat of climate change.

S. W. Jin, Y. P. Li, S. Nie, J. Sun, 2017, The potential role of carbon capture and storage technology in sustainable electric-power systems under multiple uncertainties, Renew. Sustain. Energy Rev., 80, 467-480.

G. Luderer, et al., 2013, Economic mitigation challenges: How further delay closes the door for achieving climate targets, Environ. Res. Lett., 8, 1-8.

D. Yue, F. You, 2016, Optimal Supply Chain Design and Operations Under Multi-Scale Uncertainties: Nested Stochastic Robust Optimization Modeling Framework and Solution Algorithm, AIChE J., 62, 3041-3055.

Anton A. Kiss, Edwin Zondervan, Richard Lakerveld, Leyla Özkan (Eds.)
Proceedings of the 29th European Symposium on Computer Aided Process Engineering
June 16th to 19th, 2019, Eindhoven, The Netherlands. © 2019 Elsevier B.V. All rights reserved.
http://dx.doi.org/10.1016/B978-0-128-18634-3.50035-7

Applying a Sustainability Metric in Energy, Water and Food Nexus Applications; A Biomass Utilization Case Study to Improve Investment Decisions

Ahmed AlNouss,[a,b] Sarah Namany,[b] Gordon McKay,[b] Tareq Al-Ansari [b,*]

aDepartment of Chemical Engineering, College of Engineering, Qatar University,

Doha, Qatar

bDivison of Sustainable Development, College of Science and Engineering, Hamad Bin

Khalifa University, Qatar Foundation, Doha, Qatar

talansari@hbku.edu.qa

Abstract

The demand for energy, water and food (EWF) resources will continue to increase, especially as the population is expected to reach 9 billion by 2050. The consequences of this include resource exhaustion and environmental degradation. Global pressures, such as climate change and resources depletion have encouraged the deployment of alternative energy systems and integration of carbon capture and sequestration processes. Currently, most chemicals and energy carriers are derived from finite fossil fuels which are susceptible to price fluctuation. Biomass, a renewable carbon-based fuel can be considered a promising substitute that can reduce environmental footprints in various applications. Gasification is a preferred route for handling biomass, in which the gas mixture (syngas) product is utilised to drive gas turbines and produce clean energy. Moreover, it can also be used to substitute natural gas in the petrochemical plants for methanol and ammonia production. Analysing the utilisation strategy of diverse biomass feedstocks represents a fertile research problem that can be addressed from a EWF Nexus perspective, which enables the quantification of impacts of biomass utilization strategies on the EWF systems. In this study, the utilisation strategy of biomass gasification feedstock for the poly-generation of different products is evaluated from an economic perspective. The Aspen Plus simulation models an oxygen-steam gasification technology to generate the optimal characteristics for each utilisation technique. Moreover, a sustainability metric was utilised to quantify the effect of each technique on EWF resources and to extend the investment decision making. Preliminary results generated from the simulation are integrated into a linear programming optimisation model that identifies the optimum biomass utilisation techniques that consider environmental and economic performances. The framework developed enables the selection of the optimal mix of biomass techniques that maximises sustainability indices for EWF resource systems, whilst ensuring a positive generation of the three corresponding resources. The results demonstrate that urea production and power generation are the most viable biomass utilisation techniques.

Keywords: Biomass Gasification, EWF Nexus, Sustainability, Optimisation, Decision Making

1. Introduction

The notion of producing renewable chemicals and fuels is driving sustainable development in the modern society towards a decreasing dependency on fossil fuels. The annual global production of petrochemicals is very large and implies a need to identify alternative routes to replace the fossil-based feedstocks to reduce GHG emissions as part of the global sustainable development agenda (Andersson, 2013). One of the main solutions considered for achieving large reductions in GHG emissions, is the increased production and usage of bioenergy. Considering the current total energy supply of 475 EJ, the International Panel on Climate Change (IPCC) expects that 120 to 155 EJ of the annually supplied primary energy can be extracted from biomass by 2050 (IPCC, 2011). Gasification is considered as the most flexible biomass feedstock route for the generation of various advanced biofuels, such as Fischer-Tropsch diesel or methanol. Bio-methanol produced via gasification of biomass has the potential to replace petrol in conventional combustion engines which can secure the transportation sector with renewable energy. Biomass gasification is also useful for green chemical production where green ammonia can be produced, thereby reducing the dependency on fossil fuels and reducing the emissions of greenhouse gases from the fertiliser industry (Andersson, 2013).

Numerous studies have been conducted to highlight the potential for producing value added products from biomass recycling. Arora et al. investigated the production of a small-scale ammonia plant from biomass to ensure sustainable and profitable production. The study emphasised the techno-economic benefits resulting from ammonia biomass-based production. Calculations produced using Aspen Plus simulation illustrated a 54-68% reduction in CO_2 emissions in comparison to the fossil-based conventional ammonia plants. Moreover, a wider spectrum of studies have been conducted to review the current status of the biomass technology and its utilisation in the production of value added products (Arora et al., 2016). Pike et al. discussed the wide range of opportunities to produce value added products generation from biomass. The study adopted the chemical complex analysis system to evaluate the introduction of plants producing multiple biomass-based chemicals. The developed superstructure of biomass-based chemical production system determined the optimal configuration of plants, considering economic, environmental and sustainable perspectives (Pike et al., 2008).

EWF Nexus systems have been widely used in recent years to address complex resource management challenges, and assess the significance and magnitude of the environmentally possible impacts when supplying a service or product. Integrated analysis considering an EWF Nexus approach enables the identification of key synergies and trade-offs that may exist in the design and operation of EWF sub-systems. Moreover, renewable energy technologies when integrated into EWF Nexus system analysis can address some of the trade-offs between EWF resources (Ferroukhi et al., 2015). Al-Ansari et al. developed an EWF Nexus tool based on a life cycle assessment (LCA) where EWF Nexus sub-systems are transformed from a linear system to highly efficient closed loop systems. The Nexus tool integrates biomass gasification combined cycle (IBGCC) and CO_2 capture to assess the environmental impact of a hypothetical food security scenario in Qatar. The results illustrated near relative carbon neutrality can be achieved through the integration of photovoltaic (PV), biomass gasification coupled with carbon capture for the system considered (Al-Ansari et al., 2016, 2017).

In this study, the utilisation strategy of biomass gasification feedstock for the poly-generation of different products is evaluated from an economic perspective. An Aspen

Plus model simulating gasification technology is utilised to generate the optimal characteristics for each utilisation technique. Moreover, a sustainability metric is integrated into the model in order to quantify the effect of each utilisation technique on EWF resources and to improve the investment decision.

2. Model development

Advanced system models are necessary in order to undertake reliable process economic and energy efficiency analyses of integrated biomass gasification routes. As such, a flowsheet of the biomass gasification system is simulated using Aspen Plus software evaluating Qatar's biomass characteristics. This study is an expansion of previous work (AlNouss et al., 2018) and is novel as it optimises a unique set of biomass feedstock which includes date pits, food waste, manure and bio-sludge. The simulation takes advantage of oxygen and steam in the gasification of different feedstocks to generate H_2-rich syngas, utilized in the production of value-added products i.e. methanol, urea, power through IBGCC and Fischer-Trospch liquids (FTL). Table 1 summarizes the elemental analyses of the biomass feedstocks considered in the study based on Qatar's characteristics.

Table 1: Proximate and ultimate analyses of biomass feedstock

	Manure	Dried Sewage Sludge	Date Pit waste	Food Waste
Mass Flow (tons/y)	5.27×10^5	3.65×10^4	7.60×10^3	7.0×10^3
Proximate analyses (wt %)				
Volatile matter	65.0	8.8	81.8	86.1
Fixed carbon	13.5	19.4	17.2	7.7
Ash	21.6	71.8	1.0	6.2
Moisture	27.4	8.3	5.0	75.1
Ultimate analyses (wt %)				
C	37.1	19.1	49.8	46.4
H	5.1	2.3	6.8	6.9
O	31.4	5.7	37.9	37.4
N	3.7	1.1	4.5	3.1
S	0.5	0.1	0.0	0.0
Cl	1.0	0.0	0.0	0.0
Ash	21.4	71.8	1.0	6.2
LHV (dry basis) (MJ/kg)	19.09	16.40	25.30	19.84

The generated H_2-rich syngas is utilized in the production of value-added products: methanol, urea, power through IBGCC and Fischer-Trospch liquids (FTL). Both urea and methanol production are described as petrochemical processes that utilise the produced syngas in a series of sections to produce the aforementioned value-added products. The main uses of methanol are as fuel, solvent and anti-freeze, whereas urea is mainly used as fertilizer. The liquid fuels and power production are described as emerging processes that utilise the produced syngas in a series of sections to produce the value-added products. Liquid fuels are used in many sectors such as aviation, transportation, heating and lightning, whereas power is mainly used to drive turbines. After the simulation of the four processes, an economic evaluation was conducted to quantify revenue, capital and operating costs. In addition, the EWF Nexus system considered is quantified based on the footprint of each of the three resources for every utilisation technique. Preliminary results from the simulation are integrated into a linear program to identify the optimal biomass utilisation strategies that enhance both economic and environmental performances, through minimising sustainability indexes for EWF systems while ensuring a positive generation of the three corresponding resources.

3. Results and discussion

The results from EWF footprints for each utilisation technique are quantified by comparing the consumption and generation of each resource. Table 2 summarises the main results from the economic evaluation and the EWF Nexus system. Subsequently, a sustainability metric introduced recently by (El-Halwagi, 2017), is used to quantify the effect of the footprints compared to the economic benefit for each process. To do this, the return on investment (ROI) is first calculated using equation 1, and then compared to the EWF footprints using the sustainability weighted return on investment metric (SWROIM) calculated using equation 2.

Table 2: EWF net values for the four utilization techniques

	Ammonia/ Urea	Methanol	Liquid Fuels	IBGCC
Total Capital Cost [$]	1.4E+08	1.2E+08	1.3E+08	1.4E+08
Revenue [$/y]	4.2E+07	3.1E+07	3.0E+06	1.1E+07
Water Consumption [kg/h]	4.4E+04	9.2E+04	2.0E+04	1.7E+05
Water Generation [kg/h]	5.0E+04	9.2E+04	3.6E+04	2.1E+05
Net [ton/h]	5.8E+00	-8.2E-02	1.6E+01	3.5E+01
Food Waste Consumption [kg/h]	8.0E+02	8.0E+02	8.0E+02	8.0E+02
Food/Fertilizer* [kg/kg] ((MDPS), 2018; WorldBank, 2018)	2.6E+03			
Food Generation [tons/h]	3.1E+04			
Net Food [tons/h]	3.1E+04	8.0E-01	8.0E-01	8.0E-01
Energy Consumption [kW]	4.2E+04	4.0E+04	4.2E+04	3.9E+04
Energy Generation [kW]				8.1E+04
Net Energy (MW)	-4.2E+01	-4.0E+01	-4.2E+01	4.2E+01

$$ROI_p = \frac{AEP_p}{TCI_p} \qquad\qquad \text{eq.(1)}$$

Where the term AEP abbreviates the net annual economic profit, and the term TCI abbreviates the total capital investment.

$$SWROIM_p = \frac{AEP_p\left[1 + \sum_{i=1}^{N_{Indicators}} w_i\left(\frac{Indicator_{p,i}}{Indicator_i^{Target}}\right)\right]}{TCI_p} \qquad\qquad \text{eq. (2)}$$

Where the index i is for the considered sustainability indicators apart from the net annual economic profit with $i=1,2,...,N_{indicators}$. w_i is the weighing factor indicating the relative importance ratio of the ith sustainability indicator compared to the net annual economic profit. The associated rations with EWF footprints are all assumed to be 0.25. They are manipulated to determine the effect of each footprint on the overall sustainability metric. $Indicator_{p,i}$ term corresponds to the value of the ith sustainability indicator linked with the pth alternative. The term $Indicator_i^{Target}$ represents the benchmark value of the ith sustainability indicator. The comparison between results generated from sustainability metric (SWROIM) computations for each EWF Nexus system and the corresponding return on investment (ROI) demonstrated that urea production and power generation are the only techniques selected. Methanol and liquid fuels production are excluded due to their low SWROIM value which illustrates their negative impact on sustainability. Figure 1 illustrates the results of the ROI and SWEOIM for each utilisation technique.

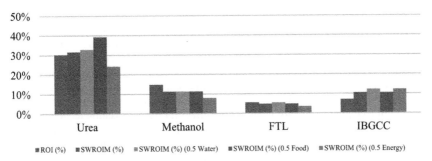

Figure 1: ROI and SWROIM results for different utilization techniques

In order to further refine the results and identify the best performing biomass utilisation techniques that considers both environmental and economic performances; a linear programming optimisation model is developed allowing the selection of optimal mix of biomass techniques that maximizes sustainability indices for EWF systems. The model, presented in Table 3 also takes into consideration the flow of resources into each application through imposing a positive net generation of EWF.

Table 3. Model formulation

Objective function	Water	$\max\sum_{i=1}^{4} w_i \times x_i^w$
	Energy	$\max\sum_{i=1}^{4} e_i \times x_i^e$
	Food	$\max\sum_{i=1}^{4} f_i \times x_i^f$
Constraints	$\sum_{i=1}^{4} nw_i \times x_i^w \geq 0$	$\sum_{i=1}^{4} x_i^w = 1$
	$\sum_{i=1}^{4} ne_i \times x_i^e \geq 0$	$\sum_{i=1}^{4} x_i^e = 1$
	$\sum_{i=1}^{4} nf_i \times x_i^f \geq 0$	$\sum_{i=1}^{4} x_i^f = 1$

Where x_i^w, x_i^e and x_i^f are decision variables representing the percentage of contribution of each technology in each sector. w_i, e_i and f_i are the SWROIM for water, energy and food, respectively, for each technique. The first three equations ensure a positive net amount of EWF such that nw_i, ne_i and nf_i are the net values defined by the difference between generation and consumption amounts of a source. The final three equations impose the sum of percentages of each type of decision variable to be 100%. The results generated support findings from the first part as urea is selected again as a sustainable biomass utilisation technique as it demonstrates the largest SWROIM for both water and food. As for energy, utilising a combination of urea generation and power production results in a high SWROIM and a positive net energy generation. The results from the two methods are illustrated in Table 4.

Table 4: Optimal sustainability indexes results

Technique	Urea	Methanol	Liquid Fuels	IBGCC
ROI (%)	32%	11%	5%	10%
SWROIM (%) (0.25 each)	33%	11%	5%	12%
SWROIM (%) (0.5 Water, 0.25 others)	39%	11%	5%	10%
SWROIM (%) (0.5 Food, 0.25 others)	24%	8%	3%	12%
SWROIM (%) (0.5 Energy, 0.25 others)	32%	11%	5%	10%
Decision variable (Water)	1	0	0	0
Decision variable (Food)	1	0	0	0
Decision variable (Energy)	0.504	0	0	0.496

4. Conclusion

There has been significant global progress worldwide to diversify resource utilization options in order to limit GHG emissions and to prolong natural resources. This study is novel as it considers an EWF Nexus framework with an emphasis on biomass utilisation to design a system that will utilize the waste biomass from built environment in Qatar to produce a high-energy combustible gas. A utilisation strategy of biomass gasification feedstocks is evaluated from an economical perspective considering oxygen-steam gasification technology. Quantification of the effect for each utilisation technique on the EWF resources is conducted in which a EWF sustainability metric is utilised to inform and enhance investment decisions. Finally, urea production demonstrated that it is the most attractive amongst the utilisation techniques considered.

5. Acknowledgment

The authors acknowledge the support of Qatar National Research Fund (QNRF) (a member of Qatar Foundation) by GSRA grant No GSRA4-1-0518-17082.

References

M.o.D.P.a.S. (MDPS), 2018, Agricultural Statistics.

T. Al-Ansari, A. Korre, Z. Nie, and N. Shah, 2016, Integration of Biomass Gasification and CO2 Capture in the LCA Model for the Energy, Water and Food Nexus, Computer Aided Chemical Engineering, 38, 2085-90.

T. Al-Ansari, A. Korre, Z. Nie, and N. Shah, 2017, Integration of greenhouse gas control technologies within the energy, water and food nexus to enhance the environmental performance of food production systems, Journal of Cleaner Production, 162, 1592-606.

A. AlNouss, G. McKay, and T. Al-Ansari, 2018, Optimum Utilization of Biomass for the Production of Power and Fuels using Gasification, Computer Aided Chemical Engineering, 43, 1481-86.

J. Andersson, 2013, Techno-economic analysis of integrated biomass gasification for green chemical production, Luleå tekniska universitet.

P. Arora, A.F.A. Hoadley, S.M. Mahajani, and A. Ganesh, 2016, Small-Scale Ammonia Production from Biomass: A Techno-Enviro-Economic Perspective, Industrial & Engineering Chemistry Research, 55, 22, 6422-34.

M.M. El-Halwagi, 2017, A return on investment metric for incorporating sustainability in process integration and improvement projects, Clean Technologies and Environmental Policy, 19, 2, 611-17.

R. Ferroukhi, D. Nagpal, A. Lopez-Peña, T. Hodges, R. Mohtar, B. Daher, and M. Keulertz, 2015, Renewable energy in the water, energy & food nexus, The International Renewable Energy Agency (IRENA).

IPCC, 2011, IPCC special report on renewable energy sources and climate change mitigation.

P. Pike, D. Sengupta, and T. Hertwig, 2008, Integrating biomass feedstocks into chemical production complexes using new and existing processes, Minerals Processing Research Institute, Louisiana State University, Baton Rouge, LA.

WorldBank, 2018, Fertilizer consumption (kilograms per hectare of arable land), https://data.worldbank.org/indicator/AG.CON.FERT.ZS

Anton A. Kiss, Edwin Zondervan, Richard Lakerveld, Leyla Özkan (Eds.)
Proceedings of the 29th European Symposium on Computer Aided Process Engineering
June 16th to 19th, 2019, Eindhoven, The Netherlands. © 2019 Elsevier B.V. All rights reserved.
http://dx.doi.org/10.1016/B978-0-128-18634-3.50036-9

Technoeconomic MINLP Optimisation of Liquid-Liquid Extraction (LLE) Cascades for Continuous Pharmaceutical Manufacturing (CPM) of Atropine

Samir Diab,[a] Nikolaos Mytis,[b] Andreas G. Boudouvis,[b] Dimitrios I. Gerogiorgis[a*]

[a] *School of Engineering (IMP), University of Edinburgh, Edinburgh, EH9 3FB, UK*

[b] *School of Chemical Engineering, National Technical University of Athens, Athens 15780, Greece*

D.Gerogiorgis@ed.ac.uk

Abstract

Continuous pharmaceutical manufacturing (CPM) has the potential to revolutionise the production of active pharmaceutical ingredients (APIs), offering operational and economic benefits over the currently dominant batch methods implemented by industry. Atropine is a nerve agent API, whose demonstrated continuous flow synthesis facilitates process modelling and optimisation. This work implements MINLP optimisation for total cost minimisation of the upstream CPM of atropine for rapid process synthesis. The process model considers reactor design from regressed reaction kinetic parameters, solute partitioning between LLE phases for different solvent systems, UNIFAC-modelled ternary liquid-liquid equilibria and mass transfer correlations for continuous LLE design. Optimisation results indicate toluene as the best (cost optimal) LLE solvent choice. This work demonstrates the utility of the described methodology for rapid process synthesis and comparative technoeconomic evaluation in early CPM process development stages.

Keywords: Continuous pharmaceutical manufacturing (CPM); Atropine; MINLP; Superstructure; Economic analysis.

1. Introduction

Continuous pharmaceutical manufacturing (CPM) is an emerging research field with the potential for significant technical, operational and economic benefits over currently prevalent batch methods (Koenig and Dillon, 2017). Despite demonstrations of active pharmaceutical ingredient (API) continuous synthesis, a lack of integrated continuous separation methods is an important obstacle (Baxendale et al., 2015); elucidation of optimal process designs is imperative for successful implementation (Teoh et al., 2015).

Atropine is a World Health Organisation (WHO) API for the treatment of nerve agents (Marrs and Rice, 2016), whose continuous flow synthesis features two plug flow reactor (PFRs) followed by liquid-liquid extraction (LLE) (Bédard et al., 2016). Systematic comparative evaluation of LLE design configurations can be implemented via MINLP optimisation. This work implements steady-state modelling and MINLP optimisation for atropine CPM, including upstream continuous flow synthesis and continuous LLE. Reactor design using kinetic parameters regressed from published data, thermodynamic models and mass transfer correlations for LLE design and an established costing methodology for pharmaceutical manufacturing are implemented. Optimisation results corresponding to cost optimal LLE design configurations and minimum total costs are then presented for different designs with an outlook on this vibrant research field.

2. Process Modelling and MINLP Optimisation

2.1. Continuous Flow Synthesis

The flowsheet for the CPM of atropine is shown in Fig. 1. The API continuous flow synthesis is demonstrated by Bédard et al. (2016), featuring three reactions in two PFRs. The first (PFR-1) features the esterification of tropine **2** (in DMF) and neat phenylacetyl chloride **3** at 100 °C to form tropine ester HCl **4** (reaction 1), the free form of which (**5**) is formed by the addition of NaOH (aq). It is assumed that PFR-1 attains the same conversion of 99% of **2** to **4** at 100 °C as reported in the literature. The second reactor (PFR-2) features the addition of formaldehyde (CH_2O) to **5** (reaction 2a) under basic conditions to produce API. An undesired elimination of API to apoatropine **6** (reaction 2b) is also reported. Interrogation of the published kinetic data for reaction 2a shows a second-order (first-order in both **5** and CH_2O) to be the most plausible rate law with an estimated second-order rate constant of $k_2 = 1.68$ L mol^{-1} h^{-1}; this allows explicit modelling of reactor performance for PFR volume calculation in the process model.

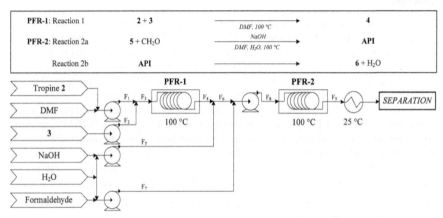

Figure 1: Flowsheet for the CPM of atropine: continuous synthesis and LLE.

2.2. Continuous Liquid-Liquid Extraction (LLE): Thermodynamics

This work considers a continuous purification via LLE following the API continuous flow synthesis. The continuous LLE is operated at $T_{LLE} = 25$ °C for partitioning of structurally similar impurities (**2**, **5**, **6**) into the extract (aqueous phase) while retaining API in the raffinate (organic phase). Candidate LLE solvents for investigation must induce rapid phase splitting with the feed solvent mixture of DMF + H_2O from the continuous API synthesis; thus, modelling of candidate CPM-LLE designs requires liquid-liquid equilibria data for the ternary solvent system DMF + H_2O + LLE solvent. Ternary systems containing candidate LLE solvents were screened for their propensity to form an immiscible mixture via UNIFAC modelling. According to these criteria, the LLE solvents considered in this work are diethyl ether (Et_2O), butyl acetate (BuOAc) and toluene (PhMe), whose ternary diagrams are shown in Fig. 2. Partition coefficients of API and impurity solutes between organic and aqueous phases for different considered solvent systems at $T_{LLE} = 25$ °C are available in the literature (Bédard et al., 2016) and are used here for solute distribution estimation and LLE modelling. Partition coefficients describe the distribution of solute components under equilibrium, i.e. non-steady-state conditions.

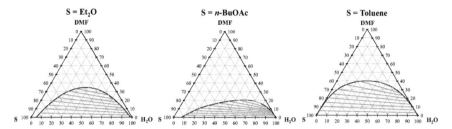

Figure 2: Ternary diagrams for the LLE systems DMF + H_2O + {Et$_2$O, BuOAc, PhMe}.

2.3. Continuous Liquid-Liquid Extraction (LLE): Mass Transfer Correlations

Calculation of inefficiencies associated with continuous (i.e., steady-state) operation compared to equilibrium conditions must be considered in the process model. The continuous LLE efficiency (E_{LLE}) is a function of the overall mass transfer coefficient (K), interfacial area (a) and tank residence time (τ_{LLE}). Here, k_i, Sh_i = phase mass transfer coefficients and Sherwood numbers, respectively, d_{32} = Sauter mean droplet diameter, D_{API} = API diffusivity, ϕ = dispersed phase volume fraction, Sc = Schmidt number, Fr = Froude number, Eo = Eotvos number, Re_i = impeller Reynolds' number, d_i, d_t = impeller and tank diameters, respectively, We = Weber number, N_i = impeller rotation speed, ρ_c = continuous phase density and σ = surface tension. The calculation of all terms uses the Skelland and Moetti (1990) correlation for continuous LLE modelling as mixer-settlers.

$$E_{LLE} = ((Ka\tau_{LLE})^{-1} + 1)^{-1} \tag{1}$$

$$K = \left(k_c^{-1} + k_d^{-1}\right)^{-1} \tag{2}$$

$$a = \frac{6\phi}{d_{32}} \tag{3}$$

$$Sh_d = \frac{k_d d_{32}}{D_{API,d}} \approx 6.6 \tag{4}$$

$$Sh_c = \frac{k_c d_{32}}{D_{API,c}} = 1.25 \times 10^{-5} Sc_c^{1/3} Fr_c^{5/12} Eo^{5/4} \phi^{-1/2} Re^{2/3} \left(\frac{d_i}{d_{32}}\right)^2 \left(\frac{d_{32}}{d_t}\right)^{1/2} \tag{5}$$

$$d_{32} = \begin{cases} 0.052 d_i We^{-0.6} \exp 4\phi & , We < 10^3 \\ 0.390 d_i We^{-0.6} & , We > 10^3 \end{cases} \tag{6}$$

$$We = \frac{d_i^3 N_i^2 \rho_c}{\sigma} \tag{7}$$

2.4. MINLP Optimisation Problem Formulation

The MINLP LLE superstructure is illustrated in Fig. 3; the location and number of LLE solvent feed points and tanks affects the LLE performance and total costs and is varied in the considered superstructure. The objective of the MINLP optimisation problem is to minimise the total plant cost (*Cost*, Eq. 8). Integer decision variables are the number of LLE tanks, N_{LLE}, allowed a maximum number of 3 (Eq. 9), binary integer variable, y_i, which determines the number and location of fresh LLE solvent feed points (Eqs. 10–11). When the sum of $y_i = 0$, a purely countercurrent LLE configuration is implemented, i.e., no fresh LLE solvent is added; when $y_i > 0$, fresh LLE solvent is fed to tank i in addition to the countercurrent extract entering tank N_{LLE} and flowing through remaining tanks.

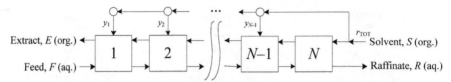

Figure 3: MINLP superstructure for the continuous liquid-liquid extraction (LLE), with continuous (tank volume, V_i, solvent feed rate, r_{TOT}) and integer variables (no. tanks, N_{LLE} and allocation of fresh solvent feed, y_i, and solvent choice).

Continuous decision variables are the total solvent-to-feed ratio (r_{TOT}), for which fresh solvent is divided equally between tanks to which a crossflow LLE solvent feed is specified (i.e., where $y_i = 1$) and constrained within values to ensure that the LLE process mixture is always fully immiscible (Eq. 13) for total LLE solvent addition, S_i (Eq. 11) and LLE tank volumes (V_i), each allowed to have a minimum volume of 1 L (Eq. 14). The problem is solved for separate instances of LLE solvent. For N_{LLE} implemented tanks, there are $N_{LLE} + 1$ continuous decision variables (V_i and r_{TOT}) and $N_{LLE} - 1$ integer decision variables (y_i), i.e. a total of $2N_{LLE}$ decision variables per instance. A multistart routine using multiple initial guesses of each decision variable is implemented in order to find as near to a global minima as possible. The considered plant capacity in all cases is $Q_{API} = 10^3$ kg API yr^{-1}. The current MINLP formulation has a small number of discrete variables, which could be solved as separate NLP instances; however, the current framework can be easily adapted to consider greater numbers of possible LLE tanks (N_{LLE}), which rapidly increases the number of discrete variables, for which applying MINLP is more suitable.

$$\min Cost = CapEx + \sum_{j=1}^{t} \frac{OpEx}{(1+k)^j} \tag{8}$$

s.t.

$$N_{LLE} \in \{1, 2, 3\} \tag{9}$$

$$y_i \in \{0,1\}, \, i = 1 \ldots N_{LLE} - 1 \tag{10}$$

$$S_i = \frac{y_j r_{TOT} F}{\sum y_j + 1} \text{ for } i = 1 \ldots N_{LLE}, j = 1 \ldots N_{LLE} \tag{11}$$

$$\sum_{i=1}^{N_{LLE}-1} y_i \leq N_{LLE} - 1 \tag{12}$$

$$0.25 \leq r_{TOT} \leq 5 \tag{13}$$

$$1 \leq V_i \tag{14}$$

Total costs (*Cost*) are calculated as the sum of capital expenditure (*CapEx*), assumed spent at year zero, and the sum of time-discounted operating expenditure (*OpEx*) over the considered plant lifetime, $t = 20$ yr. The discount rate ($k = 5\%$) accounts for inflation over the plant lifetime. Annual operation of 8,000 hr is considered. Capital expenditure includes battery limits installed costs, construction and working capital; operating expenditure is the sum of material costs, utilities and waste handling costs. The implemented costing methodology in this work is applicable to both continuous and batch API pharmaceutical manufacturing processes (Jolliffe and Gerogiorgis, 2016).

3. Results and Discussion

Fig. 4 shows the optimal design configuration for each LLE solvent choice. All solvent choices result in the same flowsheet configuration, $N_{LLE} = 3$ tanks, with an extra fresh solvent feed to the first tank, but varying optimal tank volumes and LLE solvent-to-feed ratios. Tank volumes vary, with the largest being the first tank in all design cases, with the largest tanks required for BuOAc implementation. Consideration of longer cascades (i.e., more tanks), may lead to lower unit volumes and will affect the resulting efficiency and minimum total costs. The total LLE-solvent-to-feed ratio (r_{TOT}) varies between solvents, but all are typically mid-range with respect to the constraints applied to ensure process mixtures remain fully immiscible. The LLE MINLP superstructure considered in this work (Fig. 3) can be expanded further to consider splitting the fresh feed stream as well as splitting product from intermittent stages and the as possible implementation of solvent recycling. Consideration of subsequent crystallisation process requirements on LLE product streams should also be integrated with solvent harmonisation during the early stages of design to aid CPM development and mitigate plantwide operational issues.

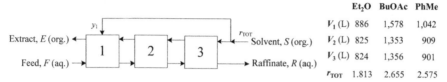

	Et$_2$O	BuOAc	PhMe
V_1 (L)	886	1,578	1,042
V_2 (L)	825	1,353	909
V_3 (L)	824	1,356	901
r_{TOT}	1.813	2.655	2.575

Figure 4: Optimal LLE MINLP superstructure and design and operating parameters corresponding to minimum plant total costs for different design assumptions.

Fig. 5 shows minimum total cost components corresponding to optimal LLE configurations presented in Fig. 4. *CapEx* is dominated by *BLIC* in all cases while material costs dominate *OpEx* due to expensive reagents. Despite high *CapEx* associated with large tank volumes, the benefits associated with increased LLE efficiency on reducing material requirements and waste is required due to the high contribution of *OpEx* components to total costs. Optimisation results show that toluene (PhMe) is the best LLE solvent choice, attaining the lowest total costs. Toluene exhibits the widest envelope of immiscibility of the LLE solvents considered; rapid and wide phase splitting allows for enhanced LLE performance. Further corroboration of optimisation results with experimental validation as well as solvent harmonisation with crystallisation processes is essential. Although toluene is more economically favourable, it has less favourable EHS criteria compared to BuOAc. Explicit consideration of solvent selection heuristics based upon EHS criteria has been useful in previous CPM efforts (Diab and Gerogiorgis, 2017).

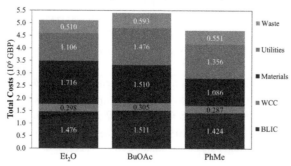

Figure 5: Minimum total cost components for different LLE solvent choices.

4. Conclusions

This work has formulated and solved a MINLP optimisation problem for the total cost minimisation of the plantwide CPM of atropine, a societally-important API with a variety of applications. Optimisation of a conceptual continuous LLE following the continuous flow synthesis for different LLE solvent choices was used to elucidate promising designs. Ternary phase equilibria were estimated via UNIFAC modelling and solute distribution between LLE phases used published partition coefficient data. The optimal LLE configuration for all cases implements three LLE tanks in series in a countercurrent arrangement with additional fresh LLE solvent fed to the first tank in the cascade. Investigation of more complex LLE superstructures accounting for greater numbers of tanks and recycle options will further elucidate optimal process design. Toluene emerges as the most economically favourable LLE solvent choice, offering significant total cost savings over other LLE designs with acceptable material efficiencies for pharmaceutical manufacturing applications. Consideration of downstream unit operation requirements for LLE solvent selection and harmonisation following the upstream CPM plant considered here will provide further insight into optimal process configuration and designs. This work demonstrates the value of conducting technoeconomic optimisation studies during the early stages of design towards economically viable end-to-end CPM.

Acknowledgements

Mr. Samir Diab gratefully acknowledges the financial support of the Engineering and Physical Sciences Research Council (EPSRC) via a Doctoral Training Partnership (DTP) PhD Fellowship (Grant # EP/N509644/1). Mr. Nikolaos Mytis acknowledges the support of an Erasmus+ Teaching Exchange Travel Scholarship. Dr. Dimitrios I. Gerogiorgis acknowledges a Royal Academy of Engineering (RAEng) Industrial Fellowship. The authors acknowledge the support of the Nagai and Great Britain Sasakawa Foundations.

References

A.C. Bédard, A.R. Longstreet, J. Britton, Y. Wang, H. Moriguchi, R.W. Hicklin, W.H. Green and T.F. Jamison, 2016, Minimizing E-factor in the continuous-flow synthesis of diazepam and atropine, *Bioorg. Med. Chem.*, 25, 23, 6233–6241.

I.R. Baxendale, R.D Braatz, B.K. Hodnett, K.F. Jensen, M.D. Johnson, P. Sharratt, J.-P. Sherlock, A.J. Florence, Achieving continuous manufacturing: technologies and approaches for synthesis, workup, and isolation of drug substance, *J. Pharm. Sci.*, 104, 3, 781–791.

S. Diab and D.I. Gerogiorgis, 2017, Process modeling and technoeconomic evaluation for continuous manufacturing of diphenhydramine, *Org. Process Res. Dev.*, 21, 7, 924–946.

H.G. Jolliffe and D.I. Gerogiorgis, 2016, Plantwide design and economic evaluation of two continuous pharmaceutical manufacturing cases, *Comput. Chem. Eng.*, 91, 269–288.

S. Koenig and B. Dillon, 2017, Driving toward greener chemistry in the pharmaceutical industry, *Curr. Opin. Green Sust. Chem.*, 7, 56–59.

T. Marrs and P. Rice, Chemical terrorism and nerve agents, 2016, *Medicine*, 44, 2, 106–108.

A.H.P. Skelland and L.T. Moetti, 1990, Mechanism of continuous-phase mass transfer in agitated liquid-liquid systems, *Ind. Eng. Chem. Res.*, 29, 11, 2258–2267.

S.K. Teoh, C. Rathi and P. Sharratt, 2015, Practical assessment methodology for converting fine chemicals processes from batch to continuous, *Org. Process Res. Dev.*, 20, 2, 414–431.

Anton A. Kiss, Edwin Zondervan, Richard Lakerveld, Leyla Özkan (Eds.)
Proceedings of the 29th European Symposium on Computer Aided Process Engineering
June 16th to 19th, 2019, Eindhoven, The Netherlands. © 2019 Elsevier B.V. All rights reserved.
http://dx.doi.org/10.1016/B978-0-128-18634-3.50037-0

Multi-product reactive distillation process for higher acrylates production

Mihai Daniel Moraru,[a,b,*] Anton Alexandru Kiss,[c,d] Costin Sorin Bildea[b]

[a]*Department of Process Technology and Development, Hexion, Seattleweg 17, 3195 ND Pernis, The Netherlands*

[b]*Department of Chemical and Biochemical Engineering, University Politehnica of Bucharest, Str. Gh. Polizu 1-7, 011061 Bucharest, Romania*

[c]*School of Chemical Engineering and Analytical Science, The University of Manchester, Sackville Street, Manchester M13 9PL, United Kingdom*

[d]*Sustainable Process Technology Group, Faculty of Science and Technology, University of Twente, PO Box 217, 7500 AE Enschede, The Netherlands*

mihai.moraru@hexion.com

Abstract

Higher acrylates are used in special applications. However, production at high capacity in continuous reactive distillation (RD) systems, throughout the whole year of only one acrylate, may be hindered by a low market and periodic demands. Thus, for the asset to be fully utilized, one may consider to build a multi-product reactive distillation system. This is a preliminary study that shows what four higher acrylates (i.e., isoamyl acrylate, cyclohexyl acrylate, 2-ethylhexyl acrylate and *n*-decyl acrylate) have in common to be considered candidates for producing them in the same column, and the methodology to design such a multi-product RD column. The systemic design method uses PSE tools to achieve the design, based solely on thermodynamics and equilibrium information.

Keywords: conceptual design, higher alcohols, process intensification, simulation

1. Introduction

Acrylates are essential chemicals used as precursors in the production of polyacrylates which are employed in a range of industries (e.g. packaging, consumer goods, and construction, automotive) and a variety of applications (e.g. coatings, paints, resins, adhesives, textiles, personal care). Acrylates with a high number of carbon atoms are more preferred in special applications. Reports state that the acrylate market was valued at B\$ 6.86 in 2016, aiming to reach B\$ 9.88 in 2022 (www.marketsandmarkets.com).

Conventional processes using strong homogeneous catalysts (i.e., acid sulfuric) are only briefly presented in the open literature (Ohara et al., 2003). A few new conceptual processes using solid-based catalysts for the synthesis of some higher-acrylates and methacrylates have been also developed, showing a high potential in overcoming the well-known drawbacks of conventional processes: corrosion, product purification, and disposal of spent catalyst, which usually lead to high operating and maintenance costs, and increasing difficulty to comply with environmental regulations (Kiss et al., 2015).

This work considers a generic perspective, by investigating the technical feasibility of producing four industrially important higher-acrylates by esterification employing the same reactive distillation (RD) process using solid catalysts. The pure component properties are estimated using group contribution methods (due to lack of experimental data in literature), followed by studying key thermodynamic properties relevant for process design. Chemical equilibrium is determined by minimizing the Gibbs energy of the system to indicate the maximum conversion possible. A preliminary RD column design is proposed using an equilibrium model. An additional separation step may be required for the recovery of one reactant (alcohol) while the limiting reactant (acrylic acid) has a conversion close to 100%. The design can be refined later, by including the reaction rate, when kinetics data is available in literature.

2. Higher acrylates and key physical properties

A higher acrylate is produced in the reaction of acrylic acid (AA) with an alcohol which has a number of carbon atoms higher than 4, following the chemical reaction:

Table 1 presents some basic properties for the four acrylates presented in this study. Two of the acrylates (*i*-AA and *2*-EHA) present some branching, one of them (CHA) has a cyclohexane ring, while the remaining (*n*-DA) is a linear acrylate. All have a relatively high molecular weight and normal boiling point.

Table 1. Basic physical properties of some high acrylates

Acrylate[†]	MW [g/mol]	T_b [°C]	DHFORM[‡] [kJ/mol]	DGFORM[‡] [kJ/mol]
isoamyl acrylate (*i*-AA)	142.2	163.8	-398.82	-208.49
cyclohexyl acrylate (CHA)	154.2	206.6	-382.42	-173.18
2-ethylhexyl acrylate (*2*-EHA)	184.3	232.4	-458.61	-183.23
n-decyl acrylate (*n*-DA)	212.3	278.6	-488.18	-163.95

[†]chemical structures:

isoamyl acrylate   cyclohexyl acrylate   2-ethylhexyl acrylate   n-decyl acrylate

[‡]DHFORM and DGFORM are the ideal gas enthalpy and energy of formation (25 °C) estimated using the Property Constant Estimation System (PCES) of Aspen Properties.

All these acrylate systems have in common important characteristics that make them candidates to be produced in the same reactive distillation system:

- From the view point of process structure, each acrylate is the highest boiler in its system and is obtained as bottom products (note that water is the lowest boiler component). In addition, all acrylate systems present heterogeneous minimum boiling azeotropes containing water in high concentration (Table 2), making thus possible to eliminate the water in the same way, in the overhead of the column: the vapors are condensed; the condensate undergoes a liquid-liquid split; the organic phase is refluxed to the column, while the water is removed from the process.

- From a mass balance perspective, similar acrylate systems catalyzed by solid catalysts present very similar space-time-yields ($t_{product}/t_{cat}/h$): 0.65 for isobutyl acrylate (Moraru et al., 2018), 1.28 for *n*-butyl acrylate (Moraru and Bildea, 2017) and 1.57 for *2*-ethylhexyl acrylate (Moraru and Bildea, 2018).

- From a heat balance perspective, all reactions are slightly endothermic, having similar reaction enthalpy (Table 2). Hence, these three main factors are good indicators that the higher acrylates can be produced in the same RD column.

Table 2. Azeotropy and reaction enthalpies of the four acrylate systems

Physical property	*i*-AA	CHA	2-EHA	*n*-DA
Azeotrope comp. / [% wt.]				
water/alcohol	50.21/49.79	70.18/29.82	80.87/19.13	96.15/3.85
water/acrylate	53.58/46.42	79.34/20.66	89.45/10.55	97.45/2.55
water/alcohol/acrylate	48.36/43.17/8.47			96.43/3.55/0.02
Enthalpy of reaction (liquid phase, 25 °C) / [kJ/mol]	15.9	16.4	27.0	35.2

3. Chemical equilibrium

Slightly endothermic / exothermic equilibrium esterification reactions are known as perfect candidates to be performed in RD systems (Kiss, 2018). As the equilibrium is shifted towards the products formation by removing water, very high or even complete per-pass conversions can be achieved. Hence, studying the chemical equilibrium gives basic info which is used in the conceptual design of the RD system. Figure 1 shows the equilibrium conversion of AA as function of temperature for several acrylate systems.

Firstly, take the *n*-butyl acrylate (*n*-BA) system. The *n*-BA (Lit) profiles, triangles and circles, represent calculated data using two equations taken from published literature, which were in turn derived from experimental data (see the right-lower corner). The *n*-BA (Aspen Database) profile is obtained by calculating K_{eq} from Gibbs free energies, for which parameters (for *n*-BA) are available in the Aspen database; although for the low temperatures the agreement is not perfect, it improves for the temperature range of practical interest (over 60 °C) where the reaction rates are higher.

Secondly, consider the *2*-EHA system. The *2*-EHA (Lit) profile uses an equation based on experimental data (see the right-lower corner). The *2*-EHA (PCES) is obtained by calculating K_{eq} from Gibbs free energies, for which the necessary parameters (for *2*-EHA) are estimated using the PCES of Aspen Properties. In this case, the agreement is very good. Thus, one may conclude that the accuracy of the predictive thermodynamic models based on group contributions is reasonable.

For the other three acrylates (*i*-AA, CHA and *n*-DA), the parameters to calculate K_{eq} are estimated by PCES. All reactions are slightly endothermic. Analyses based on experimental data are preferred, but when neither equilibrium data nor the required parameters in the Aspen database are available, then one must rely on group contribution methods to estimate the missing parameters. Results presented in Figure 1 also demonstrate that reasonable conversions can be obtained for all the alcohols considered here. However, the chemical equilibrium sets an upper bound on the achievable conversion. This can be overcome by removing one reactant (water) from the reaction mixture due to formation of the low-boiling azeotrope, and/or by performing the reaction with an excess of one reactant, achieved by refluxing the alcohol-rich organic phase from the top decanter.

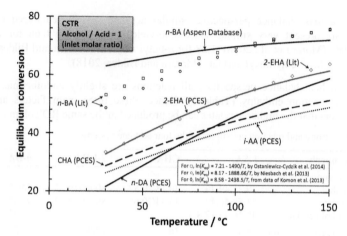

Figure 1. Equilibrium conversion for acrylic acid esterification with different alcohols, for an alcohol / acid feed molar ratio of 1.

4. Conceptual process design

For the acrylates to be all produced in the same equipment, the design has to take into account those conditions, specific to each acrylate, in which the RD is feasible. These conditions are represented here by the shaded area of the *P-T* diagram showed in Figure 2 (left). The diagram is constructed using four distinct *P-T* areas, one for each acrylate. For illustration purposes, the right-lower corner shows how this feasibility area is constructed for *2*-EHA, using the vapor pressure of the highest (acrylate) and lowest (water/alcohol azeotrope) boilers in this specific system. The area covering all acrylates spans over a large range of conditions: 60-190 °C and 0.1-6 bar. The temperature bounds come from the interval in which the reaction can be performed: the minimum temperature at which the reaction rate becomes fast enough and the maximum temperature the catalyst can withstand. The maximum pressure (about 6 bar) is given by the boiling temperature of most volatile acrylate (i.e. *i*-AA), which should be achieved by using HP steam (240 °C). The minimum pressure constraint (0.1 bar) arrives from the need of using cooling water for condensing the low boiling water-alcohol azeotropes.

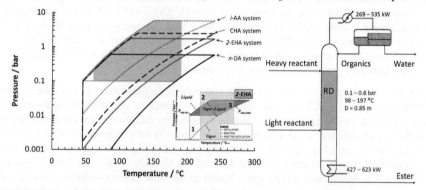

Figure 2. Pressure-Temperature conditions considered in design of the reactive distillation system (left) and reactive distillation column including the main sizes and process data (right)

Based on this feasibility window, one can conclude that it will be difficult to design a column that operates at constant pressure and similar temperature intervals, and produces all four acrylates; basically, to operate in that region where the individual feasibility windows overlap. One approach is to set the column pressure depending on the acrylate produced, and verify that the operating temperature in the column is not higher compared to the temperature the catalyst can withstand. Of course, the temperature should not be too low either. Previous studies for higher acrylates produced in reactive distillation systems (Niesbach et al., 2013) showed that above 100 °C, the reaction rate is high enough to be industrially attractive.

5. Column design

The design of the RD column that is able to produce all acrylates consists of two steps:

1. For each acrylate, design one RD column (i.e., theoretical stages and diameter) that meets certain specifications.

2. For all acrylates, select the RD column with the highest number of theoretical stages determined in the previous step, average the diameter of all columns and rate all acrylate processes in this specific column.

Each acrylate-specific design aimed to have the same production rate, and obtain a product with a purity of at least 99.5 %wt. This design step is iterative, and starts by selecting a top-pressure in the column, followed by the number of trays in each section, and for hydrodynamic reasons, a minimum reflux ratio. Then, the number of stages in each zone was varied and aimed at reducing them until the product purity cannot be achieved anymore. If the pressure can be further reduced (but still being able to use cooling water in the condenser), then a new iteration starts; if not, then the design stops and all variables of interest are recorded. Table 3 presents the results of step 1. Based on these results, in step 2 the number of stages specific to *i*-AA column are considered (i.e., the tallest column) and the diameter is calculated by averaging the column diameters. Then, each acrylate process is rated in this specific column.

The results of step 2 are given in Table 4. Start with the *i*-AA process; since the column diameter is with 0.1 m larger, the reflux had to be increased from 4 to 5.5 (again, from hydrodynamic reasons); no further modifications are required. For the CHA process, only the number of stages is updated; the hydrodynamics presents no issues since the column diameter is only 0.05 m larger; the same holds for the 2-EHA process. For the *n*-DA process, the production capacity is reduced to cope with the decrease in diameter from 0.98 to 0.85 m.

Table 3. Key design and operating parameters for each acrylate produced in individual columns

Parameter	*i*-AA	CHA	2-EHA	*n*-DA
$N_R \mid N_{RXN} \mid N_S$	1 | 4 | 4	1 | 3 | 2	1 | 3 | 2	1 | 4 | 2
D_{column} / [m]	0.74	0.80	0.85	0.98
$F_{acrylate} \mid F_{water}$ / [kg/h]	2524 | 330	2525 | 305	2535 | 247	2526 | 215
Reflux / [kg/h]	1322	1225	990	860
Purity acrylate | water / [% wt.]	99.5 | 96.3	99.5 | 96.3	99.5 | 99.6	99.9 | 99.6
$Q_R \mid Q_C$ / [kW]	519 | 508	546 | 465	486 | 340	503 | 320
$P_{top} \mid P_{bottom}$ / [bar]	0.6 | 0.609	0.3 | 0.306	0.2 | 0.203	0.1 | 0.104
$T_{top} \mid T_{bottom}$ / [°C]	96 | 146	99 | 161	110 | 172	129 | 193

Table 4. Key design and operating parameters for each acrylate produced in the same column

Parameter	i-AA	CHA	2-EHA	n-DA
N_R | N_{RXN} | N_S		1 | 4 | 4		
D_{column} / [m]		0.85		
$F_{acrylate}$ | F_{water} / [kg/h]	2524 | 330	2539 | 306	2537 | 247	2123 | 181
Reflux / [kg/h]	1814	1224	988	722
Purity acrylate | water / [% wt.]	99.5 | 96.4	99.5 | 96.4	99.5 | 99.9	100 | 99.7
Q_R | Q_C / [kW]	623 | 535	553 | 471	488 | 341	427 | 269
P_{top} | P_{bottom} / [bar]	0.6 | 0.606	0.3 | 0.305	0.2 | 0.207	0.1 | 0.115
T_{top} | T_{bottom} / [°C]	99 | 145	98 | 161	109 | 173	129 | 197

6. Conclusions

Using a PSE methodology based on physical properties and chemical equilibrium data (estimated or reported in the literature), this study shows that higher acrylates are good candidates to be produced in the same reactive distillation column. A follow-up study should reiterate this design based on reaction kinetics and mass transfer considerations.

Acknowledgements

CSB kindly acknowledges the financial support of the European Commission through the European Regional Development Fund and of the Romanian state budget, under the grant agreement 155/25.11.2016 Project POC P-37-449 (ASPiRE). AAK is thankful for the Royal Society Wolfson Research Merit Award.

References

A. A. Kiss, A. J. B. ten Kate, E. Conte, 2015, Continuous process for the esterification of an alpha, beta-unsaturated carboxylic acid and an alcohol, Patent No. WO/2015/018773.

A. A. Kiss, 2018, Novel catalytic reactive distillation processes for a sustainable chemical industry, Top. Catal., DOI: 10.1007/s11244-018-1.

T. Komon, P. Niewiadomski, P. Oracz, M. E. Jamroz, 2013, Esterification of acrylic acid with 2-ethylhexan-1-ol: Thermodynamic and kinetic study. Appl. Catal., A. 451, 127-136.

M. D. Moraru, D. A. Berinde, C. S. Bildea, 2018, Design, control and economics of a process for isobutyl acrylate production. Comput. Aided Chem. Eng. 43, 711-716.

M. D. Moraru, C. S. Bildea, 2017, Process for n-butyl acrylate production using reactive distillation: Design, control and economic evaluation. Chem. Eng. Res. Des. 125, 130-145.

M. D. Moraru, C. S. Bildea, 2018, Reaction-separation-recycle processes for 2-ethylhexyl acrylate production: Design, control, and economic evaluation, Ind. Eng. Chem. Res. 57, 2609-2627.

A. Niesbach, H. Kuhlmann, T. Keller, P. Lutze, A. Gorak, 2013, Optimisation of industrial-scale n-butyl acrylate production using reactive distillation. Chem. Eng. Sci. 100, 360-372.

T. Ohara, T. Sato, N. Shimizu, G. Prescher, H. Schwind, O. Weiberg, K. Marten, H. Greim, 2003. Acrylic acid and derivatives, in: Ullmann's Encyclopedia of Industrial Chemistry.

A.M. Ostaniewicz-Cydzik, C.S.M. Pereira, E. Molga, A.E. Rodrigues, 2014, Reaction Kinetics and Thermodynamic Equilibrium for Butyl Acrylate Synthesis from n-Butanol and Acrylic Acid. Ind. Eng. Chem. Res. 53, (16), 6647-6654.

Anton A. Kiss, Edwin Zondervan, Richard Lakerveld, Leyla Özkan (Eds.)
Proceedings of the 29th European Symposium on Computer Aided Process Engineering
June 16th to 19th, 2019, Eindhoven, The Netherlands. © 2019 Elsevier B.V. All rights reserved.
http://dx.doi.org/10.1016/B978-0-128-18634-3.50038-2

A point estimate method-based back-off approach to robust optimization: application to pharmaceutical processes

Victor N. Emenike[1,a,b], Xiangzhong Xie[1, a,b], Ulrike Krewer[a,b] and René Schenkendorf[a,b,*]

[a]*Institute of Energy and Process Systems Engineering, TU Braunschweig, Franz-Liszt-Straße 35, 38106 Braunschweig, Germany*
[b]*Center of Pharmaceutical Engineering, Franz-Liszt-Straße 35A, 38106 Braunschweig, Germany*
r.schenkendorf@tu-braunschweig.de

Abstract

In this contribution, we propose estimating the means and variances required for calculating back-off terms by using the point estimate method (PEM) as a highly efficient sampling strategy in robust process design. As case studies, we consider an upstream pharmaceutical process which involves the synthesis of 2-hydroxy-ketones via enzyme-catalyzed carboligation and a downstream pharmaceutical process that includes the continuous crystallization of ibuprofen. We show that the proposed PEM-based back-off approach is significantly faster than conventional Monte Carlo brute-force sampling methods while maintaining robust solutions with low approximation errors. In general, the efficient PEM-sampling strategy guarantees the analysis and the robust design of complex (bio)pharmaceutical process chains.

Keywords: pharmaceutical manufacturing, robust optimization, back-off approach, enzyme catalysis, ibuprofen crystallization

1. Introduction

The pharmaceutical industry has a substantial impact on the social and economic welfare of the individual and society. For the industry to continue producing high-quality and effective drugs even in the face of economic constraints, rising population and diseases, regulatory bodies and industry leaders alike have stipulated Quality by Design (QbD) as an essential paradigm. At the heart of QbD are mathematical models which are crucial for analyzing, optimizing, monitoring and controlling pharmaceutical processes (Emenike et al., 2018a,b). These models need to be properly calibrated to ensure that they reflect the physical processes they represent (Schenkendorf et al., 2018). In calibrating these models, a crucial issue that has to be dealt with is the presence of model and parameter uncertainties. A possible way to robustify processes under uncertainty is by using the back-off approach. This approach involves tightening violated constraints and shrinking the feasible region by introducing margins called back-offs. By so doing, the worst-case realization of a given process will still be feasible despite variations in the constraints (Shi et al., 2016). Moreover, these back-offs are usually calculated offline, and thus, do not lead to additional complexity of the optimization problems. Typically, Monte Carlo simulations are used to estimate the statistical moments (i.e., means and variances) required for calculating back-offs (Shi et al.,

---

[1]These authors contributed equally.

2016). However, for these means and variances to be accurately estimated, numerous Monte Carlo simulations are usually required. Thus, this could lead to high computational costs especially when a single Monte Carlo simulation of the process is computationally expensive.

Alternatively, these statistical moments can be approximated efficiently by using the point estimate method (PEM). It has been shown that the PEM is a computationally efficient and relatively accurate sampling strategy for estimating statistical moments (Schenkendorf, 2014; Xie et al., 2018b). Recently, we proposed a systematic robust optimization framework that combines the elementary process functions methodology, global sensitivity analysis, and the back-off approach (Emenike et al., 2019). A key contribution in Emenike et al. (2019) was a new back-off algorithm that uses the PEM instead of Monte Carlo simulations. We showed that the proposed PEM-based back-off approach is at least 10 times faster than the conventional Monte Carlo-based back-off approach while maintaining the quality of robust solutions. Maußner and Freund (2018) used cubature rules in lieu of Monte Carlo simulations and came to similar conclusions.

In this contribution, we build upon our original work (Emenike et al., 2019) by applying the novel algorithm in the presence of correlated parameter uncertainties and show that the robustification algorithm is not limited to upstream processes but is a versatile tool for whole pharmaceutical process chains. To this end, we apply the novel algorithm to an upstream pharmaceutical process that involves the synthesis of 2-hydroxy-ketones via enzyme-catalyzed carboligation and a downstream pharmaceutical process that includes the crystallization of ibuprofen. Details of the algorithm and the results for the case studies are presented in sections 2 and 3, respectively.

2. Methodology

A major advantage of the back-off approach to dynamic optimization under uncertainty is that its formulation is of similar complexity as the nominal dynamic optimization problem. The robust optimization problem (Problem 1) with time-varying back-offs $\mathbf{b}(t)$ is given as:

$$\underset{\mathbf{x}(\cdot),\mathbf{u}(\cdot),\mathbf{z}(\cdot)}{\text{minimize}} \quad \Phi(\mathbf{x}(t_f))) \tag{1a}$$

$$\text{subject to} \quad \dot{\mathbf{x}}(t) = \mathbf{f}(\mathbf{x}(t),\mathbf{z}(t),\mathbf{u}(t),\bar{\mathbf{p}}), \quad \forall t \in \mathcal{T}, \tag{1b}$$

$$\mathbf{g}(\mathbf{x}(t),\mathbf{z}(t),\mathbf{u}(t),\bar{\mathbf{p}}) = \mathbf{0}, \quad \forall t \in \mathcal{T}, \tag{1c}$$

$$\mathbf{h}(\mathbf{x}(t),\mathbf{z}(t),\mathbf{u}(t),\bar{\mathbf{p}}) + \mathbf{b}(t) \leq \mathbf{0}, \quad \forall t \in \mathcal{T}, \tag{1d}$$

$$\mathbf{x}(t_0) = \mathbf{x}_0, \tag{1e}$$

$$\mathbf{u}(t) \in \mathcal{U}, \tag{1f}$$

on the time horizon $\mathcal{T} := [t_0, t_f] \subset \mathbb{R}$, where $\mathbf{x}$, $\mathbf{u}$, $\mathbf{z}$ represent states, controls, and algebraic variables, respectively. $\mathbf{g}$ and $\mathbf{h}$ represent the equality and inequality constraints, respectively. As we can see from Problem 1, the dynamic optimization with back-offs is optimized at the nominal parameter vector $\bar{\mathbf{p}}$. Here, the time-varying back-offs $\mathbf{b}(t)$ in Eq. 1d are included as margins to shrink the feasible region of the dynamic optimization problem and thus, making the optimal operating conditions robust.

As pointed out by Shi et al. (2016), the solution from Problem 1 is not guaranteed to be optimum, unless the back-offs are insensitive to the decision variables. Therefore, an iterative approach is proposed to update the back-offs with the optimal design from the last iteration. The solution from Problem 1 and back-offs are consistently improved and can be exported once the back-offs converge. We depict the details regarding the iterative algorithm in Fig. 1. Moreover, we use the PEM instead of Monte Carlo simulations used by Shi et al. (2016) to derive the statistical moments required to calculate the back-offs. The PEM utilizes a relatively small number of deterministic

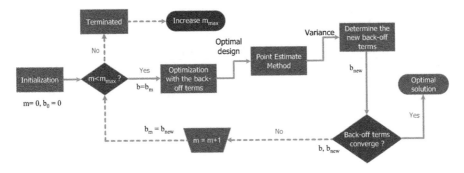

Figure 1: Computational scheme for the point estimate method-based back-off approach for robust optimization, where m is the iteration index.

samples to compute the statistical moments of system states and thus, facilitates an efficient back-off algorithm. For more details regarding the PEM, please refer to Xie et al. (2018b) and Emenike et al. (2019).

3. Case studies

3.1. Enzyme-catalyzed carboligation

First, we consider an upstream pharmaceutical process that involves an enzyme-catalyzed carboligation between propanal (A) and benzaldehyde (B) to form 2-hydroxy-ketones (BA) and benzoin (BB). Here, we aim to maximize the formation of the target product BA under the correlated parameter uncertainties specified in Xie et al. (2018a). The mechanistic model for this reaction is given as:

$$\dot{\mathbf{x}}(t) = \mathbf{f}(\mathbf{x}(t), \mathbf{z}(t), \mathbf{u}(t), \mathbf{p}) = \begin{bmatrix} \frac{u_A \cdot C_A^{in}}{V} - \frac{C_A}{V}(u_A + u_B) + r_A \\ \frac{u_B \cdot C_B^{in}}{V} - \frac{C_B}{V}(u_A + u_B) + r_B \\ -\frac{C_{BA}}{V}(u_A + u_B) + r_{BA} \\ -\frac{C_{BB}}{V}(u_A + u_B) + r_{BB} \\ -\frac{C_E}{V}(u_A + u_B) + r_E \\ u_A + u_B \end{bmatrix}, \tag{2}$$

where C_i is the concentration of species i; r_A, r_B, r_{BA}, r_{BB}, and r_E are the reaction rates for A, B, BA, BB, and E, respectively; u_A and u_B are the controlled feed rates; and C_A^{in} and C_B^{in} are the inlet feed concentrations of A and B, respectively. For details on the model and model parameters, we refer to Emenike et al. (2019). First, forward simulations by using 10,000 Monte Carlo simulations were performed on the nominal problem to determine which constraints were violated, and it was found that only the inequality constraint bounding C_{BB} was violated. Therefore, we focus on robustifying only the C_{BB} inequality constraint as shown in Eq. (3):

$$0 \le C_{BB}(t) \le 2.78 \text{ mM} - b(t), \quad \forall t \in \mathscr{T}, \tag{3}$$

where 2.78 mM is the solubility limit of BB, $\mathscr{T} := [t_0, t_f] \subset \mathbb{R}$, and final time, $t_f = 300$ min. By applying the robust optimization strategy presented in Section 2 and aiming to satisfy Eq. 3 at a probability of 99.90%, we see in Table 1 that the PEM-based back-off algorithm is able to achieve this after just one iteration of the algorithm.

Table 1: Comparison of the point estimate method-based algorithm with the Monte Carlo-based back-off algorithm for robust dynamic optimization in comparison to to the nominal case.

Scenarios	$C_{BA}(t_f)$ mM	Violation probability [%]	CPU time [s]
Nominal	3.60	57.65	4
PEM-based back-off	3.48	0.16	114
Monte Carlo-based back-off	3.49	0.13	2626

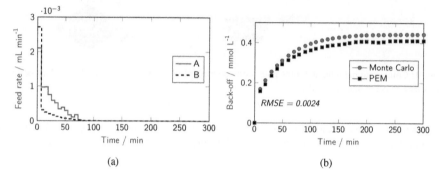

(a)   (b)

Figure 2: Results for the upstream pharmaceutical process: enzyme-catalyzed carboligation. (a) robust controls. (b) comparison between PEM and Monte Carlo simulations.

Moreover, this was achieved at a computation time that is 23 times faster than the conventional Monte Carlo-based back-off algorithm which was used as a benchmark for our algorithm (see Table 1). This speed-up is mainly due to the lower number of PEM sample points ($2 \times 13^2 + 1 = 339$) in comparison to the 10,000 Monte Carlo sample points. It is also possible to further reduce the PEM points by using a global sensitivity analysis as shown in Emenike et al. (2019). It can be seen in Fig. 2b that the time-varying back-offs calculated by both approaches are close with a marginal root-mean-square prediction error (RMSE) of 0.0024. This low RMSE validates the accuracy of our PEM-based approach. Furthermore, we note that the probability of violation and the maximum $C_{BA}(t_f)$ obtained are very close for both approaches, thus, suggesting that our PEM-based back-off approach is very accurate for the case study considered. The robust controls (see Fig 2a) lead to a maximum concentration of $3.48 \, \mathrm{mmol \, L^{-1}}$ which is 3.33% lower than the nominal value. This marginal decrease shows that the novel approach is not adversely conservative while ensuring robustness. Therefore, these results demonstrate that the PEM-based back-off strategy is very efficient and useful for the enzyme-catalyzed carboligation considered in this work.

3.2. Crystallization of ibuprofen

Second, we consider the continuous crystallization of ibuprofen in a plug-flow crystallizer (PFC) as a representative downstream pharmaceutical process. The crystal size distribution (CSD) n was chosen as an important key performance indicator for QbD. A population balance equation in combination with mass balance equations in liquid and solid phase was used to predict the evolution of the CSD along the PFC. To reduce the computational complexity, we discretized the PFC model to ordinary differential equations by using the classical method of moments. The resulting moment-based model for PFC is given in Eqs. (4) to (6):

$$\frac{d\mu_0}{dz} = \frac{B}{v} \tag{4}$$

$$\frac{d\mu_l}{dz} = \frac{BL_0^l}{v} + \frac{kG\mu_{l-1}}{v} \quad l = 1,\ldots,5 \tag{5}$$

Table 2: The mean value of mass-based mean crystal size d_{43} and the probability of a constraint violation (supersaturation) from the nominal design and the robust design with the PEM-based back-offs.

Scenarios	$\mathbb{E}(d_{43})$	Violation probability [%]
Nominal	109.3	48
PEM-based back-off	108.8	3

Liquid: $\quad \dfrac{\partial C}{\partial z} = -\dfrac{k_v \rho_s}{v}(BL_0^3 + 3G\mu_2),$ \hfill (6)

where z is the axis coordinate of the PFC, m; L_0 is the nuclei size, m; v is the superficial velocity of slurry along the PFC, $\mathrm{m\,s^{-1}}$; k_v and ρ_s are the shape factor and the crystal density, $\mathrm{kg\,m^{-3}}$, and C is the mass of solute per kg slurry, $\mathrm{kg\,kg^{-1}}$. μ_k is the kth moment which is used to describe the major information in CSD and defined with Eq. (7). B and G are the nucleation rate, $\mathrm{\#kg^{-1}\,s^{-1}}$, and the growth rate, $\mathrm{m\,s^{-1}}$, which describe the kinetics of the crystallization of ibuprofen and are determined by the degree of supersaturation S, as shown in Eqs. (8) and (9):

$$\mu_l = \int_0^\infty L^l n \, dL, \quad l = 0, \ldots, 5 \tag{7}$$

$$B = k_{b_0} S(T) \tag{8}$$

$$G = k_{g_0} \exp\left(\frac{T}{T_g}\right) S(T) \tag{9}$$

This case study aims to maximize the mass-based mean crystal size d_{43} (i.e., the ratio between μ_4 and μ_3) by manipulating the temperature along the PFC. There is an inequality constraint in the design which restricts the supersaturation of ibuprofen in the solution below the primary nucleation threshold to ensure no primary nucleation occurs. Several other inequality constraints on the yield of product and temperature gradient are also satisfied but not discussed in what follows, as they are not violated even in the presence of parameter uncertainties. Rashid (2011) estimated the values of the kinetic parameters k_{b_0}, k_{g_0}, and T_g with designed experiments and showed the estimated values are not accurate and associated with uncertainty. The parameter uncertainties are then described by Gaussian distributions and thus, are taken into account in the robust design of the PFC in this work.

For the nominal design, the parameter uncertainties are neglected. The obtained d_{43} is 109.3 μm (see Table 2). However, the inequality constraint on supersaturation is violated with a probability of 48% due to parameter uncertainties. The violation probability of inequality constraint is determined with 10,000 evaluations of the PFC model with the random samples generated from the probability distributions of kinetic parameters. The PEM-based back-off strategy introduced in Section 2 is then implemented to design a robust PFC tolerant to the parameter uncertainties, where the target violation probability of the inequality constraint is set to smaller than 1%. Results from the iterative back-off approach are depicted in Fig. 3. As we can see in Fig. 3a, the tolerance factor ε_{tol}, which represents the difference between the back-offs in the adjacent iterations, converges within 10 iterations. The resulting time-varying back-offs are plotted in Fig. 3b, in which the supersaturation is shrunk more in the middle and less on both sides of the PFC to mitigate the effect of parameter uncertainties. According to the results listed in Table 2, the d_{43} from the robust design decreases slightly when compared to the value from nominal design. The probability of constraint violation decreases to 3%. Thus, the process robustness is increased at the cost of a deteriorated performance. Although the back-off approach increases the robustness of the process significantly, the obtained violation probability 3% is still three times larger than the target value of 1%. The reason for this is that the back-offs calculated with the variances of system states are actually not accurate when their probability distributions are asymmetric, as shown in Fig. 3c.

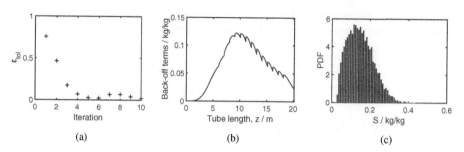

Figure 3: Results for the downstream pharmaceutical process: continuous crystallization of ibuprofen. (a) Convergence plot of the back-off terms. (b) value of the time-varying back-off terms at the last iteration. (c) probability distribution of supersaturation S at location $z = 11$m of the PFC.

4. Conclusions

In this work, we proposed a PEM-based back-off approach for the robust design of upstream and downstream pharmaceutical processes. First, the approach was implemented for the design of a fed-batch reactor for enzyme-catalyzed carboligation in the presence of parameter correlations and uncertainty. The results showed that the proposed PEM-based back-off approach is significantly faster than the conventional Monte Carlo-based back-off approach while achieving high accuracy of the robust solutions. The method was also applied to the design of continuous crystallization of ibuprofen in the presence of uncertainties in the kinetic parameters. This approach also lowered the value of constraint violation and significantly improved the robustness of the process. However, the probability of a constraint violation is still three times higher than the given target value due to the asymmetric probability distribution of system states. Future work will include non-Gaussian probability distributions for robust process design.

Acknowledgements

X. Xie acknowledges funding from the "Promotionsprogramm μ-Props" by MWK Niedersachsen. V. Emenike and X. Xie acknowledge the support from the International Max Planck Research School for Advanced Methods in Process and Systems Engineering, MPI Magdeburg.

References

V. N. Emenike, R. Schenkendorf, U. Krewer, 2018a. A systematic reactor design approach for the synthesis of active pharmaceutical ingredients. European Journal of Pharmaceutics and Biopharmaceutics 126, 75–88.

V. N. Emenike, R. Schenkendorf, U. Krewer, 2018b. Model-based optimization of biopharmaceutical manufacturing in Pichia pastoris based on dynamic flux balance analysis. Computers & Chemical Engineering 118, 1–13.

V. N. Emenike, X. Xie, R. Schenkendorf, A. C. Spiess, U. Krewer, 2019. Robust dynamic optimization of enzyme-catalyzed carboligation: A point estimate-based back-off approach. Computers & Chemical Engineering 121, 232–247.

J. Maußner, H. Freund, 2018. Optimization under uncertainty in chemical engineering: Comparative evaluation of unscented transformation methods and cubature rules. Chemical Engineering Science 183, 329–345.

M. A. Rashid, 2011. Crystallization engineering of ibuprofen for pharmaceutical formulation. PhD dissertation, Queensland University of Technology.

R. Schenkendorf, 2014. A general framework for uncertainty propagation based on point estimate methods. Second European Conference of the Prognostics and Health Management Society, PHME14, Nantes, France.

R. Schenkendorf, X. Xie, M. Rehbein, S. Scholl, U. Krewer, 2018. The impact of global sensitivities and design measures in model-based optimal experimental design. Processes 6 (4), 27.

J. Shi, L. T. Biegler, I. Hamdan, J. Wassick, 2016. Optimization of grade transitions in polyethylene solution polymerization process under uncertainty. Computers and Chemical Engineering 95, 260–279.

X. Xie, R. Ohs, A. Spiess, U. Krewer, R. Schenkendorf, 2018a. Moment-independent sensitivity analysis of enzyme-catalyzed reactions with correlated model parameters. IFAC-PapersOnLine 51 (2), 753 – 758.

X. Xie, R. Schenkendorf, U. Krewer, 2018b. Toward a comprehensive and efficient robust optimization framework for (bio)chemical processes. Processes 6 (10), 183.

Anton A. Kiss, Edwin Zondervan, Richard Lakerveld, Leyla Özkan (Eds.)
Proceedings of the 29th European Symposium on Computer Aided Process Engineering
June 16th to 19th, 2019, Eindhoven, The Netherlands. © 2019 Elsevier B.V. All rights reserved.
http://dx.doi.org/10.1016/B978-0-128-18634-3.50039-4

Design and Operation Optimization for Water and Power Cogeneration System by Reverse Osmosis and Renewable Energy Technologies

Yousef Saif,[a] Muhammad Rizwan,[a] Ali Almansoori,[a*] Ali Elkamel,[a,b]

[a]*Department of Chemical Engineering, Khalifa University of Science and Tehnology, The petroleum Institute, Abu Dhabi, P.O.Box 2533, UAE*

[b]*Department of Chemical Engineering, University of Waterloo, Waterloo, ON N2L 3G1, Canada*

ali.almanssori@ku.ac.ae

Abstract

In this study, the integration of renewable energy resources (RES) with reverse osmosis (RO) system is investigated to examine optimal design and operation of integrated water and power system over a planning time horizon. The supplied power from RES is assumed to be consumed by RO system for water production. Normally, model parameters vary over time such as water salinity, temperature, wind speed, solar radiation. Therefore, the proposed optimization problem is based on a multiperiod mixed integer nonlinear programming (MINLP) model. The MINLP model features two design and operation layers. The first layer includes design variables and constraints which are independent of time. These variables provide the capital investment requirements, and feasibility boundaries for the operation layer. The second layer involves time dependent variables and constraints to provide optimal operation and cost for the integrated system. The optimal results from the MINLP model will provide optimal system configuration and equipment size for the integrated system. Furthermore, the results will give optimal operation for the integrated system over the planning time horizon. A case study for seawater RO desalination system integrated with wind technology will be analyzed to show the application for the MINLP model.

Keywords: Renewable energy, reverse osmosis, water and power cogeneration, MINLP, multiepriod model.

1. Introduction

Water scarcity is a serious future challenge for sustainable development. Projection of water demand exhibits increasing trends due to global population growth accompanied with industrial expansions. The global water desalination market was valued at US$ 13.31 billion in 2016 and is expected to register robust growth reaching US$ 26.81 billion by 2025 (Hexa Research, 2017). Reverse osmosis (RO) is expected to witness the fastest growth because of its lower energy consumption rate. Growing demand for pure water is projected to boost the market for RO technology, and it is estimated to be worth US$ 15.43 billion by 2025. Nowadays, the generation of clean power from renewable energy sources (RES) is practical such as using wind, solar radiation, hydropower, and others (Ellabban et al., 2014). RES are abundant, moderately inexpensive, and without negative environmental impact compared to traditional fossil fuels. The application of RES as power sources for desalination technologies have witnessed considerable increase from 2% in 1998 to 23% in 2016 (REN21, 2016).

Several techno-economic studies presented research problems which examined the feasibility of RES technologies as clean energy sources for RO desalination operation. A study investigated the possible integration of photovoltaic solar technology for RO desalination operation (Monnot et al., 2018). The study showed the positive effect of RO configuration selection on the overall optimal cost. Nafey and Sharaf (2010) analyzed different solar Rankine cycle with different working fluids to find minimum treatment desalination cost by RO technology. Gökçek and Gökçek (2016) presented techno-economic study for small scale seawater RO desalination driven by wind turbines in Turkey. The aim from the study is to find the best capacity of wind turbines for reduced cost of power and water production, and reduced emission compared with grid connected system. Gökçek (2018) examined a hybrid energy system (e.g., wind, solar, diesel engine) for small scale seawater desalination in Turkey. The study results showed that a hybrid energy system provides the lowest energy and water cost.

RO desalination network has been studied extensively by many researchers to find the optimal RO configuration in desalination applications (Saif et al., 2008; Sassi and Mujtaba, 2011; Saif et al., 2014). To the best of our knowledge, the integration of RES with RO design and operation through multiperiod optimization model is not available in the literature. Therefore, the main contribution of this work is the development of integrated model for the design and operation of RES and RO integerated system for water and power production in order to satisfy water demand. The proposed optimization model is a multiperiod mixed integer nonlinear program (MINLP). The optimization model is composed by two layers. The design layer is independent of time, and it reflects the required capacities of the process equipment and capital cost. The second operation layer gives decision variables which represent the required operation of process equipment under different time periods with different values of the model parameters. In addition, the operation decision variables are constrained by the selected values for the design variables, and provide the required operation cost. In the following section, the research methodology is briefly described. The third section describes the MINLP formulation. The fourth section presents the results for seawater desalination case study integrated with wind technology. In the last section, the conclusions from this research study are detailed.

2. Methodology

Figure 1 shows the energy and water sections for the proposed research problem. It is assumed that a planning time horizon (T) is given with discrete time intervals. Within these intervals, economic and technical data for the integrated system is available. The objective is to find optimal size of power and RO equipment, and equipment operation to satisfy water demand in every time periods while minimizing total annual cost. The results from the mathematical programming formulation provide optimal RO network configuration (e.g., number of RO passes, pressure vessels, and RO modules), auxiliary equipment (e.g., high pressure (HPP) and booster (BP) pumps, pressure exchangers (PE)), stream assignments within the network, and operation over time for water section. In addition, the results provide optimal selection of RES equipment and their operation over time under minimum total annualized cost. The following section provides the mathematical programming formulation.

Design and Operation Optimization for Water and Power Cogeneration
System by Reverse Osmosis and Renewable Energy Technologies

231

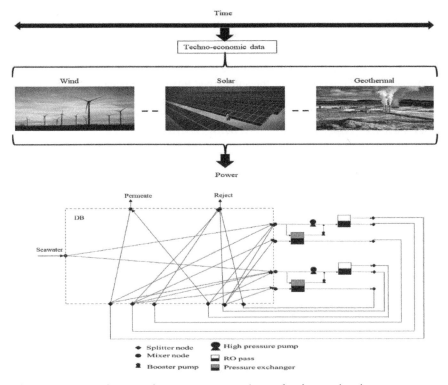

Figure 1. RES-RO integrated system representation under time variant input parameters.

3. MINLP model

The objective function of the MINLP model is to minimize the total annual cost (TAC) which is composed of the annualized capital and operation cost. The annualized capital cost (cc) of equipment (Q) represents the RO passes with their auxiliary equipment, and the RES equipment, and op represents the operation cost for the process equipment over the planning time horizon. Eq. (1) gives the total annual cost.

$$TAC = \sum_{}^{Q} cc_Q + \sum_{}^{Q,T} op_{Q,T} \tag{1}$$

The higher layer design variables (xe) are assumed to be independent of time. These design variables give operation limit for the lower operation variables (xo) as given by Eq.(2). Examples of design variables are surface area, flow, pressure, temperature, etc.

$$xp_{Q,T} \le xe_Q \quad \forall Q,T \tag{2}$$

Every RO pass produces water (wp). Water production is related to the selected number of RO modules (mr), RO pressure vessels (pr), applied pressure (p), and osmotic pressure difference (opd) between the reject and permeate side, and the pressure drop (drop) as given by Eq.(3). Water permeability is represented by the decision variable wpr which is a function of reject side physical properties (e.g., salinity, temperature, viscosity, etc.). It should worth pointing out that concentration polarization effects are considered in the MINLP formulation to give better estimation of total dissolved solid (TDS) concentration at the membrane wall. In the water section (Fig. 1), there are stream splitting and mixing in the distribution box (DB). Therefore, total water and TDS balance are required over time for the splitter and mixer nodes which give nonconvex terms.

$$wp_{RO,T} = wpr_{RO,T}mr_{RO}pr_{RO}\left(p_{RO,T} - drop_{RO,T} - opd_{RO,T}\right) \quad \forall RO,T \quad (3)$$

The energy system involves several RES. These RES have different sources of energy for power production. The power production (pwp) from RES are related to the selected number (NU) and size (SZ) of a given technology and the power that can be produced from a single unit (Q) as given by Eq. (4). Examples of power production models from single RES equipment can be found elsewhere (Maleki, 2018). The design variable is a binary variable (y) which indicates existence of a given technology and size. In addition, another binary variable is given in Eq.(4) which indicates if an RES is under operation at time interval T. Therefore, the total energy production from all RES is assumed to be consumed by RO auxiliary equipment for water demand constraint at every time period. The following section provides results for the RO seawater desalination integrated with wind technology in Tunisia.

$$pwp_{RES,NU,SZ,T} = y_{RES,NU,SZ,T}y_{RES,NU,SZ}Q_{RES,T} \quad \forall RES,NU,SZ,T \quad (4)$$

4. Case Study

Table 1 shows input data for the MINLP model to represent a case study of Tunisia (Cherif and Belhadj, 2011). The planning time is assumed to be one year with monthly discrete values. In addition, this case study represents a small scale design problem for power and water cogeneration. Table 2 shows RO membrane properties (e.g., FilmTec SW30HR-380 from Dow chemical company), and Table 3 shows different small scale wind turbines (e.g., from AEOLOS manufacturer).

Table 1. Water demand, seawater properties, and air conditions over year.

Periods, month	T1	T2	T3	T4	T5	T6	T7	T8	T9	T10	T11	T12
TDS, ppt	21	33	34	35	36	36	36	36	38	35	35	35
Seawater temp, °C	12.9	13	17	19	20.6	25.1	28	34	30	23	19	16
Air temp, °C	12	13.4	15.7	18.0	21	25	27.6	28.6	26.9	23.3	18.5	14.3
Wind speed, m/s	7.9	8	8.3	8.4	8.4	8.4	7.8	7.6	7.9	7.6	7.8	8.4
Water demand, kg/s	0.69	0.87	0.98	1.13	1.15	1.2	1.2	1.23	1.13	0.93	0.75	0.67

The optimal solution for the energy section show TAC of US$ 6504. Furthermore, the optimal selected capacity for the wind turbine is four wind turbines of 5 kW capacity. The total generated power is 94.7 kW for seawater desalination every year. This power

Design and Operation Optimization for Water and Power Cogeneration
System by Reverse Osmosis and Renewable Energy Technologies
233

is consumed for seawater desalination in order to satisfy water demand over the year. The TAC for the RO section is US$ 5681. Therefore, the combined water and energy TAC is US$ 12,185.

Table 2. RO module specifications

Active area (m^2)	35.3
Module length (m)	1.016
Feed space (mm)	0.737
Equivalent diameter (mm)	0.935
Feed flowrate range (m^3/h)	0.8-16
Maximum operating pressure (MPa)	8.3
Water permeability (kg/m^2 s MPa)	2.7×10^{-3}
TDS permeability (kg/m^2 s)	2.3×10^{-5}
Module cost ($)	1000

Table 3. Wind turbine specifications.

	Wind turbine 1 (WT1)	Wind turbine 2 (WT2)
Maximum power (kW)	2.6	7
Rated power (kW)	2	5
Cut in speed (m/s)	2	2.5
Rated wind speed (m/s)	10	10
Survival wind speed (m/s)	50	55
Generator efficiency (%)	96	96
Rotor height (m)	2.8	5.3
Cost ($)	5605	14309

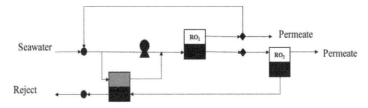

Figure 2. Optimal configuration for the RO plant.

Figure 2 shows the optimal configuration for the RO plant. It features two RO passes with permeate recycling. The recycled permeate stream is periodic when it is necessary to dilute the seawater feed stream. The mixed stream is divided into two streams for pressurization in the HPP and the PE units. Then theses streams are processed in the first RO pass with two pressure vessels and single RO module. The reject from the first RO pass flows through the second RO pass with one pressure vessel and dual RO modules to increase water recovery. The permeate streams from the first and second RO passes are combined to satisfy water demand.

5. Conclusions

This study presented a multiperiod MINLP for water and power production by RO and RES technologies. The model formulation is composed of two layers which represent the design and operation of the integrated system. The first layer provides optimal solution for the RO network configuration, optimal selection of RES equipment sizes, and capital cost. The second layer provides the required operation for the integrated system to satisfy water demand by RO technology, power production by RES technologies, and the required operation cost for the integrated system. A case study in Tunisia was analysed to show the application of the optimization model. Future work will be focused on integrating more RES technologies for improvement of the power cost and production, and examining membrane fouling effects on the desalination energy requirement.

References

A. Maleki, 2018, Design and optimization of autonomous solar-wind-reverse osmosis desalination systems coupling battery and hydrogen storage by an improved bee algorithm, Desalination, 435, 221-234.

A.S. Nafey, M.A. Sharaf, 2010, Combined solar organic Rankine cycle with reverse osmosis desalination process: Energy, exergy, and cost evaluations. Renewable Energy, 35, 2571-2580.

H. Cherif, J. Belhadj, 2011, Large scale time evaluation for energy estimation of standalone hybrid photovoltaic-wind system feeding reverse osmosis desalination unit, Energy, 36, 6058-6067.

Hexa Research, 2017, Water desalination market size and forecast, by technology (reverse osmosis, multi-stage filtration, multi-effect distillation), by source (seawater, brackish water, wastewater), and trend analysis, 2014 – 2025,

K.M. Sassi, I.M. Mujtaba, 2011, Optimal design and operation of reverse osmosis desalination process with membrane fouling, Chemical Engineering Journal, 171, 582-593.

M. Monnot, G. D. M. Carvajal, S. Laborie, C. Cabassud, R. Lebrun, 2018 , Integrated approach in eco-design strategy for small RO desalination plants powered by photovoltaic energy, Desalination, 435 , 246–258.

O. Ellabban, H. Abu-Rub, F. Blaabjerg, 2014, Renewable energy resources: current status, future prospects and their enabling technology, Renewable and Sustainable Energy Reviews, 39, 748‑764.

REN21, 2016, Renewable energy Policy Network for the 21st century, Renewables 2014, Global Status Report.

Y. Saif, A. Almansoori, A. Elkamel, 2014, Optimal design of split partial second pass reverse osmosis network for desalination applications, AIChE Journal, 60, 520-532.

Y. Saif, A. Elkamel, M. Pritzker, 2008, Global optimization of reverse osmosis network for wastewater treatment and minimization, Industrial and Engineering Chemistry Research, 47, 3060-3070.

Anton A. Kiss, Edwin Zondervan, Richard Lakerveld, Leyla Özkan (Eds.)
Proceedings of the 29th European Symposium on Computer Aided Process Engineering
June 16th to 19th, 2019, Eindhoven, The Netherlands. © 2019 Elsevier B.V. All rights reserved.
http://dx.doi.org/10.1016/B978-0-128-18634-3.50040-0

Modelling of extractive heterogeneous-azeotropic distillation in dividing wall column

Andras Jozsef Toth,[*,a] Daniel Fozer,[a] Tibor Nagy,[a] Eniko Haaz,[a] Judit Nagy,[b] Peter Mizsey,[a,c]

[a]*Department of Chemical and Environmnetal Process Engineering, Műegyetem rkp. 3., Budapest, 1111, Hungary*

[b]*Department of Building Services and Process Engineering, Műegyetem rkp. 3., H-1111, Budapest, Hungary*

[c]*Department of Fine Chemicals and Environmental Technology, Egyetemváros C/1 108., Miskolc, 3515, Hungary*

ajtoth@envproceng.eu

Abstract

The distillation based separation can be extremely complex if highly non-ideal mixtures are to be separated. In spite of different successfully applied unit operations there is always a possible way to improve the distillation technique and widen its toolbar. A novel improvement in this area is the development of the extractive heterogeneous-azeotropic distillation (EHAD). For the sake of the demonstration of the efficient use of EHAD in Dividing wall columns (DWC), two quaternary mixtures are selected for separation: Water – Ethanol – Ethyl acetate – Acetone and Water – Ethanol – Ethyl acetate – Ethylene glycol. There are real waste mixtures from pharmaceutical industry. It must be mentioned, extractive heterogeneous-azeotropic distillation method has never been investigated in dividing wall columns.

Conventional distillation column sequences and dividing wall columns are selected for comparison. Rigorous steady-state simulations are carried out using ChemCAD flowsheet simulation software. Number of trays, heat duties and Total Annual Cost (TAC) of the systems are optimized. It can be concluded, the application of the EHAD in DWCs allows also the simplification of the separation schemes and the separation reduces the energy requirements of the distillation and opens new horizons for the separation of non-ideal mixtures saving energy, money and natural resources. Using DWCs the reboiler duties can be reduced with 20% and the appropriate separation can be reached with one less column.

Keywords: extractive heterogeneous-azeotropic distillation, dividing wall column, non-ideal mixtures, flowsheet simulator

1. Introduction

The highly non-ideal mixtures can be quite often found in fine chemical industries, where the separation of the usually azeotropic mixtures are complicated with the high product purity descriptions. Szanyi et al. (2004a, b) introduced a novel kind of distillation, the extractive heterogeneous-azeotropic distillation (EHAD) that has been proved as a powerful and efficient separation method for the separation of highly non-ideal liquid mixtures. The recovery of solvents from industrial aqueous solutions has particular interest and moreover the water can be also recycled (Szabados et al., 2018). The EHAD combines the advantages of the heterogeneous-azeotropic and extractive distillations (see Fig.1). Heteroazeotropic distillation exploits the differences in volatility and liquid-liquid phase split by linking a distillation column and a phase separator. Therefore, it may also be interpreted as hybrid separation process. The heterogeneous-azeotropic option assumes that water is present in the mixture and limited immiscibility exists (Toth et al., 2016).

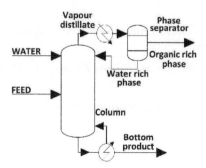

Fig. 1 The extractive heterogeneous-azeotropic distillation (EHAD) (Toth et al., 2016)

The EHAD differs from the heteroextractive distillation since no new azeotrope is formed, namely the extractive agent/entrainer is water and this component is already present in the mixtures to be separated (Toth et al., 2017). Moreover, the extractive and relative volatility changing effect of the autoentrainer/extractive agent is fully utilized and therefore the extractive effect takes place in the whole column (Szanyi et al., 2004b).

Dividing wall columns (DWCs) are todays alternative of sustainable distillation technology. Using DWCs in a distillation sequence significantly increases the number of possible arrangements. These options are worth to be considered as DWCs proved to be attractive in terms of energy consumption. Favourable energy consumption of DWCs is caused by the energy integration technique, thermal coupling (Tarjani et al., 2018). There are numerous feasible partition constructions of a DWC in the literature, but it is a common trend to investigate the properties of the original structure introduced by Asprion and Kaibel (2010) with the partition in the middle. As a systematic approach (Rong, 2011) suggests a strong connection between the conventional sequences and the DWCs with upper (DWCU) and lower (DWCL) partitions (see Fig. 2). DWCU can be considered as an alternative of the conventional direct sequence and DWLC as an alternative of the conventional indirect sequence.

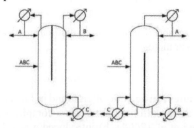

Fig. 2 DWC with Upper partition (DWCU, left) and DWC with Lower partition (DWCL, right) (Tarjani et al., 2018)

The most significant advantage of a DWC is the potential cost saving. Using a DWC can lead to cost savings up to 30% (Sangal et al., 2012) as it only requires one distillation column instead of two ones considering the separation of a three component mixture. On the other hand, thermodynamic efficiency can be increased by avoiding the remixing effect (Kiss et al., 2012). In such a way both investment and operational costs can be reduced compared to the conventional sequences (Tarjani et al., 2018).

Recent studies investigate these complex arrangements and the interest in DWCs begins to increase. Several design methods (Ramírez-Corona et al., 2015; Van Duc Long and Lee, 2012) and applications for azeotropic, extractive and reactive distillation are also developed (Yildirim et al., 2011). It has to be mentioned, EHAD has never been examined in DWC. Therefore, the aim of this work is to investigate the applicability of DWC construction in the case of extractive heterogeneous-azeotropic distillation method considering the separation of quaternary mixtures.

2. Material and methods

Two quaternary mixtures are selected for comparison: Water (Component 1) – Ethanol (2) – Ethyl acetate (3) – Acetone (4) as Mixture I and Water (1) – Ethanol (2) – Ethyl acetate (3) – Ethylene glycol (4) as Mixture II. Table 1 shows the binary and ternary azeotropes of the selected mixtures. The target of this study to create a separation process based on extractive heterogeneous-azeotropic distillation to split the compounds of these mixtures. The limit value for the composition is determined, which is min. 99.5 m/m%, except Ethanol (96 m/m%) and Ethyl acetate (96 m/m%).

Table 1 Binary and ternary azeotropes of the investigated mixtures (Szanyi, 2005)

Azeotrope type	Mixture I	Mixture II	Boil. T [°C]	Azeotropic composition [m/m%]
Binary		(1) - (2)	78	4-96
		(1) - (3)	71.3	8.3-91.7
		(2) - (3)	71.5	29.6-70.4
Ternary		(1) - (2) - (3)	70.3	8.0-8.7-83.3

ChemCAD flowsheet operator program is applied for comparison of column types. Trayed SCDS columns and UNIQUAC method is used for the calculation of the vapor-liquid equilibrium (VLE) as an equilibrium model. The optimal number of trays and heating requirements can be determined (Toth et al., 2017). First, the optimal number of trays are calculated in conventional case and then this value is used in simulation of DWC case.

3. Results and discussion

Fig. 3 and Fig. 4 show the separation alternatives of Mixture I. The separation of Mixture II in conventional and in dividing wall columns can be compared in the case of Fig. 5 and Fig. 6. The achieved product purities can be seen in flowsheet figures. First column can separate the non-azeotropic compounds of the mixtures (Acetone or Ethylene glycol) and the EHAD separation is carried out in the second column in conventional column cases. It can be seen DWCL construction is used in non-conventional case. Column II, III and IV symbolize the DWC construction in Fig. 4 and Fig. 6.

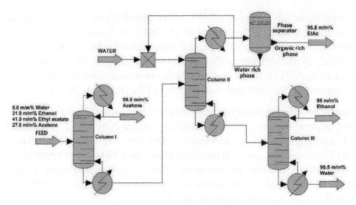

Fig. 3 Separation of Mixture I in conventional column

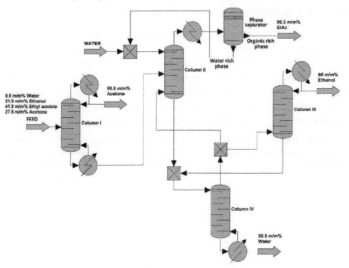

Fig. 4 Separation of Mixture I in dividing wall column (CII, CIII, CIV)

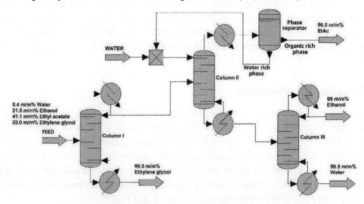

Fig. 5 Separation of Mixture II in conventional column

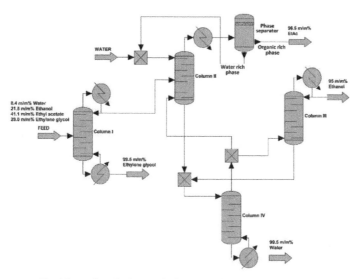

Fig. 6 Separation of Mixture II in dividing wall column (CII, CIII, CIV)

Total Annual Cost (TAC) of the optimized process is calculated according to the cost
correlations of Douglas (1988) with current M&S index (1605). Investment costs of the
distillation depend on different parameters, for e.g.: heat duty, the sizes of the column,
and purity of the products. The operating costs contain the annual costs of the steam and
water consumption. 8000 hours/year continuous operation is selected for the calculation
of the operating cost. 10-year amortization of capital cost is assumed for the total cost
estimation. The mixtures are selected for the comparison for 1000 kg/h feed stream. Valve
trays are used in flowsheet simulator (Toth et al., 2017). Table 2 shows the comparison
of two column constructions.

Table 2 Comparison of column constructions

	Mixture I		Mixture II	
	Conv.	DWC	Conv.	DWC
Feed water [kg/h]	600		800	
Total number of trays [-]	70		80	
Reboiler duty [MJ/h]	3343	2740	3837	3252
Total Annual Cost (TAC)	3206	2565	3540	2761

It can be seen the reboiler duty values are in accuracy with TAC and the DWC
constructions have lower heat duties.

4. Conclusions

The applicability of extractive heterogeneous-azeotropic distillation is tested on two non-
ideal mixtures in flowsheet simulator environment. Two column constructions are
investigated and compared: (i) conventional columns, (ii) dividing wall column. It can be
concluded both structures are capable for separation of quaternary mixtures. The
application of dividing wall column results in cheaper solutions and less energy
consumption then conventional column case, which means that DWC can be efficacious

tool for separation of highly non-ideal mixtures. Average 17% reduction can be reached in reboiler duty values and the Total Annual Cost can be reduced by up to 21%.

Acknowledgments

This paper was supported by the János Bolyai Research Scholarship of Hungarian Academy of Sciences, ÚNKP-18-4-BME-209 New National Excellence Program of Ministry of Human Capacities, NTP-NFTÖ-18-B-0154, OTKA 112699 and 128543. This research was supported by the European Union and the Hungarian State, co-financed by the European Regional Development Fund in the framework of the GINOP-2.3.4-15-2016-00004 project, aimed to promote the cooperation between the higher education and the industry.

References

N. Asprion, G. Kaibel, 2010, Dividing wall columns: Fundamentals and recent advances, Chem Eng Process 49, 139-146.

J. M. Douglas, 1988, Conceptual design of chemical processes. McGraw-Hill, New York.

A. A. Kiss, S. J. Flores Landaeta, C. A. Infante Ferreira, 2012, Towards energy efficient distillation technologies – Making the right choice, Energy 47, 531-542.

N. Ramírez-Corona, N. Ek, A. Jiménez-Gutiérrez, 2015, A method for the design of distillation systems aided by ionic liquids, Chem Eng Process 87, 1-8.

B.-G. Rong, 2011, Synthesis of dividing-wall columns (DWC) for multicomponent distillations—A systematic approach, Chem Eng Res Des 89, 1281-1294.

V. K. Sangal, V. Kumar, I. M. Mishra, 2012, Optimization of structural and operational variables for the energy efficiency of a divided wall distillation column, Comput Chem Eng 40, 33-40.

E. Szabados, A. Jobbagy, A. J. Toth, P. Mizsey, G. Tardy, C. Pulgarin, S. Giannakis, E. Takacs, L. Wojnarovits, M. Mako, Z. Trocsányi, A. Tungler, 2018, Complex Treatment for the Disposal and Utilization of Process Wastewaters of the Pharmaceutical Industry, Peri Poly Chem Eng 62, 76-90.

A. Szanyi, 2005, Separation of non-ideal quaternary mixtures with novel hybrid processes based on extractive heterogeneous-azeotropic distillation, BME, Budapest, PhD Thesis.

A. Szanyi, P. Mizsey, Z. Fonyo, 2004a, Novel hybrid separation processes for solvent recovery based on positioning the extractive heterogeneous-azeotropic distillation, Chem Eng Process 43, 327-338.

A. Szanyi, P. Mizsey, Z. Fonyo, 2004b, Optimization of nonideal separation structures based on extractive heterogeneous azeotropic distillation, Ind Eng Chem Res 43, 8269-8274.

A. J. Tarjani, A. J. Toth, T. Nagy, E. Haaz, N. Valentinyi, A. Andre, D. Fozer, P. Mizsey, 2018, Thermodynamic and Exergy Analysis of Energy-Integrated Distillation Technologies Focusing on Dividing-Wall Columns with Upper and Lower Partitions, Ind Eng Chem Res 57, 3678-3684.

A. J. Toth, E. Haaz, T. Nagy, R. Tari, A. J. Tarjani, D. Fozer, A. Szanyi, K.-A. Koczka, L. Racz, G. Ugro, P. Mizsey, 2017, Evaluation of the accuracy of modelling the separation of highly non-ideal mixtures: extractive heterogeneous-azeotropic distillation, in: Espuña, A., Graells, M., Puigjaner, L. (Eds.), Comput Aided Chem Eng. Elsevier, pp. 241-246.

A. J. Toth, A. Szanyi, K.-A. Koczka, P. Mizsey, 2016, Enhanced Separation of Highly Non-ideal Mixtures with Extractive Heterogeneous-azeotropic Distillation, Sep Sci Technol 51, 1238-1247.

N. Van Duc Long, M. Lee, 2012, Dividing wall column structure design using response surface methodology, Comput Chem Eng 37, 119-124.

O. Yildirim, A. A. Kiss, E. Y. Kenig, 2011, Dividing wall columns in chemical process industry: A review on current activities, Sep Purif Technol 80, 403-417.

Anton A. Kiss, Edwin Zondervan, Richard Lakerveld, Leyla Özkan (Eds.)
Proceedings of the 29th European Symposium on Computer Aided Process Engineering
June 16th to 19th, 2019, Eindhoven, The Netherlands. © 2019 Elsevier B.V. All rights reserved.
http://dx.doi.org/10.1016/B978-0-128-18634-3.50041-2

Optimization of an Integrated First- and Second-Generation Ethanol Production Plant with Focus on Hydrolysis Parameters

Roymel R. Carpio[a], Roberto C. Giordano[b], Argimiro R. Secchi[a,*]

[a]Chemical Engineering Program, Universidade Federal do Rio de Janeiro (UFRJ), Rio de Janeiro - RJ, 21941-914, Brazil
[b]Chemical Engineering Department, Universidade Federal de São Carlos (UFSCar), São Carlos - SP, 13565-905, Brazil
arge@peq.coppe.ufrj.br

Abstract

Despite there are many studies regarding optimization of biorefineries in the literature, most of them modelled the hydrolysis reactor as a stoichiometric reactor with a predetermined conversion. This simplification implies loss of accuracy and lack of prediction capability, because it does not account for the dependency of hydrolysis yield with important parameters such as enzyme load, solids fraction and reaction time. In this work a kinetic model of the hydrolysis reactor is combined within the whole integrated biorefinery simulation to address this gap. The process modelling and simulation was made in EMSO. Two configurations of the second-generation ethanol (E2G) production process were simulated: the first one considering the xylose biodigestion and the second one implementing the xylose fermentation. The optimization problems involved the maximization of the Net Present Value, taking four key parameters of E2G process as decision variables. The ethanol production increase was incorporated as a constraint of the optimization problem, which was varied in a range of values to obtain optimal configurations for different scenarios. No configuration was economically feasible for the realistic economic scenario considered in the studies. However, the xylose fermentation configuration presented better economic performance than the xylose biodigestion as overall.

Keywords: Sugarcane biorefinery, Modelling and optimization, Economic feasibility.

1. Introduction

The increasing energy demands and the public pressure to decrease greenhouse gas emissions, linked to the governments concern about energy security, are shifting the global energy matrix towards renewable energy technologies (Longati et al., 2018). In this sense, sugarcane biorefineries play an important role producing both biofuel and bioelectricity. Despite the several researches and industry efforts to turn second-generation ethanol production process feasible, this technology is still not consolidated and requires studies to be more sustainable and profitable (Junqueira et al., 2017).

There are many studies regarding optimization of biorefineries in the literature. For a summary of relevant works, we recommend the review of Bechara et al. (2018). However, most of them modelled the hydrolysis reactor as a stoichiometric reactor with a predetermined conversion. This simplification implies loss of accuracy and lack of prediction capability, because it does not account for the dependency of hydrolysis yield with important parameters such as enzyme load, solids fraction and reaction time. In this work we combined a kinetic model of the hydrolysis reactor within the whole integrated biorefinery simulation to address this gap.

2. Methodology

2.1. Process modelling and simulation

The biorefinery was modelled based on a standard autonomous Brazilian distillery, with a process capacity of 500 t/h of sugarcane (Costa et al., 2016). 35 t/h of sugarcane straw are brought from the field to be burnt in the boiler. The sugarcane and sugarcane straw compositions were in correspondence to Longati et al. (2018). The modelled biorefinery can produce first-generation ethanol (E1G) from sugarcane juice, second-generation ethanol (E2G) from bagasse, and electricity in an integrated process. Two different configurations of the biorefinery were modelled: (1) considering the xylose biodigestion and (2) executing the xylose fermentation. The main data used in the simulation of the biorefinery are shown in Table 1. An overall description of the process follows.

Table 1. Main data used in the biorefinery simulation (TC: ton of sugarcane).

Parameter	Value	Reference
Cleaning energy demand (kWh/TC)	5	Furlan et al. (2013)
Sugar recovery in mill (wt %)	96	Oliveira et al. (2018)
Mill energy demand (kWh/TC)	16	Bechara et al. (2016)
Sugar concentration for fermentation (^{0}Brix)	20	Furlan et al. (2013)
Glycose fermentation yield (%)	90.5	Oliveira et al. (2018)
Anhydrous ethanol purity (wt %)	99.5	Oliveira et al. (2018)
Pre-treatment solid fraction (wt %)	10	Oliveira et al. (2018)
Pre-treatment pressure (bar)	17.4	Oliveira et al. (2018)
Pre-treatment hemicellulose conversion (%)	46.53	Oliveira et al. (2018)
Hydrolysed bagasse fraction (wt %)	5-95	Becharaet al. (2016)
Hydrolysis solid fraction (wt %)	10-20	Angarita et al. (2015)
Hydrolysis Enzyme loading (FPU/g of cellulose)	5-60	Angarita et al. (2015)
Hydrolysis Residence time (h)	12-72	Angarita et al. (2015)
Xylose concentration for fermentation (g/L)	60	Longati et al. (2018)
Xylose fermentation yield (%)	66.5	Furlan et al. (2013)
Boiler steam pressure (bar)	65	Oliveira et al. (2018)
Boiler efficiency based on LHV (%)	86	Longati et al. (2018)
Turbines isentropic efficiency (%)	80	Oliveira et al. (2018)
Electric generator efficiency (%)	95.8	Oliveira et al. (2018)
Biodigester COD removal (%)	74	Ribeiro et al. (2017)
Methane production (L/kg-COD-removed)	290	Ribeiro et al. (2017)

The bagasse obtained after milling is divided in two fractions. The first one is fed in the boiler and the second one is used for E2G production. The bagasse diverted to E2G production undergoes a liquid hot water pre-treatment. After that, the liquid fraction, rich in xylose is separated from the solid fraction containing the cellulose. The xylose liquor could be used in biogas production by biodigestion or in ethanol production by fermentation. On the other hand, the solid fraction containing cellulose is fed to the enzymatic hydrolysis. The kinetic model of hydrolysis reactor proposed by Angarita et al. (2015) was used to access the dependency of hydrolysis yield on enzyme load, solid fraction and reaction time. The coupling of this kinetic model into the whole steady state simulation was made as described in Carpio et al. (2018a).

After hydrolysis reaction, the remained solid fraction (mostly lignin) is sent to the boiler and the liquid fraction (glycose liquor) is mixed to the 1G treated juice and undergoes the traditional stages of E1G. The cogeneration system includes a boiler, a back-pressure turbine and a condensing one, and produces steam and electricity to supply process demands. The electricity surplus is sold to the grid. EMSO software (Soares and Secchi, 2003) was used to perform the modelling and simulation of the biorefinery. The components and thermodynamic packages used in this work were the same of Longati et al. (2018).

2.2. Economic analysis

The economic analysis was also implemented in EMSO, coupled to the process model. This allows instant calculation of economic indexes for any feasible operational condition simulated, without requiring external or auxiliary sheet calculations. The main economic premises considered in this study are shown in Table 2.

Table 2. Main premises considered in the economic analysis.

Parameter	Value	Reference
Ethanol selling price (US\$/m^3)	584.61	MAPA (2018)
Electricity selling price (US\$/MWh)	71.19	CCEE (2018)
Sugarcane costs (US\$/t)	22.15	UDOP (2018)
Straw cost (US\$/t)	15	Bechara et al. (2016)
Enzyme cost (US\$/t)	1250	Bechara et al. (2016)
Fresh water cost (US\$/t)	0.06	Bechara et al. (2016)
Refrigeration cost (US\$/kW)	0.04	Bechara et al. (2016)
Operation time (h/year)	42000	Furlan et al. (2013)
Project life time (years)	25	Longati et al. (2018)
Construction period (years)	1	Furlan et al. (2013)
Tax Rate (%)	34	Longati et al. (2018)
Discount rate (%)	10	Bechara et al. (2016)
Depreciation strategy (%/year)	10	Longati et al. (2018)

The capital cost (CAPEX), operating costs (OPEX), cash flows (CF) and net present value (NPV) were calculated based on the methodology of Peters et al. (2003). The main equipment purchase costs were estimated from the literature (Humbird et al., 2011) and were updated and scaled according to Peters et al. (2003). The minimum ethanol selling price (MESP) corresponds to the ethanol selling price that makes NPV equal to zero.

2.3. Process optimization

The objective function of the optimization problems was the maximization of the NPV. Some key parameters of hydrolysis were selected as decision variables: hydrolysed bagasse fraction, enzyme loading, solids loading and residence time. The increasing on total ethanol production due to E2G was incorporated as an inequality constrain. The Surrogate Assisted Optimization (SAO) framework proposed by Carpio et al. (2018b) was applied for estimating an initial global solution of the optimization problems. After that, the Sequential Quadratic Programming (SQP) algorithm was used for refining the solution.

3. Results and discussion

Figure 1 shows the resulting Pareto set of NPV and MESP for different values of the constraint. The economic indexes of both configurations become worse when increasing the constraint value. It means that the additional income obtained by a larger ethanol production does not compensate the investment and operational cost involved in the E2G production process for the realistic economic scenario. This finding is in agreement with the results achieved by Bechara et al. (2016), Junqueira et al. (2017) and Longati et al. (2018).

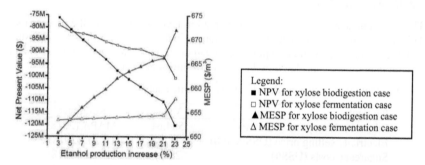

Figure 1. Pareto curve of NPV and MESP for ethanol production increase.

As overall, the economic indexes of the xylose fermentation case are better than the xylose biodigestion case. In addition, the sensitivity of the Pareto curve for xylose fermentation case is lower than for the xylose biodigestion case. It is worth mentioning the existence of knee points, for which NPV and MESP witness a greater change, at the higher values of the constraint. This behaviour is better understood by analysing the optimal values of decision variables shown in Figure 2.

The hydrolysed bagasse fraction (Fig. 2A) rises almost linearly with the constraint increase until approximately 19 %. After that value, this variable rises more gradually because it is close to the maximum value of bagasse that can be diverted to E2G without affecting the steam requirements of the biorefinery. In the case of enzyme loading (Fig. 2B), the optimal values are between 12 and 16 FPU/g. Notice that for constraint values higher than 21 % the enzyme loading rise abruptly. This behaviour is due to the impossibility of an additional increase on the hydrolysed bagasse fraction for that condition. Consequently, it is necessary to increase the enzyme loading for producing more ethanol and meet the constraint.

The optimal values for solids loading (Fig. 2C) of both configurations are mostly above 15 %. For the xylose fermentation case there is a clear tendency of increasing the solids loading as the constraint increases as well. This behaviour is justified by the higher steam demand of this configuration. Therefore, it is necessary to increase the solids loading for decreasing the steam demand and allowing a higher hydrolysed bagasse fraction. Optimal values for residence times (Fig. 2D) were mostly between 68 and 72 hours. The oscillatory behaviour of the residence time is due to the cost of hydrolysis reactors being a discrete variable that changes in steps, because the total required volume is attained by adding fixed-volume hydrolysis reactors. Consequently, there are some operating conditions where the additional ethanol produced by increasing the residence time does not compensate the cost of a new hydrolysis reactor, leading to optimal resident times below 72 hours.

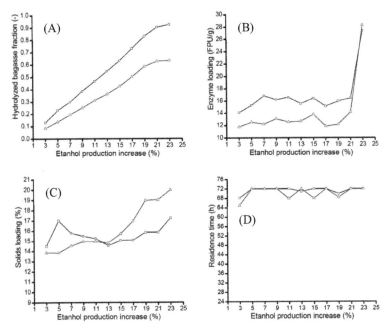

Figure 2. Optimal values of decision variables for: □ xylose biodigestion and △ xylose fermentation.

4. Conclusions

No configuration was economically feasible for the realistic economic scenario considered in this study. However, the xylose fermentation case presented better economic performance than the xylose biodigestion as overall, and particularly for high cellulosic ethanol rates. It is possible to increase the ethanol production up to 23 % in both configurations due to E2G process. However, ethanol production increase greater than 21 % leads to significant deterioration of economic indexes. Most of the optimal configurations were achieved for enzyme loading between 12 and 16 FPU/g, solids loading in the range of 14 and 17 % and residence times above 68 hours.

Acknowledgements

Financial support from CAPES (grant #9003-14-2), from CNPq (grant #302893/2013-0) and from FAPERJ (grant #E012018-236117) are gratefully acknowledged.

References

J. Angarita, R. Souza, A. Cruz, E. Biscaia, A. Secchi, 2015, Kinetic modeling for enzymatic hydrolysis of pretreated sugarcane straw, Biochemical Engineering Journal, 104, 10-19.

R. A. Bechara, A. Gomez, V. Saint-Antonin, J.-M. Schweitzer, F. Maréchal, 2016, Methodology for the optimal design of an integrated first and second generation ethanol production plant combined with power cogeneration, Bioresource Technology, 214, 441-449.

R. A. Bechara, A. Gomez, V. Saint-Antonin, J.-M. Schweitzer, F. Maréchal, A. Ensinas, 2018, Review of design works for the conversion of sugarcane to first and second-generation ethanol and electricity, Renewable and Sustainable Energy Reviews, 91, 152-164.

R. R. Carpio, F. F. Furlan, R. C. Giordano, A. R. Secchi, A kriging-based approach for conjugating specific dynamic models into whole plant stationary simulations, 2018a, Computers & Chemical Engineering, 119, 190-194.

R. R. Carpio, R. C. Giordano, A. R. Secchi, Enhanced surrogate assisted framework for constrained global optimization of expensive black-box functions, 2018b, Computers & Chemical Engineering, 10.1016/j.compchemeng.2018.06.027.

CCEE, 2018, Public auction electricity prices, Electric Energy Commercialization Chamber, www.ccee.org.br.

C. B. B. Costa, E. Potrich, A. J. G. Cruz, 2016, Multiobjective optimization of a sugarcane biorefinery involving process and environmental aspects, Renewable Energy, 96, 1142-1152.

F. F. Furlan, R. T. Filho, F. H. Pinto, C. B. Costa, A. J. Cruz, R. L. Giordano, R. C. Giordano, 2013, Bioelectricity versus bioethanol from sugarcane bagasse: is it worth being flexible?, Biotechnology for Biofuels, 6 (1), 142.

D. Humbird, R. Davis, L. Tao, C. Kinchin, D. Hsu, A. Aden, P. Schoen, J. Lukas, B. Olthof, M. Worley, D. Sexton, D. Dudgeon, 2011, Process design and economics for biochemical conversion of lignocellulosic biomass to ethanol, Tech. rep., NREL/TP-5100-47764.

T. L. Junqueira, M. F. Chagas, V. L. R. Gouveia, M. C. A. F. Rezende, M. D. B.Watanabe, C. D. F. Jesus, O. Cavalett, A. Y. Milanez, A. Bonomi, 2017, Techno-economic analysis and climate change impacts of sugarcane biorefineries considering different time horizons, Biotechnology for Biofuels, 10 (1), 50.

A. A. Longati, A. R. Lino, R. C. Giordano, F. F. Furlan, A. J. Cruz, 2018, Defining research & development process targets through retro-techno-economic analysis: The sugarcane biorefinery case, Bioresource Technology, 263, 1-9.

MAPA, 2018, Brazilian annual ethanol exports, Ministry of Agriculture, Cattle and Supply, www.agricultura.gov.br.

C. M. Oliveira, L. V. Pavo, M. A. Ravagnani, A. J. Cruz, C. B. Costa, 2018, Process integration of a multiperiod sugarcane biorefinery, Applied Energy, 213, 520-539.

M. S. Peters, K. D. Timmerhaus, R. E. West, 2003, Plant design and economics for chemical engineers, 5th Edition, Vol. 5, McGraw-Hill.

F. R. Ribeiro, F. Passos, L. V. A. Gurgel, B. E. L. Bata, S. F. de Aquino, 2017, Anaerobic digestion of hemicellulose hydrolysate produced after hydrothermal pretreatment of sugarcane bagasse in UASB reactor, Science of The Total Environment, 584, 1108-1113.

R. P. Soares, A. Secchi, 2003, EMSO: A new environment for modelling, simulation and optimisation, Computer Aided Chemical Engineering, Vol. 14, pp. 947-952.

UDOP, 2018, Sugarcane prices, Union of Biofuel Producers, www.udop.com.br.

Anton A. Kiss, Edwin Zondervan, Richard Lakerveld, Leyla Özkan (Eds.)
Proceedings of the 29th European Symposium on Computer Aided Process Engineering
June 16th to 19th, 2019, Eindhoven, The Netherlands. © 2019 Elsevier B.V. All rights reserved.
http://dx.doi.org/10.1016/B978-0-128-18634-3.50042-4

Optimization of seaweed-based biorefinery with zero carbon emissions potential

Rofice Dickson,[a] Jay Liu[a,*]

[a]Department of Chemical Egnieering, Pukyong Nationl Univresity, Busan, 48547, Korea

jayliu@pknu.ac.kr

Abstract

The superstructure-based optimization was proposed to determine optimal pathway of biorefinery, producing bioethanol. In general, the bioethanol process produces a large number of waste streams such as carbon dioxide, wastewater, and residual solid from fermentation. To utilize the aforementioned waste streams, processes such as succinic acid (SA), microalgae (MA), wastewater treatment (WWT) networks, and solid processing were integrated with bioethanol process. Based on the superstructure, technoeconomic and environmental mixed integer non-linear model was formulated and implemented in GAMS (25.0.2). The aim of the present contribution was to determine a more economically and environmentally viable process design than a standalone process. These goals were achieved by two objective functions; maximize net present (NPV) value and minimize carbon dioxide emissions (CE). To account uncertainties in process parameters, sensitivity analysis was also performed. The result indicated minimum ethanol selling price (MESP) of integrated design is about 34% lower than that of a standalone bioethanol process with more than 90% reduction in CE.

Keywords: Superstructure optimization, process synthesis, biofuels, macroalgae

1. Introduction

Development of biofuel production from renewable sources like biomass has gained significant attention due to growing energy demand, depleting fossil fuel reserves, and increasing environmental concerns such as greenhouse gas emissions. Among various biomass feedstocks, brown algae, as a 3rd generation feedstock, is considered as a promising candidate due to its sustainable cultivation, high sequestration efficiency, and absence of ethical issues such as food competition. Furthermore, brown algae contain high carbohydrates contents, at 32-60%, dry weight, and lack of lignin (Roesijadi et al., 2010). Taking into consideration the benefits of brown algae and its versatile chemical composition, this study will focus on biofuel production from brown alga *Saccharina japonica* (SJ) as a potential feedstock.

In the literature, serval bench-scale experimental studies were conducted to produce biofuels from the carbohydrates of SJ via fermentation pathway. Reith et al. (2009) utilized the carbohydrate contents of SJ and obtained ethanol yields of 0.254 kg ethanol/ kg of dry feed. Based on this yield, Fasahati et al. (2015) determined the economic viability of bioethanol production from SJ and calculated MESP of 2.39 $/gal at 80,000 t/y plant capacity. Recently, Dickson et al. (2018) conducted an optimal design of SJ-based biorefinery by using a superstructure approach to report the values of the MESP and the maximum seaweed price (MSP).

Despite the promising yields and economics, bioethanol processing produces numerous waste streams and byproducts, and is water intensive. It is reported that medium-sized biorefinery, processing 2 to 3.5 mt/y sugarcane produces 110 to 193 kt/y of CE during fermentation (Bonfim-Rocha et al., 2018). Similarly, stillage from the distillation column has high values of chemical oxygen demand, biochemical oxygen demand, and minerals. Water consumption in bioethanol plants ranges from 3 to 15 gal of water per gal of ethanol. Disposal of these waste streams without treatment can cause severe environmental issues such as contribution to global warming, deoxygenation of water reservoirs, discoloration, odors, eutrophication, acidification, and other problems. In the literature, however, little attention has been paid to simultaneously reduce all waste streams from bioethanol processing.

Based on the presented challenges and research gap, this study is the first to simultaneously integrate processes such as SA, MA, unreacted solid processing, and WWT networks with bioethanol processing. The goal of this study is to utilize all waste components from SJ biorefinery by designing an economical and environmentally friendly process by taking a superstructure approach. To achieve these goals, two objective functions were employed in the optimization: NPV and CE. The novelty of this work includes a large number of process alternatives to find the optimal design under different objective functions.

2. Methodology

2.1. Problem statement

The optimization problem is defined as determining the optimal design for macroalgae-based biorefinery, which has maximum process economics as well as minimum detrimental effects on the environment.

2.2. Superstructure development

To design an environmentally friendly biorefinery, a superstructure is developed by adding large number of design alternatives into the conventional bioethanol process. The superstructure given in Figure 1 is capable of utilizing all components of seaweed and waste streams from the bioethanol process. Seven major sections are included in the superstructure: feed pre-treatment, enzymatic hydrolysis and fermentation, enzyme production, CO_2 utilization, harvesting, purification, and WWT.

The biorefinery process starts with the feed pre-treatment. The Feed can either be pre-treated with acid thermal hydrolysis (ATH) or hot water wash (HWW). The resulting treated feed then sent to the enzymatic hydrolysis and fermentation section, where carbohydrates are converted into glucose and ultimately to ethanol. There are two alternatives for obtaining enzymes for saccharification and fermentation. Enzymes can be manufactured on-site or they can be purchased. The outlet streams from the saccharification and fermentation section consist of the gaseous, liquid, and solid product stream. The gaseous products primarily consist of CO_2 and sent to CO_2 utilization section. Two design alternatives considered for CO_2 utilization are MA production and SA production. Based on the work of Bai et al. (2015), SA production from SJ is promising and can occur by consuming glucose and CO_2 in the presence of $E.$ $Coli$. Glucose required for the SA fermentation is provided from the saccharification and fermentation section by splitting a part of glucose to CO_2 utilization section. As glucose split for the SA production will decrease the bioethanol production, therefore, upper bound on SA production is applied. In an alternative method, CO_2 can be utilized to produce microalgae. MA can be cultivated either in open ponds or photobioreactors.

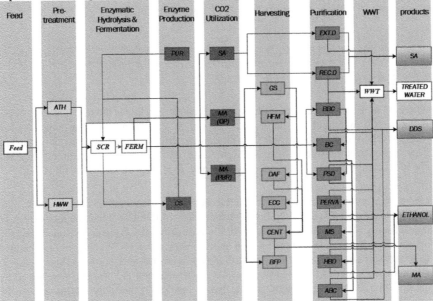

Figure 1. Superstructure for *Saccharina japonica* based biorefinery.

In harvesting section, five design alternatives are considered for MA harvesting and dewatering. The MA are harvested in gravity settler, which can be dewatered either by hallow filter membranes, diffused air flocculation, or electrocoagulation followed by centrifugation. Alternatively, belt filter press can be implemented at the outlet stream of gravity settler. The final concentration of MA from all dewatering alternative is 20 wt.%. The operating data considered for MA production is based on the work of Davis et al. (2011). In the purification section, various streams coming from the fermentation and CO_2 utilization section are processed to their desired level of purity. For example, SA can be purified either by extractive distillation or reactive distillation processes. Unreacted solids from the fermenter can be processed either before the beer column or after the beer column. Furthermore, solid processing can be performed either by centrifuge or belt filter press. As ethanol purification is an energy-intensive process, therefore, multiple design alternatives are considered in superstructure to select optimal topology for its purification. In general, two pathways included in the superstructure are conventional unit operations and novel technologies such as hybrid distillation (HD). The conventional unit operations consist of beer column, rectification column, and molecular sieves (zeolite beds) or pervaporation membranes (cross-linked vinyl alcohol). However, HD includes the combination of distillation columns and pervaporators in series. Furthermore, ethanol purification in the beer column is energy intensive. Therefore, to reduce the energy consumption, the beer column has two design alternatives: a single distillation column and pressure swing distillation (PSD). To reduce freshwater consumption, a complete WWT network incorporated into the superstructure that will treat and recycle wastewater from various process units. Process wastewater is treated using anaerobic digestion, aerobic digestion, and reverse osmosis. The treated water is assumed to be pure and is recycled to the process.

2.3. Objective function and assumptions

The objective function used for this optimization problem are maximization of the net present value (NPV) and minimization of CE, and are defined by:

$$NPV = \sum_{n=0}^{20} \frac{NCF_n}{(1+r)^n},$$

(1)

$$CE = \sum_{k} F_{k,CO2},$$

(2)

where NCF_n is non-discounted cash flow for the year n, and r is the discount rate. $F_{k,CO2}$ is the mass flow rate of CO_2 in the outlet stream k. Various assumptions considered in techno-economic analysis include 20 years project life, 10% discount rate, straight-line depreciation method over 7 years, 30% tax rate, and two-year construction time. The chemical composition of SJ reported by Roesijadi et al. (2010) was used in this work.

2.4. Optimization scenarios

Four optimization scenarios were studied to determine a sustainable biorefinery design. The scenario-1 is a base case design, which consists of traditional bioethanol process. In this scenario, all alternatives related with the utilization of CO_2 were excluded, and the optimization problem was solved with respect to maximizing NPV. The results obtained from this scenario will set targets for further improvements in the process. In scenario-2, all alternatives related to CO_2 utilization were activated and the problem was solved by maximizing the NPV. In addition, there was a restriction that only alternative can be selected for the utilization of CE. In scenario-3, all conditions were similar to that for scenario-2 except objective function which was the minimization of CE. In scenario-4, the synergistic effect of both CO_2 utilization processes was studied by removing the restriction to select only one alternative. The objective function was the maximization of NPV, whereas the second objective function was applied as a constraint in which net CE obtained from the scenario-3 was applied as an upper bound.

3. Results and discussion

The optimal topology obtained for bioethanol production and solid processing in scenario-1 consist of HWW, on-site enzyme production, ethanol purification by PSD and HD, and solid purification after the beer column. The same pathway was obtained in the rest of the scenarios for bioethanol production and solid processing. The products obtained in this scenario are bioethanol and DDS, and their production are presented in Table 1. Results indicated that NPV of this scenario is $38 MM.

Table 1. Mass balance summary.

Scenario	Ethanol yield (gal/t)	Ethanol (Mgal/y)	DDS (kton/y)	MA (kt/y)	SA (kt/y)	CO2 Produced (kt/y)	Net CE (kt/y)
1	83.94	51.37	314.80	0	0	148.7	148.7
2	73.51	44.99	275.67	0	15.30	129.6	121.8
3	83.94	51.37	314.80	62.13	0	148.7	14.9
4	73.51	44.99	275.67	50.91	15.30	129.6	12.9

In scenario-2, SA production was selected to utilize CE. The products obtained in this scenario are bioethanol, DDS, and SA, and their production are presented in Table 1. Only 6% of CO_2 is utilized in this scenario due to the upper bound on the SA production. The NPV of this scenario is \$134 MM. This improvement is attributed to the high selling price of SA, which is almost 5.5 times higher than the current wholesale price of ethanol.

In scenario-3, MA production was selected as an optimal process for the utilization of CO_2. The production rate of products obtained in this scenario are shown in Table 1. Results indicated that ~90% of CO_2 is utilized. The NPV of this scenario is \$101 MM.

In scenario-4, both SA and MA production were selected for the utilization of CO_2. The production levels of products obtained in this scenario are given in Table 1. Results indicated that ~90% of CO_2 is utilized. The NPV of this scenario is \$180 MM.

3.1. Optimal design

The comparison of all scenarios highlights that process topology obtained in the scenario-4 is both economically and environmentally superior, and therefore, selected as an optimal design. The optimal design shown in the Figure 2 has water consumption of 6.31 gal/gal of ethanol. The total capital investment, total manufacturing cost, and utility cost of optimal design are \$377 MM, \$153 MM, and \$25 MM, respectively. The total capital investment of optimal design is 55% more than that for a standalone process.

3.2. Minimum and maximum selling price of products and seaweed

The estimated MESP of optimal design is 1.31 \$/gal, which is ~34 times lower than that of scenario-1. Similarly, minimum selling price of DDS, SA, MA are 0.002 \$/kg, 1.52 \$/kg and 0.256 \$/kg. The calculated MSP is 0.127 \$/kg.

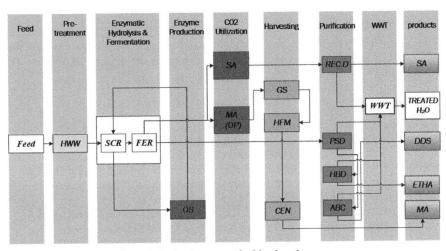

Figure 2. Optimal structure for bioethanol process

3.3. Sensitivity analysis

Sensitivity analysis was performed to evaluate the impact of key model parameters on MESP. Results presented in Figure 3 indicated that total capital investment, product selling prices, seaweed price, and IRR are the most dominant parameters that effect MESP.

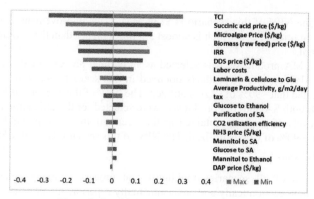

Figure 3. Sensitivity tornado chart for MESP.

4. Conclusion

A process synthesis framework for the optimization of the bioethanol process as well as optimization of CE was proposed. Multiple scenarios were studied based on different optimization criteria to determine the optimal topology. The result indicated that biofuel production from SJ is viable, at MESP of 1.31 $/gal. The proposed framework is an important decision tool for systematically analysing optimal structure for bioethanol process and reducing various pollutants.

5. Acknowledgments

This research was supported through the Basic Science Research Program of the National Research Foundation of Korea (NRF) funded by the Ministry of Science and ICT (2017R1A2B4004500).

6. Reference

Bai, B., Zhou, J. min, Yang, M. hua, Liu, Y. lan, Xu, X. hui, Xing, J. min, 2015. Efficient production of succinic acid from macroalgae hydrolysate by metabolically engineered Escherichia coli. Bioresour. Technol. 185, 56–61.

Bonfim-Rocha, L., Gimenes, M.L., Bernardo de Faria, S.H., Silva, R.O., Esteller, L.J., 2018. Multi-objective design of a new sustainable scenario for bio-methanol production in Brazil. J. Clean. Prod. 187, 1043–1056.

Davis, R., Aden, A., Pienkos, P.T., 2011. Techno-economic analysis of autotrophic microalgae for fuel production. Appl. Energy 88, 3524–3531.

Dickson, R., Ryu, J.-H., Liu, J.J., 2018. Optimal plant design for integrated biorefinery producing bioethanol and protein from Saccharina japonica: A superstructure-based approach. Energy 164, 1257-1270.

Fasahati, P., Woo, H.C., Liu, J.J., 2015. Industrial-scale bioethanol production from brown algae: Effects of pretreatment processes on plant economics. Appl. Energy 139, 175–187.

Reith, H., Huijgen, W., Hal, J. van, 2009. Seaweed potential in the Netherlands. ECN Biomass, Coal.

Roesijadi, G., Jones, S.B., Zhu, Y., 2010. Macroalgae as a Biomass Feedstock : A Preliminary Analysis. Analysis 1–50.

Anton A. Kiss, Edwin Zondervan, Richard Lakerveld, Leyla Özkan (Eds.)
Proceedings of the 29th European Symposium on Computer Aided Process Engineering
June 16th to 19th, 2019, Eindhoven, The Netherlands. © 2019 Elsevier B.V. All rights reserved.
http://dx.doi.org/10.1016/B978-0-128-18634-3.50043-6

Optimal design for integrated macroalgae-based biorefinery via mixed alcohol synthesis

Rofice Dickson,[a] Peyman Fasahati,[b] Jay Liu[a,*]

[a]*Department of Chemical Egnieering, Pukyong Nationl Univresity, Busan, 48547, Korea*

[b]*Department of Chemical Engineering and Biological Engineering, University of Wisconsin-Madison, Madison, WI 53706, USA*

jayliu@pknu.ac.kr

Abstract

A novel superstructure is developed for the biochemical conversion of macroalgae to mixed alcohols (MAs). With reference to environmental sustainability of manufacturing process, microalgae production processes are integrated to utilize CO_2 into useful products. Wastewater treatment network was modelled in the process synthesis framework to reduce freshwater consumption. Based on the superstructure, techno-economic mixed integer linear programming model was formulated. The objective function was maximization of the net present value (NPV). The results indicated that biofuel production from macroalgae is economically viable. The minimum selling price of ethanol, heavier alcohols, dry distillery solids, and microalgae are calculated to be 1.26 \$/gal, 2.3 \$/gal, 0.05 \$/kg, and 0.114 \$/kg, respectively. The maximum seaweed purchasing price is calculated to be 113 \$/ton. Furthermore, optimal design has achieved 90% reduction in CO_2 emissions (CE). Sensitivity analysis showed that the selling price of heavier alcohols and purchasing price of macroalgae are the most sensitive parameters to minimum ethanol selling price (MESP).

Keywords: Superstructure optimization, process synthesis, biofuels, macroalgae, volatile fatty acids

1. Introduction

Increasingly high energy prices, volatility of the global oil market, and consistent pressure to reduce greenhouse gases are major challenges within the transportation sector. To address these challenges, energy policies and goals are set by The United States and European Union, which have stimulated global interest in finding sustainable alternatives for replacing crude-oil derivatives (Zittel and Schindler, 2007).

Macroalgae, more specifically brown algae, as the third-generation biomass, are promising feedstock candidates for the biofuel production. Cultivation of macroalgae is considered sustainable, as it requires no arable land, irrigation water, or fertilizer. Among brown alga species, *Saccharina japonica* is extensively studied due to its high carbohydrate content, lack of lignin, and extensively available feedstock (Jiang et al., 2016). Therefore, this study focuses on the biofuel production using *Saccharina japonica* as feedstock.

There are three general pathways to produce biofuels: biochemical, chemical, and thermochemical. With reference to *Saccharina japonica*, arguments supporting biochemical conversion are the most favourable due to its ability to process feedstock with high moisture content and mild operating conditions in comparison to the alternative pathways. In general, biochemical pathway can produce MAs including ethanol, butanol, and propanol. The biochemical pathway is divided into two alternative pathways: volatile fatty acid platform (VFAP) and sugar platform (SP). In the former, volatile fatty acids (VFAs) are produced by using anaerobic digestion (AD) of the feed using a mixed culture bacterial ecosystem, which can be further processed to produce MAs. In the latter, only bioethanol is produced by extracting sugars from the biomass. Dickson et al. (2018) used a superstructure-based approach to evaluate the economics of bioethanol production from *Saccharina japonica* through SP. They estimated the MESP of 1.97 \$/gal at a plant scale of 612,000 t/y. On the other hand, techno-economic evaluation of biofuel production from VFAP at industrial scale is still limited and should be systematically evaluated in order to determine an optimal biochemical pathway.

In the literature, various bench scale experimental studies demonstrated that VFAP has higher carbon yield (g MAs/g dry feed) than the SP (Pham et al., 2012). This high yield is mainly due to the ability of mixed anaerobic bacteria to utilize all components of the biomass, including carbohydrates, proteins, and lipids, whereas in the case of SP merely carbohydrates contents of biomass are converted to bioethanol (Fasahati and Liu, 2015). Despite the promising yields, the effective and economically viable separation technologies for dehydration of the aqueous VFAs are a major obstacle to industrial scale application of VFAP. This is mainly due to the close boiling point of water and acetic acid, which makes their separation difficult as well as energy intensive by distillation. Another challenge associated with biochemical route is the massive production of CO_2 during fermentation of biomass. A potential method to mitigate direct CE from VFAP is microalgae-based biological utilization. According to Davis et al. (2016), one kilogram of microalgae consumes 1.93 kg of CO_2, which make it a suitable candidate to reduce CE from MAs production.

Based on the presented arguments, this study introduces an optimization-based process synthesis framework for MAs processes that will directly analyse the techno-economic, and environmental trade-offs using a large-scale mixed-integer linear programming model. The proposed framework simultaneously optimizes the topology of MAs manufacturing process as well as determine the optimal strategy to utilize CE produced during fermentation.

2. Methodology

2.1. Problem statement

The optimization problem is defined as determining the optimal design for MAs production process from the given set of alternatives, which has maximum process economics as well as minimum detrimental effects on the environment.

2.2. Overall process description

MAs production process starts with the partial AD of brown algae in the presence of iodoform inhibitor, at 30 PPM concentration (Granda et al., 2009). The operating conditions of AD are 5 days of retention time at 13 wt.% solid loading and 35 °C (Pham et al., 2012). The overall efficiency ranges from 0.307-0.412 g VFAs/ g dry feed. The outlet stream from the digester consists of solid, liquid, and gaseous products. Products from the digester are sent to flash drum to separate light gases such as hydrogen and carbon dioxide from the solid and the liquid products. Light gases in the vapor stream of flash drum are then sent to pressure swing adsorption to separate hydrogen from carbon dioxide, the former can be utilized during hydrogenation of VFAs to MAs. Solids are then separated from the liquid products by using solid separation technologies such as mechanical separator followed by drying. About 20 wt.% of solids are sent back to digester as an inoculum and nutrient source, while remaining fraction can be sold as animal feed called dry distillery solids. Liquid stream from the solid separation area is sent to VFAs recovery section, where VFAs are recovered at 99.9 wt.% using extraction column, rectification column, decanter, and stripping column. The concentrated VFAs are then hydrogenated for the synthesis of mixed alcohols. The hydrogenation process is a gas phase process, which takes place at 290 °C and 60 bars in the presence of cobalt catalyst to give a high alcohol yield of 97 wt.%. The catalyst consumption as well as hydrogen requirement are 0.46 mg catalyst/ kg MAs, and molar ratio of 2.1:1 (H2/VFA), respectively. The hot effluent of the hydrogenation reactor is cooled and sent to the two flash drums operating in series to recover vapours, which are recycled to the hydrogenation reactor. The bottom stream of the final flash drum consists of 25 wt.% water, 42 wt.% ethanol, 19 wt.% propanol, and 12 wt.% butanol, and is sent to the alcohol recovery unit. Herein, MAs are dehydrated by the molecular sieves, and sent to the alcohol distillation column to separate ethanol from butanol and propanol. The 99.9 wt.% purity of ethanol is obtained in the overhead stream of distillation column. Propanol and butanol are obtained in the bottom stream of column and considered as co-products.

2.3. Superstructure development

Design alternatives are added in the previously mentioned baseline process to develop a superstructure. The superstructure is shown in Figure 1 and consists of six sections: (1) fermentation and solid processing, (2) volatile fatty acids recovery, (3) hydrogenation, (4) mixed alcohols recovery, (5) utilization of carbon dioxide, and (6) wastewater treatment. The proposed superstructure contains fourteen design alternatives at various processing stages. The general mathematical model is similar to one reported in our previous work (Dickson et al., 2018). The design alternatives for solid processing include mechanical separator and centrifuge. As dehydration is energy intensive, five design alternatives are considered for recovering VFAs and MAs. VFAs can be recovered either by classical extraction/distillation processes or hybrid pervaporation (PV). The classical methods for recovering VFAs are similar to that described in Section 2.2. In PV, pervaporator is integrated into the classical process, which increases the concentration of VFAs from 5 wt.% to 10 wt.% by removing ~50 wt.% of the total water flow. Removal of this large amount of water directly impacts the process economics. Likewise, MAs can be dehydrated by three design alternatives to achieve a desired level of purity for their applications as a fuel. Dehydration can be performed by either molecular sieves, pervaporator, or vapor permeation. In all design alternatives, the target purity of ethanol is 99.5 wt.%.

To reduce CE, seven design alternatives are considered for microalgae cultivation and harvesting. Microalgae can be cultivated either in open ponds or photobioreactors. For its harvesting and dewatering, five design alternatives are considered. The microalgae are harvested in gravity settler, which can be dewatered either by hallow filter membranes, diffused air flocculation, or electrocoagulation followed by centrifugation. Alternatively belt filter press can be implemented at the outlet stream of gravity settler. The final concentration of microalgae from all dewatering alternative is 20 wt.%. The operating data and equipment costs considered for microalgae production are based on the work of (Davis et al., 2016).

A complete wastewater treatment network is incorporated that will treat and recycle wastewater from various process units including distillation columns, blowdown from the cooling tower, and blowdown from the boilers. Process wastewater is treated using anaerobic digestion, aerobic digestion, and reverse osmosis. The treated water is assumed to be pure and is recycled to the process.

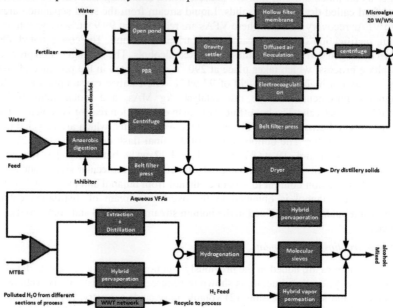

Figure 1. Superstructure for producing mixed alcohol from *Saccharina japonica*.

2.4. Objective function and assumptions

The objective function used for this optimization problem is maximization of the NPV and given in Eq. (1)

$$NPV = \sum_{n=0}^{20} \frac{NCF_n}{(1+r)^n},$$ (1)

where NCF_n is non-discounted cash flow for the year n, and r is the discount rate. Various assumptions considered in techno-economic analysis include: 20 years project life, 10% discount rate, straight line depreciation method over 7 years, 30% tax rate, and two-year construction time. The chemical composition of *Saccharina japonica* reported by Roesijadi et al. (2010) was used in the simulation. An efficiency of 0.35 g VFA/g of dry biomass is considered in AD. The selling prices of products such as ethanol, heavier alcohols, DDS, and microalgae considered in this study to calculate process revenue were 0.72 $/kg, 1.13 $/kg, 0.13$/kg, and 0.5 $/kg, respectively. Likewise, costs of raw materials such as brown algae, MTBE, cooling H$_2$O, chilled H$_2$O, H$_2$, LP steam, and electricity were 68 $/t, 1100 $/t, 0.013 $/t, 1 $/t, 1.5 $/t, 12.68 $/t, and 0.0622 $/kWh, respectively.

3. Results and discussion

The proposed process synthesis framework was implemented in GAMS (25.0.2) to determine optimal process design for MAs production process and CE utilization. The digester receives 612,000 t/y dry feed for biofuel production. The optimal manufacturing process for MAs synthesis shown in Figure 2 consists of AD, solid separation by belt filter press and dryer, VFAs dehydration by the extraction followed by distillation, hydrogenation, and MAs dehydration by molecular sieves followed by distillation. For CO_2 utilization, microalgae cultivation in open pond, harvesting by gravity settler, and dewatering by hollow filter membranes followed by centrifugation were selected as an optimal strategy. The products obtained from the biorefinery are ethanol, butanol, propanol, DDS, and microalgae. Their production rates are 32 mgal/y, 8 mgal/y, 14 mgal/y, 258 kt/y, and 49 kt/t, respectively. The NPV, TCI, TCOM, and utilities costs are $124.7 MM, $328 MM, $31 MM, $141.7 MM, respectively. By integrating microalgae process to MAs manufacturing process, CE are decreased from 117 kt/y to 11kt/y. The cost of integration of microalgae process into the MAs manufacturing is $72 MM.

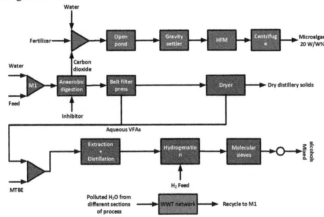

Figure 2. Optimal structure for mixed alcohol manufacturing process.

3.1. Minimum and maximum price of products and seaweed

The minimum selling price of products can be defined as the selling price of products that makes the NPV equal to zero. The estimated MESP of optimal design is 1.26 $/gal at the current whole sale price of all products. Similarly, minimum selling price of higher alcohols, DDS, and microalgae are 2.3 $/gal, 0.05 $/kg, and 0.114 $/kg.

The maximum seaweed price (MSP) can be defined as the purchasing price of seaweed that makes the NPV equal to zero. The estimated MSPP of optimal design is 111 $/ton, which is 1.63 times more than that of base case price.

3.2. Sensitivity analysis

Sensitivity analysis was performed to evaluate the effect of selling and purchasing prices of products and seaweed, respectively. Each sensitivity parameter was varied by ± 10% from the base value. The result of sensitivity analysis is presented as a tornado chars in Figure 3. Result indicated selling price of heavier alcohols and seaweed price are most dominant parameter that effect MESP.

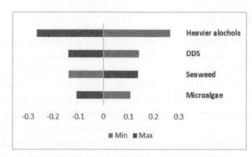

Figure 3. Sensitivity tornado chart for MESP.

4. Conclusion

An optimization-based framework for the MAs process synthesis as well as optimization of CE was proposed in this study. A rigorous techno-economic objective function (NPV) was used to investigate various economic parameters such as minimum selling price of products and MSP. The result indicated that biofuel production by VFAs route is viable; however, some challenges such as biomass price and its availability should be addressed before implementation of such biorefineries.

5. Acknowledgement

This research was supported through the Basic Science Research Program of the National Research Foundation of Korea (NRF) funded by the Ministry of Science and ICT (2017R1A2B4004500).

6. Reference

Davis, R., Markham, J., Kinchin, C., Grundl, N., Tan, E.C.D., Humbird, D., 2016. Process Design and Economics for the Production of Algal Biomass: Algal Biomass Production in Open Pond Systems and Processing Through Dewatering for Downstream Conversion.

Dickson, R., Ryu, J.-H., Liu, J.J., 2018. Optimal plant design for integrated biorefinery producing bioethanol and protein from Saccharina japonica: A superstructure-based approach. Energy 164, 1257-1270.

Fasahati, P., Liu, J.J., 2015. Impact of volatile fatty acid recovery on economics of ethanol production from brown algae via mixed alcohol synthesis. Chem. Eng. Res. Des. 98, 107–122.

Granda, C.B., Holtzapple, M.T., Luce, G., Searcy, K., Mamrosh, D.L., 2009. Carboxylate platform: The MixAlco process part 2: Process economics. Appl. Biochem. Biotechnol. 156, 107–124.

Jiang, R., Ingle, K.N., Golberg, A., 2016. Macroalgae (seaweed) for liquid transportation biofuel production: What is next? Algal Res. 14, 48–57.

Pham, T.N., Nam, W.J., Jeon, Y.J., Yoon, H.H., 2012. Volatile fatty acids production from marine macroalgae by anaerobic fermentation. Bioresour. Technol. 124, 500–503.

Roesijadi, G., Jones, S.B., Zhu, Y., 2010. Macroalgae as a Biomass Feedstock : A Preliminary Analysis. Analysis 1–50.

Zittel, W., Schindler, J., 2007. Crude oil the supply outlook.

Anton A. Kiss, Edwin Zondervan, Richard Lakerveld, Leyla Özkan (Eds.)
Proceedings of the 29th European Symposium on Computer Aided Process Engineering
June 16th to 19th, 2019, Eindhoven, The Netherlands. © 2019 Elsevier B.V. All rights reserved.
http://dx.doi.org/10.1016/B978-0-128-18634-3.50044-8

Global Optimization of Counter Current Gasketed Plate Heat Exchanger

Natália Martins,[a] Peam Cheali,[b] André Costa,[a,*] and Miguel Bagajewicz[c]

[a]*Rio de Janeiro State University (UERJ), Rua São Francisco Xavier, 524, Maracanã, CEP 20550-900, Rio de Janeiro, RJ, Brazil*

[b]*Enservpower, 1339 Pracharad 1, Bangsue, Bangkok, 10310, Thailand*

[c]*School of Chemical, Biological and Materials Engineering, University of Oklahoma, Norman, Oklahoma, 73019, USA*

andrehc@uerj.br

Abstract

This paper presents a mathematical programming approach for the design of counter current gasketed plate heat exchangers. The objective function corresponds to the minimization of the heat transfer area and the set of constraints includes the thermofluid-dynamic equations for evaluation of film coefficients and pressure drops, the heat transfer rate equation, and bounds on velocities and pressure drops. We also consider discrete geometric options. The expressions of the objective function and constraints are reformulated into a linear form, without loss of rigor, i.e. the solution of the linear problem is exactly the same of the original one. Therefore, problems related to nonconvergence or multiple local optima with different values of objective function are avoided. An example of a typical design task is employed to illustrate the performance of the proposed approach.

Keywords: Optimization, Plate heat exchangers, Design

1. Introduction

Shell-and-tube heat exchangers are the main type of thermal equipment employed in chemical process plants. However, gasketed plate heat exchangers can be a better option in several thermal tasks. Despite its limitations for more severe operational conditions, plate heat exchangers present several advantages, e.g. film coefficients are higher, cleaning procedures are easier, they are less prone to fouling problems, etc. The design optimization problem seeks to identify the plate heat exchanger associated to the minimum area, according to the available pressure drops for both streams. In our case, the design variables are the number of plates and the plate size. There is no phase change along the heat transfer surface. The thermofluid-dynamic model is based on Kakaç et al.(2012), particularly employing the equations describe in Rao et al. (2005).

2. Problem Formulation

The heat exchanger model is composed of a set of nonlinear equations, encompassing the the heat transfer rate equation, correlations for the evaluation of the heat transfer coefficients and pressure drops, and performance constraints (in the presentation of the model here, the parameters are identified by a symbol ^ on top).

2.1. Heat transfer rate equation

The heat transfer rate equation is:

$$Q = UA_{req} \Delta \hat{T}_{lm} \tag{1}$$

where U is the overall heat transfer coefficient, A_{req} is the required area and $\Delta \hat{T}_{lm}$ is the logarithmic mean temperature difference. The expression of the overall heat transfer coefficient is:

$$U = \frac{1}{1/h_h + \hat{R}f_h + \hat{t}/\hat{k}w + \hat{R}f_c + 1/h_c} \tag{2}$$

where $\hat{R}f$ is the fouling factor, $\hat{t}$ is the plate thickness, $\hat{k}w$ is the thermal conductivity of the plate material.

2.2. Convective heat transfer coefficients

The Nusselt number can be evaluated from the Reynolds and Prandtl numbers through the following correlation, where the index sSt represents the hot and cold streams ($sSt \in \{h,c\}$):

$$Nu_{sSt} = \hat{C}Re_{sSt}^{\hat{a}} \hat{P}r_{sSt}^{\hat{b}} \tag{3}$$

where the Reynolds number is expressed in relation to the hydraulic diameter:

$$Re_{sSt} = G_{sSt} \hat{D}hyd / \hat{\mu}_{sSt} \tag{4}$$

The expressions of mass flux is:

$$G = \frac{\hat{m}_{sSt}/(Nch/2)}{\hat{b} Lw} \tag{5}$$

where $\hat{m}_{sSt}$ is the mass flow rate, Nch is the total number of channels, and $\hat{b}$ is the flow channel gap.

2.3. Pressure drops

The pressure drop encompasses the head loss in the flow channels and in the distribution plate orifice:

$$\Delta P_{sSt} = f_{sSt} \frac{(Lp + Dp)}{\hat{D}hyd} \frac{G_{sSt}^2}{2\hat{\rho}_{sSt}} + 1.4 \frac{[\hat{m}_{sSt}/(\pi Dp^2/4)]^2}{2\hat{\rho}_{sSt}} \tag{6}$$

where Dp f_{sSt} is the Darcy friction factor:

$$f_{sSt} = \hat{K}Re_{sSt}^{-\hat{n}} \tag{7}$$

2.4. Performance constraints

The heat transfer area must be higher the required area according to a previously established "excess area" parameter:

$$A_{req} \leq A[100 / (100 + \hat{A}_{exc})] \tag{8}$$

where the heat transfer area depends on the plate features and the total number of plates:

$$A = \hat{\phi} L w L p (Nt - 2) \tag{9}$$

where $\hat{\phi}$ is the enlargement factor of the plate. The pressure drop of both fluids and flow velocities must be bounded according to the available values for both streams:

$$\Delta P_{sSt} \leq \Delta \hat{P}_{sSt}^{max} \tag{10}$$

$$\hat{v}^{min} \leq G_{sSt} / \hat{\rho}_{sSt} \leq \hat{v}^{max} \tag{11}$$

2.5. Objective function

The heat transfer area must be higher the required area according to a previously The objective function corresponds to the minimization of the heat transfer area:

$$\min \quad A \tag{12}$$

3. Discrete Options

It is important to observe that the design variables are discrete; therefore, its representation in the model formulation is associated to a set of binary variables, as follows:

$$Nt = \sum_{snt=1}^{sntmax} p\hat{N}t_{snt} yNt_{snt} \tag{13}$$

$$Lp = \sum_{sp=1}^{spmax} p\hat{L}p_{sp} yP_{sp} \tag{14}$$

$$Lw = \sum_{sp=1}^{spmax} p\hat{L}w_{sp} yP_{sp} \tag{15}$$

where Nt is the total number of plates (discrete options $p\hat{N}t_{snt}$ associated to the binary variables yNt_{snt}), Lp and Lw are the plate effective length and width (discrete options $p\hat{L}p_{sp}$ and $p\hat{L}w_{sp}$ associated to the binary variables yP_{sp}). Since one of the options must be selected in the solution, these constraints are complemented by:

$$\sum_{snt=1}^{sntmax} yNt_{snt} = \sum_{sp=1}^{spmax} yP_{sp} = 1 \tag{16}$$

4. Problem Reformulation

The reformulation of the problem to a linear structure employs the procedure applied by Gonçalves et al. (2017) for the optimization shell-and-tube heat exchangers. This approach involves three steps: (i) Substitution of the binary representation of the discrete design variables (Eq. (13-16)) in the heat exchanger model equations and objective function (Eq. 1-12), (ii) Reorganization of the resultant mathematical expressions in a product of binaries, and (iii) Substitution of the product of binaries by a set of linear inequalities.

The procedure is illustrated here through the substitution of the design variables in Eq. (5) by their corresponding representation using binary variables as follows:

$$G_{sSt} = \frac{[2\hat{m}_{sSt} / \sum\limits_{snt=1}^{sntmax} (p\hat{N}t_{snt} - 1)yNt_{snt}]}{(\hat{b} \sum\limits_{sp=1}^{spmax} p\hat{L}w_{sp}yP_{sp})} \tag{17}$$

Due to the nature of the binary variables and the fact that only one option can be selected (Eq. (16)), this expression is equivalent to the following representation using product of binaries:

$$G_{sSt} = \frac{2\hat{m}_{sSt}}{\hat{b}} \sum\limits_{snt=1}^{sntmax} \sum\limits_{sp=1}^{spmax} \frac{1}{p\hat{L}w_{sp}(p\hat{N}t_{snt} - 1)} yNt_{snt} yP_{sp} \tag{18}$$

Substituting the product of binaries by a continuous nonnegative variable $w_{snt,sp}$, together with the inclusion of a set of auxiliary inequalities, Eq. (18) can be substituted by the following set of linear relations:

$$G_{sSt} = \frac{2\hat{m}_{sSt}}{\hat{b}} \sum\limits_{snt=1}^{sntmax} \sum\limits_{sp=1}^{spmax} \frac{1}{p\hat{L}w_{sp}(p\hat{N}t_{snt} - 1)} w_{snt,sp} \tag{19}$$

$$w_{snt,sp} \leq yNt_{snt} \tag{20}$$

$$w_{snt,sp} \leq yP_{sp} \tag{21}$$

$$w_{snt,sp} \geq yNt_{snt} + yP_{sp} - 1 \tag{22}$$

5. Mixed-Integer Linear Programming Formulation

The application of the procedure described above yields the following linear design problem (complemented by Eqs. (10,11, 16, 19-22):

$$\min \sum\limits_{snt=1}^{sntmax} \sum\limits_{sp=1}^{spmax} \hat{\phi} pNt_{snt} pLw_{sp} pLp_{sp} w_{snt,sp} \tag{23}$$

subject to:

$$\hat{Q}_c \left\{ \sum_{sSt} \sum_{snt=1}^{sntmax} \sum_{sp=1}^{spmax} \left[\frac{\hat{D}hyd^{\hat{a}-1}}{\hat{C}\,\hat{k}_{sSt}\hat{P}r_{sSt}^{\hat{b}}} \left(\frac{\hat{b}\hat{\mu}_{sSt}}{2\hat{m}_{sSt}} \right)^{\hat{a}} p\hat{L}w_{sp}^{\hat{a}}(p\hat{N}t_{sNt}-1)^{\hat{a}} w_{snt,sp} + \hat{R}f_{sSt} \right] \right.$$

$$\left. + \frac{\hat{t}}{\hat{k}w} \right\} \le \left(\sum_{snt=1}^{sntmax} \sum_{sp=1}^{spmax} p\hat{N}t_{snt} p\hat{L}w_{sp} p\hat{L}p_{sp} w_{snt,sp} \right) \Delta \hat{T}_m \left(\frac{100}{100+\hat{A}_{exc}} \right)$$

$$\tag{24}$$

$$\Delta P_{sSt} = \left(\frac{\hat{K}}{2\hat{D}hyd\,\hat{\rho}_{sSt}} \right) \left(\frac{\hat{b}\,\hat{\mu}_{sSt}}{2\hat{m}_{sSt}\hat{D}hyd} \right)^{\hat{n}} \left(\frac{2\hat{m}_{sSt}}{\hat{b}} \right)^2 \sum_{snt=1}^{sntmax} \sum_{sp=1}^{spmax} \left[p\hat{L}w_{sp}(p\hat{N}t_{sNt}-1) \right]^{\hat{n}-2}$$

$$\left(p\hat{L}p_{sp} + p\hat{D}p_{sp} \right) w_{snt,sp} + \left(\frac{11.2\hat{m}_{sSt}^2}{\hat{\rho}_{sSt}\pi^2} \right) \sum_{sp=1}^{spmax} \left(\frac{1}{p\hat{D}p_{sp}^4} \right) yP_{sp}$$

$$\tag{25}$$

6. Numerical Results

The performance of the proposed approach is illustrated through the design of a plate heat exchanger for the thermal task described in Table 1, based on Kakaç and Liu (2002). The thermal conductivity of the plate material is 17.5 W/m°C) and the plate thickness is 0.6 mm. The hydraulic diameter associated to the heat exchanger is 4.8 mm, the enlargement factor of the area is 1.25 and the plate gap is 3 mm. The available pressure drop is 600 kPa for both streams. The fouling factor is $5 \cdot 10^{-5}$ m²K/W for the hot stream and it is null for the cold stream. The flow velocity must be between 0.4 m/s and 2.0 m/s for both streams. The minimum excess area is assumed equal to 10%.

The search space corresponds to 10 plate sizes with widths from 0.4 m to 1.3 m and lengths from 1.1 m to 2.0 m, associated to increments of 0.1 m. Additionally, an extra plate size is inserted in the search space based on a solution proposed by Kakaç et al. (2012) with width and length equal to 0.63 m and 1.35 m. The number of plates in the search space vary from 50 to 150 plates. The corresponding set of port diameters corresponds to an area of each port equivalent to 3% of the total area of the plate. The parameters associated to the correlations employed from Rao et al. (2005) are $\hat{C} = 0.218$, $\hat{a} = 0.65$, $\hat{b} = 1/3$, $\hat{K} = 21.41$, $\hat{n} = 0.301$.

Table 1: Stream data for the optimization problem.

Stream	m (kg/s)	T_i (°C)	T_o (°C)	ρ (kg/m³)	Cp (J/kg°C)	μ (mPa·s)	k (W/mK)
Hot	140	65	45	985	4183	0.509	0.645
Cold	140	22	42	995	4178	0.766	0.617

The solution obtained using the proposed design optimization procedure is compared in Table 2 with the solution based on Kakaç et al. (2012) for the same task.

Table 2: Stream data for the optimization problem.

Solution	A (m²)	Areq (m²)	Nt	Lp (m)	Lw (m)	U (W/m²ºC)	ΔP hot (kPa)	ΔP cold (kPa)
Proposed solution	102.06	92.54	96	1.35	0.63	5503	490	546
Literature	111.63	95.54	105	1.35	0.63	5330	424	471

The results in Table 2 indicate that the optimization found a solution with a smaller area, associated to a reduction of 8.6% in relation to the solution found in the literature data. The plate size is identical in both solutions, but the solution obtained using the proposed procedure has a smaller number of plates (i.e. the solution from the literature has more plates than necessary for a given excess area of 10%).

7. Conclusions

This paper presented a mathematical programming formulation for the optimization of countercurrent plate heat exchangers. Starting from a set of nonlinear equations of the heat exchanger modelling, mathematical manipulations are applied to yield a mixed-integer linear programming problem. Therefore, the global optimum of the design solution can be found without any drawbacks associated to nonconvergence issues. Due to the flexibility of the proposed approach other thermal tasks could also be addressed using the same mathematical scheme (e.g. vaporization or condensation). Possible obstacles to extend the proposed approach would be presence of thermofluidynamic models based on mathematical relations with variables that cannot be explicitly represented in relation to the design variables.

Acknowledgments

André L. H. Costa would like to thank the National Council for Scientific and Technological Development (CNPq) for the research productivity fellowship (Process 311225/2016-0) and the Rio de Janeiro State University through the Prociência Program.

References

C.O. Gonçalves, A.L.H. Costa, M.J. Bagajewicz, 2017, Shell and Tube Heat Exchanger Design Using Mixed-Integer Linear Programming, AIChE Journal, 63, 6, 1907-1922.

S. Kakaç, H. Liu, A. Pramuanjaroenkij, 2012, Heat Exchangers: Selection, Rating, and Thermal Design, CRC Press.

B.P. Rao, B.Sunden, S.K. Das, 2005, An Experimental and Theoretical Investigation of the Effect of Flow Maldistribution on the Thermal Performance of Plate Heat Exchangers, Transactions of the ASME, 127, 332-343.

Anton A. Kiss, Edwin Zondervan, Richard Lakerveld, Leyla Özkan (Eds.)
Proceedings of the 29th European Symposium on Computer Aided Process Engineering
June 16th to 19th, 2019, Eindhoven, The Netherlands. © 2019 Elsevier B.V. All rights reserved.
http://dx.doi.org/10.1016/B978-0-128-18634-3.50045-X

An optimization model for a biorefinery system based on process design and logistics

Christos Galanopoulos[a], Aristide Giuliano[b], Diego Barletta[b*], Edwin Zondervan[a]

[a]*Institute for Environmental Science and Technology (UFT), University of Bremen, Leobener Straße D, Bremen 28359, Germany*

[b]*Dipartimento di Ingegneria Industriale, Università degli Studi di Salerno, Via Giovanni Paolo II 132, I-84084 Fisciano SA, Italy*

dbarletta@unisa.it

Abstract

Design of biorefineries has been often addressed by process flowsheet optimization tools without adequately considering the relevant supply chain network. In this work, an integrated optimization algorithm including the biorefinery process flowsheet structure and biobased supply chain network was developed. A superstructure of different process pathways for a biorefinery co-producing ethanol, ethyl levulinate and electricity is built on the base of up-to-date technologies. The bio-based supply chain model was implemented to address the transportation, the inventory management and the size of the biorefinery. Mixed Integer Linear Programming (MILP) was used as a modeling approach. The efficiency of the algorithm was demonstrated by applying it to a case study consisting of a wheat straw supply chain network for bioproducts demand in Germany. The algorithm reached convergence after three iterations providing a final optimal number of biorefineries distributed in different regions of the country corresponding to a maximum Net Present Value.

Keywords: biorefinery, superstructure, bio-based supply chain, optimization, MILP

1. Introduction

A biorefinery is an industrial facility that is capable of producing multiple products from a wide variety of biomass sources. Decision-making tools and tailor-made approaches allow the appropriate exploitation of the potential of each type of biomass in power generation, heat and cooling application and as a transportation fuel (Laínez-Aguirre et al., 2015). Design of biorefineries has been often addressed by process flowsheet optimization tools without adequately considering the relevant supply chain network (Belletante et al., 2016). In particular, the optimal plant size does not depend simply on the economies of scale, but also on the biomass feedstock availability and the topology of the territory affecting logistics (transportation and storage) costs (Giuliano et al., 2018). On the other hand, works aiming at the supply chain level consider literature data or approximate correlations to estimate biorefinery technical performance, capital and operating expenditure (Galanopoulos et al., 2017). In this work, an integrated optimization algorithm including the biorefinery process flowsheet structure and the biomass and bioproduct supply chain network is developed. An original superstructure of alternative process pathways for a biorefinery co-producing biofuels and fuel addivives like ethanol "EtOH", ethyl levulinate "EL" (from levulinic acid and ethanol) and electricity is built on the basis of more recent technologies from literature.

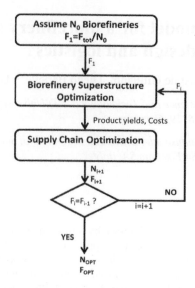

Figure 1: Graphical representation of the integrated optimization algorithm.

The bio-based supply chain model is implemented to address the logistics network, the transportation, the inventory management. The aim of the work was concentrated also on the optimal size of each biorefinery to build in a Germany region.

2. Methodology

The algorithm used to optimize the biorefinery system is presented in Figure 1. Assuming N_0 biorefineries of the same size F_1 initially, where F_1 is obtained dividing the total available biomass by N_0, the process optimization model for a single biorefinery fed by F_1 is used to optimize the flowsheet by maximizing the Net Present Value (NPV) of the single biorefinery by a MILP approach (Giuliano et al., 2015). Product flowrates, capital costs, operating costs of the single biorefinery are obtained and these data are used as input to the supply chain optimization model by Galanopoulos et al. (2018). The total system of biorefineries is then optimized by maximizing the total NPV including the supply chain costs. As a result, an updated N_i value and a new set of F_i values are obtained removing the constraints of biorefineries with equal size. The new F_i is then used for the process optimization model applied to each biorefinery of different size. In this way, the relevant process flowsheets, product flowrates, capital costs and operating costs are updated. Optimal biomass allocation, product flowrates, costs are obtained in order to design the biobased system. Convergence is achieved when the number of biorefineries and all the flowrates of feedstock for each biorefinery are the same as those obtained from the previous iteration. Finally, N_{opt} and F_{opt} are obtained.

2.1. Process Optimization Modelling

The process optimization model is based on a multiproduct lignocellulosic biorefinery superstructure. The model is obtained by Mixed Integer Linear Programming and it consists in the mathematical description of all biorefinery processes (Giuliano et al.,

2016). The original optimization mathematical model is a MINLP with integer variables for the selection of alternative technologies, after a discretization method for each non-linear variable, the model is rearranged as a MILP, in order to find the global optimal solution (Giuliano et al., 2014).

2.2. Supply Chain Modelling

Biomass is cultivated and collected at the harvesting site of each district. Then, it is either stored or transported to a biorefinery of a region where the conversion to products takes place. Similarly, the bioproducts are then transported to the demand sites to satisfy the demand. The goal is to develop a piece-wise linear model that includes the capital costs of the biorefineries. A detailed description of the supply chain network can be found in Galanopoulos et al. (2018).

3. Case study description

In Germany, the creation of a supply chain network based on cereal straw seems profitable. According to S2Biom report on cost supply (S2Biom, 2017), Germany is the second country in Europe with the highest production of cereal straw (22 Mt$_{DRY}$/y). The country is divided into 16 regions to quantify the distances in a cereal straw supply chain network in Germany. The distance between each region is evaluated using Google Maps. For the distance inside one region, the Manhattan Distance calculation (8r/3π) is used by considering that the regions are circles. To have a sustainable supply chain, 30% of all cereal straw produced in each region is assumed to be used for biorefinery purposes. Moreover, a seasonality similar to the growth of wheat is assumed. The products of the cereal straw biorefinery are bioethanol, ethyl levulinate and excess electricity. According to Wang et al. (2012), bioethanol and ethyl levulinate can be used as biofuel and fuel additive respectively for diesel/biodiesel. Ethyl levulinate was obtained by levulinic acid and ethanol equimolar reaction (Nandiwale et al., 2014), while the percentage of demand covered by the ethyl levulinate was set lower than the demand covered by the biofuel ethanol in order to obtain a similar covered demand for both products. The produced electricity can be sold to the grid. The demand of biofuel and of fuel additive is assumed equal to 10 % of the diesel demand for both products.

Table 1: Economic parameters used in the model.

Economic parameter	Value
Wheat straw cost (€/t)	100
Ethyl levulinate price (€/kg)	3.73
Ethanol price (€/kg)	0.694
Electricity price (€/MWhe)	145
Biomass transportation cost (fix €/t) + (variable €/t km)	2.64 + 0.15
Bioproduct transportation cost (fix €/t) + (variable €/t km)	2.4 + 0.17

4. Results

To develop the biomass supply chain model and process optimization model, the Advanced Interactive Multidimensional Modelling (AIMMS) software, version

4.21.5.583 64-bit, was used. CPU time to solve the supply chain model was equal to about 1 hour, for the process optimization was equal to about 30 minutes. For the process optimization the model got linear about 200 nonlinear variables. Data collected from the topology of Germany were used to find the total available wheat straw (WS). The initial number of biorefineries was assumed equal to three, because, by previous studies (Galanopoulos et al., 2018), Germany could contain about three biorefineries, considering the territory topology and availability of wheat straw in full Germany. Consequently, three biorefineries fed with 2,203,200 t/y of biomass were initially considered in the process optimization. The results of the iterative calculations are reported in Table 2. The two models converge after three iterations of the algorithm. The results show that the optimal solution is a decentralized production by means of nine biorefineries, eight with a capacity of 698,400 t/y of biomass and only one with a capacity of 871'200 t/y. Yields to products were constant for all iterations and all the biorefineries with different sizes because of constraints on covered product demands. The optimal number of biorefineries derived from a trade off between capital costs and transportation costs.

Table 2: Results of the iterations of the algorithm.

	Iteration number		
	I	II	III
Process optimization results			
Assumed number. of biorefineries for process optimization	**3**	**13**	**9**
Total straw used/total straw available (%)	100	100	98
EtOH yield (% of feedstock)	8	8	8
EL yield (% of feedstock)	10	10	10
Revenues (M€/y)	3'119	2'993	2'919
Biorefinery Operating Costs (M€/y)	1'093	1'193	1'149
Capital Costs (M€)	4'155	4'585	4'167
Supply chain optimization results			
Calculated number of biorefineries from supply chain optimization	**13**	**9**	**9**
Total straw used/total straw available (%)	100	98	98
Ethanol yield (% of feedstock)	8	8	8
Ethyl Levulinate yield (% of feedstock)	10	10	10
Revenues (M€/y)	2'993	2'919	2'919
Biorefinery Operating Costs (M€/y)	1'162	1'149	1'149
Capital Costs (M€)	4'418	4'167	4'167
Wheat straw production cost (M€/y)	845	800	800
Wheat straw & products transportation costs (M€/y)	341	337	337
NPV (M€)	30	43	43

Table 3: Biorefinery size (Mt/y of feedstock) distribution for each iteration of process optimization. Iterat. = iteration.

Iterat.	Number of biorefineries												
	1	2	3	4	5	6	7	8	9	10	11	12	13
I	2.20	2.20	2.20	-	-	-	-	-	-	-	-	-	-
II	0.94	0.87	0.81	0.78	0.70	0.53	0.52	0.44	0.36	0.30	0.23	0.09	0.05
III	0.87	0.70	0.70	0.70	0.70	0.70	0.70	0.70	0.70	-	-	-	-

In particular, the first iteration assuming only three biorefineries implied high transportation costs for the wheat straw. Therefore, next the supply chain optimization provided a result consisting in a decentralized production with 13 biorefineries with feedstock rate spanning between 0.05 and 0.94 Mt/y (Table 3). More accurate evaluation of the capital costs of smaller biorefineries, by process optimization of single plants, determined that the four smallest biorefineries, processing less than 0.3Mt/y, were deleted in the next iteration of the supply chain optimization. The straw production costs are lower in the second and third iteration compared to the first one because only 98% of available wheat straw is used as feedstock. Moreover, the transportation costs in the first iteration are almost the same with the ones in the second and third iteration as more wheat straw is used. The final result shows an increase of NPV up to 43 M€. Figure 2 shows the localization of the final biorefineries in the Germany's territory. The largest biorefinery (871'200 t/y) resulted in Rhineland-Palatinate region (dashed line in Figure 2) because WS is harvested in North West and West of Germany and from the topology results since there are no biorefineries in all its neighbour regions.

Figure 2: Biorefineries location in the map from the final iteration of the algorithm.

5. Conclusions

In this work, an integrated methodology to consider both the supply chain optimization and the process optimization was proposed. The developed MILP algorithm was tested on a biobased system transforming cereal straw into biofuels, ethanol and ethyl levulinate, in Germany. The algorithm efficiency was successfully demonstrated. In fact, three iterations were sufficient to reach the convergence of the algorithm to the optimal solution consisting in nine biorefineries located in different regions of Germany. This decentralized production resulted from a trade off between capital costs and transportation costs in a big territory. In fact, by increasing the number of biorefineries capital costs increase while biomass and bioproducts transportation costs decrease. The optimal solution derived from the maximization of the NPV.

References

S. Belletante, L. Montastruc, S. Negny, S. Domenech, 2016. Design of a Multiproduct Lignocellulosic Biorefinery through the Process Modelling of a Feasible Superstructure. Comput. Aided Chem. Eng. 38, 595–600.

C. Galanopoulos, D. Barletta, E. Zondervan, 2018. A decision support platform for a bio-based supply chain: Application to the region of Lower Saxony and Bremen (Germany). Comput. & Chem. Eng. 115, 233–242.

C. Galanopoulos, A. Odierna, D. Barletta, E. Zondervan, 2017. Design of a wheat straw supply chain network in Lower Saxony, Germany through optimization. Comput. Aided Chem. Eng. 40, 871–876.

A. Giuliano, D. Barletta, I. De Bari, M. Poletto, 2018. Techno-economic assessment of a lignocellulosic biorefinery co-producing ethanol and xylitol or furfural. Comput. Aided Chem. Eng. 43, 585–590.

A. Giuliano, R. Cerulli, M. Poletto, G. Raiconi, D. Barletta, 2016. Process Pathways Optimization for a Lignocellulosic Biorefinery Producing Levulinic Acid, Succinic Acid, and Ethanol. Ind. Eng. Chem. Res. 55, 10699–10717.

A. Giuliano, R. Cerulli, M. Poletto, G. Raiconi, D. Barletta, 2014. Optimization of a Multiproduct Lignocellulosic Biorefinery using a MILP Approximation. Comput. Aided Chem. Eng. 33, 1423–1428.

A. Giuliano, M. Poletto, D. Barletta, 2015. Process Design of a Multi-Product Lignocellulosic Biorefinery. Comput. Aided Chem. Eng. 37, 1313–1318. https://doi.org/10.1016/B978-0-444-63577-8.50064-4

J.M. Laínez-Aguirre, M. Pérez-Fortes, L. Puigjaner, 2015. Strategic Planning of Biomass Supply Chain Networks for Co-combustion Plants. Comput. Aided Chem. Eng. 36, 453–474.

K.Y. Nandiwale, P.S. Niphadkar, S.S. Deshpande, V. V. Bokade, 2014. Esterification of renewable levulinic acid to ethyl levulinate biodiesel catalyzed by highly active and reusable desilicated H-ZSM-5. J. Chem. Technol. Biotechnol. 89, 1507–1515.

S2Biom Project Report D1.8 Atlas with regional cost supply biomass potentials for EU 28, Western Balkan Countries, Moldavia, Turkey and Ukraine, 2017. https://s2biom.wenr.wur.nl/doc/S2Biom_D1_8_v1_1_FINAL_19_04_2017_CP.pdf

Z. Wang, T. Lei, L. Liu, J. Zhu, X. He, Z. Li, 2012. Performance investigations of a diesel engine using ethyl levulinate-diesel blends. BioResources 7. (4), 5972-5982.

Anton A. Kiss, Edwin Zondervan, Richard Lakerveld, Leyla Özkan (Eds.)
Proceedings of the 29th European Symposium on Computer Aided Process Engineering
June 16th to 19th, 2019, Eindhoven, The Netherlands. © 2019 Elsevier B.V. All rights reserved.
http://dx.doi.org/10.1016/B978-0-128-18634-3.50046-1

Design of smart liquid-liquid extraction columns for downstream separations of biopharmaceuticals using deep Q-learning algorithm

Soonho Hwangbo[1], Merve Öner[1], Gürkan Sin[1,*]

[1]*Process and Systems Engineering Center (PROSYS), Department of Chemical and Biochemical Engineering, Technical University of Denmark, Building 229, DK-2800 Kgs. Lyngby, Denmark*
gsi@kt.dtu.dk

Abstract

We propose smart liquid-liquid extraction columns of biopharmaceuticals using deep Q-learning algorithm. In this contribution, we demonstrated the application of the tool for design of liquid-liquid extraction process for concentration of API from fermentation broth. To this end, we present the following;1) development of property model to describe solubility of API in different solvents using the nonrandom two-liquid segment activity coefficient model, 2) design the liquid-liquid extraction process for different solvent candidates commonly used in pharma industries, 3) application of deep Q-learning algorithm to optimize liquid-liquid extraction control, and 4) perform sensitivity analysis to study effect of feed fraction of API on the performance. We have validated the developed property process modelling by comparing the existing experimental data and the characteristics of diverse solvents and using sensitivity analysis. We expect that the results from this study would contribute to further development the general framework of downstream separation for the future by extending to more downstream separation processes.

Keywords: Property process modelling, liquid-liquid extraction, deep Q-learning, control, biopharmaceuticals.

1. Introduction

The global pharmaceuticals industry enjoyed years of favorable growth –total revenues generated in 2011 were in excess of $698 billion representing an annual growth rate of 6.7% between 2007 and 2011. The industry now finds itself facing a number of challenges including a changing health care landscape, expiring patents and generic competition, pricing pressures, and a persistent economic slowdown (Fernandes 2015). One of the feasible solutions to overcome the current situation is to develop a smart modelling tool for design and synthesis of downstream separation for biopharmaceuticals. Liquid-liquid extraction (LLE), which is also called solvent extraction, is the main process that is much employed during the downstream separation. In LLE process, a liquid feed of two or more components is faced with a second liquid phase containing solvent (Seader, Henley et al. 1998). Therefore, the use of proper solvents is an inevitably important issue to obtain high yield of active pharmaceutical ingredients (APIs) and achieve great crystalline form from the product performance's point of view. The property process modelling such as the solubility, which is a chemical property referring to the ability for a given substance called solute to dissolve in solvents, can explicitly affect the general feasibility of the LLE process. As part of development of a general framework of a smart modelling tool for downstream separation process for biopharmaceuticals, this study aims to develop the property process modelling and design one of the commonly used separation step for concentration of API by using an in-silico tool and reinforcement learning. In the reinforcement learning section, a deep Q-learning algorithm to control the LLE process considering Markov decision process and deep neural networks has been investigated (Henderson, Islam et al. 2018). Sensitivity analysis of API has been simulated and the general framework of a smart LLE column for downstream separation has been proposed.

2. Problem statement

Figure 1 illustrates the overall framework of this study. Property process modelling based on thermodynamic model is developed and the LLE process is designed using the results from the property process modelling. The property process modelling is able to be constructed by either conducting experiments or applying thermodynamic models. However, the research on the property process modelling of various compounds via thermodynamic models have been actively studied because the experiments costs time and resources. Nonrandom two-liquid segment activity coefficient (NRTL-SAC) model was selected for the purpose of solubility modeling and Aspen Properties was employed to regress segment parameters. Reinforcement leaning was applied to conduct process operation optimization in the LLE process to optimize process operation.

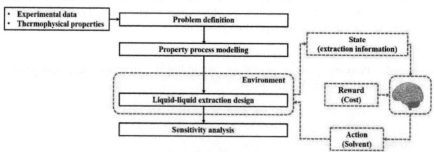

Figure 1. Overall framework of a smart liquid-liquid extraction process for downstream separation of biopharmaceuticals.

Deep Q-learning algorithm, which is one of the most dominant reinforcement learning tools, was employed to implement to design optimal control strategies (Mnih, Kavukcuoglu et al. 2015, Gu, Lillicrap et al. 2016). The LLE process corresponds to the environment and discloses LLE column information towards a deep Q-learning agent. The main role of the deep Q-learning agent optimizes parameters of the value function, which is taken into account as deep neural networks, to obtain the reward as much as possible that is the operating cost in this research. The deep Q-learning agent makes an action to manipulate information of solvents and finally the environment is newly characterized by the action. Sensitivity analysis of APIs with distinct solvents that were selected by the property process modelling has been performed.

3. Property process modelling and the LLE column design

Aforementioned thermodynamic models such as universal functional activity coefficient (UNIFAC), conductor-like screening model for real solvent (COSMO-RS), conductor-like screening model-segment activity coefficient (COSMO-SAC), NRTL-SAC correspond to liquid-phase non-ideality of organic nonelectrolytes (Chen and Crafts 2006). In this study, the NRTL-SAC model has been selected and utilized to construct the property process modelling. General mathematical expression at stages in the LLE process consists of differential equations. Solute concentrations in the raffinate phase (x_i) and the extract phase (y_i) are derived by the raffinate flowrate (R), the extract flowrate (E), backmixing coefficients (α and β), mass transfer (Q_{x_i}), and fractional holdup (h_{x_i} and h_{y_i}) and mass transfer is determined by mass transfer coefficient (K_{x_i}), interfacial area coefficient (a_i), and equilibrium concentration (x_i^*) (Eqs. (3) and (4)) (Mjalli 2005).

$$\frac{dx_i}{dt} = \frac{\left[(1+\alpha)R_{i+1}x_{i+1} + \alpha R_{i-1}x_{i-1} - (1+2\alpha)R_i x_i - Q_{x_i}\right]}{h_{x_i}} \tag{1}$$

$$\frac{dy_i}{dt} = \frac{\left[\beta E_{i+1}y_{i+1} + (1+\beta)E_{i-1}y_{i-1} - (1+2\beta)E_i y_i + Q_{x_i}\right]}{h_{y_i}} \tag{2}$$

$$Q_{x_i} = K_{x_i}a_i V(x_i - x_i^*) \tag{3}$$

The equilibrium concentration of solute is numerically connected with the mole fraction of the solute (x^{SAT}), which is able to be calculated by the entropy of fusion of the solute ($\Delta_{fus}S$), the activity coefficient of the solute (γ^{SAT}), and the melting point (T_m) (Eq. (4)) (Chen and Song 2004) .

$$\ln x^{SAT} = \frac{\Delta_{fus}S}{R}\left(1 - \frac{T_m}{T}\right) - \ln \gamma^{SAT} \tag{4}$$

The LLE process can be designed with inherent input data. In this LLE process, we mainly assume that the number of stages is 10, the system temperature is the room temperature, the reactor is adiabatic, and liquid-liquid coefficient form is calculated by the defined property method. As the feed composition, we have considered a stream after solid-liquid removal of the fermentation broth which results in a water rich (rather dilute) stream containing API with typical concentration levels. For confidentiality purposes, the identity of the API cannot be disclosed.

4. Off-policy control with deep Q-Learning

General reinforcement learning includes five components, each of which is state, state transition probability matrix, action, reward, and discount factor. State illustrates the current environment and the transition from the previous state to the next state depends on actions from the agent. All the actions are based on a policy contained in the agent and the ultimate goal of reinforcement learning is to figure out the optimal policy to maximize rewards during both exploration and exploitation. In the case of off-policy learning, experience generated from old policies can be reused and the agent learns about multiple policies while following one policy. Off-policy Q-learning converges to the optimal action-value function, and provides the optimal control solution. The general definition of the action-value function ($Q(S, A)$) is the expected return obtained by starting from the current state (S), taking an action (A), and then following the current policy (π) (Eq. (5)). Reward (R) and another state (S') are observed by taking action from the existing state using policy derived from the existing action-value function. Then, the current action-value function is updated toward a better action-value function (Eq. (6)).

$$Q_\pi(s,a) = E_\pi[G_t \mid S_t = s, A_t = a] \tag{5}$$

$$Q(S,A) \leftarrow Q(S,A) + \alpha \left(R + \gamma \max_{a'} Q(S',a') - Q(S,A) \right) \tag{6}$$

Action-value functions in this study were considered by deep neural network and the concept of experience replay was taken into account to enhance the performance of training agent. Extraction information such as flowrates of materials, molar ratio, operating temperature, and pressure represents the state of the environment and the deep Q-learning agent exports actions such as solvent flowrate to control the LLE extraction. The LLE process operation method under the optimal control strategies can be suggested with the minimization of the operating costs.

5. Results and discussion

Validation of the property process modelling and sensitivity analysis of the API mole fraction with the amounts of solvents have been performed. Figure 3 describes the predicted solubility of API with various single solvents and one binary solvents. Acetone, acetonitrile, 1-butanol, methyl tert-butyl ether (MTBE), 1,4-dioxane, ethanol, ethyl acetate, n-heptane, methyl isobutyl ketone (MIBK), isobutanol, isopropyl alcohol (IPA), and methanol were used as single solvent and the predicted mole fraction of API dissolved in those solvents shows a considerably linearity with the experimental solubility (Figure 2(A)). In the case of the binary solvents, the patterns between the predicted and the experimental values are alike but there exist visually differences until 20% of water in the binary solvents because the experiment had been conducted over the unsteady room temperature (Figure 2(B)).

The deep Q-learning algorithm has been performed to conduct process operation optimization. Designed LLE process as the environment in the deep Q-learning world manifests a total of 5 characteristics in a state which are flowrates, molar ratio, operating temperature, and pressure in the LLE process. The deep Q-learning agent has received state information and been trained via deep neural networks. In this research, two deep neural networks have been used in order to account for behaviour action-value function and target action-value function. We assumed that the internal structure of those deep neural networks are identical, with three hidden layers. The behaviour action-value function is related to an exploring policy able to extend the range of control optimality. The target action-value function is associated with the optimal policy which should be finally determined with maximizing rewards, in other words, minimizing the operating costs of the LLE process. The action of the deep Q-learning agent has been assumed as solvent information and the total of 20,000 episodes for training have been executed. The total operating costs were approximately reduced by 4.66% compared to the existing LLE process. The more real data, the better robustness and feasibility would be anticipated.

Sensitivity analysis using Aspen Plus indicates that the types of solvents play an important role in the LLE process. 94%(w/w) water in the feed stream and the room temperature in the system were assumed in the sensitivity analysis. The range between the minimum value and the maximum value of the API mole fraction in the extract stream of the LLE process is infinitesimal because used solvents (acetone, acetonitrile, 1,4-dioxane, ethanol, and methanol) are miscible with water. The API mole fraction exponentially decreases according to an increase of the quantity of solvents because used solvents (1-butanol, MTBE, ethyl acetate, MIBK, and isobutanol) are immiscible with water. Changing the number of stages in the LLE process, adding different solvents or replacing single solvents with binary solvents would be implemented with respect to sensitivity analysis.

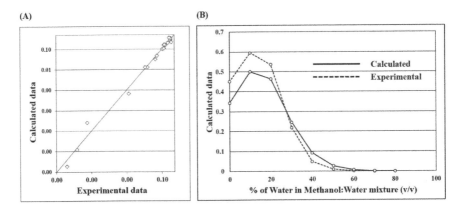

Figure 2. Solubility results from the property process modelling using thermodynamic model. (A): Solubility of API in single solvents. (B): Solubility of API in different volume fraction of water in methanol/water solvents.

6. Conclusions

An in-silico tool for the property process modelling and the LLE process has been studied and developed by using simulation tools and artificial intelligence software. We have demonstrated the application for a fermentation broth containing an API with dilute concentration (<5% wt). The main conclusions of this study are as follows: 1) NRTL-SAC model and parametric regression in Aspen Properties are able to describe solubility of API in different solvents quite satisfactorily, 2) the LLE process has been designed considering a class of solvents commonly used in pharmaceutical industry which enabled fast screening of LLE design candidates, 3) reinforcement learning such as deep Q-learning in this study has been conducted to implement the LLE process operation optimization, and 4) sensitivity analysis has been performed to clarify the connection and impact between solvents and API. Future works will extend the analysis of LLE design under uncertainty of experimental data in particular property measurements and modelling to enable robust design and solvent screening (Frutiger, Jones et al. 2018). Moreover, the LLE column design technique implemented in this study would be applied for the development of a general downstream separation framework tool able to be extend to other relevant downstream separation steps including crystallization process and chromatographic separation to offer a complete design of biopharmaceutical separation.

Acknowledgment

We would like to thank the Danish Council for Independent Research (DFF) for financing the project under the grant ID: DFF-6111600077B.

References

Chen, C.-C. and P. A. Crafts (2006). "Correlation and prediction of drug molecule solubility in mixed solvent systems with the nonrandom two-liquid segment activity coefficient (NRTL–SAC) model." Industrial & engineering chemistry research **45**(13): 4816-4824.

Chen, C.-C. and Y. Song (2004). "Solubility modeling with a nonrandom two-liquid segment activity coefficient model." Industrial & engineering chemistry research **43**(26): 8354-8362.

Fernandes, P. (2015). "The global challenge of new classes of antibacterial agents: an industry perspective." Current opinion in pharmacology **24**: 7-11.

Frutiger, J., M. Jones, N. G. Ince and G. Sin (2018). From property uncertainties to process simulation uncertainties–Monte Carlo methods in SimSci PRO/II process simulator. Computer Aided Chemical Engineering, Elsevier. **44**: 1489-1494.

Gu, S., T. Lillicrap, I. Sutskever and S. Levine (2016). Continuous deep q-learning with model-based acceleration. International Conference on Machine Learning.

Henderson, P., R. Islam, P. Bachman, J. Pineau, D. Precup and D. Meger (2018). Deep reinforcement learning that matters. Thirty-Second AAAI Conference on Artificial Intelligence.

Mjalli, F. S. (2005). "Neural network model-based predictive control of liquid–liquid extraction contactors." Chemical engineering science **60**(1): 239-253.

Mnih, V., K. Kavukcuoglu, D. Silver, A. A. Rusu, J. Veness, M. G. Bellemare, A. Graves, M. Riedmiller, A. K. Fidjeland and G. Ostrovski (2015). "Human-level control through deep reinforcement learning." Nature **518**(7540): 529.

Seader, J. D., E. J. Henley and D. K. Roper (1998). "Separation process principles."

Anton A. Kiss, Edwin Zondervan, Richard Lakerveld, Leyla Özkan (Eds.)
Proceedings of the 29th European Symposium on Computer Aided Process Engineering
June 16th to 19th, 2019, Eindhoven, The Netherlands.
http://dx.doi.org/10.1016/B978-0-128-18634-3.50047-3

Process design and techno-economic analysis of a pineapple wine production plant under the context of the Choco-Colombia region

Juan Fernando Murcia Palacios[a*], Rolando Barrera[a], Edwin Zondervan[b,]

[a] Grupo CERES-Agroindustria & Ingeniería, Universidad de Antioquia UdeA, Calle 70 No. 52-21, Medellín, Colombia

[b]University of Bremen, Leobener Str. 6, Bremen, 28359, Germany

*fernando.murcia@udea.edu.co

Abstract

Pineapple surplus in the region of Choco-Colombia, the selection process that involves its commercialization and being a rapidly perishable fruit, causes serious losses for farmers. Due to the high content of sugars, it is anticipated that discarded fruit juice can be used as a substrate for the development of bioprocesses to obtain value-added products on an industrial scale. A new model for a 1600 ton / year pineapple wine production plant has been developed with Aspen Plus® v10.0 (Aspentech, Cambridge, MA). It is observed that the cost of the raw material and the fixed manufacturing costs have the greatest impact on the operating cost with 29 and 28% respectively, the capital cost are estimated in US$ 15.52 million, on the other hand the plant generates 2210 tons of pineapple bagasse as solid waste and emits of 162.3 tons of CO_2 per year.

Keywords: modeling, simulation, techno-economic analysis, pineapple wine

1. Introduction

About 4 thousand tons of pineapple are wasted every year in the Choco region [1]. Thanks to governmental programs that have encouraged the cultivation of this fruit, in recent years the production of pineapple in the region went from 2,737 tons in 2007 to more than 8,000 tons in 2015[2]. However, such an increase in pineapple production leads to a simultaneous increase in waste generation due to the selection and elimination of components during processing. Most pineapples are eaten fresh; nevertheless, only the first-quality fruit is selected for later distribution to the markets. Therefore, fruit that does not comply with these characteristics is left to rot on farms or is sold at very low prices [1]. Although some alternatives to fresh consumption (jams, concentrates, nectars, purées, etc.) are being implemented, a high percentage of the production is still left in the fields as a waste[3]. These practices create both an ecological and an economic problem, because large amounts of organic matter have to be recycled and money must be spent on agrochemicals, labour, and machinery for both the fruit that is consumed and the fruit that is disposed of, but all the costs are borne by the fruit that is consumed. Thus, higher prices and environmental contamination result from fruit surplus[4].

Several alternatives have been proposed and implemented in some countries, mainly transformations by fermentation, with wine, vinegar and other compounds as value-added products. Despite several laboratory-scale experimental investigations of pineapple wine production, little information is available on the economics of semi-industrial or industrial production [1, 5-7]. In this work, both modeling and simulation are used to evaluate the process of transformation of pineapple juice into wine. To the best of author's knowledge, a techno-economic evaluation to the transformation of pineapple juice into wine under the context of Choco-Colombia region has not been reported so far. Aspen Plus® v10.0 was used to model and simulate the process, then the model was used to estimate the capital and operating costs, as well as the emissions of the plant.

2. Model description

Using the Aspen Plus® software a process flowsheet is presented in Fig. 1. The diagram shows the fundamental operations of the plant: the extraction of the juice, the clarification, fermentation, ageing, filtration and bottling, the process is simulated and the material and energy flows of each operation and the sizing of the equipment can be determined. Based on these values, the purchase costs of the equipment are estimated and with data from the literature assume the values corresponding to the operating costs of each unit. Currently such models (of non-conventional operations) and the related data for evaluation are not at hand. In this work we offer this valuable information. From the design and simulation, the economic analysis of the plant is presented.

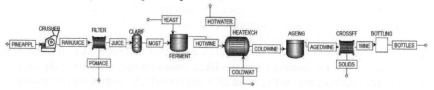

Figure 1. Aspen Plus® process flowsheet of the pineapple wine manufacturing plant

3. Outline of Process Technology

Pineapples are mechanically peeled, cored and crushed for juice extraction. The ripeness of the pineapple is judged from the sugar content in the juice; it is assumed that the pineapple juice has a 22°Brix index. Pineapple pomace is considered as a waste and the cost for its final disposal is included in the value of the raw material. Fermentation tanks made of stainless steel are used and the fermentation time is set at 15 days. Pineapple juice of a 22°Brix index when fully fermented with yeast will produce wine with an ethanol percentage of 11.5% at a rate of 1L of wine/kg of juice [8]. The fermentation is an exothermic process and the temperature in the fermentation tank must be maintained below 30°C. Therefore, cooling is required. The storage of pineapple wine results in biochemical- and physicochemical reactions that improve organoleptic characteristics and facilitate its clarification. In this case, the pineapple wine is aged for 6 months, before being bottled. Pineapple wine is stored in stainless steel tanks of 150ton capacity at 20°C, which requires cooling. Then, pineapple wine is filtered to remove all suspended particles before bottling. A suitable technology is a cross flow microfiltration. The aged and clarified pineapple wine is packaged in 0.75 L capacity glass bottles, using a high speed bottling machine at a speed of up to 5000 bottles/h.

4. Economic assessment

The economic assessment includes the purchase prices of the raw material, labor cost, industrial services, capital costs and the tentative value of sale of the finished product, the economic analysis of the production plant. Additionally, a plant lifetime of 27 years is considered, three years lower compare with a similar project using grapes, due to immediate pineapple availability. It is assumed that 50% of the required capital is covered by a loan with interest of 8% for 15 years, with a discount rate of 4%. The annual depreciation is estimated from the modified accelerated cost recovery system (MACRS) method described in Maroulis and Saravacos [9], in which, the machinery depreciates in 7 years. It assumes a production capacity equal to the installed capacity during the life time of the project. Finally, a 35% tax rate on profits is considered.

5. Results and Discussion

A flow chart of the process including the unit operations considered during the transformation of pineapple juice into wine is shown in Fig. 2. The values are based on 1000 kg of raw material. In the same diagram the requirements of the industrial services are presented in MJ. Also, Table 1 lists the material and energy requirements of the wine manufacturing plant, based on the material and energy diagram in Figure 2. The annual data corresponds to 320h/y. Labour refers only to production workers that is obtained by the counting method, both supervision and technical support are obtained by the factorial method both methods described in Maroulis and Saravacos [9].

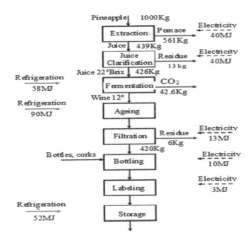

Figure 2. Material and energy balances of the pineapple wine manufacturing plant

In the extraction of the juice, pineapple peel and core are considered as residue, and the yield of this operation is taken from the literature with a value close to 44% of pulp juice per each kilogram of pineapple. In this operation, 13kg of waste is generated for each ton of pineapple, which means that from 1 ton of pineapple that enters the process only 426kg reaches the fermenter, which generates a loss of raw material close to 60%. Therefore, a strategy that generates value to these lignocellulosic wastes using superstructure optimization approach, which will be addressed in future work[10, 11].

Based on the juice input flows it the size of the fermenters should be 40 m³ of stainless steel capacity. The pineapple juice of 22 ° Brix index was inoculated with activated dry yeast (ADY) at the rate of 0.15kg / ton, and was transformed into pineapple wine with approximately 12% ethanol with a yield close to 1L of wine / kg of juice. The carbon dioxide generated during the reaction at a rate of 0.1kg CO_2 / L juice of 22 ° Brix.

On the other hand, as can be seen in Figure 1, 0MJ of electricity is required for each ton of pineapples for juice extraction, 40MJ for clarification, 13 MJ for filtration, 10 MJ for bottling and 3MJ in the labelling. While the refrigeration requirements are made in the stages of fermentation with 58MJ, aging with 90MJ and storage with 52MJ. It should be noted that water consumption is not considered during the cleaning of both the raw material and the equipment, nor the sterilization process.

Table 1. Material and Energy Requirements of the Pineapple Wine Manufacturing Plant

		Per product		**Hourly basis**		**Annual**	
Product							
Pineapple wine		1.00	kg/kg	5.00	t/h	1 600	t/y
Raw material							
Pineapples	Fr.	2.38	kg/kg	11.9	t/h	3 810	t/y
Bottles	Fg.	0.75	kg/p	6667	p/h	2. 133 333	p/y
Utilities							
Electricity	Fe.	0.05	kWh/kg	0.26	MW	82	MWh/y
Refrigeration	Fz.	0.13	kWh/kg	0.66	MW	212	MWh/y
Labour							
Manpower	M.	6.4	h/t	32.0	p	10 240	h/y

Capital costs and operating costs calculations are based on the short methods detailed in Maroulis and Saravacos [9], the size and cost of the equipment are estimated and the results are summarized in Table 2. The required capitals along with the appropriate assumptions are presented in Table 3.

Table 2. Equipment Cost Estimation of the Pineapple Wine Manufacturing Plant

Equipment	Qty	Size unit	Cost, Thousands US$
1. Fermentation tanks	20	40 ton	1000
2. Storage tanks	10	150 ton	1000
3. Crusher	1	5 ton/h	150
4. Screw press	1	5 ton/h	150
5. Heat exchanger	1	5 ton	150
6. Microfiltration	1	1 ton/h	150
7. Bottling machine	1	5 ton/h	400
			3000

It should be noted that for the economic analysis the purchase price of equipment had to be considered, these prices were updated taking by assuming a Lang factor of 4.5 because it is a new construction for food processing and to be located in an area with difficult access conditions. Although a centralized plant is considered in this work to reduce the cost of transporting the raw material, since more than 60% of the pineapple transported does not end up in the final product local storing might reduce costs significantly. In addition, it is assumed that the plant is close to the fields, the maximum distance is assumed to be 50km. In addition, losses are not considered due to the manipulation of the raw materials.

For the costs calculations the following assumptions are made: the annual operating time is 4 weeks per year, 5 days per week, 2 shifts per day and 8 hours per shift, product rate 4 ton/h, a labour cost of US $ 2.5 / h was assumed, which is representative of the unskilled workers in the Colombian context, raw material US$0.3/kg, a value three times higher than the price farmers normally receive when selling second and third quality pineapples, packaging material US$ 0.3/p, electricity cost US$ 0.11/kWh, cooling water cost US$ 0.01/kWh. and the results are presented in Figure 3. From figure 3, it is observed that the cost of the raw material is the one that has the greatest impact on the cost analysis, so if the farmers are directly involved in the pineapple wine production the cost of the raw material could decreased and the profitability of the plant could be higher.

Tabla 2. Capital Cost Estimation of the Pineapple Wine Manufacturing Plant

Purchased Equipment Cost	Ceq	3.00	M$
Lang Factor	fL	4.50	-
Fixed Capital Cost	CF	13.50	
Working Capital Cost	CW	2.02	
Total Capital Cost	CT	15.52	M$

The estimated profitability data is shown in Table 4. An internal rate of return of 23% is attractive for this type of investment. In that sense, this model can be the first step of a tool for helping processing decisions in the pineapple wine production sector. Although first result look promising, further research is needed to determine for example the amount of pineapple wine that can be diverted for the production of vinegar or premium-quality brandy.

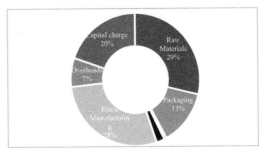

Figure 3. Operating cost estimation of the wine manufacturing plant per unit of product.

Table 4. Profitability of the Pineapple Wine Manufacturing Plant.

Profitability			
Sales Income	S	6.73	M$/y
Manufacturing Cost	CM	3.81	M$/y
Gross Profit	Pg	2.92	M$/y
Net Present Value	VPN	19.23	M$
Own Capital Cost	Co	7.59	M$
Capital Return Ratio	CRR	2.53	-
Internal Rate of Return	IRR	0.23	-

6. Conclusions

A techno-economic analysis of a plant that transforms pineapple juice into wine as the main product was carried out. The higher capital costs are related to the size of the fermentation and aging tanks, and the bottling machine. The emissions are primarily the residue or bagasse of the pineapple, which can be arranged in the field or be processed to obtain other products of interest. Moreover, this model can be the first step of a tool for helping processing decisions, making possible to vary the amount of raw material that can be transformed into pineapple wine, giving the flexible enterprise the advantage to better adapt to changes in demands that occur in the market. We are aware that this result may be significantly affected by the size of the plant, raw materials and products prices, or the volume of production and deserves a sensitivity analysis, which will be addressed in future work.

Acknowledgments

Juan Fernando Murcia Palacios express his acknowledgements to the Departamento Administrativo de Ciencia, Tecnología e Innovación (Colciencias) call 647 – 2014

References

Murcia Palacios, J.F., *Ensayos para la producción de etanol utilizando Ananas comosus de rechazo*, in *Escuela de Ingeniería*. 2013, Universidad Pontificia Bolivariana: Medellín. p. 61.
MADR, *Red de Información y Comunicación del Sector Agropecuario Colombiano (Spanish)*, M.d.A.y.D. Rural, Editor. 2018.
Grewal, H., H. Tewari, and K. Kalra, *Vinegar production from substandard fruits.* Biological wastes, 1988. **26**(1): p. 9-14.
Hidalgo, C., E. Mateo, and A.B. Cerezo, *Technological process for production of persimmon and strawberry vinegars.* International Journal of Wine Research, 2010. **2010**(1): p. 55-61.
Roda, A., et al., *Effect of pre-treatments on the saccharification of pineapple waste as a potential source for vinegar production.* Journal of Cleaner Production, 2016. **112**: p. 4477-4484.
Tropea, A., et al., *Bioethanol production from pineapple wastes.* Journal of Food Research, 2014. **3**(4): p. 60.
Roda, A., et al., *Vinegar production from pineapple wastes–Preliminary saccharification trials.* Chem. Eng. Trans, 2014. **37**.
Maroulis, Z.B. and G.D. Saravacos, *Food process design.* Vol. 126. 2003: CRC Press.
Maroulis, Z.B. and G.D. Saravacos, *Food plant economics.* 2007: CRC Press.
Nawaz, M., et al., *Design of an optimal biorefinery*, in *Computer Aided Chemical Engineering*. 2011, Elsevier. p. 371-376.
Giuliano, A., et al., *Techno-economic assessment of a lignocellulosic biorefinery co-producing ethanol and xylitol or furfural*, in *Computer Aided Chemical Engineering*. 2018, Elsevier. p. 585-590.

Anton A. Kiss, Edwin Zondervan, Richard Lakerveld, Leyla Özkan (Eds.)
Proceedings of the 29th European Symposium on Computer Aided Process Engineering
June 16th to 19th, 2019, Eindhoven, The Netherlands. © 2019 Elsevier B.V. All rights reserved.
http://dx.doi.org/10.1016/B978-0-128-18634-3.50048-5

Optimisation of Aqueous Two-Phase Systems

Emma Chandler[a], Robert Falconer [a] and Solomon Brown[a,*]

[a]*Department of Chemical and Biological Engineering, University of Sheffield, Sheffield, S1 3JD,
United Kingdom*
s.f.brown@sheffield.ac.uk

Abstract

Aqueous two-phase extraction (ATPE) is a liquid-liquid extraction (LLE) technique which is viable as a continuous protein purification unit operation for the manufacture of therapeutic proteins. A shift from batch to continuous manufacturing in this industry has been encouraged by regulatory bodies, including the Food and Drug Administration (FDA), as it is expected to increase the quality and consistency of the product and decrease manufacturing costs.

For ATPE to compete with current batch protein purification procedures, a multi-stage operation can be used to achieve a high purity and yield. However, there is a lack of reliable modelling techniques in the design of multi-stage ATPE; as a result, its design and operation is often reliant on both individual expertise and trial and error. To reduce this, there is a need to develop modelling techniques to aid in system design. In this study we present a modified equilibrium binary separation method to predict an optimal number of stages in a multi-stage system. The model is validated against data, for both traditional LLE and ATPE, in a counter-current multi-stage operation [Rosa et al., 2009a, Warade et al., 2011]. The model is then applied to a case study separation of phycocyanin from lysozyme using PEG-phosphate ATPE. The model is successfully used to predict a suitable design of a counter-current multistage system to optimise purity and yield of the target protein. The approach provides the basis with which to design general ATPE-based continuous downstream processes incorporating extraction, back-extraction and washing steps.

Keywords: Aqueous two-phase extraction, equilibrium binary separations, multi-stage optimisation.

1. Introduction

Aqueous two-phase extraction (ATPE) has been demonstrated to be capable of being a valuable alternative protein purification technique to chromatography [Rosa et al., 2010]. The unit operation is cheap relative to chromatography and, unlike chromatography, it is geared towards continuous manufacturing. Continuous manufacturing, as opposed to the traditional batch manufacturing techniques used in biomanufacturing, has been encouraged by regulatory bodies such as the FDA as it is seen as a way to reduce costs, increase manufacturing capacity and increase the consistency of the product quality [Konstantinov and Cooney, 2014]. A move to continuous manufacturing will require either a rethinking or replacement of the current downstream purification operations. However, these new manufacturing techniques still need to compete with the current manufacturing techniques as well as meet the high purity standards required of the regulatory bodies of this industry [Azevedo et al., 2009].

Currently, there are two major drawbacks to ATPE as a unit operation: the low purity / yield achieved in a single stage operation, and the lack of understanding of the phase forming mechanisms [Rito-Palomares, 2004, Ruiz-Ruiz et al., 2012]. The number of different parameters which control the phase separation and protein partitioning mean that the process optimisation is achieved through trial and error, which is both time consuming and expensive. Modelling strategies have been employed to identify key performance parameters, such as the concentration of the phase forming material (polymer(s) and salt(s)) used, and reduce the experimental workload [Rosa et al., 2007, Mao et al., 2010, Patel et al., 2018]. However, the specifics of optimising system selection still requires extensive experimental work and experience. Multi-stage techniques have been used extensively in the process industries when a separation technique is simple and cost effective but provides low purity and / or yield. In PEG-Salt ATPE the economics of the process can be further improved through using the multistage technique of back extracting the target protein into the less expensive salt rich phase, so that the more expensive polymer rich phase can be recycled [Rosa et al., 2013].

A common method for the stage-wise optimisation of equilibrium binary separations is McCabe Thiele. It was originally used to determine the number of stages for binary distillation and is still widely used in this application [Richardson et al., 2002]. The method has been demonstrated to be suitable for traditional liquid-liquid extraction (LLE) by Warade et al. [2011]. In this study a single operating line was used to optimise the number of stages for a specified purity in multi-stage counter current systems. The method was also demonstrated to be suitable for ATPS when it was applied by Rosa et al. [2009b,a], who also used a single operating line to optimise the number of stages for a required yield in ATPE. They also utilised equilibrium curves of different fractions of Chinese Hamster Ovary (CHO) cell media to predict the success of their extraction from Immunoglobulin G (IgG) [Rosa et al., 2009b]; however, the number of stages for extraction was not determined. In both cases, a single component is considered in the model the target component. In terms of traditional LLE, there are often only two components and by considering one, the other component can be inferred as one phase forming component is the target compound and the other is the contaminant. However, in ATPE, the phases are formed by the phase forming components (i.e. polymer(s), salt(s) and water) and the partitioning of the contaminants (protein, cells and solutes) is determined by the phase forming components and the environmental conditions. As such by considering only the target protein, the contaminants cannot be inferred in ATPE, and only the yield of the system can be evaluated.

This paper uses equilibrium binary separations to evaluate and optimise multi-stage ATPE. The model is validated using the experimental data in Warade et al. [2011], (counter-current multi-stage traditional LLE) and in Rosa et al. [2009a], (counter-current multi-stage ATPE). In this paper the models in Rosa et al. [2009a] and Warade et al. [2011] are interpreted for a counter-current multi-stage ATPE to evaluate both contaminants and target protein in a model separation of phycocyanin from lysozyme using a PEG phosphate ATPE. Equilibrium curves were constructed for both the target protein, phycocyanin, and the contaminant. The required number of stages to achieve the desired purity and yield were predicted using the model. Through alteration of the operating line, the system could be evaluated in other operational configurations, for instance co-current, cross-current, etc.

The work is structured as follows, Section 2 presents the model formulation developed, Section 3 presents the results from validating the model followed by the results from the model separation of phycocyanin from lysozyme and Section 4 discusses the conclusions from this work.

2. Model Formulation

In this work, we present a model for the multi-stage ATPE which incorporates the separation behaviour in each stage and that may then be used as a basis for optimisation. The model firstly assumes that while the phases are semi-miscible, the phases are treated as immiscible; this is a common assumption for ATPE. The process is isothermal so an energy balance is not used [Mistry et al., 1996, Rosa et al., 2009b,a]. It was assumed that perfect mixing was achieved at each stage and the phases are operated in equilibrium. In ATPE, several components must be considered and can be divided into the phase forming materials (polymer(s), salt(s) and water), and the protein / particulates / cells which are to be partitioned (the contaminants and target protein /cells / particulates). The partitioning of the protein is assumed to be a result of the phase forming materials. The concentration of the phase forming components and the phase volumes are assumed to be constant across the system [Rosa et al., 2009b,a]. The binary separation evaluated is the target protein from the contaminants.

Assuming X is the phase which the component / solute should be removed from and Y is the target phase, the volumes of the phases are V_X and V_Y respectively. A mass balance across an entire counter-current process can be written as:

$$V_x X_0 + V_Y Y_{n+1} = V_x X_n + V_Y Y_1 \tag{1}$$

Likewise, material balances for stage i can be written as:

$$V_x X_{i-1} + V_Y Y_{i+1} = V_x X_i + V_Y Y_i \tag{2}$$

Using equations (1) and (2) we can pose the stage-wise optimisation of the multi-stage ATPE as follows:

$$\max X_N \leq X_{Target} w \tag{3}$$

Where X_{Target} is the required concentration in phase X. If optimising for yield, X is the bottom phase and the solute / component to be considered is the target solute /component. If optimising for purity, X is the top phase and the solute / component to be considered is the contaminant solute / component. To determine the first step a mass balance across the entire system is used:

$$Y_1 = Y_{n+1} - \frac{V_X}{V_Y}(X_n - X_0) \tag{4}$$

Each stage is then evaluated as follows:

$$\left.\begin{array}{l} X_i = f(\text{equilibrium line}), \\ Y_{i+1} = Y_i - \frac{V_X}{V_Y}(X_i - X_{i-1}), \end{array}\right\} \quad i = 1,\ldots,n \tag{5}$$

Where f is the function determined for the equilibrium line. The line is determined by piece-wise linear function between the equilibrium points. To determine equilibrium points, a model separation of phycocyanin from lysozyme was carried out using a PEG-phosphate ATPE. Two equilibrium curves were generated; one for phycocyanin and one for lysozyme. Protein concentration was determined using ultraviolet visible spectroscopy.

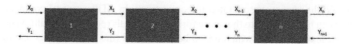

Figure 1: Depiction of a multi-stage counter current operation.

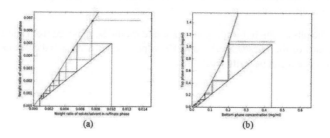

| (a) | (b) |

Figure 2: (a) McCabe Thiele diagram generated from data in Warade et al. [2011]. (b) McCabe Thiele diagram generated from data from Rosa et al. [2009a]. The dotted lines represent the stage results from the original authors. The solid line shows the results from the model in this paper.

3. Case Study

Figure 1 shows a schematic representation of the multistage counter current system where Y_i is the concentration of the phase component / solute in the target phase (% w/w) or (mg /ml) of stage i, for stages 1 to n, and X_i is the concentration of the phase component / solute (% w/w) or (mg /ml) in the opposing phase of stage i, for stages 1 to n.

The model developed above is first applied to traditional LLE and ATPE. The fit is shown above, Figure 2 (a) shows a result for traditional LLE and (b) shows a result for ATPE. It should be noted that in this model, the stages were counted off from the feed as opposed to from the target composition and so the predicted compositions are slightly different; however, the results for the number of stages were the same as the original authors.

Figure 3 shows the McCabe Thiele diagram for achieving > 99 % yield of phycocyanin using a counter-current multi-stage PEG-phosphate system. It can be seen from Figure 3 that the equilib-

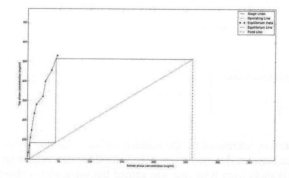

Figure 3: McCabe diagram for phycocyanin in the model PEG-phosphate ATPE.

Table 1: Stage results for lysozyme in the model PEG-phosphate ATPE.

Stage	Bottom phase (mg /ml)	Top phase (mg /ml)
1	8.91	0.503
2	0.161	0.00885

rium curve is a linear for phycocyanin before the concentration of 110 mg /ml. It is predicted that three stages were required to achieve a yield of > 99 % of phycocyanin.

Similarly, Table 1 shows the results for the concentration (mg /ml) of the contaminant, lysozyme, in each phase for each stage. The model was set up to remove > 99 % of lysozyme from the target phase using a counter-current multi-stage PEG-phosphate system, in this case two stages were required to achieve this.

4. Conclusion

In conclusion, ATPE is a developing, cheaper alternative protein purification technique which is disadvantaged by the low purity and yield achieved in a single step and the extensive experimental work required in system development and optimisation. Multi-stage operation can be used to achieve the high purities and yields required in the biopharmaceutical industry. The work has shown that the use of an equilibrium binary separation model is a viable technique in evaluating different multi-stage ATPE. The model was validated using experimental data in the literature and a case study on the purification of phycocyanin from lysozyme was carried out. It was shown that a yield of > 99 % and a purity of > 99 % could be achieved using three and two stages respectively in a counter current ATPS of PEG - phosphate. The work evaluates the different proteins separately in terms of protein concentration in each of the phases. This approach simplifies the model greatly and removes some of the complexity which is associated with ATPS, thereby further increasing the accessibility of the process.

In the future, the model could be used to optimise the stages for not only extraction protocols, but also back extraction and washing protocols as a repeating unit in a superstructure. In back extraction, conditions would be selected, usually through the addition of NaCl, to push the target protein into the salt phase. This is easier to deal with down-stream and allows the recycling of the more expensive polymer phase. For this, only a single equilibrium curve for the target protein under the new extraction protocols would be required. The washing protocol would also require a single equilibrium curve and would require looking at removal of any remaining contaminants in the salt phase, once the target protein has been extracted there, using a fresh polymer phase. Using this method, the model can be used to investigate and develop more complicated multi-stage operational techniques. Modification of the operation line can be used to investigate different multi-stage modes of operation i.e. cross current, co-current, counter-current procedures.

References

A. M. Azevedo, P. a. J. Rosa, I. F. Ferreira, and M. R. Aires-Barros. Chromatography-free recovery of biopharmaceuticals through aqueous two-phase processing. *Trends in Biotechnology*, 27(4):240–247, 2009.

K. B. Konstantinov and C. L. Cooney. White Paper on Continuous Bioprocessing. May 20-21, 2014 Continuous Symposium. *Journal of pharmaceutical sciences*, pages 1–8, 2014.

L. N. Mao, J. K. Rogers, M. Westoby, L. Conley, and J. Pieracci. Downstream antibody purification using aqueous two-phase extraction. *Biotechnology Progress*, 26(6):1662–1670, nov 2010.

S. L. Mistry, A. Kaul, J. C. Merchuk, and J. A. Asenjo. Mathematical modelling and computer simulation of aqueous two-phase continuous protein extraction. *Journal of Chromatography A*, 741(2):151–163, 1996.

N. Patel, D. G. Bracewell, and E. Sorensen. Dynamic modelling of aqueous two-phase systems to quantify the impact of bioprocess design, operation and variability. *Food and Bioproducts Processing*, 107:10–24, jan 2018.

J. F. J. F. Richardson, J. H. J. H. Harker, J. R. Backhurst, and J. M. J. M. Coulson. *Coulson and Richardson's chemical engineering. Vol. 2, Particle technology and separation processes.* Butterworth-Heinemann, 2002. ISBN 9780080490649.

M. Rito-Palomares. Practical application of aqueous two-phase partition to process development for the recovery of biological products. *Journal of Chromatography B: Analytical Technologies in the Biomedical and Life Sciences*, 807(1):3–11, 2004.

P. Rosa, A. Azevedo, I. Ferreira, S. Sommerfeld, W. Bäcker, and M. Aires-Barros. Downstream processing of antibodies: Single-stage versus multi-stage aqueous two-phase extraction. *Journal of Chromatography A*, 1216(50):8741–8749, dec 2009a.

P. A. Rosa, A. M. Azevedo, and M. R. Aires-Barros. Application of central composite design to the optimisation of aqueous two-phase extraction of human antibodies. *Journal of Chromatography A*, 1141(1):50–60, feb 2007.

P. A. J. Rosa, A. M. Azevedo, S. Sommerfeld, A. Mutter, M. R. Aires-Barros, and W. Bäcker. Application of aqueous two-phase systems to antibody purification: a multi-stage approach. *Journal of biotechnology*, 139(4):306–13, feb 2009b.

P. a. J. Rosa, I. F. Ferreira, a. M. Azevedo, and M. R. Aires-Barros. Aqueous two-phase systems: A viable platform in the manufacturing of biopharmaceuticals. *Journal of Chromatography A*, 1217(16):2296–2305, 2010. ISSN 00219673. doi: 10.1016/j.chroma.2009.11.034. URL http://dx.doi.org/10.1016/j.chroma.2009.11.034.

P. a. J. Rosa, A. M. Azevedo, S. Sommerfeld, M. Mutter, W. Bäcker, and M. R. Aires-Barros. Continuous purification of antibodies from cell culture supernatant with aqueous two-phase systems: From concept to process. *Biotechnology Journal*, 8(March):352–362, 2013.

F. Ruiz-Ruiz, J. Benavides, O. Aguilar, and M. Rito-Palomares. Aqueous two-phase affinity partitioning systems: Current applications and trends. *Journal of Chromatography A*, 1244:1–13, 2012.

A. Warade, R. Gaikwad, R. Sapkal, and V. Sapkal. Simulation of Multistage Countercurrent Liquid-Liquid Extraction. *Leonardo Journal of Sciences*, (20):79–94, 2011.

Anton A. Kiss, Edwin Zondervan, Richard Lakerveld, Leyla Özkan (Eds.)
Proceedings of the 29th European Symposium on Computer Aided Process Engineering
June 16th to 19th, 2019, Eindhoven, The Netherlands. © 2019 Elsevier B.V. All rights reserved.
http://dx.doi.org/10.1016/B978-0-128-18634-3.50049-7

Development of a biorefinery scheme to produce biofuels from waste cooking oil

Araceli Guadalupe Romero-Izquierdo[a], Fernando Israel Gómez-Castro[a], Claudia Gutiérrez-Antonio[b], Rogelio Cruz Barajas[c], Salvador Hernández[a]

[a]*Departamento de Ingeniería Química, División de Ciencias Naturales y Exactas, Campus Guanajuato, Universidad de Guanajuato, Noria Alta s/n, Guanajuato, Guanajuato, 36050, México.*

[b] *Facultad de Química, Universidad Autónoma de Querétaro, Centro Universitario, Av. Cerro de las Campanas s/n Col. Las Campanas, Santiago de Querétaro, Querétaro, 76010, México. claudia.gutierrez@uaq.mx*

[c]*Instituto Tecnológico de Ciudad Madero, Av. 1° de Mayo y Sor Juana Inés de la Cruz Col. Los Mangos, Ciudad Madero, Tamaulipas, 89440, México.*

Abstract

Biofuels are a promissory alternative to satisfy the world energy demand, and its production can be performed in a biorefinery scheme; however, few researches have been reported under this concept. According to the open literature, the raw material used to obtain renewable fuels represents roughly 60-80% of total annual cost. Thereby, the exploitation of a low-price feedstock into a biorefinery scheme is a good strategy to improve the production cost of the renewable fuels, and mitigate the environmental impact related with the processing. In this work, a biorefinery scheme using waste cooking oil (WCO) is presented, aiming to obtain biodiesel and biojet fuel simultaneously as main products. The modelling of the biorefinery scheme is performed in the process simulator Aspen Plus. The biodiesel is obtained through esterification and transesterification with ethanol, adding the refining zone to recover the ethanol; biojet fuel is produced through the hydrotreating process. The biorefinery is evaluated in terms of economic and environmental indicators, whose are compared with previously reported assessments for the separate production processes. Reductions on the processing cost and CO_2 emissions are expected regarding each individual process.

Keywords: waste cooking oil, biorefinery scheme, biofuels

1. Introduction

The depletion of fossil resources is a huge economic and environmental issue concerning the modern society, due to population growth, and the increase of energy demand. Since last decade, scientific and technological efforts have been focused on the development of novel alternatives to take advantage of renewable resources. Second and third generation raw materials have been used to produce a broad range of renewable products, mainly biofuels. However, its processing cost is high along with the price of renewable fuels. Recent studies on alternative biofuels have reported the use of agricultural wastes and waste cooking oil as promising feedstock to produce renewable products, diminishing the processing cost (Dewan et al, 2013; Gasca-González et al, 2018). The production of biofuels can be performed in a biorefinery scheme, which is a processing plant wherein biomass is converted into a broad range of renewable products; its processing routes are designed according to biomass nature and composition. Regarding petroleum refineries, a biorefinery splits the raw material in useful fractions, which are taken as internal raw material to generate the desired products (Sadhukhan et al, 2014). Therefore, due to integral and multiple use of the feedstock selected, the price of the obtained renewable products could be competitive with its fossil counterparts. On the other hand, in the transport sector the demand of diesel and jet fuel has expanded significantly, and so its environmental impact (Grote et al, 2014). Thus, the use of biodiesel and biojet fuel has been recognized as a promising strategy to diminish the generated environmental impact and partially cover the demand. Regarding biodiesel production, several techniques have been proposed to diminish its energy consumption, related costs, and improve the biodiesel yield (Hajjari et al, 2017). However, conventional processing route through esterification and transesterification reactions is commonly chosen due to its low cost (Gasca-González et al, 2018). Furthermore, the biojet fuel is an emergent biofuel, which can be produced through few processing pathways that are certified by ASTM (Gutiérrez-Antonio et al, 2018); one of them is the hydrotreating process, which is the most mature technology due to similarity with the petro-refineries (Gutiérrez-Antonio et al, 2016). Recently, advances into process operation such as novel catalyst to improve biojet fuel yield and strategies of process intensification have been proposed. In this work, a biorefinery scheme using waste cooking oil (WCO) is presented, aiming to obtain biodiesel and biojet fuel as main products. The biorefinery scheme is modelled in the process simulator Aspen Plus. The biodiesel is obtained through esterification and transesterification with ethanol; while the biojet fuel is produced through the hydrotreating process, generating green diesel and naphtha as co-products. The economic and environmental indicators for the biorefinery process are calculated, and they are compared with the previously reported assessments for biodiesel and biojet fuel individual production processes. The main contribution of this work relies on the proposal and assessment of a biorefinery scheme to convert WCO into biofuels, employing both, conventional and intensified technologies, and establishing a base structure for future enhancements.

2. Process modelling

The WCO is classified as a hazardous waste, which has severe effects on urban waste water and, thus, on fresh water bodies, due to its inadequate disposal (Hajjari et al, 2017). In Mexico were recollected 5,596,032.97 L of WCO in 2015, in agreement with government data (SEMARNAT, 2004; SEDEMA, 2015). Thus, the proposed biorefinery scheme, showed in Figure 1, has been designed to process 5,596,032.97 L/year of WCO; moreover, the scheme considers two stages of heating at 65°C and impurities removal by sedimentation as pre-treatment for the WCO. At the end of these pre-treating stages, 20% of the total volume of WCO was removed as water and suspended solids. The average density for WCO was assumed as 0.91 g/ ml. Thus, 2,004.88 kg/h were processed through simulations in Aspen Plus V.8.0. The WCO composition has been considered as 94 wt% triglycerides and 6 wt% FFA; also, according to Gasca-González et al (2018) the FFA profile in wt% is: palmitic acid (12.3%), oleic acid (24%), linoleic acid (56.6%), and linolenic acid (7.1%). It is important to highlight that several efforts to recollect the WCO have been implemented in the country; however, a well-defined supply chain has not been established yet. In the biorefinery scheme, the total WCO recollected in 2015 is divided in half after pre-treatment in order to produce biodiesel and biojet fuel; this percentage was chosen as the base scenario after a preliminary analysis to determine the proportion which allows the higher gross profit. The biodiesel process starts conditioning the WCO at 70°C, operation temperature for the esterification process. Ethanol is fed with molar ratio ethanol:oil, 6:1 and 1 wt% of sulfuric acid as catalyst; processed into a batch module. Next, the reaction products are fed to a neutralization reactor, wherein Na_2CO_3 was used to remove H_2SO_4 catalyst as Na_2SO_4 salt. The amount of Na_2CO_3 was stoichiometrically calculated regarding the H_2SO_4. The removal of Na_2CO_3 salt was realized by a filter. At once, the output stream is feeding to the transesterification reactor operated at 70°C, adding NaOH (1 wt%) as catalyst. Fresh ethanol is added to complete the 6:1, ethanol:oil molar ratio. The reaction is done into a batch module reactor. The stream leaving the transesterification reactor is feeding to decanter module, wherein two streams are splitting. In the first one, the separated biodiesel (FAEE) is fed to the washing column, operating with water (50 wt% regard FAEE); and then the excess of water is eliminated in an evaporator. The FAEE yield was 92.37%. The second stream leaving the decanter module is introduced to a neutralization reactor with H_3PO_4 (stoichiometrically calculated regarding NaOH). The Na_3PO_4 salt generated was removed by a filter. The stream leaving the neutralization reactor was rich in ethanol and water; this stream was feeding to distillation train, which includes 3 distillation columns to recover the ethanol. In the first one, the ethanol was concentrated near to the azeotropic point. In the second one, a glycerol stream was fed in 1.3:1 mass ratio, glycerol:mixture (ethanol + water). The azeotropic point was overcome and the ethanol mol purity was 99.76%. Finally, the last distillation column was used to separate water from glycerol; mole purity of 99.99% was reached for glycerol. The glycerol used to break the azeotropic point was generated as co-product in transesterification process; only 0.64% of fresh glycerol was purchased from external source to cover the glycerol/mixture ratio. The recovered ethanol and glycerol were cooled down to 25°C and recirculated to the process. It is worth to mention that the ethanol was used as alternative reactant to methanol, since it can be produced from renewable feedstock; also, is lower toxic than methanol. UNIQUAC was the thermodynamic method used to model the reaction and conditioning zones of the biodiesel process; also, the refining FAEE zone (distillation train) were modelled by NRTL method. The reaction kinetics for esterification and transesterification reactions were reported by Gasca-González et al (2018). Regarding the biojet fuel process, the WCO and hydrogen were conditioned at 380 °C and 30 bar, and fed into the hydrotreating reactor, which operates with NiMo/USY@Al-SBA-15 as catalyst. The volume ratio hydrogen:WCO was 500:1. The operation conditions, conversion, yield and distribution of products were reported by Zhang et al (2018). It is important to emphasise that the catalyst used is bifunctional, thus, the hydrotreating and hydrocracking /hydroisomerization reactions were carried out in the same equipment. Three products are obtained from the hydrotreating reactor: naphtha, biojet fuel and green diesel. A distillation train conformed by two distillation columns was designed to separate each product. The thermodynamic method used to model the conditioning of reactants and reactor zone was Peng-Robinson; while the distillation train was modelled using BK10 method. The naphtha selectivity was of 41%, biojet fuel 36% and green diesel of 84%. It is worth to mention that the biojet fuel is composed by 79.4 wt% of lineal paraffins, 1.9 wt% cycloparaffins, and 18.7 wt% aromatic compounds. Figures 2 and 3 show the biodiesel process from WCO and biojet fuel process from Jatropha curcas oil reported by Gasca-González et al (2018) and Gutiérrez-Antonio et al (2016), respectively. It is worth to mention that the processing structure for the biorefinery scheme has been constructed based on each individual process.

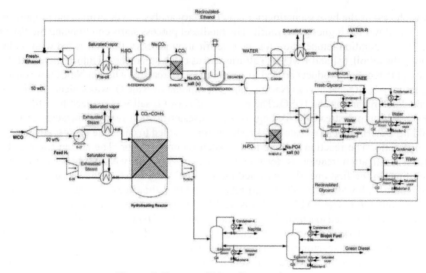

Figure 1. Proposed biorefinery scheme.

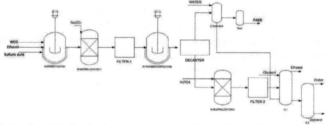

Figure 2. Biodiesel individual process extracted from Gasca-González et al (2018).

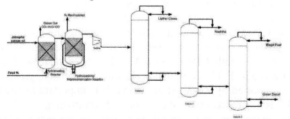

Figure 3. Biojet fuel individual process extracted from Gutiérrez-Antonio et al (2016).

3. Results

In this section, results for the proposed biorefinery scheme are presented. The TAC was obtained by Guthrie-Ulrich method (Turton et al, 2012), which take into account cost equipment, utilities cost (heating and cooling), raw materials (hydrogen and ethanol) and additional reagents (neutralisation reagents and glycerol). This estimation does not consider the cost of the heterogeneous catalyst for hydrotreating, filters cost and cost for removal equipment of CO_2-CO. Likewise, the biorefinery generates 20.4 kW of electricity; thus, its sale was considered, after covering the internal demand. In Table 1 the TAC and total CO_2 emissions per year are presented. The raw material cost represents 61.7% of TAC; also, the utilities cost is high. Regarding total CO_2 emissions, those related to the generation of vapor used in the process and those released by the hydrotreating reactor are considered. The CO_2 emissions by electricity are not considered, since the internal demand is covered by the energy produced in the biorefinery. Thus, the major CO_2 emissions are generated due to vapor production, considering a natural gas boiler with efficiency of 80%.

Table 1. TAC and total kg CO_2 emissions /year for proposed biorefinery scheme.

Utilities Cost (\$USD/year)	Equipment Cost (\$USD/year)	Raw Material Cost (\$USD/year)	Electricity Sale Cost (\$USD/year)	Total Annual Cost, TAC (\$USD/year)
\$1,158,967.54	\$1,858,623.10	\$4,826,117.42	\$19,490.04	\$7,824,218.02

Used vapor (kg CO_2/year)	CO_2 Release by hydrotreating process (kg CO_2/year)		Total Emissions (kg CO_2/year)
7,347,269,188.12	1,346,683.54		7,348,615,871.66

The comparison between the biorefinery and individual processes is made in terms of two economic indicators and two environmental indicators. The economic indicators are defined as TAC per mass unit and TAC per energy unit of main biofuel produced. The environmental indicators are defined as kg CO_2 per mass unit and kg CO_2 per energy unit of main biofuel produced. In the individual processes, the main products are biodiesel and biojet fuel, respectively; while in the biorefinery process, the sum of biodiesel and biojet fuel are considered as the main products. The proposed indicators show, in Table 2, that the biorefinery has a higher cost than biodiesel individual process, but lower than the biojet individual process. In addition, the minimum value of kg CO_2 is reached by the biorefinery scheme, regarding to each individual process; this reduction in CO_2 emissions and cost could be attributed to the use of the free-of-charge WCO, the use of bifunctional hydrotreating catalyst, and the biorefinery concept.

Table 2. Proposed economic and environmental indicators.

Indicators		Biodiesel process (Gasca-González et al, 2018)	Biojet fuel process (Gutiérrez-Antonio et al, 2016)	Biorefinery (This work)
TAC/kg biofuel	(USD/kg)	0.7651	29.915	0.7471
TAC/kJ release	(USD/kJ)	0.0006	0.021	0.0005
kg CO_2/ kg biofuel	(kg CO_2/kg)	4.0828	1769.48	0.1294
kg CO_2/ kJ biofuel	(kg CO_2/ kJ)	0.0030	1237	0.0001

4. Conclusions

A biorefinery scheme to transform WCO into biodiesel and biojet fuel as main products has been presented. The total WCO recollected in Mexico for 2015 was the processing goal; 92.37 % yield to biodiesel and 36 % selectivity to biojet fuel were obtained in this scheme. The TAC per unit of mass or energy from biorefinery process was better than the biojet fuel individual process reported; while, the total kg CO_2 emissions per mass or energy obtained were better than each individual process. Thus, the biorefinery scheme could be a promissory alternative to use WCO to produce biofuels.

5. Acknowledgments

Financial support provided by CONACyT, grants 239765 and 279753, for the development of this project is acknowledged.

References

A. Dewan, J.P. Raftery, Z. Li, M.N. Karim, 2013, Biofuel from waste agricultural product and lignocelullosic biomass, IFAC Proceedings Volumes, 46, 18, 178-186.

R. Gasca-González, F.I. Gómez-Castro, A.G. Romero-Izquierdo, E. Zenón-Olvera, C. Gutiérrez-Antonio, 2018, Design of a low-cost process for the production of biodiesel using waste cooking oil as raw material, Computer Aided Chemical Engineering, 43, 1529-1534.

J. Sadhukhan, K. Siew-Ng, E. Martínez-Hernández, 2014, Biorefineries and Chemical Processes: design, integration and sustainability analysis, 1, 20-30.

M. Grote, I. Williams, J. Preston, 2014, Direct carbon dioxide emissions from civil aircraft, Atmospheric Environment, 95, 214-224.

M. Hajjari, M. Tabatabaei, M. Aghbashlo, H. Ghanavati, 2017, A review on the prospects of sustainable biodiesel production: a global scenario with an emphasis on waste-oil biodiesel utilization, Renewable and Sustainable Energy Reviews, 72, 445-464.

C. Gutiérrez-Antonio, F.I. Gómez-Castro, J.A. De Lira-Flores, S. Hernández, 2017, A review on the production processes of renewable jet fuel, Renewable and Sustainable Energy Reviews, 79, 709-729.

C. Gutiérrez-Antonio, A.G. Romero-Izquierdo, F.I. Gómez-Castro, S. Hernández, A. Briones-Hernández, 2016, Simultaneous energy integration and intensification of the hydrotreating process to produce biojet fuel from jatropha curcas, Chemical Engineering and Processing: Process Intensification., 110, 134-145.

S. Semarnat, 2014, Subsecretaria de Gestión para la Protección Ambiental, Dirección General de Gestión Integral de Materialaes y Actividades Riesgosas, México. Consulted (10-September-2018), Web site: https://apps1.semarnat.gob.mx:445/dgeia/informe_resumen/08_residuos/cap8.html#5

S. Sedema, 2015, Inventario de Residuos Sólidos CDMX, Consulted (10-September-2018), Web site: https://www.sedema.cdmx.gob.mx/storage/app/media/IRS-2015-14-dic-2016.compressed.pdf

Z. Zhang, Q. Wang, H. Chen, X. Zhang, 2018, Hydroconversion of waste cooking oil into bio-jet fuel over a hierarchical NiMo/USY@Al-SBA-15 Zeolite, Chemical Engineering Technology, 41,3, 590-597.

R. Turton, R.C. Bailie, W.B. Whiting, J.A. Shaeiwitz, D. Bhattachayya, 2012, Analysis, synthesis and design of chemical processes, 4th edition, Prentice Hall, New Jersey, 951-982.

Anton A. Kiss, Edwin Zondervan, Richard Lakerveld, Leyla Özkan (Eds.)
Proceedings of the 29th European Symposium on Computer Aided Process Engineering
June 16th to 19th, 2019, Eindhoven, The Netherlands. © 2019 Elsevier B.V. All rights reserved.
http://dx.doi.org/10.1016/B978-0-128-18634-3.50050-3

A network model-based optimisation analysis for the utilisation of CO_2 in Qatar's chemical industries

Ali Attiq Al-Yaeeshi, Tareq Al-Ansari*, Rajesh Govindan

Divison of Sustainable Development, College of Science and Engineering, Hamad Bin Khalifa University, Qatar Foundation, Doha, Qatar

talansari@hbku.edu.qa

Abstract

A continuous increase of anthropogenic greenhouse gas (GHG) concentrations in the atmosphere since the industrial revolution has been attributed to global climate change. Mitigation technologies, such as CO_2 Capture and Utilisation (CCU) is promising where by it can reduce the global environmental footprint of CO_2. In addition, CCU adds value to the producers by enabling the increase of exports of economically valuable products to the global markets. The objective of this study is to assess the integration of CO_2 utilisation in the existing processes and technologies to create economic opportunities within the State of Qatar. The study considers CO_2 capture and subsequent utilisation as chemical feedstock for several industrial applications. The methodology includes the development of a geospatial (network) optimisation model that comprehensively models the CCU infrastructure, from the CO_2 sources to sinks considering pipeline transportation routes in order to maximise the economic benefits of CO_2 utilisation. The methodology is primarily based on a techno-economic assessment and single-objective linear programming of the proposed CO_2 utilisation network which includes Methanol, Urea and Gas-to-Liquid industries. It considers the economic life cycle of the network at the plant-level and modelling the economic objective in terms of the net present value (NPV) and internal rate of return (IRR), implemented within a multi-period optimisation formulation. The results demonstrate that by applying back-testing using the market prices of value-added products, mainly for the urea, methanol, gasoline, diesel and wax for the period of 2005 - 2018, the optimal solution of the distribution and utilisation of CO_2 within the industrial network changes reach to 5.99 Mt/y, whilst considering the revenue functions as the network objectives vary from 1.17 to 3.99 Billion US dollar per year.

Key words: CO_2 Utilisation, Linear Programming, Methanol, Urea, GTL, NPV, IRR

1. Introduction

It is widely accepted that emissions of greenhouse gases (GHGs) have contributed towards global warming. Carbon Capture and Storage (CCS) and Carbon Capture and Utilisation (CCU) are considered promising technologies to control CO_2 emissions. CCU programs avoid the need to store CO_2 in underground storage sites which in many cases remain under research and development. Incidentally, CCU enables the creation of an ecosystem which encourages the recycling of CO_2 and conversion into value-added products, such as urea, methanol, cement, and other well-known applications in addition to its possible utilisation for enhanced oil recovery (EOR). Pérez-Fortes et al. (2016)

evaluated through a techno-economic analysis the potential to combine hydrogen with captured CO_2 from a coal power plant to produce Methanol product. Although, the system demonstrated a reduction in CO_2 emissions, the project was deemed financially unattractive due to the high price of hydrogen in relation to the market price of Methanol. Anantharaman et al. (2013) pointed out that most of the studies consider average steady-state flow of CO_2 from the source into the capture unit, as opposed to variable amounts of CO_2, which impacts the operations as well as the cost at the sink. The study concluded that to optimize the cost of capturing system, the trade-off between the CO_2 capture cost and the payment of the emissions cost or tax should be established. This will lead to the deployment of an optimal investment of the capturing system and assure steady state of the CO_2 mitigation profile. However, considering multiple sinks may overcome the cost of the CO_2 capture system and ensure the steady state of the CO_2 flow, according to King et al. (2013). They indicated that the CO_2 utilisation network comprising EOR sinks could be economically attractive taking into consideration low energy prices associated with the overall operations. The objective of this study is to evaluate the optimum pathways for network integration of CCU options, considering existing processes and technologies within the State of Qatar in order to create new economic opportunities. It considers a single CO_2 capture system located at the source with the highest CO_2 emissions, thereby reducing the CAPEX and OPEX of the required compression system and pipeline network. The methodology developed considers an optimisation framework utilising Linear Programming (LP) in order to determine the sinks that maximizes revenues/profits based on CO_2 allocations and market prices of value-added products. This approach was applied to the fertilizer, methanol and GTL plants located in Mesaieed and Ras Laffan industrial zones in Qatar.

2. Source and Sink Data for CCU system

The system considered comprises of a single CO_2 source, namely Qatar Gas (QG), and five potential sinks that have been identified for the economic utilisation of CO_2, namely: Qatar Fertilizer Company (QAFCO); two plants in Qatar Fuel Additives Company (QAFAC), one utilising natural gas, whilst the other utilising hydrogen; Oryx GTL; and Pearl GTL, all located in the Mesaieed and Ras Laffan industrial zones. The optimisation model was developed where the objective is to develop a profitable allocation plan for up to 25 years (assumed as the operating lifetime of the project) to maximize the total CO_2 captured and utilised, thereby achieving maximum economic benefits from all the sinks. The related costs for these include the capital cost of capture system and plants, including the equipments at the sinks, CO_2 compression and transportation, and other operating costs.

2.1. CO_2 Source Data

The CO_2 emissions from Qatar Gas is approximately 35.8 Mt/year (Sayeed, 2016). The capture of CO_2 is presumed to be via chemical absorption using amine solvents operating at 90% efficiency in which the assumed cost of the capture system is \$40/t of CO_2 (Hildebrand, 2009). The estimated capital cost of the capture system is \$169 million.

2.2. CO_2 Compression and Transport Data

Compression is needed to overcome the pressure drop in pipelines and to meet sinks pressure requirements. The unit cost of compression and transportation per 100 km of the pipeline is approximately \$1.5/tCO_2 (Herzog et al., 2004). In this study, the total cost of compression and transport to both QAFAC and QAFCO is approximately \$0.5 million, which is also the same for both Pearl GTL and Oryx GTL plants located in Ras Laffan. Considering that the distance between Messaid and Ras Laffan industrial zones is 100km, the capital cost was estimated according to the API 5L X60 and diameter 20".

2.3. CO_2 Sinks Data

Utilisation in GTL Plant (Pearl GTL and Oryx GTL)
In addition to the sinks considered by the authors in the previous study (Al-Yaeeshi, *et al.*, 2018), CO_2 can also be utilised within the GTL plants through the integration with the Fischer-Tropsch process (Rafiee et al., 2017), where the captured CO_2 is supplied into an auto-thermal reformer (ATR). For the case of Qatar, a CO_2 network consisting of both the Pearl GTL and Oryx GTL can be developed with an uninterrupted supply of pure CO_2 at the required flow rate and pressure. Furthermore, recycling some unreacted syngas to the reforming and F–T synthesis units can increase process efficiency and significantly reduce CO_2 emissions. In addition, the process can increase the output of products of gasoline, diesel, and wax therefore increasing plant revenue.

3. Methodology

The methodology developed in this work study is an extension of the previous models by Al-Yaeeshi, et al. (2018), where the optimised allocation was based on average prices of products in the CO_2 utilisation network. For this study, the LP formulation considers CO_2 allocation from QG to QAFCO, QAFAC with NG, QAFAC with H_2, Oryx GTL and Pearl GTL constrained by their utilisation capacities. The aim is to optimise the allocation in response to price variabilities of value-added products at the sinks, thereby maximising the overall revenue of the CO_2 utilisation network.

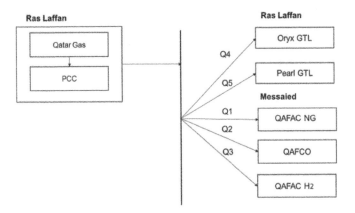

Figure 1 Proposed CO_2 utilisation network in Qatar

The decision variables used in the LP formulation are indicated in Figure 1. A detailed nomenclature of model parameters considered per industry within the CO_2 utilisation network are listed below:

Parameters related to Qatar Gas
- η: efficiency of CO_2 capture system = 0.9.
- e: CO_2 emissions rate = 15 Mt/year.
- C_1: cost factor incurred through CO_2 capture = $\eta \times e \times \$40/t\ CO_2$.

Parameters related to QAFAC (natural gas), QAFCO and QAFAC (Hydrogen), are available in (Al-Yaeeshi *et al.*, 2018). In this study, Revenue period formulation is added:

- R: Revenue factor from methanol = $\sum_{k=0}^{n} \left(\eta \times e \times q \times \frac{\$m}{t} \right)$, where n is the number of years, m is the price of the product and q is Amount of CO_2 required (kt/year) for each sink hence. In this work q is 0.6, 1.01, and 1.82 for R_2 (QAFAC NG), R_3 (QAFACO) and R_4 (QAFAC H_2) respectively

Parameters related to Oryx GTL
- D_5: pipeline distance from Qatar Gas = 5km.
- C_{51}: CAPEX of Reactors and utilities = \$2000 million.
- C_{52}: cost factor incurred through CO_2 transportation = $\eta \times e \times (d_5/100) \times \$1.5/t\ CO_2$
- R_5: revenue factor from Oryx GTL = $\sum_{k=0}^{n} \Big(\eta \times e \times ((0.0006c^2 - 0.2945c + 7662.5) * \frac{\$w}{t} + (-0.0006c^2 + 1.1319c + 1431.1) * \frac{\$d}{t} + (-0.0003c^2 + 0.2786c + 1237.1) * \frac{\$g}{t})) \Big)$
- Where n is the number of years and w, d, and g are the price of wax, diesel and gasoline respectively. In each formula, c is the desired production rate for product

Parameters related to Pearl GTL
- D_6: pipeline distance from Qatar Gas = 5km.
- C_{61}: CAPEX of Reactors and utilities plant = \$6000 million.
- C_{62}: cost factor incurred through CO_2 transportation = $\eta \times e \times (d_3/100) \times \$1.5/t\ CO_2$
- R_6: revenue factor from Pearl GTL = $\sum_{k=0}^{n} \Big(\eta \times e \times ((0.0006c^2 - 0.2945c + 7662.5) * \frac{\$w}{t} + (-0.0006c^2 + 1.1319c + 1431.1) * \frac{\$d}{t} + (-0.0003c^2 + 0.2786c + 1237.1) * \frac{\$g}{t})) \Big)^n$

Where n, c, w, d, and g are the years, desired production rate of products, prices of wax, diesel and gasoline respectively.
In addition to the reduction in CO_2 emissions, the main purpose is to optimize CO_2 allocations in order to maximize the economic returns within the utilisation network. Hence, the economic objective is given by:

Maximize $\{Q_1 \times (R_2 - C_{11} - C_{21} - C_{22} - C_{23}) + Q_2 \times (R_3 - C_{11} - C_{31} - C_{32}) + Q_3 \times (R_2 - C_{11} - C_{41} - C_{42}) + Q_4 \times (R_4 - C_{11} - C_{51} - C_{52}) + Q_6 \times (R_5 - C_{11} - C_{61} - C_{62}) \}$
subject to,
$Q_1 + Q_2 + Q_3 + Q_4 + Q_5 \leq 1$,
$Q_1 \times \eta \times e \leq 0.60 \times 10^6$,
$Q_2 \times \eta \times e \leq 1.01 \times 10^6$,
$Q_3 \times \eta \times e \leq 1.83 \times 10^6$,
$Q_4 \times \eta \times e \leq 0.36 \times 10^6$,

$Q_5 \times \eta \times e \leq 2.19 \times 10^6,$

$Q_1 \times (R_2 - C_{11} - C_{21} - C_{22} - C_{23}) \geq 0$ *(profit constraint QAFAC using natural gas)*

$Q_2 \times (R_3 - C_{11} - C_{31} - C_{32}) \geq 0$ *(profit constraints - QAFCO)*

$Q_3 \times (R_2 - C_{11} - C_{41} - C_{42}) \geq 0$ *(profit constraint - QAFAC using hydrogen).*

$Q_4 \times (R_4 - C_{11} - C_{51} - C_{52}) \geq 0$ *(profit constraints for Oryx GTL) and*

$Q_6 \times (R_5 - C_{11} - C_{61} - C_{62}) \geq 0$ *(profit constraints for Pearl GTL).*

In addition, the economic feasibility of the optimised network was evaluated using the Net Present Value (NPV) concept. The construction period and capital investment were assumed to occur in the first year, and the project life 15 years and the interest rate is 10%. The Internal rate of Return (IRR) is defined as the discount rate i at which the NPV equals to zero, and Profit to investment ratio (PIR) are part of the economic evaluation, hence;

$$NPV(t,n) = \sum_{t=0}^{n} (CF_t / (1 + i)^t)$$

where CF is the cash flow, t is the year of the cash flow, i is the discount rate, and n is the total number of years.

$NPV \geq 0$ before year 15th ; IRR $\leq$ 20%; PIR$\geq$ 0

4. Results

Table 1 indicates the optimum values for CO_2 allocations when the profit constraint is relaxed, i.e. the net revenue is maximised in the CCU network. Consequently, this also increases the annual rate of CO_2 utilisation by the sinks in the network.

Table 1. The profit constraints are relaxed.

Decision Variables (fractional amount of CO_2 from Qatar Gas)	% CO_2 Allocation
Q_1	0.045
Q_2	0.075
Q_3	0.14
Q_4	0.027
Q_5	0.16

The modelling results illustrate that when the CCU network optimisation is applied, a clear benefit is achieved in terms of generating revenues at the sinks, whilst reducing CO_2 emissions. The total CO_2 captured and transported to the sinks is 6.71 Mt/y, out of the annual emissions rate of 15 Mt/y, which corresponds to a 44.7%emissions reduction. As such, the model indicates that the CCU network is considered economically attractive when the prices of products, namely urea, methanol, wax, diesel and gasoline increases. Although it was expected that the main driver of the allocations are the product prices at the sinks, the allocation results in Table 1 were found to be constant for the period between 2005 – 2018. Furthermore, the economic evaluation yielded positive returns, as given below:

NPV = 4.43 Billion USD as the positive pay back starting between 2012 and 2013 (after 8 years)

PIR = 0.385

IRR = 16%

5. Conclusion

The modelling and analysis presented in this paper considers CCU technology to enhance the production of value-added products at the sinks such as methanol, urea, wax, diesel and gasoline, whilst reducing CO_2 emissions at the sources. The approach demonstrates the potential economic benefit of a proposed CCU network in Qatar whilst considering the market prices of value-added products. The price fluctuations of these products, however, does not significantly change the allocations in the CCU network, and as such the revenue maximisation by the network was directly linked to crude oil and commodities pricesIn addition, the economic feasibility of the network was also demonstrated by evaluating NPV, PIR and IRR which demonstrated a positive indication based on the optimal allocation for each sink although 40 % of CO_2 captured utilised. Future work will consider detailed environmental assessment in order to quantify CO_2 emissions in the network at the plant-level.

6. References

A. Attiq Al-Yaeeshi, T. Al-Ansari, R. Govindan, (2018), Computer Aided Chemical
Engineering, The potential for carbon dioxide capture and utilization within the State of
    Qatar, 28th European Symposium on Computer Aided Process Engineering,
    pp.1499-1504

A. N. Hildebrand, (2009). Strategies for Demonstration and Early Deployment of
    Carbon Capture and Storage:A Technical and Economic Assessment of Capture
    Percentage. Retrieved from:
    http://sequestration.mit.edu/pdf/AshleighHildebrand_Thesis_May09.pdf

C. W. King, G. G¨ulen, S. Cohen, and V. Nu˜ nez-Lopez, (2013). The
system-wide economics of a carbon dioxide capture, utilization, and storage network:
    Texas Gulf Coast with pure CO_2-EOR flood, Environ. Res. Lett. 8 (2013) 034030
    (16pp) ENVIRONMENTAL

Herzog, H. and Golomb, D., 2004. Carbon capture and storage from fossil fuel use.
    Encyclopedia of energy, 1(6562), pp.277-287.

M.Pérez-Fortes, A.B.Dumitriu, E. Tzimas , (2014). CO_2 Utilization Pathways: Techno-
    Economic Assessment and Market Opportunities. Energy Procedia 63 (2014) 7968
    – 7975

QAFCO,   2014.   Sustainability   Report,   Available   from:
    http://www.qafco.qa/Satellite?blobcol=urldata&blobheader=application%2Fpdf&
    blobheadername1=Content-Disposition&blobheadername2=MDT-
    Type&blobheadervalue1=inline%3B+filename%3DSustainability+report+2014+
    Final.pdf&blobheadervalue2=abinary%3B+charset%3DUTF-
    8&blobkey=id&blobtable=MungoBlobs&blobwhere=1372606173378&ssbinary=
    true[Accessed 10 Novmeber]

R. Anantharaman , S. Roussanaly , S.F. Westman and J. Huse bye, (2013). Selection of
    optimal CO_2 capture plant cap acity for better investment decisions. Energy
    Procedia 37 (2013) 7039 – 7045 GHGT-11

S. Mohammed (2016), Qatar's National Emission Inventory Report, Figshare, Availible
    from; http://creativecommons.org/licenses/by/4.0/[Accessed [Feberuary 2018]

Anton A. Kiss, Edwin Zondervan, Richard Lakerveld, Leyla Özkan (Eds.)
Proceedings of the 29th European Symposium on Computer Aided Process Engineering
June 16th to 19th, 2019, Eindhoven, The Netherlands. © 2019 Elsevier B.V. All rights reserved.
http://dx.doi.org/10.1016/B978-0-128-18634-3.50051-5

Superstructure Optimization for the Production of Fuels, Fertilizers and Power using Biomass Gasification

Ahmed AlNouss,[a,b] Gordon McKay,[b] Tareq Al-Ansari [b,*]

aDepartment of Chemical Engineering, College of Engineering, Qatar University,

Doha, Qatar

bDivison of Sustainable Development, College of Science and Engineering, Hamad Bin

Khalifa University, Qatar Foundation, Doha, Qatar

Abstract

The production of renewable fuels and decreasing the dependency on fossil fuels is an integral component of sustainable development.

As the production and utilization of petrochemicals represent an extremely important economic pillar of modern society, there exists an impetus to identify alternative routes of production in order to conserve finite resources. Furthermore, there is an additional necessity to utilize waste to produce value-added products in order to reduce greenhouse gas (GHG) emissions. Biomass, a CO_2 neutral energy source, serves as a potential basis for the production of fuels, which would have otherwise been produced from natural gas. The gasification of biomass produces a hydrogen-rich syngas, which can be utilized in the petrochemical industry to produce ammonia and methanol or processed through the Fischer-Tropsch synthesis to produce liquid fuels. In this study, the utilization strategy of biomass gasification feedstock for the poly-generation of different products is environmentally and economically evaluated. The potential production volumes of fuels and green chemicals are increased by the addition of multiple biomass sources, and thereby gaining potential positive scale effects, and by the optimization of the gasification process, in terms of operating conditions and feed blending to yield high-quality syngas. This form a superstructure network of multiple biomass feedstocks (sources) and multiple potential applications (sinks) that can be optimized to yield the most economical and environmental-friendly production configuration. The base model developed is an oxygen-steam gasification process of different feedstocks available in the State of Qatar to generate H_2-rich syngas that is utilized in the production of value-added products: methanol, urea, power through integrated biomass gasification combined cycle (IBGCC) and Fischer-Trospch liquids (FTL). The results of the optimization problem demonstrated the domination of urea generation with an overall net cost objective function of $ 0.096 per kg of biomass input and an overall net emissions objective function of 0.83 kg of CO_2-e emitted per kg of biomass input. The manure based biomass is more suitable than sludge and date pits in the resulting optimum blending option for this utilization technique.

Keywords: Biomass Gasification, Sustainability, Optimization, Superstructure, Decision Making.

1. Introduction

Converting carbon-based wastes to valuable chemicals and energy through thermochemical conversion ranging from biomass and forestry residues to pet coke, have various advantages over conventional processes. Some of these advantages are the reduction of environment harmful emissions and the ability to produce electricity independently of an external power source (Mahinpey and Gomez, 2016). Biomass, waste or otherwise is a resource which can be processed into various chemicals and fuels. Biomass gasification (BG) is one process by which biomass can be converted into value added products, therefore mitigating polluting waste disposal strategies whilst simultaneously generating useful products such as bio-fuels, bio-char, syngas, power, heat, and fertilizer. Through the production of syngas, it creates flexible pathways by which advanced biofuels can be produced, e.g., methanol, di-methyl ether or Fischer-Tropsch diesel (Andersson, 2013). The high energy source feedstock into the BG process can include, wood waste, agricultural waste, municipal solid waste (MSW), sewage treatment waste, and food waste (Kumar and Shukla, 2016). BG technology can reduce the generated carbon to hydrogen (C/H) ratio resulting in a higher calorific value content and a favourable H_2 fraction. Syngas, the main product from BG consists of carbon monoxide (CO), hydrogen (H_2), methane (CH_4) and carbon dioxide (CO_2). It is an important element in the production of environment-friendly fuels and chemicals and in the generation of power. However, various types of contaminants are associated with syngas production such as tars, sulphur inorganic compounds, particulates and nitrogenous compounds. The properties and quality of the gasification product and its associated contaminants depend on the gasifying agent, feedstock material and dimensions, reactor conditions and design, presence of sorbent and catalyst (Sikarwar et al., 2016).

Anderson et al. evaluated a techno-economic analysis of methanol and ammonia production from BG and the co-gasification of pyrolysis oil and black liquor. The results demonstrated that the recovery of a bark boiler can be replaced by a biomass gasifier. This will improve the overall energy system efficiency and economic performance of green chemical production compared to the traditional mill operation (Andersson, 2013). Sara et al. carried out a techno-economic analysis on small scale biomass gasification and purification system for the production of hydrogen and power. A sensitivity analysis was conducted in order to study the effect of hydrogen production cost on capital cost, operating cost and process efficiency. The results indicated that costs cannot be reduced to a favourable level by only increasing the efficiency of the process unless the portable purification unit cost goes down (Sara et al., 2016). AlNouss et al. studied the utilization of multiple biomass sources to find the optimal blends for the generation of different value-added products. The objective was to maximize the production of syngas while constraining the H_2 to CO ratio with a specific application value. The results demonstrated a variation in the biomass blends for the different applications with a domination for date pits biomass in most cases (AlNouss et al., 2018). The literature is rich with other studies, which used similar pathways in identifying the top value added products generated from biomass. In this study, the utilisation strategy of biomass gasification for the poly-generation of different products is evaluated from economic and environmental perspectives to identify optimal poly-generation routes. An Aspen Plus model simulating oxygen-steam gasification technology is utilised to generate the optimal characteristics for each utilisation technique.

2. Model development

In order to efficiently utilize the biomass feedstock in a poly-generation system which produces value-added products, it is essential to use advanced system models. Hence, Aspen Plus software is utilized in this study to simulate the different generation technologies. An oxygen-steam gasification process is simulated in order to generate the optimal characteristics for each utilization technique. The optimization problem is built on the basis of superstructure representation with multiple biomass sources and multiple application sinks. The ultimate goal is to utilize the optimal blends of biomass feedstock in achieving optimal polygeneration routes of different utilization techniques as illustrated in Figure 1. The main focus of this study is the production of methanol, urea, power and Fischer-Trospch liquids (FTL) from biomass.

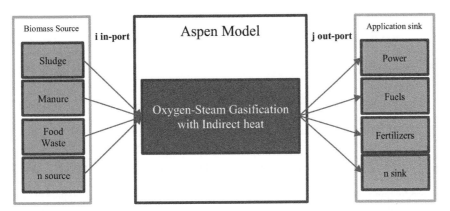

Figure 1: Superstructure representation of the biomass gasification to value added products

The first objective of the optimization problem is to maximize the production of syngas from the different biomass feedstocks, whilst constraining the specific H_2 to CO ratio of each generation technique. This was conducted partially by (AlNouss et al., 2018) and it is expanded here to capture the other optimization objectives. The H_2 to CO ratios considered the products are $H_2:CO = 2$ for Fischer-Tropsch liquids, $H_2:CO = 3$ for ammonia/urea, and $(H_2 - CO_2):(CO+CO_2) = 2$ for methanol. There is no specific ratio used for the generation of power through IBGCC. The formulation of the first objective function is presented in equations 1 and 2.

$$\text{Maximize} \quad \sum_{i=1}^{n} x_i * Syngas \qquad \forall\, i \in Biomass\ Sources \qquad \text{eq. (1)}$$

$$\text{Subject to} \quad \sum_{i=1}^{n} x_i = 1 \quad \& \quad \frac{y_{H_2}*Syngas}{y_{CO}*Syngas} = Application\ unique \qquad \text{eq. (2)}$$

Where, Syngas is the molar flowrate of the generated H_2-rich synthesis gas, y_{H_2} & y_{CO} are molar fractions of hydrogen and carbon monoxide and x is the blending fraction of each biomass feedstock.

The optimal biomass feedstock blends are then utilized in Aspen Plus to estimate the economic and environmental indicators of each utilization technique. The estimation is executed by means of the economic and energy activated analyses of Aspen Plus. These analyses are interfaces to the full software; Aspen Process Economic Analyser (APEA) and Aspen Energy Analyser (AEA). The economic and environmental outputs are used in a multi-objective optimization problem with the aim of maximizing the economic benefit and minimizing the environmental impact for the poly-generation routes. Therefore, the second and third objective functions are formulated based on the net profit and net emissions of each utilization technique multiplied by the fraction of H_2-rich syngas produced, as illustrated in equations 3 through 5.

$$Maximize \qquad \sum_{i=1}^{4} x_i * Net\ Profit_i \qquad\qquad\qquad eq.\ (3)$$

$$Minimize \qquad \sum_{i=1}^{4} x_i * Net\ Emissions_i \qquad\qquad\qquad eq.\ (4)$$

$$Subject\ to \qquad \sum_{i=1}^{4} x_i = 1 \qquad\qquad\qquad eq.\ (5)$$

Where x is the specific faction of syngas and i is the index notation for each process from 1 to 4 according to table 1. The breakdown of the profit and emission equations are illustrated in Eq. 6 through 8.

$$Net\ Profit_i = \frac{Revenue_i - TAC_i}{(Annual\ Biomass\ input)_i} \qquad\qquad\qquad eq.\ (6)$$

$$TAC_i = CC_i \frac{i(1+i)^n}{(1+i)^n - 1} + OC_i \qquad\qquad\qquad eq.\ (7)$$

$$Net\ Emission_i = \frac{(Stream\ Emissions)_i + (Utility\ Emissions)_i}{(Hourly\ Biomass\ input)_i} \qquad\qquad\qquad eq.\ (8)$$

Where, TAC is the total annualized cost, CC is the capital cost, OC is the operating cost, i is the interest rate evaluated as 20% and n is the project life evaluated as 20 years.

As the capacity of the biomass-based value added products is below the established infrastructure worldwide, therefore the upper limit was set to 1. For the minimum limit, the production capacity of each technique based on natural gas (NG) were collected and a fraction of each based on the total NG utilized in Qatar is generated as demonstrated in Table 1 (Alfadala and El-Halwagi, 2017). The results of the optimization problem is a Pareto front demonstrating the most attractive poly-generation route for the generation of value-added products.

Table 1: Fraction of maximum limit of each utilization technique

	MMTPY	Fraction
(1) Ammonia	3.8	0.032
(2) Methanol	1	0.0085
(3) FTL	0.04	0.00032
(4) Power	4.93	0.042
Total Fractions		0.083
Total NG	117.6	

Therefore, the limits of the specific fraction are summarized in equations 6 through 9.

$0.032000 \leq x_1 \leq 1$ for Ammonia production technique
$0.008520 \leq x_2 \leq 1$ for Methanol production technique
$0.000032 \leq x_3 \leq 1$ for Fischer-Tropsch liquids production technique
$0.042000 \leq x_4 \leq 1$ for power generation technique

3. Results and discussion

Considering that the biomass feedstock is optimized in order to determine the optimum blended feedstock. The results of the biomass feedstock blends optimization are illustrated in Figure 2. An economic and environmental evaluation is done to quantify capital cost, operating cost and revenue along with the environmental emissions from streams and utilities for the optimal feedstock blends, determined. Table 2 summarizes the main results from the evaluation.

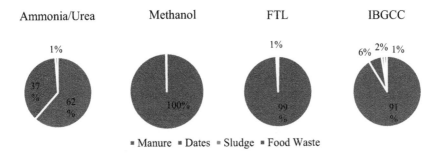

Figure 2: Biomass feedstock blending options for the different utilization techniques

The resulting optimized blends demonstrated a domination of date pits biomass for the methanol and liquid fuels options. Whereas, a domination of manure biomass is determined for the IBGCC alternative and 62:37 ratio of manure to date pits is accomplished for the ammonia/urea option. The economic and environmental results are used in a multi-objective optimization problem with the aim of maximizing the economic benefit and minimizing the environmental impact. The results of the optimization problem revealed the domination of ammonia/urea generation technique with around 95 % of the generation. The overall net cost objective function for the ammonia/urea production technique is $ 0.096 per kg of biomass input and the overall net emissions objective function is 0.83 kg of CO_2-e emitted per kg of biomass input. The rest of the distribution indicated around 4% for the IBGCC power generation and around 1% for methanol production technique.

Table 2: Results of economic and environmental evaluation

	Ammonia/ Urea	Methanol	FTL	IBGCC
Total Capital Cost [$]	2.4×10^7	2.5×10^7	1.9×10^7	1.5×10^8
Total Operating Cost [$/y]	9.7×10^6	9.7×10^6	6.0×10^6	3.7×10^7
Revenue [$/y]	5.2×10^6	6.0×10^6	3.0×10^6	1.1×10^7
Total Annualized [$/y]	1.5×10^7	1.5×10^7	9.8×10^6	6.6×10^7
Net Cost per Input [$/kg]	9.6×10^{-2}	2.4×10^{-1}	4.5×10^{-1}	9.6×10^{-2}
CO_2 Emissions (Streams) [kgCO$_2$-e/h]	9.2×10^3	6.8×10^3	3.1×10^3	6.8×10^4
CO_2 Emissions (Utilities) [kgCO$_2$-e /h]	8.3×10^1	9.8×10^2	4.1×10^2	4.6×10^3
Total CO_2 Emissions [kgCO$_2$-e/h] per input	8.3×10^{-1}	1.9×10^0	2.0×10^0	1.1×10^0

The results can be plotted in a Pareto front curve in order to inform decision making regarding the optimum biomass utilization technique. The Pareto curve resulting from the optimization of the different utilization techniques is illustrated in Figure 3.

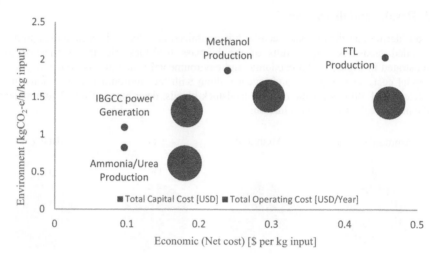

Figure 3: Pareto Curve of the optimization problem

4. Conclusions

The growing demand for global energy has motivated the utilization of renewable sources such as biomass in the generation of green fuels and chemicals. This study considers the development of a superstructure representation to capture the various biomass feedstocks and utilization techniques for the generated H_2-rich syngas through gasification. The results demonstrated the enhanced urea production as the most attractive technique in the poly-generation route.

Acknowledgment

The authors acknowledge the support of Qatar National Research Fund (QNRF) (a member of Qatar Foundation) by GSRA grant No GSRA4-1-0518-17082.

References

A. AlNouss, G. McKay, and T. Al-Ansari, 2018, Optimum Utilization of Biomass for the Production of Power and Fuels using Gasification, Computer Aided Chemical Engineering, 43, 1481-86.

J. Andersson, 2013, Techno-economic analysis of integrated biomass gasification for green chemical production, Luleå tekniska universitet.

S. Kumar, and S. Shukla, 2016, A Review on Recent Gasification Methods for Biomethane Gas Production, International Journal of Energy Engineering, 6, 1A, 32-43.

N. Mahinpey, and A. Gomez, 2016, Review of gasification fundamentals and new findings: Reactors, feedstock, and kinetic studies, Chemical Engineering Science, 148, 14-31.

H.R. Sara, B. Enrico, V. Mauro, D.C. Andrea, and N. Vincenzo, 2016, Techno-economic Analysis of Hydrogen Production Using Biomass Gasification -A Small Scale Power Plant Study, Energy Procedia, 101, 806-13.

V.S. Sikarwar, M. Zhao, P. Clough, J. Yao, X. Zhong, M.Z. Memon, N. Shah, E.J. Anthony, and P.S. Fennell, 2016, An overview of advances in biomass gasification, Energy & Environmental Science, 9, 10, 2939-77.

Anton A. Kiss, Edwin Zondervan, Richard Lakerveld, Leyla Özkan (Eds.)
Proceedings of the 29th European Symposium on Computer Aided Process Engineering
June 16th to 19th, 2019, Eindhoven, The Netherlands. © 2019 Elsevier B.V. All rights reserved.
http://dx.doi.org/10.1016/B978-0-128-18634-3.50052-7

Techno-Economic-Environmental Study for Recovery of Novel Water Source within a Power Plant - Desalination Complex

Ahmed AlNouss, Fadwa Eljack *

Department of Chemical Engineering, College of Engineering, Qatar University,

Doha, Qatar

fadwa.eljack@qu.edu.qa

Abstract

The global water supply is at an already critical level; around 3.9 billion people (47% of the world population) will be subject to water stress in 2050, according to the Organization for Economic Co-operation and Development (OECD). Unless advanced and alternative technology solutions are applied, construction of desalination facilities will continue to rise, leading to higher CO_2 emissions. While desalination allows for the production of water from highly saline sources, it is considered an energy intensive process that is largely powered by fossil fuel sources. The natural interconnections between water and energy known as water-energy nexus has been widely recognized for desalination facilities; yet, there are tremendous amounts of cooling water that are still needed for condensing steam in the thermoelectric Rankine cycle to produce electricity; and large amounts of energy are typically required to transport and treat the water. For example, over 45 thousand cubic meter per hour of water are required to run a 500 MW power plant, for cooling and other process requirements. Moreover, large amounts of water vapour exit in the effluent flue gas from the combustion process. The amount of water that can be recovered from the flue gas is sufficient to substantially reduce the need for freshwater make-up. This represents a promising opportunity to exploit synergies among water and energy systems specifically for arid regions.

In this paper, the aim is to identify suitable water recovery (dehydration hybrid) technologies that are capable of maximizing the recovery of water from flue gas in gas fired power plant-desalination plant coupled system. Specifically, compression and cooling, quenching, membrane separation and absorption alternatives are studied. The capacity of the power plant, the capacity of the desalination plant, fuel consumption of the power plant and energy requirement of the desalination facility are known. This work studies the technical, environmental and economic competing objectives when integrating the dehydration hybrid technology within the desalination-power plant complex. In this paper, the results for all the considered alternatives will be presented in terms of water recovery, energy savings, emissions reduction and economic indicators. The integrated low pressure quenching water recovery alternative has shown promising results, with up to 42% water recovery, while the integrated low pressure absorption alternative has demonstrated the highest figure in energy savings and emissions reduction with around 37%. These results can aid the decision on the suitable water recovery alternative to be used in the integrated energy-water complex.

Keywords: Energy-Water Nexus, Desalination, Flue gas, Gas-fired power plant, Techno-Environmental-Economic Analysis.

1. Introduction

Fossil-based power plants consume vast quantities of water for heat rejection, fuel preparation, power augmentation, emissions control, and cycle makeup purposes. At the same time, global water resources are becoming scarcer especially in the arid areas which necessitates more efficient and inexpensive water production processes. Although dehydration is done extensively in natural gas processing, water recovery from power plant flue gas is a new concept. Liquid desiccant dehumidification can be used to remove 64-68% water from the flue of a coal fired power plant (Martin et al., 2016). Condensing boilers can be used in the coal fired power plant to recover water and almost 15% of energy (Chen et al., 2012). Thermal membrane condensers can be used to recover heat and water from flue gasses from coal fired power plant (Wang et al., 2012). Although water recovery from coal fired power plants have been studied, gas fired combined cycle power plants are yet to get significant attention. To offset these observed escalating consumption rates, a new system must be developed to meet partial water demand of power plants. Recovering substantial portion of the water vapour present in the flue gas can act as potential source of water. The recovered water is of a quality similar to the desalinated water from reverse osmosis (RO) systems. This water can be used for various plant needs as recovered or can receive minimal treatment so that it can be used as direct-cycle makeup (Copen et al., 2005). Recently, a simultaneous heat and water recovery from flue gas was experimentally studied using membrane condensation. Different operating parameters such as fluid flowrates and temperatures were tested against process performance (Zhao et al., 2017). The results from the study can potentially guide through optimising the operational performance of membrane condensation technology for water and heat recovery. Until the moment, all the power plants in Qatar use natural gas (NG) as source of fuel and all the power plants, except one, are coupled with desalination plants to reduce the heating requirement of the desalination plant. This set up gives an opportunity to integrate the available heat in flue gas to desalination plant. Apart from desalination plants, Qatar does not have an alternative source of fresh water. With a booming economy, the need for fresh water is increasing every day in Qatar. In 2013, 70.6 Million m^3 of fresh water was consumed for industrial and domestic use in Qatar. Power plants in Qatar exhausts 30 Million m^3 of water vapour every year. With proper design, this water can be captured and integrated with desalination plants to supplement fresh water production. In addition, the heat recovered from flue gas would be integrated with the desalination plant to reduce their economic implications and environmental impacts (TokyYasir, 2018).

The aforementioned preliminary studies have shown the feasibility of a technology to recover water from industrial gases as novel sources of water. Water from flue gas, if cost-effectively separated as fresh water, is expected to have major impact on overall fresh water generation and usage capacitates in Qatar and the world. It can be reused for industrial and agricultural purposes. The water management strategies will enable encapsulating water sources from flue gas and desalination for integration. In an earlier study, (TokyYasir, 2018) examined a case of combined cycle power plant that uses both gas turbine and steam turbine to produce electricity to show the applicability of recovering water from flue gas. Specifically, compression and cooling, quenching, membrane separation and absorption alternatives are studied as potential technologies for flue gas dehydration. Detailed modelling and simulation using Aspen HYSYS V9 was done for the potential flue gas dehydration technologies. Each simulated process has multiple processing steps. For example, pressurized feed absorption has 3 steps:

compression, cooling, and absorption. Process simulation results were validated by comparison with published actual plant data in terms of energy demand. From this recent research project, a feasible source of fresh water was identified and a suitable technology was synthesized. Simulations showed that, by quenching almost 75% of the available water in the flue gas of a natural gas fired combined cycle power plant can be captured. By energy integration with a desalination plant, the energy demand for quenching was reduced by more than 50%. For further reduction in capital cost, the flow can be divided into multiple streams and other technologies like membrane filtration and adsorption can be tested in order to check for enhanced water capture to cost intensity ratio. The primary aim of this study is to valorise novel suitable water recovery technologies that are capable of maximizing the recovery of water from flue gas in gas fired power plant-desalination plant coupled system. The capacity of the power plant, the capacity of the desalination plant, fuel consumption of the power plant and energy requirement of the desalination plant are known. The study looks over the technical, environmental and economic competing objectives when integrating the dehydration hybrid technology within the desalination-power plant complex.

2. Model Development

Given the capacity of the desalination facility, its water and energy needs, the product specification or water properties, and the amount of available recovered water from hybrid dehydration technology, the aim is to develop a multi-objective optimization approach to assess the process performance targets and economic indicators. The developed optimization method and simulation track and assess the environmental impact due to the addition of the proposed hybrid water recovery technology/system. The developed tool provides flexibility in the design of water networks considering varying water quality feed, and varying objectives of utilizing the recovered water. The outcome of the presented tool is a two objectives diagram to help the decision maker in understanding the competing trade-offs in the integrated gas fired power plant/desalination plant/ and the studied water recovery technology.

The detailed simulations of the flue gas dehydration technologies using Aspen HYSYS V9 are integrated with gas fired power plant-desalination plant coupled system. Desalination process simulation models for multi-flash separation (MSF) and reverse osmosis (RO) membrane separation are considered for this study and are also developed using Aspen HYSYS along with the gas fired power plant. Figure 1 illustrates the overall configuration of the system. Each simulated process has multiple processing steps. For absorption, glycol package is used to dehydrate the flue gas stream from the power plant. The cooling alternative is a series of chiller coolers, expanders and two phase separators to recover the water from flue gas. Combining the cooling and absorption gives another alternative to be studied where the flue gas is first cooled, expanded and purified before entering the glycol absorption. Compression and cooling option adds a compression unit to the cooling system. Whereas the quenching alternative looks at recycling part of the water to the two phase separation unit to increase the separation. Finally, the membrane system utilizes the membrane unit extension modelled in Aspen HYSYS to purify the flue gas stream and recover its water content. The systems are tested under high and low operating pressures (LP and HP) to evaluate the impact on the performance of the dehydration alternative.

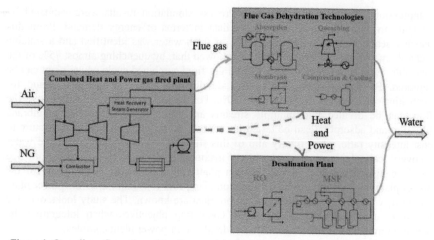

Figure 1: Overall configuration of the flue gas dehydration coupled with CHP-desalination plant

The main characteristics for the simulation models of the flue gas dehydration technologies and desalination plants are summarized in Tables 1.

Table 1: Main characteristics of the flue gas dehydration technologies and desalination plants

System	Water Recovery (%)	Water Purity (%)
LP absorption (1)	2.9	99.55
HP quenching (2)	37.9	99.95
LP quenching (3)	41.2	99.99
Compression and cooling (4)	29.9	99.99
HP cooling and absorption (5)	40.8	99.56
LP cooling and absorption (6)	38.8	99.95
Membrane separation (7)	29.4	99.91
RO desalination	15.8	99.88
MSF desalination	24.6	99.88

In addition, the characteristics of the combined heat and power (CHP) gas fired plant are highlighted in table 2.

Table 2: Main characteristics of combined heat and power (CHP) gas fired plant

CHP plant property	Value	Unit
NG feed (mainly methane)	8.3	kmol/s
Air feed (21% O2, 79% N2)	79.4	kmol/s
Exhaust temperature	100	°C
Power generated	4.5	GW

After the simulation of the different flue gas dehydration configurations in Aspen HYSYS, the built-in activated economic analysis is utilized to quantify the capital and operating costs. In addition, the activated energy analysis capabilities of Aspen HYSYS are utilized to estimate the potential heat integration between the different units in the integrated water-energy system along with the emissions of carbon dioxide equivalent. The different performance indicators are then optimized to generate a two objectives diagram of the different flue gas dehydration configurations emphasizing the environmental and economic performance. The objective of the optimization approach is to minimize the economic parameter estimated as the levelized cost of water (LCOW) expressed in Eq. (1), in addition to the environmental parameter estimated as the emissions of carbon dioxide equivalent expressed in Eq. (3).

$$LCOW\ \left(\frac{\$}{m^3}\right) = \frac{(Capital\ Cost \cdot CRF) + Operating\ Cost}{rate\ of\ water\ recovery \cdot operating\ hours}$$ Equation (1)

Taking the discount rate (r) equal to 20% and plant useful life (n) equal to 25 years,

$$CO_2\ emission\ rate\ in\ [CO_2 - e] = Q\ EF\ \eta\ GWP$$ Equation (2)

Where, CRF is the capital recovery factor calculated in Eq. (3), Q is the energy calculated for each utility type (energy per time), EF is the emission factor associated with each utility type (kg CO_2 per energy), η is the CO_2 energy source efficiency factor associated with each utility type, and GWP is the global warming potential of CO_2 considered to be 1 on this study. The annual operating hours considered for this study are 8760.

$$CRF = \frac{r(1+r)^n}{[(1+r)^n]-1}$$ Equation (3)

3. Results

The results for all the considered alternatives are presented in terms of energy savings, emissions reduction and economic indicators. Figure 2 illustrates the energy savings across the heat integration for each of the integrated flue gas dehydration system. The figure indicates a higher saving for the alternatives containing the MSF desalination plant compared to the RO ones. Nevertheless, the overall costs associated with MSF is double that of RO. The low pressure absorption option coupled with CHP and MSF units demonstrates the highest percentage of saving among the different alternatives with around 37%.

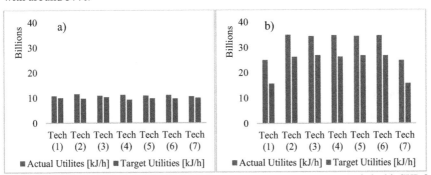

Figure 2: Energy savings among the different flue gas dehydration systems coupled with CHP for a) RO and b) MSF options

The ultimate outcome of the developed tool is a two objectives diagram to help the decision maker in understanding the competing trade-offs in the integrated gas fired power plant/desalination plant/ and the studied water recovery technology. Figure 3 illustrates the resulting economic-environmental diagram for the different integrated flue gas dehydration systems. It can be concluded from the figure that the alternatives with RO units have lower emissions compared to the ones using MSF units. In particular, the low pressure absorption and cooling alternative demonstrated the lowest LCOW with around 0.27 $/m^3 and 5.45x10^5 kg/h in terms of CO_2-e. Whereas, the compression and cooling alternative demonstrated the lowest emissions in terms of CO_2-e with around 5.19x10^5 kg/h and 0.38 $/m^3 in terms of LCOW.

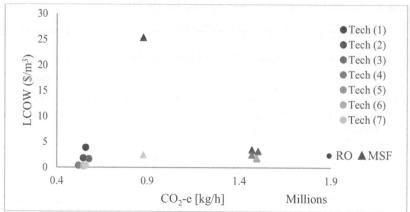

Figure 3: Economic-environmental results for the different flue gas dehydration systems coupled with CHP and RO or MSF

4. Conclusions

Water recovery from flue gas can have a major impact on overall fresh water generation and usage capacities in Qatar and the world. This study examined the techno-economic-environmental evaluation of different flue gas dehydration alternatives when integrated with gas fired power plant-desalination plant coupled system. The generated economic-environmental diagram demonstrated a much lower environmental impact for the options utilizing RO unit.

Acknowledgment

The authors acknowledge the support of Qatar University by the internal grant No QUCD-CENG-2018-2.

References

Q. Chen, K. Finney, H. Li, X. Zhang, J. Zhou, V. Sharifi, and J. Swithenbank, 2012, Condensing boiler applications in the process industry, Applied Energy, 89, 1, 30-36.

J. Copen, T. Sullivan, and B. Folkedahl, 2005, Principles of flue gas water recovery system,

C.L. Martin, B.C. Folkedahl, D.J. Dunham, and J.P. Kay, 2016, Application of liquid desiccant dehumidification to amine-based carbon capture systems, International Journal of Greenhouse Gas Control, 54, 557-65.

A. TokyYasir, 2018, Techno-Economic and Environmental Performance of Water Capture Technologies for Gas Fired Power Plants in Qatar, Qatar University.

D. Wang, A. Bao, W. Kunc, and W. Liss, 2012, Coal power plant flue gas waste heat and water recovery, Applied Energy, 91, 1, 341-48.

S. Zhao, S. Yan, D.K. Wang, Y. Wei, H. Qi, T. Wu, and P.H.M. Feron, 2017, Simultaneous heat and water recovery from flue gas by membrane condensation: Experimental investigation, Applied Thermal Engineering, 113, Supplement C, 843-50.

Anton A. Kiss, Edwin Zondervan, Richard Lakerveld, Leyla Özkan (Eds.)
Proceedings of the 29th European Symposium on Computer Aided Process Engineering
June 16th to 19th, 2019, Eindhoven, The Netherlands. © 2019 Elsevier B.V. All rights reserved.
http://dx.doi.org/10.1016/B978-0-128-18634-3.50053-9

Molecular tracking: A novel approach for multicomponent distillation column design

Nima Nazemzadeh[a], Isuru A. Udugama[b], Michael A. Taube[c], Jens Abildskov[b], Seyed Soheil Mansouri[b,*]

[a]*Department of Chemistry, Materials and Chemical Engineering "G. Natta", Politecnico di Milano, Piazza Leonardo da Vinci 32, 20133 Milano, Italy*
[b]*Process Systems Engineering Research Centre, Chemical and Biochemical Engineering Department, Technical University of Denmark, DK-2800 Lyngby, Denmark*
[c]*S&D Consulting LLC, 1227 Jackson Blvd, Houston Texas 77006, USA*
seso@kt.dtu.dk

Abstract

This paper proposes a new systematic methodology to design a distillation column with middle products (side-draw) for ideal ternary mixtures, where the middle boiling component is present at trace concentrations. The method uses a molecular tracking concept, which uses a probability function based on the thermodynamic properties of the system. The probability function expresses the possibility of upward/downward movement of a single molecule on a tray inside a column. The advantage of this method compared to other existing methods is in its capability to quickly and efficiently provide a feasible solution without relying on rigorous optimization or trial/error approaches. In addition, the inherently graphical nature of the methodology allows engineers to get an intuitive understanding of the movement of the often-complicated middle product. The methodology is demonstrated on an ideal ternary mixture of benzene and p-xylene with toluene as the trace middle boiler, where the results obtained through the molecular tracking were validated against a rigorous process simulation.

Keywords: molecular tracking, side-draw distillation, design, multi-component distillation

1. Introduction

Separation of mixtures through distillation is an established practice in many industries from petrochemicals to bio-manufacturing processes. Despite being the standard-choice for many separations, distillation typically consumes about 60 % of total required energy of chemical industries (Ma et al. 2018). Nonetheless, distillation contributes to about 3% of the total U.S national energy consumption (Seader et al., 1999). As a result, both industrial and academic practitioners have invested considerable efforts in reducing the amount of energy required to operate these units (Kraller et al., 2016), one avenue of which has been the process intensification route. One simple forms of distillation intensification at the unit operation level and in presence of trace component in the system is the replacement of sequential distillation columns by using a single side-draw distillation column. The parametric study in industrial distillation carried out by (Tedder et al., 1978) asserts that for all ternary mixtures where a low middle product purity is acceptable, a side-draw distillation should be considered as one of the possible configurations. Early stage design of distillation columns with side-draw is challenging due to lack of a simple and reliable method to efficiently obtain the (near) optimal feed and side draw locations. Today, side draw distillation columns are designed by either a trial/error or rigorous mathematical formulation, both of which are time consuming and resource intensive endeavors. This work attempts to address this through a systematic design methodology with integration of several concepts and tools including molecular tracking at its core.

2. Molecular tracking

Molecular tracking is a probability-based concept, based on the thermodynamic properties of the system. The concept evaluates the probability of a single molecule to move upwards into the vapor phase or downward into the liquid phase at a given stage of a column. The mixture existing on each stage of a distillation unit splits into vapor and liquid flows with specific vapor and liquid concentrations. The liquid moves downward to the lower tray and the vapor moves upward to the upper tray. Hence, in order to evaluate the molecules probability of moving upward or downward, the function has to be defined over the flowrates of every component on each stage., The probability function as shown in Eq. (1) can be derived (Maat, 2017). The function is defined as the ratio between the existing vapor flowrate of a component over the total outlet flowrate of the same component as expressed below:

$$\beta_i^n = \frac{y_i^n V_i^n}{y_i^n V_i^n + x_i^n L_i^n} \tag{1}$$

Here, β is the probability function, x and y are liquid and vapor compositions respectively. The variables L and V are liquid and vapor internal molar flows and i denotes the component and n is the stage number inside the column.

In molecular tracking concept, a single molecule (typically of the middle key) is tracked from the moment it enters the feed tray by comparing the output of a random number generator function with the calculated system probability value from Eq. (1). If the random number lies within the range $(0, \beta_i^n)$ the molecule is considered to have moved to the vapor phase and hence up to the stage above. This operation is repeated until the molecule leaves the column from one of the outlet streams. Figure (1) illustrates the concept of molecular tracking applied to the heavy key, light key as well as the middle boiling components. As shown in the figure, the light key component has a tendency to move directly towards the top of the column while the heavy key component has a tendency to move directly towards the bottom of the column. However, the middle boiling trace component tends to spend several steps in the middle of the column before eventually exiting the column. From a thermodynamic point of view, the tray with maximum number of hits for the middle boiling component identifies the most probable location for the side-draw as this is the location where the probability of the middle boiling molecules travelling with the vapor or liquid phases is the same (i.e. β of middle boiling component is 50%)

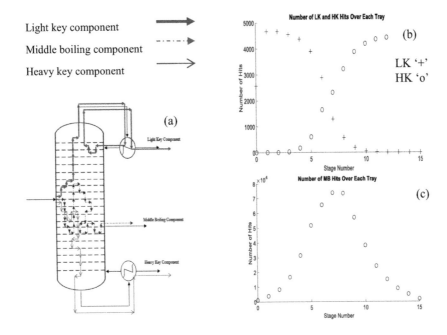

Figure 1: (a) Schematic of a side-draw distillation column with representative molecular pathways, (b) Number of hits of light key and heavy key components, (c) Number of hits of trace component versus stage number

3. Systematic design methodology based on molecular tracking

Here, a systematic hierarchical framework for designing a side-draw distillation column for a ternary mixture, with a middle boiling component at infinite dilution is proposed. In this methodology, the information of a distillation process for the hypothetical binary mixture of key components is used to design the side-draw column for the real mixture. In this work, the design methodology is presented systematically in Figure (2), and the corresponding case study is illustrated in the next section.

Methodology This methodology determines the number of stages, feed and side-draw location based on the specifications of the system. Specifications required to design the column are light key component purity in distillate and heavy key component purity in bottom stream. The reflux ratio of the final configuration of the column is implicitly calculated when the column model is solved.

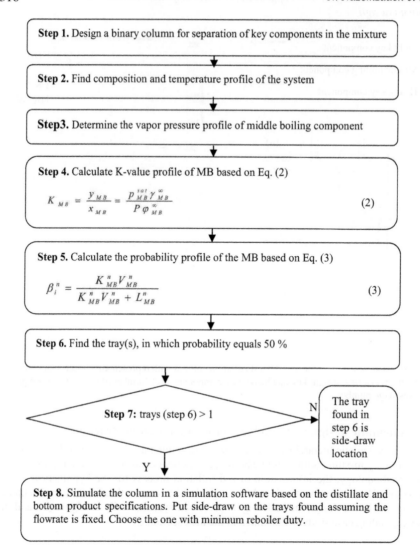

Figure 2: Workflow of methodology

4. Case study

The application of the design methodology is highlighted through a benzene and p-xylene mixture with trace amounts of toluene as an impurity. The separation process is considered isobaric at 1 atm. A comparison is carried out between this method and driving force based method for designing a side-draw column at the end of this section. The results of each step of design methodology are listed in Table (1). The outcome configuration of this algorithm shows that feed has to be located at tray 6 and side-draw has to be located at tray 7.

Table 1: Data sheet of benzene, p-xylene case study

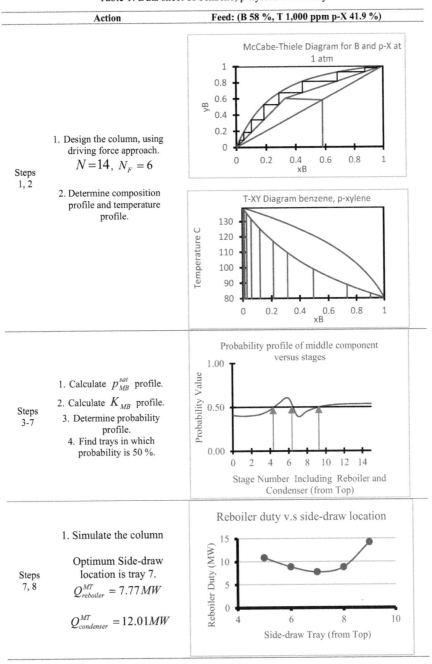

Action	Feed: (B 58 %, T 1,000 ppm p-X 41.9 %)
Steps 1, 2 — 1. Design the column, using driving force approach. $N=14,\ N_F=6$ 2. Determine composition profile and temperature profile.	McCabe-Thiele Diagram for B and p-X at 1 atm T-XY Diagram benzene, p-xylene
Steps 3-7 — 1. Calculate p^{sat}_{MB} profile. 2. Calculate K_{MB} profile. 3. Determine probability profile. 4. Find trays in which probability is 50 %.	Probability profile of middle component versus stages
Steps 7, 8 — 1. Simulate the column Optimum Side-draw location is tray 7. $Q^{MT}_{reboiler} = 7.77\,MW$ $Q^{MT}_{condenser} = 12.01\,MW$	Reboiler duty v.s side-draw location

This information has been validated against a rigorous process simulation in step 7 and 8. Comparing the rigorous process simulation results for the molecular tracking is able to narrow down the possible most energy efficient tray location for a column with a side draw purely based on thermodynamic properties (in this case to three options) and with the aid of process simulation narrow down the answer to the most energy efficient one that is illustrated in Table (1) at steps 7 and 8.

When comparing these results with driving force method proposed by Erik Bek-Pedersen and Gani (2004), the maximum driving force occurs at $D_x = 0.4$ (D_x is the liquid composition of light key component at maximum driving force) between benzene and toluene. The joint driving force diagram shows $D_s = 0.35$ (D_s is the liquid composition of light key component when two binary driving force diagrams intersect). Algorithm D2 on that paper shows that feed should be introduced at tray 5 while, side-draw should be introduced at tray 9. The simulation of this configuration in HYSYS. It can be clearly seen that molecular tracking proposes much more efficient configuration compared to driving force based method.

Conclusions

A systematic methodology to design side-draw columns for ideal ternary mixtures, where the middle component is at trace concentration level is proposed. The methodology is based on a probability function expressed in terms of thermodynamic properties of the system. The column is first designed for the key components in the mixture, and then the side-draw location is deterministically found. The side-draw is located at the stage, which the middle component (trace component) is indifferent to move either upward or downward. A case study of benzene, p-xylene and trace amount of toluene has been examined in this work. The design configuration of molecular tracking has shown less energy demand compared to the corresponding configuration of driving force. Considering that it is possible to find the side-draw location analytically by using trial/error approach, the real scope of molecular tracking is to design a dividing wall column by finding the location of dividing wall.

References

C. Maat TPC Group, 2017, Molecular tracking- a new way to analyze distillation columns, Oral Presentation, AIChE 2017 Spring Meeting – Kister Distillation Symposium, San Antonio, Texas, United States of America

D. Seader, E.J. Henley, D.K. Roper, 1999, Distillation of binary mixtures, Separation process principles, Second Edition, Page 252, John Wiley and Sons Inc., United States of America.

D.W. Tedder, D.F. Rudd, 1978, Parametric studies in industrial distillation: Part I. Design comparisons, AIChE J. 24.

E. Bek-Pedersen, R. Gani, 2004, Design and synthesis of distillation systems using a driving-force-based approach, Chem. Eng. Process. Process Intensif. 43.

Kraller, M. A.; Udugama, I. A.; Kirkpatrick, R.; Yu, W.; Young, B. R., 2016, Side Draw Optimisation of a High-Purity, Multi-Component Distillation Column. Asia-Pacific J. Chem. Eng., 11 (6)

Y. Ma, Y. Luo, S. Zhang, X. Yuan, 2018, Simultaneous optimization of complex distillation systems and heat integration using pseudo-transient continuation models, Comput. Chem. Eng. 108.

Anton A. Kiss, Edwin Zondervan, Richard Lakerveld, Leyla Özkan (Eds.)
Proceedings of the 29th European Symposium on Computer Aided Process Engineering
June 16th to 19th, 2019, Eindhoven, The Netherlands. © 2019 Elsevier B.V. All rights reserved.
http://dx.doi.org/10.1016/B978-0-128-18634-3.50054-0

Development of a Model-Based Quality-by-Control Framework for Crystallization Design

Ayşe Eren,[a] Botond Szilágyi,[a] Justin Quon,[b] Masashi Furuta,[b] Charles Papageorgiou,[b] Zoltán K. Nagy[a*]

[a]Davidson School of Cehmical Engineernig, Purdue University, 610 Purdue Mall, West Lafayette 47907, United States

[b]Takeda Oncology, 40 Landsdowne St, Cambridge 02139, United States

erena@purdue.edu

Abstract

The work proposes a combination of model-free and model-based quality-by-control (mfQbC and mbQbC) paradigms as a general framework for the optimal crystallization design with the aim of minimization of fines and agglomerates in the product. This framework provides an improved alternative to the current industrial practice, by the combined use of feedback control and mathematical models for rapid design of robust crystallization processes. The implementation of the proposed mbQbC framework enhanced the prediction of crystallization events and was able to achieve better control of the crystallization processes by providing controlled heating/cooling cycles, for de-agglomeration and fines destruction. The information for parameter estimation and optimization calculations was collected from the experiments in mfQbC part, which additionally also provided a rapid design of robust operating conditions, which subsequently in the mbQbC approach were improved to achieve optimal operation.

Keywords: Optimization, modelling, control, crystallization, design.

1. Introduction

Batch crystallization is used substantially in purification of the active pharmaceutical ingredients (APIs) in the pharmaceutical industries. Particle size has a significant effect on the quality of drugs and on the efficiency of downstream processes such as filtration, milling, centrifugation, drying, granulation, and tableting (Rawlings et al., 1993). A narrow crystal size distribution (CSD) at the desired mean crystal size is crucial for efficient downstream processes and desired critical quality attributes (CQAs) of the final product, therefore crystallization control strategies such as model-based control approaches, automated direct nucleation control (ADNC), supersaturation control (SSC) or temperature control (T-control) have been developed to achieve desired CSD (Simon et al., 2018). Current industrial practice for the design of operating conditions generally uses a quality-by-design (QbD) framework, based on exploring the design space by experimentation, which can be time consuming even with a well thought experimental design. More recently, a novel and faster alternative, the quality-by-control (QbC) framework has been introduced as a new paradigm that uses feedback control (model-free or model-based) to automatically find the optimum operating profiles that lead to the manufacturing of final product with desired CQAs, rather than applying open-loop experimentation.

The new sequential QbC approach proposed consists of the combination of the mfQbC approach where first closed loop feedback control is used to automatically identify the design space and feasible region of operation, while also providing a robust, although probably suboptimal, operating procedure. This is followed by the implementation of a mathematical model that uses the information from experimental part for parameter estimation and model-based optimization to provide an optimal refined operating procedure. The experimental control strategy provides the first important step of improving the product quality and phase diagram information of the system. MbQbC provides the ability to predict crystallization phenomena or to enhance the control of crystallization processes. Worlitschek (2004) showed that a developed deterministic model for solution thermodynamics, crystal growth, and nucleation enhanced the control of the crystallization of paracetamol from ethanol. After optimization, the determined cooling profile was good enough to obtain the desired monomodal particle size distribution and supersaturation. Hermanto, Braatz et al. (2010) showed that an integrated batch-to- batch and nonlinear model predictive control (B2B-NMPC) strategy based on a hybrid model can be used to control the polymorphic transformation of L-glutamic acid. Nagy (2009) showed that a lower model-free approach can be used to operate the system in the phase diagram in combination with a higher-level model-based approach to maintain product uniformity. Acevedo et al. (2017) showed that model-based design can also be used for the design of model-free direct nucleation control (DNC) for the optimal operation in the case of continuous crystallization.

A critical step of model-based approaches is the parameter estimation of the crystallization kinetics, which requires the solution of the population balance equations (PBE) of the crystallization model. For efficient parameter estimation, model-based optimization, and real-time model predictive control, it is imperative to have fast and accurate solution. Various techniques have been proposed for the solution of PBMs, including analytical solution-based approaches, such as method of moments, quadrature method of moments, or method of characteristics, or direct numerical solutions such as finite volume method (FVM) or Monte-Carlo simulations, which have also been applied along with the solution of the optimization problem (Omar and Rohani, 2017). In this work, the model-free and model-based QbC approaches were combined for the optimal design of crystallization systems with the aim of minimization of fine formation and agglomeration of paracetamol (PCM) crystals, as the model compound. Although PCM is well-studied, only the parameters for the nucleation and growth kinetics have been determined so far. This work will be the first study that estimates all kinetic parameters for the primary and secondary nucleation, growth, dissolution, agglomeration and de-agglomeration mechanisms for the crystallization of PCM by developing a novel QbC framework combining model-free and model-based techniques.

2. Experimental Methods, Model Development, Parameter Estimation, and Process Optimization

Four types of batch experiments were performed to understand the system dynamics, seed production and for crystallization kinetics parameter estimation of the crystallization of paracetamol (PCM) from isopropyl alcohol (IPA). Seeded linear cooling and heating experiments were used for determination of the crystal count during secondary nucleation. These were followed by several direct nucleation control (DNC) experiments with different cooling/heating rates to keep the crystal count within certain thresholds.

DNC experiments provided the information about the primary and secondary nucleation curves in the phase diagram. After determining the metastable zone width (MSZW) according to these curves, a seeding point and set point were selected for the SSC experiments. The temperature data generated from SSC experiment gave the cooling profile required to operate below the secondary nucleation curve (e.g. growth zone) in the phase diagram. The cooling curve provided was approximated by a sequence of three linear cooling ramps and was used in an open-loop temperature control experiment to show that the simplified profile can produce similar product. Data from all experiments were used to estimate nucleation, growth, agglomeration, dissolution and de-agglomeration kinetic parameters. UV/Vis spectrophotometer, focused beam reflectance measurement (FBRM), and Particle Vision Measurement (PVM) were used as PAT tools to measure concentration, particle count, morphology and size. In addition, Malvern Mastersizer 3000 and Nikon SMZ1500 microscope were used for offline characterization of size distribution and crystal morphology.

A mathematical model is required for mbQbC that describes the crystal birth, growth, and death due to nucleation, growth, agglomeration, dissolution, and de-agglomeration. A 1D Population Balance Model (PBM) with size-independent growth and dissolution, including size-dependent agglomeration and de-agglomeration kernels (1) was used to model the system for the supersaturated and desaturated regions along with corresponding mass balances equations (2).

$$\frac{\partial n(L,t)}{\partial t} + G\frac{\partial n(L,t)}{\partial L} = B\delta(L - L_m) - \int_0^\infty \beta(t,L,\lambda)n(L,t)n(\lambda,t)d\lambda$$

$$+ \frac{1}{2}\int_0^L \frac{\beta(t,(L^3-\lambda^3)^{1/3},\lambda)}{(L^3-\lambda^3)^{2/3}} \times n(t,(L^3-\lambda^3)^{\frac{1}{3}})n(t,\lambda)d\lambda, \text{if } \sigma > 0 \tag{1}$$

$$\frac{\partial n(L,t)}{\partial t} - D\frac{\partial n(L,t)}{\partial L} = \int_L^\infty b(L|\lambda)S(\lambda)n(t,\lambda)d\lambda - S(L)n(t,L), \text{if } \sigma < 0$$

$$\frac{dC}{dt} = \begin{cases} -k_V\rho_C\left(3G\int_0^\infty L^2n(L,t)dL\right), \text{if } \sigma > 0 \\ \\ k_V\rho_C\left(3D\int_0^\infty L^2n(L,t)dL\right), \text{otherwise} \end{cases} \tag{2}$$

$$B = B_p + B_b, B_p = k_p\sigma^p, B_b = k_b\sigma^b A_c, G = k_g\sigma^g exp\left(-\frac{E_A}{RT}\right), \beta(\lambda,L) = k_{ag}F(\lambda^3 + L^3),$$
$$D = k_d(-\sigma)^d, S(\lambda) = k_{br} F(\lambda^3) \tag{3}$$

The model was solved by using the high-resolution FVM (HR-FVM) during parameter estimation and optimization calculations. Parameter estimation calculations were done to estimate 10 parameters in the crystallization events (3) which are also used in PBEs. The equations are given for primary and secondary nucleation, growth, agglomeration, dissolution, and de-agglomeration, respectively. Size dependent de-agglomeration and agglomeration selection functions F are described by hyperbolic tangent functions using the crystal crystals sizes for both cases. Optimizations were carried out for the temperature profile (T-profile), in three steps: a) first a preliminary stochastic global optimization of a crude T-profile defined by 10 discrete temperature points was performed to provide a good starting point for the b) gradient-based optimization (sequential quadratic programming-SQP) for refinement of the solution and c) SQP-based

optimization of a smoother T-profile (defined by 20 discrete temperatures), using as
starting point the outcome of b). For global optimization, a custom implementation of
Covariance Matrix Adaptation Evolution Strategy (CMA-ES) was applied. The objective
function (4) was defined to minimize each term: the product fine index, product
agglomeration index, sharpness of T-profile and agglomerates index during the
crystallization, respectively. The weight factors (w_i) were set by preliminary
optimizations so to ensure that the sub-objective values are in the same order of
magnitude around the optimum. Note that changing the values of weight factors also
changes the optimal solution. This is a subjective decision, which is taken based on
detailed process understanding. In Eq. (4) N_A is the number of agglomerates, L is the
length of the crystals, n is the population density. The product fine index is the ratio of
the number of fine crystals to the total number of crystals in the product CSD; the product
agglomeration index is the ratio of the agglomerates in the same product CSD. Sharpness
of the T-profile was defined as the gradient of the profile to be minimized for smoother
operation and the last term is defined as the total number of agglomerated crystal fraction
during the crystallization rather than only in the product CSD.

$$OF = 100 \left[\frac{\int_0^{L_f} L^3 n(L, t=t_f)dL}{\int_0^{L_{max}} L^3 n(L, t=t_f)dL} \right]^2 + w_1 100 \left[\frac{N_A(t=t_f)}{\int_0^{L_{max}} n(L, t=t_f)dL} \right]^2$$

$$+ w_2 \sum_{i=2}^{N} (t_i - t_{i-1}) \left(\frac{T_i - T_{i-1}}{t_i - t_{i-1}} \right)^2 + w_3 100 \int_0^{t_f} \left[\frac{N_A(t)}{\int_0^{L_{max}} n(L, t)dL} \right]^2 dt \tag{4}$$

3. Results and Discussion

The experiments performed in the mfQbC framework were seeded cooling
crystallization, DNC, followed by SSC, and a T-control experiments. The benefits of this
procedure are to obtain detailed information about the system's phase diagram/operating
zone, as well as to produce the product obtained from the close-loop SSC experiment by
a more practical, simplified cooling crystallization (T-control). Volume-based crystal size
distribution and microscopy images showed that similar products were achieved. Data
from each controlled experiment was used as input for the parameter estimation
calculations in the model-based approach.

Param.	Value	Dev.	Units
k_p	10.35	± 0.71	$\#/m^3s$
p	2.63	± 0.21	-
k_b	$1.19 \cdot 10^6$	$\pm 0.25 \cdot 10^6$	$\#/m^3s$
b	0.88	± 0.05	-
k_g	$4.56 \cdot 10^{15}$	$\pm 0.65 \cdot 10^{15}$	m/m^3s
g	1.61	± 0.11	-
E_A	89044	± 7184	kJ/mol
k_d	1.95	± 0.03	m/m^3s
k_{ag}	$1.46 \cdot 10^{-14}$	$\pm 0.25 \cdot 10^{-14}$	$\#/m^3s$
k_{br}	$1.08 \cdot 10^{-2}$	$\pm 0.11 \cdot 10^{-2}$	$\#/m^3s$

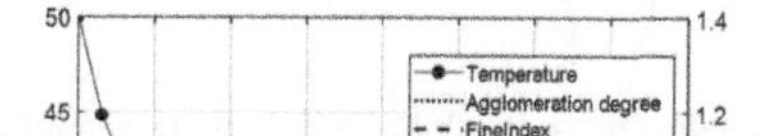

Fig. 1. (a) Estimated kinetic parameters; (b) Optimum temperature profile and the evolution of the
agglomeration degree and fine index during the optimum operation.

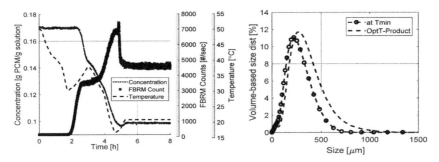

Fig. 2. (a) Experimental results of the optimum temperature profile; (b) Volume-based size distribution of the crystals from the minimum temperature point and the end of the same experiment.

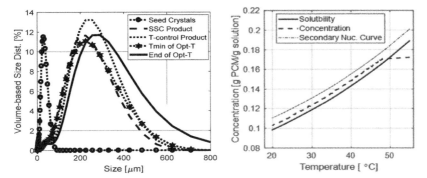

Fig. 3. (a) Volume-based size distribution of the seed crystals used and products from SSC and T-control experiments; (b) Operation profile of SSC experiment in growth region.

The combined framework is designed so that the two parts to be complementary to each other. Collected data from mfQbC was used in parameter estimation and optimization calculations in mbQbC. Estimated parameters (Fig. 1) were used in the model for optimization calculations. The optimum temperature profile (T-opt) was obtained by the three step optimization calculations as described. The resulting profile exhibited two heating cycles including a small heating ramp at the end. T-opt was tested by an unseeded cooling crystallization experiment. Results show that the model predicts the nucleation accurately, and the system is heated before detectable nucleation by FBRM counts. Although the system was in the heating region the primary nucleation still occurred, but the first heating cycle was able to slow down the nucleation event. In addition, the 4 °C heating at the end was efficient to destroy fine crystals and to induce de-agglomeration. During the experiment, two samples were taken at the minimum temperature point and at the end to understand the effect of the last heating cycle. Microscopy images and the size distributions of the samples before and after this heating cycle showed that this small heating ramp (4 °C) was enough for de-agglomeration and elimination of fine crystals (Fig. 2), which could be observed by the corresponding FBRM peak before the decrease in the counts (2,500 counts/sec), respectively. The strength of fine elimination and de-agglomeration of the T-opt by predicting nucleation correctly can be emphasized by the comparison of the products from SSC, T-control and T-opt experiments. The size distribution (Fig.3) shows that, T-opt product contains more larger crystals and less fines. The model-free direct design approach provided automatically a T-profile from SSC experiment that was implemented easily using a simple T-control experiment. While this is easy to develop and implement, this may not be the optimum operating profile especially for systems that tend to agglomerate or produce significant number of fines due to attrition, breakage or some secondary nucleation. The model-based optimization provided a T-profile that reinforces fine dissolution and de-agglomeration (Fig. 3). The shift in the distribution of the end-sample from the T-opt experiment shows that fines elimination is significant when compared to samples from other experiments or different time moment of the same experiment.

4. Conclusions

A new hybrid (model-based and model-free) QbC framework for crystallization design was developed that can predict the crystallization process and keep the measured CQAs at their desired values, while using feedback control approaches efficiently. This framework was developed to provide the optimum operating procedure for crystallization systems. The model could even predict the primary nucleation time and apply heating cycle before detectable nucleation. The experimental validation of the approach demonstrated that the desired fine dissolution was achieved, agglomerated index was significantly decreased and the mean crystal size of the CSD could be increased accordingly, indicating the potential benefits of the new approach as a novel and efficient design of crystallization systems governed by complex phenomena.

Acknowledgements

Financial support from Takeda Pharmaceuticals Int. Co. is gratefully acknowledged.

References

Acevedo, David, Yang Yang, Daniel J. Warnke, and Zoltan K. Nagy. 2017. "Model-Based Evaluation of Direct Nucleation Control Approaches for the Continuous Cooling Crystallization of Paracetamol in a Mixed Suspension Mixed Product Removal System." *Crystal Growth and Design* 17 (10): 5377–83. doi:10.1021/acs.cgd.7b00860.

Hermanto, Martin, Richard Braatz, and Min-Sen Chiu. 2010. "Integrated Batch-to-Batch and Nonlinear Model Predictive Control for Polymorphic Transformation in Pharmaceutical Crystallization." *AIChE Journal* 57 (4): 1008–19. doi:10.1002/aic.

Nagy, Zoltan K. 2009. "Model Based Robust Control Approach for Batch Crystallization Product Design." *Computers and Chemical Engineering* 33 (10): 1685–91. doi:10.1016/j.compchemeng.2009.04.012.

Omar, Hecham M., and Sohrab Rohani. 2017. "Crystal Population Balance Formulation and Solution Methods: A Review." *Crystal Growth & Design* 17 (7): 4028–41. doi:10.1021/acs.cgd.7b00645.

Rawlings, James B., C.W. Sink, and S.M. Miller. 1993. "Control of Crystallization Processes." *Handbook of Industrial Crystallization*, 201–30. doi:10.1016/B978-075067012-8/50011-2.

Simon, Levente L., Elena Simone, and Kaoutar Abbou Oucherif. 2018. *Crystallization Process Monitoring and Control Using Process Analytical Technology. Computer Aided Chemical Engineering.* 1st ed. Vol. 41. Elsevier B.V. doi:10.1016/B978-0-444-63963-9.00009-9.

Worlitschek, Jörg, and Marco Mazzotti. 2004. "Model-Based Optimization of Particle Size Distribution in Batch-Cooling Crystallization of Paracetamol." *Crystal Growth and Design* 4 (5): 891–903. doi:10.1021/cg034179b.

Anton A. Kiss, Edwin Zondervan, Richard Lakerveld, Leyla Özkan (Eds.)
Proceedings of the 29th European Symposium on Computer Aided Process Engineering
June 16th to 19th, 2019, Eindhoven, The Netherlands. © 2019 Elsevier B.V. All rights reserved.
http://dx.doi.org/10.1016/B978-0-128-18634-3.50055-2

Towards development of a decision support tool for conceptual design of wastewater treatment plants using stochastic simulation optimization

Resul Al, Chitta Ranjan Behera, Krist V. Gernaey, Gürkan Sin[*]

Process and Systems Engineering Center (PROSYS), Department of Chemical and Biochemical Engineering, Technical University of Denmark, Building 229, 2800 Kgs. Lyngby, Denmark

gsi@kt.dtu.dk

Abstract

Available treatment technologies for wastewater are diversifying as the industry is undergoing a paradigm shift from considering wastewater as a waste to treat to an increasingly valuable source for energy production and resource recovery. With the purpose of addressing the problem of determining optimal plant network for wastewater treatment plants, we develop a new decision support tool (SPDLab) relying on a novel simulation optimization based process synthesis framework and a library of rigorous process models. The capabilities of SPDLab are demonstrated with a case study for designing an energy surplus WWTP. The Benchmark Simulation Model No. 2 (BSM2) (Gernaey et al., 2014) plant layout is populated with additional options for primary treatment technologies, such as a rotating belt filter with or without polymer addition, and mainline treatment options including also fixed film activated sludge (IFAS) technology. A side stream treatment with partial nitrification-Anammox process is also included in the superstructure. Results obtained show that the combination of efficient carbon recovery with main stream Anammox and anaerobic digester produces the most net energy among the investigated alternatives.

Keywords: Process synthesis and design, wastewater treatment plant design, simulation-based optimization, Monte Carlo simulation.

1. Introduction

The design of domestic wastewater treatment plants (WWTPs) has seen an unprecedented shift since the inception of the widely used activated sludge process. The priority for a design engineer was mainly to ensure effective removal of organic pollutants from wastewater. However, with the ever growing demands on the WWTP, such as population growth leading to increased pollutant loads, stringent environmental laws, demand for energy neutrality and contributing to circular economy, the layout of WWTP looks more gigantic than ever. The WWTP design intricacy has been further exacerbated by the remarkable innovation and availability of novel treatment technology (both matured and emerging) in the market. Therefore, given the steadily growing number of competing treatment technologies and ever-ambitious performance goals, the need for the use of simulation, optimization, and systematic process synthesis methodologies for engineering design of WWTPs is becoming more pronounced among design professionals.

Accurate modelling of highly complex biological processes in WWTPs require use of rigorous (non-linear) bio-process models such as ASM1 (Henze et al., 2006), ADM1 (Batstone et al., 2002), etc. Such models remain too complex for use in traditional process synthesis approaches such as superstructure optimization using mathematical programming due to the highly nonlinear process equations (Chen et al., 2018). The main contribution of this paper is the development and application of a new simulation optimization-based process synthesis approach to explore more rigorously alternative WWTP networks using a model library of high-fidelity mechanistic bio-process models. For this purpose, a decision support tool for sustainable process synthesis and design, SPDLab, has been developed to assist design professionals with the implemented methodology. SPDLab provides computational tools for interfacing with complex bio-process models implemented in a Simulink environment and searches for an optimal plant layout configuration for the given design objective. The process synthesis methodology consists of three major steps. First, a superstructure containing all different design configurations is created using combinatorial synthesis and expert knowledge approach (Bozkurt et al., 2015). Second, design degrees of freedoms of each configuration are investigated with Monte Carlo simulations and promising configurations are selected for the third step, which imposes user-defined effluent quality constraints to rank and select optimal plant layouts with preliminary design.

2. Methodology

Simulation is an established tool for evaluating and predicting the performance of complex engineering systems. Stochastic simulation optimization, also referred to as simulation optimization, uses simulation to find values of decision variables that will optimize the system's key performance indicators (KPI) of interest, which are obtained by performing stochastic simulations like Monte Carlo simulations. Promoted by recent advancements in computing power, simulation optimization allows one to work with arbitrarily complex simulation models, eliminating the need to keep model complexity to mathematically tractable forms as required by deterministic optimization frameworks (Pasupathy et al., 2011). A step-by-step overview of the proposed simulation optimization based process synthesis and design methodology is shown in Table 1.

Table 1: Overview of proposed methodology for early stage design of WWTPs.

Step 1	Generation of a superstructure containing all the different plant layouts using combinatorial synthesis and expert knowledge
Step 2	Design space exploration of each alternative plant layout with Monte Carlo simulations
Step 3	Ranking and selection of optimal plant layouts

2.1. Step 1: Superstructure generation

A superstructure is postulated to represent all practical plant layouts, which can be selected as an alternative plant design by the decision support tool, using combinatorial synthesis together with expert knowledge. Combinatorial synthesis allows exhaustive exploration of all different combinations of technologies whereas expert knowledge is used to exclude layouts with an infeasible sequence of treatment units from further investigation.

Towards development of a decision support tool for conceptual design of
wastewater treatment plants using stochastic simulation optimization

327

2.2. Step 2: Design space exploration

For each treatment technology, there exist several design degrees of freedom, such as the volume ratio of aerobic and anaerobic tanks in an activated sludge system, which needs to be selected by the designer and significantly affects the plant performance. Therefore, to achieve desired effluent quality levels, one often needs to explore these design degrees of freedom for every different technology. For this purpose, design-related parameters of each technology included in a given layout are gathered in a global parameter space, i.e. the design space, which is then sampled using a uniform space filling sampling design such as Latin hypercube sampling (LHS). The resulting design space is explored with Monte Carlo simulations to identify promising plant layouts which will provide optimized performance results by also satisfying imposed effluent constraints.

2.3. Step 3: Ranking and selection (R&S)

Among the methods developed for solving simulation-based optimization problems are ranking and selection (R&S), black-box search methods, surrogate model based methods, and sample path approximation, etc. For a detailed review of these methods, the work of Xu et al. (2015) can be consulted. For problems with a finite number of solutions in the search space, such as optimal plant layout among the alternatives contained in the superstructure, R&S procedures can be directly applied to find the most promising plant layout for the given design objective. To further assist the decision-maker in identifying promising layouts, results of Monte Carlo simulations are exposed to the performance constraints to filter out infeasible solutions and then ranked according to the design objective.

3. A decision support tool for process design of WWTPs: SPDLab

3.1. The model library and the user interface

The SPDLab model library (shown in Figure 1) encompasses models representing both conventional and emerging treatment technologies. The primary clarifier works based on gravity settling and is modelled as presented in Gernaey et al. (2014), whereas the rotating belt filter, which is an emerging technology, works based on cake filtration and sieving and is modelled as presented in Boiocchi et al. (2018), and Behera et al. (2018).

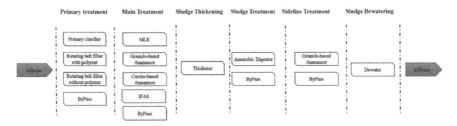

Figure 1: The model library of SPDLab is shown for different treatment steps in WWTPs.

For mainstream nutrient removal the Modified Ludzack-Ettinger (MLE) system is used based on the ASM1 principle (Gernaey et al., 2014). Anammox based nutrient removal for both mainstream and side stream is modelled using a one-dimensional biofilm concept. The integrated fixed-film activated sludge (IFAS) system is a retrofitted version of the MLE system, where the aerobic tanks are filled with carrier in order to enhance the nitrogen loading rate. For sludge treatment, the anaerobic digestion (AD) system is modeled using the ADM1 (Batstone et al., 2002). The sludge thickening and dewatering are modeled using the approach of Gernaey et al., (2014). To design each unit, several widely used design parameters such as sludge retention time (SRT), hydraulic retention time (HRT), surface over flow rate (SOR), nitrogen removal rate (NRR), recycle ratio (RR), carrier filling etc. are used while sampling the design space using LHS. Figure 2 shows the SPDLab's user interface, which was developed in the Simulink modelling environment.

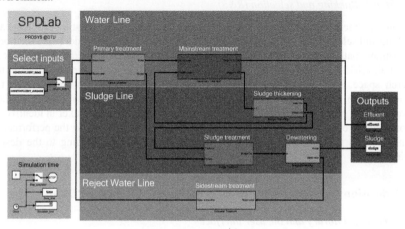

Figure 2: The main user interface of the decision support tool

3.2. A case study: Designing an energy surplus WWTP

The main objective of this case study is to illustrate the proposed methodology outlined in Table 1. To this end, a scenario is considered where the primary objective is to build an energy surplus WWTP for a benchmark municipal wastewater stream (Gernaey et al., 2014) with a plant capacity of 100,000 PE. Figure 3 depicts the synthesis problem along with the design flows and the effluent quality limits imposed in the case study.

Figure 3: Design flows and performance goals considered in the case study.

4. Results and discussion

Following the proposed methodology, a total of 80 different plant layouts were generated in step 1 with a combinatorial synthesis approach, and step 2 explored automatically the generated design space of each layout with Monte Carlo simulations using a LHS of size 100. Results are shown for net energy production of feasible designs in Figure 4. Furthermore, the solutions are screened and ranked (see Figure 5) by enforcing the effluent quality limits (COD < 100 mg/L, TN < 10 mg/L and NH_4^+ < 1 mg/L) and the plant KPIs such as methane gas production, aeration energy demand and sludge production, etc., are calculated for each design. Besides, the net energy is calculated by subtracting the aeration energy consumption from the energy produced via the methane gas. The energy modelling at this stage is kept intentionally simple as the primary objective of this work is to assess the methodology.

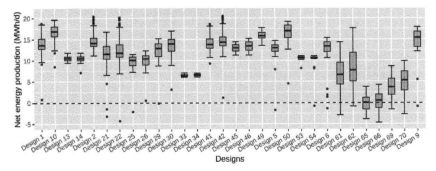

Figure 4: Comparing net-energy production of all potential plant layouts.

The top five feasible designs selected by the tool for building an energy surplus WWTP are shown in Table 2, which picks main stream Anammox as an efficient carbon recovery technology together with an AD unit. This combination also agrees well with the available process knowledge, i.e., increasing biogas production by diverting more carbon to the AD unit and then treating the low COD/TN load wastewater with Anammox technology. In this way the aeration energy demand can be reduced significantly as the Anammox process needs significantly less oxygen compared to the conventional activated sludge process (Morales et al., 2015).

Table 2: Top 5 promising plant layouts selected by SPDLab for energy surplus WWTP design.

Selected Configuration	Aeration Energy (kWh/d)	Methane Production (kWh/d)	Net Energy (kWh/d)
PC – Anx_carrier – Thickener – AD – Dewater	3662	19452	15790
RBF w/ polymer – Anx_carrier – Thickener – AD – Dewater	3795	18987	15192
PC – Anx_granule – Thickener – AD – Dewater	3721	18109	14388
PC – Anx_carrier – Thickener – AD – Dewater – Anx_granule_side	3546	17777	14231
PC – Anx_granule – Thickener – AD – Dewater – Anx_granule_side	3880	18018	14138

5. Conclusions

This paper presented a new methodology and a tool for process synthesis and preliminary design of WWTP networks using simulation optimization. The tool is targeted at exploring alternative WWTP designs for a given wastewater stream and design objective/constraints. The case study results demonstrate that SPDLab can provide decision makers with valuable insights during the early-stage design of WWTP networks with its rigorous search and advanced visualization capabilities for identifying promising plant layout configurations. Furthermore, development of a fully-fledged commercial decision support tool allowing also for multi-objective design optimization, extension of the model library to newly arising treatment technologies, and integration of other early stage design tools, such as sustainability analysis, are planned as future work.

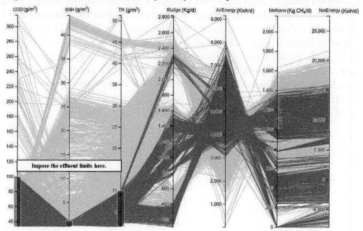

Figure 5: Comparison of all feasible designs after imposing effluent quality constraints.

Acknowledgements: The authors acknowledge funding from the EU Horizon 2020 research and innovation programme under the Marie Skłodowska-Curie grant agreement no.675251 as well as the funding from the Water Joint Programming Initiative under the PIONEER_STP project.

References

C.R. Behera, D. Santoro, K.V. Gernaey, G. Sin, 2018, Organic carbon recovery modeling for a rotating belt filter and its impact assessment on a plant-wide scale, Chemical Engineering Journal, 334, pp.1965-1976.

D.J. Batstone, J. Keller, I. Angelidaki, S.V.Kalyuzhnyi, S.G. Pavlostathis, A. Rozzi, W.T.M. Sanders, H. Siegrist, V.A. Vavilin, 2002, The IWA anaerobic digestion model no 1 (ADM1), Water Science and Technology, 45(10), pp.65-73.

H. Bozkurt, A. Quaglia, K.V. Gernaey, G. Sin, 2015, A mathematical programming framework for early stage design of wastewater treatment plants, Environmental Modelling & Software, 64, 164–176.

J. Xu, E. Huang, C.H. Chen, L.H. Lee, 2015, Simulation Optimization: A Review and Exploration in the New Era of Cloud Computing and Big Data, Asia-Pacific J. Oper. Res., 32, 1550019.

K.V. Gernaey, U. Jeppsson, P.A. Vanrolleghem, and J.B. Copp, 2014, Benchmarking of control strategies for wastewater treatment plants, IWA Publishing.

M. Henze, W. Gujer, T. Mino, M.C.M. van Loosdrecht, 2000, Activated Sludge Models ASM1, ASM2, ASM2d and ASM3, IWA Scientific and Technical Report 9, IWA Publishing, London.

N. Morales, Á.V. del Río, J.R. Vázquez-Padín, R. Méndez, A. Mosquera-Corral, J.L. Campos, 2015, Integration of the Anammox process to the rejection water and main stream lines of WWTPs, Chemosphere, 140, pp.99-105.

R. Boiocchi, F. Giaccherini, F. Khan, C. DeGroot, A. Sherratt, D. Santoro, Dynamic Modelling And Validation Of A Rotating Belt Filter For Primary Wastewater Treatment, 4th ecoSTP conference, Ontario, Canada.

X. Chen, R. Al, C.R. Behera, G. Sin, 2018, Process Synthesis, Design, and Control of Wastewater Treatment Plants, Elsevier Reference Module in Chemistry, Molecular Sciences and Chemical Engineering, pp. 1–14.

Anton A. Kiss, Edwin Zondervan, Richard Lakerveld, Leyla Özkan (Eds.)
Proceedings of the 29th European Symposium on Computer Aided Process Engineering
June 16th to 19th, 2019, Eindhoven, The Netherlands. © 2019 Elsevier B.V. All rights reserved.
http://dx.doi.org/10.1016/B978-0-128-18634-3.50056-4

Targeting of sustainable chemical processes using data envelopment analysis: application to liquid fuels for transportation

Daniel F. Rodríguez-Vallejo,[a] Ángel Galán-Martín,[a] Gonzalo Guillén-Gosálbez[a,*] Benoît Chachuat[a]

[a]Department of Chemical Engineering, Centre for Process System Engineering, Imperial College London, South Kensington Campus, London SW7 2AZ, United Kingdom

g.guillen05@imperial.ac.uk

Abstract

In this paper we proposed a framework aimed to improve the sustainability of chemical processes based on the combination of data envelopment analysis and process system engineering tools. Given a set of chemical process alternatives, each characterised by techno-economic and environmental performance indicators, the framework discerns between efficient (optimal) and inefficient (suboptimal) processes in the sense of these indicators. We develop an approach to quantifying the closest targets for an inefficient process to become efficient, while avoiding unattainable targets by accounting for thermodynamic limitations in that process in terms of mass and energy flow constraints. We demonstrate the capabilities of the framework through a case study that involves the assessment of a methanol production process with CO_2 captured from power plants and H_2 derived from fossil fuels, in comparison to ten fuel alternatives. We find that this methanol fuel is presently suboptimal in comparison with other fuels. Making it competitive would require a significant reduction in hydrogen price, which is unrealistic in the short term. Alternatively, the methanol fuel could become competitive upon combining H_2 derived from fossil fuels with sustainably produced H_2 via wind-powered electrolysis.

Keywords: data envelopment analysis, chemical process targeting, sustainability, practical closest targets, process synthesis.

1. Introduction

The development of more sustainable chemical processes with good performance in the three sustainability pillars (i.e. economic, environmental and social) has recently attracted growing interest in the process systems engineering literature (Azapagic and Perdan, 2014). A wide range of methods for process design have been put forward, either based on heuristics or super-structure optimisation. These approaches often focus on optimising profit as unique criterion while disregarding other environmental and social indicators (Yuan and Eden, 2016). Furthermore, they are often based on a given chemical route and do not compare flowsheets based on alternative reaction pathways, which can be sometimes radically different. Last but not least, in the process of identifying the optimal solution to the problem, suboptimal alternatives are discarded without providing any analysis on why they underperform compared to others and on how they could be improved so as to become competitive. This piece of information, however, is highly relevant and insightful for those developing new chemical routes that are at present suboptimal but could become competitive via targeted improvements. The sustainability assessment is further complicated by the existence of multiple indicators on the basis of which the process design alternatives need to be compared against each other.

Acknowledging these gaps in the literature, this work presents a framework that combines data envelopment analysis (DEA) (Cook and Seiford, 2009) with process systems engineering tools (Grossmann and Guillén-Gosálbez, 2010), with a view to improving the sustainability of chemical processes and products, and supporting decision-makers towards more sustainable design solutions. We demonstrate the capabilities of the framework on a real case study assessing eleven transportation liquid fuels: a new methanol process obtained from CO_2 captured from power plants and H_2 from fossil fuels, and ten existing alternatives.

2. Methodology

The proposed DEA framework comprises three steps, which are detailed next.

2.1. Step 1. Simplified input-output model representation

The first step consists of gathering information from a detailed process simulation of the candidate design in order to develop a simplified input-output model representation to be used in the DEA model in Step 2. In essence, this model relates a set of elementary mass and energy flows Z_f ($f = 1 \ldots F$) to the key performance indicators (KPIs), treated either as inputs $x_{\ell,i}(Z_1, \ldots, Z_F)$ or outputs $y_{\ell,j}(Z_1, \ldots, Z_F)$ of the decision making unit (DMU). For instance, Z_f could comprise the flows of raw materials and utilities in connection to DMU inputs, or products and emissions in connection to DMU outputs. In turn, thermodynamic limits in the system can be enforced by restricting the flows, e.g. in the form of inequality constraints $g(Z_1, \ldots, Z_F) \leq 0$, and these restrictions are then reflected on the KPIs. For instance, these constraints could represent the minimum amount of raw materials and energy that the process would consume under the assumption of a 100 % yield and a full heat integration of streams to meet the minimum utility requirements dictated by a composite curve.

2.2. Step 2. Enhanced closest-target DEA model

In this step the simplified input-output model from Step 1 is combined with a closest-target DEA model. Our enhanced DEA model projects inefficient DMUs onto the efficient frontier by minimising the distance to target (according to a given metric), while accounting for the thermodynamic limits of the process so as to prevent unrealistic targets. A certificate of infeasibility for this model is an indication that the candidate design may not be projected onto the efficient frontier within the design envelope dictated by the thermodynamic limits. The model takes the form of a mixed-integer program, either linear (MILP) or nonlinear (MINLP) depending on the nature of the simplified input-output model. This step is divided into three sub-steps.

2.2.1. Step 2.1 Definition of attributes

The attributes are classically labelled as inputs or outputs according to whether they are to be maximised (DMU outputs) or minimised (DMU inputs). A tailored approach to sustainability assessment in process synthesis and design entails the selection of a single DMU output, corresponding to the functional unit in LCA; while all of the economic, environmental and social indicators are normalized in reference to the functional unit.

2.2.2. Step 2.2 Characterization of the efficient frontier

Given a set of n DMUs $k = 1 \ldots K$, each consuming m inputs $x_{k,i}$ $(i = 1 \ldots I)$ and generating n outputs $y_{k,j}$ $(j = 1 \ldots J)$, the question about whether or not a DMU ℓ is efficient can be answered via the solution of the following LP model (Galán-Martín et al. 2016):

$$\max \theta_\ell^* = \sum_{j=1}^J v_j \, y_{\ell,j}^* \tag{1}$$

$$\text{s.t. } \sum_{i=1}^I u_i \, x_{\ell,j}^* \tag{2}$$

$$\sum_{j=1}^J v_j \, y_{k,j} - \sum_{i=1}^I u_i \, x_{k,i} \leq 0 \quad k = 1 \ldots K, \ k \neq \ell \tag{3}$$

$$u_i, v_j \geq 0, \ i = 1 \ldots I, \ j = 1 \ldots J \tag{4}$$

where u_i and v_j denote the linear weights of outputs and inputs, which are treated as variables to be optimised; and the relative efficiency score θ_ℓ^* indicates whether the DMU ℓ is efficient ($\theta_\ell^* = 1$) or inefficient ($\theta_\ell^* < 1$) in comparison to the other DMUs. The best-practice or efficient frontier consists of the subset $E \subset \{1, \ldots, K\}$ of all efficient DMUs and may be used as a benchmark to define improvement targets for the inefficient units.

2.2.3. Step 2.2 Target setting with thermodynamic limits

In the second step, the simplified input-output model from Step 1 is combined with a closest-target DEA model, based on the work by Aparicio et al. (2007). Our enhanced DEA model projects inefficient DMUs onto the efficient frontier by minimising the distance to target (according to a given metric), while accounting for the thermodynamic limits of the process so as to prevent unrealistic targets. A certificate of infeasibility for this model is an indication that the candidate design may not be projected onto the efficient frontier within the design envelope dictated by the thermodynamic limits. The model takes the form of a mixed-integer program, either linear (MILP) or nonlinear (MINLP) depending on the nature of the simplified input-output model. The targets for an inefficient DMU $\ell \notin E$ are computed by solving the model represented by Eqs. (5)-(15).

$$\min \ \sum_{f=1}^F \left| \frac{Z_f - Z_f^{\text{ref}}}{Z_f^{\text{ref}}} \right| \tag{5}$$

$$\text{s.t. } \sum_{k \in E} \lambda_k x_{k,i} = x_{\ell,i}(Z_1, \ldots, Z_F), \ i = 1 \ldots I \tag{6}$$

$$\sum_{k \in E} \lambda_k y_{k,j} = y_{\ell,j}(Z_1, \ldots, Z_F), \ j = 1 \ldots J \tag{7}$$

$$g(Z_1, \ldots, Z_F) \leq 0 \tag{8}$$

$$\sum_{j=1}^J v_j y_{k,j} - \sum_{i=1}^I u_i x_{k,i} + d_k = 0, \ \forall k \in E \tag{9}$$

$$d_k \leq M(1 - b_k), \ \forall k \in E \tag{10}$$

$$0 \leq \lambda_k \leq Mb_k, \ \forall k \in E \tag{11}$$

$$b_k \in \{0,1\}, \ \forall k \in E \tag{12}$$

$$d_k \geq 0, \ \forall k \in E \tag{13}$$

$$u_i \geq 1, \ i = 1 \dots I \tag{14}$$

$$v_j \geq 1, \ j = 1 \dots J \tag{15}$$

The main degrees of freedom in this model are the modified mass and energy flows Z_f in order to make the DMU ℓ efficient. The objective function in Eq. (5) minimises relative deviations between Z_f and the original flows Z_f^{ref}. The improvement targets are enforced in Eqs. (6)-(7), where λ_k are the weights assigned to each efficient DMU (belonging to the reference set E). These targets are constrained by thermodynamic limits in the system via the generic inequality constraints in Eq. (8). The linear constraints in Eq. (9) combined with the big-M constraints in Eqs. (10) and (11) determine the peer group of the DMU ℓ. A binary variable b_k equal to 1 indicates that the DMU k belongs to the peer group, in which case $d_k = 0$ and $\sum_{j=1}^{J} v_j y_{k,j} = \sum_{i=1}^{I} u_i x_{k,i}$, and the corresponding weight λ_k can be adjusted freely (provided that the constant M is set to a large enough positive value). Otherwise, having b_k equal to 0 forces $\lambda_k = 0$ when the DMU k does not belong to the peer group of the DMU ℓ (Aparicio et al., 2007).

3. Case study in liquid fuels for transportation

We illustrate the capabilities of the enhanced DEA framework through the sustainability assessment of liquid fuels for transportation, which could be potentially employed in the automotive fleet powered by internal combustion engines. Our main objective is to assess methanol produced from H_2 derived from fossil fuels, and compare it with ten alternative transportation liquid fuels including gasoline, bio-gasoline, Fischer-Tropsch naphtha from natural gas, ethanol produced from three different sources (i.e. corn, sugarcane, switchgrass), liquid hydrogen produced from three sources (i.e. natural gas, coal, biomass), and methanol employing electrolysis powered by wind as a source of H_2. The methanol production process of interest is based on the work by Gonzalez-Garay and Guillen-Gosalbez (2018). If this process were found to be inefficient, a further objective is to quantify practical improvement targets that would make it competitive. The scope of our analysis follows a well-to-wheel (WTW) approach, which is further decomposed into well-to-pump (WTP) and pump-to-wheel (PTW) contributions (Greet, 2016). Two indicators are used to assess the performance of the liquid fuels: the total driving cost (DC) and the global warming potential (GWP) per driven mile. Both indicators are defined as inputs to be minimised, while the output is set to 1 driven-mile.

4. Results and discussion

The results in Figure 1 show that four fuels are efficient ($\theta_\ell^* = 1$), namely gasoline, EtOHsc-85, Bio-gasoline and 85-MeOH$_{\text{re}}$ and therefore, they constitute the efficient frontier which in turn may be used as a benchmark to define the improvement targets for our fuel of interest 85-MeOH$_{re}$. Gasoline shows the lowest price, but the second highest GWP, being overcome only slightly by FT-naphtha. Ethanol from sugarcane has a very similar cost to gasoline, but a lower GWP. Bio-gasoline and methanol based on H$_2$ from renewable electrolysis are the cleaner fuels, showing the lowest GWP. On the other hand, ethanol from corn or switchgrass, hydrogen-based fuels, and our fuel of interest (85-MeOH$_f$) are all deemed inefficient. The comparison confirms that liquid H$_2$ from coal, natural gas and biomass perform significantly worse than the other fuels, both in terms of DC and GWP. This is principally due to the high cost and energy consumption associated to the transport and storage stages (IEA, 2013). Observe also that our fuel 85-MeOH$_f$ shows the second highest DC, just behind methanol employing renewable electrolysis as source of H$_2$ (85-MeOH$_{re}$). For the targets definition, we consider three cases: 1) H$_2$ flow defined as variable; 2) H$_2$ cost as variable (flows defined as constant); and 3) H$_2$ produced from two different sources, namely fossil fuels and wind-powered electrolysis. Case 1 is proved to be infeasible. Therefore, our fuel 85-MeOH$_f$ cannot be projected onto the efficient frontier by modifying the sole flow of H$_2$ subject to the stoichiometric limit defined by the reaction that governs the process (Gonzalez-Garay and Guillen-Gosalbez 2018). In Case 2 (see Figure 1), it is found that 85-MeOH$_f$ could reach the target defined by its peers, 85-EtOH$_{sc}$ and Bio-gasoline, on the efficient frontier, but this would call for a 60% reduction in H$_2$ price, down to 1.17 US\$/kg. In practice however, such a large drop is unlikely given the current state-of-the-art in H$_2$ production technology (Gonzalez-Garay and Guillen-Gosalbez, 2018). In case 3, 85-MeOH$_f$ could also reach the target defined by its peers, 85-MeOH$_{re}$ and Bio-gasoline, on the efficient frontier, by allowing for a mix of H$_2$ from fossil fuels and wind-powered electrolysis. This projection increases DC by 7.9 % and reduces GWP by 9.4 % with respect to their initial values, which is enabled by: (i) the reduction of the total H$_2$ flow to the stoichiometric lower bound which represents a decrease of 14.5 % compared with the initial H$_2$; and (ii) the use of a 26-74 % mix of H$_2$ from fossil fuels and wind-powered electrolysis, respectively, which suggests that our fuel 85-MeOH$_f$ may only become competitive upon substituting a majority of the H$_2$ feedstock from fossil fuels by a more sustainable production route, despite the resulting increase in fuel price.

5. Conclusions

This paper has presented a systematic framework for improving the sustainability of chemical processes, based on the synergistic combination between DEA and process synthesis tools. Our approaches improves the capabilities of standard DEA models and process targeting methodologies by providing realistic targets for suboptimal processes. Its main advantages are four-fold: (i) Applicability in the presence of multiple sustainability KPIs; (ii) Discernment between the efficient and inefficient options among a set of candidate designs, thereby defining an efficient frontier; (iii) Identification of quantitative targets for the inefficient process, which are at a minimum distance of the best-practise frontier in terms of mass and energy flow modifications; and (iv) Definition of realistic targets that account for the thermodynamic limits of the underlying process, by embedding a (simplified) model of the sustainability KPIs in terms of the process mass and energy flows into the enhanced closest-targets DEA model.

The application of the DEA framework to the case study reveals that for the methanol fuel 85-MeOH$_f$ the current price of H$_2$ is a major impediment to its competitiveness, the sole reduction of the H$_2$ flow from fossil fuels does not allow to reach the best-practise frontier when the stoichiometric limits are taken into account. However, if flexibility is introduced in the H$_2$ source by mixing H$_2$ from fossil fuels and wind-powered electrolysis, it is found that 85-MeOH$_f$ could indeed become competitive due to a reduction in GWP despite an increase in its DC.

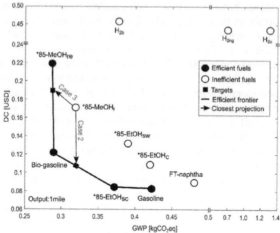

Figure 1. Results of the enhanced DEA framework applied to the transportation fuels case study (*Fuels blending 15 % of regular gasoline).

References

Aparicio, Juan, José L. Ruiz, and Inmaculada Sirvent. 2007. "Closest Targets and Minimum Distance to the Pareto-Efficient Frontier in DEA." *Journal of Productivity Analysis* 28 (3): 209–18. doi:10.1007/s11123-007-0039-5.

Azapagic, Adisa, and Slobodan Perdan. 2014. "Sustainable Chemical Engineering: Dealing with 'Wicked' Sustainability Problems." *AIChE Journal* 60 (12). Wiley Online Library: 3998–4007.

Centre for Transportation Research-Energy Systems Division. 2016. "GREET."

Cook, Wade D., and Larry M. Seiford. 2009. "Data Envelopment Analysis (DEA) - Thirty Years On." *European Journal of Operational Research* 192 (1): 1–17. doi:10.1016/j.ejor.2008.01.032.

Galán-Martín, Ángel, Gonzalo Guillén-Gosálbez, Laurence Stamford, and Adisa Azapagic. 2016. "Enhanced Data Envelopment Analysis for Sustainability Assessment: A Novel Methodology and Application to Electricity Technologies." *Computers & Chemical Engineering* 90. Elsevier Ltd: 188–200. doi:10.1016/j.compchemeng.2016.04.022.

Gonzalez-Garay, Andres, and Gonzalo Guillen-Gosalbez. 2018. "SUSCAPE: A Framework for the Optimal Design of SUStainable ChemicAl ProcEsses Incorporating Data Envelopment Analysis." *Chemical Engineering Research and Design* 137. Institution of Chemical Engineers: 246–64. doi:10.1016/j.cherd.2018.07.009.

Grossmann, Ignacio E., and Gonzalo Guillén-Gosálbez. 2010. "Scope for the Application of Mathematical Programming Techniques in the Synthesis and Planning of Sustainable Processes." *Computers and Chemical Engineering* 34 (9). Elsevier Ltd: 1365–76. doi:10.1016/j.compchemeng.2009.11.012.

International Energy Agency (IEA). 2013. "Production of Alternative Transportation Fuels: Influence of Crude Oil Price and Technology Maturity," 46.

Yuan, Zhihong, and Mario R. Eden. 2016. "Superstructure Optimization of Integrated Fast Pyrolysis-Gasification for Production of Liquid Fuels and Propylene." *AIChE Journal* 62 (9): 3155–76. doi:10.1002/aic.15337.

Anton A. Kiss, Edwin Zondervan, Richard Lakerveld, Leyla Özkan (Eds.)
Proceedings of the 29th European Symposium on Computer Aided Process Engineering
June 16th to 19th, 2019, Eindhoven, The Netherlands. © 2019 Elsevier B.V. All rights reserved.
http://dx.doi.org/10.1016/B978-0-128-18634-3.50057-6

Production scheduling of semi-continuous milk processing facility

Utkarsh Konge[a] and Sivakumar Subramanian[a,*]

[a]*TCS Research and Innovation, Tata Research Development and Design Centre, Tata Consultancy Services, Pune 411013, India*
*sivakumar.subramanian1@tcs.com

Abstract

Production scheduling of a semi-continuous multi-product plant with multiple units working in series or parallel mode is a challenging problem. Furthermore, characteristics like limited inventory and single continuous packing campaigns add to its complexity. In this work, an MILP formulation with continuous time representation is implemented to maximize the production of a milk processing facility. Unlike the batch processes where the batch sizes in the time intervals are the key variables, in the semi-continuous process considered, the time duration for which the process is active in each time interval becomes the key variable. A schedule which maximizes the production is generated for each day so that a minimum market requirement is satisfied for each product. The results obtained can further be used to find the bottlenecks and help improve the productivity of the facility.

Keywords: MILP, Scheduling, Semi-continuous Process, Dairy Plant Scheduling

1. Introduction

High competition in process industries has led manufacturers to prioritize optimization of existing production operations. This is where optimal scheduling of the facility plays an important role. Harjunkoski et al. (2014) presented the impact of optimal scheduling for various industries. The case presented in Bongers and Bakker (2008) saw a significant increase in production due to optimal scheduling. This motivated a rich set of literature showcasing scheduling optimization in food industry. Most of the production plants in food processing industry work in semi-continuous mode as the production is flexible and production equipment can be utilized more efficiently. As discussed by van Elzakker et al. (2012) characteristics like multi-stage production, limited inventory, intermediate cleaning, and single continuous packing campaigns are representative of a typical FMCG industry. These characteristics were modelled for a semi-continuous ice-cream manufacturing process. Kopanos et al. (2010) discussed the scheduling of yoghurt production in detail. In both works, the stages of pasteurization, standardization, and homogenization were considered as a single stage. The schedule for downstream stages is thrown over the wall to this stage.

Most of the milk derivatives like ice-cream, yoghurt, milk powder and so on, have pasteurized and standardized milk as a precursor. This makes it imperative to schedule the process of pasteurization and standardization of milk. Bilgen and Dogan (2015) optimized the production planning of a milk pasteurization facility which comprised of raw milk tanks, pasteurization unit, intermediate storage tanks and so on. The work presented in this paper aims at developing optimal schedule for a similar semi-continuous process with characteristics like limited intermediate storage and single continuous packing campaign. The model is expressed as an MILP formulation with continuous representation of time. A decomposition method is implemented to solve the problem in a reasonable time. Results obtained were used to find the bottlenecks of the process and improve the process further.

2. Problem Statement

Bylund (2003) discussed the pasteurization process in detail. It depicts the significance of various process components like milk silos, intermediate storage tanks, pasteurizer, standardization unit and so on. The semi continuous dairy plant, considered based on the discussion in Bylund (2003), is shown in Figure 1. This production facility converts raw milk into standardized milk, which is then converted into Stock Keeping Units (SKU). Raw milk is received in the silos at the beginning of each day. It is then processed in a pasteurization unit which operates in continuous mode. In a standardization unit, cream is separated from the raw milk in a continuous mode and collected in separate Cream Storage Tanks. The pasteurization unit and standardization unit work in continuous mode consecutively. Hence, these are considered as a single unit in the process. Apart from cream, the standardization unit produces standardized milk. This standardized milk is then stored in the intermediate storage tanks which is then converted into SKUs by the packaging lines. Changing the operation from one fat content to other on the pasteurizer stage can be done without any additional setup time or intermediate cleaning. As there are various types of intermediate products based on the fat content, multiple storage tanks are required to avoid mixing. The packaging lines operate in continuous mode with feed from the intermediate tanks. Typically, packaging lines can process multiple types of SKUs with different rates. Additional setup time or intermediate cleaning may be required while changing the mode from one SKU to other on the packaging lines. In Kopanos et al. (2010), typical daily production line shutdowns are modelled due to hygienic requirements. Similar shutdowns are modelled in the presented facility where the packaging lines are allowed to run only for 18 hours a day. At the end of the scheduling horizon (week) the levels of all the intermediate products are constrained to be zero. The objective of the scheduling problem is to maximize the total production subject to continuous single product packing campaign, limited intermediate storage and some minimum production of each SKU.

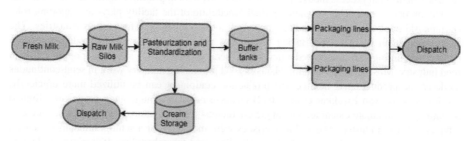

Figure 1: Schematic overview of a milk processing plant

3. Formulation

The key decision variables in this optimization problem are: (i) the start time of each stage in the production line, (ii) the amount of each SKU to be produced on each day of the week and on each packaging line, (iii) the order in which the SKUs and the intermediate products are processed. To keep track of the levels of intermediate products, a continuous time formulation is implemented. The start and completion times of products on the pasteurization stage and the packaging lines are considered as events for the formulation. A slot is created between two events and since the processes are continuous, the time for which each stage is active in a slot is a key variable too. The binary variables denoting the start and end of a particular process for a specific product in the given slot are used to find the slots in which the process is active. The time of processing in each slot can be equated to this slot length. Let $\Delta t_{i,l,p,k}$ denote the time for which a process line p was active processing product i in slot l on day k. Let $s_{i,l,p,k}$ and $f_{i,l,p,k}$ be the binary variables denoting the start and end of this process in slot l respectively. The relation between these variables are captured in constraints (1)-(3). The variable $S_{l,k}$ denotes the starting time of slot l on day k. M is large value compared to $\Delta t_{i,l,p,k}$. *nslots* is the total number of slots given.

$$\Delta t_{i,l,p,k} \geq S_{l+1,k} - S_{l,k} - M \times \left(1 - \sum_{lm \in \{1,2,3,...,l\}} (s_{j,lm,p,k} - f_{j,lm,p,k})\right) \tag{1}$$

$$\Delta t_{i,l,p,k} \leq S_{l+1,k} - S_{l,k} + M \times \left(1 - \sum_{lm \in \{1,2,3,...,l\}} (s_{j,lm,p,k} - f_{j,lm,p,k})\right) \tag{2}$$

$$\Delta t_{i,l,p,k} \leq M \times \left(\sum_{lm \in \{1,2,3,...,l\}} (s_{j,lm,p,k} - f_{j,lm,p,k})\right) \tag{3}$$

$$\forall i \in Products, p \in ProcessLines, l \in slots \setminus \{nslots\}, k \in Days$$

The levels of each intermediate product is updated at each event so that the input from the pasteurization stage adds to the level at previous event and the output to the packaging lines reduces it. The total capacity of intermediate storage is limited. To model this, the storage amount is divided into various bins. The parameters U_{cap}^r and L_{cap}^r are the upper and lower bounds of the bins respectively. Computation of these bounds is explained with an example here. Consider three tanks each with capacity of 1000 kg. The index r will run from 1 to 3 (total number of tanks). The set of parameters is as shown in constraints (4).

$$\{(L_{cap}^1, U_{cap}^1), (L_{cap}^2, U_{cap}^2), (L_{cap}^3, U_{cap}^3)\} = \{(0, 1000), (1000 + \varepsilon, 2000), (2000 + \varepsilon, 3000)\} \tag{4}$$

Here ε is a small value compared to tank capacity. A binary variable keeps track of the bin in which the level of each intermediate product lie in each slot on each day. Now, to implement the maximum capacity constraint, the sum of U_{cap}^r for the bins in which the levels lie, is constrained to be less than or equal to the maximum capacity. Let the binary variable denoting whether the level of intermediate product j is in bin r in slot l for day k be $z_{j,r,l,k}$. The constraints capturing the relations are equations (5) and (6). The constraints (7) ensure that the levels are in exactly one bin for a given intermediate product, slot and day. The variable $R_{j,l,k}$ represents the amount of intermediate product j at the start of slot l on day k. *MPast* is a large value as compared to $R_{j,l,k}$. I is the set of intermediate products.

$$R_{j,l,k} \geq L_{cap}^r - MPast \times (1 - z_{j,r,l,k}) \qquad \forall j \in I, r \in bins, l \in slots, k \in Days \tag{5}$$

$$R_{j,l,k} \leq U_{cap}^r + MPast \times (1 - z_{j,r,l,k}) \qquad \forall j \in I, r \in bins, l \in slots, k \in Days \tag{6}$$

$$\sum_{r \in bins} z_{j,r,l,k} = 1 \qquad \forall j \in I, l \in slots, k \in Days \tag{7}$$

Since raw milk has a very short shelf-life, all the milk procured on a particular day must be pasteurised and stored in the intermediate storage. The input stream of the pasteurizer, which is converted into intermediate products with different fat content, has a constant flowrate. But the output flowrate depends on the type of intermediate product being produced. Cream is produced as a side product and stored in storage tanks of limited capacity. The pasteurized milk can be kept overnight in the tanks and used for production on the following day. For the first day of the

Intermediate Product	Output flowrate (kg/h)
Z1 (Low fat)	2199.5
Z2 (Medium fat)	2256.6
Z3 (High Fat)	2348.1

Table 1: Pasteurizer output flowrates of intermediate products

week, it is assumed that the tanks are empty at the beginning of the day. Packaging lines can start packing the products only when some buffer time has elapsed after the start of pasteurization of the corresponding intermediate product. Sequence dependent changeover is implemented on the packaging lines. When a product is assigned to a particular packaging line, some minimum amount of it has to be processed on the line. To maintain the hygiene of the plant, the fillers or the packaging lines are allowed to run only for 18 hours a day. Finally, the constraints ensuring meeting of the market demand and the mass balance between the intermediate products and the SKUs are enforced. Apart from these constraints, the regular scheduling constraints like non-preemptive assignment of units and sequencing of the products are enforced.

3.1. Decomposition

For the given case, the scheduling for the whole week turned out to be a difficult problem to solve due to the size of the problem. Hence, the problem was divided into smaller problems by decomposing the temporal dimension. In each of the smaller sub-problem, scheduling optimization was carried out for just one day with the objective of maximizing the production. Through the constraints of the model, it was ensured that the daily production of each product was more than the daily average requirement to satisfy the weekly target. The level of each intermediate product at the end of the day was recorded and was used to initialize the level of each intermediate product at the start of the following day. The sub-problems are solved for all the seven days of the week. A schematic of the decomposition method is given in Figure 2. The advantage of such a decomposition is that if in the optimal schedule for a day, the initial levels of the intermediate product are equal to the levels at the end of the day, then the problem need not be solved for the next day as it would have the same optimal schedule.

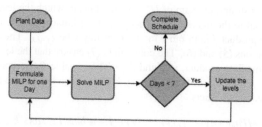

Figure 2: Decomposition strategy

4. Results and Discussion

The problem was formulated in Pyomo 5.5.1(Hart et al. (2017), Hart et al. (2011)) and solved using COIN-OR Cbc (Forrest et al. (2018)). For one day of scheduling, the MILP formulation consisted of 1281 variables and 2726 constraints and was solved within 120 seconds on a system with i5-2400 (3.10 GHz) processor and 10 GB RAM. The continuous time representation consisted of 20

SKU	Rates (kg/h)		Intermediate Product	Min Req.(kg)	Optimal production (kg)
	S1	S2			
A	600	540	Z3	30000	32899
B	900	600	Z2	20000	20000
C	-	600	Z1	15000	15000
D	540	540	Z1	7500	7500
E	720	780	Z3	15000	22399
F	600	-	Z2	2500	2500

Table 2: Packaging Rates, Minimum and Optimal production

events. The input flow rate of the pasteurization stage is 2400 kg/h. The output flow rates of various intermediate products are given in Table 1. The maximum capacity of the Raw Milk silos is 15000 kg. There are four intermediate storage tanks each with capacity of 5000 kg. The facility has two packaging lines namely S1 and S2. The packaging rates for the SKUs on each line are given in Table 2 along with the corresponding intermediate product. The sequence dependent changeover for the packaging lines ranges from 0.25 to 0.5 h. The minimum required quantity and the optimal production of the products are given in in the last column of Table 2. The products A and E are produced more than the minimum required value (9 % and 49 % more, respectively). Rest of the products met their demands exactly. The excess production of A and E can be explained by the fact that both A and E are produced with the intermediate product with the highest flow rate (Z3). This ensures high availability of intermediate product required for the production. The packaging rate of product E is high on both the packaging lines. Thus, more of this product can be processed in less time. Figure 3 depicts the optimal schedule for one day. Figure 4 depicts the time profile of quantities of intermediate products stored in the intermediate tanks. As the initial and final levels of all the intermediate products is same, the same schedule is optimal for all the days.

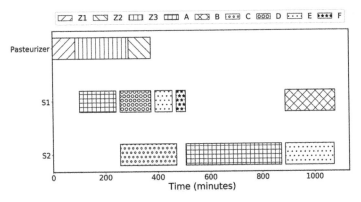

Figure 3: Gantt Chart of the schedule

As evident from the Figure 3, the packaging lines S1 and S2 are not being used to the fullest as there is some idle time apart from the sequence dependent changeover. This can be attributed to low capacity of the raw milk silos. This is explained even by Figure 4 in which the levels of all the intermediate products drop to zero at the end of the day. To improve the utilization of S1 and S2, the capacity of raw milk silo, in other words, the procurement of raw milk, should be increased. Additional optimization simulations can be performed to find the capacity of silos which enable

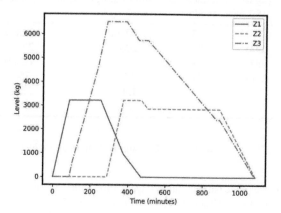

Figure 4: Levels of intermediate products

the packaging lines to be utilized to the fullest.

5. Conclusion

An MILP model was formulated for a semi-continuous milk processing facility. The process characteristics typical of an FMCG industry were successfully modelled. A decomposition algorithm was developed, implemented, and successfully tested. An optimal schedule was obtained using an open source solver. The results obtained were used to draw insights to further improve the performance of the plant. The framework developed here provides a good foundation to simulate additional scenarios and to further increase the throughput of the plant by varying the silo capacity. This naturally transitions into simultaneous synthesis and scheduling optimization problem.

References

B. Bilgen, K. Dogan, 2015. Multistage Production Planning in the Dairy Industry: A Mixed-Integer Programming Approach. Industrial & Engineering Chemistry Research 54 (46), 11709–11719.

P. M. Bongers, B. H. Bakker, 2008. Validation of an Ice cream factory operations model. In: ESCAPE 18 proceedings.

G. Bylund, 2003. Dairy processing handbook. Tetra Pak Processing Systems AB.

J. Forrest, T. Ralphs, S. Vigerske, LouHafer, B. Kristjansson, jpfasano, EdwinStraver, M. Lubin, H. G. Santos, rlougee, M. Saltzman, Jul. 2018. coin-or/Cbc: Version 2.9.9.

I. Harjunkoski, C. T. Maravelias, P. Bongers, P. M. Castro, S. Engell, I. E. Grossmann, J. Hooker, C. Méndez, G. Sand, J. Wassick, 2014. Scope for industrial applications of production scheduling models and solution methods. Computers & Chemical Engineering 62, 161 – 193.

W. E. Hart, C. D. Laird, J.-P. Watson, D. L. Woodruff, G. A. Hackebeil, B. L. Nicholson, J. D. Siirola, 2017. Pyomo–optimization modeling in python, 2nd Edition. Vol. 67. Springer Science & Business Media.

W. E. Hart, J.-P. Watson, D. L. Woodruff, 2011. Pyomo: modeling and solving mathematical programs in Python. Mathematical Programming Computation 3 (3), 219–260.

G. M. Kopanos, L. Puigjaner, M. C. Georgiadis, 2010. Optimal Production Scheduling and Lot-Sizing in Dairy Plants: The Yogurt Production Line. Industrial & Engineering Chemistry Research 49 (2), 701–718.

M. A. H. van Elzakker, E. Zondervan, N. B. Raikar, I. E. Grossmann, P. M. M. Bongers, 2012. Scheduling in the FMCG industry: An Industrial Case Study. Industrial & Engineering Chemistry Research 51 (22), 7800–7815.

A. S. Wallerand, R. Voillat, F. Maréchal, 2016. Towards optimal design of solar assisted industrial processes: Case study of a dairy. Tech. rep., University of Ljubljana.

Anton A. Kiss, Edwin Zondervan, Richard Lakerveld, Leyla Özkan (Eds.)
Proceedings of the 29th European Symposium on Computer Aided Process Engineering
June 16th to 19th, 2019, Eindhoven, The Netherlands. © 2019 Elsevier B.V. All rights reserved.
http://dx.doi.org/10.1016/B978-0-128-18634-3.50058-8

Fast Bypass Selection Method during the Heat Exchanger Network Synthesis

Rupu YANG,[a*] Cong Toan Tran,[a] Assaad Zoughaib[a]

[a]CES-MINES ParisTech, PSL Research University, CES (Center for Energy efficiency of Systems), 5, rue Léon Blum, 91120 Palaiseau, France

rupu.yang@mines-paristech.fr

Abstract

This paper provides a new and fast method to select bypass during the heat exchanger network (HEN) synthesis stage. An indicator, namely disturbance over utility (DoU), was introduced to measure the maximum simultaneous disturbance rejection ability over the utility consumption. Together with a physical distance study, they can select the bypass placement fast and efficiently. DoU can select preferable heat exchangers to place bypass, and compare different HENs. For a given HEN with specified bypass strategies, the higher the DoU is, the larger the disturbance rejection ability per unit utility consumption, which was solved by a non linear programming (NLP) model. The physical distance study utilizes the structural information to discard potential inverse response and compare response time of different bypasses. The method has been applied into two alternative HENs, illustrating the process to select better HEN and find preferable bypass placement strategies. The main goal of this work is to contribute to HENs synthesis, by proposing a fast and efficient bypass selection method to decide the control structure.

Keywords: heat exchanger network synthesis, bypass selection, simultaneous disturbance, inverse response, time response

1. Introduction

The operational performance of HEN is largely dependent on the control structure, which deserves to be set up at design stage (Escobar et al., 2013). The manipulation of HEN is usually achieved through the operation of bypass and utility when the system is facing disturbance. While the number of utility is often not adequate to meet the HEN control requirement, thus bypasses are required in the HEN, and they usually denoted as manipulated variables (MVs). A challenging work is how to find optimal bypass placement strategy considering the simultaneous disturbance rejection, utility consumption and dynamic performance fast and efficiently.

During the past decades, many approaches were put forward to select the bypass for HENs by studying the trade-off between disturbance rejection ability, investment cost and dynamic performance. For explicit disturbance, flexibility index is widely accepted as the criteria to iterate the synthesis stage, along with checking the disturbance range individually (Yan et al., 2001)(Escobar et al., 2013). Chen and Hung (2004) agreed that the individual disturbance cannot guarantee the feasibility of the network when simultaneous disturbance occurs. The simultaneous disturbance analysis is especially important when disturbances are not explicit, for example, the HEN integrated with renewable energy systems. For a given HEN, the disturbance rejection is actually the heat load redistribution process limited by the constraints in MVs and the utility cost.

The disturbance rejection ability is a static problem, while the dynamic part is mainly about the control problems and time response, and it largely depends on the control strategy and specific controller. The following discussion is based on decentralized control scenario with PID as controller, which is the most commonly selection for HENs. Escobar et al. (2013) applied PID controller in MATLAB to study the dynamic performance of different bypass selections without consideration of the potential inverse response. In decentralized control scenario, the presence of right half plane (RHP) zeros might evoke the inverse response, and lead to control difficulty which ought to be avoided(Skogestad and Postlethwaite, 2005). The presence of inverse response in HENs comes from different downstream pathways with contrary effect on the same controlled variable (CV). The time response is the time delay between two stable conditions when MV functions, and the faster the better. Lersbamrungsuk and Srinophakun(2009) introduced the structural time delay (physical distance from MV to CV) to represent time response. We employ the same idea to compare different bypass placement strategies.

In this context, we aim to propose a fast and efficient method to select control structure during the HEN design. The method employs disturbance-over-utility (DoU), coupling with RGA-number, inverse response and physical distance to find a preferable bypass selection. The calculation of DoU involves optimization, while the whole method is trying to locate a good result by integrating static and dynamic criteria.

2. Bypass selection process

Figure 1 presents the integration of bypass selection in HEN sequential design process. In this paper we focus only on the control structure selection step. To reach the preferable bypass placement strategies, RGA-number and DoU will help to select preferable heat exchangers to place bypass, then potential inverse response and physical closeness will be employed to evacuate the most appealing bypass. RGA-number has been widely accepted as an efficient tool to quantify the interaction between different control loops and here it is also calculated with the same method as (Chen and Hung, 2004) (Escobar et al., 2013).

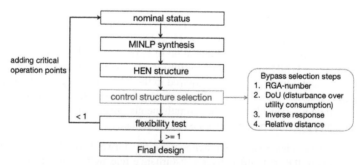

Figure 1: Bypass selection during the HEN synthesis

2.1 NLP model to calculate DoU

The HEN model regards the heat exchanger (HX) as the knot throughout each process stream, and for each stream there are '2*number of knots + 1' stages of temperature by assuming that bypass is on every side of all HXs. The simplified thermal effectiveness method (Knut W. Mathisen, 1994) was selected to describe the energy balance of HX. The method is based on the simple relationship between the thermal effectiveness of the cold and the hot side (P^c and P^h) as in equation (4). With the constraint that P^c and P^h are within 0 and 1. For each heat transfer process, the heat transfer between two streams can be described as following:

$$P^h[i,j,k,l] = \frac{1 - \exp(-N_{tu}^h[i,j,k,l](1 - R^h[i,j,k,l]))}{1 - R^h[i,j,k,l]\exp(-N_{tu}^h[i,j,k,l](1 - R^h[i,j,k,l]))} \qquad (1)$$

$$R^h[i,j,k,l] = CP_h[i,j,k,l]/CP_c[i,j,k,l] \qquad (2)$$

$$N_{tu}^h[i,j,k,l] = UA[i,j,k,l]/CP_h[i,j,k,l] \qquad (3)$$

$$P^c[i,j,k,l] = R^h[i,j,k,l]P^h[i,j,k,l] \qquad (4)$$

$$P^h[i,j,k,l] = (T[i,2k-1] - T[i,2k])/(T[i,2k-1] - T[j,2l-1]) \qquad (5)$$

$$P^c[i,j,k,l] = (T[j,2l] - T[j,2l-1])/(T[i,2k-1] - T[j,2l-1]) \qquad (6)$$

Where i, j stand for the hot and cold stream of a HX; k, l stand for the order of knot that the HX lies in each stream; CP_h, CP_c are the heat capacity flow of hot and cold streams separately, U is the heat transfer coefficient, A is the transfer area; and T is the temperature. DoU is depicted as equation (7), d_i is the disturbance item, $d_{i,o}$ is the nominal value of that disturbance, and $W_{utility}$ is the utility consumption. The product can be interpreted as the volume by which the system can operate normally, the larger the DoU the better the disturbance rejection ability of HEN and utility consumption. It helps to select preferable HXs to place bypass and can also act as controllability indicator of HEN.

$$DoU = Max(\prod \left| \frac{d_i}{d_{i,o}} - 1 \right| / W_{utility}) \qquad (7)$$

The constraint information to reach DoU is as following:

$$MV_y \in (0,1) \qquad (8)$$

$$CV_x \in (CV_{x,o} - \alpha, CV_{x,o} + \alpha) \qquad (9)$$

$$W_{utility} \le load_{i,max} \qquad (10)$$

$CV_{x,o}$ is the nominal value of CV_x, α represents the allowable range of CV.

2.2 Potential inverse response

Inverse response is a typical obstacle to achieve preferable control performance (Skogestad and Postlethwaite, 2005). It possibly occurs when there are different downstream pathways from a MV to a CV, and especially when those effects arrive at different velocity with contrary trend. Firstly, an algorithm will find the possible downstream pathway for a MV-CV pairing and the relationship between them. Then if the longest pathway dominates the integral effect and is contrary to the effect of other pathways, the inverse response will highly come out. By definition, the pathway length is the number of physical steps required from MV to CV. Refer to Figure 2 as example, when bypass at hot side of HX3 is changed, there are two downstream paths to affect y1 dotted curves illustrating.

Path 1: 3H->4H->4C->2C->y1, (4), +
Path 2: 3H->3C->1C->1H->2H->2C->y1, (6), -

where H and C stand for hot and cold side of HX; the number in the bracket stands for the pathway length. When the bypass increases, positive effect "+" means that the corresponding path will increase y1 while negative effect "-" means that it will decrease y1. In this example, path 1 is shorter physically, and if the effect of path 2 dominates the final variance of y1, the inverse response is expected to present. The integral effect can be read from bypass gain matrix directly.

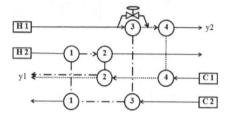

Figure 2: Example of two downstream paths with opposite effect

2.3 Physical distance

The physical distance of certain control pairings can be represented by the longest downstream path among the selections. Taking Figure 2 as example again, compare two pairings P1 and P2 as shown in Table 1. For P1, path 2 is the longest one that requires 6 steps, which dominates the time response and requires 6 steps. For P2, path 2 dominates the time response and only requires 4 steps. Thus P2 is preferable in term of time response aspect. The above inverse response detection and physical distance study is carried out with a program in Python automatically.

Table 1: Result of physical distance of two pairings

P1, 3H-y1/4H-y2	P2, 2H-y1/4H-y2
Path 1: 3H->4H->4C->2C->y1, (4), +	Path 1: 2H->2C->y1, (2), -
Path 2: 3H->3C->1C->1H->2H->2C->y1,(6), -	Path 2: 4H->4C->2C->y1, (4), -
Path 4: 4H->4C->2C->y1, (3), -	Path 3: 4H->y2, (1), +
Path 3: 3H->4H->y2, (2), +	
Path 5: 4H->y2, (1), +	

3. Case study

The case study that involves two hot streams and two cold streams is a classical case discussed in many studies (Yan et al., 2001)(Escobar et al., 2013) (Masoud et al., 2016). The two alternative designs consist of three HXs and two coolers, as shown in Figure 3. The pinch method aims to reach the maximum energy recovery and leads to HEN1, while the superstructure approach aims to find the minimum total annualized cost leads to HEN2. The heat capacity flow of each stream is 10, 15, 20, 30 (kW/K) separately, heat transfer coefficient is 0.16 (kW/(m^2·K)) and their supply and target temperatures are also listed in the Figure 3. The four stream outlet temperatures are CVs with ± 1K allowable operational range. In addition to two utilities acting as MVs, two bypasses are required to help the system to reject disturbance, and inlet temperature variation of C1 and C2 are expected disturbance with unknown range.

RGA-number in Table 2 was calculated from the gain matrix result in Table 1. Pairings E1E3 and E2E3 are both perfect pairings in two structures according to the interpretation of RGA-number. The DoU results are presented in Table 3, the pairing

E1E3 in both structures get the largest DoU value which represents structure's maximum disturbance rejection region under the same utility cost. It can also be concluded that HEN1 is better than HEN2. Then physical distance result can help to select desirable bypass shown in Table 4 (pairing 1H3H means bypass at hot side of exchanger 1 and 3 will control y1and y2 separately). For all the pairings there exist three paths from MV to CV, while they all present the same change direction as bypass fluctuate, regardless of inverse response. Pairings 1C3H and 1C3C share the same longest path which is smaller than other choices, and 1C3C present smaller integral distance than 1C3H. Therefore, 1C3C in HEN1 is the best bypass selection both in static and dynamic aspects.

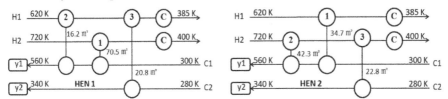

Figure 3: HENs in case study

Table 2: Gain matrix of HEN

	HEN1			HEN2		
	E1	E2	E3	E1	E2	E3
C1	-0.0376	-0.0511	0	-0.0259	-0.0501	0
C2	-0.0051	0.0195	-0.0331	-0.0081	0.0167	-0.0333

Table 3: RGA result

HEN1, pairings	RGA-number	HEN2, pairings	RGA-number
E1E2	1.0488	E1E2	1.9362
E1E3	0	E1E3	0
E2E3	0	E2E3	0

Table 4: DoU result

HEN1, pairings	DoU*1,000	HEN2, pairings	DoU*1,000
E1E3	63.3	E1E3	62.6
E2E3	62.6	E2E3	62.3

Table 5: Physical distance analysis

Pairings	Pathway	Longest path	Integral distance
1H3H (1H-y1,3H-y2)	P1: 1H->1C->2C->y1, - P2: 3H->3C->y2, - P3: 1H->1C->2C->2H->3H->3C->y2,-	P3 (6)	11
1H3C	P1: 1H->1C->2C->y1, - P2: 3C->y2, - P3: 1H->1C->2C->2H->3H->3C->y2, -	P3 (6)	10
1C3H	P1: 1C->2C->y1, - P2: 3H->3C->y2, - P3: 1C->2C->2H->3H->3C->y2, -	P3(5)	9
1C3C	P1: 1C->2C->y1, - P2: 3C->y2, - P3: 1C->2C->2H->3H->3C->y2, -	P3(5)	8

4. Conclusion

The work provides a new method to select bypass during HENs synthesis, considering the simultaneous disturbance analysis and prediction of dynamic performance with pure static calculation. The method proposed an indicator DoU to represent the maximum disturbance rejection region over utility consumption, it can be used to compare the operability of different HENs, and select preferable exchangers to control HEN. A physical distance method is used to reject the potential inverse response and compare the response time of various bypass selections. The case study had shown the applicability of the method, they can reach optimal result quickly and efficient since only in static calculation is required. It deserves to be mentioned that the static result cannot guarantee the desirable dynamic performance, and a dynamic study is required to confirm the solution found by the method. Finally, it can be seen that implementing the method directly in the synthesis step is possible, and that allows designing HEN by considering simultaneously a main objective (energy consumption or cost) and disturbance rejection ability.

5. Acknowledgments

The authors are very grateful for the grants from China Scholarship Council (CSC).

References

Chen, C., Hung, P., 2004. Simultaneous Synthesis of flexible heat-exchange networks with uncertain source-stream temperatures and flow rates. Industrial & Engineering Chemistry Research 43(18), 5916–5928.

Escobar, M., O.Treirweiler, J., E.Grossmann, I., 2013. Simultaneous Synthesis of Heat Exchanger Networks with Operability Considerations: Flexibility and Controllability. Computers & Chemical Engineering 55, 158–180.

Knut W. Mathisen, 1994. Integrated design and control of heat exchanger networks. Ph.D. Thesis. University of Trondheim - NTH, Norway.

Lersbamrungsuk, V., Srinophakun, T., 2009. Structural Controllability Evaluation for Heat Exchanger Networks, in: Proceedings of the 7th Asian Control Conference. 835–840.

Masoud, I.T., Abdel-Jabbar, N., Qasim, M., Chebbi, R., 2016. Methodological framework for economical and controllable design of heat exchanger networks: Steady-state analysis, dynamic simulation, and optimization. Applied Thermal Engineering. 104, 439–449.

Skogestad, S., Postlethwaite, I., 2005. Multivariable feedback control: analysis and design, chapter 5, Chichester, New York, Brisbane, Toronto, Singapore, John Wiley & Sons.

Yan, Q.Z., Yang, Y.H., Huang, Y.L., 2001. Cost-effective bypass design of highly controllable heat-exchanger networks. AIChE Journal. 47(10), 2253–2276.

Anton A. Kiss, Edwin Zondervan, Richard Lakerveld, Leyla Özkan (Eds.)
Proceedings of the 29th European Symposium on Computer Aided Process Engineering
June 16th to 19th, 2019, Eindhoven, The Netherlands. © 2019 Elsevier B.V. All rights reserved.
http://dx.doi.org/10.1016/B978-0-128-18634-3.50059-X

Integrating Oil Refineries and Bio-refineries: Upgrading Acetone, Butanol and Ethanol to High-Value Products

Elham Ketabchi, Laura Pastor-Perez, Tomas Ramirez Reina, Harvey Arellano-Garcia*

Department of Chemical and Process Engineering, University of Surrey, Guildford, GU27XH, United Kingdom

*h.arellano-garcia@surrey.ac.uk

Abstract

In this work, an integration systems approach connecting an oil refinery and a bio-refinery is proposed. These plants can be connected through various pathways such as on-site power generation, utility systems and syngas production with the feed of refinery residue, bio-oil and other streams. One important pathway that is the focus in this work represents the production of chemicals produced via biomass sources into the petrochemical and transportation industry as valuable products. Focusing on the latter route of integration, the upgrading of Acetone, Butanol and Ethanol produced by sugar fermentation via bacterial species, has been chosen as a pathway to produce valuable products that could be utilised in both the chemical sector and the transportation industry. There is little current literature regarding this upgrading process, making it a relatively novel option of producing valuable products.

The reaction systems studied consist of the self-condensation of the alcohols and cross condensation of alcohols and acetone using active metals supported on basic supports as catalysts at high temperatures and pressure in a batch reactor. Moreover, catalysts syntheses were conducted successfully to verify the proposed integration approach. The results have shown an outstanding performance for the catalysts in terms of conversion and selectivity, having conversions as high as 90%. The catalysts have also proven to yield valuable products with broad market options in the chemical Industry. In conclusion, this route has shown promising results in terms of providing valuable C_2-C_{15} products, useful for both the petrochemical industry and the transportation sector while using economically favourable catalysts in comparison with previous studies.

Keywords: Integration, oil refinery, bio-refinery, ABE, long-chain hydrocarbons.

1. Introduction

One of the main issues that many manufacturing sectors such as oil refineries are facing is that they are not performing as efficient as the past due to various factors. These factors could be environmental, economic, etc. A main factor that should be considered for oil refineries is their dependency on crude oil, the main feedstock of the process. Following this, the price fluctuation in crude oil has a direct impact on this industry. The price increase will force a rise in the search for fossil fuel substitutes from renewable and sustainable sources becoming a driving factor towards cheaper feedstocks, such as biomass. Another major factor impacting the oil refinery that should be taken into account represents the strict environmental regulations that have raised the cost of producing clean fuels (Fahim, M. F., Alsahhaf, T. A., & Elkilan, 2010)(Leffler, 2008). As global energy consumption increases, as does the production of greenhouse gases like CO_2. The latter increase has caused the scientific community to look towards the "green" production of fuels and chemicals that were once dependant entirely on fossil fuels. The depletion of fossil fuels has also prompted interest in the production of fuels and chemicals that are compatible with petroleum liquids such as biomass-based products. Similar processes and approach to the refining industry that could be combined with the existing refining processes can be seen in bio-refineries. Using non-fossil fuel-based feedstocks, the bio-refinery produces low-value fuels and high-value materials and chemicals. Biomass conversion such as the production of ethanol and butanol through ABE (Acetone, Butanol and Ethanol) fermentation (Gupta and Demirbas, 2010) in which sugar is fermented using the bacteria genus Clostridium (Qureshi *et al.*, 2010)(Qureshi and Ejezi, 2008), is a well-recognized drop-in fuel option. Following upgrading and conversion, the products from the ABE mixture are compatible with fuel or chemicals, making the process an attractive option for the transportation and chemicals industry.

The focus of this work is to produce chemicals through the upgrading of ABE and to incorporate it in the proposed integration system aiming to decrease both dependency on fossil fuel and reduce greenhouse gas emissions. This process has been carried out previously in literature but with strong emphasis on the utilisation of noble metal-based catalysts. Amongst the noble metals, Pd has been proven to work better when compared to other noble metals such as Pt, Rh, Ru and Ir (Goulas *et al.*, 2017). Although they have performed efficiently towards converting ABE to valuable products, the economic aspect of these catalysts should also be considered as the process of ABE production is an expensive process in itself (Bîldea *et al.*, 2016). Therefore, one of the main aims of this work is to be able to achieve valuable products whilst using economically viable catalysts based on transition metals.

2. Methodology

The integration system proposed, presented in Figure 1, depicts various routes to connect the oil refinery with bio-refining processes. These connections are through utility

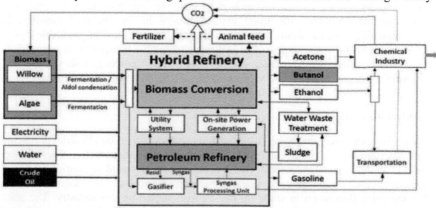

Figure 1. Schematic of proposed integration routes between an oil refinery and bio-based processes.

systems, on-site power generation, production of ABE through biomass fermentation and further upgrading to chemicals and many more. Focusing on the latter route, the fermentation of sugar in this case, produces a mixture of acetone, butanol and ethanol. These products can either be transformed into pyrolysis oil through the pyrolysis unit or used to produce bio-fuels via self-condensation of the alcohols and cross condensation of the alcohols with acetone, known as upgrading, that can also blend with the gasoline produced from the oil refinery. This will form part of the whole picture that is provided through experimental work which can be directly applied to the integration system.

This process as can be seen in Figure 1 starts from using sugar as an input to the ABE fermentation unit while bacterial species such as Clostridium acetobutylicum ferment sugar producing the ABE mixture. This is then combined with extractive fermentation using a water-immiscible solvent of glyceryl tributate. Following this, a series of distillations occur separating the extractant phase from the ABE mixture (Sreekumar *et al.*, 2015). The ABE mixture obtained will then go through an upgrading process leading to the production of longer chained hydrocarbons.

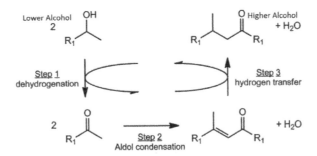

Figure 2. Guerbet reaction pathway adapted from (Shimura *et al.*, 2013)

The upgrading reactions have been carried out in the laboratory using the mixture of reactants with the same molar ratio of 3:6:1 acetone:butanol:ethanol, as representative composition obtained from the sugar fermentation reactor. The reaction was then carried out in a pressure vessel at high temperature and pressures using an activated transition metal on basic support with the condition of purging air trapped in the reactor with N_2 to ensure an oxygen-free atmosphere. This upgrading reaction requires active catalysts which have been synthesised using the wet impregnation method that have also been proven successful through various characterisation methods such as XRD, BET, TPR, TGA, Raman, etc. The reaction route, also known as the Guerbet reaction, forms branched or unbranched products which is demonstrated in Figure 2. This reaction typically consists of three steps being the dehydrogenation of a primary alcohol, then a base catalysed aldol coupling reaction followed by the hydrogenation of an α,β -unsaturated aldehyde (Chakraborty *et al.*, 2015). Most industrial Guerbet reactions have been carried out over homogenous catalysts, usually corrosive bases using a soluble metal complex producing Guerbet alcohols. Throughout the process water is produced that must be removed by the addition of a desiccant such as CaO (Patel *et al.*, 2015). However, due to the disadvantages of these catalysts, mainly being their corrosive nature, hetergenous catalysts have been chosen in this reaction using a basic support and transition metal active phases.

Following the reaction, the products were analysed using a GC-MS for quantification and identification purposes. Using the results obtained from this, the conversion and selectivity were calculated using the following equations:

$$ABE \; Conversion \; (\%) = \frac{n_{Initial \; ABE} - n_{Unreacted \; ABE}}{n_{Initial \; ABE}} \times 100 \tag{1}$$

$$Selectivity \; (\%) = \frac{n_{Initial \; ABE}}{n_{Initial \; ABE} - n_{Unreacted \; ABE}} \times 100 \tag{2}$$

Where n is the number of total moles of reactants or product.

3. Results and Discussions

The catalysts have demonstrated exceptional results in terms of conversion and selectivity rates both having values up to 90%. They have also been successfully synthesised proven by the characterisation methods which due to space limitations are not presented in this paper. The BET analysis has shown the mesoporosity of the samples while also depicting the textural properties of the catalysts. The XRD has also clearly shown the presence of the metals and the support giving information about the crystal structure of the powder samples. The Raman spectroscopy carried out also proved the presence of the elements in each catalyst while providing information about the bonding structure of the sample. Due to the nature of the upgrade, which includes hydrogen transferring, the redox properties of the catalysts must be a relevant factor therefore TPR was carried out.

TGA conducted has demonstrated the weight loss and/gain occurring while heating the sample. This also demonstrates carbon loss associated with organic compounds attached to the samples after reaction which is a good indication that the reaction has proceeded successfully.

In terms of the products obtained, a range of hydrocarbons from C_2-C_{15} was identified using the GC-MS. The quantification of the products was carried out by establishing GC response factors of the main products identified, by the injection of samples with known concentrations prepared using standards. Following this, the conversion and selectivity was then calculated using Equations 1 and 2 which can be seen in table 1 and Figure 4.

Table 1. Selectivity of products in the range of C_2-C_{15} with the corresponding catalysts

Catalyst	Selectivity (%)	
	C_2-C_7	C_8-C_{15}
Active catalyst 1	60	5
Active catalyst 2	90	4
Active catalyst 3	43	14

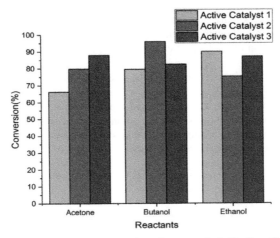

Figure 3. Demonstrating conversion of reactants individually with the
corresponding catalyst

As demonstrated in Figure 3, all the catalysts are active in this upgrading reaction displaying very high conversion levels. As demonstrated in this figure, catalyst 1 is more selective towards ethanol conversion while catalyst 2 converts more butanol in comparison with the rest. This could be due to the fact that the catalysts are favorable towards the cross condensation of alcohols and acetone i.e. catalyst 1 is promoting the reaction between ethanol and acetone as well as ethanol dimerization (Zhu *et al.*, 2017) while the second catalyst is more favorable towards the reaction between butanol and acetone.

Using the data obtained and Equation 2, the selectivity was calculated considering all products in all concentrations presented in Table1. Catalyst 2 shows outstanding selectivity towards hydrocarbons in the range of C_2-C_7. However, catalyst 3 with the high conversion of 84.5% has demonstrated high selectivity in comparison with the others regarding the range of C_8-C_{15} which depending on the application of the products could also be the desired catalyst. Catalyst1 has also shown promising results with high conversions of 82.92% while favoring the products of C_2-C_7. However, the aforementioned catalyst demonstrated higher ability to push the reaction towards the production of higher carbon number chemicals, as high as C_{15}, when compared to the other catalysts.

Overall, among the catalysts, the second catalyst especially exhibits an excellent performance of 88.92% conversion and performing with the highest selectivity and yield amongst the selected products that were in significant concentrations.

Further details about the catalyst will be discussed in the presentation.

4. Conclusions

The successfully synthesized catalysts proven through various characterization techniques have performed effectively in terms of producing valuable range of chemicals from biomass-based sources. All catalysts have been able to convert the ABE reactants to the long chain hydrocarbons with significantly high conversion levels while also demonstrating reasonable selectivity towards the identified added value products.

Catalyst 2 has been chosen as the best performing catalyst in terms of conversion and selectivity. Nevertheless, the third catalyst has demonstrated notable performance to produce longer chain hydrocarbons and the first catalyst was able to push the reaction towards the production of the highest carbon number hydrocarbon in comparison to the rest.

Finally, taking all of this into account, it has been shown that this route delivers valuable chemicals that can facilitate the integration of a bio and a traditional refinery. One of the key parameters to be optimized is the catalytic reaction to obtain high value chemicals from ABE. This work showcases that transition metal-based catalysts are effective materials for this process and open new avenues for research in the catalysts design towards an optimized ABE upgrading pathway.

References

Bîldea, C. S. *et al.* (2016) 'Enhanced Down-Stream Processing of Biobutanol in the ABE Fermentation Process', *Computer Aided Chemical Engineering*, 38, pp. 979–984. doi: 10.1016/B978-0-444-63428-3.50168-5.

Chakraborty, S. *et al.* (2015) 'Highly Selective Formation of n-Butanol from Ethanol through the Guerbet Process: A Tandem Catalytic Approach', *Journal of the American Chemical Society*, 137(45), pp. 14264–14267. doi: 10.1021/jacs.5b10257.

Fahim, M. F., Alsahhaf, T. A., & Elkilan, A. E. (2010) *Fundamentals of Petroleum Refining*. Edited by 1st. Oxford: Elsevier.

Goulas, K. A. *et al.* (2017) 'ABE Condensation over Monometallic Catalysts: Catalyst Characterization and Kinetics', *ChemCatChem*, 9(4), pp. 677–684. doi: 10.1002/cctc.201601507.

Gupta, R. and Demirbas, A. (2010) *Gasoline, Diesel and Ethanol Biofuels from Grasses and Plants*. 1st edn. Cambridge, England: Cambridge University Press.

Leffler, W. L. (2008) *Petroleum Refining in Nontechnical Language*. 4th edn. Tulsa, Oklahoma: PenWell.

Patel, A. D. *et al.* (2015) 'Analysis of sustainability metrics and application to the catalytic production of higher alcohols from ethanol', *Catalysis Today*, 239, pp. 56–79. doi: 10.1016/j.cattod.2014.03.070.

Qureshi, N. *et al.* (2010) 'Production of butanol (a biofuel) from agricultural residues: Part II - Use of corn stover and switchgrass hydrolysates', *Biomass Bioenergy*, 34(4), pp. 566–571.

Qureshi, N. and Ejezi, T. (2008) '"a superior biofuel" production from agricultural residues (renewable biomass): recent progress in technology', *Biofuels, Bioprod. Biorefin*, 2(4), pp. 319–330.

Shimura, K. *et al.* (2013) 'Self-coupling of secondary alcohols by Ni/CeO2catalyst', *Applied Catalysis A: General*. Elsevier B.V., 462–463, pp. 137–142. doi: 10.1016/j.apcata.2013.04.040.

Sreekumar, S. *et al.* (2015) 'Production of an acetone-butanol-ethanol mixture from Clostridium acetobutylicum and its conversion to high-value biofuels', *Nature Protocols*, 10(3), pp. 528–537. doi: 10.1038/nprot.2015.029.

Zhu, Q. *et al.* (2017) 'Upgrade of Solvent-Free Acetone-Butanol-Ethanol Mixture to High-Value Biofuels over Ni-Containing MgO-SiO2Catalysts with Greatly Improved Water-Resistance', *ACS Sustainable Chemistry and Engineering*, 5(9), pp. 8181–8191. doi: 10.1021/acssuschemeng.7b01837.

Anton A. Kiss, Edwin Zondervan, Richard Lakerveld, Leyla Özkan (Eds.)
Proceedings of the 29th European Symposium on Computer Aided Process Engineering
June 16th to 19th, 2019, Eindhoven, The Netherlands. © 2019 Elsevier B.V. All rights reserved.
http://dx.doi.org/10.1016/B978-0-128-18634-3.50060-6

Heat-Integrated Reactive distillation processes to produce Ethyl Levulinate: Design and Optimization including Environmental, Safety and Economics Aspects

J.A. Vazquez-Castillo, [a,*] G.Contreras-Zarazúa,[b] J.G. Segovia-Hernandez [b]

*a Faculty of Chemical Sciences Autonomous University of Chihuahua, Circuito Universitario 8, Campus II, Chihuahua,Chih. 31125,

b Deparment of Chemical Engineering University of Guanajuato, Noria Alta S/N, Guanajuato,Gto., 36000 , Mexico.

vazquezcastillo@gmail.com

Abstract

This study provides optimally designed reactive distillation (RD) processes for the production of ethyl levulinate, taking into account costs, environmental impact and safety. The thermally coupled RD process is the most appealing with major energy savings in the range of 9.6-54.3% lower than other RD processes, reduced environmental impact in the range of 5.7-51% lower ECO 99 index value and similar process safety less than 2% difference compared to other RD processes considered. The lower energy requirement of the thermally coupled process was reflected in the lowest energy use to produce ethyl levulinate (1.667 GJ/ton.).

Keywords: Ethyl Levulinate, Reactive Distillation, Cost and Safety of chemical processes, Multi-objective optimization.

1. Introduction

Ethyl Levulinate (EL) is a valuable chemical whose utilization is extended in multiples industries, EL distinguishes as a product with the potential to be used as a replacement of the fuel additives such as Methyl Tert-Butyl Ether (MTBE) y el Tert-Amyl Methyl Ether (TAME), the industry related with the production of ethyl Levulinate can be considered in its infancy however the forecast for the ethyl Levulinate demand indicates that 49.1 tons will be demanded by the year 2022 with a worth value in the market of 11.8×10^6 USD (Grand View Research, 2017). An appealing route to avoid the use of harmful solvents and larger amounts of energy is the reaction between the levulinic acid with ethanol to obtain ethyl Levulinate (Fernandes et al., 2012), however, this route is limited by the equilibrium of the reaction, in order to overcome the limitation, the implementation of Reactive Distillation is relevant, even more the heat integration and thermally coupling of these designs adds significant improvements to be consistent with the philosophy of seek for sustainable processes.

In this work, the evaluation of the TAC, the ECO 99 and the Individual Risk (IR) of proposals of processes based on heat integrated and thermally coupled reactive Distillation to produce Ethyl Levulinate is introduced, as these proposals involve the handling of organic compounds, which are the most common source of fires and explosions in industry, in addition to the traditional economic and sustainable evaluation, a quantitative risk analysis is highly desirable.

2. Methodology

Ethyl Levulinate is produced through the reaction of the Levulinic Acid with Ethanol, the reaction is showed in the Eq. (1).

$$C_5H_8O_3 + C_2H_5OH \underset{k_2}{\overset{k_1}{\rightleftharpoons}} C_7H_{12}O_3 + H_2O \qquad (1)$$
$$\quad A \qquad\qquad B \qquad\qquad\qquad C \qquad\quad D$$

From the Equation 1: A=Levulinic Acid; B= Ethanol; C=Ethyl Levulinate; D=Water.

The kinetics equation and the kinetic parameters were taken from a previous work by Tsai, 2014. In this work the Hayden-O'Connell model was selected as the thermodynamic model to properly estimate the vapor-liquid equilibrium. The binary interaction parameters of the components were taken from a previous work by Resk et al. (2014). Four different reactive distillation configurations are studied; the alternatives and the schemes of these configurations are shown in Figure 1 these consist in: Conventional Reactive Distillation Process (CRDP); Thermally Coupled Reactive Distillation (TCRD); Reactive Distillation With heat Integration (RDHI) and Reactive Distillation with Thermally Coupled and heat Integration (THRD). All of the sequences consist of a reactive distillation column (RDC) and two separation columns RC-1 and RC-2. The first separation column, RC-1, performs the separation of the by-product water from the main product, ethyl levulinate (EL) and the unreacted Levulinic Acid (LA), in the second separation column, RC-2, the separation of the Ethyl Levulinate and the Levulinic Acid is carried out, the Levulinic Acid is returned to the RDC column. In all cases, the feed flow of Ethanol and fresh Levulinic Acid were 100 kmol/h. The topology of these processes was taken from the previous work by Novita et al. (2017), however, in this work a rigorous multi-objective optimization algorithm is implemented, and three key factors are simultaneously evaluated, even more through the optimization strategy would help to contrast and eventually to carry out the selection of the optimal designs in terms of multiple objectives as the proposed in this work.

The total annual cost has been computed using the Guthrie methodology. Five years was assumed as a payback period, whereas carbon steel is considered as construction material for the process equipments. The operating costs included cooling utilities, heating utilities, and 8400 hours of yearly operation for each alternative have been considered.The ECO 99 is used to calculate the environmental impact. This approach is based on the evaluation of three impact categories: human health, ecosystem quality, and resources depletion. This method has been successfully implemented in the environmental evaluation of chemical processes (Quiroz-Ramirez et al 2017). According to the importance of three major impact categories the weighting for ECO 99 was realized as follows: damages to human health and damage to ecosystem quality are of equal importance, thus these were equally weighted while the damage to the resources was considered to be half of importance in weighting. The individual risk is an index used to quantify the safety of a process and it is calculated through a quantitative risk analysis where the damage caused by an accident is identified and quantified. For the cases of study seven possible incidents have been identified, these are divided in two categories. Instantaneous incidents are: Boiling liquid expanding vapour explosion (BLEVE), unconfined vapour cloud explosion (UVCE), flash fire and toxic release, whereas the continuous release incidents are: jet fire, flash fire and toxic release. The calculations of the individual risk were carried out for a reference distance of 50 m, the complete set equations to calculate the IR is showed by Medina-Herrera et al. 2014.

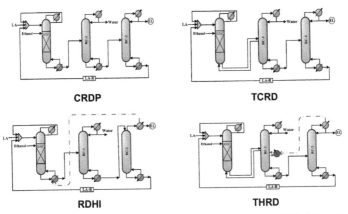

CRDP   TCRD

RDHI   THRD

Figure 1. Reactive distillation processes to produce Ethyl Levulinate.

The multi-objective optimization problem was solved using the mathematical technique called Differential Evolution with Tabu List (DETL) by Sharma, S., & Rangaiah, G. P. (2010). The values of the parameters required by DETL method are: Population size (NP): 200 individuals, Generations Number (GenMax): 500, Tabu List size (TLS): 100 individuals, Tabu Radius (TR): 0.01, Crossover fractions (Cr): 0.8, Mutation fractions (F): 0.3.The DETL method together with objective function were implemented in a hybrid platform involved, which linked Aspen Plus™ and Microsoft Excel™ through Visual Basic™. The design variables for the different processes are offered in the Table 1.

Table 1. Design variables for the processes separation of furfural.

Decision Variables	CRDP	TCRD	RDHI	THRD
Number of stages, RDC	X	X	X	X
Number of reactive stages	X	X	X	X
Heat duty of RDC, kW	X		X	
Distillate flow, kmol h^{-1}	X	X	X	X
Diameter of RDC, m	X	X	X	X
Number of stages, RC-1	X	X	X	X
Feed stage, RC-1	X	X	X	X
Reflux ratio of RC-1	X	X	X	X
Interlinking flow, kmol h^{-1}		X		X
Bottom flow of RC-1, kmol h^{-1}	X	X	X	X
Diameter of RC-1, m	X	X	X	X
Withdrawal side stage of RC-1				X
Side flow of RC-1, kmol h^{-1}				X
Number of stages, RC-2	X	X	X	X
Feed stage, RC-2	X	X		X
Reflux ratio of RC-2				X
Bottom flow of RC-1, kmol h^{-1}	X	X	X	X
Heat duty of RC-2, kW	X	X		
Diameter of RC-2, m	X	X	X	X

Total number of variables	15	15	13	17

Finally, the overall optimization problem can be mathematically expresed as in Eq. (2) and Eq. (3):

$$\min \quad Z = \{TAC; ECO\,99; IR\} \qquad (2)$$

$$\text{Subject to:} \quad y_{i,F} \geq x_{i,F}$$
$$w_{i,F} \geq u_{i,F} \qquad (3)$$

The objective functions are restricted to satisfy the purity ($y_{i,F}$) and molar flowrate ($w_{i,F}$) especifications of Ethyl Levulinate and Water. The purity required for Ethyl Levulinate (EL) and Water was 99.5 mol%.

3. Results

The Pareto charts obtained for all of the reactive distillation processes at the end of the optimization process are offered in the Figure 2. Each point in the graphics represents a solution or design that meets the purity requirements with the best values of the three objective functions under evaluation.

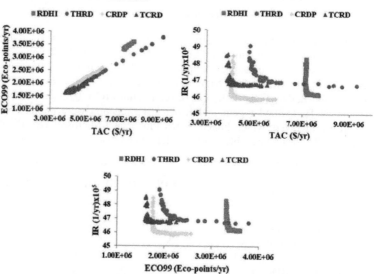

Figure 2. Pareto charts of the RD processes.

The shape of the Pareto TAC vs ECO99, in the Figure 2, is explained relating the influence of total energy consumed by each process and the amount of steel required to build the equipments in the ECO 99 calculation. The Pareto front of IR vs TAC for all the processes exhibits a trend of opposite objectives for IR and TAC, this behaviour indicates that the selection of a design with the lowest TAC, it necessarily causes the value of IR to increase, therefore, the solutions that offer the best trade-offs between the two objectives are those located in the curve zone of the Pareto Chart for these sequences; the Pareto front of IR vs ECO 99, the shape of the Paretos of all the processes exhibits a similar trend as the IR vs TAC Pareto for these same sequences. In the optimal designs of all the sequences, the larger reflux ratios and reboiler duties the higher utilization of heating services and electricity for cooling services, these larger values have a direct contribution in the increment of the ECO 99 values. According to the behaviour of the Paretos of the objective functions IR vs ECO 99 and IR vs TAC, which is the same behaviour for both combinations of indexes, it is possible to assert that the best optimal designs of the processes CRDP, THRD and TCRD are found in the zone of the Pareto that compensates both objectives, this is the curve zone as explained above. Therefore, the selection of a design that compensates the IR index with the TAC, this choice directly equilibrates the IR index with the ECO 99. The Table 2 provides the design variables of the selected designs of the Pareto charts of the processes.

Table 2. Design variables of optimal designs of reactive distillation processes.

Design Variables	CRDP	TCRD	RDHI	THRD
Topology of columns				
Number of stages, RDC	83	93	48	58
Number of reactive stages, RDC	2-45	2-63	2-23	2-37
Number of stages, RC-1	26	23	32	19
Number of stages, RC-2	31	34	16	16
Feed stage, RC-1	13	15	21	15
Feed stage, RC-2	21	27	1	14
Withdrawal side stage, RC-1	——	——	——	14
Diameter of RDC, m	1.009	1.334	1.04	1.17
Diameter of RC-1, m	1.170	1.036	1.13	1.60
Diameter of RC-2, m	1.080	1.090	1.07	1.88
Operating conditions				
Top pressure (atm)	1	1	1	1
Distillate flow, kmol h^{-1}	493.73	441.58	532.464	342.606
Tray holdup, l	44.004	76.951	46.687	59.442
Reflux ratio of RC-1	0.5371	0.5819	0.9651	1.152
Reflux ratio of RC-2	——	——	——	0.7045
Heat duty of RDC, kW	3019.1	0	10211.3	0
Heat duty of RC-1, kW	2738.9	4830.7	3226.57	6750.52
Heat duty of RC-2, kW	1698.8	1839.3	1122.45	2052.30
Interlinking flow, kmol h^{-1}	——	151.44	——	272.922
Side flow of RC-2, kmol h^{-1}	——	——	——	24.7091
Bottom flow of RC-1, kmol h^{-1}	118.68	119.813	117.416	125.435
Bottom flow of RC-2, kmol h^{-1}	18.7575	19.9172	17.4219	25.6693
Temperature bottom , RDC (°C)	118.95	117.70	117.94	117.15
Temperature bottom, RC-1 (°C)	227.31	232.07	227.47	228.638
Temperature bottom, RC-2 (°C)	247.83	267.91	230.42	235.69
Molar flowrates of process streams				
Ethyl Levulinate stream, kmol h^{-1}	99.5081	99.877	99.5036	99.7631
Water stream, kmol h^{-1}	99.6249	99.990	99.5128	99.9929

Continue Table 2

Purity of EL product and by-product water (mol%)			
Ethyl Levulinate	0.9964	0.9998	0.9951	0.9999
Water	0.9957	0.9981	0.9950	0.9979
Performance indexes			
Energy per ton. of **EL** produced (**GJ**/ton. **EL**)	1.8712	1.6676	3.6539	2.2033
Utilities cost (million \$/yr)	3.8125	3.7141	6.9426	5.0005
Equipment cost (million \$)	0.2544	0.2305	0.2767	0.2218
TAC (million \$/yr)	4.0670	3.9447	7.2193	5.2224
Eco99 (million Eco-points/yr)	1.7803	1.6592	3.3916	2.1465
IR $(1/yr)*10^5$	45.994	46.766	46.1502	46.962

4. Conclusions

The multi-objective optimization taking into account simultaneously the total annual cost, environmental impact and process safety, revealed that the thermally coupled reactive distillation (TCRD) process has the lowest energy use (1.667 MJ/kg EL) with major energy savings (9.6-54.3% lower than other RD processes), reduced environmental impact (5.7-51% lower ECO 99 index value) and similar process safety (less than 2% difference compared to other RD processes considered). Thus, the TCRD process is suggested as the best process alternative to produce ethyl levulinate, although there is room for further selection of other feasible RD processes where other tradeoffs among the indicators may be devised.

References

Grand View Research. Ethyl Levulinate Market Worth $11.8 Million by 2022. (2016). http://www.grandviewresearch.com/press-release/global-ethyl-levulinate-market.

Fernandes, D. R., Rocha, A. S., Mai, E. F., Mota, C. J., & Da Silva, V. T. (2012). Levulinic acid esterification with ethanol to ethyl levulinate production over solid acid catalysts. Applied Catalysis A: General, 425, 199-204.

Tsai C. Y., Kinetic Behavior Study on the Synthesis of Ethyl Levulinate over Heterogeneous Catalyst (2014), Master Thesis, NTUST, Taiwan.

Resk, A. J., Peereboom, L., Kolah, A. K., Miller, D. J., & Lira, C. T. (2014). Phase Equilibria in systems with levulinic acid and ethyl levulinate. Journal of Chemical & Engineering Data, 59(4), 1062-1068.

Novita, F. J., Lee, H. Y., & Lee, M. (2017). Energy-efficient design of an ethyl levulinate reactive distillation process via a thermally coupled distillation with external heat integration arrangement. Industrial & Engineering Chemistry Research, 56(24), 7037-7048.

Medina-Herrera, N., Jiménez-Gutiérrez, A., & Mannan, M. S.; Development of inherently safer distillation systems. Journal of Loss Prevention in the Process Industries, 2014, 29, 225-23

Quiroz-Ramírez, J. J., Sánchez-Ramírez, E., Hernández-Castro, S., Segovia-Hernández, J. G., Ponce-Ortega, J. M.; (2017). Optimal planning of feedstock for butanol production considering economic and environmental aspects, ACS Sustainable Chemistry & Engineering, 5(5), 4018-4030.

Sharma, S., & Rangaiah, G. P. (2010). A hybrid multi-objective optimization algorithm. In 5th International Symposium on Design, Operation, and Control of Chemical Processes (pp. 1494-1503)

Anton A. Kiss, Edwin Zondervan, Richard Lakerveld, Leyla Özkan (Eds.)
Proceedings of the 29th European Symposium on Computer Aided Process Engineering
June 16th to 19th, 2019, Eindhoven, The Netherlands. © 2019 Elsevier B.V. All rights reserved.
http://dx.doi.org/10.1016/B978-0-128-18634-3.50061-8

Risk-conscious approach to optimizing bioenergy investments in the Brazilian sugarcane industry

Victoria M. Mutran[a,b], Celma O. Ribeiro[a], Claudio O. A. Nascimento[a] and Benoît Chachuat [b,*]

[a]Escola Politécnica da Universidade de São Paulo, São Paulo, Brazil
[b]Centre for Process Systems Engineering, Imperial College London, London, United Kingdom
b.chachuat@imperial.ac.uk

Abstract

Deciding price policies in order to attract new investments on renewable energy generation remains a challenge to many public policy-makers. This is particularly relevant to the Brazilian sugarcane industry, which has experienced a significant reduction in new bioenergy projects in recent years. Since investment costs thereof are expressive, a producer's willingness to increase energy generation is highly dependent on market conditions. Herein, we propose an optimization model based on portfolio theory to assess different price policies for attracting investment, where historical variations in sugar, ethanol and spot-market electricity prices are accounted for. Results obtained on a representative case study highlight the significant role played by regulated market prices in mitigating financial risks in the sugarcane business. The analysis enables a better understanding of investors' behavior according to their aversion to risk. It could support policy-makers with more effective pricing in the regulated market to keep promoting bioenergy generation.

Keywords: sugarcane, bioenergy, portfolio optimization, risk analysis, CVaR

1. Introduction

The Brazilian sugarcane industry is an example of a successful concerted public effort towards reducing a country's dependency on fossil fuels. In addition to its contribution to the energy sector with ethanol production, sugarcane mills now play an important role in the national electricity matrix. Cogeneration with bagasse—the fibrous residue after sugarcane stalks are crushed to extract their juice—currently holds a share of about 7% of the installed capacity in Brazil. Albeit significant, this share is still far from the industry's full potential, since less than half of all Brazilian mills are currently exporting electricity to the grid. All of Brazil's sugarcane mills are self-sufficient in energy through the use of bagasse for cogeneration of steam and power, but a majority still operates with low efficiency. Because the investment costs for new technologies to improve energy generation are high, a producer's willingness to invest is very sensitive to the market conditions and the prices practiced by the power sector.

Electricity in Brazil may be sold in either one of two ways: the free market and the regulated market. The former consists of a spot market, whereby prices are highly sensitive to the local weather conditions. The latter presents long-term contracts (e.g. over 20-25 years) with a determined rate (tariff) for the supplied power, in the form of power auctions organized by the Brazilian government. Since the free market is inherently high risk, new projects for renewable energy generation are usually enabled by the regulated market. However, the Brazilian government is yet to propose effective policies to incentivize the production of bioelectricity, withholding many producers from wanting to bear the costs for modernizing their cogeneration systems and connect to the distribution network to sell electricity (Hofsetz and Silva, 2012). The absence of new installed capacity of bioelectricity into the Brazilian matrix in 2019 illustrates this trend perfectly.

Several studies have analyzed scenarios to increase power generation from the sugarcane bagasse. Grisi et al. (2012) applied an optimization model to decide the best economical combinations of sugar, bioethanol, biogas and electricity for production in a sugarcane mill. They highlighted the role of the regulated market in incentivizing sales of surplus power and showed that these sales could increase profits significantly. However, their assessment did not account for price risks, nor did it consider investments on new technologies to increase power production.

Accounting for risks in production and investment decisions is paramount in the sugarcane sector, especially since sugar, ethanol and spot electricity prices have been historically volatile. Hence, recent studies have applied Portfolio Theory to assess production decisions in the sugarcane sector (Carpio and Souza, 2017; Dutenkefer et al., 2018), but technological routes on bioenergy generation in the sugarcane sector have not been assessed yet in light of price risks, to the best of our knowledge.

This paper presents a risk-conscious assessment of investments on bioelectricity projects in sugarcane mills, through the application of a portfolio optimization strategy. Detrimental price scenarios are accounted for by means of the Conditional-Value-at-Risk (CVaR), a single tail risk-measure which is amenable to a fully linear optimization formulation using historical price data. The main objective of the analysis is to gain a better understanding of the role played by price policies on the increase of surplus power generation in the sugarcane sector, while accounting for the impact of bioelectricity sales on the sugar-ethanol business.

The proposed model is presented in Sec. 2. The case study of a generic sugarcane mill is introduced in Sec. 3, whereby investment decisions are assessed with regards to different scenarios of regulated market prices for electricity. The results of this case study are presented and discussed in Sec. 4, and final conclusions are drawn in Sec. 5.

2. Methodology

Our approach consists of modeling the production decisions related to the use of resources in the sugarcane mill and optimizing the trade-off between annual profit and risk in order to assess investments in new bioelectricity capacity.

2.1. Process Model

Production decisions in sugarcane processing plants generally relate to using available resources to produce a range of products that yield the largest economic profit. The resources comprise juice, bagasse, molasse and vinasse, denoted by the set $I = \{ju, bag, mol, vin\}$, whereas the products consist of sugar, ethanol, fertilizer, free electricity and regulated electricity denoted by $J = \{su, et, fert, free, reg\}$.

Assuming a predetermined amount of sugarcane to be crushed during the season, denoted here by the parameter Ca, and given a yield of juice extracted in the milling process, a producer needs to choose the amount that will be sent to both sugar and ethanol processes at the onset of the season:

$$r_{ju,su} + r_{ju,et} = \gamma_{ju}Ca \tag{1}$$

where the decision variable $r_{i,j}$ denotes the amount of each resource $i \in I$ used for the production of product $j \in J$; and γ_i is the yield of resource i. The product (sugar) and byproduct (molasse) in the sugar production process are described by:

$$x_{su} = \theta_{ju,su} r_{ju,su} \tag{2}$$

$$r_{mol,et} = \gamma_{mol} x_{su} \tag{3}$$

where the decision variable x_j denotes the amount of product j; and $\theta_{i,j}$ are process conversion parameters describing the average yields from resource i to product j. Both juice and molasse can be used as inputs to the ethanol generation process, whereas vinasse, a residue of ethanol distillation, is widely used as a fertilizer in sugarcane plantation areas:

$$x_{et} = \theta_{ju,et} r_{ju,et} + \theta_{mol,et} r_{mol,et} \tag{4}$$

$$r_{vin,fert} = \gamma_{vin} x_{et} \tag{5}$$

$$x_{fert} = \theta_{vin,fert} r_{vin,fert} \tag{6}$$

Lastly, but not least importantly, the main residue from the milling process, bagasse, is used in all of Brazilian sugarcane mills as a fuel for thermal, mechanical and electrical energy through the use of power-steam cogeneration systems. Our main objective herein is to assess investments to upgrade bioelectricity from bagasse according to various free and regulated electricity price scenarios. Technological routes to increase energy recovery from bagasse are discussed by Dantas et al. (2013), who identify the use of condensation turbines within a Rankine cycle plant as the most competitive alternative for generating surplus electricity. Accordingly, we consider both a traditional Rankine cycle (base-scenario) and a Rankine cycle with a condensation turbine (improved scenario), so the surplus electricity available for commercialization in the sugarcane mill is such that:

$$x_{free} + x_{reg} \leq G_{base} z_{base} + G_{imp} z_{imp} \tag{7}$$

$$z_{base} + z_{imp} = 1 \tag{8}$$

where $z_k \in \{0,1\}$ is the investment decision variable; G_k is a parameter for the annual surplus electricity expected in each configuration $k \in K$ of the cogeneration process, with the set $K = \{base, imp\}$; and the surplus electricity production is separated into free and regulated market sales, which present different prices and risks.

2.2. Portfolio Optimization

The goal of the model is to enable risk-conscious decisions regarding product mix and investment in the sugarcane industry. We assume that product prices are the only source of uncertainty, so the optimization model chooses the best production portfolio to maximize profits in the case of detrimental price scenarios. Consequently, the decisions are based on historical records for sugar, ethanol and spot market electricity prices. Such information from past scenarios is used to robustify decisions against potential future short-falls, on account of historical market fluctuations. The validity of our results therefore relies on the assumption that future market conditions can be captured by such historical price records over several years.

As risk measure, we apply the Conditional-Value-at-Risk (CVaR), a coherent and convex, one-tailed measure. Following Rockafellar and Uryasev (2000), CVaR is amenable to a tractable, fully linear formulation, and optimizing CVaR has been shown to indirectly optimize other risk measures such as variance and Value-at-Risk (VaR) as well. Thus, given $q = 1 \ldots Q$ historical price observations, $p_{j,q}$ and production costs, c_j for each product $j \in J$, alongside investment costs, $\$_k$ for each technology $k \in K$, the proposed portfolio optimization model may be stated as:

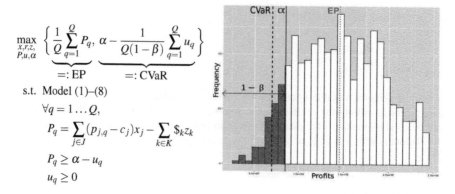

$$\max_{\substack{x,r,z,\\P,u,\alpha}} \left\{ \underbrace{\frac{1}{Q}\sum_{q=1}^{Q} P_q}_{=:\,\text{EP}}, \; \underbrace{\alpha - \frac{1}{Q(1-\beta)}\sum_{q=1}^{Q} u_q}_{=:\,\text{CVaR}} \right\}$$

$$\text{s.t. Model (1)--(8)}$$

$$\forall q = 1 \ldots Q,$$

$$P_q = \sum_{j\in J}(p_{j,q}-c_j)x_j - \sum_{k\in K}\$_k z_k$$

$$P_q \geq \alpha - u_q$$

$$u_q \geq 0$$

where P_q are auxiliary variables denoting the profit in each scenario $q = 1 \ldots Q$; α is a decision variable corresponding to the VaR at confidence level β; and $u_q, q = 1 \ldots Q$ are auxiliary variables introduced in the formulation in order to reduce it to a linear problem. Note that this is a bi-objective optimization problem, seeking a trade-off between expected profit (EP) and risk (CVaR). Also note that minimizing risk comes to maximizing the CVaR in our formulation. We apply the ε-constraint approach to construct the Pareto frontier here (Miettinen, 1999).

3. Case Study

A case study is defined based on a generic sugarcane plant in order to demonstrate the proposed portfolio optimization model for product mix and investments decisions in the sugarcane sector. This plant processes 3 million tonnes of sugarcane per year, an average-size plant in Brazil. The initial configuration of the cogeneration system is a traditional Rankine cycle running with a 67 bar boiler at 520°C and generating an average surplus electricity of 53 kWh per tonne of sugarcane processed. As the investment alternative, we consider the addition of a condensation turbine that increases surplus power generation to an average of 83 kWh per tonne.

The parameters used in the model are taken from the literature. Production and investment costs are from Grisi et al. (2012) and Dantas et al. (2013), respectively, while process yields and waste generation rates are derived from the Open Sugarcane Process Simulation Platform (Castro et al., 2018). The selling prices of sugar, ethanol and spot market electricity correspond to historical price records at a weekly frequency between 2002 and 2018. These prices are all expressed for the same base-year (2010 US$) by discounting the effect of inflation, before using them to estimate the expected profit and risk.

Since the regulated market does not present price variations within the contracted supply period, and since those prices are set during the energy auctions prior to making the investments, a sensitivity analysis is performed to assess how different price policies practiced by the government could affect investment and production decisions in the sugarcane sector. The range of regulated market prices used in this analysis is US$50-100 per MWh, based on the average prices practiced in Brazilian renewable energy auctions over the past 10 years. The results obtained are presented and discussed in the following section.

4. Results and Discussion

The model predicts two distinct investment behaviors within the range of regulated electricity prices investigated in the sensitivity analysis (US$50-100 per MWh): one when the price in the regulated market is lower than or equal to the expected price of the free market, and the other one when it is higher. This is expected since the regulated prices are not subject to variations and

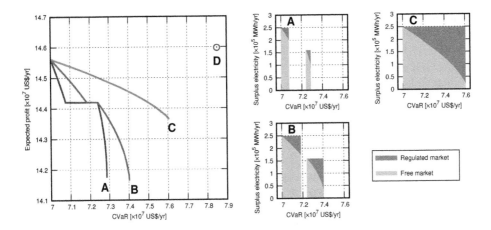

Figure 1: Efficient frontiers and annual surplus electricity sales in the free and regulated markets for different regulated price scenarios. **A**: US$50/MWh; **B**: US$60/MWh; **C**: US$70/MWh; **D**: US$80/MWh.

are essentially risk-free. Consequently, when regulated prices are greater than the expected value of prices in the free market, a decision-maker will always choose to sell to the regulated market. Given the expected free market price of US$78 per MWh, this latter behavior is clearly seen in Fig. 1 (scenario **D**).

For lower prices practiced in the regulated market (scenarios **A–C**), there is a tendency for producers to prefer selling at spot market price. As price policies of renewable energy auctions in Brazil become more efficient, they attract sales to the regulated market and thereby generate more interest in investing towards surplus energy generation. Notice that for low regulated market prices, such as US$50-60 per MWh, only a risk-inclined investor would choose to invest in new bioelectricty projects, aiming most of their surplus electricity sales to the free market. This analysis corroborates the results of two auctions performed by the Brazilian government in 2011, with average prices of US$52 and US$57 per MWh, which led to significantly less contracted energy compared with the subsequent auctions in 2013, with average prices of US$65 and US$68 per MWh.

Another relevant aspect of this analysis is the disparity of portfolio choices for different risk levels. For lower prices in the regulated market in particular (scenarios **A–B**), a risk-inclined decision aiming to maximize the expected profit only, presents significant difference with a risk-averse decision. For instance, for the regulated market price of US$60 per MWh, a risk-inclined optimization model would recommend investing in a condensation turbine and selling all of the surplus electricity to the free market, a particularly risky strategy with regard to short-falls.

The efficient frontiers for all four price scenarios is shown on the left plot in Fig. 1. Recall that in our bi-objective optimization formulation, increasing the CVaR reduces risk. Therefore, the risk-neutral scenarios originate from the left and have the greatest expected profits, while risk-averse scenarios are on the right. The three frontiers for which regulated market prices are lower than the expected price in the free market (scenarios **A–C**) all originate from the same point, where a risk-inclined producer would sell all of its surplus electricity to the free market. For regulated price scenarios in the range of US$50-60 per MWh, the Pareto frontier presents a significant jump because the decision to invest is not made until the risk level is quite high. Below this threshold, the investment is not made, but surplus power is sold entirely to the free market. The sales decisions only change among prices in this range when risk starts playing a more important role than expected profit in the investor's decisions. Regulated prices of US$70 per MWh or higher are sufficiently attractive to promote the investment, and we no longer observe a jump in the Pareto frontier. There is furthermore a clear tendency for risk-averse profiles to prefer the regulated market in all of the regulated price scenarios.

There is also a notable gain in efficiency as the prices in the regulated market increase. Although it is expected, this result is interesting as it shows a change in the trade-off between risk and profit among the scenarios. Clearly, raising the regulated market price reduces the gap between the expected profits in risk-averse and risk-inclined strategies. This shows how long-term electricity contracts may play a relevant role as a strategy to mitigate price risks of other products in the sugarcane business.

Finally, as far as assisting price policies to attract more bioelectricity investments is concerned, the sensitivity analysis of the portfolio decisions allows a better understanding of the regulated market prices that would be attractive to sugarcane producers. The results obtained with the cost conditions of the case study suggest that a price range between US$65-70 per MWh would raise the interest of risk-averse investors in implementing a condensation turbine to increase their surplus electricity generation. Naturally, there are other market aspects that may influence a producer's willingness to invest, such as economic and political uncertainties in Brazil. However, by evidencing the impact of long-term energy contracts on reducing the overall price risks of the sugarcane business and proposing economically attractive prices for the energy auctions, policymakers are more likely to succeed in increasing the share of bioelectricity in the national matrix.

5. Conclusions

This paper has presented a portfolio optimization model to address investment decisions in the Brazilian sugarcane sector. Price risks are accounted for by means of the Conditional-Value-at-Risk, in combination with historical price records of sugar, ethanol and spot market electricity, to enable risk-conscious decisions that are robust to potential shortfalls. A sensitivity analysis has been conducted for a variety of regulated market prices and risk-aversion profiles. Results obtained on a representative case study confirm that the decision to invest on bioenergy projects is highly sensitive to the price policies practiced in the regulated market, evidencing also the importance of bioelectricity sales on the economic performance of sugarcane mills. Typical optimal solutions also present a large sensitivity towards the level of risk, which confirms the need to account for market price variations in the analysis. The developed risk-conscious optimization framework therefore provides a more robust tool to assist policy-makers and to incentivize bioenergy projects in the Brazilian sugarcane industry.

Acknowledgements: The authors thank São Paulo Research Foundation (FAPESP) under grants 2015/50684-9, 2017/17530-3 and 2018/08255-1 for student scholarships and financial support.

References

L. Carpio, F. Souza, 2017. Optimal allocation of sugarcane bagasse for producing bioelectricity and second generation ethanol in Brazil: Scenarios of cost reductions. Renewable Energy 111, 771–780.

R. E. N. Castro, R. M. B. Alves, A. Hawkes, C. A. O. Nascimento, 2018. Open Sugarcane Process Simulation Platform. Computer Aided Chemical Engineering 44, 1819–1824.

G. Dantas, L. Legey, A. Mazzone, 2013. Energy from sugarcane bagasse in Brazil: An assessment of the productivity and cost of different technological routes. Renewable & Sustainable Energy Reviews 21, 356–364.

R. M. Dutenkefer, C. O. Ribeiro, V. M. Mutran, E. E. Rego, 2018. The insertion of biogas in the sugarcane mill product portfolio: A study using the robust optimization approach. Renewable & Sustainable Energy Reviews 91, 729–740.

E. F. Grisi, J. M. Yusta, R. Dufo-Lopez, 2012. Opportunity costs for bioelectricity sales in Brazilian sucro-energetic industries. Applied Energy 92, 860–867.

K. Hofsetz, M. Silva, 2012. Brazilian sugarcane bagasse: Energy and non-energy consumption. Biomass & Bioenergy 46, 564–573.

K. Miettinen, 1999. Nonlinear Multiobjective Optimization. Springer.

R. T. Rockafellar, S. Uryasev, 2000. Optimization of Conditional Value-at-Risk. Journal of Risk 2, 21–41.

Anton A. Kiss, Edwin Zondervan, Richard Lakerveld, Leyla Özkan (Eds.)
Proceedings of the 29th European Symposium on Computer Aided Process Engineering
June 16th to 19th, 2019, Eindhoven, The Netherlands. © 2019 Elsevier B.V. All rights reserved.
http://dx.doi.org/10.1016/B978-0-128-18634-3.50062-X

Production of chemicals from syngas: an enviro-economic model-based investigation

Andrea Bernardi[a], Jose E. A. Graciano[a] and Benoît Chachuat[a,*]

[a]*Centre for Process Systems Engineering, Department of Chemical Engineering, Imperial College London, SW7 2AZ, UK*
b.chachuat@imperial.ac.uk

Abstract

Syngas has traditionally been derived from fossil fuels, but alternative production routes have attracted significant interest recently, such as syngas from biomass gasification, electrolysis of water, or electrocatalytic reduction of CO_2. The composition of the produced syngas can vary drastically, in addition to presenting large price differences. The main contribution of this paper is a systematic, model-based comparison of three syngas conversion technologies, namely methanol, DME and Fisher-Tropsch syntheses, for a range of syngas compositions. The key performance indicators in this comparison are the break-even price of syngas, the carbon efficiency, and the energy return on energy investment. The results suggest that DME synthesis is the most promising technology both economically and in terms of carbon efficiency, while methanol synthesis presents the best energy efficiency.

Keywords: methanol, DME, Fisher-Tropsch, process simulation, techno-economic analysis, carbon efficiency, energy efficiency

1. Introduction

Syngas – a gas mixture made primarily of CO and H_2 – provides a flexible feedstock for a variety of chemical syntheses, including methanol (MeOH) and dimethyl ether (DME) production and higher hydrocarbons via Fischer-Tropsch (FT) synthesis. A majority of the syngas worldwide is currently produced from fossil hydrocarbon feedstock and carries a large environmental burden. In response to this, alternative routes to syngas generation have received significant attention, including biomass gasification, co-generation of CO and H_2 via electrochemical and solar routes, and catalytic reduction of CO_2 into CO (Foit et al., 2017). Many of these sustainable syngas production processes are at a much lower technological readiness level compared with syngas from fossil feedstock, and their integration within existing plants may not be so straightforward because the obtained syngas composition can vary drastically depending on the feedstock or selected route. There is also significant uncertainty about the projected price of sustainable syngas in a scaled-up production. This cursory analysis suggests that there exist significant opportunities for better integration and optimization across syngas production and conversion processes.

A number of research studies have been conducted on this topic in recent years. Trippe et al. (2013) compared direct DME synthesis and FT synthesis, using syngas from biomass gasification. They assumed that the syngas composition could be varied without incurring a penalty, and therefore considered optimal $H_2:CO_x$ ratios of 1 for direct DME synthesis and of 2 for the FT synthesis. They furthermore used simplified models (Gibbs reactor) of the DME and FT reactors to conduct the assessment. Hankin and Shah (2017) compared methanol and DME syntheses (both direct and indirect) using CO_2 and H_2 as feedstock. They considered different layouts, including electrocatalytic cells (SOECs) and a separate water-gas-shift reactor prior to the reactor in order to adjust the $CO:CO_2:H_2$ ratio for each conversion technology, and they also used equilibrium models in their assessment.

The main objective of this paper is to conduct an assessment of alternative technologies for the production of fuels/chemicals from syngas, by accounting for different $H_2:CO_x$ ratios. Our focus is on three syngas conversion processes, namely FT, MeOH and indirect DME synthesis. Direct DME synthesis was not included in the analysis due to its much lower optimal syngas composition ($H_2:CO_x$ ratio close to 1; see Peng et al. (1999)) compared with the other three processes. A distinctive feature of our analysis is that it relies on detailed kinetic models of the various syntheses, which were calibrated against experimental data. We furthermore consider process flowsheets that are flexible enough to operate under different syngas compositions, not merely at the optimal syngas composition. Finally, the technologies are assessed in terms of their environmental and energy efficiency, alongside their economic performance.

2. Methodology

State-of-the-art process flowsheets for FT, MeOH, and DME syntheses are simulated using Aspen Plus® (FT, DME) and Aspen Hysys® (MeOH). Both simulation environments are also used to conduct the techno-economic analysis, using the information provided by the detailed models, which include mass and energy balances, thermodynamic properties and kinetics. Specifically, the kinetic rate expressions are taken from the works of Todic et al. (2013), Graaf et al. (1988) and Bercic and Levec (1993) for FT, MeOH and DME, respectively. All of these models have been calibrated against experimental data from dedicated measurement campaigns.

The influence of the syngas composition is analyzed by simulating each process with different $H_2:CO_x$ inlet ratios in the range of 1.6–2.4 and a fixed $CO:CO_2$ ratio of 10, as shown in Table 1. The molar flow rate, pressure and temperature are kept constant at 8000 mol.hour^{-1}, 24 bar and 80°C, as well the concentration of inerts (N_2, H_2O and CH_4) that are inherent to the syngas production process.

Three key performance indicators (KPIs) are used to assess and compare the syngas conversion processes. The *break-even price* (BEP) indicator represents the highest price we should be willing to pay for syngas in order for the conversion process to remain economically feasible, here considering a process life-time of 30 years and in the price scenario of Europe 2017. The *carbon efficiency* (CE) indicator accounts for the fraction of carbon from the syngas that ends up in the fuel products. Lastly, the *energy return on energy investment* (EROI) is the amount of energy in the products divided by the amount of energy provided to the process, considering chemical, thermal and electrical energy all together. An important difference between the MeOH, DME and FT processes is that the latter is a net producer of electricity, a saleable co-product that can improve both the BEP and EROI indicators.

Table 1: Molar composition of the different syngas streams used in the process simulation

x_i	$H_2:CO_x$				
[mol%]	1.6	1.8	2	2.2	2.4
H_2	59.7%	62.4%	64.7%	66.7%	68.5%
CO	33.9%	31.5%	29.4%	27.5%	25.9%
CO_2	3.4%	3.1%	2.9%	2.8%	2.6%
N_2, H_2O, CH_4	1.0%	1.0%	1.0%	1.0%	1.0%

Fischer-Tropsch liquids synthesis. The FT plant considered herein is based on the work of Graciano et al. (2018a,b), which comprises six main units: Fischer-Tropsch reacion, water-gas shift (WGS), upgrading, separation, Rankine cycle, and gas turbines (top row of Fig. 1). In the proposed arrangement, the syngas is mixed with H_2 surplus from the WGS unit to adjust the $H_2:CO$ ratio to 2 (unless this ratio is already higher than 2). Then, the mixture feeds into the slurry bubble FT reactor filled with cobalt catalyst, producing the paraffin and olefin that compose the synthetic oil (synoil). This synoil is sent to the separation section to be fractionated into gasoline, kerosene, diesel, and wax products. The upgrading unit is responsible for converting both heavy synoil and recycled wax into lighter and more valuable fractions. The unconverted syngas from the FT unit passes through a WGS unit that converts part of the CO into H_2, before feeding into the FT reactor and the upgrading unit. The thermal energy produced by the exothermic FT reactions is recovered by the Rankine cycle unit and converted into electricity, while the gas turbine unit produces additional electricity by burning the tail gas from the WGS unit.

Methanol synthesis. The MeOH plant is simulated based on the process flowsheet developed by Van-Dal and Bouallou (2013) (middle row of Figure 1). This process comprises only two units: methanol reaction and separation. The former mainly consists of a compressor train and an adiabatic reactor filled with a fixed amount of copper-based catalyst and operating at 78 bar. The latter comprises a sequence of two flash drums and a distillation column, which separate the unconverted syngas and purify the methanol product to the product grade (AA grade), respectively. A heat integration analysis of the process reveals that the heat produced in the reactor is sufficient to cover the process needs, so no external heating utility is needed. By contrast, cooling water and electricity are still required and need to be supplied by external sources.

We consider two alternative copper-based catalysts with the objective to compare their effect on the methanol synthesis. The kinetic data of the first catalyst (Catalyst I) is taken from Van-Dal and Bouallou (2013), which relies on the model by Bussche and Froment (1996). The kinetic data for the second catalyst (catalyst II) is taken from Ng et al. (1999) work, which have been used to calibrate the model by Graaf et al. (1988). The amount of catalyst was adjusted in such a way that a conversion close to the equilibrium is obtained at the reactor outlet; the corresponding amounts of catalyst I and II are 44.7 and 26.6 tons, respectively.

Dimethyl ether synthesis. The process flowsheet for indirect DME production comprises two steps, methanol synthesis and methanol dehydration (middle and bottom rows of Figure 1). The methanol produced from a given syngas composition is mixed with the recycle

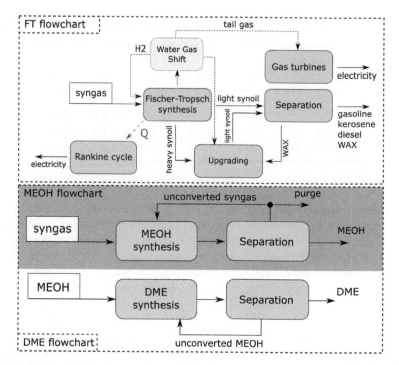

Figure 1: Schematic diagrams for the FT process (top), MeOH process (middle), and DME process (bottom)

stream and heated up to 275°C in a furnace, before entering a jacketed tubular reactor to undergo DME synthesis. Then, the unreacted methanol is separated from the produced water and DME by a train of two distillation columns and recycled back to the reactor. Because water is the only impurity present in the recycle stream, a purge stream is not necessary here.

The kinetic model used in the simulation was initially calibrated against data from a double bed reactor fed with syngas and producing methanol and DME. The model was also tested against experimental data of DME synthesis from methanol, showing a good agreement with the experimental data (Bernardi et al., 2019).

3. Results and discussion

The process simulation results are summarized on Fig. 2. A first observation is that the $H_2:CO_x$ ratio of the syngas has a large effect on the three KPIs, which all pass through a maximum in the investigated range 1.6-2.4.

Economic performance. We start by noting that the catalyst choice has a great effect on the economic performance of the MeOH process, both in terms of capital and operating costs. The catalyst may also modify the optimal syngas composition. The FT process is found to be economically superior to the MeOH process for both catalysts, albeit the MeOH process with catalyst II becomes competitive with the FT process for $H_2:CO_x > 2$. Thereafter, catalyst II is selected to produce methanol in the first step of indirect DME production due to its superior economic performance compared to catalyst

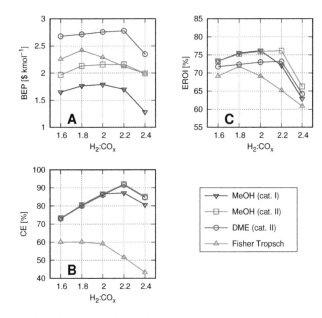

Figure 2: Comparison between MeOH, DME and FT processes in terms of break-even price (**A**), carbon efficiency (**B**), and energy efficiency (**C**)

I. DME is found to be the most profitable product by a large margin, for all analyzed $H_2:CO_x$ ratios even considering a conservative price for the DME (e.g. Chinese market). These results are in agreement with Trippe et al. (2013), who predicted a slightly better economic performance for gasoline from DME compared with gasoline from FT.

Carbon conversion efficiency. The FT process presents the lowest carbon efficiency, around 60% for $H_2:CO_x \leq 2$ and decreasing to about 40% thereafter. This decline is attributed to the H_2 recycle needed for adjusting the $H_2:CO = 2$ at the FT reactor inlet. By contrast, the CE of the MeOH process is consistently over 70%, and it presents a maximum above 90% with catalyst II at the $H_2:CO_x$ ratio of 2. The effect of catalyst selection on the CE is rather low; the main difference being noticeable for $H_2:CO > 2$ due to catalyst I requiring a larger recycle stream. Lastly, there is hardly any difference in CE between the MeOH and DME processes, due to the near-100% conversion of the methanol dehydration in DME synthesis.

Energy efficiency. The most favorable EROI is consistently obtained for the MeOH process, and passes a maximum of about 75% for both catalysts around $H_2:CO_x = 2$. (Recall that the EROI calculation accounts for the chemical energy of the syngas feed, so the resulting EROI may not be greater than 100%.) A fast decline in the EROI is observed for larger $H_2:CO_x$ ratios, due to the increase in the recycle flowrate of unconverted syngas. Unlike CE, the EROI indicator is lower in the DME process than in its MeOH counterpart alone, a consequence of the extra process complexity and exergetic losses. Finally, the FT process presents the worst performance in terms of EROI. At its optimal syngas ratio $H_2:CO_x = 1.8$, it has a similar performance as the DME process nevertheless. This behavior is again explained by the higher complexity of the FT plant in comparison with the other two processes, which results in larger exergetic losses overall.

4. Conclusions

This paper has presents a systematic, model-based comparison between different syngas conversion technologies for the production of liquid transportation fuels. Our results show that the production of DME is the most attractive technology in both economic and carbon efficiency terms, while methanol synthesis has the best performance in terms of energy efficiency. It is also noteworthy that the techno-economic analysis provides quantitative price targets for novel syngas generation technologies. Our current investigations aim at completing the sustainability assessment by looking at additional environmental impacts and comparing different geographical locations (UK, US, South America and China).

Acknowledgements: This paper is based upon work supported by the Engineering and Physical Sciences Research Council (EPSRC) under Grant EP/N010531/1 and EP/P016650/1 "Flexible routes to liquid fuels from CO_2 by advanced catalysis and engineering". Financial support from Shell and FAPESP through the "Research Centre for Gas Innovation - RCGI" (FAPESP Proc. 2014/50279-4), ANP (Brazil National Oil, Natural Gas and Biofuels Agency) through the R&D levy regulation, and CNPq Brasil (Conselho Nacional de Desenvolvimento Científico e Tecnológico - Proc. 200470/2017-5) is gratefully acknowledged.

References

G. Bercic, J. Levec, 1993. Catalytic dehydration of methanol to dimethyl ether – Kinetic investigation and reactor simulation. Industrial & Engineering Chemistry Research 32 (11), 2478–2484.

A. Bernardi, L. Gomoescu, J. Wang, C. C. Pantelides, D. Chadwick, B. Chachuat, 2019. Kinetic model discrimination for methanol and DME synthesis using Bayesian estimation. IFAC-PapersOnLine (to appear).

K. M. V. Bussche, G. F. Froment, 1996. A steady-state kinetic model for methanol synthesis and the water gas shift reaction on a commercial Cu/ZnO/Al$_2$O$_3$ catalyst. Journal of Catalysis 161 (1), 1–10.

S. R. Foit, I. C. Vinke, L. G. J. de Haart, R.-A. Eichel, 2017. Power-to-syngas: An enabling technology for the transition of the energy system? Angewandte Chemie International Edition 56 (20), 5402–5411.

G. Graaf, E. Stamhuis, A. Beenackers, 1988. Kinetics of low-pressure methanol synthesis. Chemical Engineering Science 43 (12), 3185–3195.

J. E. Graciano, B. Chachuat, R. M. Alves, 2018a. Conversion of CO_2-rich natural gas to liquid transportation fuels via trireforming and Fischer-Tropsch synthesis: Model-based assessment. Industrial & Engineering Chemistry Research 57 (30), 9964–9976.

J. E. Graciano, B. Chachuat, R. M. Alves, 2018b. Enviro-economic assessment of thermochemical polygeneration from microalgal biomass. Journal of Cleaner Production 203, 1132–1142.

A. Hankin, N. Shah, 2017. Process exploration and assessment for the production of methanol and dimethyl ether from carbon dioxide and water. Sustainable Energy & Fuels 1 (7), 1541–1556.

K. L. Ng, D. Chadwick, B. Toseland, 1999. Kinetics and modelling of dimethyl ether synthesis from synthesis gas. Chemical Engineering Science 54 (15-16), 3587–3592.

X. Peng, A. Wang, B. Toseland, P. Tijm, 1999. Single-step syngas-to-dimethyl ether processes for optimal productivity, minimal emissions, and natural gas-derived syngas. Industrial & Engineering Chemistry Research 38 (11), 4381–4388.

B. Todic, T. Bhatelia, G. F. Froment, W. Ma, G. Jacobs, B. H. Davis, D. B. Bukur, 2013. Kinetic model of Fischer-Tropsch synthesis in a slurry reactor on Co-Re/Al$_2$O$_3$ catalyst. Industrial & Engineering Chemistry Research 52 (2), 669–679.

F. Trippe, M. Fröhling, F. Schultmann, R. Stahl, E. Henrich, A. Dalai, 2013. Comprehensive techno-economic assessment of dimethyl ether (DME) synthesis and Fischer–Tropsch synthesis as alternative process steps within biomass-to-liquid production. Fuel Processing Technology 106, 577–586.

E. S. Van-Dal, C. Bouallou, 2013. Design and simulation of a methanol production plant from co$_2$ hydrogenation. Journal of Cleaner Production 57, 38–45.

Anton A. Kiss, Edwin Zondervan, Richard Lakerveld, Leyla Özkan (Eds.)
Proceedings of the 29th European Symposium on Computer Aided Process Engineering
June 16th to 19th, 2019, Eindhoven, The Netherlands. © 2019 Elsevier B.V. All rights reserved.
http://dx.doi.org/10.1016/B978-0-128-18634-3.50063-1

A new index for chemical process design considering risk analysis and controllability

Nancy Medina-Herrera,[a*] Salvador Tututi-Avila,[b] Arturo Jiménez-Gutierrez[c]

[a] *Universidad Autonoma de Nuevo León, Agronomy School, Francisco Villa s/n, Ex Hacienda el Canadá, General Escobedo, N.L, 66451, MEXICO*

[b] *Universidad Autónoma de Nuevo León, Department of Chemical Engineering, Av. Universidad s/n, Ciudad Universitaria, San Nicolas de los Garza, NL, 66451, MEXICO*

[c] *Department of Chemical Engineering, Instituto Tecnológico de Celaya, Av. Tecnológico s/n, Celaya, Gto. 38010 MEXICO*

nancy.medinahr@uanl.edu.mx

Abstract

Safety and controllability are two important items that complement the economic analysis commonly done during a process design. Such factors are typically carried out once the process has been designed. Although some approaches have been proposed to include controllability properties from the design stage of the process, safety is still addressed after the design has been completed, so that safety devices are added to mitigate the consequences of potential accidents. Inherent safety is the most effective risk management approach, since actions can be taken to avoid accidents instead of mitigating their consequences. However, inherent safety is not a straightforward procedure, nor universal, and sometimes in conflict with other properties or parameters of the process. This manuscript describes a new index to account for inherent safety and controllability. The combination of a conditions number that accounts for controllability and a distance likely to cause death that emerges from the application of a quantitative risk analysis for the process was used as a basis. Three mathematical relationships were explored in the search for a suitable combination of such indices. The procedure was applied to a case study dealing with a distillation system design. Results show how the values obtained from the proposed index can give an initial assessment of the combined effect of risk and controllability as part of the design of a process.

Keywords: controllability, design, inherent safety, risk analysis.

1. Introduction

The concepts associated with inherent safety provide an effective tool for risk management. Inherent safety relies on the principles of elimination, minimization, moderation, substitution and simplification. The objective of inherent safety is to avoid risk instead of diminishing its consequences. The effectiveness of inherent safety depends on the stage of the plant life it is applied, being the design stage the most effective. The decisions based on inherent safety must be evaluated carefully, since inherent safety principles sometimes show conflicts among them. For instance, the minimization principle states that a process is safer when hazardous materials inventory is reduced, but dynamic performance might work against safety if inventory is reduced. Thus, it is important to assess safety in early stages of process design including this type of self-conflicting behavior. Recently, a comprehensive review of process safety indices has been published (Roy et al., 2016). From this collection, some highlighted indexes are discussed here. Dow Fire & Explosion Index (DF&EI) was the first proposed index to account for safety in the mid-60's. There have been several works to assess inherent safety since it was defined in the 80's. The first index related to inherent safety was proposed by Heikkila et al (1996). This index is similar to DF&EI and considers two main parts of the process: chemicals properties and process conditions. Khan and Amyotte (2004) have published an integrated inherent safety index, named I2SI. This index is more complex and considers process control within inherent safety.

Most of the indices published so far are semi-quantitative, but many times weight factors are used to rank their importance. This semi-quantitative characteristic results in different processes with similar conditions so that material properties may get the same rating, which is not totally accurate. A quantitative risk analysis (QRA) has been shown as a proper tool to account for safety (Medina-Herrera et al., 2014). A QRA performs a more detailed study and provides a more exact risk measurement because probabilities and consequences are considered (AIChE, 2000).

The Morari resilience index (MRI) can be used to discriminate among process alternatives; the larger its value, the more controllable the process is. Another important index is the condition number (CN) related to system sensitivity against input disturbances. Small values are desired. Another important index is the relative gain array number (RGA$_{No}$) which gives information about the controlled and manipulated variables in the frequency domain; pairings with low RGA$_{No}$ values are preferred. All these indices provide a good basis to account for controllability, but a suitable approach to include both controllability and process safety is needed.

In this work, we propose a quantitative approach for process design that accounts for inherent safety considering both risk and controllability. In terms of risk, we use a QRA approach to obtain a distance likely to cause death, which relates to material inventory. For controllability, we test two indices, namely the condition number and the relative gain array. From a set of design candidates, the indices are normalized, and three mathematical relationships between risk and controllability are explored.

2. Safety Indices Calculation

2.1. Design approach

A set of initial designs (P) is considered to evaluate the performance of each design using the proposed indexes. Once the candidates are set, they are subjected to a combined controllability and QRA analysis. The approach is carried out using ASPEN Tech and MATLAB as software tools. In Aspen Plus steady state simulations are carried out, simulations are then exported to Aspen Dynamics, and the results are transferred to MATLAB, where indexes are computed.

2.2. Controllability analysis

In terms of controllability, a singular value decomposition procedure is carried out, from which the condition number CN$_i$ is evaluated. Regularly, a matrix of gain is obtained for the process at zero frequency and a singular value decomposition analysis is carried out. In this work, we followed the methodology proposed by Gabor and Mizsey (2008) to make calculations using a linearized state-space model system of every candidate i. The linearized state space model can be obtained with the Control Design Interface module. The methodology also computes MRI and RGA$_{No}$.

2.3. Quantitative risk analysis

QRA was implemented to assess the risk of a chemical inside process, following the methodology described in Medina-Herrera et al. (2014). The methodology is based on frequency and consequences analyses. First, catastrophic scenarios are identified from potential failures within the system using a bow tie procedure, and frequencies are calculated from literature data on failures. Then, a consequence analysis is performed for every catastrophic scenario previously identified. In brief, the consequences analysis implies quantification of the amount of material released, dispersion calculations, characterization of the scenario, and finally quantification of consequences. The models for consequence analysis were taken from CCPS Guidelines for Quantitative Risk Analysis in Chemical Process (AIChE, 2000). After the application of QRA, DD_i is obtained, which represents the distance of affectation such that there is a 50% chance of death in case of a catastrophic event. DD_i was selected because it can be calculated as measurement of risk even when layout is not yet defined, in an early design stage.

2.4. Normalization

After controllability and risk indices are individually evaluated, a normalization procedure is needed, since such indices have values with different orders of magnitude, and they also depend on the system of units.

When the set P was evaluated and controllability and risk indicators were obtained for each candidate i, a normalization procedure was used taking as a basis the highest value of each index, DD_i and CN_i, within the set P, that is,

$$\left. \begin{array}{l} DD_N^i = \dfrac{DD^i}{Maximum(DD^i)} \\[4mm] CN_N^i = \dfrac{CN^i}{Maximum(CN^i)} \end{array} \right\} \forall i \in P \qquad (1)$$

As a result, the normalized indices are bound between zero and one, and they can be subject to numerical comparison on a consistent basis.

2.5. Basic mathematical relationships: Indices

After the indicators are obtained with similar orders of magnitude, they can be used to rank process alternatives from controllability and risk considerations. Even when the relationship between such items is complex, we can establish that they are related to the process safety. Facing the lack of knowledge about the relationship between controllability and risk to assess safety, we followed the methodology by Ni et al. (2010) to create indices with two different inputs, and derived three basic mathematical relationships. As a result, a proposed safety index, SI, was developed, and three versions of such an index were created. The objective of testing three different relationships is aiding in the analysis to understand whether risk and controllability are additive, factored or follow a balanced relationship.

The first version SI_1 is the addition of both criteria, distance likely to cause death (DD_N) and condition number (CN_N).

$$SI_1 = DD_N + CN_N \tag{2}$$

The second version, SI_2, is the product of both inputs,

$$SI_2 = DD_N * CN_N \tag{3}$$

For both additive and product relationships, the smaller the value of the index, the safer the process is.

The third version we explore is a fraction given by the distance likely to cause death divided by the condition number (see Eq. (4)). In this case, a value close to one means that the process is balanced from both controllability and safety considerations, which may not necessarily be desirable. A value higher than one would indicate that risk is a more important criterion than controllability, and vice versa.

$$SI_3 = DD_N / CN_N \tag{4}$$

These three versions arise from the lack of knowledge on the relationship between risk and controllability. It deemed convenient to calculate and evaluate all three alternatives for an initial insight into behavior of the proposed index.

3. Case Study and Results

The case study was taken from the CCPS Example of the guidelines for chemical process quantitative risk analysis (AIChE, 2000). The distillation system is a single column that separates n-hexane and n-heptane. The feed stream has 60,120 kg/h of a binary mixture with 58%wt of n-hexane. The purity specification for the top product is 0.9 on a weight basis, with a flowrate of 36,000 kg/h. The column has 16 equilibrium stages and the top pressure is 4.9 atm. The internal diameter calculated by ASPEN Plus was 2.7 meters. The residence time for sump was fixed at 6 minutes, and for reflux drum at 12 min using a 2D=L rule for tank dimensions. The QRA performed with the CCPS Guidelines has been used to analyze process risk. The objective of this example is to describe the methodology for the proposed index calculations along with the analysis of results. The hydraulic variables considered for this example were diameter and residence time for the reflux drum and sump. Such hydraulic variables affect both criteria, controllability and risk. In order to define the set of designs P, we took the CCPS design as the base case, which has a diameter of 2.71m and 12 and 6 min of residence time on the reflux drum and sump. Other designs were considered by varying the diameter from half the base diameter to three times that value, such that D = [0.5Dbase, 0.75Dbase, Dbase, 1.5Dbase, 2Dbase, 3Dbase] where Dbase=2.71m. As for the residence time, a range was fixed from 1 minute to 20 minutes, assuming equal values for both tanks. It should be noted that the base case assumes residence times of 12 and 6 minutes. When the diameter was varied, the designs were set with a residence time of 10 min for reflux drum and sump, and when residence time was varied, the diameter was kept fixed at 2.71m (in that case, the residence time was the same for reflux drum and sump).

The results obtained are illustrated in Figure 1. We can observe that there is no significant difference using CN_N or RGA_{NoN} for the controllability component. We also observe that for the range analyzed, the trend seems not to be linear. The index presents almost the same value from 0.5 times diameter to the base diameter; after that point, increasing the diameter has a more pronounced effect on the three forms of the safety index, which means that increasing the diameter to improve controllability conflicts with the safety parameter. The safest design is the base case, according to SI_1 and SI_2. The design with three times diameter (3D) is more balanced between controllability and risk, as given from the results of SI_3, while for the base design controllability has a higher weight than risk ($SI_3 < 1$), which means that changing the diameter is not recommended for an inherently safer process. In part b, we observe that the contribution of the two controllability indicators used here is similar for the three safety indices. It is important to notice that for this variation range (1min -20 min) the trend seems to be linear. From SI_1 and SI_2, a residence time of 1 minute is the safest option. From the results of SI_3, the same trend is observed; decreasing residence time has a lower impact on risk with respect to the effect on controllability. Residence time has therefore an important effect on safety, as given from the risk evaluations conducted here.

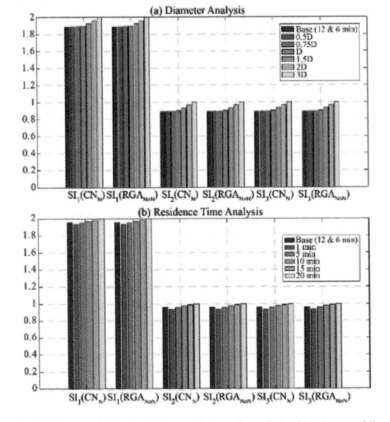

Figure 1. CCPS case study Results of Proposed Indexes for analysis of (a) changes of diameter and (b) changes of residence times

Conclusion

A combined index that accounts for risk and controllability has been described. After normalizing the individual indices chosen for each item between zero and one, three types of relationships were explored. The results of the application to a case study taken from the CCPS publication showed that implementing the minimization principle of inherent safety can lead to a conflict with controllability properties, which calls for a careful consideration of risk and controllability during the design stage of a process. The approach given in this work attempts to contribute in that direction. It is worthy of mention that there is not a general guideline whether reducing inventory, which is called for from the minimization principle of inherent safety, is a correct policy when controllability is considered. The results of the application to the case study show this type of conflict. It is important to notice that this methodology has being implemented in case studies on steady state and it has not been implemented in an intrinsically dynamic system, such as a batch process. Further work is needed to consolidate these initial efforts towards the development of a useful index that combines risk and controllability and that can be used during the design stage of a chemical process.

References

AIChE, A. I. of C. E. (2000). *Guidelines for Chemical Process Quantitative Risk Analysis*. (C. for C. P. Safety, Ed.) (2nd ed.). New York, New York.

Gabor, M., & Mizsey, P. (2008). A Methodology To Determine Controllability Indices in the Frequency Domain. *Industrial & Engineering Chemistry Research*, *47*(14), 4807–4816.

Heikkilä, A.-M., Hurme, M., & Järveläinen, M. (1996). Safety considerations in process synthesis. *Computers & Chemical Engineering*, *20*(Supplement 1), S115–S120.

Khan, F. I., & Amyotte, P. R. (2004). Integrated inherent safety index (I2SI): A tool for inherent safety evaluation. *Process Safety Progress*, *23*(2), 136–148.

Medina-Herrera, N., Grossmann, I. E., Mannan, M. S., Jimenez-Gutierrez, A., & Jiménez-Gutiérrez, A. (2014). An approach for solvent selection in extractive distillation systems including safety considerations. *Industrial & Engineering Chemistry Research*, *53*(30), 12023–12031.

Medina-Herrera, N., Jiménez-Gutiérrez, A., & Grossmann, I. E. (2014). A mathematical programming model for optimal layout considering quantitative risk analysis. *Computers & Chemical Engineering*, *68*, 165–181. https://doi.org/10.1016/j.compchemeng.2014.05.019

Medina-Herrera, N., Jiménez-Gutiérrez, A., & Mannan, M. S. (2014). Development of inherently safer distillation systems. *Journal of Loss Prevention in the Process Industries*, *29*, 225–239. https://doi.org/http://dx.doi.org/10.1016/j.jlp.2014.03.004

Ni, H., Chen, A., & Chen, N. (2010). Some extensions on risk matrix approach. *Safety Science*, *48*(10), 1269–1278. https://doi.org/http://dx.doi.org/10.1016/j.ssci.2010.04.005

Roy, N., Eljack, F., Jiménez-Gutiérrez, A., Zhang, B., Thiruvenkataswamy, P., El-Halwagi, M., & Mannan, M. S. (2016). A review of safety indices for process design. *Current Opinion in Chemical Engineering*, *14*, 42–48. https://doi.org/10.1016/j.coche.2016.07.001

Anton A. Kiss, Edwin Zondervan, Richard Lakerveld, Leyla Özkan (Eds.)
Proceedings of the 29th European Symposium on Computer Aided Process Engineering
June 16th to 19th, 2019, Eindhoven, The Netherlands. © 2019 Elsevier B.V. All rights reserved.
http://dx.doi.org/10.1016/B978-0-128-18634-3.50064-3

An MILP model for safe multi-floor process plant layout

Jude O. Ejeh[a], Songsong Liu[b] and Lazaros G. Papageorgiou[a,*]

[a]*Centre for Process Systems Engineering, Department of Chemical Engineering, University College London, Torrington Place, London WC1E 7JE, United Kingdom;*
[b]*School of Management, Swansea University, Bay Campus, Fabian Way, Swansea SA1 8EN, United Kingdom;*

Abstract

In this work, a mixed integer linear programming (MILP) model is presented to obtain the optimal layout of a multi-floor chemical process plant with minimum risk in fire and explosion scenarios. Layout decisions determine the spatial arrangement of process plant equipment on available land area considering the equipment interconnections, dimensions, costs, general operability, as well as associated structures and auxiliary units. Optimal decisions ought to strike a balance between risk and cost savings. Previous attempts to include safety considerations in the layout decision making process have been restricted to minimise connection and risk costs alone, with some unrealistic assumptions on safety distances for mostly single floor layout cases. The model presented adopts the Dow's Fire & Explosion system to quantify risk in order to determine the optimal multi-floor plot layout simultaneously with more realistic constraints for safety distance calculations. The optimal layout design obtained minimises costs attributed to the installation of connecting pipes, pumping, area-dependent construction of floors, land purchase, as well as the risk associated with fire and explosion events by inherent and passive strategies.

Keywords: multi-floor plant layout; safety; optimisation; MILP

1. Introduction

Right from conceptualisation to plant decommissioning, it is quite important that safety assessments be carried out for every aspect of a chemical process plant design project (Khan and Amyotte, 2004). Improper safety considerations at each stage of design or operation can result in fatalities, injuries, disruption of production activities within the plant and its neighbouring environment. Amidst a range of factors that contribute towards the overall safety levels, a study has shown that 79% of process plant accidents were attributed to design errors, the most critical being poor layout (Kidam and Hurme, 2012). Layout design determines the spatial arrangement of chemical process plant units considering their interconnections based on pre-defined criteria. These units may be process vessels in which unit operations are carried out, storage facilities, work centres or departments, and their spatial arrangement affect capital and operating costs, efficiency of plant activities, and of particular concern to this work, the overall safety levels within the plant and the immediate environment. From an optimisation point of view, safety considerations in layout designs have been considered in the past. While a great deal of research has focused on the economic aspects alone - piping, construction and operating costs associated for a layout configuration, an ideal plant layout design ought to establish a balance between risks and costs. In a recent review, Roy et al. (2016) outlined available safety metrics for process design and their level of application. One of the key indices applicable to layout design with numerical quantification is the Dow Fire and Explosion Index (F&EI). The Dow F&EI was developed by American Dow Chemical Company (American Institute of Chemical Engineers, 1994) and is currently a widely applied method for hazard evaluation of chemical and industrial processes (Wang and Song, 2013). It estimates the hazards of a single unit based on the chemical properties of the material(s) within it, and the potential economic risk such equipment poses to itself and neighbouring structures with or without the installation of protection devices. A similar concept was adopted by Penteado and Ciric (1996) in a mixed integer non-linear programming (MINLP) model where financial risks associated with potential events from process units were modelled as cost functions with an overall objective to minimise the net present cost of a single floor layout. The choice of safety devices was also made available to reduce the associated risk levels. Patsiatzis et al. (2004) proposed a mixed integer linear programming (MILP) model solely based on the Dow F&EI to minimise the total cost associated with connecting process units by pipes, financial risks and the purchase and installation of protection devices. Other research activities have built on these to include multi-floor considerations (Park et al., 2018), human risk considerations, and in more recent times by employing the Domino Hazard Index (López-Molina et al., 2013).

In this work, an MILP model is proposed to address the multi-floor process plant layout problem with safety considerations, which are quantified using the Dow F&EI. Readers may consult the Dow's F&EI Hazard Identification guide (American Institute of Chemical Engineers, 1994) for detailed steps to calculate this metric. The proposed model will minimise the total cost attributed to pipe connections, pumping, floor construction, land purchase, installation of protection devices and financial losses in the event of an accident, which prior to this work has not been simultaneously addressed. Safety distances between equipment items are also modelled in a new way - from the opposing boundaries of equipment items as compared to the midpoints as previously done in order to better capture the actual distances between equipment for risk quantifications. Tall equipment items spanning through consecutive floors are also considered with the model determining the optimal number of floors and the equipment floor and spatial arrangements.

In the rest of the paper, the problem description is outlined in section 2. In section 3 the mathematical model is proposed and its computational performance is shown with a relevant case study in section 4. Final remarks are given in section 5.

2. Problem Description

The problem is as follows: *Given* a set of process plant units ($i \in I$), their dimensions - length (l_i), breadth (d_i) and height (h_i) - and connectivity network with space and unit allocation limitations, a set of potential floors for layout with respective floor height (FH), a set of pertinent equipment item ($i \in I^{pe}$), a set of protection device configurations available for each pertinent item ($p \in P_i$), with associated costs (C_{ip}^p) and loss control credit factor if installed on an equipment item; *determine* the total number (NF) and area of floors (FA), the protection device configuration, p, to be installed on each pertinent equipment item, and the plot layout *so as to* minimise the total plant layout and safety costs.

It is assumed that the geometries of all process plant equipment are rectangles, with horizontal connection distances taken as the rectilinear distance from the geometrical centres in the x-y plane. Vertical connection distances are taken from a design-specified height on each equipment. For safety considerations, all rectilinear distances are taken from the boundaries of equipment items to evaluate the probability, magnitude and impact of an incident. Equipment items are allowed to rotate by 90° and those with heights greater than the floor height can extend through consecutive floors but must start from the base of a floor.

3. Mathematical Formulation

The mathematical formulation constitutes an extension of model A.1 in Ejeh et al. (2018) for the multi-process plant layout problem and by Patsiatzis et al. (2004). All constraints in model A.1 (Ejeh et al., 2018) apply with the following modifications/additions. First of all, the distance constraints written for connected equipment items ($f_{ij} = 1$) (Patsiatzis et al., 2004), are further written for pairs of items (i, j) including a pertinent item, $i \in I^{pe}$, and any other item j, i.e., $\zeta = \{(i, j) : i \in I^{pe}, j \neq i\}$.

For safety considerations, the rectilinear distances between equipment items taken from the geometrical centres no longer seem to be a valid assumption. This is especially true for process plants having large and/or tall equipment items where rectilinear distances from the geometrical centres may have a high value but the equipment items are physically close to each other. A more valid assumption will be to calculate the separation distances from the equipment boundaries as illustrated in Figure 1, as an event on a pertinent item i can emanate at any point within the item up to its boundaries.

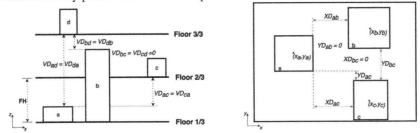

Figure 1: Vertical and horizontal safety distances between equipment items

For vertical separation distances between any two equipment items i and j (VD_{ij}), the distance is taken from the top of j to the bottom of i if i is on a higher floor than j, and if the reverse is the case, from the top of i to the bottom of j. However, if both i and j are on the same floor, i.e., $N_{ij} = 1$, the vertical separation distance is taken to be zero. The conditions stated above are modelled by Eqs. (1) - (3) where S_{ik}^s is a binary variable with a value of 1 if item i starts at floor k, and η_{ij}^u and η_{ij}^d are positive variables evaluated by Eqs. (4) - (6).

Horizontal separation distances are also calculated from the item boundaries in the x and y planes as XD_{ij} (Eqs. (7) - (11)) and YD_{ij} (Eqs. (12) - (16)) respectively (Figure 1). A value of zero is assigned to these distances if the opposing boundaries of an item i is not strictly to the right or left (in the x plane), or above or below (in the y plane) j. That is, items i and j overlap at any point on either the x or y plane. The binary variable W_{ij}^{xo} is assigned a value of 1 if item i is strictly to the right or left of item j or 0 otherwise. The same applies for W_{ij}^{yo} if item i is strictly above or below j. The relative distances between items i and j in the x plane are represented by R_{ij} and L_{ij} if i is to the right of j, and if i is the left of j respectively. A_{ij} and B_{ij} represent the relative distances in the y plane if i is above j, and if i is below j respectively. $E2_{ij}$ is a non-overlapping binary variable and BM is a large number (Patsiatzis et al., 2004). Given these modifications, the total safety distance, TD_{ij}^s, between equipment items i and j is then calculated by Eq. (17).

$$VD_{ij} \leq FH\sum_k (k-1)(S_{jk}^s - S_{ik}^s) - h_i + \eta_{ij}^u + BM \cdot N_{ij} \qquad \forall\, (i,j) \in \zeta \qquad (1)$$

$$VD_{ij} \geq FH\sum_k (k-1)(S_{jk}^s - S_{ik}^s) - h_i + \eta_{ij}^u - BM \cdot N_{ij} \qquad \forall\, (i,j) \in \zeta \qquad (2)$$

$$VD_{ij} \leq BM \cdot (1 - N_{ij}) \qquad \forall\, (i,j) \in \zeta \qquad (3)$$

$$\eta_{ij}^u - \eta_{ij}^d = 2FH\sum_k (k-1)(S_{ik}^s - S_{jk}^s) + h_i - h_j \qquad \forall\, (i,j) \in \zeta \qquad (4)$$

$$\eta_{ij}^u \leq BM \cdot W_{ij}^z \qquad \forall\, (i,j) \in \zeta \qquad (5)$$

$$\eta_{ij}^d \leq BM \cdot (1 - W_{ij}^z) \qquad \forall\, (i,j) \in \zeta \qquad (6)$$

$$x_i - x_j + 2L_{ij} \geq \left(\frac{l_i + l_j}{2}\right) - BM(1 - W_{ij}^{xo}) \qquad \forall\, (i,j) \in \zeta \qquad (7)$$

$$XD_{ij} \leq R_{ij} + L_{ij} - \left(\frac{l_i + l_j}{2}\right) + BM(1 - W_{ij}^{xo}) \qquad \forall\, (i,j) \in \zeta \qquad (8)$$

$$XD_{ij} \geq R_{ij} + L_{ij} - \left(\frac{l_i + l_j}{2}\right) - BM(1 - W_{ij}^{xo}) \qquad \forall\, (i,j) \in \zeta \qquad (9)$$

$$XD_{ij} \leq BM \cdot W_{ij}^{xo} \qquad \forall\, (i,j) \in \zeta \qquad (10)$$

$$W_{ij}^{xo} \geq 1 - E2_{ij}\,|_{j>i} - E2_{ji}\,|_{i>j} \qquad \forall\, (i,j) \in \zeta \qquad (11)$$

$$y_i - y_j + 2B_{ij} \geq \left(\frac{d_i + d_j}{2}\right) - BM(1 - W_{ij}^{yo}) \qquad \forall\, (i,j) \in \zeta \qquad (12)$$

$$YD_{ij} \leq A_{ij} + B_{ij} - \left(\frac{d_i + d_j}{2}\right) + BM(1 - W_{ij}^{yo}) \qquad \forall\, (i,j) \in \zeta \qquad (13)$$

$$YD_{ij} \geq A_{ij} + B_{ij} - \left(\frac{d_i + d_j}{2}\right) - BM(1 - W_{ij}^{yo}) \qquad \forall\, (i,j) \in \zeta \qquad (14)$$

$$YD_{ij} \leq BM \cdot W_{ij}^{yo} \qquad \forall\, (i,j) \in \zeta \qquad (15)$$

$$W_{ij}^{yo} \geq E2_{ij}\,|_{j>i} + E2_{ji}\,|_{i>j} \qquad \forall\, (i,j) \in \zeta \qquad (16)$$

$$TD_{ij}^s = XD_{ij} + YD_{ij} + VD_{ij} \qquad \forall\, (i,j) \in \zeta \qquad (17)$$

The area of exposure and maximum probable property damage cost constraints are as described in Patsiatzis et al. (2004) using the modified total distance, TD_{ij}^s.

The objective function (Eq. (18)) is the minimisation of the total cost attributed to connection, pumping, land purchase, construction, financial risk and the installation of protective devices. The financial risk is evaluated from the actual maximum probable property damage cost (Ω_i) (Patsiatzis et al., 2004) and μ_{ip} is a binary variable with a value of 1 if protection device configuration p is to be purchased and installed on pertinent item $i \in I^{pe}$. C_{ij}^c, C_{ij}^v, C_{ij}^h, LC, $FC1$ and $FC2$ represent the connection cost, vertical pumping cost, horizontal pumping cost, area-dependent land purchase cost, fixed floor construction cost and area-dependent floor construction cost respectively.

$$min\sum_i \sum_{j\neq i: f_{ij}=1} [C_{ij}^c TD_{ij} + C_{ij}^v D_{ij} + C_{ij}^h (R_{ij} + L_{ij} + A_{ij} + B_{ij})] + FC1 \cdot NF$$

$$+FC2\sum_s AR_s \cdot NQ_s + LC \cdot FA + \sum_i \Omega_i + \sum_{i,p\in P_i} C_{ip}^p \cdot \mu_{ip} \tag{18}$$

4. Case study

The model proposed was applied to an Ethylene oxide plant (Figure 2) (Patsiatzis et al., 2004). Six protection device configurations are made available for installation, with the first configuration having no protection device purchased or installed. Full details for the configurations, the characteristic protection devices in each, and the associated cost and loss control credit factor can be found in Patsiatzis et al. (2004). The model was solved to global optimality using GAMS modelling system v25.0.2 with the CPLEX v12.8 solver on an Intel® Xeon® E5-1650 CPU with 32GB RAM. It had 260 discrete and 386 continuous variables with 894 equations, and obtained a total cost value of 480,114.4 rmu in 33s.

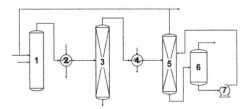

Figure 2: Flow diagram of Ethylene Oxide plant

Figure 3 shows the optimal layout plot with safety considerations. With the inclusion of fire and explosion scenarios, an additional floor is required compared to the layout results without safety considerations (Ejeh et al., 2018). Out of the total cost of 480,114.4 rmu, 175,000 rmu was attributed to the installation of protection devices, 187,535.4 to financial risks and 117,579.0 rmu to connection, pumping and construction costs. The latter cost quota is much larger when compared to the case without safety considerations, 66,262 rmu (Ejeh et al., 2018), owing to additional separation distances between equipment items, a larger floor area (30m× 30m compared to 20m× 20m), as well as the cost of the additional floor constructed.

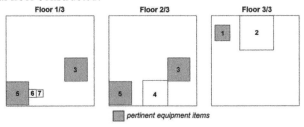

Figure 3: Optimal layout results

For the case where safety was not considered and no protection device was installed, the financial risk was calculated, based on the layout results obtained in Ejeh et al. (2018), to be 935,820.9 rmu. In the optimal solution with safety considerations, protection devices were installed on all the pertinent equipment items - 1, 3 and 5 - to reduce the probability and magnitude of an incident. The total cost of purchase and installation was 175,000 rmu, with a reduced financial risk of 187,535.4 rmu. Hence, the cost of protection devices, financial risk, and other layout costs combined is much less for the case where safety is considered and protection devices are installed than if they were not. This provides for a more informed balance between cost savings and financial risks.

5. Concluding remarks

An MILP model (extended from Ejeh et al., 2018 and Patsiatzis et al., 2004) was proposed for the multi-floor process plant layout problem considering connection, pumping, construction, financial risk and protection device installation costs in fire and explosion scenarios. The model successfully described tall equipment items spanning through multiple floors with more accurate safety distance calculations obtained from the boundaries of neighbouring equipment items within similar floors and on different floors. The proposed model was applied to a 7-unit case study having 3 pertinent equipment items and 6 protection device configurations. 3 floors were obtained for the optimal solution, with a larger floor area and total cost compared to the same case without safety considerations. Overall, the proposed model is proved to be able to optimise the installation of protection devices and significantly reduce the risk associated with fire and explosion, resulting in a substantial decrease in probable property damage cost, much higher than the required additional safety device purchase, installation, connection, pumping and construction costs. Future work will seek to apply the model to larger case studies with more complex connection networks.

Acknowledgement

JOE acknowledges the financial support of the Petroleum Technology Development Fund (PTDF).

References

American Institute of Chemical Engineers, 1994. Dow's Fire & Explosion Index Hazard Classification Guide. Vol. 7. John Wiley & Sons, Inc., Hoboken, NJ, USA.

J. O. Ejeh, S. Liu, M. M. Chalchooghi, L. G. Papageorgiou, 2018. Optimization-Based Approach for Process Plant Layout. Ind. Eng. Chem. Res. 57 (31), 10482–10490.

F. I. Khan, P. R. Amyotte, 2004. Integrated Inherent Safety Index (I2SI): A Tool for Inherent Safety Evaluation. Process Saf. Prog. 23 (2), 136–148.

K. Kidam, M. Hurme, 2012. Design as a Contributor to Chemical Process Accidents. J. Loss Prev. Process Ind. 25 (4), 655–666.

A. López-Molina, R. Vázquez-Román, M. S. Mannan, M. G. Félix-Flores, 2013. An Approach for Domino Effect Reduction Based on Optimal Layouts. J. Loss Prev. Process Ind. 26 (5), 887–894.

K. Park, D. Shin, W. Won, 2018. Risk Based 3-Dimensional and Multifloor Plant Layout Optimization for Liquefied Natural Gas (LNG) Liquefaction Process. Korean J. Chem. Eng. 35 (5), 1053–1064.

D. I. Patsiatzis, G. Knight, L. G. Papageorgiou, 2004. An MILP Approach to Safe Process Plant Layout. Chem. Eng. Res. Des. 82 (5), 579–586.

F. D. Penteado, A. R. Ciric, 1996. An MINLP Approach for Safe Process Plant Layout. Ind. Eng. Chem. Res. 35 (4), 1354–1361.

N. Roy, F. Eljack, A. Jiménez-Gutiérrez, B. Zhang, P. Thiruvenkataswamy, M. El-Halwagi, M. S. Mannan, 2016. A Review of Safety Indices for Process Design. Curr. Opin. Chem. Eng. 14, 42–48.

J. Wang, W.-H. Song, 2013. Fire and Explosion Index Calculation Method Incorporating Classified Safety Measure Credits. J. Loss Prev. Process Ind. 26 (6), 1128–1133.

Anton A. Kiss, Edwin Zondervan, Richard Lakerveld, Leyla Özkan (Eds.)
Proceedings of the 29th European Symposium on Computer Aided Process Engineering
June 16th to 19th, 2019, Eindhoven, The Netherlands. © 2019 Elsevier B.V. All rights reserved.
http://dx.doi.org/10.1016/B978-0-128-18634-3.50065-5

A Generalized, Nonsmooth Operator for Process Integration

Caroline J. Nielsen[a,*] and Paul I. Barton[a]

[a]*Massachusetts Institute of Technology, 77 Massachusetts Ave., Cambridge, MA 02139, USA*
cjn1994@mit.edu

Abstract

This work presents a novel, generalized method for solving resource targeting problems for process integration. The approach uses nonsmooth systems of two equations per resource to simulate the process under optimal resource reuse. The resulting equation system, including process models, is solved using new advances in the automatic generation of LD-derivatives to supply generalized derivative elements to nonsmooth equation-solving methods. Therefore, this method can be used to solve for process variables in addition to resource targets and retains the same number of equations regardless of the number of resource sources and sinks in the problem. An illustrative example of combined mass and water integration is included to demonstrate the strengths and flexibility of this approach.

Keywords: Process integration, Targeting, Process design, Nonsmooth equations

1. Introduction

Process integration methods have been widely proposed and utilized to minimize resource use through optimal reuse. These approaches were initially considered for heat recovery in heat integration problems (Linnhoff and Flower, 1978) and were then extended to the recovery of materials in mass exchange networks (MENs) and water allocation problems (El-Halwagi and Manousiouthakis, 1989; Dhole et al., 1996). In recent years, integration methods have also been applied beyond these traditional areas to new problems, such as hydrogen allocation, carbon planning, and even inventory problems (Alves and Towler, 2002; Munir et al., 2012; Castillo and Mahalec, 2013). There is a significant body of work on solving these integration problems; however, although the underlying integration problem is the same for each application, the existing solution methods are specific to one resource type and not immediately generalizable.

Process integration problems consist of two stages, first, determining the minimum attainable fresh and waste resource flows, and second, designing a resource conservation network that can approach these targets. The focus of this work is the former resource targeting problem. By eliminating the network design step and avoiding simultaneous superstructure approaches that scale poorly with problem size, resource targeting is able to consider resource usage and constraints efficiently when screening and optimizing plant designs.

The simplest class of targeting approaches are graphical pinch analysis and cascade (also referred to as transshipment) formulations. These approaches are easy to use and physically intuitive, but are applicable to only a limited number of scenarios and are usually unable to solve for process variables. Therefore, they cannot be used to simulate systems with known resource targets or for simultaneous process integration and optimization. To address these limitations for heat integration, Navarro-Amoros et al. (2013) proposed a cascade-type model that uses disjunctions to determine temperature intervals. Alternatively, Duran and Grossmann (1986) developed a "pinch location method," which avoids the construction of temperature intervals by using an optimization formulation with nonsmooth inequalities that is solved using smoothing approximations or as a disjunctive program (Grossmann et al., 1998). However, all of these approaches either require approximations or solving nonconvex MINLPs, and they scale either cubically or quadratically with the number of hot and cold streams in the problem.

To avoid approximations and improve scaling, Watson et al. (2015) reformulated the inequalities in the pinch location method to a create a simple system of nonsmooth equations to simulate heat integration systems. In this work, we extend the approach of Watson et al. to develop compact nonsmooth operators that can be applied beyond heat integration to the general integration problem. The result is a solution method that scales well with problem size, requires only equation-solving approaches, and can solve for process variables while simultaneously considering the integration of multiple resources.

2. Problem Statement

Consider a set of resources types under consideration for integration, T. Using the notation for general resource integration presented by Foo (2013), for each resource type $n \in T$, there exists a fresh resource supply, $R_{SR,n}$, and a waste resource flow, $r_{SK,n}$, a set of sources, SR_n, with constant states $S_{i,n}$ that change in quality from $Q_{i,n}^{in}$ to $Q_{i,n}^{out}$, and a set of sinks, SK_n, with states $s_{j,n}$ that change in quality from $q_{j,n}^{in}$ to $q_{j,n}^{out}$. The source and sink states determine the extent to which a resource transfer $R_{i,n}$ or $r_{j,n}$ will affect the quality according to $R_{i,n} = S_{i,n}\Delta Q_{i,n}$ or $r_{j,n} = s_{j,n}\Delta q_{j,n}$ respectively, and the quality is selected such that higher values indicate higher purity resources.

Table 1: State and qualities for common integration types.

Integration Type	Quantity	Quality	State
Heat	heat transfer rate	temperature	heat capacity flow rate
Mass	contaminant mass load flow rate	concentration in reference stream	scaled solvent mass flow rate
Water	water mass flow rate	negative cumulative contaminant mass load flow rate	inverse contaminant concentration, sorted by increasing concentration

The states and qualities for common integration problems are given in Table 1. Note that for mass integration problems, concentrations and flow rates are transformed to their corresponding values in a specified reference stream using equilibrium relations. Additionally, in water allocation problems, the sources and sinks must be sorted by increasing concentration, and the qualities are the negative of the cumulative contaminant flow rates of the sources or sinks in this order to ensure that high purity water flows have higher quality values.

Given this system, we want to be able to solve the following problem for a selection of unknowns from the vector of process variables, $\boldsymbol{x}$, and the $|T|$ vectors of resource utilities, $\boldsymbol{y}_n = (R_{SR,n}, r_{SK,n})$:

$$\boldsymbol{0} = \mathbf{h}(\boldsymbol{x}, \boldsymbol{y}_1, \ldots, \boldsymbol{y}_{|T|}),$$

$$\boldsymbol{y}_n = \underset{\boldsymbol{y}_n, R_{1,n}, \ldots, R_{K_n-1,n}}{\arg\min} R_{SR,n}, \quad \forall n \in T,$$

$$\text{s.t.} \quad 0 = R_{SR,n} - R_{1,n} + \sum_{i \in SR_{1,n}} S_{i,n} \Delta Q_{1,n} - \sum_{j \in SK_{1,n}} s_{j,n} \Delta q_{1,n},$$

$$0 = R_{k-1,n} - R_{k,n} + \sum_{i \in SR_{k,n}} S_{i,n} \Delta Q_{k,n} - \sum_{j \in SK_{k,n}} s_{j,n} \Delta q_{k,n}, \quad \forall k \in \{2, \ldots, K_n - 1\},$$

$$0 = R_{K_n-1,n} - r_{SK,n} + \sum_{i \in SR_{K_n,n}} S_{i,n} \Delta Q_{K_n,n} - \sum_{j \in SK_{K_n,n}} s_{j,n} \Delta q_{K_n,n},$$

$$0 \leq R_{k,n}, \quad \forall k \in \{1, \ldots, K_n - 1\}.$$

This problem consists of a process model, $\mathbf{h}$, dependent on resource utilities and process variables, and embedded resource minimization problems parametric in the process variables. These minimization problems are constrained by resource balances and feasibility constraints for resource transfer. While a number of formulations of these constraints have been presented in the literature, for the sake of example, here we use the transshipment formulation of Papoulias and Grossmann (1983), which ensures that resource flows, $R_{k,n}$, are positive from high to low quality between the K_n quality intervals that have quality changes $\Delta Q_{k,n} = \Delta q_{k,n}$.

3. Operator Formulation

Our approach to solving the general integration problem is using explicitly nonsmooth equations to express the solutions of the embedded minimization problems. This formulation results in two equations per resource n in addition to the process model. Neglecting the index n for clarity, these two equations can be written as

$$0 = \sum_{i \in SR} S_i (Q_i^{in} - Q_i^{out}) - \sum_{j \in SK} s_j (q_j^{out} - q_j^{in}) + R_{SR} - r_{SK}, \tag{1}$$

$$0 = \min_{p \in P} \{RBP_{SK}^p - RBP_{SR}^p\} + r_{SK}, \tag{2}$$

where P is the finite index set of pinch point candidates and

$$RBP_{SR}^p := \sum_{i \in SR} S_i [\max\{0, Q^p - Q_i^{out}\} - \max\{0, Q^p - Q_i^{in}\}$$

$$- \max\{0, Q^{min} - Q^p\} + \max\{0, Q^p - Q^{max}\}], \quad \forall p \in P,$$

$$RBP_{SK}^p := \sum_{j \in SK} s_j [\max\{0, (Q^p - \Delta Q_{min}) - q_j^{in}\}$$

$$- \max\{0, (Q^p - \Delta Q_{min}) - q_j^{out}\} + \max\{0, (Q^p - \Delta Q_{min}) - q^{max}\}$$

$$- \max\{0, q^{min} - (Q^p - \Delta Q_{min})\}], \quad \forall p \in P,$$

where $Q^{min,max}$ and $q^{min,max}$ are the minimum and maximum qualities across the sources or the sinks, respectively, ΔQ_{min} is the minimum feasible quality difference for resource transfer to occur, and the source qualities at the potential pinch points are

$$Q^p = \begin{cases} Q_i^{in}, & \forall p = i \in SR, \\ q_j^{in} + \Delta Q_{min}, & \forall p = j \in SK. \end{cases}$$

Here, Equation 1 is the overall resource balance, and Equation 2 is the resource balance below potential resource transfer pinch points. Equation 2 uses a simple nonsmooth expression to ensure that the resource balance is nonnegative below all potential pinch points and zero below at least one of these potential pinch points, i.e. resource transfer is always feasible and at least one pinch point exists to ensure optimality. The expressions for $RBP_{SR,SK}^p$ are the cumulative source and sink resources below the potential pinch point quality. The nonsmooth max terms capture the position of the inlet and outlet qualities of the source or sink in relation to the potential pinch point quality. Nonphysical extensions to the cumulative resource quantities are also included, which avoid additional singular regions or infinite solutions by ensuring the difference between the source and sink resource balances is always defined.

These two equations replace the embedded minimization problem for each resource and we solve the resulting system of equations with a nonsmooth equation solving method such as the semismooth or LP Newton methods (Facchinei et al., 2014). In the past, these methods have been limited by the ability to calculate useful generalized derivative elements automatically. However, using recent work by Khan and Barton (2015), we calculate LD-derivatives using a vector forward mode of automatic differentiation which computes elements of the B-subdifferential for piecewise differentiable functions. Therefore, we are able to automatically compute generalized derivative elements to achieve local quadratic convergence for these nonsmooth equation-solving methods.

4. Example: Dephenolization and recycling of aqueous wastes

Adapting the problem presented by El-Halwagi (2012), we consider an oil recycling facility that uses steam strippers to remove sulfur and other light compounds from the oil streams. The main contaminant of concern in the stripper condensates is phenol, which can be removed through transfer to the oil streams in a MEN. Here, we consider the possibility of reuse of the stripper condensate after dephenolization to reduce both fresh water consumption and wastewater production. We wish to determine the minimum attainable fresh and waste water flow rates as well as the phenol concentrations and water flow rates throughout the system. We require that no external utilities are used in the MEN and that the concentrations of the two stripper condensates are the same when they exit the MEN. We also assume that there are phenol concentration limits in the boilers that limit the inlet concentrations to the strippers and that the mass of phenol transferred in the strippers is constant. (This assumption can be replaced by more complex stripper models if desired.) The parameters for this system are given in Table 2.

To solve this problem, we used two integration operators, one for the allocation of water and one for the mass exchange of phenol. We obtained the sorted mass fractions required to determine the states and qualities for the water allocation problem using a simple bubble sort algorithm. Because this algorithm applies a fixed number of min

Table 2: System parameters for dephenolization example.

Stream	Flow rate (kg/h)	Inlet mass fraction	Outlet mass fraction
Lube Oil	5	0.005	0.015
Gas Oil	3	0.010	0.030
Stripper 1 steam	2.5	0.005	z_2
Stripper 2 steam	z_1	0.002	z_4
Stripper 1 wastewater	2.50	z_2	z_3
Stripper 2 wastewater	z_1	z_4	z_5
Fresh water	z_6	-	-
Wastewater	z_7	-	-

Stripper 1 mass load: 0.11 kg/h
Stripper 2 mass load: 0.03 kg/h

Equilibrium relation for lube oil: $y = 2.00x_1$
Equilibrium relation for gas oil: $y = 1.53x_2$
Minimum MEN concentration difference: $\varepsilon = 0.001$

and max functions for a given input size, it allows us to automatically calculate LD-derivatives for the sorting process that can be supplied to nonsmooth equation-solving methods (Watson et al., 2015). In addition to the integration operators, we also included process equations describing the constant mass transfer in the strippers and equating the MEN water outlet concentrations. The result was a nonsmooth system of 7 equations which we solved for 7 unknowns using a semismooth Newton method to give $z = (0.84, 0.049, 0.013, 0.038, 0.013, 2.27, 2.27)$. For a range of initial guesses, the semismooth Newton method quickly converged to the solution in 3 to 9 iterations. The mass and water composite curves for this solution are given in Figure 1 and demonstrate that our solution method produces the optimal pinch behavior.

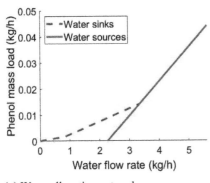

(a) Water allocation network.

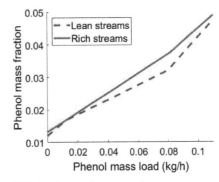

(b) Mass integration network.

Figure 1: Composite curves for the optimized dephonolization system.

5. Conclusions

We have developed an approach for solving process integration problems using compact, nonsmooth operators. These operators are generalizable to the integration of any resource and can be combined to simultaneously consider multiple resources coupled by a process model. These operators also only require equation-solving methods, can solve for process variables, and are only two equations per resource regardless of the number of sources and sinks in the problem. As a result, we have formulated a readily adaptable approach that significantly reduces problem complexity and can provide computationally tractable solutions to a wide variety of large-scale integration problems.

6. Acknowledgments

We are grateful to the OCP Group for providing financial support for this research and to the Université Mohammed VI Polytechnique - MIT Research Program for supporting and facilitating this collaboration.

References

J. J. Alves, G. P. Towler, 2002. Analysis of Refinery Hydrogen Distribution Systems. Industrial Engineering and Chemistry Research 41, 5759–5769.

P. A. C. Castillo, V. Mahalec, 2013. Inventory Pinch Algorithm for Gasoline Blend Planning. AIChE Journal 59 (10), 3748–3766.

V. R. Dhole, N. Ramchandani, R. Tainsh, M. Wasilewski, 1996. Make your process water pay for itself. Chemical Engineering 103 (1), 100–103.

M. A. Duran, I. E. Grossmann, 1986. Simultaneous optimization and heat integration of chemical processes. AIChE Journal 32 (1), 123–138.

M. M. El-Halwagi, 2012. Sustainable Design Through Process Integration. Elsevier.

M. M. El-Halwagi, V. Manousiouthakis, 1989. Synthesis of Mass Exchange Nextworks. AIChE Journal 35 (8), 1233–1244.

F. Facchinei, A. Fischer, M. Herrich, 2014. An LP-Newton method: nonsmooth equations, KKT systems, and nonisolated solutions. Mathematical Programming 146, 1–36.

D. C. Y. Foo, 2013. Process Integration for Resource Conservation. Taylor & Francis Group.

I. Grossmann, H. Yeomans, Z. Kravanja, 1998. A rigorous disjunctive optimization model for simultaneous flowsheet optimization and heat integration. Computers and Chemical Engineering 22, S157–S164.

K. A. Khan, P. I. Barton, 2015. A vector forward mode of automatic differentiation for generalized derivative evaluation. Optimization Methods and Software 30 (6), 1185–1212.

B. Linnhoff, J. R. Flower, 1978. Synthesis of heat exchanger networks: I. Systematic generation of energy optimal networks. AIChE Journal 24 (4), 633–642.

S. M. Munir, Z. A. Manan, S. R. W. Alwi, 2012. Holistic carbon planning for industrial parks: a waste-to-resources process integration approach. Journal of Cleaner Production 33, 74–85.

M. A. Navarro-Amoros, J. A. Caballero, R. Ruiz-Femenia, I. E. Grossmann, 2013. An alternative disjunctive optimization model for heat integration with variable temperatures. Computers and Chemical Engineering 56, 12–26.

S. A. Papoulias, I. E. Grossmann, 1983. A structural optimization approach in process synthesis - II: Heat recovery networks. Computers and Chemical Engineering 7 (6), 707–721.

H. A. J. Watson, K. A. Khan, P. I. Barton, 2015. Multistream heat exchanger modeling and design. AIChE Journal 61 (10), 3390–3403.

Anton A. Kiss, Edwin Zondervan, Richard Lakerveld, Leyla Özkan (Eds.)
Proceedings of the 29th European Symposium on Computer Aided Process Engineering
June 16th to 19th, 2019, Eindhoven, The Netherlands. © 2019 Elsevier B.V. All rights reserved.
http://dx.doi.org/10.1016/B978-0-128-18634-3.50066-7

Analysis of Process Alternatives for Energy-Efficient Bioethanol Downstream Processing

Dinis S. Nunes[a], José F.O. Granjo[a*], Belmiro P.M. Duarte[a,b] and Nuno M.C. Oliveira[a]

[a]*CIEPQPF, Department of Chemical Engineering, University of Coimbra, Rua Sílvio Lima — Polo II, 3030–790 Coimbra, Portugal*
[b]*Coimbra Polytechnic-ISEC, Dept. Chemical & Biological Engineering, Portugal*
josegranjo@eq.uc.pt

Abstract

This work addresses the production of gasohol using gasoline as a separation agent, an alternative approach to processes that recover and dehydrate ethanol before its blending with gasoline. Experimental data was used to build the thermodynamic model used to predict phase equilibrium and thermophysical properties. Two configurations for the direct manufacture of E10 gasohol were analyzed. Process I is extraction-based whereas Process II is extractive distillation-based. The processes were compared with each other in terms of energy needs as well as with a state-of-art process where ethanol dehydration is performed with molecular sieves (Process MS). The results show that Processes I and II are energetically favorable, and consume, after process optimization and heat integration, 30% less heat than Process MS, for ethanol concentrations in fermentation broths between 2 and 10 wt%. Furthermore, estimated ethanol separation costs are approximately $0.19/kg·ethanol for a 5 wt% feed.

Keywords: Ethanol separation; Gasohol direct production; Process design; Heat integration; Techno-economic analysis

1. Introduction

The pursuit of alternative sources of energy prompted global research and industrial developments of biofuels. Ethanol (produced from diverse sources) falls into this class and is typically marketed in blends with gasoline (as gasohol) for road transport vehicles. The downstream processing of fuel-grade ethanol involves the removal of the solids fraction and secondary products from the broth, followed by concentration and dehydration to prevent phase separation in fuel systems. This step is energy-intensive because of the need of separating the water, and challenging by the existence of a binary azeotrope in the ethanol/water mixture which hinders the economic performance of the process.

Several separation systems are described in literature for the recovery and dehydration of ethanol, including pressure-swing distillation (Black, 1980), liquid-liquid extraction (Neves et al., 2011), salt-effect distillation (Zeng and Li, 2015), and azeotropic, extractive and dividing-wall distillation operations (Singh and Rangaiah, 2017). Kubička et al. (2013) describes an arrangement coupling a distillation pre-concentration step followed by molecular sieves, which adsorb the reminiscent water out of ethanol with great energy efficiency. Configurations including membrane separation units (e.g., pervaporation, vapor permeation) for water removal in the vicinity of azeotrope mixture after a previous ethanol concentration step were also successfully implemented (Vane, 2008).

All the aforementioned configurations have a common feature. They are designed to produce anhydrous ethanol. However, this approach may be economically sub-optimal if the product is to be marketed as a blend with gasoline rather a pure fuel or chemical. Another option is to consider hydrocarbon streams to be incorporated from diverse sources in ethanol separation systems, or simply pre-blending gasoline with ethanol on-site. Potential opportunities for heat and process integration could arise, besides the utilization of hydrocarbon cuts as solvents for water elimination.

Schemes for the direct production of gasohol were developed in previous contributions wherein gasoline fractions work as solvents in extraction columns where the final product is obtained from a concentrated aqueous solution of ethanol (Kyle, 1981; Stacey et al., 2016) or as entrainers in extractive distillation systems (Black, 1980; Chianese and Zinnamosca, 1990). Estimates indicate achievable energy savings of 17–68% for both methods compared with classical azeotropic distillation methods. Nevertheless, no rigorous process simulation is provided to quantify in detail the operating conditions, materials and energy requirements (Stacey et al., 2016); besides the process optimization and heat integration were not addressed (Black, 1980; Kyle, 1981; Chianese and Zinnamosca, 1990). Noticeably, a techno-economical analysis of processes that incorporate gasoline fractions in ethanol separation can benefit potential users and complement existing references.

Consequently, this work examines the production of gasohol using gasoline as a separating agent, focusing on techno-economic aspects involving different process designs and comparing their performance to the benchmark. We developed a modeling framework to describe accurately phase equilibria and thermophysical properties of mixtures (Section 2). Subsequently, two main configurations were simulated in Aspen Plus®, analyzed at base case conditions (i.e., close to the ones reported in the literature). Specifically, they are compared against each other and with a benchmark alternative – Process MS – regarding the energy consumption for achieving ethanol concentrations in broth in 2–10 wt% (Section 3). Next, process optimization and pinch analysis were carried out to estimate the minimum energy needs for both processes (Section 4). Moreover, heat exchanger networks (HENs) were also optimally designed for minimum total cost using systematic strategies, with the ethanol production cost estimated and compared with those reported in literature. Finally, the paper closes in Section 5 with a summary of the main findings.

2. Modeling framework

The scope of analysis is the separation of ethanol, where a simplified broth composition is assumed, i.e., the secondary products and solids were previously removed. Therefore, the components in the stream are water, ethanol, and gasoline. The latter may be modeled as an assay with different cuts of hypothetical components or as a single hypothetical component, with the pure and mixing thermophysical parameters estimated from petroleum distillation-curves. However, classical equations-of-state are usually inadequate to describe liquid phase non-idealities of mixtures containing polar components, like water and ethanol (Carlson, 1996). Consequently, gasoline was considered as a single pseudo-component, wherein pure thermophysical properties are estimated using a distillation-curve ASTM D86 presented in Andersen et al. (2010) and the API methods (Aspentech, Inc., 2016). Phase equilibrium is modeled considering the vapor as an ideal gas and non-ideality in liquid phase is modeled with NRTL model (Renon and Prausnitz, 1968).

2.1. Data regression

The binary interaction parameters of NRTL model were fitted to an experimental data set collected from several works containing 40 tie-lines of the ternary water-ethanol-gasoline system, plus 23 points of VLE and 9 of excess molar enthalpy for the binary ethanol-gasoline. The fitting strategy followed here is similar to that in Granjo et al. (2014), where data points were weighted uniformly and phase stability conditions were explicitly included in the mathematical formulation. Regression results show a good agreement between experiments and model predictions, since the global

Table 1: NRTL parameters for water(1)-ethanol(2)-gasoline(3). $\tau_{ij} = a_{ij} + b_{ij}/T$, $\alpha_{ij} = \alpha_{ji}$.

i	j	a_{ij}	a_{ji}	b_{ij}/K	b_{ji}/K	α_{ij}
1	2†	3.8173	-1.3047	-263.33	-0.62597	0.10000
1	3	17.881	9.0361	-2773.7	-1495.0	0.24115
2	3	-0.20257	-0.27569	515.11	722.30	0.4837

†1-2 pair fixed. Values from `NISTV100` `NIST-IG` database (Aspentech, Inc., 2016).

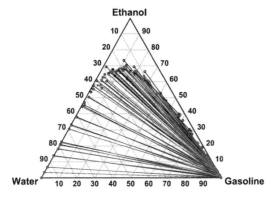

Figure 1: Experimental (black, empty) and predicted (red,filled) tie-lines (wt%).

average relative deviation (ARD) is 5.3% with an ARD of 0.7% in tie-line predictions (check Figure 1).

3. Process simulation & benchmark

Two processes described in literature are used for benchmark. In Process I, the broth stream is pre-concentrated up to the vicinity of the azeotropic concentration (∼90 wt% ethanol), and then fed to an extraction column, with the gasohol leaving the extract while raffinate goes to a gasoline recovery distillation column (Kyle, 1981). Process II is similar to Process I, but the extraction column is replaced by an extractive distillation arrangement where the product leaves in the bottoms and the distillate is decanted (Black, 1980). Processes I and II are represented in Figure 2 and Figure 3, respectively. To assess the thermal efficiency, energy requirements of Processes I and II were estimated for ethanol concentrations in feed within 2–10 wt%. It was considered a continuous processing plant with an hourly capacity of approximately 2 tonnes of ethanol (dry mass) and 8322 h/y of operation.

For a comparative analysis, energy needs were calculated for a liquid saturated feed with 2–10 wt% ethanol and (i) a *Single Column* system comprehending an ethanol/water distillation column operating at 1 atm, with total condenser and producing a distillate with 93.5 wt% ethanol; (ii) a *Double Column* system consisting on a stripping column followed by a concentration distillation column (with total condenser), both at 1 atm and producing a distillate with 93.5 wt% ethanol; and (iii) Process MS involving a dehydration step with molecular sieves preceded by a double-column distillation system. The total number of stages (NT) and the feed stage (NF) in D101 and D102 were estimated with the approximate methods of Fenske-Underwood-Gilliland, whereas the reboiler duties and reflux ratio were optimized to find the minimum energy consumption. NT_{D101} and NF_{D101} in Single Column/Process I are 30 and 12, respectively. NT_{D101}, NT_{D102}, and NF_{D102} in Double Column/Process II/Process MS are 26, 34, and 20, respectively. The operating conditions of D102 and the extraction column in Figure 2 are similar to the ones in Kyle

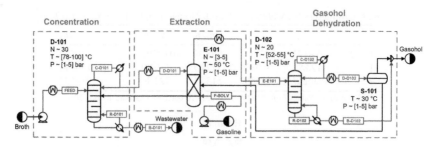

Figure 2: Process flowsheet diagram of Process I.

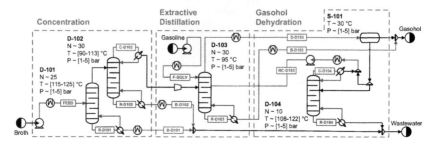

Figure 3: Process flowsheet diagram of Process II.

(1981), whereas the conditions D103 and D104 of Figure 3 are similar to the ones reported in Black (1980).

Figure 4 shows that Processes I and II are energy-efficient, since their heat duties to produce E10 gasohol at base case conditions are, respectively, within 5.1–14.1 MJ·heat/kg·ethanol and 4.8–13.8 MJ·heat/kg·ethanol for ethanol concentrations in feed between 10 wt% and 2 wt%. This means that Process I requires on average 0.9 MJ·heat/kg·ethanol of heat to produce E10 gasohol from near-azeotropic composition, while Process II needs about 1.6 MJ·heat/kg·ethanol. These figures are competitive with those reported in Singh and Rangaiah (2017) considering other technologies (0.7–5.1 MJ·heat/kg·ethanol). Both processes also compare well with Process MS, since molecular sieves are reported to spend 1–2 MJ·heat/kg·ethanol to produce 99.5 wt% ethanol from ethanol/water azeotropic distillates (Vane, 2008).

4. Process optimization and heat integration

Once the performance of Processes I and II at base case conditions were found, the goal is to determine the operating conditions that minimize the total hot utilities consumption. For such a purpose a mathematical program was formulated and then solved in Aspen Plus® V10 using BOBYQA (Powell, 2009), where reboiler duties and reflux ratios of all distillation columns in Processes I and II were optimized to minimize energy consumption. The total number of stages, feed stages and operating pressures remain fixed. Afterwards, pinch analysis was carried out with ASPEN Energy Analyzer to find the theoretical minimum energy usage for both processes with $\Delta T_{\min} = 10\,°C$. Dashed lines in Figure 4 show that modifications in operating conditions and heat integration can significantly reduce the energy needs of Processes I and II to 3.8–14.0 MJ·heat/kg·ethanol and 3.5–12.2 MJ·heat/kg·ethanol, respectively, for ethanol concentrations in broth between 10 wt% and 2 wt% which represent energy savings up to 30% compared to Process MS. Practically, the lower energy consumptions are due to (i) the reduction in heat requirements for solvent recovery; and (ii) the heat integration between the pre-concentration distillation columns and the gasoline

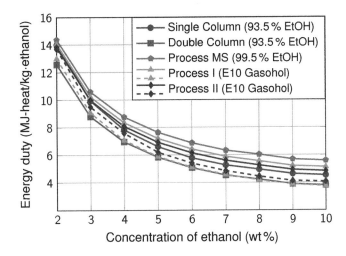

Figure 4: Energy duty vs. ethanol concentration in feed for the various process configurations. Dashed lines represent the Processes I and II optimized for minimum energy requirements.

recovery/extractive distillation columns.

4.1. HEN optimal design and ethanol production cost

Now we consider the plant capacity and the optimal operating conditions obtained before, and design optimal HENs for both processes. A concentration of 5 wt% of ethanol in the broth is used for demonstration. The optimal design of HENs for minimum total cost was determined with Aspen Energy Analyzer, which uses a sequential procedure where superstructures similar to those proposed by Yee et al. (1990) are built and solved as MILP problems to provide feasible HENs satisfying the heat load distributions. Finally, ethanol production cost was estimated from capital and manufacturing costs for a 15 years life plant. Figure 5 shows the optimal HEN found for Process I. It is observed that the overhead vapor and the bottom streams of D-101 (respectively, C-D101 and B-D101) are the main heat sinks and are used to heat the feeding stream, pre-heat the solvent and in the reboiler of D-102. Regarding the production costs, Processes I and II have similar figures (respectively, $0.17/kg·ethanol and $0.19/kg·ethanol) and they are in the lower decile of the costs range indicated by Singh and Rangaiah (2017), i.e. $0.03–3.65/kg·ethanol. However, a fair comparison in this case is hard due to the different concentrations of ethanol in the fermentation broths and the set of assumptions used in techno-economic analyzes.

5. Conclusions

This contribution addresses the direct production of gasohol where gasoline is employed as separating agent. It is demonstrated that Processes I and II are energetically favorable relatively to Process MS, especially after optimization and heat integration. Specifically, total energy savings can reach up to 30% for ethanol concentrations in feed within 2–10 wt%. The results show that these alternative processes can be very competitive (production costs ca. $0.19/kg·ethanol) when gasoline can blend on ethanol production site or the integration with a petrochemical plant is possible. The capital costs involved are potentially low as the retrofitting of existing distillation facilities would require a limited number of modifications. Future works may include the simultaneous optimization and heat integration of multi-effect and/or dividing-wall distillation systems seeking for further decrease of energy and capital costs.

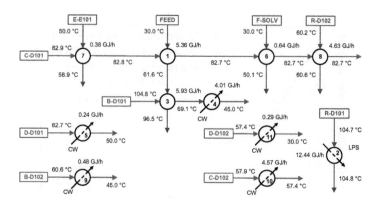

Figure 5: Heat exchanger network of Process I. (CW) cooling water. (LPS) low pressure steam.

6. Acknowledgments

This work was carried out under the Project inpactus – innovative products and technologies from eucalyptus, Project N. ° 21874 funded by Portugal 2020 through European Regional Development Fund (ERDF) in the frame of COMPETE 2020 n°246/AXIS II/2017 for the post-doctoral grant of José F.O. Granjo and under the Project "MultiBiorefinery - Multi-purpose strategies for broadband agro-forest and fisheries by-products valorisation: a step forward for a truly integrated biorefinery" (POCI-01-0145-FEDER-016403) for the research grant of Dinis S. Nunes.

References

V. F. Andersen, J. E. Anderson, T. J. Wallington, S. A. Mueller, O. J. Nielsen, 2010. Distillation Curves for Alcohol–Gasoline Blends. Energy Fuels 24 (4), 2683–2691.

Aspentech, Inc., 2016. Aspen physical property system V9, Bedford, MA, USA.

C. Black, 1980. Distillation modeling of ethanol recovery and dehydration process for ethanol and gasohol. Chem Engng Prog 76 (9), 78–85.

E. C. Carlson, 1996. Don't gamble with physical properties for simulations. Chem Engng Prog 92 (10), 35–46.

A. Chianese, F. Zinnamosca, 1990. Ethanol dehydration by azeotropic distillation with a mixed-solvent entrainer. Chem Eng J 43 (2), 59–65.

J. Granjo, N. Oliveira, J. Coutinho, 2014. Systematic parameter estimation for equilibria data with thermodynamic consistency metrics and phase stability. In: CHEMPOR 2014. September 10-12th, Porto, Portugal.

D. Kubička, I. Kubičková, J. Čejka, 2013. Application of molecular sieves in transformations of biomass and biomass-derived feedstocks. Catalysis Reviews 55 (1), 1–78.

B. G. Kyle, 1981, Low energy process of producing gasoline-ethanol mixtures, U.S. Patent 4297172 A.

C. M. Neves, J. F. Granjo, M. G. Freire, A. Robertson, N. M. Oliveira, J. A. Coutinho, 2011. Separation of ethanol–water mixtures by liquid–liquid extraction using phosphonium-based ionic liquids. Green Chem 13 (6), 1517–1526.

M. J. D. Powell, 2009. The BOBYQA algorithm for bound constrained optimization without derivatives. Tech. Rep. DAMTP 2009/NA06, Department of Applied Mathematics and Theoretical Physics, Cambridge University.

H. Renon, J. M. Prausnitz, 1968. Local compositions in thermodynamic excess functions for liquid mixtures. AIChE J 14 (1), 135–144.

A. Singh, G. P. Rangaiah, 2017. Review of technological advances in bioethanol recovery and dehydration. Ind Eng Chem Res 56 (18), 5147–5163.

N. T. Stacey, A. Hadjitheodorou, D. Glasser, 2016. Gasoline preblending for energy-efficient bioethanol recovery. Energy Fuels 30 (10), 8286–8291.

L. M. Vane, 2008. Separation technologies for the recovery and dehydration of alcohols from fermentation broths. Biofuels, Bioprod Biorefin 2 (6), 553–588.

T. F. Yee, I. E. Grossmann, Z. Kravanja, 1990. Simultaneous optimization models for heat integration — I. Area and energy targeting and modeling of multi-stream exchangers. Comput Chem Eng 14 (10), 1151–1164.

L. Zeng, Z. Li, 2015. A new process for fuel ethanol dehydration based on modeling the phase equilibria of the anhydrous MgCl$_2$ + ethanol + water system. AIChE J 61 (2), 664–676.

Anton A. Kiss, Edwin Zondervan, Richard Lakerveld, Leyla Özkan (Eds.)
Proceedings of the 29th European Symposium on Computer Aided Process Engineering
June 16th to 19th, 2019, Eindhoven, The Netherlands. © 2019 Elsevier B.V. All rights reserved.
http://dx.doi.org/10.1016/B978-0-128-18634-3.50067-9

A Model based analysis in applying Anderson–Schulz–Flory (ASF) equation with CO2 Utilisation on the Fischer Tropsch Gas-to-liquid Process

Ali Attiq Al-Yaeeshi,[a] Ahmed AlNouss,[a,b] Gordon McKay,[a] Tareq Al-Ansari [a,*]

[a] Divison of Sustainable Development, College of Science and Engineering, Hamad Bin Khalifa University, Qatar Foundation, Doha, Qatar

[b] Qatar University, College of Engineering, Department of Chemical Engineering, Qatar

talansari@hbku.edu.qa

Abstract

Industrial emissions of CO_2 have observed a rapid increase since the industrial revolution and is accepted as a major contributor towards global warming. Despite the low market demand for the captured CO_2, carbon capture and storage has not seen commercial deployment due to questions regarding economic feasibility. As such, carbon capture and utilisation (CCU) is considered as an alternative and commercially viable CO_2 reduction approach, which can contribute effectively to the economy and environment. In CCU systems, captured CO_2 is utilised as a feedstock in other processes which require CO_2. This includes the synthesis of chemicals and materials such as Fischer-Tropsch Gas-to-liquid (GTL) production. The purpose of this paper is to evaluate the production of LPG, gasoline, diesel and wax using a Fischer-Tropsch (FT) GTL process model utilising mainly synthetic and captured CO_2 as a raw material. The aim is to assess the effects of reforming methods, recycle ratio of syngas mixture on the process efficiency. The reforming unit of this study includes both; auto-thermal reforming (ATR) and steam-methane reforming (SMR), to form synthesis gas (syngas). Moreover, the application of the Anderson–Schulz–Flory (ASF) equation on the product distribution of FT synthesis is studied to investigate the growth probability of hydrocarbons (α) affected by CO_2 utilisation. This GTL process is modelled using Aspen HYSYS software, and mainly includes a feeding unit, a reforming unit, an FT synthesis unit, upgrading and separation units and recycling units. The unreacted syngas mixture is recycled to the FT synthesis unit to enhance process efficiency and reduce the required amount of fresh feed. This work indicates that the optimal application of ASF with CO_2 captured can increase the production rates of paraffin's and olefins depending on the variation of α and H_2/CO. Initial results demonstrated promising results for an SMR case with around 27% and 4% increase in CO and H_2 production; respectively, when introducing CO_2 with around 38% mass flowrate of natural gas. The ATR case demonstrated less potential with only 9% increase in CO production when introducing the same flow rate of CO_2. The findings of this study include the effect of this increase on the production of fuel liquids such as gasoline and diesel and the optimization of ASF and H_2/CO ratio when introducing the captured CO_2. These results can have a positive impact on enhancing the overall process efficiency and reduce significantly the environmental impact.

Keywords: CO_2 Utilisation, ASF, Auto-Thermal Reforming, Steam-Methane Reforming, Gas-to-Liquid.

1. Introduction

Conversion of gas to liquids in what is known as (GTL) through the Fischer-Tropsch process has increased in production globally comparing to 2010 by 150% in 2015 and is expected to reach 500% by 2025 after commissioning of large scale plants in South Africa and Uzbekistan (EIA, 2017). The main purpose of the GTL process is to convert natural gas (NG) into synthesis products mainly hydrogen and carbon monoxide and subsequently to refined products such as LPG, gasoline, diesel and wax. GTL products contribute effectively to the environmental performance due to the low sulphur and aromatic fuels derived from the process as synthetic fuels. In addition, the process has low emissions of carbon monoxide, nitrogen oxides, hydrocarbons, and other components. Hence, synthetic fuels (GTL products) are considered green fuels, which have an added benefit of reducing the dependence on conventional fuels (Shell, 2018). Although the process is considered as environment-friendly, the GTL process with the Fischer Tropsch Synthesis (FTS) reaction has a very high cost breakeven value when compared to the conventional refinery product (Wood *et al.*, 2012). The GTL process consists of five main sections: pre-reforming, reforming, FT synthesis, upgrading and product fractionation. Upon conversion of the NG into syngas through different reforming technologies, the syngas is converted to liquid hydrocarbons in the FT reactor. These liquid hydrocarbons are then processed in the upgrading unit using hydrogen and separated as refined products in a fractionation column. There are different types of reformers used for syngas production. The main reformers include; Steam Methane Reforming (SMR) and Partial Oxidation Reformer (POX). However, some other reforming units can used, such as dry methane reforming (DMR) and Auto Thermal Reforming (ATR) (Baltrusaitis and Luyben, 2015). The cost and the efficiency of producing a stable molecule pair of CO and H_2 (syngas) form a challenge to these techniques. As part of the GTL process, CO_2 can be utilised as a raw material or as part of recycling process to shift the chemical equilibrium in the aforementioned reformers and upgrade syngas quality. As such, the process design parameters, which need to be considered include: reactor/process design, effect of operating conditions, and the amount of CO_2 where each element is affecting the overall efficiency of the hydrocarbon products distribution including H_2/CO ratio of syngas and catalyst selectivity. The economic feasibility for CO_2 utilisation in the GTL process was studied by Zhang et al. (2014) based on two models. The first model to feed fresh CO_2 to the reforming unit and the FT synthesis unit to produce the required hydrocarbons. The second model considered fresh CO_2 as a direct feed to the FT synthesis unit only. The study targeted the process CAPEX and OPEX, and it was concluded that the two processes are environmentally friendly and economically feasible at large-scales. Rafiee et al. (2017) explored feeding captured CO_2 into the GTL plants' SMR or ATR processes. The economic feasibility demonstrates a benefit for both the emitters and consumers considering low project costs. Applied a multi-objective optimization which considered minimising of CO_2 emissions, while maximising carbon efficiency and mass flow of wax was demonstrated (Panahi et al., 2018) . The results indicated a high wax production rate and carbon efficiency, albeit with higher CO_2 emission than the base case.

The objective of this work is to evaluate the production of LPG, gasoline, diesel and wax using a GTL process model utilizing mainly FT synthetic and captured CO_2 as raw materials. The aim is to assess the effects of reforming methods and recycle ratio of syngas mixture on the process efficiency. The reforming units considered in this study include both; ATR and SMR, to form syngas. Moreover, the application of the Anderson–

Schulz–Flory (ASF) equation on the product distribution has been studied to investigate the growth probability of hydrocarbons (α) affected by CO_2 utilisation.

2. Process model of GTL

In addition to the sinks considered by the authors in the previous study (Al-Yaeeshi, et al., 2018), the system considered is comprised a single CO_2 source and multiple GTL plants located in close proximity. The optimization model is developed for each GTL plant based on different reformer technologies, where the objective function is to maximise the total CO_2 utilised taking into consideration the highest production of LPG, gasoline, diesel and wax. This can ensure lower harmful emissions to the environment and increased economic benefits. Hence, it is important to assess the efficiency of integrating the CO_2 into SMR and ATR and compute the enhancements in the output production. The data are related to a specific CO_2 source; namely from Qatar Gas (QG), and multiple GTL sinks for CO_2 utilisation; namely Oryx GTL, and Pearl GTL in the Ras Laffan industrial zone.

2.1. GTL Process Technology

The feed consisting of NG and steam with O_2 in the case of ATR enters a Gibbs Reactor, where NG is reformed to mainly CO and H_2. The syngas produced is first purified from water and then sent to the FT section to produce the higher carbon molecules. The effluent from the FT reactor is purified in a 3-phase separator to remove water and recycle back the unreacted CO and H_2 for what's known as Tail gas. The high hydrocarbon content stream is send to the upgrading section, where the higher molecules are cracked with H_2 into smaller ones. The cracked effluent is finally sent to the fractionation unit where the unreacted H_2 is first recycled to the hydrocracking unit and the product is distilled into LPG, gasoline, diesel, and wax. Part of the wax is recycled back to the upgrading unit to increase the efficiency of the section (Figure 1).

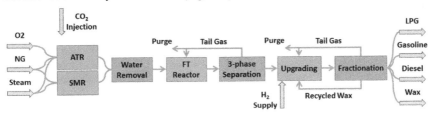

Figure 1: Process flow diagram of GTL plant

2.2. CO₂ Source Data

Emissions of CO_2 from Qatar Gas is approximately 35.8 Mt/year (Sayeed, 2016). The capturing of CO_2 is processed by chemical absorption using amine solvents, with the maximum achievable capture removal efficiency of 90%. The captured CO_2 is transferred though a pipeline connected to Pearl GTL and Oryx GTL plants.

2.3. CO2 Sinks Data (Pearl GTL and Oryx GTL)

The Pearl GTL is the largest GTL plant on the global scale. Utilising ATR technology, it produces LPG, naphtha, kerosene, diesel and base oils. It is supplied with 1.6 billion cubic feet per day of lean methane-rich gas from the Qatar north gas field. The capacity of plant 260,000 bbl/day divided as 120,000 bbl/day upstream products and 140,000 bbl/day GTL products (Shell, 2018). Oryx GTL utilizes ATR technology and is supplied with 330,000 cubic feet per day of lean methane-rich gas from the Qatar North gas field to produce 34,000 barrels per day of liquids with 24,000 barrels of GTL diesel, 9,000 barrels of naphtha and 1,000 barrels of liquefied petroleum gas (QP, 2018).

3. Methodology

This study develops a simulation model of a GTL plant which integrates CO_2 as raw feed to attain optimal production of hydrocarbon products based on integrated SMR and ATR reformers. The model assumes the captured CO_2 is pure and reaches the sinks at the required pressure of the GTL process at a given capacity which is not exceeded. The simulation is developed using Aspen HYSYS-V9 using the parameters listed in Table 1.

Table 1. Model parameters

Parameter	NG	Steam (ATR)	O₂ (ATR)	Steam (SMR)
Flow (T/d)	1.54×10^4	6.49×10^3	1.72×10^4	4.87×10^4
T (C)	25	500	144	500
P (bar)	1	25	25	25
	Reformer	**FT**	**Hydrocracking**	**Fractionator**
T (C)	1050	250	345	Top P: 1 bar
P (bar)	23	24	80	Bottom P :1.5 bar
	1ˢᵗ Purge (ATR)	**2ᵉᵈ Purge (ATR)**	**1ˢᵗ Purge (ATR)**	**2ᵉᵈ Purge (ATR)**
%	5	5	8	1

The scenarios considered vary depending on plant capacity, reformer types, and feed rate of CO_2 into Oryx GTL and Pearl GTL. It is considered that the plant capacity for the two trains is 34000 bbl/day with 15372 ton/d of NG feed flow rate with molar steam to carbon ratio (S/C) of 0.4, and oxygen to carbon ratio of 0.6 in the case of ATR. However, the steam to carbon ratio in the case of SMR will increase to a ratio of 3 with zero oxygen while the NG will remain the same. The CO_2 injection to the ATR/SMR reformer has been varied between 500-2500 ton/d to examine its effect on the production rates of the refined products compared to the ATR case with zero CO_2 feed. The target is for the H_2/CO ratio to be in the acceptable range and to maximise the production. The main constraint used in the model is the appropriate ratio of H_2: CO which does not exceed a ratio of 2 in the case of ATR (Aasberg-Petersen et al., 2003) and 3 in case of SMR (Rafiee et al., 2017) without CO_2 injection, to ensure optimal synthesis gas after the reformers. A carbon mass balance has been applied to estimate the FT products distribution according to the Anderson-Schulz-Flory model, illustrated in Eq. (1) (Krishna and Sie, 2000).

$$W_n = Cn \, (1 - \alpha)^2 \, \alpha^{n-1}$$
                                                                    Eq. (1)

Where, W_n is weight fraction of a particular product characterized by the carbon number (Cn) and chain growth probability (α).

4. Results

The results demonstrated a higher rates of refined products with the addition of CO_2 for both cases. In the base case of the ATR reformer with zero injection of CO_2, an H_2/CO ratio of 2.15 is achieved after the ATR reformer, and a ratio of 3.1 is achieved before the

FT reactor. These ratios were reduced significantly with the addition of CO_2 to the system. As illustrated in Figures 2a and 3a, the H_2/CO ratio before the FT reactor performance declined. Furthermore, production rates of LPG, gasoline, diesel and wax demonstrated increasing trends. Moreover, the SMR reformer indicated a high production of LPG and wax in comparison with the base reference case of ATR and conversely to gasoline and diesel, where the results demonstrated a substantial decrease. Furthermore, it can be deduced that in case of the ATR the total production of the refined products is larger in comparison to the SMR. Furthermore, the CO_2 rate to the system has a significant impact on the H_2/CO ratio after the SMR and before the FT reactor as illustrated in Figure 2b. This contributes positively to the overall process as it will reduce the needed purge rate and increase the production rates of refined products.

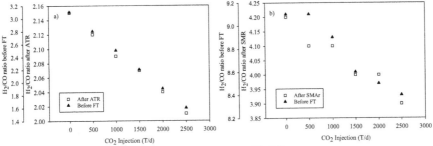

Figure 2: Impact of CO_2 injection on H_2/CO ratio in a) ATR and b) SMR

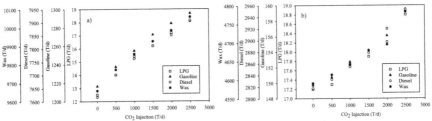

Figure 3: Production trend of refined products in a) ATR and b) SMR with CO_2 injection rates

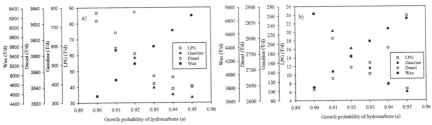

Figure 4: Impact of (α) in a) ATR and b) SMR on production trend of refined products

The study of varying growth probability of hydrocarbons is conducted to examine the effect on production rates and to identify the optimal location of α. The results of the ATR case, illustrated in Figure 4a, indicate an increasing trend for the wax with the increase in α, while the three remaining products illustrated a declining trend. The diesel production indicated a peak around 0.92α at approximately 3630 T/d. The SMR case demonstrated a declining trend in the production of LPG and gasoline with the increase of α. Whereas, the production rates of diesel and wax demonstrated an increasing trend with a peak value of around 0.95α in the case of Diesel.

5. Conclusion

The study demonstrates the suitability of integrating CO_2 into GTL plants in order to increase production rates of finished products, reduce rogue CO_2 emissions and to generate economic benefits. The GTL plants considered in this study consist of two different reforming operations, ATR and SMR. The base reference considered is the ATR with zero CO_2, after which the injection of CO_2 is studied at varying rates between 500-2500 tonne per day to monitor the refined production rates. The results demonstrated a significant enhancement, however the LPG and wax in the case of the SMR are larger than the base reference case, although the purge and the H_2/CO is higher for the case after the reformer and before the FT reactor. Future studies should include the computation of net emissions of CO_2, and the economic viability considering process steam and heat energy requirements.

References

A. Attiq Al-Yaeeshi, T. Al-Ansari, R. Govindan, 2018, Computer Aided ChemicalEngineering ,The potential for carbon dioxide capture and utilization within the State of Qatar, 28th European Symposium on Computer Aided Process Engineering, pp.1499-1504.

A. Rafiee, M. Panahi, and K.R. Khalilpour, 2017, CO2 utilization through integration of post-combustion carbon capture process with Fischer-Tropsch gas-to-liquid (GTL) processes, Journal of CO2 Utilization, 18, 98-106.

C. Zhang, K.-W. Jun, K.-S. Ha, Y.-J. Lee, and S.C. Kang, 2014, Efficient Utilization of Greenhouse Gases in a Gas-to-Liquids Process Combined with CO2/Steam-Mixed Reforming and Fe-Based Fischer–Tropsch Synthesis, Environmental Science & Technology, 48, 14, 8251-57.

D.A. Wood, C. Nwaoha, and B.F. Towler, 2012, Gas-to-liquids (GTL): A review of an industry offering several routes for monetizing natural gas, Journal of Natural Gas Science and Engineering, 9, 196-208.

EIA, 2017, Global gas-to-liquids growth is dominated by two projects in South Africa and Uzbekistan, U.S. Energy Information Administration, International Energy Outlook 2017, Accessed 14/11/2018, https://www.eia.gov/todayinenergy/detail.php?id=33192

J. Baltrusaitis, and W.L. Luyben, 2015, Methane Conversion to Syngas for Gas-to-Liquids (GTL): Is Sustainable CO2 Reuse via Dry Methane Reforming (DMR) Cost Competitive with SMR and ATR Processes?, ACS Sustainable Chemistry & Engineering, 3, 9, 2100-11

K. Aasberg-Petersen, T.S. Christensen, C. Stub Nielsen, and I. Dybkjær, 2003, Recent developments in autothermal reforming and pre-reforming for synthesis gas production in GTL applications, Fuel Processing Technology, 83, 1, 253-61.

M. Panahi, A. Rafiee, S. Skogestad, and M. Hillestad, 2012, A Natural Gas to Liquids Process Model for Optimal Operation, Industrial & Engineering Chemistry Research, 51, 1, 425-33.

M. Panahi, E. Yasari, and A. Rafiee, 2018, Multi-objective optimization of a gas-to-liquids (GTL) process with staged Fischer-Tropsch reactor, Energy Conversion and Management, 163, 239-49.

QP, 2018, Subsidiaries and join venture details Accessed 14/11/2018, https://www.qp.com.qa/en/QPActivities/Pages/SubsidiariesAndJointVenturesDetails.aspx?aid=3

R. Krishna, and S.T. Sie, 2000, Design and scale-up of the Fischer–Tropsch bubble column slurry reactor, Fuel Processing Technology, 64, 1, 73-105.

Shell, 2018, Shell qatar project and sites https://www.shell.com.qa/en_qa/projects-and-sites/pearl-gtl.html

S. Mohammed (2016), Qatar's National Emission Inventory Report, Figshare, Availible from; http://creativecommons.org/licenses/by/4.0/ [Accessed Feberuary 2018]

Anton A. Kiss, Edwin Zondervan, Richard Lakerveld, Leyla Özkan (Eds.)
Proceedings of the 29th European Symposium on Computer Aided Process Engineering
June 16th to 19th, 2019, Eindhoven, The Netherlands. © 2019 Elsevier B.V. All rights reserved.
http://dx.doi.org/10.1016/B978-0-128-18634-3.50068-0

Scalable manufacturing of nanostructured materials by atomic layer deposition in fluidized bed reactors

J.Ruud van Ommen,[a,*] Fabio Grillo,[a,b] Johan Grievink[a]

[a]*Dept. of Chemical Engineering, Delft Univ. of Technology, Delft, the Netherlands*

[b]*Dept. of Materials, ETH Zurich, Zurich 8093, Switzerland*

J.R.vanOmmen@TUDelft.nl

Abstract

Atomic layer deposition (ALD) is a gas-phase coating technique that can be used to coat nanoparticles in a fluidized bed reactor. ALD is based on the alternating supply of two precursors, which makes it an inherent dynamic process. We discuss a multi-scale, multi-phase mass transfer-diffusion-reaction model capable of predicting the evolution of surface coverage of particles at different local operating conditions. The dynamic ALD-reactor model can be extended with operational scenarios. The reactor design combined with the scenarios has many degrees of freedom, yielding ample opportunities to optimize the process with efficient utilization of precursors.

Keywords: particle technology, nanotechnology, fluidization, ALD, nanoparticles

1. Introduction

Nanostructured particles (e.g., core-shell nanoparticles or nano-decorated micro-particles) have high a potential in applications such as catalysis and energy storage, but also in medicine and food. However, from designing products incorporating nanostructuring to produce them in large quantities is not trivial. Gas-phase coating using atomic layer deposition (ALD, a variant of chemical vapour deposition) can be used to provide the surface of a particle with either an ultrathin continuous coating or a decoration of nanoclusters. When carried out in a fluidized bed or a pneumatic reactor, ALD is an attractive way of producing nanostructured particles with excellent scale-up potential (Salameh et al., 2017). Even nanopowders can be treated with this process. This is facilitated by the fact that during fluidization they are not present as individual particles but as very dilute agglomerates of several hundreds of microns.

2. Atomic Layer Deposition in a Fluidized Bed

Atomic layer deposition (ALD) is a gas-phase coating technique that is being increasingly used in the semi-conductor industry to provide microchips with coatings on the order of 1-10 nm. It enables digital control over the amount of deposited material by relying on sequential self-limiting surface reactions. In ALD the compound to be deposited is synthesized directly on the substrate surface instead of being deposited from the vapour phase as in other thin film techniques such as chemical vapor deposition (CVD), from which ALD is derived. The synthesis of the desired compound is typically split into two steps, each step follow by a purge. Each reaction step involves self-saturating chemisorption reactions between a precursor and the substrate surface. The precursor is provided for a certain period of time, which is typically called the pulse time. The purge step after the precursor pulse is crucial to preserve the self-limiting nature of ALD reactions, as it prevents the intermixing between different precursors, and between precursors and reaction by-products, which might result in uncontrolled deposition. By repeating these steps in a cyclic fashion one can grow the desired material with a resolution set by the amount of material deposited in each cycle referred to as growth per cycle (GPC), which is usually a fraction of a monolayer. This in principle translates into an atomic-level control over the material properties (Van Bui et al., 2017).

Since ALD is a surface-driven process, its use is not limited to wafers and other flat substrates, but it can also be used to obtain conformal coatings on substrates with complex geometries such as high-aspect-ratio structures for electronic devices, porous media and powders (Van Bui et al., 2017, Longrie et al., 2014, Puurunen, 2005). Especially its application to powders is interesting: 70% of the industrial processes involve powders, and there is an increasing demand for nanostructured powders. By applying ALD to a fluidized bed, we have a precise, versatile and scalable way of making such powders.

3. Modelling ALD in a Fluidized Bed Reactor

Fluidized bed ALD is an interesting process from a dynamics point of view, since the fluidized bed dynamics (gas residence time and particle mixing ~ seconds) is combined with very fast ALD reaction kinetics (<< 1s) and relatively slow precursor pulse times (~ minutes), in order to provide enough precursor molecules to cover all surface. In order to analyze the interplay between these phenomena, we developed a multiscale model to describe this process (Grillo et al., 2015), which will be briefly recapped here.

Our dynamical model captures the essential features of the coupling between the precursor transport, from the reactor- to the particle-scale, and the kinetics of the ALD surface reactions. During ALD in fluidized bed reactors, the precursor transport takes place on at least three different length scales: (1) from the inlet of the reactor throughout the bulk of the gas phase, (2) from the bulk of the gas phase to the outer surface of the particles, and (3) from the outer surface of the particles to their inner porous structure. We therefore describe the precursor transport via two sub-models: the one describing the transport across the length scales (1-2), which we refer to as the "reactor-scale", and the second describing the transport within the inner structure of the particles (3), which we refer to as the "particle-scale". Next to the precursor transport we also account for the precursor consumption arising from the gas-solid reactions taking place on the surface of the particles. In particular, to retrieve the self-limiting nature of ALD surface reactions our model also incorporates the detailed balance of the surface coverage of active sites prescribed by the stoichiometry of the chemistry of choice.

The reactor-scale model is based on the two-phase theory of bubbling fluidization. The latter accounts for the uneven distribution of gas within a fluidized bed of cohesive powders such as many nanostructured particles. It assumes that the gas flow at the reactor inlet is distributed between two phases: the emulsions phase, characterized by a high density of particles, and the bubble phase, which instead contains only gas. The gas flow in the bubble phase is approximated to be plug flow; the emulsion phase is assumed to be fully mixed. Furthermore, the two phases exchange precursor through interphase mass transfer mediated by both diffusion and convection, and the precursor can reach the particles only in the emulsion phase through mass transfer. The reactor-scale precursor transport model therefore translates into the following system of differential equations:

$$\frac{\partial C_b}{\partial t} + u_b \frac{\partial C_b}{\partial z} = -K_{be}(C_b - C_e) \tag{1}$$

$$\varepsilon_e \frac{dC_e}{dt} = \frac{u_e}{H}(C_{in} - C_e) + \frac{K_{be}\delta}{H(1-\delta)}\int_0^H (C_b - C_e)dz - K_{ga}\frac{6(1-\varepsilon_e)}{d_p}\left(C_e - C_p|_{r=R_p}\right) \tag{2}$$

where $C_b, C_e, C_p|_{r=R_p}, C_{in}, u_b, u_e, \varepsilon_e, \delta, z, H, K_{be}, K_{ga}$ are the concentration of precursor in the bubble phase, in the emulsion, at the particles outer surface, at the reactor inlet; the gas velocity in the bubble, and in the emulsion; the gas volume fraction in the emulsion phase; the total volume fraction of the bubble phase; the vertical distance from the inlet of the reactor; the total height of the reactor; the bubble-to-emulsion mass transfer coefficient; and the gas-to-particle mass transfer coefficient, respectively.

The precursor transport at the particle-scale is modeled in terms of diffusion and reaction of dilute species within porous spheres. Nanostructured particles such as nanoparticle agglomerates may present a hierarchical porous structure: pores of different sizes at different length scales. This means that the transport model should take into account that the diffusion rates are a function of the position within the pore network. Nevertheless, if the transport through the pore network is limited along a preferential direction (e.g., the radius of the nanoparticle agglomerate), then its description can be reduced to a diffusion problem within mono-dispersed porous media in spherical coordinates:

$$\epsilon_p \frac{\partial C_p}{\partial t} = \frac{D_p}{r^2}\frac{\partial}{\partial r}\left(r^2 \frac{\partial C_p}{\partial r}\right) + g(C_p, \boldsymbol{\theta}) \tag{3}$$

$$D_p \frac{\partial C_p}{\partial r}|_{r=R_p} = K_{ga}\left(C_e - C_p|_{r=R_p}\right) \tag{4}$$

where $C_p, D_p, r, R_P, \varepsilon_p, g, \boldsymbol{\theta}$ are the concentration within the particles, the diffusion coefficient, the radial distance, the radius of the particle, the particle porosity, the reaction term arising from the surface reaction kinetics, and the surface coverage of the active sites, respectively. As already argued in our previous work (Grillo et al., 2015), this treatment is suitable for describing the precursor transport through both nanoparticle agglomerates and nano-porous particles presenting mono-dispersed pores.

The precursor model at the particle scale is coupled to the kinetics of the ALD surface reactions via the evolution of the surface coverage of the active sites:

$$\frac{\partial \boldsymbol{\theta}(\mathbf{r})}{\partial t} = f(C_p(r), \boldsymbol{\theta}, \mathbf{v}) \tag{5}$$

where $\mathbf{v}$ are the reaction rates associated with the surface reactions. The latter balance can assume varying degree of complexity depending on the number and nature of the active sites and of the gas-solid reactions involved in the surface chemistry behind the ALD scheme of choice.

4. Operation

The ALD fluidized bed reactor is by nature operated in a non-stationary way: precursor pulses are alternated with purges by inert gas. Figure 1 gives a schematic of the operation: after loading the reactor with particles, a precursor pulse is given (e.g., a metal precursor), then a purge with inert gas (typically nitrogen) to remove byproducts and possible excess precursor, followed by a pulse of the second precursor (e.g., an oxidizer), and finally again a purge with inert gas. The length of the pulse and purge periods depends on parameters such as surface area of the substrate, concentration of the precursors, and reaction rate. The precursor pulse and purge periods typically last a few minutes.

The precursor pulse and the purge step are characterized by several processes that take place at different time scales. Analyzing the relative order of magnitude of such time scales offers a clue into the scalability and controllability of the process. With regard to the precursor pulse, we already shown through a time scale analysis that all the relevant chemical and physical processes are typically faster than the rate at which the precursor is supplied by as much as five orders of magnitude. This allows one to tailor the precursor pulsing time such that just enough precursor is being supplied to for saturating all the available surface. In other words, no precursor will be wasted.

A key aspect that our model currently does not take into account is the time scale associated with the purging of excess precursor and reaction by-products. In fact, as already pointed out elsewhere (Onn et al., 2018), the purging step in ALD on powders is particularly cumbersome compared to ALD on flat substrates. This is mainly due to two phenomena that slow down the purging process: (1) capillary condensation of precursor within small pores and (2) delayed desorption kinetics caused by the fact that, once desorbed, a molecule has a high probability of adsorbing on another location, either within the porous structure of the same particle or even on other particles within the fluidized bed, before leaving the reactor. The purging dynamics during ALD on powders certainly merits investigation because, on the one hand, the effective purging of unreacted precursor is essential to the self-limiting nature of ALD, and on the other hand excessively long purging times undermine the overall throughput of the process. The model presented here represents a starting point in this regard because it can be readily integrated with a set of equations describing the desorption kinetics of excess precursor.

The amount of precursor to be fed is determined by the surface area in the reactor. Often, it is not possible to exactly know this quantity. In that case, it can be attractive to monitor the outlet of the reactor for a breakthrough of the precursor, e.g. by a mass spectrometer. Since the precursor concentration in the outlet approaches a block wave (Grillo et al., 2015), it is possible to quickly respond to a decrease in precursor concentration.

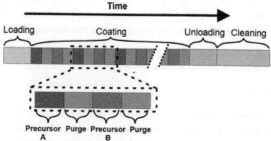

Figure 1. Schematic of the operation of a fluidized bed reactor for ALD

5. Dynamic reactor model with operational scenarios

The reactor operation with its sequence of precursor additions and pulses can be modelled by including the species mass balances, the energy balance, and the transfer and reaction rate equations. The result is a mix of partial differential equations for the bubbly phase, ordinary differential equations for the emulsion phase with algebraic equation for rate laws. The resulting reactor model is written in a compact way, where $x(z,t)$ represents the internal physical state (concentrations, temperature, pressure and fluxes) of all matter (in gas & in solid particles) in the reactor at position z at time t:

$$\frac{\partial x}{\partial t} = f(\frac{\partial x}{\partial z}, x; p, d) \tag{6}$$

The physical parameters are denoted by p, while d is the set of the reactor design parameters.. The model equations are first-order in the spatial derivative of the states as shown in eq. (1). The radial coordinate (r) and the associated concentration dependency in eq. (3) and (4), are assumed to have been approximated by discretization or by orthogonal collocation, considerably extending the number of states at position z.

There is a boundary condition at entrance $z = 0$: $\qquad x(0,t) = g(t)$ $\qquad$ (7)

as well as an initial condition for $t = 0$: $\qquad x(z,0) = x_0$ $\qquad$ (8)

Let this initial condition correspond to a fully fluidized bed in a steady state at the end of the loading, just before any precursor addition will start. The particles are supposed to be in a clean state at $t = 0$.

During the sequence of precursor additions and pulses the model equations remain invariant. It is the inlet boundary condition that changes per addition and pulse. Let the sequence of additions and pulses be denoted by j ($j = 1, 2, ...N$), while the starting time of inlet operation j by T_j and it is running till time T_{j+1}. For inlet operation j one has:

Inlet condition: $\qquad x_j(o, t) = g_j(t) \qquad$ for $T_j < t \leq T_{j+1}$ $\qquad$ (9)

Initial condition: $\qquad x_j(z, T_j) = x_{j-1}(z, T_j) \quad$ for $0 < z < H$ and $t = T_j$ $\quad$ (10)

The inlet condition reflects the feeding conditions during inlet operation j, while the initial condition for this operation j is equal to the final state at the end of the previous operation j -1. In pulsing intervals the inlet concentrations of precursors are zero.

The product quality at the end of the last operation, pulse $N(Q_N)$ can be related to the process state $x_N(H,T_N)$:

$$Q_N = h(X_N(H, T_N) \tag{11}$$

Given the operational policies as the set $\{g_j(t), T_j \,|\, j = 1, .. ,N\}$ and the initial condition (8) one can simulate the evolution of states $x(z,t)$ over time t by means of (6), (9) & (10). Then it becomes possible to perform sensitivity analyses of the end state, $x_N(H,T_N)$ with respect to the:

- physical parameters (p);
- design parameters (d),
- the starting times of pulses $\{T_j; j=1, .. , N\}$ and
- piece-wise constant pulse inlet conditions $\{g_j(t) = g_j \;; j=1, .. , N\}$.

Furthermore one can analyse operational features such as stability and system time constants by determining the eigenvalues of the Jacobian matrix of the differential equations at reactor exit $z = H$. The ultimate objective is, given a certain product specification (Q_N^*), to obtain an optimum operational policy $\{T_j^*, g_j^*, j = 1, .., N\}$ and reactor design (d^*). I.e., an optimum is sought for an economic objective function, while making full use of the precursors. The many degrees of freedom process has, likely make it sustainizable (Jorat & Manousiouthakis, 2018): for the right set of parameters, it can be operated in a sustainable manner.

6 Conclusions

The typically fast kinetics of ALD surface reactions enable the complete uptake of the added precursor, even in the limit of high surface coverages. This has been shown by multi-scale modelling of physical phenomena in the reactor. The same multi-scale model used to analyze the precursor utilization is also amenable to the incorporation of the desorption kinetics of excess precursor. Such extended model can inform the choice of the optimal purging time. The alternation of precursor pulses and purging steps translates into many degrees of freedom. These can be used to optimize the process in line with a given economic objective function, while ensuring nearly full consumption of the supplied precursors. A mathematical model of the reactor with its operational scenarios is formulated as the starting point for such optimizations.

References

Grillo, F., Kreutzer, M. T. & Van Ommen, J. R. 2015. Modeling the precursor utilization in atomic layer deposition on nanostructured materials in fluidized bed reactors. Chemical Engineering Journal, 268, 384-398.

Jorat, M. & Manousiouthakis, V. 2018. Sustainability identification for infinite-dimensional systems. AIChE annual meeting, paper 62c.

Longrie, D., Deduytsche, D. & Detavernier, C. 2014. Reactor concepts for atomic layer deposition on agitated particles: A review. Journal of Vacuum Science & Technology A, 32, 010802.

Onn, T., Küngas, R., Fornasiero, P., Huang, K. & Gorte, R. 2018. Atomic layer deposition on porous materials: Problems with conventional approaches to catalyst and fuel cell electrode preparation. Inorganics, 6, 34.

Puurunen, R. L. 2005. Surface chemistry of atomic layer deposition: A case study for the trimethylaluminum/water process. Journal of Applied Physics, 97, 1-52.

Salameh, S., Gómez-Hernández, J., Goulas, A., Van Bui, H. & Van Ommen, J. R. 2017. Advances in scalable gas-phase manufacturing and processing of nanostructured solids: A review. Particuology, 30, 15-39.

Van Bui, H., Grillo, F. & Van Ommen, J. R. 2017. Atomic and molecular layer deposition: off the beaten track. Chemical Communications, 53, 45-71.

Anton A. Kiss, Edwin Zondervan, Richard Lakerveld, Leyla Özkan (Eds.)
Proceedings of the 29th European Symposium on Computer Aided Process Engineering
June 16th to 19th, 2019, Eindhoven, The Netherlands. © 2019 Elsevier B.V. All rights reserved.
http://dx.doi.org/10.1016/B978-0-128-18634-3.50069-2

Effect of Non-Ideal Kinetics on Hybrid Reactive Distillation Models for Selectivity Engineering

Deepshikha Singh, Antarim Dutta, Ankur Gaur, Shabih Ul Hasan*

Department of Chemical Engineering, Motilal Nehru National Institute of Technology, Allahabad 211004, India

shasan@mnnit.ac.in

Abstract

Multi-reaction schemes comprise of highly non-ideal mixtures (such as alcohols, esters, aldehydes, ethers, water, etc.) can be quite often found in fine chemical industries. Previous work [Hasan et al., 2014] has looked at finding the designs for simple and complex hybrid RD columns targeting to obtain the desired selectivity for ideal kinetics and in the present work we extend it to cover non-ideal kinetics. In particular, it is found that in case of non-ideal kinetics the single feed hybrid RD models to be used are strongly dependent on the number of components involved in a multireaction scheme, contrary to our earlier work for ideal kinetics in which the hybrid RD models used were depends on the number of products that undergo further side reactions and is applicable for any number of components. The developed method is applicable to single reactant as well as multi-reactants single-feed hybrid RD columns, provided all the reactants should be saddle in the residue curve map and is limited to four components.

Keywords: Hybrid Reactive Distillation, Non-ideal kinetics, Design, Selectivity

1. Introduction

Reactive Distillation (RD) which is a combination of reaction and distillation in a single functional unit can also be effectively used to obtain desired selectivity in multi-reaction schemes comprises of highly non-ideal mixtures. The present work concerns the design and selection of type of single feed hybrid RD models depending upon whether the given reaction kinetics is ideal or non-ideal. A van de Vusse type hypothetical reaction scheme having ideal and non-ideal kinetics is used as an example, with the capability of the new approach demonstrated in terms of its ability to provide promising designs of hybrid RD models to obtain desired selectivity in multireaction schemes.

2. Design Methodology

The methodology starts with non-reactive distillation column (non-RD) and then introduces the reaction related attributes. For non-RD, we use the concept of visualization of the locus of feed stage compositions (LFSCs) in 3D composition space. For reaction related attributes we view the column as a reactor and relate it to the conventional reactors for which geometric interpretation is well studied through the attainable region approach. Glasser et al. (1987) presented geometrical interpretation of CSTR in terms of process vectors viz. reaction and mixing. In order to know whether a point in the composition space is attainable or not, they derived a condition that the rate vector at that point is collinear with the mixing vector of feed and product stream. The component material balance of CSTR gives the required condition. It must be noted that the reaction takes place at the product composition in the case of CSTR. On the other hand, in an arbitrary reactor (R), if the composition at which reaction takes place is different than the product composition, then the collinearity condition is no longer valid. The composition at which reaction takes place is dependent on the type of reactor. One can control this composition by introducing separation attributes as is done the case of reactive distillation.

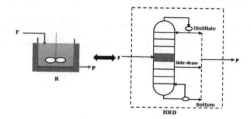

Fig. 1. Analogy between Arbitrary reactor (R) and hybrid RD Column (HRD) with side draw

Now, as shown in Fig.1, let us consider a side draw hybrid column with single reactive stage. It may be noted that the reaction in the column does not take place at a composition corresponding to that of the product (P). The overall product composition is the one obtained by virtually mixing the distillate and bottom streams. The composition of the reactive stage depends on the distillation attributes such as reflux ratio, feed location, number of stages, etc. Therefore, the next exercise is to know – which are the points in the composition space that can be the potential reactive stage composition(s) giving the desired selectivity corresponding to the point of desired product composition. The following section determines the surface of such feasible reactive stage compositions.

2.1. Surface of Reactive Stage Compositions (SRSCs)

Consider an equimolar van de Vusse type reaction scheme Eq. (1) with one reacting component A having all the reactions irreversible, except B to A, with first, second and third reactions are of 1st order while the fourth reaction A to D is of 2nd order. The feed is pure reactant A and the kinetic rate constants are given by $[k1 \ k2 \ k3 \ k4] = [2 \ 1 \ 1 \ 3]$. The non-ideal kinetics is given by Eq. (2) and for ideal kinetics (Table 1) the value of activity coefficients of all components is taken as unity.

$$A \underset{undesired(k_2)}{\overset{desired(k_1)}{\rightleftarrows}} B \xrightarrow{undesired(k_3)} C$$

$$A \xrightarrow{undesired(k_4)} D \tag{1}$$

$$\left[r_A \ r_B \ r_C \ r_D \right] = \left[-k_1\gamma_A x_A^* - k_4\gamma_A^2 x_A^{*2} + k_2\gamma_B x_B^*, \ k_1\gamma_A x_A^* - k_2\gamma_B x_B^* - k_3\gamma_B x_B^*, \ k_3\gamma_B x_B^*, \ k_4\gamma_A^2 x_A^{*2} \right] \tag{2}$$

The material balances for components A and B on any arbitrary reactor are given by

$$x_{A,P} - x_{A,0} = \tau . \sum_{k=1}^{nR} r_{k,A}(x^*) \tag{3}$$

$$x_{B,P} - x_{B,0} = \tau . \sum_{k=1}^{nR} r_{k,B}(x^*) \tag{4}$$

where τ is the residence time and nR represents number of reactions
Divide (3) by (2) we get,

$$\frac{x_{B,P} - x_{B,0}}{x_{A,P} - x_{A,0}} = \frac{r_B}{r_A} = \frac{k_1\gamma_A x_A^* - k_2\gamma_B x_B^* + k_3\gamma_B x_B^*}{-k_1\gamma_A x_A^* - k_4\gamma_A^2 x_A^{*2} + k_2\gamma_B x_B^*} \tag{5}$$

where $x_{i,p}$ is the product composition of component i, $x_{i,0}$ is the inlet composition of component i and x^* denotes the compositions at which the reaction takes place in the reactor. The LHS of Eq. (5) is the slope of line joining points A (x_{A0}, x_{B0}) and P (x_{AP}, x_{BP}) as shown in Fig. 2. It should be noted that point P is on ABD plane in Fig. 2 and since Eq. (5) is independent of x_{CP}, its value is not required for plotting the SRSCs.

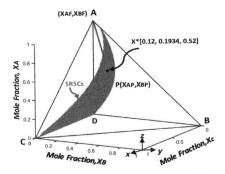

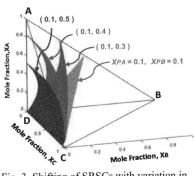

Fig. 2. Surface of reactive stage compositions (SRSCs).

Fig. 3. Shifting of SRSCs with variation in desired selectivity

Hence, for any desired point P in the composition space, Eq. (5) gives a relation between x_A^* and x_B^*. One can plot the SRSCs for the quaternary mixture by taking a meshgrid of [x_A^*, x_C^*] and plot x_B^* compositions [by solving a non-linear equation (Eq. 5) at each point of meshgrid; with γ being calculated by *WILSON* model] as shown in Fig. 2. Figure 3 indicates that with increase in the desired selectivity keeping conversion fixed, the feasible reactive stage compositions get reduced.

2.2. Effect of non-ideal kinetics and thermodynamic models on SRSCs

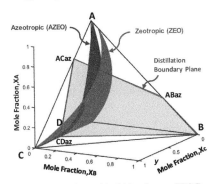

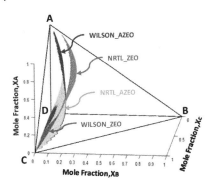

Fig. 4. Effect of non-ideal kinetics on SRSCs for ZEO and AZEO mixtures.

Fig. 5. Effect of thermodynamic models on SRSCs for ZEO and AZEO mixtures.

In case of azeotropic systems, non-ideal vapor-liquid equilibrium and distillation boundaries [for multicomponent azeotropic mixture in Fig.4, see Hasan et al., 2014; Section 4 (Example 3)] are responsible for the contraction of the feasible reactive stage compositions required for the design of hybrid RD column. Figure 4 shows that if non-ideality is present in kinetics as well then these feasible reactive stage compositions reduces further and thereby increase the design complexity for RD systems. Figure 5 indicates that there is no effect of thermodynamic models (WILSON & NRTL) on the surface of reactive stage compositions both for zeotropic as well as azeotropic mixtures.

2.3. Selection of Single Feed Hybrid RD Models

Hasan et al. (2014) proposed a design algorithm for ideal kinetics in which the type of hybrid RD models to be used in order to obtain the feasible design of desired selectivity is strongly dependent on the nature of reaction schemes i.e. whether in a complex reaction scheme one, two or more products undergo further side reaction(s). If one product undergoes further side reaction, then simple hybrid RD column (SHRD) is capable to give desired selectivity and if two product undergoes further side reaction then hybrid RD column with side draw is to be used. In the present example (Eq.1) although only one product undergoes further side reaction, due to the presence of non-ideal kinetics it is found that the desired selectivity is achievable by using simple hybrid RD model in a three component multi-reaction scheme while for four components multi-reaction scheme hybrid side-draw RD model is needed. The design procedure of which is explained in the next section.

2.4. Design Procedure

Consider a simple hybrid side-draw RD column with one reactive stage (Fig. 6a) and a reactor-separator system (Fig. 6b). A systematic methodology that uses intersection of LFSCs with the selected reactive stage composition (X^*) to obtain feasible designs of desired selectivity using hybrid RD column for the reaction scheme given by Eq. (1) is described. The approach presented here exploits the fact that if we split the reaction and distillation attributes of the hybrid RD column (Fig. 6a), then the new configuration (Fig. 6b) gives the same performance as that of a hybrid RD column. If the feed stage in the RD column is the reactive stage, then the column profiles of non-RD and RD column coincide for the same distillation attributes. This would be made clear with the following example.

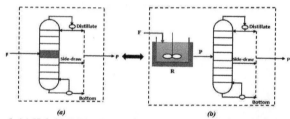

Fig. 6. (a) Hybrid (RD) column. (b) Reactor separator system (Non-RD).

A simplified equimolar van de Vusse type reaction scheme with only one reacting component with rate constants, [k1 k2 k3 k4] = [2 1 1 3] is chosen as an illustrative example (see Eq. 1). The reaction takes place in the liquid phase and the assumption of constant molar overflow is valid. Following are the proposed step-by-step design procedure to obtain desired selectivity using hybrid RD column with side draw:

Step 1: Select any point P (Fig. 2) according to the desired selectivity of intermediate product, B in the composition space. This point represents the overall output composition of hybrid RD column with side draw (Fig. 6b), obtained by virtually mixing distillate, side draw and bottoms streams. Hence, it can be considered as the feed to Non-RD column in Fig. 6a.

Step 2: Join point P (0.3, 0.275) with A (1, 0) to calculate the slope of line AP, and hence obtain the SRSCs using Eq. (5) as shown in Fig. 2.

Step 3: Select any X^* on the curve of SRSCs as shown in Fig. 2. For the present example we have selected $X^* = [x_A{}^* \, x_B{}^* \, x_C{}^*] = [0.52, 0.1934, 0.12]$.

Step 4: Find the composition of all the components in the hypothetical feed that is sent to the non-RD distillation column (Fig. 6b) by using the material balances given by Eq.

(7), Eq. (8) and Eq. (9). The composition of C is related to the extent to which individual reactions take place, which in turn depends on the Damkohler number (Da) number i.e. the ratio of characteristic liquid residence time to the characteristic reaction time (Eq. 6).

$$Da = \left(\frac{W_{cat} * k_{ref}}{F} \right) \tag{6}$$

We determine Da by applying material balance for either component A (Eq. 7) or component B (Eq. 8) for any arbitrary reactor in which reaction takes place at the selected composition, X^*. Further, by using material balance for component C (Eq. 9), one can find the composition of C in the feed to the distillation column. Composition of D can be obtained by summation equation.

$$x_{A,0} - x_{A,P} + Da \left(\frac{-k_1 \gamma_A x_A^* - k_4 \gamma_A^2 x_A^{*2} + k_2 \gamma_B x_B^*}{k_{ref}} \right) = 0 \tag{7}$$

$$x_{B,0} - x_{B,P} + Da \left(\frac{k_1 \gamma_A x_A^* - k_2 \gamma_B x_B^* + k_3 \gamma_B x_B^*}{k_{ref}} \right) = 0 \tag{8}$$

$$x_{C,0} - x_{C,P} + Da \left(\frac{k_3 \gamma_B x_B^*}{k_{ref}} \right) = 0 \tag{9}$$

Step 5: Specify the number of stages and feed location (say N=12, Nfl=7th stage) with Reboiler as first stage. Side draw location depends on the volatility of that product whose composition is required to be adjusted through side draw to obtain the desired selectivity; in the present case it is component C. Hence, if the volatility of component C is less than the volatility of the reactant A then the side draw location is below the feed location (Sd= 6th stage).

Step 6: Find the operating parameters such that the feed stage of Non-RD column coincides with the selected reactive stage composition, X^*. To obtain this intersection draw the family of curves (FOC) representing LFSCs obtained for a range of distillate to feed ratio (D:F) and boil-up to feed ratio (V:F) ratios by choosing initially some arbitrary value of side draw to feed ratio (say SD=0.1) as shown in Fig. 7.

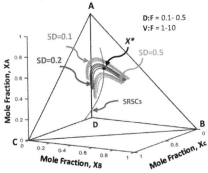
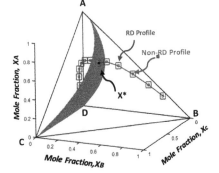

Fig. 7. FOC for a range of D:F at different values of V:F and S:F representing LFSCs.

Fig. 8. Identical column profiles in triangular diagram

Range of D:F can be decided based on whether or not one of the LFSCs crosses the curve of SRSCs containing selected reactive stage composition, X^*, while the V:F ratio can start from any small value till the performance becomes insensitive at higher values.

It should be noted that there is one curve that corresponds to the range of $D{:}F$ at a given value of SD and $V{:}F$. Now if one considers the range of $V{:}F$ too then a family of curves can be plotted. Fig. 7 shows three such families for a range of distillate to feed ratio (*0.1-0.5*) and boil-up to Feed ratio (*1-10*) at three different values of SD. It can be clearly seen in Fig. 7 that the reactive composition, X^* of interest lies in the vicinity of curves obtained for $SD{=}0.2$.

Step 7: Next step is to consider the range of side draw to feed ratio, near the value $SD{=}0.2$ and narrow down the ranges of $D{:}F$ and $V{:}F$ ratios based on the results shown in Fig. 7. The values of three operating parameters viz. SD, $V{:}F$, and $D{:}F$ at which the exact intersection of feed stage of Non-RD column with the selected reactive stage composition, X^* is found are 0.22, 3.225 and 0.321, respectively. The column profile for Non-RD side draw column in 3D composition space (Fig. 8) is then plotted.

Step8: Obtain the column profile for RD, with the feed as pure A and the feed stage as the reactive stage, using the same design and operating parameters as used for the Non-RD case. The profiles coincide (Fig. 8) to indicate that the design is feasible. Hence, the desired selectivity for the given reaction scheme with non-ideal kinetics is attainable through hybrid side-draw RD column with design specifications given in Table 1.

Table 1. Design specifications for hybrid RD Models for ideal and non-ideal reaction kinetics

Kinetics Type	Ideal Kinetics [Hasan et al., 2014]		Nonideal Kinetics [Present work]	
Reaction Scheme	Eq. (1)		Eq. (1)	
Rate Constants	*[k1 k2 k3 k4] = [2 1 1 3]*		*[k1 k2 k3 k4] = [2 1 1 3]*	
Column configuration	Non-RD SHRD Model	RD SHRD Model	Non-RD Side Draw Model	RD Side Draw Model
Number of components, NC	4	4	4	4
Volatility Order	B > A > C > D	B > A > C > D	B > A > C > D	B > A > C > D
Number of stages, N	12	12	12	12
Feed location, Nfl	6th Stage	6th Stage	7th Stage	7th Stage
Feed flow rate, F	1	1	1	1
Side draw location, Sdl	-	-	6th Stage	6th Stage
Feed composition, Xf	(0.30, 0.275, 0.0701, 0.3549)	(1, 0, 0, 0)	(0.3, 0.275, 0.0816, 0.3434)	(1, 0, 0, 0)
Number of reactive stages, Nr	-	1	-	1
Location of Reactive stage, Nrl	-	6th Stage	-	7th Stage
Damkohler Number, Da	-	0.3641	-	0.4741
Distillate to feed ratio, $D{:}F$	0.3775	0.3775	0.321	0.321
Vapor to feed ratio, $V{:}F$	2.315	2.315	3.225	3.225
Side draw to feed ratio, $S{:}F$	-	-	0.22	0.22
End Compositions after mixing the distillate and bottom streams	(0.3, 0.275, 0.0701, 0.3549)	(0.30, 0.275, 0.0701, 0.3549)	(0.3, 0.275, 0.0816, 0.3434)	(0.3, 0.275, 0.0816, 0.3434)

3. Conclusions

A combined graphical-simulation algorithm for the design and selection of type of hybrid RD models is developed considering both ideal and non-ideal kinetics. For same reaction scheme, volatility order, and number of components it is found that for ideal kinetics SHRD and for non-ideal kinetics hybrid RD side draw model is capable to obtain the desired selectivity. The next step of the algorithm is to extend its applicability for mixtures (including multiazeotropic) containing more than four components.

References

D. Glasser, D. Hildebrandt, C. Crowe, 1987, A geometric approach to steady flow reactors: The attainable region and optimization in concentration space, Ind. Eng. Chem. Res., 26, 1803-1810.

S.U. Hasan, S.M. Mahajani, R.K. Malik, 2014, Selectivity Engineering with Simple and Complex Hybrid Reactive Distillation Columns, Ind. Eng. Chem. Res.,53, 18526–18538.

Anton A. Kiss, Edwin Zondervan, Richard Lakerveld, Leyla Özkan (Eds.)
Proceedings of the 29th European Symposium on Computer Aided Process Engineering
June 16th to 19th, 2019, Eindhoven, The Netherlands. © 2019 Elsevier B.V. All rights reserved.
http://dx.doi.org/10.1016/B978-0-128-18634-3.50070-9

Integrated Design of Solvents and Processes based on Reaction Kinetics from Quantum Chemical Prediction Methods

Christoph Gertig[a], Kai Leonhard[a] and André Bardow[a,b,*]

[a]*Institute of Technical Thermodynamics, RWTH Aachen University, Schinkelstrasse 8, 52062 Aachen, Germany*
[b]*Institute of Energy and Climate Research (IEK-10), Forschungszentrum Juelich, Wilhelm-Johnen-Strasse, 52425 Juelich, Germany*
andre.bardow@ltt.rwth-aachen.de

Abstract

The choice of the employed solvent often strongly influences the performance of chemical processes. To obtain optimal process designs, we propose a method for the integrated in silico design of solvents and reaction-based processes. The search space of possible solvent molecules is explored by a genetic optimization algorithm which is directly linked to gradient-based process optimization. Thereby, the process performance of the designed solvent is evaluated. While most approaches for such integrated design problems are based on group contribution methods and limited to equilibrium properties, we here propose a quantum mechanics-based approach to capture reaction kinetics. The integrated design method is successfully applied to the design of solvent and process for a carbamate cleavage reaction. The presented method allows for efficient design of a large number of promising solvents within the integrated reaction solvent and process design.

Keywords: computer-aided molecular design, process design, quantum mechanics

1. Introduction

The performance of chemical processes largely depends on the occurring chemical reactions, which are in turn influenced by the choice of solvent (Reichardt, 1990). Thus, the selection of optimal solvents is essential in the design of reaction-based processes. As the number of potential solvents is theoretically unlimited, systematic solvent design methods have been developed. The success of such methods depends on the evaluation of candidate solvents. For a reliable evaluation, first, a sound prediction of solvent impacts on the reactions is essential and second, the objective used for the evaluation should reflect the performance of candidate solvents in the process.

The sound prediction of solvent impacts on reactions has been addressed by several solvent design methods (Papadopoulos et al., 2018). Struebing et al. (2013) calculate reaction kinetics from surrogate models fitted to few data points derived from quantum chemical calculations. Austin et al. (2018) propose a design method where reaction kinetics are predicted for every candidate solvent based on transition state theory and a correction term fitted to experiments. However, in these approaches, solvents are assessed based on reaction rate constants as design objective and the designed solvents are likely different from those showing optimal performance in the chemical process. The approach proposed by Zhou et al. (2015) overcomes this disadvantage by employing a process model allowing for the process-based assessment of the designed solvents. However, the solvent impact on reaction kinetics is predicted with a simplified model fitted to few available experimental data points, which does not guarantee good extrapolation.

To overcome the limitations of previous approaches, we here propose an integrated reaction solvent and process design approach using a sound prediction of reaction kinetics combined with a process-based assessment of solvents. The required reaction rates are determined by fully predictive, quantum chemistry-based computations. Experimental data is not needed and only used for validation. To reduce the computational effort such that large molecular design spaces can be explored, we separate the computation of solvent-independent and solvent-dependent quantities required for calculating reaction rates. Detailed process optimizations are employed for the process-based solvent assessment. To demonstrate the proposed approach for integrated reaction solvent and process design, we apply it to the case study of a carbamate cleavage process.

2. Approach for the Integrated Reaction Solvent and Process Design

The integrated solvent and process design problem is formulated based on the general computer-aided molecular and process design (CAMPD) problem by Gani (2004):

$$\max_{x,y} f(x,y) \qquad \text{process-based objective}$$

$$
\begin{aligned}
\text{s.t.} \quad & g_1(x,y) = 0 && \text{process model} \\
& g_2(x,y) = 0 && \text{property models} \\
& g_3(y) = 0 && \text{chemical feasibility of molecules} \\
& c_1(y) \leq 0 && \text{constraints on molecular and thermodynamic properties} \\
& x \in X \subset \mathbb{R}^n, y \in Y.
\end{aligned}
\tag{1}
$$

The process-based objective $f(x,y)$ (e.g., a product yield) depends on n continuous process variables x (e.g., temperatures) contained in the operation range X and on the molecular structure of the inert solvent y contained in the molecular design space Y. The equality constraints $g_1(x,y)$ correspond to the process model (see section 2.2) and the equality constraints $g_2(x,y)$ to models for kinetic and thermodynamic properties (see section 2.1). Constraints $g_3(y)$ ensure feasibility of the molecular structures y, e.g., by ensuring correct valency of all atoms in a molecule. Inequality constraints $c_1(y)$ limit molecular properties like the number of atoms in the molecule as well as thermodynamic properties like boiling points. The solution of the integrated design problem is the combination of the optimal solvent with its optimal process conditions.

2.1. Prediction of Reaction Kinetics and Thermodynamic Properties

Reaction rate constants are predicted based on transition state theory (Eyring, 1935) from the activation barrier $\Delta G^{\ddagger}$ between the reactants and the transition state. The activation barrier $\Delta G^{\ddagger}$ is computed in two steps for a reaction in an inert solvent (Kröger et al., 2017):

1. Geometries of reactants and transition states are optimized and vibrational frequencies are determined with b3lyp and TZVP basis set using the software Gaussian

09 (Frisch et al., 2009). Electronic energies are calculated with DLPNO-CCSD(T) and aug-cc-pVTZ basis set using the software ORCA (Neese, 2018). Next, the activation barrier $\Delta G^{\ddagger}$ in an ideal gas state is computed with the statistical thermo-dynamics package TAMkin (Ghysels et al., 2010).

2. Solvation effects are accounted for based on Gibbs free energies of solvation G^{solv} of reactants and transition states. We predict G^{solv} using the COSMO-RS method (Eckert and Klamt, 2002) implemented in the COSMOtherm software (Eckert and Klamt, 2017).

Step 1 is the computationally most demanding step, but is independent of the solvent and thus needed only once per reaction. COSMO-RS is also used for predicting normal boiling points and vapor pressures as well as activity coefficients used to fit parameters for the NRTL model (Renon and Prausnitz, 1968). NRTL is used to efficiently compute activity coefficients in process optimization.

2.2. Process Modeling

Process models are formulated as differential-algebraic systems of equations (DAE) based on balance equations. Further, the models contain algebraic equations describing phase equilibria and the NRTL equations. Process models are implemented in MatLab (The MathWorks, Inc., 2015) and solved with the DAE solver ode15s.

2.3. Solution of the Integrated Design Problem

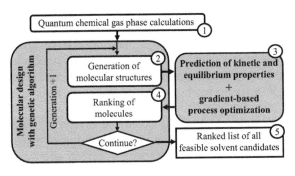

Figure 1: Flowsheet of the solution approach to the integrated design problem.

To solve Problem 1, first, the quantum-chemical gas phase calculations are performed (step 1 in Figure 1). Next, the actual integrated design problem is solved with a hybrid optimization scheme. The molecular structure of the solvent is optimized with the genetic optimization algorithm LEA3D as proposed for non-reactive systems by Scheffczyk et al. (2017). For this purpose, candidate solvent molecules are generated by connecting 3D molecule fragments from a given library (step 2). Full 3D structural information is maintained in this step. Next, the 3D molecular structures are used to predict kinetic and thermodynamic properties of the resulting reaction systems based on quantum chemistry and to optimize processes with the candidate solvents (step 3). For this purpose, we use gradient-based optimization with fmincon in MatLab (The MathWorks, Inc., 2015). Based on the final objective function values of the process optimizations, the candidate solvents are ranked (step 4) and refined (step 2). Steps 2 to 4 are repeated for a predefined number of iterations before a ranked list of all feasible solvents is returned (step 5).

3. Case Study: Thermal Cleavage of Cyclohexyl Carbamate

The thermal cleavage of methyl carbamates to isocyanates and methanol is part of a production route of industrially impor- tant isocyanates (Six and Richter, 2000). Carbamate cleavage reactions are strongly endothermic (Leitner et al., 2018) with an unfavorable reaction equilibrium almost completely on the reactants' side. To avoid the fast back-reaction, methanol has to be continuously removed from the reactor. As methanol is volatile at typical reaction temperatures around 200 °C, it can be removed by stripping with an inert gas like nitrogen (Cao et al., 2015). In this work, we consider the cleavage of cyclohexyl carbamate (CHC) in a batch reactor with nitrogen stripping and a flash for recycling flushed out isocyanate and solvent (Figure 2).

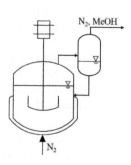

Figure 2: Batch process for CHC cleavage.

3.1. Prediction of Reaction Rate Constants

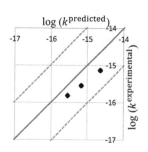

Figure 3: Log-log plot of experimental vs. predicted rate constants.

Alcohols and carbamates have an autocatalytic effect on car- bamate cleavage reactions (see e.g., Thiele (1979)). There- fore, we consider the completely non-catalytic cleavage re- action as well as autocatalysis by carbamate and methanol molecules. Suitable experimental data for direct valida- tion of the predictions for the autocatalytic carbamate cleav- age is not available in the literature. However, the carba- mate cleavage can be considered as reverse reaction of the isocyanate-alcohol reaction (Thiele, 1979). Moreover, dif- ferent aliphatic isocyanates (Lorenz et al., 1984) and differ- ent alcohols (Sardon et al., 2013) have been shown to re- act with similar rate in isocyanate-alcohol reactions. Thus, we use rate constants determined experimentally by Lorenz et al. (1984) for the reaction of the cycloaliphatic isocyanate group in isophorone diisocyanate with butanol for compar- ison (Figure 3). The deviation of our predictions from the experimental values is much less than one order of magnitude, which can be considered a very good agreement (Kröger et al., 2017). Moreover, we aim at comparisons of solvents such that several errors can- cel. Thus, the chosen prediction methods for rate constants are regarded as suitable for the reactions under consideration in this work.

3.2. Specifications for the Integrated Solvent and Process Design

As process objective $f(x,y)$, the yield of isocyanate is chosen and defined as the final amount of isocyanate devided by the initial amount of carbamate in the reactor. The free process variables x are the temperature T^{flash} in the flash (cf. Figure 2) and the volume flow of nitrogen $\dot{V}_{N_2}$. We set a constant reactor temperature of $T^R = 200\,°C$, a pressure of $p = 4\,bar$, a reactor volume $V^R = 1\,m^3$ and a reaction time of $t^R = 10\,h$. A library of 3D fragments is used for the genetic optimization of solvent structures y in 25 generations with a maximum of 40 molecules per generation. Alkanes, aromates, ketones, ethers, esters, nitro- and nitrile compounds are suitable solvents for carbamate cleavage (see

Ephraim et al. (1958) and Merger et al. (1983)) and according fragments are provided. As only inert solvents are desired, protic substances are not considered because they may react with the produced isocyanate. As inequality constraints $c_1(y)$, the number of non-hydrogen atoms in solvent structures y is limited to a maximum of 20 and a minimal normal boiling point of the solvents of 176 °C, which is 10 °C higher than the normal boiling point of the produced isocyanate, is required to prevent solvent evaporation.

3.3. Results of the Integrated Solvent and Process Design

The solution of the integrated solvent and process design problem takes about 6 days using an Intel Xeon CPU E5-1660 v3 @ 3.00 GHz with 16 virtual processor cores. The design results in an optimal process with the inert solvent n-undecane and an isocyanate yield of 68%. The temperature in the flash is $T^{\text{flash}} = 20.5\,°\text{C}$ and the nitrogen flow rate is $\dot{V}_{N_2} = 0.72\,\text{m}^3\,\text{min}^{-1}$, which is in a similar range as the experimental conditions used by Cao et al. (2015). 176 designed solvents meet all constraints (Figure 4). Interestingly, solvent selection based

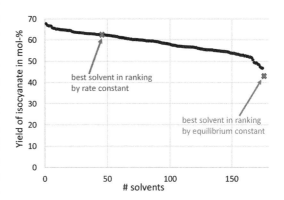

Figure 4: Yields of optimized carbamate cleavage processes for 176 designed feasible solvents.

on equilibrium constants of the cleavage reaction fails (solvent benzaldehyde, 43% yield). The reason is that methanol removal prevents the control of the process by reaction equilibrium. A selection based on the rate constant of carbamate cleavage results in a good solvent (i-icosane, 62% yield), but not in the best solvent. The reason is that a tradeoff between high rate constants and favorable vapor-liquid equilibrium properties is important to achieve maximum product yield. This tradeoff is only captured by integrated solvent and process design, which clearly shows the strength of the proposed approach.

4. Conclusion

An approach is presented for the integrated design of reaction solvents and processes which overcomes the limits of previous approaches. Our approach uses quantum chemistry-based predictions of reaction kinetics and thermodynamic properties and thus avoids simplified models. The integrated solvent and process design problem is solved with a hybrid optimization scheme combining genetic optimization of solvent structures and gradient-based process optimization. In a case study of a carbamate cleavage process, the strength of the integrated design compared to a solvent selection by equilibrium or rate constants is demonstrated.

Acknowledgements:

We thank the German Federal Ministry of Education and Research for funding of the Project Carbon2Polymers (03EK30442C). Simulations were performed with computing resources granted by RWTH Aachen University under project rwth0284.

References

N. D. Austin, N. V. Sahinidis, I. A. Konstantinov, D. W. Trahan, 2018. COSMO-based computer-aided molecular/mixture design: A focus on reaction solvents. AIChE Journal 64 (1), 104–122.

Y. Cao, H. Li, N. Qin, G. Zhu, 2015. Kinetics of the decomposition of dimethylhexane-1,6-dicarbamate to 1,6-hexamethylene diisocyanate. Chinese Journal of Chemical Engineering 23, 775–779.

F. Eckert, A. Klamt, 2002. Fast solvent screening via quantum chemistry: COSMO-RS approach. AIChE Journal 48 (2), 369–385.

F. Eckert, A. Klamt, 2017. COSMOtherm, C3.0, release 1701, COSMOlogic GmbH & Co KG, Leverkusen.

S. Ephraim, A. Woodward, R. Mesrobian, 1958. Kinetic Studies of the Reaction of Phenyl Isocyanate with Alcohols in Various Solvents. Journal of the American Chemical Society 80 (6), 1326–1328.

H. Eyring, 1935. The Activated Complex in Chemical Reactions. The Journal of Chemical Physics 3, 107–115.

M. J. Frisch et al., 2009. Gaussian 09, Gaussian Inc., Wallingford, CT.

R. Gani, 2004. Computer-aided methods and tools for chemical product design. Chemical Engineering Research and Design 82 (11), 1494–1504.

A. Ghysels, T. Verstraelen, K. Hemelsoet, M. Waroquier, V. van Speybroeck, 2010. TAMkin: a versatile package for vibrational analysis and chemical kinetics. Journal of Chemical Information and Modeling 50 (9), 1736–1750.

L. C. Kröger, W. A. Kopp, K. Leonhard, 2017. Prediction of Chain Propagation Rate Constants of Polymerization Reactions in Aqueous NIPAM/BIS and VCL/BIS Systems. The Journal of Physical Chemistry B 121 (13), 2887–2895.

W. Leitner, G. Franciò, M. Scott, C. Westhues, J. Langanke, M. Lansing, C. Hussong, E. Erdkamp, 2018. Carbon2Polymer–Chemical Utilization of CO2 in the Production of Isocyanates. Chemie Ingenieur Technik 90 (10), 1504–1512.

O. Lorenz, H. Decker, G. Rose, 1984. NCO-Prepolymere aus Diisocyanaten mit unterschiedlich reaktiven NCO-Gruppen. Die Angewandte Makromolekulare Chemie: Applied Macromolecular Chemistry and Physics 122 (1), 83–99.

F. Merger, G. Nestler, R. Platz, F. Towae, H. Hellbach, 1983. Verfahren zur Herstellung von Isocyanaten durch thermische Spaltung von Urethanen, DE 3142627, BASF.

F. Neese, 2018. Software update: the ORCA program system, version 4.0. Wiley Interdisciplinary Reviews: Computational Molecular Science 8 (1), 1327.

A. I. Papadopoulos, I. Tsivintzelis, P. Linke, P. Seferlis, 2018. Computer-Aided Molecular Design: Fundamentals, Methods, and Applications. In: Reference Module in Chemistry, Molecular Sciences and Chemical Engineering. Elsevier, https://doi.org/10.1016/B978-0-12-409547-2.14342-2.

C. Reichardt, 1990. Solvents and solvent effects in organic chemistry, 2nd Edition. VCH, Weinheim.

H. Renon, J. M. Prausnitz, 1968. Local compositions in thermodynamic excess functions for liquid mixtures. AIChE Journal 14 (1), 135–144.

H. Sardon, A. C. Engler, J. M. Chan, J. M. García, D. J. Coady, A. Pascual, D. Mecerreyes, G. O. Jones, J. E. Rice, H. W. Horn, et al., 2013. Organic acid-catalyzed polyurethane formation via a dual-activated mechanism: unexpected preference of N-activation over O-activation of isocyanates. Journal of the American Chemical Society 135 (43), 16235–16241.

J. Scheffczyk, L. Fleitmann, A. Schwarz, M. Lampe, A. Bardow, K. Leonhard, 2017. COSMO-CAMD: A framework for optimization-based computer-aided molecular design using COSMO-RS. Chemical Engineering Science 159, 84–92.

C. Six, F. Richter, 2000. Isocyanates, organic. Ullmann's Encyclopedia of Industrial Chemistry.

H. Struebing, Z. Ganase, P. G. Karamertzanis, E. Siougkrou, P. Haycock, P. M. Piccione, A. Armstrong, A. Galindo, C. S. Adjiman, 2013. Computer-aided molecular design of solvents for accelerated reaction kinetics. Nature chemistry 5 (11), 952–957.

The MathWorks, Inc., 2015. MATLAB R2015b.

L. Thiele, 1979. Isocyanatreaktionen und Katalyse in der Polyurethanchemie. Fortschrittsbericht. Acta Polymerica 30 (6), 323–342.

T. Zhou, K. McBride, X. Zhang, Z. Qi, K. Sundmacher, 2015. Integrated solvent and process design exemplified for a Diels-Alder reaction. AIChE Journal 61 (1), 147–158.

Anton A. Kiss, Edwin Zondervan, Richard Lakerveld, Leyla Özkan (Eds.)
Proceedings of the 29th European Symposium on Computer Aided Process Engineering
June 16th to 19th, 2019, Eindhoven, The Netherlands. © 2019 Elsevier B.V. All rights reserved.
http://dx.doi.org/10.1016/B978-0-128-18634-3.50071-0

Novel refrigeration cycle configurations for performance improvements in LNG processes at small scale

Fernando Almeida-Trasvina* and Robin Smith

Centre for Process Integration, School of Chemical Engineering and Analytical Science, The University of Manchester, Manchester M13 9PL, UK

hector.almeidatrasvina@manchester.ac.uk

Abstract

The refrigeration cycles employed in the LNG industry are highly energy-intensive. The costs associated to the shaft work energy required for refrigerant compression usually dominates the overall operating costs of the LNG plant. In this work, four different single mixed refrigerant (SMR) cycle configurations, including the commercial PRICO cycle and the CryoMan cycle, are studied for energy-efficiency improvements in the production of LNG at small scale (i.e. up to 1 million tonnes per annum, MTPA). The cycle configurations are based on structural modifications applied to the PRICO cycle. The four configurations are first optimised to minimise shaft work demand, so analysis is carried out in the scenario in which each cycle fully exploits their corresponding configuration. Additionally, the complexity of the SMR cycles, in terms of number of compression stages is kept similar, so the energy savings can be associated to the structural modifications only. From the four SMR cycles, the CryoMan cycle is the most energy-efficient, achieving saving of around 8.5% compared to the commercial PRICO cycle. The exergy analysis applied to their multi-stream heat exchangers (MSHE) suggests that the structural modifications allow reducing the refrigeration duty at the lowest temperature level to bring energy savings.

Keywords: LNG, small scale, refrigeration cycle, SMR cycles.

1. Introduction

Small scale production of liquefied natural gas (LNG), i.e. up to 1 MTPA, is becoming commercially attractive. To liquefy a natural gas stream (to around –160 °C), energy-intensive refrigeration cycles are usually employed. The shaft work energy required for refrigerant compression strongly dominates the overall operating costs of the LNG plant. Thus, minimising shaft work energy demand of a given cycle configuration leads to minimising operating costs. The PRICO single mixed refrigerant (SMR) cycle is the commercial benchmark SMR cycle for small scale production of LNG.

The energy-efficiency of mixed refrigerant cycles can be improved by structurally modifying its configuration, as shown by Almeida-Trasvina and Smith (2018) for cascade cycles in large scale production of LNG. However, little research has been done in structural modifications to mixed refrigerant cycles for LNG processes at small scale. He et al. (2019) optimised the energy-efficiency of an SMR cycle consisting of two MSHE stages but with a flash unit before the first MSHE unit. Aslambakhsh et al. (2018) optimised the PRICO cycle considering both operating and capital costs. Nguyen et al. (2018) optimised the energy-efficiency of the PRICO cycle for five different natural gas feeds. Morosuk et al. (2015) analysed the PRICO cycle using exergy analysis for improving its energy-efficiency. Mehrpooya and Ansarinasab (2015) assessed two SMR cycles using an exergoeconomic analysis.

In this paper, the energy-efficiency performance of four different SMR cycles is studied. The SMR cycle configurations are based on structural modifications applied to the PRICO cycle, and are taken from Zheng (2009). The SMR cycles are first optimised in a case study for small scale production of LNG. The complexity of the SMR cycles (in terms of number of compression stages) is kept similar, so differences in energy performance can be associated to their structural modification only. Exergy analysis is applied to each configuration so as to bring insights of how each structural modification allows achieving energy savings.

2. Configuration of the single mixed refrigerant (SMR) cycles

Figure 1 shows the four SMR cycles studied in this paper. The PRICO cycle is shown in Figure 1a. In the MultiStream cycle (Figure 1b), the structural modification consists in splitting the refrigerant stream flow rate into two streams before entering the MSHE, each with an independent evaporating pressure. In the PreFlash cycle (Figure 1c), the structural modification consists in using a flash unit; the resulting refrigerant streams would then have different compositions between each other. In the CryoMan cycle (Figure 1d), the main refrigerant stream is also split into two streams using a flash unit, and the resulting flash outlet streams are partially mixed to create the two refrigerant streams that provide cooling in the MSHE.

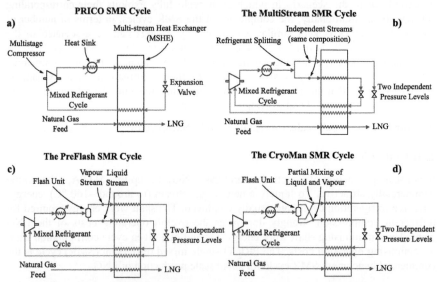

Figure 1. SMR configurations: a) PRICO; b) MultiStream; c) PreFlash; d) CryoMan.

The configurations of the SMR cycles are defined to have a total of three compression stages for refrigerant compression, in order to have similar complexity across the SMR cycles since compressors are major contributors to capital costs and also impact on energy performance (Mokhatab et al., 2014, Ch. 3.2).

3. Optimisation of the SMR cycle configurations

The operating variables of the four SMR cycles are optimised in order to analyse their best performance, i.e. the scenario in which the SMR cycles are fully exploiting their corresponding structural modifications to reduce the energy demand.

All the four SMR cycle configurations are optimised to minimise the specific shaft work energy demand (Equation 1) in a case study to produce LNG at small scale. The data of the natural gas is taken from Fahmy et al. (2016), and is given in Table 1. The natural gas feed flow rate is equivalent to LNG production of 1.0 MTPA. It is assumed that the minimum temperature approach for heat exchange in the MSHE is 2 °C; a maximum pressure ratio of 3.5 has been defined for any compression stage.

$$\frac{W^{Total}}{\dot{m}_{LNG}} = \frac{\sum_{i=1}^{n} W_i^{Stg}(\phi)}{\dot{m}_{LNG}} \tag{1}$$

The optimisation strategy followed in this work is similar to that employed by Almeida-Trasvina and Smith (2018) for the optimisation of cascade refrigeration cycles for large scale production of LNG. The strategy consists in applying a stochastic algorithm to search the solution space (using Genetic Algorithm) and avoid local optima, and the best solution found is fed to an SQP solver to refine the solution.

Table 1. Natural gas specifications for the case study.

Flow rate [kg·s⁻¹]	31.71
Inlet pressure [bar]	63.0
Inlet temperature [°C]	25.0
Outlet temperature [°C]	−161.0
Composition [mole fraction]	
Methane	0.98385
Ethane	0.01070
Propane	0.00090
n-Butane	0.00020
CO_2	0.00005

The results from the optimisation are presented in Table 2. The CryoMan cycle is the most energy-efficient of the four SMR cycles. The CryoMan cycle performance is equivalent to a specific shaft work demand of 28.67 MW·MTPA LNG⁻¹, whereas that of the PRICO cycle is 31.32 MW·MTPA LNG⁻¹. That is, the CryoMan cycle achieved energy savings of around 8.5% compared to the PRICO cycle.

The results in Table 2 suggest that manipulating the refrigerant composition brings energy savings. The modification applied to the PreFlash cycle (i.e. the flash unit) implies splitting the refrigerant stream into two streams that have different composition with respect to each other (unlike with the MultiStream cycle). Energy savings of 3.22% are achieved by the PreFlash cycle compared to the MultiStream cycle.

Table 2. Energy-efficiency comparison between the SMR cycles (relative to PRICO cycle).

	PRICO SMR Cycle	MultiStream SMR Cycle	PreFlash SMR Cycle	CryoMan SMR Cycle
Compression Stages	3	3	3	3
LNG production [MTPA]	1.00	1.00	1.00	1.00
Specific shaft work [MW·MTPA⁻¹ LNG]	31.32	30.47	29.38	28.67
Energy savings [%]	—	+ 2.71%	+ 6.19%	+ 8.46%

The CryoMan SMR cycle allows manipulating further the refrigerant composition by partially mixing the flash unit outlet streams. Energy savings of around 2.78% are achieved by the CryoMan SMR cycle relative to the PreFlash SMR cycle.

4. Exergy analysis of the SMR cycles

In refrigeration cycles, exergy is defined as the minimum shaft work input (Equation 2) needed to provide refrigeration at a given temperature, assuming a thermodynamically reversible process (Venkatarathnam, 2008, Ch. 1.4). Equation 2 suggests that the exergy increases either as the refrigeration temperature (T_{Evap}) decreases, or as the refrigeration duty (Q_{Evap}) increases. The term in brackets on the right-hand side of the equation is widely known as the Carnot factor. Alternatively, exergy can be expressed as in Equation 3, which implies that the exergy demand is also dependent on the nature of the refrigerant mixture employed (values of enthalpies and entropies).

$$Ex = -W_{rev} = Q_{Evap}\left(\frac{T_{Cond}}{T_{Evap}} - 1\right) \tag{2}$$

$$Ex = n\left[\left(h_{out} - h_{in}\right)_{Evap} - T_{Cond}\left(s_{out} - s_{in}\right)_{Evap}\right] \tag{3}$$

Exergy analysis is applied to the SMR cycles, by plotting the exergy composite curves (from Equation 2) of the MSHE for each SMR cycle. The exergy composite curves are the analogue of the conventional composite curves, but the temperature axis in the latter is replaced by the Carnot factor. The area between the exergy composite curves represents exergy loss, associated to the temperature difference needed for heat transfer.

Figure 2 shows the exergy composite curves for each optimised SMR cycle. As can be implied from Equation 2, the area between the exergy composite curves is minimised at the cold end of the process across the four SMR cycles. Moreover, the overall exergy losses are gradually reduced with each of the structural modifications applied. The exergy losses in the MSHE for the PRICO cycle are equivalent to 2.71 MW, whereas in the CryoMan cycle the exergy losses are equivalent to only 1.13 MW, i.e. the losses are reduced by around 58%.

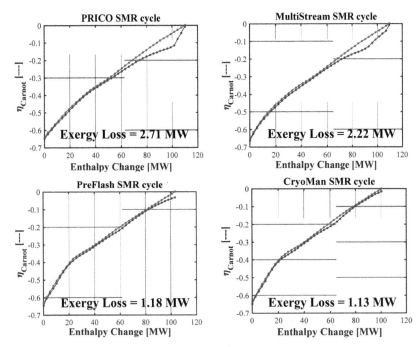

Figure 2. Exergy composite curves of MSHE for each SMR cycle.

The main results from the exergy analysis over the MSHE unit for each SMR cycle are shown in Table 3. The exergy efficiency in Table 3 is defined as the ratio of overall exergy change of the natural gas stream (15.72 MW) to the total shaft work demand for refrigerant compression. The exergy duty in the MSHE is calculated for both composite curves at intermediate temperatures using Equation 3.

Table 3. Summary of exergy performance results for each SMR cycle.

	PRICO SMR cycle	MultiStream SMR cycle	PreFlash SMR cycle	CryoMan SMR cycle
Shaft work demand [MW·MTPA LNG^{-1}]	31.32	30.47	29.38	28.67
Exergy Duty MSHE [MW]	54.79	53.12	44.06	43.17
Exergy Losses MSHE [MW]	2.71	2.22	1.18	1.13
Exergy Efficiency [%]	50.19	51.59	53.50	54.83

As shown in Table 3, the exergy duty in the MSHE is decreased by around 9.1 MW when the flash unit is introduced, since the refrigerant flow rate in the low pressure stream (at the lowest temperature level) is significantly reduced. Also, the flash unit helps reducing the exergy losses by creating two different refrigerant compositions that yield a reduced area between the composite curves (see Figure 2).

In the CryoMan cycle, partial mixing of the streams leaving the flash unit allows to reduce further the flow rate of the stream at the lowest temperature level, and also to reduce the exergy losses by manipulating the refrigerant composition of each resulting stream. Thus, the exergy demand further reduced, bringing the corresponding savings in shaft work demand.

5. Conclusions

The structural modifications applied to the PRICO cycle were demonstrated to bring significant energy savings – up to 8.46 % with the CryoMan cycle – for configurations with similar level of complexity in terms of number of compression stages, and for the same liquefaction duty. The results from the exergy analysis suggest that structural modifications should be applied with the aim to reduce the refrigeration load at the lowest temperature level. Additionally, creating different refrigerant compositions and manipulating refrigerant flow rates allow minimising the exergy losses in the MSHE.

Further study is still needed on the implications of structural modifications in the configuration of LNG mixed refrigerant cycles. More insights would be useful to further develop and optimise novel LNG refrigeration cycles more systematically.

References

Almeida-Trasvina, F. & Smith, R. (2018). Design and Optimisation of Novel Cascade Refrigeration Cycles for LNG Production. *In:* Friedl, A., Klemeš, J. J., Radl, S., Varbanov, P. S. & Wallek, T. (eds.) *Computer Aided Chemical Engineering.* Elsevier. Vol. 43, 621-626.

Aslambakhsh, A. H., Moosavian, M. A., Amidpour, M., Hosseini, M. & AmirAfshar, S. (2018). Global cost optimization of a mini-scale liquefied natural gas plant. *Energy,* 148, 1191-1200.

Fahmy, M. F. M., Nabih, H. I. & El-Aziz, M. R. A. (2016). Investigation and performance improvement of the propane precooling cycle in the propane precooled mixed refrigerant cycle liquefaction process. *Industrial & Engineering Chemistry Research,* 55(10), 2769-2783.

He, T., Liu, Z., Ju, Y. & Parvez, A. M. (2019). A comprehensive optimization and comparison of modified single mixed refrigerant and parallel nitrogen expansion liquefaction process for small-scale mobile LNG plant. *Energy,* 167, 1-12.

Mehrpooya, M. & Ansarinasab, H. (2015). Exergoeconomic evaluation of single mixed refrigerant natural gas liquefaction processes. *Energy Conversion and Management,* 99, 400-413.

Mokhatab, S., Mak, J. Y., Valappil, J. V. & Wood, D. A. (2014). *Handbook of Liquefied Natural Gas.* Kidlington, Oxford, UK: Gulf Professional Elsevier, Inc.

Morosuk, T., Tesch, S., Hiemann, A., Tsatsaronis, G. & Bin Omar, N. (2015). Evaluation of the PRICO liquefaction process using exergy-based methods. *Journal of Natural Gas Science and Engineering,* 27, 23-31.

Nguyen, T.-V., Rothuizen, E. D., Markussen, W. B. & Elmegaard, B. (2018). Thermodynamic comparison of three small-scale gas liquefaction systems. *Applied Thermal Engineering,* 128, 712-724.

Venkatarathnam, G. (2008). *Cryogenic Mixed Refrigerant Processes.* New York, NY, USA: Springer Science+Business Media LLC.

Zheng, X. (2009). *Design and Integration of Refrigeration and Power Systems.* Ph.D. Thesis. Centre for Process Integration, The University of Manchester. Manchester, UK

Anton A. Kiss, Edwin Zondervan, Richard Lakerveld, Leyla Özkan (Eds.)
Proceedings of the 29th European Symposium on Computer Aided Process Engineering
June 16th to 19th, 2019, Eindhoven, The Netherlands. © 2019 Elsevier B.V. All rights reserved.
http://dx.doi.org/10.1016/B978-0-128-18634-3.50072-2

Involving the Water-Energy-Food Nexus in Integrating Low-Income and Isolated Communities

Brenda Cansino-Loeza[a], J. Betzabe González-Campos[b], José María Ponce-Ortega[a*]

[a] *Chemical Engineering Department, Universidad Michoacana de San Nicolás de Hidalgo, Francisco J. Múgica S/N, Ciudad Universitaria, 58060, Morelia, Michoacán, México.*

[b] *Institute for Chemical and Biological Research, Universidad Michoacana de San Nicolás de Hidalgo, Morelia, Michoacán 58060, Mexico.*

jmponce@umich.mx

Abstract

This work presents a general mathematical programming model for satisfying water, energy and food needs in isolated and low-income communities involving different process integration approaches. The problem consists in determining the optimal and sustainable configuration to satisfy the energy, water and food demands. Also, the use of waste-to-energy technologies is proposed aiming to obtain valuated products from wastes to reduce the environmental impact. A multi-objective analysis is presented considering the consumption of fresh water, the greenhouse gas emissions and the cost of the integrated system as objective functions. As case study, the community with the lowest index of poverty and marginalization from the State of Guerrero in Mexico is presented. The results show that it is possible to satisfy the water, energy and food needs in isolated communities accounting for integrated processes.

Keywords: Water-Energy-Food Nexus, Isolated community, Polygeneration, Optimization, Process integration.

1. Introduction

Water, energy and food are critical resources for meeting the social demands and socioeconomic development of communities and societies around the world (Fuentes-Cortés and Ponce Ortega, 2017). Nevertheless, there are communities that do not have access to energy and, consequently, there is a lack of access to water and food. Many rural communities or small towns still do not have access to these resources mainly due to their geographic location that makes difficult the interconnection with the electrical grid (Sánchez et al., 2015). Moreover, the provision of water from the public network is a big problem. Satisfying the basic needs of inhabitants in isolated communities is a problem that is closely related to the water-energy-food nexus due to the inhabitants consume considerable amounts of resources to meet their demands (Martínez-Guido et al., 2017). Water, energy and food are inextricably interrelated and each of them depends on others (Zhang and Vesselinov, 2017). The water-energy-food nexus is considered to achieve a sustainable development that allows maintaining the security of these resources and promote economic growth without affecting the environment considerably. However, the inadequate management of these resources may also produce significant environmental impacts. Currently, alternative energy sources have been used to decrease the environmental impact. Also, there have been reported several studies related to the use of renewable energies implemented in isolated communities to generate electric energy (Ahadi et al., 2016). Furthermore, other researches have focused on distributed generation to produce electricity in remote places by isolated systems due to the generation units are close to the consumers and the transmission energy losses are negligible; examples of this type of generation are polygeneration systems, which can be defined as the simultaneous production of two or more energy utilities and products, seeking to take advantage of the maximum potential of the consumed resources. It has been demonstrated that polygeneration systems reduce fuel consumption, operational costs and consequently reduce the environmental impact, which is associated to the greenhouse gas emissions. There are many studies that propose the use of different schemes of distributed generation to meet the energy demands at a household level. Other researches have been focused on integrating different processes to take advantage of the available resources in residential complexes (Nuñez-López et al., 2018). Nevertheless, none of the previous mentioned works have considered the water-energy-food nexus involving a polygeneration system that allows to decrease the use of fresh resources and the environmental impact in an isolated community.

Another important challenge to decrease the environmental impact is planning a sustainable waste management system. In this context, Diaz-Barriga-Fernandez et al. (2017) proposed a multi-objective optimization approach for the strategic planning of a municipal solid waste management system considering recycle, reuse, transportation, separation and distribution of solid wastes. The management of municipal solid waste has been identified as one of the global challenges that must be carefully faced to achieve sustainable goals, recent researches have focused on proposing processes that convert waste-to-energy or valuated products. Matsakas et al. (2018) investigated the conversion of municipal solid waste to energy and chemicals by biological and thermochemical treatments that are among the most used technologies.

However, none of the previous researches has focused on studying different types of solid waste treatments in a low-income municipality to be a community in which their needs can be met through the proper management of their resources and recycled wastes. In addition, no research has been conducted to address the integration of water-energy-food nexus and the management of solid wastes in isolated communities, which can help to reduce the environmental impact and improve the living conditions of the inhabitants. Faced with this problem, it is needed to implement a system capable of integrating the energy-water-food nexus so that the needs of the inhabitants of the isolated community can be met. In this context, a polygeneration system is an attractive option to provide electricity, heating and cooling to the community, satisfying the energy demands making proper management of water and the resources which in turn will facilitate the food production and consequently the access to food.

2. Problem Statement

This work presents a mathematical programming model for the design of a residential polygeneration system in an isolated community considering the water-energy-food nexus (Figure 1). The problem consists in determining the optimal and sustainable configuration to satisfy the energy, water and food demands of the inhabitants. To meet energy demands, the existence of different cogeneration units such as Internal

Combustion Engines, Fuel Cells, Microturbines and Stirling Engines were contemplated. In addition, there was considered the use of of renewable energies such as solar collectors, aerogenerators and solar panels to help to satisfy the energy demands of the community. Water demand was satisfied by rainwater collection systems and wells, it was proposed the use of rainwater collection systems for provide water in the community, agriculture activities, cattle activities and gardening. Wastewater generated in the community was sent to blackwater and greywater treatment plants. The treated greywater was used in gardening, cattle and agriculture. Different types of crops and animal production were considered to satisfy the food demands of the inhabitants. The agriculture activities involve the production of peanut, jicama, corn, lemon, mango, papaya, and sorghum, and the livestock activities are related to the bovine, porcine, ovine, goat and bird production. On the other hand, the generated municipal solid wastes are separated in plastic, metal, paper, glass and non-recyclables, the latter can be treated in process plants such as pelletization, incineration, gasification, pyrolysis and anaerobic digestion to obtain pellets, steam, natural gas and pyrolysis oil that can be used as an energy source or can be sold.

The objective functions of the problem are to minimize the consumption of fresh water, the greenhouse gas emissions and the cost (Eq. (1)).

$$OF = \{ \min Cost; \; \min Water; \; \min GHGE \} \tag{1}$$

The economic objective function (*Cost*) considers the minimization of the total annual cost associated to satisfy the needs of the community, which includes operating and capital costs for each needed unit and the sales associated with animals, crops, pyrolysis oil, natural gas, biogas, pellets and recyclable products. Additionally, the environmental objective function involves the minimization of fresh water consumption (*Water*) and the minimization of greenhouse gas emissions (*GHGE*) produced by the cogeneration units and the process plants for non-recyclable wastes. To solve this problem, in this paper is proposed the superstructure shown in Figure 1 to satisfy the demand.

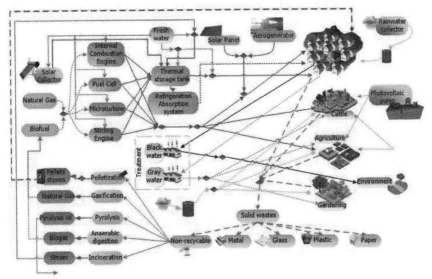

Figure 1. Proposed superstructure.

3. Case Study

There is considered the community of "Cochoapa el Grande", located in the State of Guerrero in Mexico with coordinates 17° 12' N 98° 27' O as case study, this community has been listed as the municipality with the highest index of poverty and marginalization in the country, mainly due to its geographical location which coincides with a mountainous zone called "Sierra Madre del Sur". The difficult access to the community as well as the irregular distribution of their localities causes that the water supply of the public network represents a severe problem and consequently agricultural and livestock activities are affected. Therefore, there is difficult access to food. Likewise, there is a lack of electric power, affecting the provision of services that are essential for human, social and economic development. Faced with this problem, there is proposed a polygeneration system capable of integrate energy, water and food demands of this isolated community.

4. Results

The proposed model corresponds to a Mixed-Integer Linear Programming problem and it was implemented in the software GAMS. The mathematical model consists of 3,138 continuous variables, 21 binary variables and 1,561 equations.
The points obtained from the functions to minimize water consumption, greenhouse gas emissions and cost are shown in Table 1.

Table 1. Results obtained for each scenario evaluated.

	Min Water	Min GHGE	Min Cost
Cost ($)	161,000,000	161,000,000	-27,903,000
Water (m^3/y)	3,060,000	3,088,500	3,178,700
GHGE (t CO_2/y)	147,400,000	12,790,000	900,200,000

For the evaluated scenarios, water consumption does not vary significantly between the different solutions. If we compare the minimum consumption of fresh water scenario and the minimum cost scenario, which represents the highest consumption of fresh water, this only increase approximately 4 %. The selected cogeneration technologies for the case of minimizing the consumption of fresh water are represented by a Microturbine, a Fuel Cell and a Stirling Engine, while in the case of minimizing emissions a Fuel Cell is proposed, and in the case of minimizing costs the selected technology was the Microturbine. The case for minimizing the emissions selects the Fuel Cell for power generation. In the case of minimum consumption of fresh water, fuel requirements increase by 28 %. On the other hand, in the case of minimizing costs, 46 % more fuel is required than in the case of minimizing emissions, which causes a greater generation of greenhouse gases. For solid waste management, the processing plants selected in the scenario of minimizing emissions are the pelletization and pyrolysis plants. In the case of minimum consumption of fresh water, the pelletization, pyrolysis and incineration plants are selected, which represents a considerably increase in the GHGE and, in the case of minimizing costs, gasification, incineration and pelletization plants are selected.

Table 2. Results for the multi-stakeholder analysis.

	Stakeholder weights			Objectives			% Dis
	COST	**WATER**	**GHGE**	**COST**	**WATER**	**GHGE**	**% Dis**
Case	($U.S./y)	(m³/y)	(t CO₂/y)	($U.S./y)	(m³/y)	(t CO₂/y)	
1	4	3	3	-24,770,000	3,063,700	96,820,000	4.75
2	3	4	3	-24,770,000	3,063,700	96,820,000	4.75
3	3	3	4	-24,770,000	3,063,700	96,820,000	4.75
4	2	7	1	-15,080,000	3,060,000	96,820,000	5.42
5	1	2	7	-14,950,000	3,084,100	21,580,000	9.38
6	7	1	2	-26,990,000	3,070,400	96,820,000	6.24
7	8	1	1	-26,990,000	3,070,400	96,820,000	6.24
8	1	8	1	-15,080,000	3,060,000	96,820,000	5.42
9	1	1	8	-24,660,000	3,094,200	12,790,000	10.18

Due to the conditions of the community and because of the lack of processes to generate energy and manage the resources, very high costs are presented, which lead to an exponential increase in greenhouse gas emissions, as well as an increase in the use of water. This can be attributed to the fact that in the case of minimizing costs, it is sought to obtain the maximum production of animals and crops for sale. In the same way, the gasification and pyrolysis plants are selected to make use of the natural gas generated in the gasification plant and thereby reduce the cost associated with the purchase of natural gas and obtain profits from the sale of pyrolysis oil.

Because the objectives are in conflict, the methodology of Multi-stakeholder Optimization is used in this work with the purpose of finding a balance between the objective functions and giving feasible solutions to the problem. In addition, a dissatisfaction analysis is included in each of the proposed feasible solutions. The dissatisfaction of each of the objective functions, as well as the total dissatisfaction for each of the scenarios is presented in Table 2. There were randomly generated weights and it was calculated the percentage of dissatisfaction.

The results obtained in general show that in cases were the objective has a greater weight in the GHGE objective present a greater percentage of dissatisfaction. Moreover, it is possible to obtain better results in cases were the weights are distributed between the three objectives, as Cases 1, 2 and 3, with 4.5% of dissatisfaction, which is the lowest percentage of dissatisfaction of all the evaluated feasible solutions.

5. Conclusions

This paper has presented a multi-objective optimization approach for the optimal design of a polygeneration system applied in a low-income and isolated community. The proposed model is capable to determine the optimal configuration of technologies that meet the demands of water, energy and food of the community accounting for economic and environmental objectives. There were evaluated different scenarios for the minimum cost of the integrated system, the minimum fresh water consumption and the minimum greenhouse gas emissions generated. To trade-off the proposed objectives, it is presented a multi-stakeholder approach which is capable to find the compromise solution which is the point where the objectives are minimized simultaneously. As case study, it was considered the community of Cochoapa el Grande, which is the community with the lowest human development index of Mexico. There were generated different feasible solutions and it was evaluated the dissatisfaction percentage of each one. The results show that the compromise solution is very close of the Utopian Point, which indicates that is possible to obtain a solution that satisfies almost entirely the minimum of the objectives. It should be noticed that in the generated feasible solutions the dissatisfaction increases when it is assigned a major priority to the GHGE objective. On the other hand, the lowest percentage of dissatisfaction corresponds to the cases in which the priorities are distributed between the three objectives.

6. Nomenclature

OF	Objective functions
GHGE	Greenhouse gas emissions

References

A. Ahadi, S.K. Kang, J.H. Lee, 2016, A novel approach for optimal combinations of wind, PV, and energy storage system in diesel-free isolated communities. Applied Energy, 170, 101-115.

A.D. Diaz-Barriga-Fernandez, J.E. Santibañez-Aguilar, N. Radwan, F. Nápoles-Rivera, M.M. El-Halwagi, J.M. Ponce-Ortega, 2017, Strategic planning for managing municipal solid wastes with consideration of multiple stakeholders. ACS Sustainable Chemistry and Engineering, 5(11), 10744-10762.

L.F. Fuentes-Cortés, J.M. Ponce-Ortega, 2017, Optimal design of energy and water supply systems for low-income communities involving multiple-objectives. Energy Conversion and Management, 151, 43-52.

J.M: Núñez-López, E. Villicaña-García, B. Cansino-Loeza, E. Rubio-Castro, J.M. Ponce-Ortega, 2018, Involving acceptability in the optimal design of total integrated residential complexes involving the water-energy-waste nexus. ACS Sustainable Chemistry and. Engineering, 6(6), 7390-7402.

S.I. Martínez-Guido, J.B. González-Campos, M.M. El-Halwagi, J.M. Ponce-Ortega, 2017, Sustainable optimization of food networks in disenfranchised communities. ACS Sustainable Chemistry and. Engineering, 5(10), 8895-8907.

L. Matsakas, Q. Gao, S. Jansson, U. Rova, P. Christakopoulos, 2017, Green conversion of municipal solid wastes into fuels and chemicals. Electronic Journal of Biotechnology, 26, 69-83.

A.S. Sánchez, E.A. Torres, R.A. Kalid, 2015, Renewable energy generation for the rural electrification of isolated communities in the Amazon Region. Renewable Sustainable Energy Reviews, 49, 278-290.

X. Zhang, V.V. Vesselinov, 2017, Integrated modeling approach for optimal management of water, energy and food security nexus. Advances in Water Resources, 101, 1-10.

Anton A. Kiss, Edwin Zondervan, Richard Lakerveld, Leyla Özkan (Eds.)
Proceedings of the 29th European Symposium on Computer Aided Process Engineering
June 16th to 19th, 2019, Eindhoven, The Netherlands. © 2019 Elsevier B.V. All rights reserved.
http://dx.doi.org/10.1016/B978-0-128-18634-3.50073-4

Integration of Consumer Preferences and Heuristic Knowledge in the Design of Formulated Products: Application to a Cosmetic Emulsion

Javier A. Arrieta-Escobar[a,b]*, Fernando P. Bernardo[c], Alvaro Orjuela[b], Mauricio Camargo[a], Laure Morel[a], Laurent Wendling[d]

[a]ERPI (Equipe de Recherche sur les Processus Innovatifs) - University of Lorraine - 8, rue Bastien Lepage, 54010 Nancy Cedex, France
[b]Department of Chemical and Environmental Engineering- Universidad Nacional de Colombia - Sede Bogotá, Colombia
[c]GEPSI-PSE Group, CIEPQPF, Department of Chemical Engineering - University of Coimbra, Portugal
[d]LIPADE (Laboratoire d'Informatique Paris Descartes) - Paris Descartes University - 45 rue des Saints Pères, 75270 Paris Cedex 06, France
arrietae1@univ-lorraine.fr

Abstract

In this work, an optimization-based methodology to design formulated products, incorporating heuristic rules, property models and also quantified customer preferences, is proposed and applied to a skin moisturizer. The relative importance of each product attribute valued by customers is first quantified and then related parameters progressively incorporated in an optimization-based method that generates plausible alternative formulations. The proposed method can be useful to accelerate the selection among alternative formulations, moreover in a benchmarking process.

Keywords: Product design, Consumer assessment, Heuristics, Emulsions, Skin moisturizer

1. Introduction

In the highly competitive market, consumer acceptance has become an important factor in the formulated product design process. Besides key physicochemical properties of the final product, it is of paramount importance to account for the performance of the product as perceived by the final consumer. Therefore, the prediction of acceptability is essential in product development, especially in the domain of cosmetic products, whose performance assessment integrates not only functional but also sensorial characteristics (Wortel and Wiechers, 2000).

Here, a recently proposed methodology (Arrieta-Escobar et al., 2018, 2017) to find a set of plausible product formulations, based on mixed-integer programming and incorporating heuristic rules (modelled as algebraic restrictions), is extended to include the consumer assessment. Starting with a list of attributes directly valued by consumers, the importance level of each of them as well as their interactions are determined from data of usability tests made on an on-market product, by using fuzzy measures (Grabisch, 1995). These consumer parameters can then be incorporated into the optimal design problem formulation, progressively and accordingly to their level of importance but also depending on the availability of models or heuristics correlating them with product composition. This stepwise procedure may result in a reduction in the number of lab scale tests and alternatives preceding to consumer testing. Our main objective is to illustrate the application of this methodology using a skin moisturizer as a case study.

2. Consumer assessment methodology

In "Affective Engineering" or "Kansei Engineering" approaches, usability tests are made to unveil the subjective and even unconscious perception of the user (Nagamachi, 1995). Recently a methodology to integrate the user's perception and identify the importance and interaction of consumer attributes, based on fuzzy measures was proposed by Camargo et al. (2014). This methodology combines a Hybrid Kansei Engineering approach (Matsubara and Nagamachi, 1997), which uses a prototype or mock-up to elicit the product attributes, with a fuzzy integral analysis, namely the Choquet integral (Choquet, 1954). The main advantage of this approach is the possibility to consider the attributes relevance, based on the user's preferences, and the interactions among them. Here, the aforementioned methodology was adapted for cosmetic emulsions in order to understand the importance level (Shapley index) along with the interactions among the attributes (Murofushi and Soneda indices) using a composite index. The main stages of this methodology are described in detail in the original paper, and here only some aspects will be mentioned in the context of a skin moisturizer example (see Figure 1).

Figure 1: Consumer assessment methodology. Adapted from (Camargo et al., 2014)

Consumer attributes reported in the literature (Parente et al., 2010) are classified in 8 groups (thickness, ease of spreading, stickiness, easy of absorption, freshness, residues, greasiness/oiliness and moisturization) and an on-the-market product (Bioderma® Atoderm Ultra-nourishing Cream) is chosen for the usability test. For that, a questionnaire was prepared, in which the participants were told to apply the product on their arms, and to answer two questions corresponding to each one of the 8 groups of attributes, using a 5-level ordinal scale from "not at all" to "very much" (Osgood, 1959). Two additional questions about product's acceptability allow the algorithm in the fuzzy integral analysis to "learn" how important the attributes were to the overall performance.

3. Skin moisturizer case study

A skin moisturizer can be described as a cosmetic product that provides a healthy skin feeling thanks to the use of moisturizing agents (humectants and emollients), typically delivered in the form of an oil in water (O/W) emulsion, stabilized with a combination of emulsifiers (mostly nonionic surfactants) and thickeners (Barel et al., 2001).

3.1. Ingredients, property models and heuristics

Skin moisturizer emulsifiers are usually a suitable combination of at least two nonionic surfactants (Rieger and Rhein, 1997) used at a minimum level of 2% and up to 5% (Rähse, 2013). The final HLB value of the combination – 1 part of medium HLB (9-15), 3 to 6 parts of high HLB (>16) and 2 to 6 parts of low HLB (<8) – should be between 8 and 15 to assure O/W emulsions. Also, a total surfactants/oil ratio of 1:4 to 1:6 should be kept to stabilize the resulting emulsion (Iwata and Shimada, 2013). The classical empirical HLB model is here adopted: HLB of the surfactant mixture should approximately match the HLB required by the oil mixture: HLB = RHLB.

Water-soluble polymers are added as thickeners to provide consistency and stability to the emulsion (Iwata and Shimada, 2013). The primary feeling (consistency at first contact) is correlated to the high viscosity η_1, perceived on the onset of flow of the product, under low applied stresses. In contrast, the secondary feeling (consistency during spreading) corresponds to a much lower final viscosity η_2, when the product is being applied under higher stresses (the emulsion has a strong shear-thinning behavior). Composition-viscosity data for polymer thickened aqueous solutions are available, based on which one has constructed linear models of $\log(\eta_1)$ and $\log(\eta_2)$ as a function of polymer concentration and also total content in oils.

Emollients are the main moisturizing agents and improve the spreadability of the product. A proper combination of at least one emollient of high, one of medium, and one of low spreading types, provides the complete profile for a well-performing product (Ansmann et al., 2005). The after-feel provided by the emollients is related to their greasiness value (γ), which can be calculated as a weighted average from individual values (scale from 1 to 5), available for a wide range of products (Mentel et al., 2014). Similarly, the RHLB value of the emollients mixture is estimated from individual values obtained directly from the providers or from other sources (Pensé-Lhéritier, 2016).

All formulations consider a fixed amount of mandatory ingredients, i.e. the humectant (3% Glycerol) and the preservative (0.7% Cosgard®).

3.2. Optimization of the formulation

Table 1 shows the most relevant design variables and a short formulation of the optimization problem. Thirty-six possible ingredients were considered (vector y and x have dimension 36): Six emulsifiers, three polymer thickeners, three fatty alcohols and twenty-four emollients. The complete list of adopted heuristics is not here reported. The resulting model is a small MINLP problem, easily solved in less than 1 s using GAMS/BARON.

Table 1. Product design variables and problem formulation.

Binary variables y (choice of ingredients) and continuous variables x (wt %)	Problem formulation
Emulsifiers: y_r, x_r Thickening polymers: y_n, x_n Fatty alcohols: y_m, x_m High spreading emollients: y_i, x_i Medium spreading emollients: y_j, x_j Low spreading emollients: y_k, x_k	Find vectors y and x that minimize cost, subject to: Heuristics of typical amounts and combinations of ingredients $2.0 \leq \gamma \leq 2.4$ $120 \leq \eta_1 \leq 500$ Pa.s, $0.023 \leq \eta_2 \leq 0.500$ Pa. s HLB = RHLB

4. Results and discussion

Thirty-two female users of moisturizers (average age 31 years old) tested the commercial product and completed the questionnaire. Table 2 contains the resulting average scores of each attribute, along with the normalized Shapley, Murofushi and Soneda and composite indices. Under the latter metric, "ease of absorption" (0.29), "freshness" (0.25) and "residues" (0.20), are the most important attributes. Noteworthy is that these attributes also have the highest values of mutual interactions (Table 2 only shows the sums of the total interactions as normalized interactions).

Table 2. Scores, normalized values of Shapley (relative weights), Murofushi and Soneda (interactions), and composite indices.

Attribute	Symbol	Score	Normalized relative weights	Normalized interactions	Normalized composite index
Thickness	V	0.46	0.13	0.08	0.07
Spreadability	S	0.75	0.04	0.07	0.02
Stickiness	P	0.45	0.15	0.11	0.11
Ease of absorption	A	0.35	0.20	0.22	0.29
Freshness	F	0.31	0.21	0.18	0.25
Residues	R	0.30	0.15	0.20	0.20
Greasiness	G	0.74	0.05	0.06	0.02
Moisturization	H	0.61	0.07	0.08	0.04
Overall performance	C	0.43			1.00

A first basic formulation (Formulation 0) was generated solving the problem specified in Table 1. In this case, 3 of the 8 attributes of Table 2 are already addressed (at least partially): "Thickness" and "Spreadability" (through the imposed viscosity limits, which were determined from sensorial tests on general purpose creams), and also "Greasiness" (through the limits imposed on the greasiness value γ). In a second stage, the "residues" attribute (R) was then chosen as the next attribute to be considered, since, among the remaining 5 attributes, it is the most informative one and the easiest to evaluate (it has by itself a composite index of 0.20 and the highly correlated trio (A+F+R) adds up to 0.74). Formulation 0 and the commercial reference sample were then evaluated in this attribute, with results shown in Figure 2 (left side). The poor performance of Formulation 0 is clear.

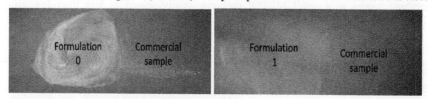

Figure 2. "Residues" of the analyzed formulations compared with the commercial sample.

In a third stage, the optimization of product formulation was readdressed, now including an additional heuristic to correct residues excess: add up to 2% of low HLB emulsifier so as to reduce the micro-foam formation (Institute of Personal Care Science, 2016). With this extra restriction (and allowing RHLB to deviate up to one unit from HLB), the optimization resulted in Formulation 1 (also shown in Figure 2 – right side). Both Formulations 0 and 1 are presented in Table 3 and their rheological profiles in Figure 3.

Figure 2 clearly shows that the additional heuristic worked very well, with Formulation 1 presenting a level of white residues very similar to that of the commercial sample.

Integration of Consumer Preferences and Heuristic Knowledge in the
Design of Formulated Products: Application to a Cosmetic Emulsion

437

Regarding rheology, both Formulations 0 and 1 have profiles similar to that of the commercial reference and in agreement with the simple viscosity models adopted in the optimization. Formulation 1 is thus a good candidate to customer satisfaction regarding attributes V, S, R and G (attributes A and F to the extent of their correlation with R too).

Table 3. Computer-generated alternative formulations for skin moisturizers.

Ingredient	Cost (USD/kg)	Formulation 0	Formulation 1
Water A		60.00%	60.00%
Xanthan gum	35	1.10%	1.10%
Cetyl Alcohol	7.4	4.00%	4.00%
Polysorbate 60	15.5	0.50%	0.50%
PEG-100 Stearate	9.8	1.50%	1.50%
Glyceryl Stearate SE	8.9		1.00%
Sorbitan Stearate	12.5	1.30%	0.70%
Isopropyl Myristate	16.7	5.60%	6.80%
Paraffinum Liquidum	12.2	2.70%	3.20%
Persea Grattisima Oil	16.7	1.00%	1.00%
Water B		18.60%	16.50%
Glycerol		3.00%	3.00%
Preservative (Cosgard)		0.70%	0.70%
	Total	100%	100%
	Cost (USD/kg)	2.50	2.77

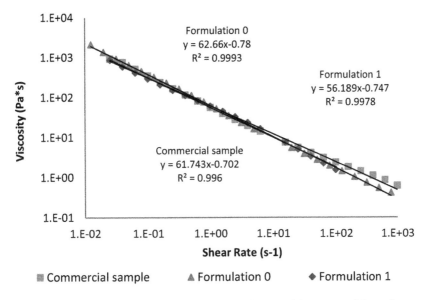

Figure 3. Rheological profile of the two formulations studied and of the commercial sample.

5. Conclusions

We have proposed an optimization-based methodology for the design of formulated products, which incorporates consumer assessment data along with available heuristic rules, and presented a case study of a skin moisturizer. Although not all product attributes were here addressed, the example provided illustrates how the proposed method can guide the selection among alternatives, according to the relative importance given by consumers to different product attributes and available information correlating product performance and acceptance with its composition.

Acknowledgments

This work was financially supported by the Universidad Nacional de Colombia within the framework of the research project QUIPU 202010026994.

References

A. Ansmann, P. Busch, H. Hensen, K. Hill, H.-U. Krächter, M. Müller, 2005. Personal Care Formulations, in: Handbook of Detergents, Part D, Surfactant Science. CRC Press, Boca Raton FL. 207–260.

J.A. Arrieta-Escobar, F.P. Bernardo, A. Orjuela, M. Camargo, L. Morel, 2018. Incorporation of Heuristic Knowledge in the Optimal Design of Formulated Products: Application to a Cosmetic Emulsion. Comput. Chem. Eng. In press.

J.A. Arrieta-Escobar, F.P. Bernardo, A. Orjuela, M. Camargo, L. Morel, 2017. An Integrated Methodology for Emulsified Cosmetic Product Formulation Using Integer Programming with Logical Constraints, in: Espuña, A., Graells, M., Puigjaner, L. (Eds.), Computer Aided Chemical Engineering. Elsevier B.V., Barcelona, Spain, 985–990.

A. O. Barel, M. Paye, H.I. Maibach, 2001. Handbook of Cosmetic Science and Technology. Marcel Dekker, New York - Basel.

M. Camargo, L. Wendling, E. Bonjour, 2014. A fuzzy integral based methodology to elicit semantic spaces in usability tests. Int. J. Ind. Ergon. 44, 11–17.

N. Choquet, 1954. Theory of capacities. Ann. l'Institut Fourier 5, 131–295.

M. Grabisch, 1995. Fuzzy integral in multicriteria decision making. Fuzzy Sets Syst 69, 279–298.

Institute of Personal Care Science, 2016. Free formulas/Videos (accessed 3.7.18) URL https://personalcarescience.com.au/Freeformulas-Videos/FreeVideos-448/

H. Iwata, K. Shimada, 2013. Formulas, Ingredients and Production of Cosmetics. Springer.

Y. Matsubara, M. Nagamachi, 1997. Hybrid Kansei Engineering System and design support. Int. J. Ind. Ergon. 19, 81–92.

M. Mentel, S. Wiechers, A. Howe, P. Biehl, J. Meyer, 2014. Senses- A Scientific Tool for the Selection of The Right Emollient. SOFW 140, 8–15.

M. Nagamachi, 1995. Kansei Engineering: A new ergonomic consumer-oriented technology for product development. Int. J. Ind. Ergon. 15, 3–11.

C.E., Osgood, 1959. Semantic Space Revisited. WORD 15, 192–200.

M.E. Parente, G. Ares, A.V. Manzoni, 2010. Application of two consumer profiling techniques to cosmetic emulsions. J. Sens. Stud. 25, 685–705.

A.-M. Pensé-Lhéritier (Ed.), 2016. Conception des produits cosmétiques : La formulation, 1st ed. Lavoisier Tec&Doc, Paris.

W. Rähse, 2013. Design of Skin Care Products, in: Bröckel, P.D.-I.U., Meier, D.W., Wagner, D.-I.G. (Eds.), Product Design and Engineering: Formulation of Gels and Pastes. Wiley-VCH Verlag GmbH & Co. KGaA, Weinheim, Germany, 273–313.

M.M. Rieger, L.D. Rhein (Eds.), 1997. Surfactants in Cosmetics, 2nd ed, Surfactants Science Series. Marcel Dekker, New York.

V. a. L. Wortel, J.W. Wiechers, 2000. Skin sensory performance of individual personal care ingredients and marketed personal care products. Food Qual. Prefer. 11, 121–127.

Anton A. Kiss, Edwin Zondervan, Richard Lakerveld, Leyla Özkan (Eds.)
Proceedings of the 29th European Symposium on Computer Aided Process Engineering
June 16th to 19th, 2019, Eindhoven, The Netherlands. © 2019 Elsevier B.V. All rights reserved.
http://dx.doi.org/10.1016/B978-0-128-18634-3.50074-6

Economic Study of the Urea Alcoholysis Process for Dimethyl Carbonate Production

Juan Javaloyes-Antón[a,*], Daniel Vázquez[a], Juan D. Medrano-García, José A. Caballero[a]

[a]Institute of Chemical Process Engineering. Universito of Alicante, Alicante, Spain

javaloyes.anton@ua.es

Abstract

In this work, we study the techno-economic feasibility of the urea alcoholysis process for the continuous manufacture of dimethyl carbonate. We propose a superstructure for the urea alcoholysis process based on patents and research articles found in literature. In this superstructure, different reaction and separation alternatives have been considered leading to 54 feasible flowsheets. Due to the complexity of some unit operations (reactive distillation columns, azeotropic distillation columns) and the reduce number of alternatives (or at least not prohibitive), we performed an exhaustive search to determine the most profitable flowsheet using Aspen Plus. Results prove the feasibility of this process, as long as a good catalyst is employed in the process.

Keywords: dimethyl carbonate, urea alcoholysis, process simulator, Aspen Plus.

1. Introduction

Dimethyl carbonate (DMC) is a non-toxic chemical that stands out thanks to its versatile use as reagent and solvent. DMC is employed as a substitute of dimethyl sulfate and methyl halides in methylation reactions, and as carbonylation agent to replace phosgene in the production of polycarbonates. DMC could also be used as a fuel additive since it has a higher oxygen content (53%) than the MTBE or TAME. However, the current price of DMC still prohibitively expensive to use as fuel additive (Ryu and Gelbein, 2006).

Different technologies to produce DMC have been studied, although a few of them are industrially exploited (Pacheco and Marshall, 1997). The commercial routes to make DMC that are currently in operation are: the older commercial process based on the phosgenation of methanol; and the greenest processes: liquid phase oxidative carbonylation of methanol (ENIChem), vapor phase oxidative carbonylation of methanol (Covestro and Ube), and transesterification of ethylene carbonate with methanol (Asahi Kasei). In addition, there is a developing process with some promise: the urea alcoholysis.

The urea route allows the production of DMC using urea and methanol as raw materials, which are abundant and not especially expensive. It also avoids the use of phosgene, carbon monoxide, nitric oxide and ethylene oxide, which are present in the commercial routes aforementioned. The most promising chemical scheme to obtain DMC form urea and methanol is based on a two-step reaction.

First, urea is converted to the intermediate methyl carbamate (MC) by reaction with methanol (Reaction 1a). Then, the carbamate is further reacted with methanol in the presence of a catalyst to produce DMC (Reaction 1b). The first reaction is thermodynamically favorable. In the work of Wang et al. (2007) it is also noted that a high conversion of urea to MC can be reached quickly. However, the critical aspect associated with this route is the highly unfavorable equilibrium of the second step reactions, whose equilibrium constant is about $2.08 \cdot 10^{-3}$ at 300 K. This reaction is endothermic, therefore, a positive effect on the equilibrium is observed rising the temperature. Nevertheless, the gain on the equilibrium constant value is not so pronounces as to overcome the problems raised by the reaction thermodynamics, as it is shown in Table 1 (Wang et al., 2007). In addition, the component N-methyl methyl carbonate (NMMC) has been detected as the main byproduct, which is formed from the reaction of DMC with MC.

Beside the unfavorable thermodynamics of Reaction 1b, the synthesis of DMC from urea alcoholysis is a very attractive route since it avoids the hazards of using dangerous compounds, and would allow the synthesis of DMC starting from carbon dioxide, since the co-product ammonia can be recycled to the synthesis of urea (NH_3+ CO_2 → urea + water). The commercial success of this route basically depends on the development of an appropriate catalyst to the second reaction step, and the design of suitable reaction arrangements in order to carry out the second step reaction on a large industrial scale.

Remark that a large amount of works in academia and industrial literature can be found about this topic. However, as far as the authors are aware, the academia papers are mainly focus on the study of the reaction mechanisms and catalyst. And the patents, even though they describe the process for large scale production, all the examples that they provide are laboratory scale. Thus, the main aim of this work is to provide a preliminary techno-economic assessment for the urea alcoholysis process, based on the rigorous simulation of possible large industrial scale flowsheets.

$$NH_2CONH_2 + CH_3OH \rightleftharpoons NH_2COOCH_3 + NH_3 \qquad a)$$

$$NH_2COOCH_3 + CH_3OH \rightleftharpoons CH_3COOCH_3 + NH_3 \qquad b)$$

$$- -$$

$$NH_2CONH_2 + 2\,CH_3OH \rightleftharpoons CH_3COOCH_3 + 2\,NH_3 \quad c)$$

Reaction 1. a) Methyl carbamate (MC) formation. b) DMC formation. c) Global reaction.

Table 1. Temperature dependence of the equilibrium constant for reactions 1a and 1b.

T (K)	K – Reaction 1a	K – Reaction 1b
300	203.88	$2.08 \cdot 10^{-3}$
350	120.88	$4.30 \cdot 10^{-3}$
400	86.07	$7.20 \cdot 10^{-3}$
450	70.27	$1.04 \cdot 10^{-3}$
500	62.74	$1.37 \cdot 10^{-3}$
550	58.40	$1.66 \cdot 10^{-3}$
600	57.65	$1.92 \cdot 10^{-3}$

2. Superstructure for the DMC production process from Urea

The superstructure for the DMC production process form urea and methanol given in Figure 1 is considered. This superstructure consists of the following three main sections:

2.1. Reaction and ammonia recovery section

As discussed in the previous section, DMC is produced form the reaction of methanol with urea in a two-step reaction. The first reaction is thermodynamically favorable. However, the second one has a low equilibrium constant. Thus, as other equilibrium reactions (such as the production of diphenyl carbonate from phenol and DMC), Reaction 1b is best carried out in a reactive distillation column (Ryu and Gelbein, 2002). Under these conditions, the following alternatives have been considered. On the one hand, a continuous stirred-tank reactor (R-101) can be used for the production of MC without catalyst. Then the byproduct NH_3 is removed be means of a distillation column (C-101). This column can operate at lower or higher pressure than R-101. Depending on the operating pressure, around 7 or 14 bar respectively, refrigerated water or cooling water will be use in the column condenser as cold utility. C-101 bottoms product is fed to the reactive distillation column C-102, where MC is converted to DMC. This column strips the product DMC and co-product NH_3 form the reaction mixture, shifting the equilibrium to the product side. C-102 can operate with a total or partial condenser. The C-102 overhead stream, containing most of the unreacted MeOH, NH_3, CO_2 and some DMC is mixed with a stream coming from the distillation section with similar composition, and fed to the C-103 column. In this column, NH_3 is recovered as top product, and the bottom product, containing MeOH and some DMC, is recycled back to the reaction section.

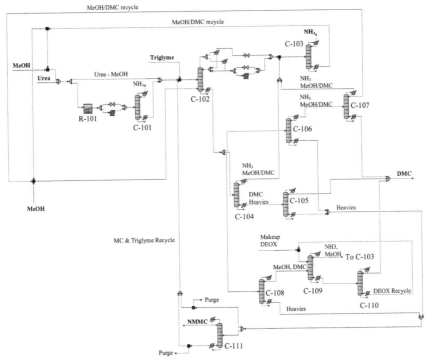

Figure 1. Superstructure for the production of DMC from urea and methanol.

As in the previous ammonia recovery column (C-101), the refrigerant fluid in the condenser of C-103 can be refrigerated water or cooling water depending on the column operating pressure. On the other hand, reactive distillation column R-102 can be used as the single reactor to carry out the two-step reaction.

The reaction of MC with methanol to DMC takes place in the presence of a catalyst. Different heterogeneous and homogeneous catalyst have been studied so far. In the present work, the homogeneous catalyst triglyme is used according to the US patent 6,392,078(Ryu and Gelbein, 2002).

2.2. Distillation section

The crude DMC from the bottom product of C-102 is diverted to the distillation section. This stream, containing NH3, unreacted MeOH, DMC product and heavier compounds (NMMC, unreacted MC and triglyme) has to be separated into three main streams: high purity DMC product stream, a MeOH recycle stream (which will contain DMC and NH3), and a stream containing the heavy compounds (NMMC, MC and triglyme).
The binary system MeOH-DMC has a homogeneous azeotrope which makes the separation somewhat more complex. Fortunately, this azeotrope is pressure dependent, increasing the percentage of MeOH with pressure (Romano, 1976). For instance, at one bar the azeotrope composition of MeOH is around to 85 mol%, and at 15 bar around to 96 mol% (Yunhai et al., 2005). This allows for using pressure distillation to improve the MeOH-DMC separation.

Two different sequences are considered in the superstructure shown in Figure 1 based on exploiting this change in the azeotropic composition with pressure. The direct sequence (C-104 and C-105 columns), and the indirect sequence (C-106 and C-107 columns).

In the direct sequence, C-104 column operates at around 12 bars. At higher pressures, the temperature in the reboiler overcomes 240°C, which prevent from using high pressure steam (41 barg, 254 °C) as hot utility. The overhead product from C-104 is a mixture of MeOH-DMC close to the azeotrope composition and all the NH$_3$ in C-102 bottom product, while the bottom product contains DMC and the heavier compounds. The C-104 column bottoms are fed to C-105 distillation column where high purity DMC is obtained as top product. The column bottoms, containing NMMC, MC and triglyme are sent to the catalyst and MC recovery section. C-105 column operates close to atmospheric pressure. In the indirect sequence, the C-106 column splits the bottom product of the reactive distillation column into a stream containing all the NH$_3$, MeOH and DMC as top product, and a stream containing the heavier compounds (NMMC, MC and triglyme) as bottom product. The C-106 bottoms are diverted to the catalyst and MC recovery section. The overhead product is fed into the high-pressure C-107 column. In this column (C-107), high purity DMC is obtained from the bottoms, and a mixture of MeOH-DMC close to the azeotrope composition with the NH$_3$ as top product. The C-106 column operates at atmospheric pressure, and C-107 at 12-16 bar. A third alternative has been considered in the superstructure based on extractive distillation (C-108, C-109 and C-110). For instance, the US Patent No. 5,214,185 (Nishihira et al., 1993) disclosed the separation of the DMC-MeOH mixture by using dimethyl oxalate (DMOX) as solvent, and US Patent No. 6,392,078 (Ryu and Gelbein, 2002) assert that diethyl oxalate (DEOX) has more desirable properties than DMOX. The extractive distillation sequence proposed in Figure 1 can be used either with DMOX and DEOX. Preliminary simulations have shown that both solvents are effective, and in or work we selected DMOX.

2.3. Catalyst and methyl carbamate recovery section

The bottom product of C-105, C-106 or C-108 depending on whether the direct sequence, indirect sequence or extractive sequence is selected respectively, is sent to the catalyst and MC recovery section. In this section, part the undesired product NMMC is removed by means of C-111 column or a purge, in order to control the build-up of this component in the system. If the purge is selected, a bleed of 3-5% is performed in the stream. If the distillation column is selected, most of the NMMC is removed from the system and the performance of the process improves, at the expense of using an additional column.

3. Results

An exhaustive search is performed using the flowsheeting program Aspen Plus to determine the most profitable flowsheet based on raw material, products, and utility costs. Actually, the existence of dominated solutions avoids the need of simulation all 54 alternatives. For instance. The composition specifications of the effluent heavy stream from the distillation section is the same independently of the selected distillation arrangement. If we compare all the alternatives resulting from fixing the direct distillation sequence followed by C-111 column (9 alternatives), with the alternatives resulting from fixing the direct distillation sequence followed by the purge in order to control the build-up of byproduct NMMC (9 alternatives), it is possible to determine that the use of C-111 column gives the best results. Thus, the remaining branches of the decision tree that uses purges to control the amount of NMMC can be cut-off (18 alternatives).

The main results for the best flowsheet are summarized in Table 1. The best flowsheet consists of the following columns: C-102 with partial condenser, C-103 at low temperature, C-104, C-105 and C-111 (Figure 2). The yearly DMC plant production rate was fixed to 52 Kton/y, based on 8,000 operating hours per year. The price for the raw materials and products were taken from different webs (www.icis.com, www.mathanex.com, and www.alibaba.com), and the prices for the utility services from Turton et al. (2008).

Table 1. Results for the best flowsheet simulation

Materials	ton/h	$/ton	$MM/y	Utilities	MW	$/MWh	$MM/y
Feed stock			**22.40**	**Hot utility**			**9.30**
MeOH	4.97	340.0	13.53	LPS (5 barg)	9.35	50.6	3.78
Urea	4.98	221.5	8.82	MPS (10 barg)	0.05	53.4	0.02
Triglyme	0.01	830.0	0.05	HPS (41 barg)	10.77	63.7	5.49
Products			**48.33**	**Cold utility**			**0.63**
DMC	6.50	830.0	43.16	CW (30°C)	13.17	1.3	0.14
NH3	2.69	240.0	5.17	RW (5°C)	3.91	15.9	0.50
Operating Costs ($MM/y)							32.32
Product Sales – Feed Costs ($MM/y)							25.93
Profit Value ($MM/y)							**16.00**

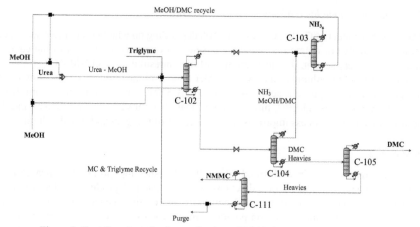

Figure 2. Best flowsheet for the production of DMC from urea and methanol

4. Conclusions

The urea process for making DMC is a promising alternative to the current processes, since it avoids the hazards of using dangerous compounds, and also would allow the synthesis of DMC starting from carbon dioxide. The results of this preliminary techno-economic study show that, if a catalyst that permit overcome the kinetic barriers of the second step reaction is developed in the future, DMC could be synthesized with considerable annual positive cash flows.

Acknowledgments.

The authors gratefully acknowledge the financial support by the Spanish Ministry of Economy, Industry and Competitiveness CTQ2016-77968-C3-02P, FEDER, UE.

References

Nishihira, K., Yoshida, S., Tanaka, S., 1993. Continuous process for preparing dimethyl c. US Patent 5,214,185.

Pacheco, M.A., Marshall, C.L., 1997. Review of Dimethyl Carbonate (DMC) Manufacture and Its Characteristics as a Fuel Additive. Energy & Fuels 11, 2–29.

Romano, U., 1976. Recovery of DMC from its azeotropic mixture with methanol. DE Patent 2,607,003.

Ryu, J.Y., Gelbein, A.P., 2006. Process for making dialkyl carbonates. US 7,074,951 B2.

Ryu, J.Y., Gelbein, A.P., 2002. Process and catalyst for making dialkyl carbonates. US Patent 6,392,078.

Turton, R., Baile, R.C., Whiting, W.B., 2008. Analysis, synthesis and design ofchemical processes. Pearson Education.

Wang, M., Wang, H., Zhao, N., Sun, Y., 2007. High-Yield Synthesis of Dimethyl Carbonate from Urea and Methanol Using a Catalytic Distillation Process. Ind. Eng. Chem. Res. 46, 2683-2687.

Yunhai, S., Honglai, L., Kun, W., Wende, X., Ying, H., 2005. Measurements of isothermal vapor-liquid equilibrium of binary methanol/dimethyl carbonate system under pressure. Fluid Phase Equilib. 234, 1–10.

Anton A. Kiss, Edwin Zondervan, Richard Lakerveld, Leyla Özkan (Eds.)
Proceedings of the 29th European Symposium on Computer Aided Process Engineering
June 16th to 19th, 2019, Eindhoven, The Netherlands. © 2019 Elsevier B.V. All rights reserved.
http://dx.doi.org/10.1016/B978-0-128-18634-3.50075-8

Effect of Ambient Conditions on Boil Off Gas Generation in LNG regasification terminals

Philips Prince Pokkatt[a] and Rajagopalan Srinivasan[a]

[a] Department of Chemical Engineering, Indian Institute of Technology Madras, Chennai, 600036, India

raj@iitm.ac.in

Abstract

Liquefied natural gas has started to establish itself as the fuel of choice across the globe, evident from its sustained growth over the last three decades. As a result, more regasification terminals are coming up every year. Hence, it is critical to develop technologies which make sure the plants are operated efficiently. This paper studies the generation and management of Boil Off Gases (BOG) in LNG regasification terminals. The effect of time varying ambient temperature on the BOG generation is studied, and ways to improve the operational efficiency of BOG compressors are suggested.

Keywords: LNG, Ambient temperature, Regasification, BOG compressor

1. Introduction

As the global population increases, world's energy demand stands to double by the year 2050. Natural gas is believed to have a significant role in driving this rising demand. Gas is the fastest growing hydrocarbon market today. Natural Gas (NG), being the cleanest fossil fuel, has become the fuel of choice in many of the developed and emerging economies. NG demand is expected to grow at an average of 2% per year which is twice the rate of total worldwide energy demand. Natural gas is transported to India as Liquefied Natural Gas (LNG) through specially designed ships known as LNG carriers. Natural gas is converted to liquefied natural gas (LNG) by refrigeration below -162°C; this reduces its volume by 600 times. LNG is imported to the regasification terminal, where it is stored, vaporized and distributed to the customers.

Processes involved in the regasification are energy intensive. Vaporizers, used for conversion of LNG to natural gas uses major share of energy consumption in the plant. Although the storage tanks are provided with extensive insulation, the heat ingress into them cannot be avoided. This leads to the vaporization of LNG producing Boil off Gases (BOG). Excessive buildup of BOG causes surge in the storage tank pressure. For the safe operation of the plant, the tank pressure must be kept much below the designed level of the pressure. Hence, it is imperative that the BOG is timely taken out and either liquefied or sent to distribution line. The pressure in the distribution line is over the range of 75bar which is significantly higher when compared to pressure of the BOG which is nearly 1.17 bar. So, the warm BOG produced are liquefied in the recondenser and sent back into the storage tank, causing the temperature to rise. BOG is transported to the recondenser through BOG compressor. The composition of BOG and LNG is quite different, with the former having more methane and latter having relatively heavier hydrocarbons. The BOG management process is also an energy intensive one.

BOG management is one of the most challenging tasks in the operation of a regasification terminal. Most studies assume a constant BOG rate while devising energy efficient ways to condense BOG and transport them back to the storage tank. In reality, BOG generation is not constant and it fluctuates in the course of a day. For estimating the BOG generation rate, modeling of the storage tank is cardinal and it also enables us to study the dynamics of the regasification terminal, closer to the reality. In the paper, we studied the effect of ambient conditions on the variation in the BOG generation. Further, we also propose methodologies to reduce to energy consumption in the operation of BOG compressors.

2. Various Models of BOG in Literature

BOG management holds a major role in reducing the energy consumption in the plant. Effects of BOG generation often cause ripple effects in other operations in the plant. Different studies have incorporated these effects in their models. The fluctuation in the BOG generation causes change in the level of LNG in the recondenser.(Shin et al., 2008) studied the effect the above occurrence can have on the high pressure LNG pump (which pumps LNG from the recondenser to the vaporizer) e.g. cavitation of the pump and equipment vibration.(Park et al., 2012) proposed a retrofit design the form of intermittent cooling of the BOG before its compression, saving compression costs. But many of those studies like above, were done on the underlying assumption of constant BOG generation. Studies by (Saleem et al., 2018) brought better insights into factors affecting BOG generation, by studying the heat ingress magnitude and convective heat transfer in the LNG storage tank. Most models also assumed that the vapor and liquid phases in the LNG tank are at same temperature and composition. (Effendy et al., 2017) studied the BOG generation in the storage tank by taking into account the temperature and composition variation which exists in the different phases. In their model, the storage tank is considered to be composed of four subsystems, namely, vapor, liquid, flash, recirculation subsystems. Also, the heat leaks from the surroundings to the liquid and vapor subsystems are accounted for separately.

The temperature of the liquid subsystem is governed by the following energy balance:

$$\frac{dT_L}{dt} = \frac{4}{\pi D_T^2 \rho_L h}\left[-\frac{\lambda \dot{m}_e}{C_{p,L}} + \left(1 - \bar{f}_F\right)\dot{m}_r\left(T_v - T_L\right) + \frac{\dot{Q}_L}{C_{p,L}}\right] \tag{1}$$

$$\dot{Q}_L = U_{side}\left(\pi D_T h\right)\left(T_a - T_L\right) + U_{bottom}\frac{\pi D_T^2}{4}\left(T_{bottom} - T_L\right) + U^*\frac{\pi D_T^2}{4}\left(T_V - T_L\right) \tag{2}$$

where T_L is the temperature of liquid phase, D_T is diameter of the storage tank, ρ_L is the density of liquid phase, h is the height of liquid in storage tank, λ is the latent heat of vaporization, $\dot{m}_e$ is the LNG evaporation rate, $C_{p,L}$ .specific heat capacity of liquid subsystem, $\bar{f}_F$ is the fraction of liquid phase in the flash subsystem, $\dot{m}_r$ is the rate of recirculation liquid returning back to the tank, T_V is the temperature of the vapor phase, $\dot{Q}_L$ is rate of heat leak into the liquid subsystem, T_{bottom} is the temperature of bottom of the storage tank, U_{side}, U_{bottom}, U^* are the overall heat transfer coefficients at storage tank shell, bottom and the vapor-liquid interface respectively

The temperature of the vapor subsystem is governed by the following energy balance:

$$\frac{dT_V}{dt} = \frac{\left[\dot{m}_E\left(T_L - T_V\right) + \left(T_F - T_V\right)\left(1 - \overline{f}_B\right)\overline{f}_F\dot{m}_R + \dfrac{\dot{Q}_V}{C_{p,V}} \right]}{m_V} \tag{3}$$

$$\dot{Q}_V = U_{top}A_{top}\left(T_a - T_V\right) + U_{side}\left(\pi D_T\left(H - h\right)\right)\left(T_a - T_V\right) + U^*\frac{\pi D_T^2}{4}\left(T_L - T_V\right) \tag{4}$$

where, U_{top} is the overall heat transfer coefficient at top of the storage tank, T_F is the temperature of the flash subsystem, $\overline{f}_B$ is the fraction of boil off stream, $\dot{Q}_V$ is the total heat transfer into vapor phase, $C_{p,V}$ is the specific heat capacity of vapor phase.

Rate of change of mass in the vapor subsystem is governed by the follow equation:

$$\frac{dm_V}{dt} = -\frac{\pi D_T^2}{4}\rho_V\left[\frac{dh}{dt} + \frac{\left(H - h\right)}{T_V}\frac{dT_V}{dt} \right] \tag{5}$$

Total amount of BOG generated is given by:

$$\dot{m}_B = \dot{m}_E + \overline{f}_F\dot{m}_R - \frac{dm_V}{dt} \tag{6}$$

where $\dot{m}_B$ is the rate of BOG generation.

As heat leaks into the tank, the LNG boils and the BOG generated has to be managed so that the pressure of the tank remains within the safety limits. This is typically done by a BOG compressor as it transports the vapor into the liquefaction system. BOG compression being energy intensive, it is critical to optimize the operation of the process.

3. Effect of Ambient Conditions on Boil Off Gas Generation

We consider a regasification terminal operated in the holding mode i.e. LNG is not transferred from the carrier ship to the storage tank.

The objective of this paper is to demonstrate the effect of ambient weather conditions on the generation of Boil off Gas (BOG) and optimal operation of BOG compressor in a LNG regasification terminal. The LNG storage tank and recirculation pipeline are modeled by utilizing the model proposed by (Effendy et al., 2017). The regasification plant modeled has eight storage tanks, and ten cooling lines connecting the jetties to the storage tanks. The storage tank is assumed to be operated in an isobaric regime so that any BOG generated will be evacuated from the tank. The simulation is run for a span of 16 days.

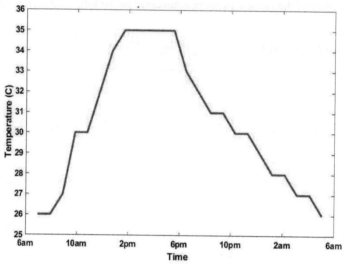

Figure 1: Ambient temperature profile in Hazira, India

In order to understand the effect of ambient temperature, the temperature profile in Dahej, where India's largest regasification terminal is situated was considered. On a typical day in November, the temperature was observed to be rising quickly after sunrise from 26 °C to 35 °C in six hours, then remaining fairly constant at 35 °C for five hours and slowly cooling to 26 °C over twelve hours. The first and last temperature regime fitted for a quadratic and linear fit respectively. It is assumed here that a given day starts at 6 a.m. in the morning (around sunrise).

$$
Ambient\,Temperature(K) = \begin{cases} 1 < t_k < 7 \rightarrow 0.107 * x^2 + 0.536 * x + 298 \\ \qquad 8 < t_k < 12 \rightarrow 308 \\ 13 < t_k < 24 \rightarrow -0.601 * x + 313.46 \end{cases} \tag{7}
$$

The above ambient temperature function was incorporated into the model proposed by Effendy et al. (2017) and the BOG generated thereof was calculated. The variation of BOG generation rate on a given day due to the change in ambient conditions is shown in Figure 2.

Figure 3 shows the BOG generation over a 16-day period for three different conditions – ambient conditions constant at 25 °C, ambient conditions constant at 30.5 °C (median temperature of the profile in Figure 1) and ambient temperature varying as per Figure 1. From this, it can be readily inferred that there is significant fluctuation in the BOG generation over the course of a day, and this fluctuation also depends with the inventory level of the LNG in the tank. The BOG generated is recompressed back to liquid using compressors – the substantial variation in BOG generation rates described above, therefore, motivate a study of suitable operations regimes for the compressor network.

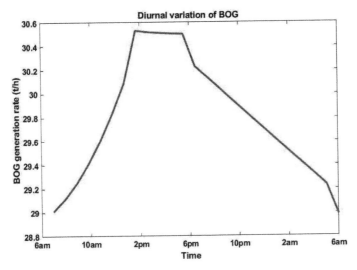

Figure 2: Variation of BOG generation resulting from the ambient conditions in Figure 1

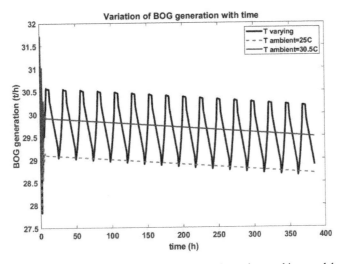

Figure 3:Comparison of BOG generation rate for various ambient models

4. Effect on Compressor Operations

The compression cost can be significantly reduced by improving the operation of the compressor network for processing a specified amount of BOG. (Shin et al., 2007) proposed a method to minimize the power consumption using mixed integer linear problem (MILP) formulation, which improved the operational policies based on safety analysis on the dynamics of the tank pressure. Hence, for reducing the energy consumption in a regasification terminal, it is important to optimize the operation of the BOG compressors.

In our study of compressor operations, following Shin et al. (2007) we assume that at load levels of 0, 50%, 75%, and 100%, the current requirement by the compressor is 65 A, 115 A, 127 A, and 145 A, respectively. Given the voltage of 6900 V, the corresponding amount of energy consumed is 449 kW, 794 kW, 876 kW, and 1000 kW. Table 1 shows the energy consumed by BOG compressors when operated at different loads. The quantity and quality i.e. the flow rate and enthalpy, of the BOG generated by the LNG train vary depending upon the operating conditions in the plant, as well as on the mode of operation.

As the BOG generation rate changes significantly over time, optimizing the compressors could save significant amounts of energy. A simple analysis reveals a reduction of over 13% on a given day in compressor energy consumption when BOG compressors are operated differently over the course of the day. Further, as evident from Figure 3, the BOG generation profiles are different from day to day depending on the inventory, so the energy optimal mode and the savings potential would also vary on a daily basis and motivates real-time optimization.

5. Conclusions

As the size of LNG regasification plants grow, and multiple LNG trains are connected, the complexity of BOG management also increases. BOG management is a multifaceted problem requiring study of hydraulics, transient behavior and compressoroperations. This paper has demonstrated that the effects of ambient temperature on the rate of BOG generation is significant and motivates daily optimization of compressors' operation modes. Further, we believe such studies would educate new designs of regasification terminals in tropical regions.

References

Effendy, S., Khan, M.S., Farooq, S., Karimi, I.A., 2017. Dynamic modelling and optimization of an LNG storage tank in a regasification terminal with semi-analytical solutions for N 2 -free LNG. Comput. Chem. Eng. 99, 40–50. https://doi.org/10.1016/j.compchemeng.2017.01.012

Park, C., Song, K., Lee, S., Lim, Y., Han, C., 2012. Retrofit design of a boil-off gas handling process in liquefied natural gas receiving terminals. Energy 44, 69–78. https://doi.org/10.1016/j.energy.2012.02.053

Saleem, A., Farooq, S., Karimi, I.A., Banerjee, R., 2018. A CFD simulation study of boiling mechanism and BOG generation in a full-scale LNG storage tank. Comput. Chem. Eng. 115, 112–120. https://doi.org/10.1016/j.compchemeng.2018.04.003

Shin, M.W., Shin, D., Choi, S.H., Yoon, E.S., 2008. Optimal operation of the boil-off gas compression process using a boil-off rate model for LNG storage tanks. Korean J. Chem. Eng. 25, 7–12. https://doi.org/10.1007/s11814-008-0002-9

Shin, M.W., Shin, D., Choi, S.H., Yoon, E.S., Han, C., 2007. Optimization of the Operation of Boil-Off Gas Compressors at a Liquified Natural Gas Gasification Plant. Ind. Eng. Chem. Res. 46, 6540–6545. https://doi.org/10.1021/ie061264i

Anton A. Kiss, Edwin Zondervan, Richard Lakerveld, Leyla Özkan (Eds.)
Proceedings of the 29th European Symposium on Computer Aided Process Engineering
June 16th to 19th, 2019, Eindhoven, The Netherlands. © 2019 Elsevier B.V. All rights reserved.
http://dx.doi.org/10.1016/B978-0-128-18634-3.50076-X

An MPCC Reactive Distillation Optimization Model for Multi-Objective Fischer–Tropsch Synthesis

Yizu Zhang [a], Cornelius M. Masuku [a,b] and Lorenz T. Biegler [a,*]

[a]*Department of Chemical Engineering, Carnegie Mellon University, Pittsburgh, PA 15213, USA.*
[b]*Department of Civil and Chemical Engineering, University of South Africa, Private Bag X6, FLORIDA, 1710, South Africa.*
lb01@andrew.cmu.edu

Abstract

In the design of a reactive distillation column, aspects such as column configuration, catalyst loading, tray temperature, and side extraction rates should be well considered. Though preferences in Fischer–Tropsch (FT) synthesis may vary, it is acknowledged that the final product contains a wide range of hydrocarbons including fuel gas, gasoline, diesel, and linear wax. We previously developed an equation-oriented framework for optimal synthesis of integrated reactive distillation systems for FT processes (Zhang et al., 2018).

Here, we extend the mass, equilibrium, summation, and heat equations to a mathematical programming with complementarity constraints model to deal with possible dry trays in the non-reactive sections. The purpose of describing disappearing phases is to avoid infeasibilities due to multiple bilinear terms in the model for complicated model structures. The model is implemented by solving initialization steps and a sequence of nonlinear programming problems to determine an optimal structure and operating conditions.

Design specifications for multiple products could be set as individual objectives to determine design limits. Moreover, a balance of multi-objectives could be reached by formulating the reactive distillation model as a multi-objective optimization problem. In this work, we employ the augmented ε-constraint method. The results show that significant design insights can be gained from the Pareto-optimal front regarding acceptable trade-offs amongst various objectives.

Keywords: Equation-Oriented Optimization Framework, Mathematical Programming with Complementarity Constraints, Vapor–Liquid Equilibrium Modeling, Low-Temperature Fischer–Tropsch, Process Intensification.

1. Introduction

The Fischer–Tropsch (FT) reaction is generally assumed to be kinetically determined (Lu et al., 2017) with an Anderson–Schulz–Flory product distribution that describe the product range with a single parameter α (Eze and Masuku, 2018). This presents a challenge in optimizing for a specific product range (Masuku et al., 2015). We recently presented an equation-oriented reactive distillation (RD) model for a typical low-temperature FT processes favoring wax production to overcome the selectivity challenges (Zhang et al.,

2018). In this study, we introduce a method to solve multi-objective optimization (MOO) in FT RD syntheses. The next section discusses relevant model formulation based on a previous study from Zhang et al. (2018). The third section focuses on the implementation procedure by solving a sequence of NLPs and initialization steps to determine optimal structure and operating conditions with multiple objectives. An example is given for a typical low-temperature FT process in the fourth section, along with results, discussions and model validations. The last section summarizes the key points and conclusions of the paper.

2. Model Reformulation

Figure 1 shows the superstructure of the FT RD synthesis problem along with the basic nonreactive stage model as the building block for the purple tray sections. Here, the mass and heat balance equations from Zhang et al. (2018) are extended with stream connection variables γ for each stream and bypass variables ζ for each stage. As bypass variables are used to deal with the optimization of stage numbers, the equilibrium equations for non-reactive stage model with bypass are reformulated as follows (Dowling and Biegler, 2015):

$$\zeta_k \gamma_{v,k+1} V_{k+1} y_{i,k+1} + \zeta_k \gamma_{l,k-1} L_{k-1} x_{i,k-1} - V_k^* y_{i,k}^* - L_k^* x_{i,k}^* = 0 \tag{1.1}$$

$$L_k x_{i,k} = L_k^* x_{i,k}^* + (1 - \zeta_k) L_{k-1} x_{i,k-1} \tag{1.2}$$

$$V_k y_{i,k} = V_k^* y_{i,k}^* + (1 - \zeta_k) V_{k+1} y_{i,k+1} \tag{1.3}$$

$$y_{i,k}^* = \beta_k K_{i,k} x_{i,k}^*, \quad \beta_k = 1 - S_k^L + S_k^V \tag{1.4}$$

$$0 \le S_k^V \perp V_k^* \ge 0, \quad 0 \le S_k^L \perp L_k^* \ge 0 \tag{1.5}$$

$$\sum_i y_{i,k} = \sum_i x_{i,k} = \sum_i y_{i,k}^* = \sum_i x_{i,k}^* = 1 \tag{1.6}$$

where S_k^L and S_k^V are non-negative slack variables for the liquid and vapor phases leaving stage k respectively. β_k is the slack variable to relax phase equilibrium. When both phases are present, $V, L \ge 0$ and $S_k^L = S_k^V = 0$, here $\beta = 1$ is not relaxed (Burgard et al., 2018). However, if the liquid phase disappears ($L = 0$), S_k^L moves away from zero and $\beta_k \le 1$, thus relaxing (1.4). Also note that, γ_k are connecting variables to connect adjacent stages when modifying column structure, ζ_k are bypass variables indicating the existence of stage k. The purpose of describing disappearing phases is to avoid infeasibility issues of bilinear terms in the model when column structure becomes complicated.

For the multi-objective optimization We employ the augmented ε-constraint method proposed by Mavrotas (2009) to formulate the reactive distillation model into the following MOO problem:

$$\textbf{Problem}(\varepsilon_i) \min f_1(x) - \rho(\sum_{i=2}^p s_i/r_i), \text{ s.t. } f_i(x) + s_i \le \varepsilon_i, \, i = 1, \dots, p, \tag{2}$$

where $\rho > 0$ is a small penalty parameter, and $r_i > 0$ and $s_i \ge 0$ are the range constants and the slack variables for the ith objective function, respectively.

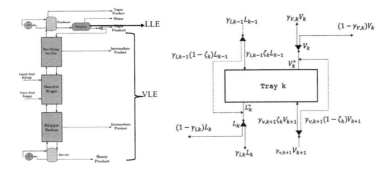

Figure 1: FT reactive distillation superstructure and nonreactive stage model

3. Implementation and Initialization Procedures

The **Algorithm** to find column structure and operating conditions for a multi-objective FT RD production is given below in the form of pseudo-code.

1. Set initial column structure with non-reactive and reactive trays. Set iteration $j = 1$.

2. **If** max. outer loop iteration times reached: **goto** 7; **else**: Implement **base case** run.

3. Implement **adiabatic case** run.

4. Determine $\{f_1^j, f_2^j, ..., f_p^j\}$, $\{\overline{f_1^j}, \overline{f_2^j}, ..., \overline{f_p^j}\}$, q_i^j, δ_i^j, r_i^j for multiple objective functions;
   Pos$^j = \emptyset$; **Pof**$^j = \emptyset$; **I**$^j = \{\zeta^j |$ Obj$_{\min} = f_i^j, \forall i = 1$ to $p\}$.

5. Set $\varepsilon_{i,0}^j = \overline{f_i^j}, \forall i = 2$ to p;
   while $\varepsilon_i^j - \delta_i^j \geq \underline{f_i^j}, \forall i = 2$ to p **do**:

   > **update** ε_i^j by δ_i^j;
   >
   > solve $\{\mathbf{x}, \mathbf{f(x)}\} = \mathbf{Problem}(\varepsilon_i^j)$;
   >
   > **If** ($\{\mathbf{x}\} \not\subset \mathbf{Pos}^j$ **or** $\{\mathbf{f(x)}\} \not\subset \mathbf{Pof}^j$):
   >
   > > **Pos**$^j = $ **Pos**$^j \cup \{\mathbf{x}\}$, **Pof**$^j = $ **Pof**$^j \cup \{\mathbf{f(x)}\}$, **I**$^j = $ **I**$^j \cup \{\zeta\}$;
   > >
   > > **If** $\{\mathbf{x}\} = $ *null*: skip; **else**: skip;

   end while

6. Visualization of **Pof**^{j} and analyze to get **Pof**^{j}.
   If (desired subset of **I**^{j}=**I**$^{j-1}$ **and/or** max$\{ |\frac{f_1^{j-1} - f_1^j}{f_1^{j-1}}|, |\frac{f_2^{j-1} - f_2^j}{f_2^{j-1}}|, ..., |\frac{f_p^{j-1} - f_p^j}{f_p^{j-1}}|\} \leq \varepsilon$):
   goto 7; **else**: update column structure from **I**^{j}, $j = j + 1$, **goto** 2.

7. Fix column structure from desired subset of **I**^{j}.

The core of the algorithm lies in two nested loops. In each iteration of the outer loop (steps 2-6), denoted by iteration number j, a new column structure is explored; the inner loop (step 5) transforms the whole objective space as a rectangular axis-parallel domain with respect to objectives f_2 to f_p under a fixed and continuous column structure search space. The output of the outer loop gives information on bypass variables from single-objective and multi-objective optimizations. These results give us information to add or remove additional trays, which updates the outer loop with a new structure.

The **base case** and **adiabatic case** mentioned in steps 2 and 3 refer to the stage model formulations in Zhang et al. (2018) with the updated MPCC reformulation introduced in Section 2. The MPCC reformulation aims to deal with infeasibility issues caused by dry trays or trays with total bypass, which relaxes equilibrium constraints for disappearing phases. The **adiabatic case** reformulates the **base case** into an optimization problem by defining heat duty as an objective to minimize.

In step 4, $\underline{f_i^j}$, $\overline{f_i^j}$ denote the respective lower and upper bounds of the ith objective function in outer loop j; the results are obtained by setting f_i^j as a single objective. In step 5, by dividing the range of the ith objective function to q_i^j equal intervals using $\delta_i^j = (\overline{f_i^j} - \underline{f_i^j})/(q_i^j - 1)$, the original rectangular optimal search space, denoted by vertices $\{\underline{f_1^j}, \overline{f_1^j}\} \times ... \times \{\underline{f_p^j}, \overline{f_p^j}\}$, is gradually reduced, leading to poorer solutions. The detailed implementation of **update** could be found in the flowchart of the AUGMECON method in Mavrotas (2009). The **Pos**^{j} and **Pof**^{j} sets collect exclusive Pareto-optimal set and corresponding Pareto-optimal front values. $\mathbf{I}^j$ is the exclusive set of bypass variables obtained from single-objective (in step 4) and multi-objective optimizations (in step 5). These three sets provide information for visualization of Pareto-optimal front and column structure modification. If the given optimal search space is infeasible, i.e., no **Pos**^{j} and **Pof**^{j} are found, or if the same result is found with different optimal search spaces, the results are not recorded, ε_i^j is further updated, and the inner loop continues.

The entire optimal search space is visited through the equally-spaced gridding in step 5. Through visualization of MOO Pareto curve in step 6, we get a better sense of the tradeoffs among multiple objectives. By restricting attention to the subset of choices that are Pareto-efficient (where a gain in one objective leads to a significant loss of another objective), we extract values of corresponding ζ obtained and update the column structure to the next outer loop iteration. The determination of the desired subset is based on preference of the decision maker.

The termination conditions in step 6 could be interpreted as: if no change of bypass variables is observed between the last two outer loop iterations (no indications on column structure change) and/or no great improvements of single objectives from column structure modifications, the outer loop terminates. It should be mentioned, the outer loop also terminates when the "maximum outer loop iteration times" is reached in step 2. The value of "maximum outer loop iteration times" and threshold of improvement ε in step 6 are preferences of the decision maker. $\varepsilon > 0$ is normally set to around 1%, with which all absolute values of normalized improvements on single objectives are compared. With the improvement of column structure after each outer loop, values of $\underline{f_i^j}, \forall i$ are normally smaller under the convention of minimization problems.

4. Case Study Results and Discussions

In this section we consider reactive distillation with low temperature Fischer-Tropsch kinetics, where we minimize -(wax mass flow rate) as the main objective is f_1 and minimize -(naphtha purity) and -(diesel purity) are subsidiary objectives, f_2 and f_3, respectively. Catalyst loading of reactive stages are fixed during simulation and optimization; heat duty is freed on reactive trays and are minimized to zero for non-reactive trays during **adiabatic case** run; 1000 [$kmol/hr$] syngas ($H_2 : CO = 2 : 1$) (Kapfunde et al., 2018) is fed to the last reactive tray; pressure of the column is fixed at 21 [bar]; temperature of condenser is fixed at 35 °C; temperature range of reactive stages is from 190 °C to 260 °C; liquid extraction fraction (γ_l) for naphtha and diesel streams are freed from [0,1] after step 3. Also, the following carbon number cut specifications from the previous work (Zhang et al., 2018), naphtha (C_5-C_7), fuel gas (C_1-C_4), gasoline (C_8-C_{12}), diesel (C_{13} to C_{18}), wax (C_{19}-C_{56}) are defined.

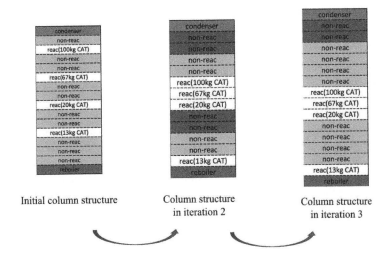

Figure 2: Typical evolution of RD column structure through MOO algorithm. Trays in green are non-reactive trays; those in dark green are from update, those in light green are results from the previous iteration.

The optimal column structure and operating conditions are found through the implementation of **Algorithm** introduced in the previous section over three major iterations. A typical evolution of the column structure (e.g., for $f_1^* \approx -822$) can be observed in Figure 2. From results of **base case** and **adiabatic case** runs, we found that the maximum diesel purity is found on the tray above the last reactive tray; this was set as location for diesel product side-draw all along. The Pareto-front for the three-objective optimization study is shown in Figure 3. The Pareto-front and utopia point (red star) is shown for the final iteration. The three-objective optimization case can then be studied by visiting a uniformed grid of ε_i of the defined **Problem**, and selecting the desired subset of the Pareto-front to provide bypass variable information. The iterations terminate because modification of column structure leads to improved single objectives by less than 1%. For instance, by selecting one Pareto set of interest, we could get 821.73[kg/hr] bottom liquid wax mass flow rate, 0.934 naphtha purity in the top liquid and 0.706 diesel purity on stage 14. This corresponds to the rightmost column in Figure 2.

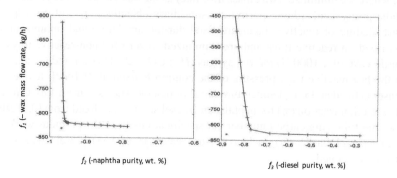

Figure 3: Pareto fronts for three-objective optimization

5. Conclusions

Since the FT reaction produces a range of products, we described a multi-objective optimization model that could be used to optimize the production of one product whilst restricting the negative impact on other valuable products. The model considers disappearing phases in the reactive distillation calculations and uses bypass variable information to avoid large computational efforts on the multi-objective case. The column structure is determined from the Pareto optimal set.

References

A. Burgard, J. Eason, J. Eslick, J. Ghouse, A. Lee, L. Biegler, D. Miller, 2018. A smooth, square flash formulation for equation-oriented flowsheet optimization. Computer Aided Chemical Engineering 44, 871–876.

A. Dowling, L. Biegler, 2015. A framework for efficient large scale equation-oriented flowsheet optimization. Computers & Chemical Engineering 72, 3–20.

P. Eze, C. Masuku, 2018. Vapour–liquid equilibrium prediction for synthesis gas conversion using artificial neural networks. South African Journal of Chemical Engineering 26, 80–85.

N. Kapfunde, C. Masuku, D. Hildebrandt, 2018. Optimization of the thermal efficiency of a fixed-bed gasifier using computational fluid dynamics. Computer Aided Chemical Engineering 44, 1747–1752.

X. Lu, X. Zhu, C. Masuku, D. Hildebrandt, D. Glasser, 2017. A study of the Fischer–Tropsch synthesis in a batch reactor: rate, phase of water, and catalyst oxidation. Energy & Fuels 31, 7405–7412.

C. Masuku, D. Hildebrandt, D. Glasser, 2015. Reactive distillation in conventional Fischer–Tropsch reactors. Fuel Processing Technology 130, 54–61.

G. Mavrotas, 2009. Effective implementation of the ε-constraint method in multi-objective mathematical programming problems. Applied Mathematics and Computation 213, 455–465.

Y. Zhang, C. Masuku, L. Biegler, 2018. Equation-oriented framework for optimal synthesis of integrated reactive distillation systems for the Fischer–Tropsch processes. Energy & Fuels 32, 7199–7209.

Anton A. Kiss, Edwin Zondervan, Richard Lakerveld, Leyla Özkan (Eds.)
Proceedings of the 29th European Symposium on Computer Aided Process Engineering
June 16th to 19th, 2019, Eindhoven, The Netherlands. © 2019 Elsevier B.V. All rights reserved.
http://dx.doi.org/10.1016/B978-0-128-18634-3.50077-1

Techno-economic analysis of alternative reactive purification technologies in the lactic acid production process.

Roberto Gasca-González,[a] Oscar A. Prado-Rubio,[b] Fernando I. Gómez-Castro,[a] Javier Fontalvo-Alzate,[b] Eduardo S. Pérez-Cisneros,[c] Ricardo Morales-Rodriguez[a],*

[a]*Departamento de Ingeniería Química, División de Ciencias Naturales y Exactas, Campus Guanajuato, Universidad de Guanajuato, Noria Alta S/N, Guanajuato, Gto. 36050, México.*

[b]*Departamento de Ingeniería Química, Universidad Nacional de Colombia, Km 9 vía al Aeropuerto La Nubia, Campus La Nubia, Bloque L, Manizales, Caldas, Colombia.*

[c]*Departamento de Ingeniería de Procesos e Hidráulica, Universidad Autónoma Metropolitana-Iztapalapa, Av. San Rafael Atlixco 186, 09340, México, D.F., México.*
ricardo.morales@ugto.mx

Abstract

Lactic acid is one of the most important organic acids on the market due to its wide field of applications. The bio-production of lactic acid has acquired great attention due to the environmental and energy benefits; however, its production bottleneck by fermentation is the cost of the separation and purification stages, representing about 50% of total production cost. Therefore, reducing such costs through the development and design of purification technologies is mandatory. This work presents a techno-economic assessment for lactic acid bio-production process from the residues of the sugar industry, using different alternatives of separation and purification technologies, namely reactive distillation and reactive extraction. The design of the separation systems was performed in Aspen Plus and Matlab. The lactic acid production processes were evaluated to determine the economic feasibility of each separation strategy based on the total annual cost (TAC) and return of investment. It is shown that reactive extraction reduced the total annual cost and energy requirements with respect to reactive distillation by 44% and 37.5%, respectively. Additionally, the return on investment using reactive extraction is 1.2 years faster. Therefore, the reactive extraction process appears as a promising alternative to increase profitability of lactic acid bio-production within a biorefinery. Finally, it is important to highlight that this work discusses the design of a novel reactive extraction system for lactic acid recovery; and, to the best knowledge of the authors, this emerging technology is still under experimental development and has not been extensively investigated from a simulation perspective.

Keywords: Lactic acid production, Aspen plus, Reactive distillation, Reactive extraction

1. Introduction

In a bio-economy, the production of high value-added products from renewable resources, such as biomass, has been established as a strategy to reduce the environmental impact generated by human activities. Biomass can be used to produce biofuels and other chemicals, thus, decreasing our dependency on fossil fuels as feedstocks. Particularly, one of the chemical products that can be obtained from biomass is lactic acid (LA). Great interest has been placed on this compound due to its diverse applications in the chemical, pharmaceutical, food and plastic industries. More recently, research has focused on LA due to the possibility of transforming it into polylactic acid (PLA), which is considered a biodegradable polymer with applications in the production of packaging, sutures and medical applications in drug delivery systems (Serna et al., 2005). Lactic acid can be produced by chemical synthesis, but it has been estimated that ~90% of the total worldwide production is by bacterial fermentation, since this process uses cheap renewable raw materials, low processing temperatures and low energy consumption (Udachan et al., 2014). However, the bio-production of lactic acid is challenging, especially in the downstream stage, where several separation and purification steps are needed to recover the lactic acid from the fermentation broth. Specifically, it is difficult to obtain high purities of lactic acid mainly due to the high affinity with water and its decomposition at high temperatures. Therefore, separation and purification stages represent up to 50% of total production costs (Komesu et al., 2015).

Several separation techniques have been proposed for lactic acid recovery such as precipitation, distillation, solvent extraction, adsorption and membrane separation processes such as reverse osmosis, electrodialysis, ultrafiltration and ultrafiltration (Prado-Rubio et al., 2009). Despite the efforts, there are still some challenges to overcome, which could be solved at industrial scale, for instance, high equipment cost, solvent recovery and high energy consumption (Komesu et al, 2015). Therefore, the objective of this work is to use a systematic design methodology to perform a techno-economic assessment of the lactic acid bioproduction process, using residues of the sugar industry as main feedstock. Reactive distillation and reactive extraction processes have been investigated to determine their economic feasibility based on total annual cost (TAC) and recovery time. The obtained results showed both technologies potential and could be used as driving force for further technologies development for Lactic acid production.

2. Methodology

For this analysis a calculation base of 28,886.6 kg/h of sugar cane bagasse was considered. The composition of the sugarcane bagasse used was: cellulose (68.22 % w/w), lignin (29.19 % w/w) and xylene (2.59 % w/w). The design of the lactic acid bio-production process used in this paper has been previously proposed by Mendez-Alva et al. (2018). The bio-production stages including pre-treatment, enzymatic hydrolysis and fermentation stages were taken from Morales-Rodriguez et al. (2016). For the separation and purification stages, they have been based on the studies of Pérez-Cisneros et al. (2015), Su et al. (2013) and Pérez et al. (2016). The process was simulated in the software Aspen Plus V8.8 complemented by integrating a Matlab code where it was necessary. The phase equilibrium has been modeled using the NRTL and Hayden-O'Connell thermodynamic methods, according with a previous work (Méndez-Alva et al., 2018), which employed the NRTL parameters of the National Renewable Energy Laboratory (NREL) database (Wooley and Putsche, 1996).

2.1. Reactive distillation
The scheme shown in Figure 1 was used for the purification of LA by reactive distillation (Su et al., 2013). This separation scheme is composed by four sections: pre-concentrator,

esterification, hydrolysis and the alcohol recovery. The process begins feeding lactic acid aqueous solution (30% w/w) from a filtration and precipitation process to the pre-concentrator column. The pre-concentrator column is used to remove excess water from the feed stream. Lactic acid esterification is performed using methanol in a molar ratio of 2:1 alcohol to acid and using Amberlyst 15 as a catalyst at a concentration of 2.5% w/w. Subsequently, in the hydrolysis section, the lactic ester is hydrolyzed back into lactic acid and alcohol using Amberlyst 15 at the same concentration. Finally, at the recovery section the alcohol is separated from the water and other impurities. The alcohol is recirculated to the esterification section while the water can be recirculated to the hydrolysis section. The kinetic model of Sanz et al. (2004) was used to represent the esterification and hydrolysis reaction. The distillation columns presented in this paper have been modeled with the RADFRAC module in Aspen Plus.

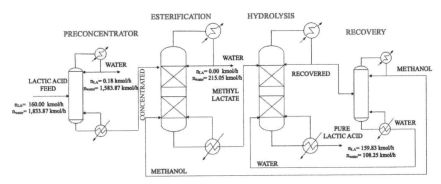

Figure 1. Lactic acid purification process by reactive distillation (Su et al., 2013).

The design of reactive distillation columns was a combinatorial optimization problem with total annual cost (TAC) as objective function. A strategy based on sensitivity analysis was performed to design of the separation scheme considering as degrees of column freedom: number of stages (N), the number of reactive stages (N_{rxn}), feed stage of LA (N_{FLA}) and feed stage of alcohol (N_{FOH}). The design methodology for the reactive and non-reactive distillation columns is presented in Figure 2, where ND is the number of designs obtained in the combinatorial problem. The equilibrium stages, the reactive stages of the column as well as the purities of the required products must be specified, while the position of the feed stages to the column are automatically varied by Aspen Plus. Subsequently, considering the all possible designs obtained through sensitivity analysis, the design that minimizes the total annual cost is selected.

2.2. Reactive extraction

On the other hand, the purification of LA by reactive extraction has been proposed to separate the LA from the fermentation broth using trioctylamine (TOA) and 1-dodecanol as diluent (Pérez et al., 2016). The process has been simulated using the EXTRACT module in Aspen Plus. However, the simulator does not have the binary interaction parameters between amine and system components in its database for the NRTL model; therefore, these parameters could be estimated by the UNIFAC method or employ the NRTL parameters and a chemical equilibrium model with distribution coefficients for this system previously published by Pérez et al. (2016). In this simulation, the parameters estimated by the UNIFAC method were used since the phase equilibrium could not being reproduced using the parameters reported by Pérez et al. (2016).

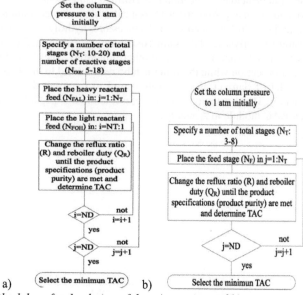

a)   b)

Figure 2. Methodology for the design of the: a) reactive and b) non-reactive distillation columns.

The reactive extraction separation scheme is presented in Figure 3. The extraction was carried out in a counter-current column feeding an aqueous solution of LA (30% w/w) using a molar ratio of 1:1 amine to acid and keeping a concentration of 0.8 mol/L (of TOA in 1-dodecanol). In this system, there is a chemical reaction between LA and TOA producing an amine-lactate complex. This complex promotes separation and provides a greater degree of separation. The extract stream is a mixture of LA-TOA and 1-dodecanol, while the refining stream contains water and a small part of 1-dodecanol. The extract is sent to a distillation column to separate the solvent and TOA from LA and reuse it in the extraction unit.

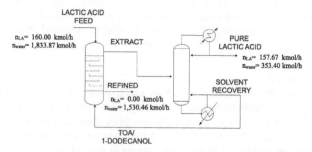

Figure 3. Lactic acid purification process by reactive extraction.

For the design of the extraction column the equilibrium stages have been determined through the equilibrium model reported by Pérez et al. (2016), which considers the distribution coefficient, the equilibrium constant of the chemical reaction and the mass balances. It is important to mention that the equilibrium model considers that LA is the only compound transferred from the aqueous phase to the organic phase. The analysis of the best design for the extraction column in terms of TAC was limited because the chemical structure of the amine lactate complex changes according to the molar feed ratio. The calculations required the integration of Aspen Plus and Matlab through COM objects since the reactive extraction module was not available in Aspen Plus as a unit operation.

3. Results

Computer-assisted simulation enabled the design of both purification schemes and the economic evaluation of both technologies using Aspen Economic Analyzer.

The best design of the reactive distillation purification scheme consists of four distillation columns: The pre-concentrator column with 8 stages and the feed stream is introduced at the stage number 4. The esterification column has 17 stages and 5 reactive stages (12-16), feeding the stream leaving the concentrator column through stage number 7, while the methanol stream is fed through stage number 13. The hydrolysis column has 30 stages and 25 reactive stages (5-29), feeding the methyl lactate stream through stage number 10, while the water stream is fed through stage number 20. Finally, the column has 14 stages and the stream containing the methanol-water mixture is fed through stage number 6. The separation system operates at 1 atm pressure and the esterification and hydrolysis reactions are carried out at a temperature of 353.15 K.

The reactive extraction process consists of one extraction column and one distillation column. The extraction column has 5 stages, where La is fed at stage number 1, while TOA and diluent are fed at stage number 5, the extraction column operates at 1 atm and 316.1 K. The distillation column has 11 stages and is fed at stage number 7. Both LA purification designs achieved a purity of 88% w/w.

Table 1 presents a comparison of the economic evaluation for both technologies and Table 2 presents a comparison of the energy requirements of both purification schemes.

Table.1 Costs for the proposed purification processes.

Analysis	Reactive distillation	Reactive extraction
Total Capital Cost (USD)	93,107,800.00	93,107,800.00
Total Operating Cost (USD/y)	49,011,200.00	27,654,000.00
Desired Rate of Return (%/y)	20	20
Return of investment (Year)	2.7	1.48
Equipment Cost (USD)	672,500.00	536,500.00
Total Annual Cost (USD/y)	53,666,590.00	27,680,825.00

Table.2 Energy requirements for the proposed purification processes.

Purification process	Heat Duty (kW)
Reactive distillation	31,601.00
Reactive extraction	19,771.00

The economic evaluation of both technologies has shown that reactive extraction substantially reduces the total annual cost of LA purification by 44% compared to reactive distillation. Also, using reactive extraction for LA purification reduces the energy requirements of the purification stage with respect to the use of reactive distillation by 37.5%.

4. Conclusions

A techno-economic analysis of the LA reactive purification technologies has been carried out. Both processes have been designed and analyzed using CAPE tools. The use of reactive extraction in LA purification promises to substantially reduce total LA production costs and energy requirements. However, this technology according to Technology Readiness Level (TRL) is still under development (TRL 3 - TRL 7) because the exact nature of the chemistry involved in acid absorption is unknown and the chemical structure of the complex varies according to several factors, such as: the concentration of the LA in the aqueous phase, the type of diluent and the molar amine to acid feed ratio. Therefore, efforts should be made to provide more reactive extraction system understanding that allows to have more accurate prediction useful for detailed design. However, this work is the starting point for the development of a methodology for the design and simulation of reactive extraction systems for LA recovery in Aspen Plus. Finally, reactive distillation presents a total annual cost and much higher energy requirements, however, the results obtained are much more reliable because it is a mature technology (TRL 8 - TRL 9), which has already been tested industrially.

References

L. Serna, A. Rodriguez, 2005, Producción biotecnologíca de ácido láctico: Estado del arte, Ciencia y Tecnología Alimentaria, 5, 1, 54-65 (Spanish).

I.S. Udachan, A.K. Sahoo, 2014, A study of parameters affecting the solvent extraction of lactic acid from fermentation broth, Brazilian Journal of Chemical Engineerig, 31, 3, 831-827.

A. Komesu, P.F. Martins, B.H. Lunelli, J. Oliveira, R.M. Filho, M.R.W. Maciel, 2015, The effect of evaporator temperature on lactic acid purity and recovery by short path evaporation, Separation Science and Technology, 50, 10, 1548-1553.

C.Y. Su, C.C. Yu, I.L. Chien, J. D. Ward, 2013, Plant-wide economic comparison of lactic acid recovery processes by reactive distillation with different alcohols, Industrial and Engineering Chemistry Research, 52, 32, 11070-11083.

J. A. Méndez-Alva, E.S. Pérez-Cisneros, D. Rodriguez-Gomez, O.A. Prado-Rubio, B. Ruiz-Camacho, R. Morales-Rodriguez, 2018, Computer-aided process simulation, design and analysis: lactic acid production from lignocellulosic residues, Computer Aided Chemical Engineering, 44, 463-468.

R. Morales-Rodriguez, E.S. Pérez-Cisneros, J. de los Reyes-Heredia, D. Rodriguez, 2016, Evaluation of biorefinery configuration through a dynamic model-based platform: Integral operation for bioethanol and Xylitol Co-production from lignocellulose, Renewable Energy, 89, 135-143.

E. S. Pérez-Cisneros, L. Avilés-Cabrera, V. Medina-Bañuelos, M. Sales-Cruz, A. Ochoa-Tapia, T. Viveros-García, R. Lobo-Ohemichen, 2015, A computational platform for simulation, Design and analysis of a Poly(Lactic) Acid production process from different lignocellulosic raw materials, Comput.-Aided Chem. Eng., 37, 1187-1192.

O.A. Prado-Rubio, S.B. Jørgensen, G. Jonsson, 2009, Lactic Acid Recovery in Electro-Enhanced Dialysis: Modelling and Validation. Comput.-Aided Chem. Eng., 26, 1406-1410.

R. Wooley, V. Putsche, 1996, Development of an ASPEN PLUS physical property database for Biofuels Components, National Renewable Energy Laboratory, NREL/MP-425-20685.

M.T. Sanz, R. Murga, S. Beltrán, J.L. Cabeza, 2004, Kinetic study for the reactive system of lactic acid esterification with methanol: Methyl lactate hydrolysis reaction, Ind. Eng. Chem. Res, 43,9, 2049-2053.

A.D. Pérez, S. Rodríguez-Barona, J. Fontalvo, 2016, Liquid-liquid equilibria for trioctylamine/ 1-dodecanol/ Lactic Acid/ Water system at 306.1m 310.1 and 316.1 K: Experimental data and prediction, Journal of Chemical and Engineering Data, 61, 7, 2269-2276.

Anton A. Kiss, Edwin Zondervan, Richard Lakerveld, Leyla Özkan (Eds.)
Proceedings of the 29th European Symposium on Computer Aided Process Engineering
June 16th to 19th, 2019, Eindhoven, The Netherlands. © 2019 Elsevier B.V. All rights reserved.
http://dx.doi.org/10.1016/B978-0-128-18634-3.50078-3

Optimal design of post combustion CO_2 capture processes based on phase-change solvents

Panagiotis Kazepidis[a,b], Athanasios I. Papadopoulos[a], Panos Seferlis[a,b], Felipe A. Perdomo[c], Amparo Galindo[c], George Jackson[c], Claire S. Adjiman[c]

[a]Chemical Process and Energy Resources Institute (CPERI) – Centre for Research and Technology – Hellas (CERTH), Thermi-Thessaloniki 57001 Greece

[b]Department of Mechanical Engineering, Aristotle University of Thessaloniki, Thessaloniki 54124, Greece

[c]Department of Chemical Engineering, Centre for Process Systems Engineering, Imperial College London, London SW7 2AZ, UK

seferlis@auth.gr

Abstract

The current work addresses the investigation of phase-change solvents behaviour during the design of post-combustion CO_2 capture processes. The use of phase-change solvents leads to energetic gains due to their lower regeneration energy demands. The latter are enhanced in this work by the consideration of systematic structural and operating modifications imposed on a reference absorption/desorption flowsheet. Such modifications are realized with the help of a rigorous and flexible model that can represent the phase-change behaviour and includes stream redistribution options that aim to enhance the main process driving forces. An aqueous N-methylcyclohexylamine (MCA) solution is employed in an effort to exploit the solvent's phase separation behaviour towards the reduction of the total process cost and energy requirements.

Keywords: CO_2 capture, optimal design, phase change solvents, MCA, N-methylcyclohexylamine.

1. Introduction

Solvent-based absorption/desorption processes represent a mature technology for post-combustion CO_2 capture. A major drawback is the high regeneration energy requirements which prohibit the wide industrial adoption of such systems. Phase-change solvent processes are emerging as a new and promising technology which enables up to 50% reduction in regeneration energy requirements (Pinto et al., 2014). This is achieved through the use of solvents which exhibit phase-change behavior due to the appearance of a second liquid phase upon reaction with CO_2 and possibly a subsequent increase of temperature. This enables the use of a physical process usually in the form of a decanter to separate the two liquid phases; one of them can be partially or totally recycled directly to the absorber, whereas the other is transferred to the desorber, resulting in significant energy reduction. Despite the obvious advantages, there is very limited research addressing modelling and design of such systems, leaving considerable space for performance improvements. The very few reported studies pertain to technoeconomic assessment of specific solvents using commercial software, with no systematic optimisation approaches reported to date (Raynal et al., 2011; Pinto et al., 2014).

In this work, a rigorous and flexible model that can represent the phase-change behaviour of absorption/desorption CO_2 capture processes is proposed. The column models are based on the orthogonal collocation on finite elements (OCFE) technique tailored to three phase systems that support a sufficiently accurate but also computationally tractable process representation. The main advantages include the transformation of discrete process characteristics into continuous decision variables, and the ability to represent and track sharp changes of important variables such as concentration and temperature profiles along the column domain. The model is also employed in the context of a superstructure representation which supports optimisation.

2. Methodology

2.1. Modelling framework

The use of phase-change solvents (PCS) systems in CO_2 capture processes provides the opportunity for enhanced performance as well as the reduction of process energetic demands and economic resources through the exploitation of their liquid-liquid phase separation capabilities. The optimum design of three-phase flowsheets is challenging because it requires (a) a systematic modelling approach able to capture transitions between vapour-liquid (VLE) and vapour-liquid-liquid (VLLE) equilibria regimes, and (b) an underlying framework, which is sufficiently flexible to account for the interactions of the large number of the desired structural and operating features.

The modeling framework employed in this work to meet requirement (a) is based on the OCFE approximating technique (Dalaouti and Seferlis, 2006; Damartzis and Seferlis, 2010) to model three-phase reactive separation systems. The separation column is divided into column sections, defined as the column segment between two successive feed or draw streams. A section is further subdivided into finite elements (FE) of variable size. Within each finite element a given number of collocation points (CP) are defined based on the degree of polynomial approximation. These points are selected as the roots of the discrete Hahn family orthogonal polynomials. A finite element is illustrated in Figure 1 (left) with the two liquid and vapour flows leaving and entering the collocation points.

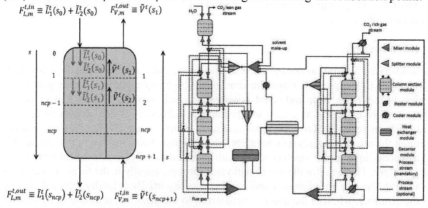

Figure 1: Three-phase OCFE presentation (left), superstructure with indicative placement of liquid-liquid phase separator (right)

Eq. (1) – (5) represent the main equations of a VLLE model with NC components and n collocation points under the assumption of a dispersed second liquid phase. Eq. (1) is the material balance and Eq. (3) the energy balance at collocation point j that corresponds to a location in the column s_j; x_i^{L1} and x_i^{L2} are the molar fractions of each component in the two liquid phases and y_i^V is the vapour molar fraction of each component. The reactive absorption is incorporated implicitly in the phase equilibrium model. In Eq. (3) symbol H represents the enthalpies of each phase and ΔH is the heat of reaction. The equilibrium between the vapour and the $L1$ phase is presented in Eq. (4) by K_i^V, whereas Eq. (5) is the equilibrium between the two liquid phases, represented by K_i^L. The dispersed liquid phase (2nd liquid phase) does not interact with the vapour phase and therefore only two interfaces are considered; vapour – liquid $L1$ and liquid $L1$ – liquid $L2$.

$$L1_i(s_j + 1) + L2_i(s_j + 1) - L1_i(s_j) - L2_i(s_j) + V_i(s_j - 1) - V_i(s_j) = 0 \tag{1}$$

$$x_i^{L1}(s_j) = \frac{L1_i(s_j)}{\sum_{i=1}^{NC} L1_i(s_j)}, x_i^{L2}(s_j) = \frac{L2_i(s_j)}{\sum_{i=1}^{NC} L2_i(s_j)}, y_i^V(s_j) = \frac{V_i(s_j)}{\sum_{i=1}^{NC} V_i(s_j)} \tag{2}$$

$$\begin{aligned} &L_1^t(s_j + 1)H^{L1}(s_j + 1) + L_2^t(s_j + 1)H^{L2}(s_j + 1) + V^t(s_j - 1)H^V(s_j - 1) - \\ &L_1^t(s_j)H^{L1}(s_j) - L_2^t(s_j)H^{L2}(s_j) - V^t(s_j)H^V(s_j) + \Delta H = 0 \end{aligned} \tag{3}$$

$$y_i^V(s_j) = K_i^V(s_j)x_i^{L1}(s_j) \tag{4}$$

$$x_i^{L2}(s_j) = K_i^L(s_j)x_i^{L1}(s_j) \quad i = 1, \dots, NC, \quad j = 1, \dots, n \tag{5}$$

2.2. Design framework

The model shown for the column section is directly adapted on the superstructure proposed by Damartzis et al. (2014) for two-phase post-combustion CO₂ capture processes. The superstructure, shown in Figure 1 (right) consists of modules representing generic process tasks (e.g., reactive, separation, heat transfer) and interconnecting streams emulating material flows. Reactive separation and liquid-liquid phase change processes may be represented by different modules through the column section. Additional information is reported in Damartzis et al. (2014) pertaining to heat transfer tasks. Several different modules may be connected in the same flowsheet using a broad set of stream types (e.g., recycle, bypasses and so forth). The proposed generic tasks account for (a) reaction, mass and heat exchange between different phases within each module, and (b) stream mixing and splitting to enable distribution of materials among different modules. This representation enables the reproduction of any potentially desired representation of solvent-based CO₂ capture processes. For clarity, the liquid-liquid separator is illustrated before the heat exchanger in Figure 1 (right), but it can also be placed after the heat exchanger and connected in any desired way to the columns as in Figure 2.

The combination of the superstructure approach with the OCFE representation introduces important advantages in process optimization. The element length becomes a design variable that indicates the number of stages or equivalent packing height in the column. Accordingly, the size of the separation column can be deduced from the sum of element lengths comprising the column plus the discrete stages, if any, such as the distinct feed stages, reboilers and condensers. Hence, the integer variable denoting the number of stages becomes continuous. Further avoidance of integer variables is achieved by the continuous representation of the location of side feed or draw streams in the columns. Temperature and composition profiles in the column are approximated by continuous Lagrange polynomials of position inside the column. Finally, OCFE supports a significant reduction in terms of the total number of model equations without compromising the resolution of the model, by enabling the solution of the material and energy balances of the equilibrium model on a reduced number of collocation points.

3. Implementation

To investigate the effect of PCS on the optimal design of CO_2 capture processes a N-methylcyclohexylamine (MCA) 35 wt % aqueous solution is considered. MCA is a cyclic secondary aliphatic amine, which has been shown to demonstrate enhanced CO_2 capture capabilities (Jeon et al. 2014; Zhuang et al., 2016) is used. The flowsheet investigated in this work is shown in Figure 2. In addition to the absorption and desorption columns a liquid-liquid phase separator is employed to exploit the phase-split exhibited by MCA.

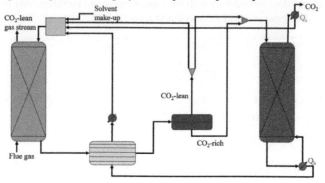

Figure 2: Flowsheet structure used in optimal design.

In the case of MCA, phase separation occurs at 90°C, so the liquid-liquid phase-separator (LLPS) is positioned after the intermediate heat exchanger. In principle, the superstructure may be used to investigate various structural flowsheet options. In this work, for the first time the performance of MCA through systematic process design is investigated and a new structural design option in phase-change flowsheets is explored. After the phase separation, the CO_2-rich phase is directed to the stripper column, whereas the CO_2-lean stream may be recycled entirely or partially to the absorber top through a splitter. The fraction of the CO_2 lean stream leaving the LLPS is a degree of freedom in optimisation. This design option is considered to investigate the trade-off between the regeneration energy requirements and the effects of absorber size on the total process cost. The only flowsheet proposed to date for PCS allows for complete recycle of the CO_2-lean stream to the absorber, leaving the interplay of regeneration energy-absorber size unexplored. A total of seven design decision variables is considered including the split fraction after the LLPS, the pressure in the columns, the reboiler temperature, the amine flowrate as well as the column sizes. The objective function is expressed as the sum of the total process capital and operating expenses as follows:

$$F = \underbrace{\sum_{i=1}^{N_{sep}} C_{sep,i} + \sum_{i=1}^{N_{HEX}} C_{HEX,i} + \sum_{i=1}^{N_{pump}} C_{pump,i}}_{CAPEX} + \underbrace{C_{steam} + C_{cool} + C_{amine}}_{OPEX} \qquad (6)$$

CAPEX terms reflect the annualized capital costs of the separation, the heat exchangers and the pumping equipment, whereas the OPEX terms stand for the costs of steam in the reboiler, water (both process and cooling) and the fresh amine used in the system. Employed initial conditions as well as process specifications are listed in Table 1.

The CO_2 vapour pressure (P_{CO2} in kPa) with respect to loading (a mol CO_2 / mol amine) and temperature (T) is represented by Eq. (7) which is fitted from experimental VLLE data (Tzirakis et al., 2018), with R^2 =0.96 for T=40 °C, 60 °C, and 90°C. For MCA and H_2O in the vapour phase ideal behavior is assumed. The heat of reaction (*ΔH* in J/mol) is calculated using Eq. (7) derived by a polynomial approximation (Oexmann, 2011):

Table 1: Initial conditions and process specifications.

Initial Conditions		Specifications	
Vapour flow in absorber (mol/s)	320	CO_2 Absorption (%)	≥90
CO_2 composition in flue fas (% v/v)	14.11	Cooler temperature (K)	≥313
Vapour inlet temperature (K)	298	Condenser temperature (K)	313

$$log10(P_{CO2}) = 21.65 - 19.81 \cdot a - \frac{7343}{T} - 75720 \cdot \frac{a^2}{T^2} + 721500 \cdot \frac{a}{T^2} + 5435 \cdot \frac{a}{T} \quad (7)$$

$$\Delta H = -R \cdot (-7343 - 2 \cdot 75720 \cdot \frac{a^2}{T} + 2 \cdot 721500 \cdot \frac{a}{T} + 5435 \cdot a) \quad (8)$$

4. Results and discussion

Table 2 presents the optimal solution for MCA (MCA[opt]) compared to an optimal solution obtained for monoethanolamine (MEA) 30 wt %. Two more cases are explored, namely MCA[1] and MCA[2], where the split fraction after the liquid-liquid phase separator is fixed at specific values, one lower and one higher than the optimal solution. This enables the investigation of the effect of the split fraction in the overall performance.

Table 2: Design optimization results

Case	MCA[1]	MCA[opt]	MCA[2]	MEA
CO_2-lean phase split ratio (%) to stripper	20	28.63	50	-
Equivalent Stages:				
Absorber / Stripper	24 / 26	22 / 26	22 / 27	11 / 27
Reboiler Temperature (K)	376.58	376.87	377.35	393.15
Phase Split Ratio (%) (rich/lean)	30.63	30.63	30.63	-
Bottom Pressure (bar):				
Absorber / Stripper	1 / 1	1 / 1	1 / 1	1.9 / 1.8

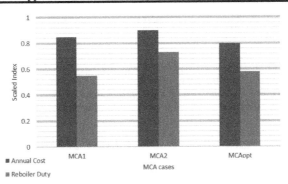

Figure 3: Both reboiler duty and annual cost of MCA aqueous phase split ratio cases, all values scaled with respect to MEA case, values lower than 1 indicate better performance than MEA.

Optimization results reveal that all the cases using MCA exhibit lower operating pressures in both columns as well as reduced operating temperature in the reboiler than MEA. The second liquid phase is formed above 363.15 K, so this is the target temperature in the decanter for the liquid-liquid phase separation that must be provided by the heat exchanger. Reduced reboiler duty (2.3 GJ/ton CO_2) by 42.5 % at a lower temperature level by 16.2°C is required in the optimised MCA case compared to the conventional MEA case (4.0 GJ/ton CO_2). This is a significant advantage of the phase-change solvent capture system. When the recycle of the CO_2-lean stream to the absorber increases (i.e. in MCA[1]), a larger absorber column is needed in order to achieve the overall CO_2 capture specification. A large recycle of the aqueous liquid stream reduces the total amount of CO_2 captured per pass. Eventually, this results in lower regeneration energy, due to lower volume in the desorber, but at a higher investment cost, as shown in Figure 3. MCA performs better even at pressures of 1 bar (thermodynamic data were available only for this pressure). Potential increase of pressure in the desorber would further improve the capture performance.

5. Conclusions

The optimal design of an amine-based post-combustion CO_2 capture process using a phase-change solvent was presented. The process was modelled using a rigorous, equilibrium-based model, able to accurately represent the underlying physical and chemical phenomena, coupled with the OCFE technique for model size reduction. An aqueous MCA solution was used as a representative phase-change solvent, aiming to investigate the impact of phase-splitting behaviour. Stream redistribution possibilities and a flowsheet that takes advantage of the two liquid phases that are formed, were generated using a generalized process design superstructure. Design optimization results indicate a substantial energy reduction in the reboiler and subsequent reduction in the total annual cost compared with a reference plant operating with a MEA solvent, making phase-change solvents a promising alternative for further investigation.

Acknowledgements

This project has received funding from EU Horizon 2020 program under agreement 727503 - ROLINCAP – H2020-LCE-2016-2017/H2020-LCE-2016-RES-CCS-RIA

References

N. Dalaouti, P. Seferlis, 2006, Comput. Chem. Eng., 30 (8), 1264–1277.

T. Damartzis, A. I. Papadopoulos, P. Seferlis, 2014, Clean Technol. Environ. Policy, 16(7), 1363–1380.

T. Damartzis, P. Seferlis, 2010, Ind. Eng. Chem. Res., 49 (7), 3275–3285.

N., Mac Dowell, Pereira, F.E., Llovell, F., Blas, F.J., Adjiman, C.S., Jackson, G., Galindo, A., 2011, J. Phys. Chem. B, 115 (25), 8155-8168.

B. Huepen, E. Y. Kenig, 2010, Ind. Eng. Chem. Res., 49 (2), 772–779.

S. Bin Jeon, S. W. Cho, S. S. Lee, 2014, S. Y. Jang, K. J. Oh, J. Taiwan Inst. Chem. Eng., 45(5), 2673-2680

J. Oexmann, 2011, Post combustion CO_2 capture: Energetic evaluation of chemical absorption processes in coal fired steam power plants, PhD Thesis, Tech Universität Hamburg-Harburg.

D. D. D. Pinto, S. A. H. Zaidy, A. Hartono, 2014, H. F. Svendsen, Int. J. Greenh. Gas Control, 28, 318–327.

L. Raynal, P. A. Bouillon, A. Gomez, P. Broutin, 2011, Chem. Eng. J., 171(3), 742-752.

J. Rodriguez, N. Mac Dowell, F. Llovell, C. S. Adjiman, G. Jackson, A. Galindo, 2012, Mol. Phys., 110 (11–12), 1325–1348.

F. Tzirakis, I. Tsivintzelis, A. I. Papadopoulos, P. Seferlis, 2019, Solubility of CO_2 in methylcyclohexylamine, Chem. Eng. Sci., 199, 20-27.

Q. Zhuang, B. Clements, J. Dai, L. Carrigan, 2016, Int. J. Greenh. Gas Contr., 52, 449-460.

Anton A. Kiss, Edwin Zondervan, Richard Lakerveld, Leyla Özkan (Eds.)
Proceedings of the 29th European Symposium on Computer Aided Process Engineering
June 16th to 19th, 2019, Eindhoven, The Netherlands. © 2019 Elsevier B.V. All rights reserved.
http://dx.doi.org/10.1016/B978-0-128-18634-3.50079-5

Optimization of a hydroformulation process in a thermomorphic solvent system using a commercial steady-state process simulator and a memetic algorithm

Tim Janus[a,b], Maximilian Cegla[a,b], Sabine Barkmann[b] and Sebastian Engell[a,b]

[a]ZEDO, Dortmund e.V., Joseph-von-Fraunhofer-Str. 20, 44227 Dortmund, Germany
[b]TU Dortmund University - Process Dynamics and Operations, Emil-Figge-Str. 70, 44227 Dortmund, Germany
tim.janus@tu-dortmund.de

Abstract

The economic evaluation of alternative process configurations is an important step in process development. It should be based on optimization to correctly investigate the potential of different process routes and process variants. In many companies, such design studies are performed using block-oriented flowsheet simulators such as Aspen Plus to utilize the extensive model libraries and the ease of model building. We developed an optimization framework that integrates a process simulator (specifically Aspen Plus) with a memetic algorithm (MA). This MA combines an evolution strategy (ES) with derivative-free (DFO) local search methods. The ES addresses the global optimization of all design variables, whereas the DFO method locally optimizes the continuous sub-problems that arise by fixing the discrete variables. In this work, the performance of the memetic algorithm is evaluated for different local methods, involving different DFO methods or the internal equation-oriented optimization engine of Aspen Plus. We discuss the results and the efficiency of the different local methods.

Keywords: Chemical process synthesis, Flowsheet simulation, Aspen Plus, Memetic algorithms, Flowsheet optimization

1. Introduction

Chemical process design in industrial practice is usually done by an interdisciplinary team in an iterative process of comparing the performances and costs of alternative process configurations. In many companies, such design studies are performed using block-oriented flowsheet simulators as e. g. Aspen Plus. The optimization of a chemical process is a challenging task as the models that represent the process units, e. g. a reactor, are in general nonlinear. Discrete decisions like the number of stages and the feed stage of a distillation column enlarge the complexity of the optimization problem. In this case, the optimization of a chemical process is a mixed integer nonlinear program (MINLP). In research usally equation-based models are used (see e. g. Urselmann et al. (2011)). From an industrial perspective this approach has the disadvantage that the extensibility and applicability of the models heavily rely on the experts who created them. Often, as in Waltermann and Skiborowski (2017), a tailor-made initialization procedure is needed to converge the model. In contrast, Aspen Plus offers a large model library and the models are initialized automatically. We therefore investigated the coupling of external process simulators, like Aspen Plus, to optimization methods. The biggest drawback from an optimization perspective is the lack of derivative information in commercial process simulators such that optimization of these flowsheets is not as efficient as the optimization of equations-based models with mathematical programming. In this contribution we extend the approach of Urselmann and Engell (2015), to include features of Aspen Plus that can utilize derivative information. We demonstrate the performance of our approach for a case study that has been studied extensively in other work.

2. Optimization Method - Memetic Algorithm

The optimization of a chemical process can be mathematically formulated by:

$$\min f(\mathbf{x}, \mathbf{y}, \mathbf{z}) \text{ subject to } g_i(\mathbf{x}, \mathbf{y}, \mathbf{z}) \leq 0$$

A cost function f will be minimized in respect to a set of constraints g_i. The variables are divided in three sets, where $\mathbf{x}$ denotes the discrete design variables, $\mathbf{y}$ the continuous design variables and $\mathbf{z}$ the state variables of the process. $\mathbf{x}$ and $\mathbf{y}$ represent degrees of freedom that are determined by an optimization method and $\mathbf{z}$ represents variables that are calculated by the process simulator and are also used by the cost function.

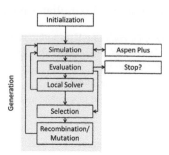

Figure 1: Memetic Algorithm

2.1. Memetic Algorithm

Urselmann et al. (2011) proposed a memetic algorithm to solve MINLPs that formulate an optimization problem for chemical processes. A memetic algorithm is the combination of an evolutionary algorithm, e. g. an evolution strategy (ES), with a local solver (meme). The ES is referred to as the 1st stage and fixes the discrete design variables and provides an initialization of the continuous optimization variables in the NLP problem. The meme solves the NLPs in a more effective manner than the ES and is referred to as the 2nd stage. Figure 1 shows the memetic algorithm. In an initialization step a generation of size μ, i. e. a set of solution candidates, is generated, where the design variables $\mathbf{x}$ and $\mathbf{y}$ are initialized within their bounds by a random uniform distribution. The individuals are simulated by Aspen Plus and then evaluated by the cost function. A meme then computes a local minimum of the continuous sub-problem using Aspen Plus evaluations. After solving the sub-problem for all members of the population the MA is initialized. Then the MA generates a set of λ offspring individuals and evaluates them to select the new μ individuals of the next population. These two steps are repeated until a stop criterion, e. g. the maximum number of function-evaluations, is fulfilled. To generate an offspring, two parents are randomly chosen from the population and act as an input for a recombination operator that generates a new offspring. This offspring is further modified by a mutation operator before it is evaluated.

2.2. Aspen Plus Equation-oriented Mode

Traditionally Aspen Plus uses a sequential modular approach to simulate the flowsheet. Meanwhile, an equation-oriented (EO) mode of Aspen Plus has been implemented which solves the underlying model equations simultaneously. The sequential modular mode is used as an initialization strategy. Aspen Plus supports simulation and optimization in the EO mode. The EO mode distinguishes between calculated and constant types of variables and every variable of the EO mode is initialized by a default type that can be changed. Constant variables are inputs from Aspen Plus, e. g. the reflux ratio. If a constant variable is changed to calculated the underlying equation system becomes over-determined and if a calculated variable is changed to constant it becomes under-determined. Fixing the value for a calculated product purity is permitted if a constant variable, e. g. reflux ratio, is changed to calculated accordingly, such that the equation system is not under-determined. In this way a specification is defined and is realized if the computations are successful. The EO mode supports an internal local optimizer which has access to derivatives. Variables are marked as degrees of freedom and a cost function is defined in EO mode optimization. The drawback of the internal optimizer is that it does not support arbitrary cost functions, due to technical limitations. In this work we extend the MA by two local solvers, which exploit the EO mode of Aspen Plus. The first meme uses the EO mode simulation to realize specifications and the second meme applies the Aspen Plus internal optimizer to perform a local optimization of an approximated cost function.

3. Flowsheet Optimization of the Hydroformulation of 1-Dodecene

As a case study, the homogeneously catalyzed hydroformulation of 1-dodecene in a thermomorphic solvent system (TMS) is investigated. This case study has been investigated by various groups within the TR SFB Inprompt. Steimel and Engell (2016) optimized this case study based on a simpler model and cost function using an equation-oriented model. The process consists of a reaction step, a decanter and a distillation column, two recycles and includes complex kinetics (Kiedorf et al. (2014)) and uses liquid-liquid separation modelled according to (Merchan and Wozny (2016)) to recover the expensive homogeneous rhodium-based catalyst from the reaction mixture. Due to the coupling of the separation units with the reactor a simple objective function as e. g. the selectivity of the reaction is not sufficient (see Hentschel et al. (2014)). A data-based model describing the catalyst loss is employed, since this loss greatly influences the overall costs.

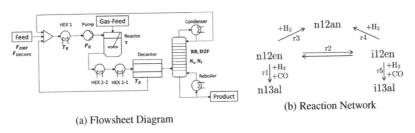

(a) Flowsheet Diagram   (b) Reaction Network

Figure 2: TMS model with DoFs and Specifications

3.1. The Aspen Plus Flowsheet

Figure 2a illustrates the Aspen Plus flowsheet that represents the process. The degrees of freedom are highlighted in bold. The feed flows of the reactant dodecene and the solvents decane and DMF flow are pre-heated and pressurized. The optimizer can change the solvent ratio by adapting F_{DMF} and F_{DECANE}, the residence time τ, the temperature T_R and the pressure P_R to alter the performance of the reaction, in which 1-dodecene reacts to tridecanal. The basic scheme of the reaction network is shown in Figure 2b and is implemented in Aspen Plus. The reacted mixture is cooled down by two heat-exchangers. The first heat exchanger is operated with cooling water and the second heat exchanger is either operated with ammonia or with cooling water depending on the decanter temperature T_E, which is varied by the optimizer. The decanter uses the miscibility gap of the mixture at lower temperature to separate it in a polar phase that contains the catalyst and an unpolar phase that contains the product containing both tridecanal isomers. The polar phase is recycled back to the reactor and the unpolar phase is further purified in a distillation column. The optimizer varies the stage count N_s, the feed position N_F, the distillate to feed ratio $D2F$ and the reflux ratio RR of the column.

Table 2: Variants of Memetic Algorithm

Name	Local Solver	Avg. Costs	Best Costs	Best Purity	Fails
ES-SPECS	EO Sim.	3443 ± 4.76 € / T	3439 € / T	99.00 %	37.6 ± 1.7 %
ES-CATOPT	EO Opt.	3449 ± 3.05 € / T	3445 € / T	99.18 %	26.6 ± 2.5 %
ES	None	3506 ± 5.23 € / T	3500 € / T	99.40 %	27.7 ± 4.0 %
ES-NOMAD	NOMAD	3594 ± 40.6 € / T	3549 € / T	99.49 %	6.1 ± 0.7 %
ES-CMAES	CMAES	3728 ± 217 € / T	3554 € / T	99.43 %	17.5 ± 1.6 %

3.2. Catalyst Loss and Cost Estimation

Our approach supports the definition of arbitrary cost functions. Here the cost function is an indicator of the costs per ton of product depending on the amount of catalyst loss:

$$f(\mathbf{x}, \mathbf{y}, \mathbf{z}) = \frac{C_{OU} + C_{Mat}}{8000 \cdot \dot{m}_{Product}} + Penalty$$

With $C_{Mat} = C_{Raw} + C_{Cat} + C_{Makeup}$ and C_{OU} equals the sum of the capital and utility costs of every operation unit, as proposed by Turton et al. (2008). The capital costs are pressure dependent, e. g. a reactor operated by a pressure of thirty bar instead of twenty raises the capital costs by approximately 45 %. We fitted a 2nd order polynomial model to describe the catalyst loss based on the temperature and solvent data measured by Brunsch and Behr (2013). The catalyst loss is represented by:

Table 1: Model Parameters

a	0.00112
b_1	−0.1743
c_1	6.9086
b_2	0.2033
c_2	1.7474

$$Loss = (a \cdot DMF_p^2 + b_1 \cdot DMF_p + c_1) \cdot (b_2 \cdot T + c_2)$$

where the parameters are defined in Table 1. T represents the temperature in the decanter and DMF_p represents the fraction of DMF of the solvent. With this loss term the costs for catalyst loss regarding the volume flow $\dot{V}_F$ of the decanter is calculated by $C_{Cat}(\dot{V}_F) = \dot{V}_F \cdot Loss \cdot C_{Rhodium}$. The penalty term of the form $Penalty = 4000 + v \cdot 10000$ is used to penalize the constraint violation. Here v represents the constraint violation in molar fraction of the tridencanal purity in the bottom flow of the distillation column.

4. Optimization Results

The optimization problem contains 10 design variables (see Table 3). The purity of the sum of iso- and n-tridecanal is specified as 99 mol % in the bottom stream of the distillation column. We compare the results of several variants of the MA, which are summarized in Table 2. The parameters for the ES are $\mu = 10$ (generation-size), $\lambda = 20$ (number of offsprings) and $\kappa = 5$ (maximum age of an individual) which have been determined in previous studies as a robust setting for a range of problems. We compare the performance of a traditional ES with four MA variants that differ in their meme, i. e.

Table 3: Boundaries of Design Variables

Variable	Unit	Lower	Upper	BFS
T_R	[C°]	80	120	111.34
P_R	[bar]	15	30	23.06
τ	[h]	0.1	5	4.49
T_E	[C°]	-5	25	-5
N_s	unitless	4	40	27
N_f	unitless	2	dynamic	6
$D2F$	unitless	0.6	0.95	0.61
RR	unitless	0.1	15	0.17
F_{dmf}	[kmol/h]	20	100	81.44
F_{dode}	[kmol/h]	20	100	20.76

we test four different local optimization
strategies. The Aspen Plus equation-oriented (EO) optimization and the EO simulation represent
two memes. The former minimizes the catalyst loss and the latter fixes the tridecanal specification.
The derivative free methods (DFO), covariance matrix evolution strategy (CMAES) and the solver
NOMAD represent the other two memes. These peformed best from a set of DFO methods which
have been compared by Urselmann et al. (2016) for water-ethanol-benzene separation case study.

4.1. Cost Distribution

The best found solution (BFS) is shown in Table 3 which has the cost distribution shown in Figure
4. The raw material costs have the biggest impact on the cost. The heat exchangers and the column
cause the main equipment costs. The catalyst and solvent makeup costs are only a small fraction
of the entire costs of the BFS. The HEX2-1 may use ammonia if the target temperature is below
5 C° and this increases the costs considerably. Nonetheless, the optimizer chooses a decanter
temperature of -5 C° because the cost of using ammonia is compensated by the reduction of
catalyst loss. The high fraction of DMF in the solvent is also chosen by the optimizer to reduce
the loss of catalyst. The design parameters of the reactor are chosen such that there is a good
trade-off between selectivity and conversion to reduce the size of the recycle. The high influence
of the pressure on the capital costs of the reactor causes the pressure to be below the upper bound.

4.2. Convergence Behavior and Runtime

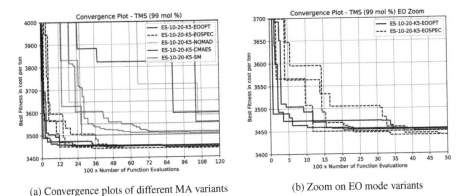

(a) Convergence plots of different MA variants   (b) Zoom on EO mode variants

Figure 3: Convergence Plots of three runs of different MA variants

Figure 3 shows the convergence
of three runs for each MA variant, i. e. lines of the same type
represent different runs of the
MA variant that is identified in
the legend. Table 2 shows the
average and best costs, the best
purity and the average percentage of failed simulations and
is ordered ascending by costs.

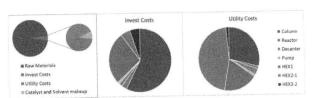

Figure 4: Cost Distribution of Optimal Solution

The memes using Aspen Plus features perform best, as they can access derivatives. All the Aspen Plus meme variants found an optimum that is closer than one percent to the optimal solution
after 40 % of the optimization time, i. e. after 4.800 function evaluations which are processed in
ten hours on a i7-4790S CPU with 3.20 GHZ. Here 99 % of the time is spent in the Aspen Plus

simulation which is solved in 8.4 seconds on average. The best found solution was detected by the variant that fixes the specification, since a distillation column that operates at a high purity is more expensive. Nonetheless the optimization of the catalyst loss with Aspen Plus leads to a faster convergence in the early stage of the optimization. Although the variants that use DFO methods fail less, the ES variant that does not make use of a local optimization performs better than the DFO variants. This means that the function evaluations used by the DFO methods are not worth the effort. At least at the early stages of the optimization, i. e. using these function evaluations in the ES leads to a faster convergence. Both variants ES and ES-CATOPT fail approximately in 27 % of the simulations. However the ES-SPECS variant fails 10 % more often such that the fraction of failed simulation is traded for a solution that fulfills the specification accurately.

5. Conclusion

Based on the case study of the hydroformylation of 1-dodecene into tridecanal we showed that the new implemented memes that use the equation-oriented (EO) mode of Aspen Plus and therefore utilize derivative information speed up the convergence. As long as the derivative information is not accessible by external tools, the benefit of the ease of modeling larger processes using a process simulator is traded for significantly higher computation times of the optimization. For the example it turned out that in general a MA that uses a derivative-free method (DFO) as a local solver does not outperform a pure evolution strategy with respect to speed of convergence. We therefore propose that a DFO based local optimization should only be performed in the later stages of the optimization.

Acknowledgements

This work is part of the Collaborative Research Centre Integrated Chemical Processes in Liquid Multiphase Systems. Financial support from the Deutsche Forschungsgemeinschaft (DFG) is gratefully acknowledged through TRR 63. The financial support by the German Federal Ministry of Education and Research for the research project SuperOpt (01LY1614) is gratefully acknowledged. The responsibility for the contents rests with the authors.

References

Y. Brunsch, A. Behr, 2013. Temperature-controlled catalyst recycling in homogeneous transition-metal catalysis : Minimization of catalyst leaching. Angewandte Chemie - International Edition 52, 1586–1589.

B. Hentschel, A. Peschel, H. Freund, K. Sundmacher, 2014. Simultaneous design of the optimal reaction and process concept for multiphase systems. Chemical Engineering Science 115, 69–87.

G. Kiedorf, D. Hoang, A. Mller, A. Jrke, J. Markert, H. Arellano-Garcia, A. Seidel-Morgenstern, C. Hamel, 2014. Kinetics of 1-dodecene hydroformylation in a thermomorphic solvent system using a rhodium-biphephos catalyst. Chemical Engineering Science 115, 31 – 48.

V. A. Merchan, G. Wozny, 2016. Comparative evaluation of rigorous thermodynamic models for the description of the hydroformylation of 1-dodecene in a thermomorphic solvent system. Industrial & Engineering Chemistry Research 55 (1), 293–310.

J. Steimel, S. Engell, 2016. Optimization-based support for process design under uncertainty: A case study. AIChE Journal 62 (9), 3404–3419.

R. Turton, R. C. Bailie, W. B. Whiting, J. A. Shaeiwitz, 2008. Analysis, synthesis and design of chemical processes. Pearson Education.

M. Urselmann, S. Barkmann, G. Sand, S. Engell, 2011. A memetic algorithm for global optimization in chemical process synthesis problems. IEEE Transactions on Evolutionary Computation 15 (5), 659–683.

M. Urselmann, S. Engell, 2015. Design of memetic algorithms for the efficient optimization of chemical process synthesis problems with structural restrictions. Computers and Chemical Engineering 72, 87–108.

M. Urselmann, C. Foussette, T. Janus, S. Tlatlik, A. Gottschalk, M. T. Emmerich, S. Engell, T. Bäck, 2016. Selection of a DFO Method for the Efficient Solution of Continuous Constrained Sub-Problems within a Memetic Algorithm for Chemical Process Synthesis. Proceedings of the GECCO Conference 2016, 1029–1036.

T. Waltermann, M. Skiborowski, 2017. Conceptual Design of Highly Integrated Processes Optimization of Dividing Wall Columns. Chemie Ingenieur Technik - Special Issue Prozess Optimierung 89 (5), 562–581.

Anton A. Kiss, Edwin Zondervan, Richard Lakerveld, Leyla Özkan (Eds.)
Proceedings of the 29th European Symposium on Computer Aided Process Engineering
June 16th to 19th, 2019, Eindhoven, The Netherlands. © 2019 Elsevier B.V. All rights reserved.
http://dx.doi.org/10.1016/B978-0-128-18634-3.50080-1

Exergy analysis for energy integration in a bioethanol production process to determine heat exchanger networks feasibility

J. Cristóbal García-García[a], Jaime D. Ponce-Rocha[b], Danahe Marmolejo-Correa[c,d], Ricardo Morales-Rodriguez[b*]

a División de Ciencias e Ingenierías Universidad de Guanajuato, Loma del Bosque 103, León, Guanajuato. 37150, México.

b Departamento de Ingeniería Química, División de Ciencias Naturales y Exactas, Universidad de Guanajuato, Noria Alta S/N, Guanajuato, Gto. 36050, México.

cCollege of Sciences and Arts, Maryville University, 350 Maryville University Drive, St. Louis, Missouri, 63141, USA

dDepartment of Engineering, St. Charles Community College, 4601 Mid Rivers Mall Drive, Cottleville, Missouri, 63376, USA

ricardo.morales@ugto.mx

Abstract

In this study, Exergy Analysis (EA) and Energy Integration (EI) analyses are employed as decision factors to select the best heat exchanger network (HEN) configuration and applied to improve a bioethanol production process plant by evaluating its irreversibilities. The results of EI and EA reveal that the HEN configuration A6 allows to obtain a value of rational efficiency for the process of 87.88 % (an increasing of 12.33 % respect to base case scenario) by a diminution of the process irreversibilities of 28.85 MW. With this HEN configuration, the equipment cost increases by $158,432.57 with a decrease on services cost of 750,615.06 $/year, obtaining an energy saving of 21.37 MW.

Keywords: Exergy, Energy Integration, Bioethanol production

1. Introduction

The world is starting to face energy resources depletion and non-renewable resources are the most employed as a fuel in the auto transport sector. The use of non-renewable resources has also showed negative environmental consequences for some decades, which has been catalogued as one of the main global problems that the nations aim to solve, figuring in the list of Sustainable Development Goals that might be reached in 2030 (United Nations General Assembly, 2015). Thus, different alternatives to minimize the negative effects are being evaluated, among them it is the use of alternative fuels such as bioethanol. Bioethanol is an organic biofuel that is obtained from lignocellulosic biomass, a renewable substrate that through a process of numerous unit operations could be converted in an ethanol solution with high purity grade. The second-generation bioethanol production process has begun to be commercially feasible, however, improvements in the process performance are still necessary to reduce production cost.

EA is useful to evaluate thermodynamic efficiency of chemical processes by the calculation of its irreversibilities. EI is a tool that allows development and analysis of several HEN configurations that seeks energy benefits by exchanging the available energy between process streams that may contribute in the reduction of the total cost of the process. Usually, the cost of the process is considered a performance criterion for selection of the best HEN, leaving apart the thermodynamic criteria for the best HEN selection. Therefore, the objective of this works is employing these two tools to design and evaluate HEN configurations in a bioethanol production process, aiming to reduce energy consumption and determine thermodynamic efficiency by using a computer-aided based approach.

2. Exergy Analysis

Exergy is the maximum theoretical work obtainable from a given thermodynamic state when this reaches thermo-mechanical and chemical equilibrium with a reference state on environmental conditions entering in a state called "dead state" (Kotas, 1995). In open systems, exergy content can be classified by its origin: a) exergy accompanying energy flows and b) exergy accompanying material flows. In material flows, excluding kinetic, potential, nuclear and electromagnetics effects, exergy can be then divided into: thermo-mechanical or physical exergy and chemical exergy (Marmolejo-Correa and Gundersen, 2015).

Thermo-mechanical exergy in Eq. (1) is defined by differences in enthalpy (h-h_0) and entropy (s-s_0) from the current conditions of the system (T, P) to the ambient conditions (T_0, P_0), where T and P stand for temperature and pressure, respectively. Chemical exergy for a non-ideal mixture is shown in Eq. (2), where x_i are the mole fractions, ε_i are the standard chemical exergy and γ_i are the activity coefficient of each component. The irreversibility rate (I) in bioethanol production plant is calculated developing an exergy balance as shown in Eq. (3), where, E_i and E_o are the net exergy rates entering and leaving the system, respectively. ΣE^Q is the net exergy flow accompanying the energy entering in heat exchangers and leaving in coolers, and, ΣE^W is the net exergy flow accompanying the work applied to process. The rational efficiency is a measure of the process performance and is defined by Kotas (1995) as it is illustrated in Eq. (4), this is a relation between useful exergy in the products and exergy driven to the system.

$$e^{ph} = h - h_0 - T_0 \left(s - s_0 \right) \tag{1}$$

$$e^{ch} = \sum_{i=1}^{n} \varepsilon_i^0 x_i + \sum_{i=1}^{n} x_i ln x_i \gamma_i \tag{2}$$

$$I = E_i - E_o + \Sigma E^Q + \Sigma E^W \tag{3}$$

$$\psi = 1 - I / \Delta E_i \tag{4}$$

EA has been previously applied in bioethanol production processes, reporting overall analyses to the complete process configurations (Ojeda et al., 2011; Silva Ortiz and de Oliveira Jr, 2014, Zeineb et al., 2018). However, these studies simulate the process employing other feedstocks and in some cases the papers do not include an EI analysis.

Regarding to exergy calculation, the simulation software employed in this work provides the calculation of physical exergy, but it is necessary to calculate the chemical exergy, in order to obtain the net exergy that material flows contain. Therefore, the usage of computational tools linked to the simulator is a useful strategy. The methodology applied to link the computer-aided tools was already described in a previous work (García-García et al, 2018), thus, it was possible to obtain the exergy balances stage by stage and in overall plant in the bioethanol production process studied.

3. Energy Integration

The EI task relies on proposing several configurations of heat exchanger networks with the aim of minimizing the utility consumption, employing as a performance criterion to determine the best configuration the energy savings, total costs and heat exchangers areas. The EI could be achieved employing the pinch analysis, which provides a systematic methodology for energy saving in process and total sites heat integration (Goodarzvand-Chegini and GhasemiKafrudi, 2017). The exergy analysis has been successfully employed for the EI in previous studies, for example, Janka, A. et al (2018) employed this methodology to evaluate the energy integration in distillation technologies focusing on dividing-wall columns. Goodarzvand-Chegini and GhasemiKafrudi (2017) developed an exergy analysis to improve the heat integration efficiency in a hydrocracking process. On the other hand, Staine and Favrat (1996) proposed a pinch analysis method extended to include exergy factors in the process. The state of the art does not show this type of thermodynamic and process design approach for bio-based production processes, for example for bioethanol production, which is divided in diverse stages and includes several unit operations that need and release energy. Therefore, this work employs the exergy analysis as a performance criterion to select the best HEN obtained by a pinch analysis on a bioethanol production process, the selection also considers the lowest cost on services and equipment.

4. Bioethanol Production Process

The second-generation bioethanol production plant was simulated employing the Aspen Plus v. 8.8 process simulator and divided into six stages: pretreatment, overliming, saccharification, fermentation, separation and waste treatment. The data for the equipment and initial conditions of the streams was taken from (Sánchez et al., 2013). The process simulation was carried out taking wheat straw as raw material with a mass flowrate of 7,752.13 kg/h with composition in mole fraction of 0.47 of water, 0.34 of cellulose, 0.15 of xylan, 0.05 of lignin and traces of ash. In the saccharification section, the cellulose that cannot be dehydrated during the pretreatment section is converted into glucose, with the help of enzymes that favour its reaction. During fermentation the fermentable sugars present in the stream are converted into ethanol by *Zymomonas mobilis*. The separation stage employs a system of sequential distillation columns that allows obtaining high-purity ethanol that can be used as biofuel. Finally, in the waste treatment stage, the residual streams are conduced to biological treatment where three streams are obtained: residual solids, biogas and treated water. The Figure 1 shows a bioethanol process diagram, the streams labelled with points indicate the entering and exit streams using blue and red points, respectively. It is important pointing out these streams are used in the exergy analysis lately.

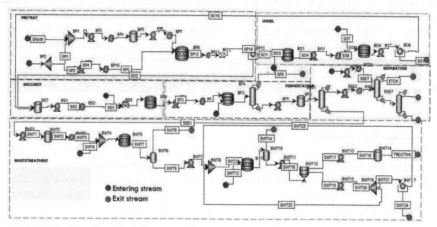

Figure 1. Bioethanol production process diagram

5. Results

The methodology proposed by García-García et al. (2018) was used in this study for calculating the irreversibility rate and rational efficiency, and the previous results were used as the base case scenario. The results of thermal exergy in streams are show in Table 1. The EI analysis was performed employing the computational tool HINT (Martin and Mato, 2008).

Six HEN configurations were designed and analysed (Table 2). The energy integration and exergy analysis considered the usage of direct flame, high, middle and low pressures steams as heating0 utilities, and cooling water and Freon as cooling utilities. In Table 2 could be observed that the equipment cost increased in all proposed configurations, due to the number of heat exchangers; in base case scenario the number of heat exchangers were 18 while in all the proposed configurations were 23. It can be also observed that the configurations allow a decrease in the utilities cost in all configurations with energy savings of 21.37 MW, that in fact it was equal in all configurations. Employing only this information obtained from EI analysis was difficult to select the best configurations, because the results are very similar. However, the use of exergy analysis results provided an important and additional information that allowed making a better selection of the best HEN option. Table 2 also shows that the rational efficiency was improved by the selection of any of the proposed HEN, but it was more effectively improved with the configurations A1 or A6 that represents the higher rational efficiency. Comparing the results of energy integration and exergy analyses was possible to select the configuration A6 as the best because improved in 12.10 % the rational efficiency and represents one of the minimum equipment cost in the configurations constructed (US$ 158,432.56).

The minimum energy requirements for configuration A6 are shown in form of a heat cascade (see Figure 2).

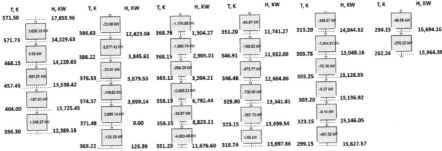

Figure 2. Cascade diagram to determine the energy requirements in scenario A6

Table 1. Exergy of streams that entering and leaving the production process

Category	Stream	e^{ph}, MW	e^{ch}, MW	$e^{ph} + e^{ch}$, MW
Inlets	GRAIN	0.000	23,293.067	23,293.067
	SP1	0.000	2,425.025	2,425.025
	SO3	0.000	136.798	136.798
	SO7	0.216	48.916	49.132
	SS4	0.000	183.514	183.514
	SF4	0.000	138.666	138.666
	SSE5	0.000	50,021.701	50,021.701
	SWT4	0.000	22.033	22.033
	SWT12	0.000	5.873	5.873
Outlets	SO11	0.218	324.830	325.066
	SF6	0.717	343.591	344.308
	SSE10	489.309	50,018.981	50,508.290
	SSE11	29.081	138.182	167.263
	ETOH	7.955	15,170.858	15,178.813
	SWT8	0.010	204.708	204.719
	SWT14	0.678	0.000	0.678
	TREATW	7.734	2,654.332	2,662.066
	SWT24	0.731	11,665.444	11,667.171

Table 2. Results of EI and Exergy analysis

Configuration	Equipment cost, US$	Utilities cost, US$/year	Rational efficiency, %	Irreversibility, MW	Energy Saving, MW
Base case	225,151.88	1,715,486.19	75.55	44.76	0
A1	457,430.13	964,871.13	87.88	15.91	21.37
A2	383,584.45	964,871.13	83.96	21.06	21.37
A3	385,959.90	964,870.46	83.76	21.33	21.37
A4	388,128.80	964,870.48	83.55	21.42	21.37
A5	387,922.24	964,871.13	83.88	21.15	21.37
A6	383,584.45	964,870.47	87.65	16.22	21.37

Conclusions

The results reveal that without EI and employing utilities to cover the total energy requirements the rational efficiency and total irreversibility of the process are 19.92% and 68,187.75 KW, respectively. Employing the energy integration and exergy analysis was found that the configuration A6 represent the better option to improve the process performance with a rational efficiency value of 87.65%, total irreversibility of 16.22 MW and savings energy of 21.37 MW. The implementation of both, EI and exergy analysis demonstrates to be a useful methodology to determine the best HEN configuration in accordance with the energy savings and thermodynamic feasibility.

Acknowledgments

The authors acknowledge the partial financial support by the Mexican Bioenergy Innovation Centre, Bioalcohols Cluster (249564) and the Universidad de Guanajuato for the development of this project.

References

C. García-García, D. Marmolejo-Correa, J. Cárdenas-Guerra, R. Morales-Rodríguez, 2018, Exergy Analysis o fan Extractive Distillation Column for Reducing Energy Consumption in a Bioethanol Production Process, Computer-Aided Chemical Engineering, 43, p. 513-518.

F. Goodarzvand-Chegini and E. GhasemiKafrudi, 2017, Application of exergy analysis to improve the heat integration efficiency in a hydrocracking process, Energy and Environment, pp. 1-16.

A. Janka, T. Nagy, A. Toth, E. Haaz, 2018, Thermodynamic and Exergy Analysis of Energy-Integrated Distillation Technologies Focusing on Dividing-Wall Columns with Upper and Lower Partitions, Industrial and Engineering Chemistry Research.

T.J. Kotas, 1995, The Exergy Method of Thermal Plant Analysis, Elsevier.

D. Marmolejo-Correa and T. Gundersen, 2015, A new efficiency parameter for exergy analysis in low temperature processes, International Journal of Exergy, 17, pp. 135-170.

A. Martín and F. A. Mato, Hint: An educational software for heat exchanger network design with the pinch method, Education for chemical engineers, Vol. 3, pp 6-14, 2008.

K. Ojeda, E. Sánchez and V. Kafarov, 2011, Sustainable ethanol production from lignocellulosic biomass - application of exergy analysis. Energy, 36, pp. 2119-2128

A. Sánchez, V. Sevilla-Güitrón, G. Magaña and L. Gutierrez, 2013, Parametric analysis of total cost and energy efficiency of 2G enzymatic ethanol production. Fuel, 113, pp. 165-179

P. Silva Ortiz and S. de Oliveira Jr., 2014, Exergy analysis of pretreatment processes of bioethanol production based on sugarcane bagasse, Energy, 76, pp. 130-138.

F. Staine and D. Favrat, 1996, Energy integration of industrial processes based on the PINCH analysis method extended to include exergy factors, Applied Thermal Engineering, Vol.16, No.6, pp 497-507.

United Nations General Assembly, 2015, Session 70th

W. Zeineb, K. Zouhour, L . Boulbaba, B. Rachid, H. Noureddine, 2018, Exergetic Analysis of Bioethanol Production from Tunisian Waste Dates, The Open Waste Management Journal, pp. 19-32.

Anton A. Kiss, Edwin Zondervan, Richard Lakerveld, Leyla Özkan (Eds.)
Proceedings of the 29th European Symposium on Computer Aided Process Engineering
June 16th to 19th, 2019, Eindhoven, The Netherlands. © 2019 Elsevier B.V. All rights reserved.
http://dx.doi.org/10.1016/B978-0-128-18634-3.50081-3

ProCAFD: Computer-aided Tool for Sustainable Process Synthesis, Intensification and Hybrid solutions

Anjan K.Tula[a], Mario R. Eden[a], Rafiqul Gani[b*]

[a] Department of Chemical Engineering, Auburn University, Auburn, AL 36849, USA
[b] PSE for SPEED, Skyttemosen 6, Allerød, DK-3450, Denmark

rgani2018@gmail.com

Abstract

Process industry is always in quest for innovative designs which are both efficient, safe and sustainable. The feasible search space of all unit operations that can be combined to generate process flowsheet alternatives for a given synthesis problem can be large and difficult to manually navigate in order to determine the best processing route. Therefore, it is helpful to utilize computer-aided methods and tools to enumerate, analyze and determine within the design space, the more sustainable processes. In this paper, an integrated computer-aided method and corresponding software-tool that's capable of generating and searching the entire design space for more sustainable process options is presented. In this work a comprehensive analysis method consisting of economic, life cycle, sustainability and process safety indicators is used to identify process bottlenecks on the selected alternative which are translated to design targets. Matching of these design targets minimizes/eliminates the process hot-spots and, thereby generating non-trade-off innovative process designs.

Keywords: Process synthesis, ProCAFD, Process Optimization, Process Safety.

1. Introduction

Due to increased emphasis by governments concerning environment, public health and safety through regulatory enforcements and growing competitiveness through globalization, the process industry is moving towards the design of innovative, more sustainable processes. Since synthesis problems are by nature combinatorial and open ended, several approaches have been proposed, these approaches can be broadly classified into three main classes of methods. (1) Rule based heuristic methods, which rely on rules based on a combination of experience, insights and engineering knowledge (data) to solve the synthesis problem; (2) Mathematical programming-based methods, where the best flowsheet alternative is determined from network superstructure optimization. This approach requires one to define and represent the network of alternatives in a mathematical form and solve the resulting mathematical problem using suitable solvers. (3) Hybrid methods that combines different approaches to solve the synthesis problem. Simultaneous based process synthesis approaches require the generation of a superstructure which contains a finite number of processing units with their corresponding interconnections. The resulting superstructure is solved by, using equations that describe the equipment, connectivity together with the process constraints and specifications. Even though it is advantageous to perform simultaneous optimization of the flowsheet structure and operating conditions there are few limitations. The major limitations of this approach are that the solution of the synthesis problem heavily depends on the superstructure of the alternatives considered. So, in order to find the optimal process topology, the original search space should constitute the optimal pathway. Also, since the process synthesis problem is by default nonlinear in nature, the solution to such optimization problem is difficult. Since applying only knowledge-based methods or optimization-based methods often over simplifies or complicates the process synthesis problem, a more logical way is to use hybrid methods where we can leverage the advantages of the two approaches while still keeping the complexity of the synthesis problem manageable. his work focuses on the development of hybrid method and computer aided software tool (ProCAFD) capable of enumerating all feasible alternatives within the entire search space and efficiently evaluate them. This work also focuses on introducing new analysis methods related to process safety along with economic, sustainability, and life cycle assessments during selection of process alternatives. This paper also shows successful application of ProCAFD on different case studies where different options are highlighted such as generation of integrated/hybrid/intensified configurations based on problem formulation.

2. ProCAFD architecture based on 3-stage Framework for Innovation

An overview of the 12-step method, which is an extension of the synthesis method proposed by Tula et al. (2015), is presented in Figure 1. The method is based on 3 stage approach for innovation proposed by Babi et al. (2015). Brief overview of the steps involved in the method are given below:

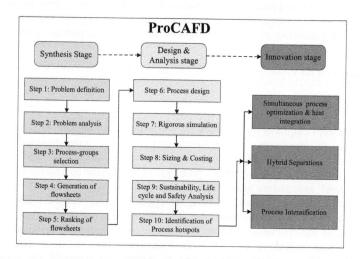

Figure 1: Sustainable process synthesis-design and analysis method (in ProCAFD)

<u>Problem Definition</u>: In this step the synthesis problem is defined along with process specifications, design constraints and performance criteria against which the generated alternatives are screened.

<u>Problem Analysis:</u> In this step, analysis is done to generate information through use of knowledge bases and physical insights methods to solve the synthesis. The outcome of this analysis includes, i) List of all chemical species in the synthesis problem, including

reaction intermediates and/or any mass transfer agents, ii) Reactions, if needed, to convert the given raw materials to desired products, iii) List of all the possible separation tasks along with feasible separation techniques.

Process-groups selection: The selection and initialization of the process groups is based on analysis carried in step 2. This is carried out in three tasks: i) selection and initialization of inlet and outlet process-groups, (based on step 1 information) ii) selection and initialization of reaction process-groups, and iii) selection and initialization of separation process-groups.

Generation of Flowsheets: In this step, the initialized process-groups are combined using connectivity and logical rules to generate structurally feasible process alternatives. These rules also safeguard against any combinatorial explosion that is generally associated with generate and test approaches.

Ranking of Flowsheets: In this step, different flowsheet property models are used to calculate flowsheet properties which are used to screen and rank the generated alternatives. The flowsheet property models are based on a group contribution *(GC)* approach, where the property of the entire flowsheet is estimated using contributions of individual process-groups present. Flowsheet models are available for carbon footprint, energy consumption, product recovery and, product purity

Process Design: Operational design parameters of the selected process alternative(s) are calculated in this step. This is achieved through the following two tasks: i) the resolution of the mass and energy balance, and ii) calculation of flowsheet design parameters of the process unit operations in the flowsheet structure through reverse simulation. The separation factors and temperature data required for performing mass and energy balance are obtained from the process-group definitions and driving force available. Design parameters for separation process-groups (such as distillation, extractive distillation, and flash), are estimated based on the driving force (DF), while attainable region theory is used to design reactor networks.

Rigorous Simulation: ProCAFD is integrated with commercial simulators like PROII, ASPEN where the design is automatically setup using rigorous models to verify performance of the selected alternatives.

Sizing & Costing: In this step, equipment sizing, and costing calculations are performed for all equipment in the process flowsheet. The sizing and costing values are estimated using ECON (Kalakul et al. 2014).

Analysis: The results of the rigorous simulation, sizing and costing (stream summary, equipment sizing, energy balance etc.) are used to perform economic, safety, sustainability and life cycle analyses.

- *Economic Analysis*: The mass and energy balance results from the rigorous simulation are used to calculate the capital and utility costs for each unit operation which are used to identify hotspots involving high operational and capital costs.
- *Sustainability Analysis*: This analysis is based on an indicator-based methodology (Carvalho et al., 2013), which identifies critical flow paths within the process. Here analysis is done on both open (where a chemical species enters and leaves the process) and closed paths (like recycle loops where mass and energy are recycled without going out of the process). The main indicators, which are estimated, include material value added (MVA), energy and waste cost (EWC), total value added (TVA).
- *Life Cycle Analysis*: This analysis is used for environmental assessment of the selected process alternative. This is carried out through LCSoft (Kalakul et al. 2014) that helps to quantify potential environmental impacts of chemical process. The main factors which are estimated in this analysis are Carbon Footprint (CF),

Human Toxicity Potential by Ingestion (HTPI), Human Toxicity Potential by Exposure (HTPE) and Global Warming Potential (GWP).

- *Process Safety Analysis*: This analysis is based on Dow's (1987) scoring system to estimate the inherent safety of the process alternative. This method considers different aspects like process conditions, chemicals involved, and equipment types etc. to identify different hazards in the plant. The total inherent safety index is a combined score of chemical inherent safety and process inherent safety. While the chemical inherent safety index considers reactions hazards and chemical hazards; process inherent safety index takes process and equipment conditions

Identification of Hotspots: The indicators from the analysis step are used to identify the process hotspots (Babi et al., 2015), which are in turn used to set design targets for overall process improvement

Innovative Designs: In this step, different strategies/methods are applied individually to the selected alternative to target the hot-spots for overall process improvement.

- *Simultaneous Process Optimization and Heat Integration:* Simultaneous process optimization and heat integration approach is applied to the analyzed base case design, to target process hot-spots involving high operational costs. In this approach, rigorous models from the process simulator are used to calculate the process inputs, which are sent to an integrated heat integration module to estimate the minimum utility requirements. Both module results are used in the optimizer to minimize the total utility of the process. In this method, the heat integration module is based on the condensed LP transshipment model for calculating the minimum utility consumption.

- *Hybrid Separations:* A generalized method based on Tula et al. (2016) for synthesis-design of hybrid distillation-membrane systems is applied to replace the distillation columns in the base case design with a hybrid system to reduce the operational cost substantially. Tula et al. (2016) showed that 30-50 % of energy savings can be achieved for any distillation column by replacing the less efficient region of the distillation operation with membrane based separation technique.

- *Process Intensification:* Phenomena based intensification method proposed by Babi et al. (2015) is applied in this step. This approach breaks tasks into phenomena within the unit operations involved. These phenomena are analyzed and re-combined using combination rules to generate new and/or existing unit operations that constitute the (more sustainable) flowsheet alternatives which satisfy the set design targets.

Case Study

2.1. Synthesis stage:

The synthesis problem definition is to develop an energy efficient process to produce cumene from propylene and benzene. This reaction is exothermic and typical operating conditions are 600 K at atmospheric pressure. In this problem definition, the propylene stream has propane as impurity. As a process specification, the minimum purity of cumene should be 99.5 wt%. A total of 10 binary pairs are formed from 5 compounds present in the synthesis problem. For this synthesis problem, a total 155 process-groups are selected and initialized, which include 148 separation tasks process groups, 6 inlet/outlet process groups and 1 reaction process group. A total of 240 process alternatives are identified, and the best alternative with respect to energy consumption is shown in Figure 2. The objective from the problem definition step is to find an energy efficient process so, energy consumption property model is used in this case study. Different flowsheet models can be used to screen the alternatives based on the problem definition.

2.2. Design & Analysis stage:

In this stage the selected process alternative (Figure 2) is designed and simulated using rigorous models. Based on the simulation results economic, safety, sustainability and life cycle analyses are performed on the base case. From economic analysis the heat exchangers on the recycles streams (HE3, HE5) along with HE4 share 57% of total equipment cost and 42% of the total utility cost. These results are also complemented by sustainability analysis, which showed a high energy and waste cost (EWC) associated with closed path 3 and loss of material (MVA) for propylene in open path 5. Life cycle analysis showed high carbon footprint associated with heat exchangers HE3 & HE5. LCA analysis also flagged environmental impact from the purge stream AB-P. Safety analysis on the process alternative gave a combined score (total inherent safety index) of 18. The identified hotspots are translated into design targets: Increase plant profit, reduce energy consumption, and improve LCA/sustainability indicators while maintaining the product purity and production rates (kept as the base case values).

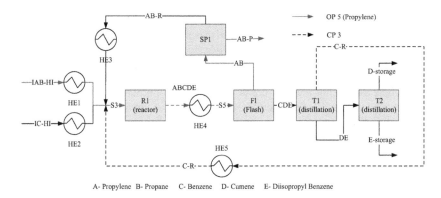

A- Propylene   B- Propane   C- Benzene   D- Cumene   E- Diisopropyl Benzene

Figure 2 : Selected base case design for further analysis. The open and closed paths (OP, CP).

2.3. Innovation stage:

In this case study, simultaneous optimization and heat integration strategy is used to satisfy the design targets set in stage 2. The process is optimized to maximize the operational profit (Fobj= Revenue – Cost) and the heat integration targeting heat exchangers (HE3, HE4, and HE5). The operational profit has increased by 28% in the optimized case mainly due to reduction of heating and cooling utilities. Since the purge stream ratio is optimized to maximize the profit, waste generation is also reduced which also reduced the environmental impact.

Table 1 shows the application of ProCAFD on various industrially important processes. In all the cases, ProCAFD was able to generate numerous alternatives quickly that are truly innovative and that have not been reported in the literature. This is because the work-flow and data-flow of ProCAFD is organized in such way that all the steps can be performed very fast, consistently and reliably to solve the complete synthesis-design and innovation problem. More details on the solutions can be obtained from the authors.

Table 1 : Solved case examples using ProCAFD. Where improvement is wrt utilities consumption

Case Study	Alternatives Generated	Innovation Strategy	Improvement
Production of Benzene	64	Simultaneous Opt, & Heat Integration	67.0%
Separation of Alkanes	184	Hybrid Separations	60.5%
Production of Cumene	240	Simultaneous Opt, & Heat Integration	27.6%
Production of Biodiesel	502	Process Intensification	24.3%
Production of DMC	53	Process Intensification	86.7%

3. Conclusions

In this work, the main achievement is the development of a computer-aided method and its software to systematically solve complex process synthesis and design problems, which facilitates more efficient and innovative solutions. This work also focuses on extension of previous method to include comprehensive analysis involving sustainability, life cycle, safety and economic in early states of process synthesis. The developed method and software differ significantly from conventional synthesis-design methods/tools as it is not iterative nor is it based solely on mathematical optimization techniques to synthesize an optimal solution. It is a hybrid method based on decomposition-based approach where in the complexity of the synthesis problem is decomposed into a set of sub-problems and solved sequentially.

References

D. K. Babi, J. Holtbruegge, P. Lutze, A. Gorak, J.M. Woodley, R. Gani, 2015, Sustainable Process Synthesis-Intensification, Computers & Chemical Engineering, 81, 218-44.

A. Carvalho, H.A. Matos, R. Gani, 2013, SustainPro - A tool for systematic process analysis, generation and evaluation of sustainable design alternatives, Computers & Chemical Engineering, 50, 8-27.

Dow Chemical Company. 1987. DOW's Fire & Explosion Index Hazard Classification Guide. 6th ed. New York: American Institute of Chemical Engineers

S. Kalakul, P. Malakul, K. Siemanond, R. Gani, 2014, Integration of Life Cycle Assessment Software with Tools for Economic and Sustainability Analyses and Process Simulation for Sustainable Process Design, Journal of Cleaner Production, 71, 98-109.

A. K. Tula, B. Befort, N. Garg, K. V. Camarda, R. Gani, 2017. Sustainable Process Design & Analysis of Hybrid Separations, Computers & Chemical Engineering, 105, 96-104.

A. K. Tula, M. R. Eden, R. Gani, 2015, Process synthesis, design and analysis using a process-group contribution method, Computers & Chemical Engineering, 81, 245-259.

Anton A. Kiss, Edwin Zondervan, Richard Lakerveld, Leyla Özkan (Eds.)
Proceedings of the 29th European Symposium on Computer Aided Process Engineering
June 16th to 19th, 2019, Eindhoven, The Netherlands. © 2019 Elsevier B.V. All rights reserved.
http://dx.doi.org/10.1016/B978-0-128-18634-3.50082-5

A multi-objective multi-period optimization of carbon integration networks in industrial parks

Dhabia M. Al-Mohannadi[a,*], Patrick Linke[a,] Nialy Shah[b]

[a]*Department of Chemical Engineering, Texas A&M University at Qatar, Education City, PO Box 23874, Doha, Qatar*
[b]*Department of Chemical Engineering, Imperial College of London, London, United Kingdom*
dhabia.al-mohannadi@qatar.tamu.edu

Abstract

The direct link between climate change and anthropogenic industrial activity resulted in a need more prominent than ever to cut emissions. At the Paris climate conference (COP21), 195 countries adopted a legally binding global climate deal to put the world on track to avoid dangerous climate change effects. This sets a challenge for many countries to draft sustainable climate policies by 2030. Climate change has social, environmental and economic consequences. Therefore, it is important to understand the impact of these interconnected factors on climate strategies. Multi-period carbon integration allows carbon reduction over a certain time horizon. The multi-period planning approach identified allocation of carbon dioxide between sources and potential sinks in each period, compared cost elements simultaneously and resulted in a low cost network across all periods. In this work the approach was expanded to evaluate two conflicting objectives. An example was solved to assess climate policies under two objectives. Good carbon reductions were achieved.

Keywords: Optimization, carbon dioxide reduction, renewable energy, sustainability, climate policy

1. Introduction

Policy-making entities have proposed ambitious carbon dioxide emission reduction targets as a means of mitigating global warming effects. Many policies are drafted yearly, in an attempt to successfully reduce carbon dioxide emissions. Most of the policies are outlined for regulatory reasons, by prescribing a required target, over a specified time horizon. Different carbon dioxide emission reduction strategies that are often dictated by over time GHG emission targets, (Huisingh et al. 2015). While other policies define individual emission reduction targets across different industrial sectors, especially ones associated with carbon dioxide point sources that result in considerable emissions (Pinho and Madaleno, 2011). A number of conventional methods may be applied to reduce carbon dioxide emissions such as energy efficiency, carbon capture utilization and storage (CCUS) and the use of renewable energy. Energy management techniques have been implemented by works like Klemeš and Kravanja (2013) and Varbanov et al. (2004) among others. In CCUS, which minimizes emissions by allocating the CO_2 source to sinks for storage, sequestration and utilization. Works such as Boot-Handford et al. (2014) offer a review of possible CO_2 storage sinks, while work such as Al-Mohannadi and Linke (2016), optimized CO_2 networks converting CO_2 to value added products in sinks among others that can be found at Foo and Tan (2016). Moreover, emissions are reduced further by the use of renewable energy. Carbon dioxide emission reduction policies may prescribe appropriate target emission goals or specific technologies to achieve their reduction goal such as the European Commission Climate Action Plan of 20-20-20, which specifies carbon reduction by 20% by the year 2020 using 20% renewable technology for energy production and 20% increase in energy efficiency.

Carbon dioxide emission targets are often proposed for a point in time in the future. Multi-period carbon integration methods allow carbon reduction schemes to be identified over certain a time horizon. The same target may be achieved in various ways, depending on how the carbon reduction policy is being implemented over time. Therefore, this work studies the effects that result from incorporating different objectives over a given time horizon onto carbon integration networks, using a multi-period approach (Al-Mohannadi et al, 2016). Economic or environmental objectives often have a trade-off that works such as Jing et al (2018) used in energy planning. This work expands the representation by Al-Mohannadi et al, (2016) to evaluates the impact of different time dependent policies onto CCUS–RE decisions, using a multi-period carbon integration approach and understanding the trade-offs between economic and the reduction targets through assessments of multiobjectives. The next sections include a brief description of the problem statement, and is followed by an illustrative example.

2. Description and problem statement

The overall goal is the identification of climate strategies under two conflicting constraitnts which are to achieve the maximum economic and maximum environmental preforamnce in terms of carbon reduction. The challenge is to identify the most promising network allocations from the possible reduction alternatives found for each objective.

The problem addressed requires setting a number of periods, knowing for each period the number of plants and their locations. Based on the existing plants, the total CO_2 emission from the cluster is known with defined CO_2 emission sources in terms of flowrates, compositions, condition (temperature and pressure). A given total power requirement of the cluster, a common utility system with known power demand and supply. In addition, to reduce emissions further renewable power generations options are available with known limits and prices. The model was solved for each objective using "What's Best 9.0" Lindo Global solver for MS-Excel 2010 via a desktop PC with Intel Core i7 Duo processor, 8 GB RAM and a 32-bit operating System (Lindo, 2006). Next, a Pareto curve is constructed to evaluate the performance of each objective. The next section illustrates the concept.

3. Case Study

The proposed concept is illustrated in the following case study, which is an industrial cluster that includes a set given plants. The plants are Oil refinery, Steel production, a fertilizer production facility producing both ammonia and urea in addition to a Natural Gas Fired Power Plant which main information is shown in Table 1. In the industrial clusters, plants and processes were included to reduce carbon dioxide footprint such as a Renewable solar power plant, Enhanced Oil Recovery (EOR), Saline Storage, and a Methanol plant, which is also shown in Table 1.

Table 1: Carbon Integration Data obtained from Al-Mohannadi et al, (2016)

Plants		CO₂ Composition. (wt%)	CO₂ Flow (t/d)	Sink fixation (t CO₂ emitted/ t CO₂ captured)	CO₂ Cost (USD/ t CO₂)
Sinks	Enhanced Oil Recovery (EOR)	0.94	6317	0	-30
	Methanol (MEOH)	0.99	1710	0.098	-21
	Fertilizer Complex - Urea	0.99	1126	0.39	-15
	Saline Storage	0.94	8317	0	8.6
Sources	Fertilizer Complex -CO₂ amine unit	1	977	0	0
	Steel-iron mill	0.44	3451	0	29
	Power Plant-gas turbine	0.07	9385	0	43
	Oil Refinery-boiler	0.27	1092	0	35

Carbon dioxide treatment efficiency parameters, treatment removal, power needed for the compression and transmission were taken from Al-Mohannadi and Linke, (2016). Transmission data including sizes and costs of pipeline and compression were obtained using the method proposed by Kwak, (2016). For a given time frame of five periods over 10 years, the network was first optimized to achieve the maximum economic benefit. The allocation of the network is shown in Table 2.

Table 2: Maximum Economic Benefit Carbon Dioxide Allocation (Period – P, T – Treated Source, U- Untreated Source)

Source	Period	Flow type	EOR	MEOH	UREA	Storage
Fertilizer Complex	P1	T1	-	-	-	-
		U1	977	-	-	-
	P2	T2	-	-	-	-
		U2	977	-	-	-
	P3	T3	-	-	-	-
		U3	977	-	-	-
	P4	T4	-	-	-	-
		U4	977	-	-	-
	P5	T5	-	-	-	-
		U5	977	-	-	-
Iron and Steel Production	P1	T1	2,309	825	-	-
		U1	317	-	-	-
	P2	T2	2,309	825	-	-
		U2	317	-	-	-
	P3	T3	2,309	825	-	-
		U3	317	-	-	-
	P4	T4	2,309	825	-	-
		U4	317	-	-	-
	P5	T5	2,309	825	-	-
		U5	317	-	-	-
Oil Refinery	P1	T1	207	885	-	-
		U1	-	-	-	-

Source	Period	Flow type	EOR	MEOH	UREA	Storage
	P2	T2	207	885	-	-
		U2	-	-	-	-
	P3	T3	207	885	-	-
		U3	-	-	-	-
	P4	T4	207	885	-	-
		U4	-	-	-	-
	P5	T5	207	885	-	-
		U5	-	-	-	-
	P1	T1	2,507	-	-	-
		U1	-	-	-	-
	P2	T2	2,507	-	-	-
		U2	-	-	-	-
Power Plant	P3	T3	2,507	-	-	-
		U3	-	-	-	-
	P4	T4	2,507	-	-	-
		U4	-	-	-	-
	P5	T5	2,507	-	-	-
		U5	-	-	-	-

The network resulted in a total profit of 395 million USD. The most profitable sinks, EOR and methanol, were supplied from the sources that has the lowest treatment needed. Next, the network was optimized to achieve the maximum environmental benefit. The network allocation flows are provided in Table 3.

Table 3: Maximum Environmental Benefit Carbon Dioxide Allocation (Period – P, T – Treated Source, U- Untreated Source)

Source	Period	Flow type	EOR	MEOH	UREA	Storage
	P1	T1	-	-	-	-
		U1	-	-	-	977
	P2	T2	-	-	-	-
		U2	-	-	-	977
Fertilizer Complex	P3	T3	-	-	-	-
		U3	-	-	-	977
	P4	T4	-	-	-	-
		U4	-	-	-	977
	P5	T5	-	-	-	-
		U5	-	-	-	977
	P1	T1	2,795	-	-	656
		U1	-	-	-	-
	P2	T2	2,795	-	-	656
		U2	-	-	-	-
Iron and Steel Production	P3	T3	2,795	-	-	656
		U3	-	-	-	-
	P4	T4	2,795	-	-	656
		U4	-	-	-	-
	P5	T5	2,795	-	-	656
		U5	0	-	-	-
Oil Refinery	P1	T1	207	-	-	885

A multi-objective multi-period optimization approach of carbon
integration networks in industrial parks
    491

Source	Period	Flow type	EOR	MEOH	UREA	Storage
		U1	-	-	-	-
	P2	T2	207	-	-	885
		U2	-	-	-	-
	P3	T3	207	-	-	885
		U3	-	-	-	-
	P4	T4	207	-	-	885
		U4	-	-	-	-
	P5	T5	207	-	-	885
		U5	-	-	-	-
	P1	T1	3,314	-	-	4,194
		U1	-	-	-	-
	P2	T2	3,314	-	-	4,194
		U2	-	-	-	-
	P3	T3	3,314	-	-	4,194
Power Plant		U3	-	-	-	-
	P4	T4	3,314	-	-	4,194
		U4	-	-	-	-
	P5	T5	3,314	-	-	4,194
		U5	-	-	-	-

When the maximum capture target was imposed without any economic constraint, the network resulted in a cost of -600 million USD and 68 thousand CO_2 captured across all periods. The same structure, sources to sinks, connections were chosen. As EOR and Storage had the largest capacities to reduce CO_2 and the highest efficiency of fixating CO_2. The network also activated the maximum allowed renewable power.

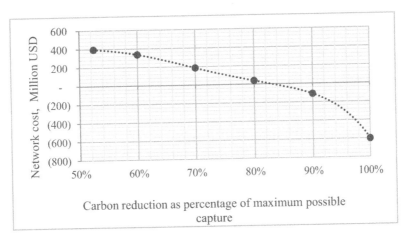

Figure 1: Pareto Optimal Solution of the bi-objective problem

From Figure 1, it can be seen that none of the points within Pareto front were identical, in terms of both of the specified objectives. However, the optimum points for the cost objective, still reduced a good amount of CO_2.

4. Conclusions

The approach takes into account multiple time periods, multiple processes including renewable power generation, CCUS, treatment, compression and transmission options needed to develop carbon dioxide allocation networks. The network optimization problem has been formulated as a MILP and can robustly and quickly be solved for industrial clusters of typical size. Different scenarios for an industrial park were explored using the proposed approach and compared using Pareto curve. The approach gives the regulator or policy makers a tool to develop future mitigation strategies and compare plans.

Acknowledgement

Dhabia M. Al-Mohanandi gratefully acknowledges the support received from the Qatar Research Leadership Program (QRLP), which is part of Qatar Foundation Research Division.

References

C. Pinho, M. Madaleno, 2001, CO₂ emission allowances and other fuel markets interaction. Environmental Economics and Policy Studies. Environmental Economics and Policy Studies. 13, 3, 259–281

D. Foo, R. Tan, 2016, A review on process integration techniques for carbon emissions and environmental footprint problems, Process Safety and Environmental Production, 103B, 291-307

D. Huisingh,Z. Zhang,J. Moore,Q. Qiao, Qi, Q. Li,2015, Recent Advances in Carbon Emissions Reduction: Policies, Technologies, Monitoring, Assessment and Modeling. Journal of Cleaner Production. 103,1-12

D.M. Al-Mohannadi, P. Linke, 2016, On the Systematic Carbon Integration of Industrial Parks for Climate Footprint Reduction Journal of Cleaner Production, 112, 4053-4064

D.M. Al-Mohannadi, S. Y. Alnouri, S.K. Binshu, P Linke, 2016, Multiperiod Carbon Integration. 136, 150-158

G. Kwak, 2016, A Systematic approach to optimize the cost of carbon integration network. Masters Thesis, Texas A&M University at Qatar, Doha, Qatar

J.J. Klemeš, Z. Kravanja, 2013, Forty years of Heat Integration: Pinch Analysis (PA) and Mathematical Programming (MP). Curr. Opin. Chem. Eng., 2, 461-474

Lindo, 2006, What'sBest! 9.0 - Excel Add-In for Linear, Nonlinear, and Integer Modeling and Optimization; Lindo Systems: Chicago, IL

M.E. Boot-Handford, J.C. Abanades, E.J. Anthony, M.J. Blunt, S. Brandani, N. Dowell, J. R. Fernández, M. Ferrari, R. Gross, J. P. Hallett, R. Haszeldine, P. Heptonstall, A. Lyngfelt, Z. Makuch f, Enzo Mangano, Richard T. J. Porter j, Mohamed Pourkashanian k, Gary T. Rochelle, N. Shah, J. Yao, P. Fennell, 2014, Carbon capture and storage update. Energy & Environmental Science, 7, 1, 130-189

P.S. Varbanov, S. Doyle, R. Smith, 2004. Modelling and Optimization of Utility Systems. Chemical Engineering Research and Design, 82, 5, 561-578

R. Jing, X. Zhu, Z. Zhu, W. Wang, C. Meng, N. Shah, N. Li, Y. Zhao, 2018, A multi-objective optimization and multi-criteria evaluation integrated framework for distributed energy system optimal planning, Energy Conversion and Management,166, 445-462

Anton A. Kiss, Edwin Zondervan, Richard Lakerveld, Leyla Özkan (Eds.)
Proceedings of the 29th European Symposium on Computer Aided Process Engineering
June 16th to 19th, 2019, Eindhoven, The Netherlands. © 2019 Elsevier B.V. All rights reserved.
http://dx.doi.org/10.1016/B978-0-128-18634-3.50083-7

Improved problem constraints modeling based using classification

Elisabet Capón-García[a*], Edrisi Munoz[b], Luis Puigjaner[c]

[a] *ABB Switzerland Ltd., Segelhofstrasse 1K, 5405 Baden-Dättwil, Switzerland*

[b] *Centro de Investigacion en Matemáticas A.C., Jalisco S/N, Mineral y Valenciana 36240, Guanajuato, Mexico*

[c] *Chemical Engineering Department, EEBE, Universitat Politècnica de Catalunya, Av. Eduard Maristany, 10-14, 08019 Barcelona, Spain*

elisabet.capon@ch.abb.com

Abstract

A general classification agent has been developed based on a semantic model for supporting the modelling of problems in the chemical modelling domain. Two case studies are used to illustrate the proposed approach, which stands for a routine that solves the modelling task easily and quicker and less error-prone approach in comparison to the traditional problem.

Keywords: first-principles, mathematical modelling, chemical processes, semantic modelling.

1. Introduction

Currently, chemical and other process industries, such as food, agriculture or pharmaceutical, evolve in a highly dynamic and changing environment. Indeed, the globalization of trade, product customization and stricter environmental and societal requirements, among others, seriously challenge the performance and operation of the process industry. Indeed, time response and solution quality for critical problems are critical issues that motivate the development of new solutions.

In such scenario, enterprises strive to remain competitive by improving their functional, technological and operational advantage. Although chemical processes are intrinsically complex, the underlying chemical and physical phenomenal can be explained by a self-contained set of mathematical expressions and models, which derive from physical laws and experimental. In this sense, the quick and flexible development of models that fundamentally support: (i) the understanding of the underlying phenomena and (ii) the implementation of advanced decision support systems, is a crucial issue in the process industry.

Mathematical models use equations and concepts in order to describe a systems and particular situations with the aim of explain, predict and simulate them. The advances in computers systems in recent years have allowed an exponential growth in scientific computation, enhancing the capacity for solving mathematical models with algorithms, easier to treat and solve. In this sense problem modelling has become a key activity where process activities exists as base for make more efficient the mathematical optimization task.

This objective of this work is to support the automatic generation of constraints design by using semantic modelling and mathematical programming, based on problem classification. An intelligent agent proposes a set of model equations which help to understand how those set of constraints can be built up. Besides, the proposed system makes use of semantic technologies enhancing the comprehension among decision variables and parameters. Thus, model constraints using semantic networks link relationship among different components of the system, concepts, physical laws and principles of the phenomenon based on standard conceptualizations.

2. Problem statement

The starting point when posing a model for solving a problem in the chemical process domain mainly consists of defining the problem features, namely the elements which represent the system and describe its behavior, as well as the system parameters and variables.

Hence, a multi-label classification problem can be associated with process modeling. Therefore, given (i) a set of process features (attributes) and (ii) a set of existing mathematical equations related to such problem features (labels); the objective is to match a given instance with a subset of the features in (i) with its corresponding equations in (ii). A goodness function for each label will be used to check the ability of the classification approach to select the appropriate labels (ii).

3. Methodology

On the one hand, an ontology has been created comprising the chemical engineering domain described in Section 3.2. Therefore, Section 3.1 presents the basis for the ontology development. Ultimately, this work develops a software platform in Jython, which is integrated with the semantic model derived as presented in Section 3.1 using OWLAPI, and stands as an improved modeling tool in the chemical process domain.

Different areas in the chemical engineering domain, including basic unit operation principles, transport phenomena, reaction kinetics and thermodynamics, have been revised in order to collect and examine the most relevant formulae (Cameron and Hangos, 2001). In this sense, it is essential to work out the expressions in a very precise and thorough way, since every imaginable system and process configuration has to be considered to account for all possible cases. As a result, a complete table of equations with their attributes has been built up. In summary, 102 distinct equations have been classified to enable a complete and most realistic description of a given system or chemical process. In order to select the appropriate equations, 39 system attributes have been specified. The full description of the knowledge base is provided in Section 3.2.

3.1. Semantic modelling

Ontologies stand for a formal specification of the domain, that is, a body of formally represented knowledge based on conceptualizations, which are abstract, simplified views of the physical or procedural elements. On the one hand, the ontology elements should be part of the model intended to represent a system for some purpose, managing the relationships that hold among the elements of the model, thus allowing the ontology to be usable. On the other hand, reusing ontologies requires not only consideration of the ontologies, but also of the tasks for which they are intended. The base of this work lies down in the use of an ontology that deals with diversity in scheduling problem representation and allows effective data sharing and information flow. Ontologies are hierarchical domain structures that provide a domain theory, have a syntactically and semantically rich language, and a shared and consensual terminology (Klein et al. 2002). The body of knowledge for this ontology stems from the chemical engineering modelling domain, and a PDCA methodology (Munoz et al., 2012) has been used to create the ontology. The final ontology, called Chemical Engineering Ontology (ChEnOn), contains 154 classes, 33 object properties and 21 data properties.

3.2. Modelling domain and classification approach

The chemical engineering domain can be broadly classified in different knowledge areas. In this work, we have considered mass, energy and momentum balances, as well as mass and heat transfer equations, and thermodynamics and reaction kinetics. Besides, classification approaches are described for each knowledge area, presented next.

3.2.1. Mass balances

First of all, the conservation principle of mass was considered. In general, there are three distinct systems that have to be considered: the isolated system, the closed system and the open system in relation to the surrounding environment. All three systems have to be taken into account to fully study the conservation principles of mass, energy and momentum in every real case example. For mass, there is no difference between the isolated and closed system, since mass can only be exchanged in an open system. The first mass balances for a closed system were stated and the descriptor "State" was introduced to differentiate between a steady state system and a transient state system. These two characteristic, yet clearly opposite attributes of a system were the first guiding principle on how to distinguish and classify equations. In total there are three different situations possible in a closed system. The first two systems time-independent described with the attribute steady state, while the third system's components change their mass due to the reaction, which results in a transient state system. To differentiate between the first two systems, a new descriptor and its corresponding attributes were introduced, being "Components" and "Single Component" and "Multiple Components", respectively. Also the descriptor "Reaction" with an attribute "Generation" was proposed. All these parameters and equations are part of the ontological model, where each equation was inserted as a class with a descriptive name and a unique ID code, while the descriptors and its attributes were put into object properties of the ontology. If now a system possesses or an equation fulfils a certain attribute, the corresponding cell between them was marked with a 1 or else with 0. In this way 16 different mass balance equations could be identified and expressed with the help of additional system descriptors like "Mass Flow" (Attributes: Feed, Mass Outflow), "Evolution" (Accumulation/Depletion) and "I/O Structure" (Single Stream, Multiple Streams).

3.2.2. Energy balance

Next, the conservation law of energy and its energy balances for the three aforementioned systems: isolated, closed and open was considered. The approach was similar to the determination of the mass balances and 21 different energy balances could be formulated, covering all imaginable system configurations. To be able to differentiate between these energy balances, additional categories to the old ones of system descriptors and their attributes had to be proposed, namely "Heat", with the attributes consisting of "Heat Inflow", "Heat Outflow", "Conduction", "Convection" and "Radiation", as well as "Work" with "Work Input" and "Work Output" as the corresponding attributes.

For the derivation of the energy balances, it was assumed that the kinetic and potential energy of the system are negligible.

3.2.3. Momentum balance

To conclude with the conservation principles, the conservation law of momentum was examined and similar to the energy balances, 21 momentum balances could be postulated. Since most of the momentum balances are simply correlated to the mass balances, only one additional attribute "Force" had to be added in order to account for the sum of gravitational, friction, pressure and shearing forces, which might act on the system. As a result of the conservation principles in chemical systems and processes, 58 different equations could be found to describe a potential real life system.

3.2.4. Mass transfer

For this purpose, the descriptor "Diffusion" and five more attributes being "Dilute Solution", "Concentrated Solution", "Membrane", "Diffusion", and "Convection" have been created. With these, nine more equations concerning diffusion in different systems could be classified and added to the list of classes of the ontology.

3.2.5. Heat transfer

Another examined aspect of transport phenomena includes the heat transfer to or from a given system. Heat transfer is a very common issue in chemical engineering. Again the focus was put on the most practical and applicable heat transfer equations and eight common heat transfer equations could be ascertained. For these equations, no further descriptors and attributes had to be assigned, since heat transfer had already been accounted for by the derivation of the energy balances. The transport phenomena encompasses a total of 17 equations.

3.2.6. Reaction kinetics

Alongside the classical and convenient reactor kinetics of batch, semibatch, CSTR and PFR, a numerous of typical reactions were investigated and postulated. A total of 19 reaction kinetic equations were amassed with 10 more attributes required to differentiate and classify them all.

3.2.7. Thermodynamics

Last but not least, thermodynamics and its equations of state were put into consideration and eight of the vast number of equations has been chosen according to their applicability and frequency of usage. The five specified attributes regarding the thermodynamic equations were "Ideal", "Non-Ideal", "Empirical", "Gas" and "Liquid". The last two attributes correspond to the phase of the considered fluid.

4. Case study

The applicability of the proposed equations has been tested in two different systems, namely a tank system and an equilibrium stage. The case studies allow to understand the usability of the proposed framework. This validation allows for the direct evaluation of the work and gives insights in the usefulness of having such a tool.

4.1. Tank system

The first example deals with a standard tank system, where both input and output streams are constant and all initial conditions like volume, temperature and concentration of the solution inside the tank are known. The feed stream has constant composition, concentration and temperature and identical properties of both solutions to water as well as perfect mixing are assumed. The goal is to determine the time evolution of the tank level, its concentration and its temperature.

As a first step, the system attributes were determined from the problem description: Open system, transient state, accumulation (since inflow was greater than outflow), single input/output stream, single component, no generation (reaction), no heat or work flows. The time evolution of the tank level is directly correlated to the mass inside the tank, hence a mass balance was required that is described by all the above-mentioned attributes. The overall set of equations proposed by the developed agent consist of M4, M16 and E12 (Figure 1). From the proposed set of equations to the problem solution, a few set of adjustments are required. M4 had to be slightly modified, since volume and not mass was targeted, and integrated to give an exact answer in the form of an analytical expression. M6, which relates mass and concentration, could be used to find an analytical expression for the time evolution of the concentration. In order to determine the temperature evolution of the system, E12 underwent some changes, namely the conversion of the equation from energy to temperature, and the equation could eventually be integrated and the temperature profile of the system with respect to the time was obtained. This methodical way of solving the problem by determining system attributes and supporting agent proved to be very successful and timesaving.

Problem Description	System Attributes	Set of Equations		Problem Solution
Tank (Area: A = 2 m², Height: H) filled with 0.8 m³ (V) of 0.15 wt% (c_0) NaCl solution at 35°C (T_0). At constant feed (Q_1) of 0.20 wt% (c_0) NaCl solution at 25°C (T_1) and outflow (Q_2), determine time evolution of tank level, concentration and temperature.	Open System, Transient State, Accumulation, Single I/O-Stream, Single Component, No Generation (Reaction), No Heat or Work Flows, Perfect Mixing, Ideal Solution (density ρ, heat capacity c_p)	$\frac{dm}{dt} = F - Out$ $\frac{dm_i}{dt} = \frac{d(Vc_i)}{dt}M_i$ $\frac{dE}{dt} = F\,h_F - Out\,h_{Out}$	[M4] [M16] [E12]	Tank level: $\frac{dm}{dt} = \rho A\frac{dH}{dt} = Q_1 - Q_2$ $H(t) = H_0 + \frac{(Q_1 - Q_2)}{\rho A}\cdot t$ Concentration: $\rho\frac{dm}{dt} = c\frac{dV}{dt} + V\frac{dc}{dt} = \rho Q_1 c_1 - \rho Q_2 c$ $\frac{dc}{dt} = \frac{Q_1\cdot(c_1 - c)}{\rho V}$ $c(t) = (c_0 - c_1)\cdot e^{-\frac{Q_1}{V}t} + c_1$ Temperature: $\frac{dE}{dt} = mc_p\frac{dT}{dt} = Q_1 c_p T_1 - Q_2 c_p T$ $\frac{dT}{dt} = \frac{(Q_1 - Q_2)\cdot(T_1 - T)}{m}$ $T(t) = (T_0 - T_1)\cdot e^{-\frac{(Q_1 - Q_2)}{m}t} + T_1$

Figure 1. Problem description and solution for a single tank system.

4.2. Equilibrium stage

The following example covers the traditional equilibrium stage of a distillation column. In a distillation column, two streams with different compositions enter an arbitrary stage in counter-current mode, where some components inside the stage change from the liquid phase to the vapour phase or vice versa and the compositions of the two streams leaving the stage are assumed to be in thermodynamic equilibrium. The task is to determine all possible equations to fully describe and solve the system.

The task requires to find the appropriate mass and energy balances, as well as the thermodynamic equilibrium expression. For this purpose, the following system attributes were identified: Open system, steady state, neither accumulation nor depletion, no generation (reaction), multiple input/output streams, multiple components, no heat or work flows (adiabatic), gas-liquid equilibrium, ideal system (assumption). The developed agent proposed equations M9, E15 and T7 (Figure 2), which had to be adequately adapted. With these three equations, the overall mass balance of the stage, the mass balances of each component, the energy balance of the stage and the equilibrium condition for each component between liquid and gas phase could be obtained. From there, the system was explicitly solvable, which underlined the usefulness of working with system attributes and having the effective classification matrix.

Problem Description	System Attributes	Set of Equations	Problem Solution
Modelling of a Single Stage in a Distillation Column.	Open System, Steady State, No Depletion or Accumulation, No Generation (Reaction), Multiple I/O-Streams, Multiple Components, No Heat or Work Flows, Gas-Liquid Equilibrium, Ideal	$0 = \sum_{s=1}^{S} F_i - \sum_{s=1}^{S} Out_i$ [M9] $0 = \sum_{s=1}^{S}\sum_{i=1}^{C} h_{F,i}(F_i)_s - h_{Out,i}(Out_i)_s$ [E15] $p y_i = x_i p_i^s$ [T7]	Mass Balance: $0 = V_{i+1} + L_{i-1} - V_i - L_i$ Component Balance: $V_{i+1}y_{i+1} + L_{i-1}x_{i-1} = V_i y_i + L_i x_i$ Energy Balance: $0 = h_{V_{i+1}}V_{i+1} + h_{L_{i-1}}L_{i-1} - h_{V_i}V_i - h_{L_i}L_i$ Equilibrium Condition: $y_i = m_i x_i$ with $m_i = \frac{p_i^s}{p}$

Figure 2. Problem description and solution for an equilibrium stage.

5. Conclusions

This work presents an intelligent agent which is capable of recognizing the system attributes, and links them to specific equations from the areas of conservation principles, transport phenomena, reaction kinetics and thermodynamics. The agent is based on a semantic model and has been programmed in Java. It has proved to be very helpful in quickly finding the appropriate set of equations to determine or solve for certain properties of the system in a systematic and methodical way. Likewise, a general classification algorithm has been develop to assist in the assignment of the problem to the correct equations. What this all amounts to is that the overall definition of a chemical engineering problem can be monitored on a regular basis and mistakes or inaccuracies in the table are removed at an early stage. As a future work, the developed framework is a cornerstone for a larger enterprise wide framework, which processes the information and data required for the model fitting and problem optimization. The overall framework should be designed such that it is capable of managing, structuring and delivering information as required by the constraints, thus being able react to production system changes or modeling changes, based on flexible data and information structures.

Acnowledgements
Financial support received from the Spanish "Ministerio de Economía, Industria y Competitividad" and the European Regional Development Fund, both funding the research Project AIMS (ref. DPI2017-87435-R), and from the "Generalitat de Catalunya" (AGAUR 2017-SGR-1092-CEPEiMA)" is thankfully acknowledged

References
I. Cameron and K. Hangos, 2001, Process Modelling and Model Analysis. Elsevier.
M. Klein et al, 2002, Ontology versioning and change detection on the web. In 13th international conference on knowledge engineering and knowledge management (EKAW02), pp. 197–212.
E. Muñoz et al. (2012). Towards an ontological infrastructure for chemical batch process management. Comp. & Chem. Eng., 34, 668–682.

Anton A. Kiss, Edwin Zondervan, Richard Lakerveld, Leyla Özkan (Eds.)
Proceedings of the 29th European Symposium on Computer Aided Process Engineering
June 16th to 19th, 2019, Eindhoven, The Netherlands. © 2019 Elsevier B.V. All rights reserved.
http://dx.doi.org/10.1016/B978-0-128-18634-3.50084-9

Bioethanol Production with Cyanobacteria by a Two-Stage Fermentation Strategy

Romina Lasry Testa[a], Claudio Delpino[a], Vanina Estrada[a], M. Soledad Diaz[a,*]

[a] *Planta Piloto de Ingeniería Quimica (PLAPIQUI), Universidad Nacional del Sur (UNS)-CONICET, Camino La Carrindanga Km 7, Bahía Blanca 8000, Argentina*

sdiaz@plapiqui.edu.ar

Abstract

In this work, we study *in silico* photoautotrophic bioethanol production with *Synechocystis* sp. PCC6803 by a two-stage approach in two bioreactors in series. In the first stage the conditions are set for the maximization of growth rate, with optimal conditions of light intensity and carbon sources, while in the second a state of nitrogen limited conditions that tends to maximize ethanol production instead of growth rate is considered. Both stages are optimized by Flux Balance Analysis with different objective functions: Maximization of biomass for the first stage and Minimization of ATP production for the second. A previously developed genome scale metabolic network model is used for the optimizations. Results are promising into considering this strategy experimentally.

Keywords: Synechocystis, Bioethanol, FBA, Nitrogen limitation, phosphorus limitation.

1. Introduction

In recent years cyanobacteria have been considered as promising candidates to become cell factories in the context of systems biology research. This is due to the fact that these microorganisms are capable of growing only on ambient carbon dioxide and minimal inorganic nutrients. More specifically, photoautotrophic bioethanol production has been widely studied with mutant strains of *Synechocystis* sp. PCC6803 (*Synechocystis*) harboring the genes *pdc* and *adh* from the ethanol producing bacterium *Zymomonas mobilis*, achieving experimental production rates of 0.261 g L^{-1} day^{-1} (Dienst *et al.*, 2014).

Mathematical models of metabolism are useful into quantifying the metabolic capabilities of the microorganism and predicting experimental results through optimization problems. The most useful kind of models are genome scale metabolic networks (GEMs), that include information of all the enzymes, reactions and metabolites, with their corresponding stoichiometry, in the genome of the considered microorganism. GEMs allowed the development of *in silico* strategies to improve the production of high added value products. One of these strategies is coupling the production of the compound of interest to growth by the identification of a set of reactions to eliminate ("knock-outs"),based on a bi-level programming approach, where the knock-outs are represented by binary variables, resulting in MILP programming problems (Chowdhury et al., 2015). In previous work (Lasry Testa et al., 2017) we applied a modification of this strategy to a previously developed GEM of *Synechocystis* to couple bioethanol production to growth with good results, but requiring a high number of genetic interventions.

In this work we propose a two-stage ethanol production approach in two bioreactors in series to improve ethanol production based on nutrient limiting conditions. In the first stage the conditions are set to maximize growth rate, while in the second stage the conditions are set to limit growth and allow for ethanol production. For the second stage, two different limiting nutrients are considered: Nitrogen and Phosphorus. A similar strategy has been used to produce bioethanol with yeast (Gowtham et al., 2014), but is has not been applied to cyanobacterial to our knowledge so far. We evaluate our model against fluxomic experimental data for a nitrogen limited state (Nakajima et al., 2017). Namakoshi et al. (2016) provide experimental evidence on ethanol production under nitrogen-limited conditions by a mutant strain of *Synechocystis* harbouring deletions for both glycogen and PHB synthesis pathways.

2. Materials and Methods

2.1. Genome Scale Metabolic Network Model and Conditions

We consider a genome scale metabolic network model (GEM) of the cyanobacteria *Synechocystis* that contains 709 reversible and irreversible reactions, 80 exchange reactions and 535 metabolites. The ethanol production pathway is added by incorporating the heterologous gene *pdc* from Zymomonas mobilis, which encodes for the enzyme pyruvate decarboxylase (PDC) that catalyzes the non-oxidative decarboxylation of pyruvate (PYR) to produce acetaldehyde (ACAL) and CO_2. Carbon is considered to be taken up as carbon dioxide (CO_2) and bicarbonate (HCO^{3-}). HCO^{3-} uptake is active by a Na^+ dependent ATP consuming transporter, while CO_2 uptake is passive with the posterior conversion to HCO^{3-}. The CO_2 from intracellular decarboxylation is considered to be converted into HCO^{3-} by a reversible reaction (Nogales et al., 2012). For all the optimizations performed in this work, photoautotrophic growth is considered, and carbon uptake is restricted to 3.7 mmol gDW^{-1} h^{-1}, divided into CO_2 and HCO^{3-}, with all other possible carbon sources set to 0. For the light uptake an upper bound of 100 mmol gDW^{-1} h^{-1} is considered. Nitrogen is considered to be taken up as nitrate, while phosphorous is taken up as orthophosphate, both through active transport. For the TCA cycle, we take into account two possibilities, proven to be functional by experimental data: (a) The γ- aminobutyric acid shunt (GABA shunt) and (b) the enzymes 2-OGDC and SSDHA.

The model is built in SBML format with the tools provided in COBRA Toolbox and is then turned into the GAMS Data eXchange (GDX) format to be used in the GAMS environment (GAMS Development Corporation, Washington, DC).

2.2. Flux Balance Analysis and evaluation against experimental data

Flux Balance Analysis (FBA) is used to determine the flux distribution of a metabolic network under a specific steady state condition. It consists of a linear programming (LP) problem, which is defined with the steady state mass balances of the network (Eq. (2)), the lower and upper bound on fluxes (Eq. (3)) and an objective function. In this work we consider two different objectives functions (Eq. (1)): (a) Maximization of biomass production and (b) minimization of ATP production.

$$\max v_{biomass} \ (\min v_{ATP \ production})\tag{1}$$

$$\sum_j S_{i,j} v_j = 0\tag{2}$$

$$LB_j \leq v_j \leq UB_j\tag{3}$$

To evaluate the GEM against experimental fluxomic data, Flux Variability Analysis (FVA) is considered. FVA is a strategy derived from FBA, where the fluxes of all the reactions in the model are maximized and minimized subject to FBA constraints (Maranas and Zomorrodi, 2016). In the evaluation, the lower and upper confidence bounds of the experimental data are set as bounds for the corresponding reactions in the GEM and the bounds for all other reactions are obtained by FVA. The resulting flux distribution must be feasible and have the same growth rate as reported in the experimental data.

2.3. Two stage production approach

In this *in silico* bioethanol production strategy we consider a first stage were conditions of carbon and light uptake are set for the strain to be in exponential growth phase, where all the carbon flux is directed towards biomass production. This stage is simulated by FBA with biomass objective function (Maximization of Biomass). Then, the biomass produced in the first stage is transferred to a second stage where the conditions are set for the growth to be in stationary phase. For this, we consider two different cases of nutrient limitation that allow for the redirection of carbon flux to the production of biofuels. This stage can also be simulated by FBA with an objective function of ATP production minimization, characteristic of the stationary growth phase where growth rate tends to zero, as the growth and death rates are balanced. The limitations considered are nitrogen and phosphorus. Experimental evidence reveals ethanol production under nitrogen limited conditions in a mutant of *Synechocystis* incapable of glycogen and PHB storage (Namakoshi et al., 2016). With this approach we simulate a nitrogen limited scenario according to experimental values and study the case of phosphorus limitation with different scenarios as there is no experimental evidence to validate it.

3. Results

For both limitation cases we modify our GEM eliminating glycogen and PHB storage as this favours biofuel production (Namakoshi et al., 2016). The first stage of the approach presented in section 2.3 is the same for both cases as it is not limited by any other nutrient than carbon or light. The FBA optimization provides a maximal growth rate of 0.089 h^{-1} for the first bioreactor, which is consistent with experimental data for these conditions.

3.1. Nitrogen limited conditions

We evaluated our model against experimental fluxomic data from Nakajima et al. (2017) as described in section 2.2. The growth rate reported in this study is 0.015 h^{-1}. We evaluate our model for this growth rate to obtain the nitrogen uptake that corresponds to the experimental flux distribution, which results in a flux of 0.135 mmol gDW^{-1} h^{-1}. With this uptake value we run FVA and obtain a very accurate correlation between the experimental values and the flux distribution obtained (Table 1), showing that our model is capable to reproduce nitrogen limitation. We only find significant difference for the reaction converting Fumarate to Malate (FUM -> MAL) which is probably due to the different modelling of the TCA cycle. Nakajima et al. (2017) consider the Glyoxylate Shunt and the OGDH complex which are proven to not be present in cyanobacteria. Based on the evaluation against experimental data, we chose to consider a case of nitrogen uptake restricted with an upper bound of 0.135 mmol gDW^{-1} h^{-1} to assure that the uptake is feasible and limiting, experimentally. This value and the growth rate of 0.015 h^{-1} are fixed, and ATP production is minimized by FBA with a result of 6.285 mmol gDW^{-1} h-1. These conditions provide an ethanol production of 1.547 mmol gDW^{-1} h^{-1}.

3.2. Phosphorus limited conditions

As there is no experimental data available on cases of phosphorus limitation, we chose to simulate a set of cases for different phosphorus uptakes to study the possibilities for ethanol production in the second stage. The phosphorus uptakes considered are 6: 0.03, 0.025, 0.02, 0.015, 0.01 and 0.005 mmol gDW^{-1} h^{-1}, respectively. For each of the uptakes maximum growth rate, maximal ethanol production rate and minimal ATP production are obtained with FBA and reported in Figure (1) a, b and c respectively. We can see that as the upper bound on phosphorus uptake decreases the maximal biomass production also decreases, leaving more carbon flux available to be redirected towards ethanol production, which has the opposite tendency. The minimal ATP production required for each state decreases as growth rate, since the ethanol production pathway does not require the production of ATP, contrary to biomass production. We chose the case of 0.01 mmol gDW^{-1} h^{-1} of phosphorus uptake as the best one as the growth rate of 0.014 h^{-1} is very close to the case considered for nitrogen limitation. For this case the ethanol production is 1.57 mmol gDW^{-1} h^{-1} and the minimal ATP production is 6.269 mmol gDW^{-1} h^{-1}.

Table 1: *Experimental and Model flux distributions*

	Our Model	Nakajima et al (2016)		Our Model	Nakajima et al (2016)
G6P -> RU5P	0.389	0.349	GAP -> DHAP	0.938	0.937
RU5P -> RUBP	1.229	1.191	PGA -> GAP	1.166	2.167
RUBP -> 2 PGA	1.229	1.191	PGA -> 2PG	0.192	0.192
DHAP + E4P -> S7P	0.821	0.803	2PG -> PEP	0.193	0.192
PYR -> ACCOA	0.111	0.111	PYR -> PEP	0.444	0.406
ACCOA -> CIT	0.048	0.049	GLU -> AKG	0.042	0.042
CIT -> ACONI	0.048	0.049	SUC -> FUM	0.028	0.027
ACONI -> ICIT	0.048	0.049	FUM -> MAL	1.081	0.039
ICIT -> AKG	0.048	0.048	MAL -> OAA	0.498	0.049
GLU -> ABUT	0.02	0.021	X5P -> RU5P	0.569	0.572
4ABUT -> SUCSAL	0.02	0.021	R5P -> RU5P	0.269	0.269
SUCSAL -> SUCC	0.022	0.021	S7P + GAP -> R5P + X5P	0.282	0.281
MAL -> PYR	0.583	0.537	F6P + GAP -> E4P + X5P	0.288	0.29
F6P -> G6P	0.395	0.366	S7P + GAP -> E4P + F6P	0.539	0.521
FBP -> F6P	0.145	0.136	G6P -> GLYC	0.37	0.372
GAP + DHAP -> FBP	0.145	0.136			

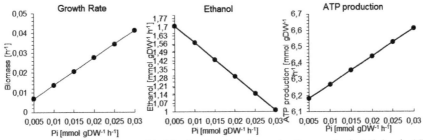

Figure 1: a) Growth rate, b) Maximal ethanol production and c) Minimal ATP production required for 6 different phosphorus scenarios

4. Discussion

To compare the results obtained for the two cases of limitation with data from bibliography, we assume experimental culture conditions to calculate ethanol production rates. The initial biomass concentration (X_0) considered is of 0.078 gDW L^{-1}. For the first stage we consider growth in exponential phase and calculate the final biomass concentration assuming a cultivation time of 2 days (t) and a growth rate (μ) of 0.089 h^{-1} (see section 3). According to Eq. (4), the final biomass concentration for the first stage is 5.589 gDW L^{-1}. This value is the same for both cases of nutrient limitation.

$$\ln X - \ln X_0 = \mu t \tag{4}$$

For the second stage the culture is considered to be in stationary phase, so the net growth rate is 0. With these assumptions the ethanol production is calculated based on the final biomass concentration of the first stage, considering a cultivation time of 1 day. For both stages, a light limitation function is considered to include shade effect of biomass (Laiglecia et al., 2013). The ethanol production for both limitation cases, compared with the case of the coupled mutant presented in Lasry Testa et al. (2017) are shown in Figure 2.

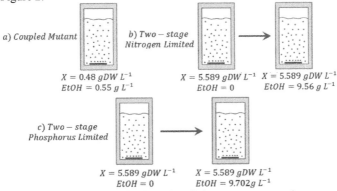

Figure 2: Ethanol and biomass productions for all the cases compared

Numerical results show a very similar ethanol production for the nitrogen and phosphorus cases, with an increase of only ~1.5% for the phosphorus case. In contrast, the results obtained for the two-stage approach are more promising than the ones obtained in previous work for a coupled mutant obtained by a set of genetic interventions, and higher than the best result of 332 mg L^{-1} reported by Namakoshi et al. (2016). These results are obtained for constant illumination, so the cultivation needs to be carried out in a closed photobioreactor at industrial scale, where the main obstacle would be the cost of the system compared with open ponds. However, encouraging new photobioreactor designs are beginning to be available to address these difficulties (Johnson et al., 2018)

5. Conclusions

In this work, we have addressed photoautotrophic ethanol production by the genetically modified cyanobacterium *Synechocystis* sp. PCC 6803 with a novel strategy trough mathematical modelling. The ethanol productions obtained for both limitation cases are promising as they are higher than the best experimental results from bibliography. The model could be successfully evaluated against experimental data for nitrogen limited conditions, but no experimental data is available for the phosphorus case. Mathematical models of metabolism become more reliable with the inclusion of experimental values. The results obtained are encouraging into testing this kind of approach in experimental studies.

References

Chowdhury, A., Zomorrodi, A.R., Maranas, C.D., 2015. Bilevel optimization techniques in computational strain design. Comput. Chem. Eng. 72, 363–372.
Dienst, D., Georg, J., Abts, T., Jakorew, L., Kuchmina, E., Börner, T., Wilde, A., Dühring, U., Enke, H., Hess, W.R., 2014. Transcriptomic response to prolonged ethanol production in the cyanobacterium Synechocystis sp. PCC6803. Biotechnol. Biof.. 7, 21.
Gowtham, Y.K., Miller, K.P., Hodge, D.B., Henson, J.M., Harcum, S.W., 2014. Novel two-stage fermentation process for bioethanol production using Saccharomyces pastorianus. Biotechnol. Prog. 30, 300–310.
Johnson, T.J., Katuwal, S., Anderson, G.A., Gu, L., Zhou, R., Gibbons, W.R., 2018. Photobioreactor Cultivation Strategies for Microalgae and Cyanobacteria. Biotechnol. Prog. 34, 811–827.
Laiglecia, J., Estrada, V., Vidal, R.V., Florencio, F.J., Guerrero, M.G., Soledad Diaz, M., 2013. Dynamic flux balance analysis of a genetic engineered cyanobacterium for ethanol production. Parameter estimation. Chem. Eng. Trans. 32, 955–960.
Lasry Testa, R., Delpino, C., Estrada, V., Diaz, M.S., 2017. Metabolic network desgin of Synechocystis sp. PCC 6803 to obtain bioethanol under autotrophic conditions. Comput. Aided Chem. Eng. 40, 2857–2862.
Maranas, C.D., Zomorrodi, A.R., 2016. Optimization Methods in Metabolic Networks. John Wiley & Sons, Inc.
Nakajima, T., Yoshikawa, K., Toya, Y., Matsuda, F., Shimizu, H., 2017. Metabolic flux analysis of the synechocystis sp. PCC 6803 ΔnrtABCD mutant reveals a mechanism for metabolic adaptation to nitrogen-limited conditions. Plant Cell Physiol. 58, 537–545.
Namakoshi, K., Nakajima, T., Yoshikawa, K., Toya, Y., Shimizu, H., 2016. Combinatorial deletions of glgC and phaCE enhance ethanol production in Synechocystis sp. PCC 6803. J. Biotechnol. 239, 13–19.
Nogales, J., Gudmundsson, S., Knight, E.M., Palsson, B.O., Thiele, I., 2012. Detailing the optimality of photosynthesis in cyanobacteria through systems biology analysis. Proc. Natl. Acad. Sci. 109, 2678–2683.

Anton A. Kiss, Edwin Zondervan, Richard Lakerveld, Leyla Özkan (Eds.)
Proceedings of the 29th European Symposium on Computer Aided Process Engineering
June 16th to 19th, 2019, Eindhoven, The Netherlands. © 2019 Elsevier B.V. All rights reserved.
http://dx.doi.org/10.1016/B978-0-128-18634-3.50085-0

Application of plate heat exchangers into heat exchanger networks retrofit with fixed structure

Kexin Xu*, Robin Smith

Centre for Process Integration, School of Chemical Engineering and Analytical Science, The University of Manchester, M13 9PL, UK.
kexin.xu@ manchester.ac.uk

Abstract

Heat exchanger enhancement technologies have been widely used into heat exchanger networks (HENs) retrofit. However, the heat recovery is limited through the enhancement, which is restricted by the geometry of existing heat exchanger. Plate heat exchangers are widely used in energy-intensive process industries to increase heat recovery and reduce greenhouse gas emissions with the features of small minimum temperature approach and high effectiveness. Thus, plate heat exchangers are taken into consideration to replace conventional heat exchanger in crude oil preheat trains to enhance heat transfer coefficient and reduce energy consumption. A major limitation of applying plate heat exchanger is lack of reliable optimization method to quantity the energy saving effectively. Due to the high installation cost of plate heat exchangers, the optimization is based on the trade-off between energy reduction and capital cost. This work proposes a new methodology of application of plate heat exchanger in HENs retrofit with a fixed network structure. A change in one component in heat exchanger networks can have an effect on other downstream heat exchangers. Therefore, the proposed methodology also presents a way of eliminating the need for additional heat transfer area after replacement, while ensuring the stream target temperatures are met. Case studies highlight the benefits of the new approach.

Keywords: plate heat exchanger, heat exchanger network retrofit, energy saving

1. Introduction

With the growth of energy consumption and the increase of CO_2 emissions, it is more and more important to improve heat transfer efficiency. Heat exchanger network retrofit is a cost-effective way to increase heat recovery based on the existing heat exchanger network in process industries. Plate heat exchanger, including gasket plate heat exchanger and welded plate heat exchanger, is one of the most high-efficiency heat transfer equipment. Compared with conventional shell-and-tube heat exchangers, plate heat exchangers could significantly increase energy efficiency with minimum approach temperature as low as 2 °C, decrease the possibility of fouling and reduce the fuel consumption and CO_2 emissions. Thus, plate heat exchangers can be considered to improve the energy performance of an existing heat exchanger network.

Established techniques and methodologies for the retrofit of HENs focus on modifying the existing HENs to obtain energy savings and overcome network bottlenecks. Pinch analysis, mathematical programming and hybrid methods are the three main retrofit methods in existing heat exchanger networks. There are several reports in literature dedicated to the retrofit of HENs based on these methods. Sreepathi and Rangaiah

(2014) presented a detailed review of the different methods for HEN retrofit. The book by Smith (2005) has full chapters that introduce the fundamentals of energy targets, capital and total cost targets, and network design of HENs.

In the recent years, there has been an increasing number of research applying heat transfer enhancement techniques in HEN retrofit. Adding inserts and fins in the existing heat exchangers, which could increase the heat transfer coefficient, are the two main techniques in heat transfer enhancement. Heat transfer enhancement increases heat recovery and can also reduce the energy consumption. (Akpomiemie and Smith, 2015) However, for heat transfer enhancement to be effective, one of the film coefficients must be controlling. Besides, although heat transfer enhancement techniques can be performed during the normal shutdown time, the potential risk of damaging the heat exchangers when adding inserts or fins is not negligible. Thus, to overcome these drawbacks, this work presents a new retrofit method that provides insights into the application of plate heat exchangers into heat exchanger network in order to reduce the network energy consumption and increase heat recovery. However, there is no published literature shows the possibility of integrating plate heat exchanger into traditional shell-and-tube heat exchanger networks and quantity the potential effect on energy saving.

The main objective of this work is to develop cost effective retrofit methods for HENs with plate heat exchangers. The benefit of retrofit profit of the existing heat exchanger network is highlighted.

2. Methodology

This section presents a retrofit design methodology of application of plate heat exchanger into an existing fixed structure HEN. The methods, including identify the best candidate heat exchanger to replace, apply plate heat exchanger and set up non-linear model to rebalance network, are detailed in this section.

2.1. Identification of heat exchanger candidate to replace
Utility path is used to identify candidate heat exchanger and sensitivity analysis is used to determine the rank of identified exchangers.

2.1.1. Identification of utility paths
A utility path is a connection between two utilities through process heat exchangers. To develop a cost effective retrofit method of an existing HEN without structure modification and additional heat transfer area, the exchangers to be replaced must be on a utility path so that heat loads can be shifted along the path (Linnhoff and Hindmarsh, 1983). A change in a HEN can affect the performance of other components; thus, the utility path can also be used in the rebalance the HEN after replacement of shell-and-tube heat exchangers. For a simple network, utility paths can be specified by inspection. However, for a complex HEN, Incidence Matrix Approach is used to identify utility paths in the HEN (Akpomiemie and Smith, 2015).

2.1.2. Sensitivity analysis

Sensitivity analysis is used to identify the best heat exchangers, which can bring the most energy saving among others, to be replaced by plate heat exchangers. It also helps users to select the sequence of replacement. Kotjabasakis and Linnhoff (1986a) are the first researchers that proposed sensitivity analysis. This method is based on the equation:

$$Q = UA\Delta T_{LM}F_T \tag{1}$$

In which Q is the total heat load, W; U is the overall heat transfer coefficient, W/(K·m²); A is surface area of heat exchanger, m²; ΔT_{LM} is the logarithmic mean temperature difference; F_T is the correction factor. The key point of sensitivity analysis is increasing the inlet temperature of key utility, which is identified as the one that have the most energy consumption, by adjusting the heat transfer coefficient, surface area and correction factor of candidate heat exchangers. Wang (2012) developed a mathematical model to identify the high sensitivity heat exchangers. He concluded that the amount of energy saving largely depended on the distance between the heat exchanger and the key utility. Easy implementation and short computation time are the main advantages of sensitivity analysis.

2.1 Application of plate heat exchangers

After the best heat exchangers for replacement are identified, plate heat exchangers need to be applied in the replacement of selected shell-and-tube heat exchangers. The plate heat exchanger model used in this paper is from Xu et al. (2017) , where the effects of multi-pass flow arrangement, plate geometries and chevron angle on heat transfer behavior are considered in the model. The input process stream data are derived from candidate heat exchangers. The maximum heat transfer coefficient of the single plate heat exchanger can be derived from the optimization model in GAMS.

2.2 Optimization of HEN

Application of plate heat exchangers to replace the conventional heat exchanger in the existing HEN can affect the other heat exchangers performance. After replacement, the heat transfer coefficient of new plate heat exchanger significant increased, which leads an increase of the inlet temperature of the next heat exchanger in the hot stream and a decrease of the inlet temperature of the next heat exchanger in cold stream correspondingly. These changes could further affect the other components. To rebalance the HEN, the heat loads of heat exchangers need to be relocated. The heat loads can be shifted through the utility paths. Thus, an optimization method to retrofit an existing heat exchanger network without additional heat transfer area and topology modification is proposed. Plate heat exchangers may decrease energy consumption but the high installation cost of plate heat exchanger may be a significant negligible. Thus, there is a trade-off between energy saving and total retrofit cost. The objective of this optimization problem is to maximize retrofit profit. The total cost of retrofit includes the implementation cost of bypass, the capital cost of plate heat exchangers, the cost of adding heat transfer area only if the heat exchangers are not on the utility path. To achieve target temperatures of the process problem and maintain the existing heat exchanger areas (exclude the candidate heat exchangers to be replaced) are the two main constraints of the design.

Objective Function: *Maximize Retrofit Profit* = Profit from energy saving – Total cost of retrofit

Constraints: $A_{ex} = A_E$ $\forall_{\text{exchangers (excluded the candidate heat exchanges)}}$

$TT_s = TT_E$ $\forall_{\text{streams}}$

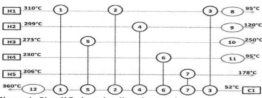

Figure 1. Simplified crude oil preheat train

Variables: heat load for all exchangers on a utility path

heat transfer coefficient for candidate heat exchanger

3. Case study

A simplified preheat train is used to illustrate the benefit of application of plate heat exchanger into retrofit design of HEN in a fixed network structure. The existing structure of the network is shown in Figure 1. There are in total 12 exchangers, and five hot streams and one cold stream. The objective of this study is to maximum the retrofit profit of applying plate heat exchangers into existing network without adding area and structure change. Table 1 summarized the cost parameters used in this study. The streams properties are assumed to be constant. To quantify the retrofit profit, the operating time is fixed as one year.

The first step is to identify the best heat exchanger to replacement. It can be inspected from the Figure 1 that only process heat exchanger 7 is not on the utility path. Thus, heat exchanger 1, 2, 3, 4, 5 and 6 are selected to further sensitivity analysis. According to the result of sensitivity analysis, heat exchanger 5 is the most sensitive exchanger which can bring the most benefit of energy saving. Thus, heat exchanger 5 is identified to be replaced by the plate heat exchanger. To maximum retrofit profit, the heat duties of heat exchanger 5 and corresponding cold utility exchanger 10 are set as variables. After inputting the process stream data of exchanger 5 into the optimization model of a single plate heat exchanger in GAMS, the maximum heat transfer coefficient can be derived with the number of 3.75 m², which is a significant increase compare with shell-and-tube heat exchangers.

The optimization procedure is conducted to rebalance the network by using global solver on LINDO Systems What's Best!. The heat duty of exchanger 5 is increased by 814.96kW and the utility consumption in exchanger 10 decreases to 0. Although the heat load of heat exchanger 5 increases, the area of exchanger 5 decreases from 183.85 m² to 23.83 m² by applying the plate heat exchanger. Three bypasses are implemented

Table 1. Cost data of case study

Utility cost data	Retrofit cost data
Hot Utility Cost: 400 ($/kW y)	Cost of Installation of plate heat exchangers: 2.5*2070*A0.85($)
Cold Utility Cost: 5.5 ($/kW y)	Implementing By-pass: 5000 ($)
	Cost of increasing heat exchanger area: 6000 + 200 * A ($)

Table 2. Results of replacement

	Parameter	Replace E5	Replace E5&E1	Replace E5&E1(allowing extra area on E2 & E3)
Retrofit Cost	Replacement	$76,630	$272,893	$324,287
	Increasing Area	$0	$0	$199,323
	Implementing By-pass	$15,000	$15,000	$15,000
	Total Cost	$91,631	$287,893	$539,110
Retrofit Profit	Utility Savings	$296,684	$296,604	$494,325
	Net Saving (Utility Savings – Total Cost)	$205,054 (~3.5% of initial utility cost)	$8,702 (~0.5% of initial utility cost)	-$44,785
	Payback	0.31 yr	0.97 yr	1.09 yr

to reduce the duty of heat exchangers. The results of retrofit cost and retrofit profit are detailed in Table 2 with the initial utility cost of $5,801,396.

The procedure is repeated until the net saving starts to decrease since the retrofit objective is to maximize retrofit profit. According to the sensitivity analysis, the next heat exchanger to be replaced is heat exchanger 1. The results after replacement of heat exchanger 5 and heat exchanger 1 are listed in Table 5. The net saving after replacing heat exchanger 1 is smaller than only replacing heat exchanger 5, which violates the objective function, thus the replacement is stopped after replacing heat exchanger 5. The main reason that limits the net saving is the limited utility saving which is restricted to the fixed area of heat exchanger 2 and heat exchanger 3. Thus, another trail allowing extra area on heat exchanger 2 and 3 is carried out.

The comparisons between application of plate heat exchanger and enhancement (Akpomiemie and Smith, 2015) are also highlighted in Table 3. The retrofit profit of replacement is $11,217.97 smaller than enhancement due to the high installation cost of

Table 3. Comparison of replacement and enhancement

	Parameter	Replacement	Enhancement
Retrofit Cost	Replacement	$76,630.58	$3,981.16
	Increasing Area	$0	$0
	Implementing By-pass	$15,000	$15,000
	Total Cost	$91,630.58	$18,981.16
Retrofit Profit	Utility Savings	$296,684.13	$237,252.68
	Net Saving	$205,053.55	$216,271.52

plate heat exchanger. However, the replacement is more environmental friendly since utility saving in replacement is $59,431.45 larger than enhancement. Thus, heat transfer enhancement is a cost effective retrofit method. However, when one of the film coefficients is not controlling, applying plate heat exchanger to replace shell-and-tube heat exchanger can be regarded as an alternative option for retrofit, which can bring more energy saving at the same time.

4. Conclusions

A new retrofit method for heat exchanger networks based on the application of plate heat exchangers has been proposed in this work. The case studies highlight the retrofit benefit of the new methods. Compared to the traditional heat transfer enhancement technologies, replacing the shell-and-tube heat exchangers with plate heat exchangers can significantly increase the heat recovery and decrease energy consumption with smaller heat transfer area. However, the installation cost of plate heat exchanger is relatively high. Thus, plate heat exchangers can be used as an alternative retrofit option when one of the heat transfer film is not controlling. The savings are constrained, as all of the existing matches, except the new plate heat exchangers, are being maintained at their original sizes.

References

Akpomiemie, M. O. & Smith, R. (2015). Retrofit of heat exchanger networks without topology modifications and additional heat transfer area. Applied energy, 159, 381-390.

Linnhoff, B. & Hindmarsh, E. (1983). The pinch design method for heat exchanger networks. Chemical Engineering Science, 38(5), 745-763.

Kotjabasakis, E. & Linnhoff, B. (1986a). Sensitivity tables for the design of flexible processes (1)—How much contingency in heat exchanger networks is cost-effective? Chemical engineering research & design, 64(3), 197-211

Smith, R. (2005). Chemical process: design and integration: John Wiley & Sons.

Sreepathi, B. K. & Rangaiah, G. (2014). Review of heat exchanger network retrofitting methodologies and their applications. Industrial & engineering chemistry research, 53(28), 11205-11220.

Wang, Y., Pan, M., Bulatov, I., Smith, R. & Kim, J.-K. (2012). Application of intensified heat transfer for the retrofit of heat exchanger network. Applied energy, 89(1), 45-5

Xu, K., Smith, R., Zhang, N. (2017). Design and optimization of plate heat exchanger networks. *27th European Symposium on Computer Aided Process Engineering.* Barcelona.

Anton A. Kiss, Edwin Zondervan, Richard Lakerveld, Leyla Özkan (Eds.)
Proceedings of the 29th European Symposium on Computer Aided Process Engineering
June 16th to 19th, 2019, Eindhoven, The Netherlands. © 2019 Elsevier B.V. All rights reserved.
http://dx.doi.org/10.1016/B978-0-128-18634-3.50086-2

Clustering alternative product formulations using graphs

Fernando P. Bernardo[a]*, Javier A. Arrieta-Escobar[b]

aGEPSI-PSE Group, CIEPQPF, Department of Chemical Engineering, University of Coimbra, Portugal
bERPI (Equipe de Recherche sur les Processus Innovatifs) - University of Lorraine - 8, rue Bastien Lepage, 54010 Nancy Cedex, France
bernardo@eq.uc.pt

Abstract

This work proposes the use of graph partitioning tools to identify clusters in a possible large space of plausible product formulations, with each cluster representing a significantly different design alternative that deserve to be tested. The partitioning tools are used to find clusters in a large set of previously generated alternatives, and are also incorporated into a mixed-integer programming problem whose solution generates clustered alternatives (within a feasible space defined by available models and heuristics). An example of a cosmetic emulsion is provided.

Keywords: product design, formulated products, graph partitioning, cluster analysis

1. Introduction

Computer-aided design of formulated products, moreover of those having characteristic microstructural attributes, is hindered by the lack of quantitative reliable property models. It is then important to develop tools able to handle qualitative knowledge (Zhang *et al.*, 2017), including lists of often used ingredients, databases of known successful formulations, and a variety of heuristic rules regarding typical combinations of ingredients, amounts used, known effects, synergies and antagonisms. We have recently proposed a method to generate alternative product formulations, based on mixed-integer programming and using propositional logic to model heuristic rules as algebraic restrictions (Arrieta-Escobar *et al.*, 2017, 2018). The list of plausible alternatives thus generated may be long, due to acknowledged uncertainty in the assumed models and heuristics, and therefore it may not be clear what smaller subset of alternatives really deserves to be manufactured and tested.

Here, we propose the use of graph partitioning tools to identify clusters of formulations within a given space of feasible alternatives. Formulations belonging to a given cluster have a certain similarity between them and should be as dissimilar as possible to formulations belonging to other clusters. Therefore, an exploratory design of experiments should include at least one instance from each cluster. As a first contribution to this problem, the only clustering criterion here adopted is the qualitative composition of the formulation, such that similarity between formulations is defined by the number of shared components. Two subproblems are addressed: (i) to find clusters in a given, possibly large, set of alternative formulations (previously generated using e.g. integer programming and/or constructed from databases of product formulations); (ii) to simultaneously generate and cluster alternative formulations obeying to a given set of property models and heuristic constraints.

2. Matrix and graph representations of a set of product formulations

Given a set of available components, $C = \{c_1, ..., c_{NC}\}$, a product formulation is defined by a vector yV of binary variables, with dimension NC, indicating which components are present in the formulation, and a corresponding vector xV of mass fractions.

Solely in terms of qualitative composition (i.e., regardless of xV values), a set of NF alternative formulations, $F = \{f_1, ..., f_{NF}\}$, may be represented by a list of vectors yV organized in a matrix $Y = (y_{fc})_{NF \times NC}$, with $y_{fc} = 1$ if component c is present in formulation f, for all $c \in C, f \in F$. An equivalent representation is that of a bipartite graph $G = (C, F, E)$, with vertex sets C and F, and edge set E. Edge $f - c$ exists if and only if the corresponding matrix entry $y_{fc} = 1$. Figure 1 illustrates both matrix and graph representations.

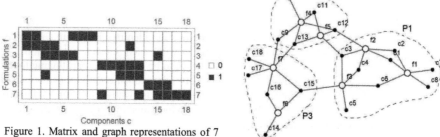

Figure 1. Matrix and graph representations of 7 product formulations (f1 to f7), each one having a subset of 18 possible components (c1 to c18). A partition in three clusters is shown: in the matrix, clusters correspond to diagonal blocks; in the graph, clusters are delimited by dashed lines.

3. Clustering of alternative product formulations

Given a set of product formulations F represented by a 0-1 matrix Y as above defined, the problem of partitioning F in NP clusters may be stated as: "find row and column permutations of Y in order to obtain NP diagonal blocks and minimizing the number of external elements "1" outside the diagonal blocks". Figure 1 (left) represents a possible solution to this problem with 3 clusters corresponding to 3 diagonal blocks and 5 external elements. Cluster P1, for instance, has formulations f1, f2 and f3, and components c1 to c8. Each external element represents a component from one cluster that is used in a formulation belonging to a different cluster, and therefore the number of external elements is a measure of similarity between clusters that should be minimized.

The same clustering is shown on graph format (Figure 1, right). The external elements of matrix Y here correspond to external edges, which are those connecting vertices located in different clusters. External edges are also designated by cut edges, since their removal decomposes the graph into NP disconnected subgraphs. For this reason, the set of external edges is designated by edge separator.

Using graph language, our problem of partitioning F in NP clusters is thus a problem of graph partitioning by edge separator (known in the graph literature as GPES): "given a set of product formulations F and its graph representation $G = (C, F, E)$, divide the graph into NP subgraphs (also designated by partitions or clusters) minimizing the number of external edges".

Graph partitioning is a better studied problem than sparse matrix rearrangement. In addition, the latter is often solved first translating the matrix into an equivalent graph and then applying graph partitioning methods (Aykanat *et al.*, 2004). Graph partitioning is thus the basic clustering technique here used, although the representation in the matrix form is preferred for its simplicity.

The graph partitioning problem is an NP-complete combinatorial optimization problem, well studied in multiple contexts (e.g. parallel computing, sparse matrix computations, VLSI design, biological and social networks, data mining). Exact solutions using, for instance, integer programming are in practice limited to relatively small graphs with some hundreds of vertices. For larger graphs, several heuristic algorithms are available with different performances in terms of computational time/quality of solutions (Fjallstrom, 1998). Here, we use integer programming to generate and simultaneously cluster a small set *F* of alternative formulations (section 4), and a heuristic algorithm to find clusters in large given sets. In particular, we use the multilevel algorithm of the publicly available tool hMeTiS (Karypis and Kumar, 1998). In its simpler form, hMeTiS only requires two inputs: the number of partitions *NP* and the allowed difference in the cardinality of different partitions (in Karypis Lab, MeTiS is the standard tool for large graphs partitioning, but if the focus is on solution quality rather than on computational efficiency then hMeTiS in advised; hMeTiS is a tool to partition hypergraphs, which are generalization of graphs, and thus may also be applied to our relatively simple graphs *G*).

4. Simultaneous generation and clustering of alternative formulations

Here, we present a new optimization formulation that extends the one presented in Arrieta-Escobar *et al.* (2017, 2018), in order to solve the following problem: "find the *NF* most dissimilar formulations of *NC* components (dissimilarity in qualitative composition defined by *yV*), obeying to a set of product design constraints (e.g., composition, performance and cost)". Using a graph representation, what is here being equated is how to connect two given sets of vertices (components *C* and formulations *F*) in order to obtain well defined clusters of components *c* around each formulation *f*. In other words, this is a graph partitioning problem with edges $f - c$ still to be decided and with each cluster having one and only one formulation (*NP* = *NF*). Further, the decision about the edges is subject to the condition that the set of edges connected to each *f* must define a feasible product formulation (according to the available product models).

The standard 0-1 formulation for graph partitioning is adopted (Boulle, 2004), with two sets of binary variables: $y_{fc} = 1$ if component *c* is chosen to be in formulation *f*, and $v_{fc} = 1$ if component *c* is located in cluster *f* (but not necessarily belongs to formulation *f*). Then, edge $f - c$ exists if and only if $e_{fc} = y_{fc} \cdot v_{fc} = 1$. The goal is to minimize the number of external edges (*NEE*) equal to the total number of edges (*NE*) minus the number of internal edges (*NIE*):

$$\min_{y_{fc}, x_{fc}, v_{fc}} NEE = \sum_{f,c} y_{fc} - \sum_{f,c} e_{fc} \tag{1.1}$$

$$s.t. \quad e_{fc} \leq a_{fc}, e_{fc} \leq v_{fc}, e_{fc} \geq a_{fc} + v_{fc} - 1, \forall f, c \tag{1.2}$$

$$\sum_f y_{fc} = 1, \forall f, c \tag{1.3}$$

$$v_{fc} = 0, \forall c, ord(f) = ord(c) + 1, ..., NF \tag{1.4}$$

$$g(yV_f, xV_f, p_f) \leq 0, yV_f = \{y_{fc}, \forall c\}, xV_f = \{x_{fc}, \forall c\}, , \forall f \tag{1.5}$$

$$y_{fc}, v_{fc} \in \{0,1\}, 0 \le e_{fc} \le 1, 0 \le x_{fc} \le 1 \qquad (1.6)$$

Restrictions (1.2) are a linear formulation of $e_{fc} = y_{fc} \cdot v_{fc} = 1$; equations (1.3) impose that each component belongs to only one cluster; equations (1.4) are anti-degeneracy constraints (c_1 must belong to cluster f_1, c_2 must belong either to f_1 or to f_2, and in general c_k must belong to one of the first kth clusters); restrictions (1.5) represent the available product models, relating the composition of formulation f (vectors yV_f and xV_f) with performance metrics p_f (cost included) and imposing desired limits to these metrics. Although variables $e_{fc} \in \{0,1\}$, they may be treated as continuous due to restrictions (1.2). The decision variables are the composition of all NF formulations (y_{fc}, x_{fc}) plus the assignment of components to clusters (v_{fc}). The total number of binary variables (y_{fc} and v_{fc}) is $2NF \cdot NC$.

For a graph with NE edges, NEE is an absolute measure of the partitioning quality. When comparing solutions for graphs of different dimensions, the fraction of external edges should be used instead: $FEE = NEE/NE$.

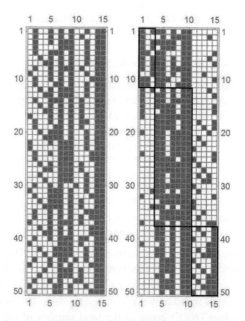

Figure 2. Set of 50 alternative formulations, before (left) and after (right) clustering. Order of components before clustering: {i3, i4, i5, i9, j2, j6, j7, j8, k3, k5, m1, m2, m3, r2, r3}. Order of components after clustering: {i4, k5, m3, j2, j7, j8, k3, m1, r2, r3, i3, i5, i9, j6, m2}. Clustering metrics: $NE = 375$, $NEE = 174$, $FEE = NE/NEE = 0.46$.

5. Example of a cosmetic emulsion

Here, the above proposed tools are applied to the example of Arrieta-Escobar *et al.* (2017, 2018). This is the formulation of a hair conditioner (which is an o/w emulsion), from an initial list of 32 possible ingredients organized in 6 subsets: emollients of type i ($i1$ to $i9$), emollients of type j ($j1$ to $j8$), emollients of type k ($k1$ to $k7$), fatty alcohols ($m1, m2$), thickening polymers ($n1, n2, n3$) and cationic surfactants ($r1, r2, r3$). Known heuristic rules (regarding amounts and combinations of ingredients), together with models for product viscosity and greasiness index, define a space of feasible formulations of the type $g(yV, xV) \leq 0$. All optimization problems here formulated are MILP problems and were solved using GAMS/CPLEX.

Through successive solution of the problem "min $Cost, s.t. g(yV, xV) \leq 0$", and using binary cuts to prohibit previous solutions, a rank of 50 formulations with increasing cost (only of raw-materials) is generated. These formulations (Figure 2, left) use 15 different components and have a cost between 0.884 and 0.952 USD/kg. They are then clustered using hMeTiS and with the additional constraint of a minimum of 3 components by cluster. As shown in Figure 2 (right), the result for $NP=3$ is poor, with FEE being quite large (0.46). For larger values of NP, the partitioning quality is even worse. One then concludes that, within this set F of 50 formulations, significantly different subsets of alternatives cannot be identified, which means that F is not diverse enough to there identify a reduced number of exploratory experiments.

Next, the most dissimilar NF formulations obeying to $g(yV, xV) \leq 0$ and also subject to an upper limit on cost ($Cost_f \leq Cmax, \forall f$) are generated by solving the optimization problem (1.1)-(1.6). Figure 3 and Table 1 shows results for different input values of NF and $Cmax$. Set $F1$ contains the three most dissimilar formulations within the considered design space, with only 5 external edges (corresponding to shared components $m2, r2$ and $r3$) of a total of 19, and thus a value of $FEE=5/19=0.26$.

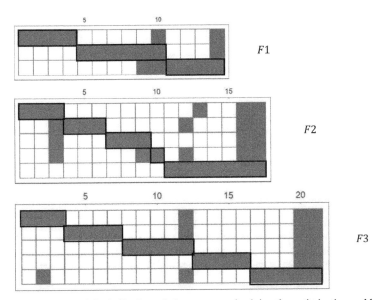

Figure 3. Sets of dissimilar formulations generated solving the optimization problem of section 4. The order of components (columns of the matrices) is shown on Table 1.

Table 1. Data regarding the sets of formulations represented in Figure 3 (*Cmax* is in USD/kg).

Set	*Em*	*Cmax*	*FEE*	Components
F1	3	1.1	0.26	{i5, j2, k3, m1, i4, j6, j7, k2, m2, r2, i9, j8, k5, r3}
F2	5	1.1	0.47	{i9, k5, m2, i3, j6, k6, i5, j2, k3, i4, i7, j7, j8, k2, m1, r2, r3}
F3	5	1.3	0.36	{i2, j2, k5, i3, j1, j7, k6, i4, j5, j8, k4, m2, i9, j6, k2, m1, i5, j4, k3, r2, r3}

Table 2. Data regarding set *F3*. Cost is *Cmax*=1.3 USD/kg for all formulations.

Formulation	Emollients	Emollients mass percentage
f_1	i2, j2, k5	1.3, 2.8, 1.9; Total = 6.0%
f_2	i3, j1, j7, k6	2.0, 1.5, 1.5, 1.0; Total = 6.0%
f_3	i4, j5, j8, k4	1.1, 1.0, 2.9, 1.0; Total = 6.0%
f_4	i9, j6, k2	1.9, 2.7, 1.5; Total = 6.1%
f_5	i5, j4, k3	2.3, 1.7, 1.0; Total = 6.0%

Keeping *Cmax* at the same level and increasing *NF* to 5, one obtains set *F2* that uses more components but has less dissimilar formulations (*FEE*=0.47). Relaxing *Cmax* to 1.3 USD/kg, the more diverse set *F3* is obtained, with *FEE* decreasing to 0.36. Additional data regarding set *F3* is given in Table 2. For other input values of *NF* and *Cmax*, the same tendency is observed: a more diverse set of alternatives (low value of *FEE*) come at the price of more expensive formulations.

6. Conclusions

The proposed graph representation and graph partitioning tools are able to identify significantly different alternatives within a space of plausible product formulations (possible large due to uncertain models and heuristics) and thus may be very useful to design an exploratory set of experiments or to build different product lines from a given set of ingredients. Several extensions and refinements of the proposed tools are still to be done, namely the use of additional clustering criteria apart from qualitative composition of the formulation, which was the only one here considered.

References

J.A. Arrieta-Escobar, F.P. Bernardo, A. Orjuela, M. Camargo, L. Morel, 2017, An Integrated Methodology for Emulsified Cosmetic Product Formulation Using Integer Programming with Logical Constraints, in: A. Espuña, M. Graells, L. Puigjaner (Eds.) ESCAPE-27, Computer-Aided Chemical Engineering, Elsevier, Amsterdam, 985-990.

J.A. Arrieta-Escobar, F.P. Bernardo, A. Orjuela, M. Camargo, L. Morel, 2018, Incorporation of heuristic knowledge in the optimal design of formulated products: Application to a cosmetic emulsion, Comput. Chem. Eng., In press.

C. Aykanat, A. Pinar, Ü.V. Çatalyüurek, Permuting sparse rectangular matrices into block-diagonal form, 2004, SIAM J. Sci. Comput., 25, 1860-1879.

M. Boulle, Compact Mathematical Formulation for Graph Partitioning, Optimization and Engineering, 5 (2004) 315-333.

P.-O. Fjällström, Algorithms for graph partitioning: a survey, Linköping Electronic Articles in Computer and Information Science, 3 (1998).

G. Karypis, V. Kumar, hMeTiS. A Hypergraph Partitioning Package. Version 1.5.3, in, Department of Computer & Engineering, University of Minnesota, 1998.

L. Zhang, K.Y. Fung, X. Zhang, H.K. Fung, K.M. Ng, 2017, An integrated framework for designing formulated products, Comput. Chem. Eng., 107, 61-76.

Anton A. Kiss, Edwin Zondervan, Richard Lakerveld, Leyla Özkan (Eds.)
Proceedings of the 29th European Symposium on Computer Aided Process Engineering
June 16th to 19th, 2019, Eindhoven, The Netherlands. © 2019 Elsevier B.V. All rights reserved.
http://dx.doi.org/10.1016/B978-0-128-18634-3.50087-4

Analysis of the Tri-Reforming of Methane in a Membrane Reactor

Samuel S. Q. Jardim, José E. A. Graciano and Rita M. B. Alves[*]

Universidade de São Paulo, Escola Politécnica, Department of Chemical Engineering, Avenida Prof. Luciano Gualberto, trav. 3, 380, São Paulo, 05508-010, Brazil
rmbalves@usp.br

Abstract

This paper analyses the tri-reforming of methane as a reactive way to use natural gas rich in carbon dioxide, without a previous separation. The tri-reforming of methane (TRM) produces syngas suitable for GTL processes and also avoids coke deposition, depending on specific process conditions. For this reason, a thermodynamic analysis was conducted to investigate the possible operating regions to avoid coke formation; then, an operating point was determined by maximizing the CO_2 conversion at a fixed H_2: CO ratio. The given results suggested that the use of large amounts of oxygen are necessary to overcome the coke formation and to increase the syngas yield. In those conditions, the reactor may present hot spots that damage the reactor catalyst. A porous membrane reactor that distributes oxygen along the reactor dropped the sharp thermal profile; the hot spot was mitigated, obtaining 94 % of methane and 30 % of carbon dioxide conversion.

Keywords: membrane reactor, tri-reforming of methane, carbon dioxide, syngas.

1. Introduction

Natural gas is one of the most available sources of energy and a feedstock to the chemical industry. However, in many exploitation sites, the high content of the associated carbon dioxide increases the production cost. For example, in the new Brazilian petroleum off-shore fields, the associated CO_2 is usually between 8 and 18 % and, in some cases, up to 79 % (Gaffney et al., 2010). The elevated CO_2 content in NG requires separation previously to its commercialization, increasing the energy requirement and the production cost. An alternative to mitigate this problem is to use the associated CO_2 as a constituent block to produce added-value products, by combining CO_2 and CH_4 to produce syngas.

Tri-reforming of methane (TRM) is a synergetic combination of Steam Methane Reforming (SMR: $CH_4 + H_2O \rightleftharpoons 3\,H_2 + 1\,CO$), Dry Reforming (DMR : $CH_4 + CO_2 \rightleftharpoons 2\,H_2 + 2\,CO$) and Partial Oxidation of Methane (POM: $CH_4 + 0.5\,O_2 \rightarrow 2\,H_2 + 1\,CO$), able to convert both methane and carbon dioxide into syngas. The POM is an exothermic reaction which provides energy for endothermic SMR and DMR. As a result, TRM can operate adiabatically, unlike conventional reformers, which demand external heat. Moreover, the coke formation is mitigated due to the introduction of oxygen when compared to DMR and SMR processes. Despite several thermodynamic studies in the literature, less attention has been paid to industrial pressures (> 20 bar) and none to adiabatic conditions. As a result, the benefits reported, such as CO_2 conversion over 90 % (Zhang et al., 2014), might not hold true at industrial conditions. The equilibrium analysis in these conditions is a good alternative to determine the best operating point for the membrane reactor and to verify if the TRM is: (i) able to efficiently convert the carbon dioxide and (ii) suitable for the downstream process in a GTL plant.

Additionally, the presence of fast and exothermic reactions makes the reactor design challenging, creating hot spots that can damage the reactor materials and threaten the process viability. For example, Arab Aboosadi et al. (2011) optimized a TRM reactor for hydrogen production but obtained a hot spot near to the melting point of nickel (1455 °C), which can easily deteriorate the catalyst activity. The use of a membrane to distribute oxygen along the reactor can be a promising technology to better control the kinetics and the temperature profile of the TRM, as initially proposed by Rahimpour et al. (2012). However, the requirement of large permeation fluxes and severe operating conditions promote the use of porous membranes in detriment of the perm-selective ones. Indeed, α-alumina membranes may be an interesting choice for this application, since they are chemically stable and their permeability can be easily adjusted to a required value (Alibrando et al., 1997; Coronas and Santamaría, 1999; Godini et al., 2014).

In the present work, the TRM is investigated over a large range of feed composition, for an adiabatic operation at 25 bar, aiming to increase the syngas production from a CO_2-rich NG. The initial thermodynamic analysis is conducted using a simplified equilibrium reactor to determine the operating condition that maximizes the CO_2 conversion, syngas yield and prevent coke formation. After that, the obtained optimum operating point is applied to study the behaviour of a phenomenological membrane reactor, in which the ideal oxygen distribution over the membrane is determined by a sensitivity analysis.

2. Modelling

The thermodynamic analysis is performed to convert CO_2-rich natural gas (CO_2: CH_4 = 0.5) into syngas. This process was simulated by an equilibrium reactor model (*RGibbs* in Aspen Plus V8.8®), considering seven gaseous species (CH_4, CO_2, H_2O, O_2, CO, H_2, N_2) and solid carbon (C), subjected to the elemental balance at constant pressure (25 bar) and isenthalpic operation (adiabatic). The thermodynamic behaviour of the fluid was predicted by the Peng-Robson equation of state. A parametric analysis is conducted to evaluate the influence of water and oxygen ratio (H_2O: CH_4, O_2: CH_4) in four defined metrics, namely: coke yield (Y_{coke}), syngas yield (Y_{syngas}, eq. 1), CO_2 conversion (X_{CO_2}) and syngas quality (H_2: CO).

$$Y_{syngas} = \left[(F_{H_2}^{out} + F_{CO}^{out}) - (F_{H_2}^{in} + F_{CO}^{in}) \right] / (4 F_{CH_4}^{in}) \tag{1}$$

After that, the operating point for the membrane reactor was determined by maximizing the CO_2 conversion, subjected to: syngas ratio equal to 1.6; syngas yield greater than 70%; absence of solid carbon (coke); and inlet and outlet temperature limited to 900 and 1000 °C, respectively. The set of independent variables was defined as: the inlet composition of oxygen, water and feed stream temperature. The stated optimization problem was solved with the SQP method implemented in Aspen Plus V8.8®.

The first-principle membrane reactor was modelled as a packed bed tube with an inert porous membrane wall. Oxygen was fed through both feed stream and membrane, from an outer compartment (shell). On the proposed shell side, the oxygen was fed at 900

°C and 29.5 bar. The reactor had 6 m in length, 0.1 m in inner diameter and 0.43 in bed porosity. The nickel catalyst had 0.015 m in diameter and 2100 kg/m^3 in density. The TRM kinetics were the same used in Arab Aboosadi et al. (2011). The permeation through the α-alumina porous membrane was modeled by Darcy's equation (eq. 2a) for flow in porous media (B$_0$ = 2 × 10^{-16} m^2 and $\delta_{membrane}$ = 1.5 mm) and the pressure drop was determined by Ergun's equation (Salehi et al., 2016).

$$J_{O_2} = \frac{B_0\,\rho_{gas}}{\mu\,\delta_{membrane}}(P_{shell} - P_{tube}) \tag{2a}$$

$$\frac{dF_i}{dz} = A_t \rho_{bed} \sum^q v_i r_q + J_{O_2}\,\pi D \tag{2b}$$

$$\frac{dH_{total}}{dz} = J_{O_2}\,\pi D\,h_{O_2} \tag{2c}$$

A plug-flow regime was assumed with uniform concentrations in the cross-section area. Additionally, no heat conduction is accounted trough the wall (membrane). The resulted 1D-pseudo-homogenous model (eq. 2) was implemented in Aspen Custom Modeler® (ACM). The system of differential algebraic equations was discretized by backward finite difference method with 300 internal nodes, resulting in a system with (75,156) algebraic equations, solved by a Newton-like method.

3. Results and Discussion

3.1. Thermodynamic analysis

Coke production is one of the major problems encountered in industrial reformers. It is responsible for catalyst deactivation, requiring a high proportion of steam to methane in the feed stream (between 2 to 3). Tri-reforming requires less water due to the presence of a stronger oxidant - O$_2$. As observed in Figure 1(a), the minimal oxygen amount to mitigate the coke formation is above 40 %. For oxygen feeds below this proportion, more water is required.

The syngas yield is positively affected by both water and oxygen (Figure 1(b)), due to the SMR and the raise of the adiabatic temperature. The yield is more sensitive to oxygen, growing up to a maximum of 0.73 for 55 % of oxygen (O$_2$:CH$_4$) and 100 % of water (H$_2$O:CH$_4$). The excess of oxygen is also responsible for a decrease in the syngas selectivity, as a result of the higher conversion of methane into carbon dioxide and water (total combustion). In conclusion, both coke and syngas yield profiles stress that a high proportion of oxygen is required for adiabatic operation at 25 bar. However, this imposes a challenge to the reactor design because this high content of oxygen might produce temperatures over the safe operating limits.

The syngas ratio (H$_2$: CO) grows with water (Figure 1 (c)), as a result of the higher syngas ratio provided by the SMR. On the other hand, it decreases with oxygen, due to the rise of the adiabatic temperature, favoring the DMR. Within the coke free region, the syngas ratio tends to be lower than 2.0. Consequently, more water is needed (> 100 %) to attain syngas ratios stoichiometrically suitable for methanol and Fischer-Tropsch plants (around 2). As observed in Figure1(d), the carbon dioxide conversion is more influenced by steam

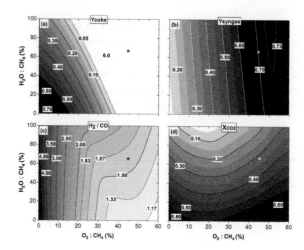

Figure 1: TRM thermodynamic equilibrium analysis at 25 bar, 900°C and 50 % of CO_2: CH_4

than oxygen, due to the presence of the water-gas-shift reaction ($H_2O + CO \rightleftharpoons CO_2 + H_2$). By simultaneously comparing the syngas ratio and CO_2 graphs it is possible to observe a trade-off (Figure1 (c),(d)). If syngas ratios of 2 or higher are desired, the corresponding CO_2 conversion is low. Conversely, in order to convert the most of the CO_2, the syngas ratio should be the lowest possible. In other words, the maximum conversion of CO_2 is at an active constraint on the syngas quality, which is set at a minimum value of 1.6 (a useful value for some special schemes of Fischer-Tropsch synthesis (Graciano et al., 2018)).

The described optimization found an optimum operating point with the inlet composition of $CH_4 : CO_2 : H_2O : O_2 = 1 : 0.5 : 0.679 : 0.4522$, at 900 °C and 25 bar. This condition resulted in conversions of 31.2 % of CO_2 and 93 % of CH_4 with 71 % of syngas yield, as indicated by the asterisk shown in Figure 1.

3.2. Membrane Reactor

Since a large amount of oxygen is required for adiabatic operation, it is important to know how the oxygen distribution affects the reactor performance, especially the thermal behavior. Therefore, the effect of the oxygen partition (proportion of oxygen injected at the feed to the one permeated through the porous membrane, $O_{2,feed} | O_{2,membrane}$) is shown in Table 1 and Figure 2. As verified, the kinetic model deviates slightly from the equilibrium results, favoring more conversion of CO_2 and CH_4. The oxygen partition does not significantly shift the overall reactor performance. In contrast, the thermal behavior changes drastically (Figure 2). For example, at 0 % oxygen partition (no oxygen distribution through the membrane) the temperature goes up to 1650 °C, far away from

Table 1: Overall results of oxygen partition in the membrane reactor

$O_{2,feed} | O_{2,membrane}$	equilibrium	0%l100%	20%l80%	40%l60%	60%l40%	80%l20%	100%l0%
O_2/CH_4 at feed	45%	45%	36%	27%	18%	9%	0%
$J_{O_2} (mol/m^2 s)$	-	0.00	0.10	0.20	0.30	0.40	0.51
X_{CH_4}	0.93	0.94	0.94	0.94	0.94	0.94	0.93
X_{CO_2}	0.31	0.33	0.33	0.33	0.33	0.33	0.33
Y_{syngas}	0.71	0.71	0.71	0.71	0.71	0.71	0.71
H_2/CO	1.60	1.58	1.58	1.58	1.57	1.57	1.57

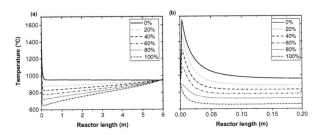

Figure 2: Temperature profile of the membrane reactor for different oxygen partitions, full (a) and zoomed (b) profile.

the melting point of nickel (1455 °C). Cold spots also occur, especially at low oxygen feed because the inlet oxygen is not enough to overcome the endothermic reactions. Despite different profiles for the oxygen distribution, their temperatures coincide at the reactor end (about 950°C). The partition results indicate that a sharp temperature profile is unavoidable. There will always be either a hot or a cold spot due to the extreme enthalpy and reaction velocities at the reactor inlet. Since a hotspot is undesirable for safety reasons, a partition of 80 % is chosen for the porous membrane study.

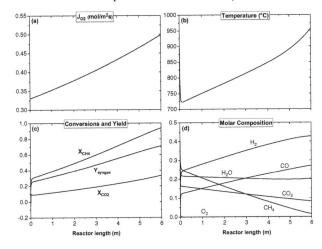

Figure 3: Profile of the membrane reactor using 80 % of oxygen partition. The shell pressure is fixed at 29.5 bar.

Figure 3 shows the reactor behaviour operating at the conditions determined in the thermodynamic analysis and oxygen partition study. As observed in Figure 3 (a), the permeation flux grows from 0.33 up to 0.50 mol/m^{2}s due to the pressure drop in the catalytic bed. Therefore, the transmembrane pressure, pressure drop and the permeability of the membrane should be well designed and controlled to prevent an undesired flux of oxygen. As expected, the temperature profile (Figure 3(b)) reveals no hot spot but rather a cold spot in the inlet region followed by a smooth growth up to the equilibrium temperature, from 725 to 953°C. The conversions and syngas yield profiles (Figure 3(c)) have similar behaviors, a sharp increase at the inlet due to the fast reforming reactions, followed by a smoother growth caused by the temperature increase. The methane and carbon dioxide conversions go up to 94 % and 33.5 % with syngas yield of 71 %. The molar composition shows the same trend with a very steep change at the inlet (Figure 3(d)). Oxygen is extremely low since it reacts faster as soon as it is introduced in the reactive mixture.

4. Conclusions

The TRM thermodynamic analysis revealed that the adiabatic operation demands substantial oxygen feed to obtain high syngas yields and to avoid coke formation, around half of the methane feed. Moreover, there is a trade-off between the CO_2 conversion and the syngas ratio; CO_2 is converted at the expense of hydrogen production. The membrane reactor showed to be a good alternative to safely provide a high amount of oxygen. The reactor consumed 93 % of the methane and 32 % of the carbon dioxide feed, producing 71 % of the methane into syngas at a 1.6 ratio. As shown, different ratios of oxygen partition do not change the overall reactor performance. No matter how the oxygen is partitioned, drastic temperature behavior is found in the inlet region, either by hot spot or cold spot. However, the chosen oxygen partition of 80 % makes the operation possible by keeping the temperature profile within the limits imposed by the catalyst. The porous membrane imposes a non-uniform distribution of oxygen that grows with the reactor length. As a result, over-oxidation can occur due to the low methane pressure in the outlet region. In short, the proposed porous membrane reactor can perform TRM adiabatically, processing natural gas with high CO_2 content without previous separation.

Acknowledgments: The authors gratefully acknowledge support from FAPESP and SHELL Brasil through the "Research Centre for Gas Innovation – RCGI" (FAPESP Proc. 2014/50279-4), hosted by the University of São Paulo, and the support given by ANP (Brazil's National Oil, Natural Gas and Biofuels Agency) through the R&D levy regulation.

References

M. Alibrando, H. S. Ã. Hahm, E. E. Wolf, 1997. Partial oxidation of methane to synthesis gas on a Rh / TiO 2 catalyst in a fast flow porous membrane reactor. Catal. Letters 49, 1–12.

Z. Arab Aboosadi, A. H. Jahanmiri, M. R. Rahimpour, 2011. Optimization of tri-reformer reactor to produce synthesis gas for methanol production using differential evolution (DE) method. Appl. Energy 88 (8), 2691–2701.

J. Coronas, J. Santamaría, 1999. Catalytic reactors based on porous ceramic membranes. Catal. Today 51 (3-4), 377–389.

C. Gaffney, et al., 2010. Exame e avaliação de dez descobertas e prospectos selecionadas no play do pré-sal em águas profundas na bacia de santos, brasil. Documento acessado no endereço eletrônico http://www. anp. gov. br.

H. R. Godini, A. Gili, O. Görke, U. Simon, G. Hou, G. Wozny, feb 2014. Performance analysis of a porous packed bed membrane reactor for oxidative coupling of methane: Structural and operational characteristics. Energy and Fuels 28 (2), 877–890.
URL http://pubs.acs.org/doi/10.1021/ef402041b

J. E. Graciano, B. Chachuat, R. M. Alves, 2018. Conversion of CO2-Rich Natural Gas to Liquid Transportation Fuels via Trireforming and Fischer-Tropsch Synthesis: Model-Based Assessment. Ind. Eng. Chem. Res. 57 (30), 9964–9976.

M. R. Rahimpour, Z. Arab Aboosadi, A. H. Jahanmiri, 2012. Synthesis gas production in a novel hydrogen and oxygen perm-selective membranes tri-reformer for methanol production. J. Nat. Gas Sci. Eng. 9, 149–159.

M. S. Salehi, M. Askarishahi, H. R. Godini, O. Görke, G. Wozny, 2016. Sustainable Process Design for Oxidative Coupling of Methane (OCM): Comprehensive Reactor Engineering via Computational Fluid Dynamics (CFD) Analysis of OCM Packed-Bed Membrane Reactors. Ind. Eng. Chem. Res. 55 (12), 3287–3299.

Y. Zhang, S. Zhang, J. L. Gossage, H. H. Lou, T. J. Benson, 2014. Thermodynamic analyses of tri-reforming reactions to produce syngas. Energy & Fuels 28 (4), 2717–2726.

Anton A. Kiss, Edwin Zondervan, Richard Lakerveld, Leyla Özkan (Eds.)
Proceedings of the 29th European Symposium on Computer Aided Process Engineering
June 16th to 19th, 2019, Eindhoven, The Netherlands. © 2019 Elsevier B.V. All rights reserved.
http://dx.doi.org/10.1016/B978-0-128-18634-3.50088-6

Design of a novel sour water stripping unit

Umer Zahid [a*], Ali Al-Qadri [a], Baqer Al-Mousa [a], Ali Al-Nasser [a], Usama Ahmed [a]

[a] *Department of Chemical Engineering, King Fahd University of Petroleum and Minerals, Dhahran, 34464, Saudi Arabia*

uzahid@kfupm.edu.sa

Abstract

This study focusses on the design and simulation of sour water stripping (SWS) unit in the refinery setup for the reuse of sour water. In this study, process simulation has been performed to analyze the energy saving and cost reducing prospects in the sour water stripping unit. First, a base case design has been simulated using a reference sour water stripping unit data. The developed model is validated against the plant data in order to ensure the model validity. A novel design has been proposed in this study that can reduce the energy requirement by 53 % compared to the conventional designs. The results of this study provide a meaningful analysis in terms of energy and economic considerations to improve the performance of the sour water units in the refineries.

Keywords: Sour water stripping, energy efficiency, process simulation, economic analysis.

1. Introduction

Refineries around the world process thousands of barrels of crude oil every day for the production of various petroleum products. The oil refineries generate considerable amounts of sour water from various processes that should be treated before the water can be reused or disposed of. In a typical refinery setup, the stripped sour water can be reused in the crude de-salter section for the removal of chloride salts to inhibit the formation of HCl in the downstream distillation columns (Lieberman, 2013). The stripped water can also be used in the hydrotreater unit for the removal of ammonia sulfide which otherwise could lead to a serious plugging of the condensers in the presence of CO_2 (Gai et al., 2008). Many studies in the past have focused on how to reduce the energy requirement of the sour water stripping process while meeting the environmental regulatory requirements. Sour water strippers can be configured in a variety of ways including column configurations, condensing and reboiler system and stripping methods.

Weiland and Hatcher (Weiland and Hatcher, 2012) studied the sour water stripping process employing a rate based simulation model using ProTreat. Their results showed that depending on the stream rate and H_2S to NH_3 ratio, the overall tray efficiency can vary widely between 15 to 45 %. Bellen (Bellen, 2009) described a step-by-step guide to the design and operation of sour water stripper and showcased the process simulation using Aspen HYSYS and PRO/II simulators. Nabgan et al. (Nabgan et al., 2016) compared the operational performance of single column and double column SWS process using Aspen HYSYS. Their results showed that 100% of NH_3 was stripped in the two columns model whereas only 24% was stripped using the single column model. Sharma and Nag (Sharma and Nag, 2009) analysed the design modifications in the sour water stripping unit installed at one of the refineries in the India to enhance the H_2S recovery from the sour water before it is fed to the stripper. The simulated the SWS process using Chemcad and showed that approximately 7.5 % more H_2S can be recovered compared to the base design by installing a hot flash drum upstream of the stripper column.

Although, SWS systems have been installed and operational in the industry since decades, however, not enough effort has been done to improve their design and performance. With growing concerns on the environmental issues and energy efficiency improvements in the industry, there is a need to look into SWS system which is an important unit in the refineries. Most of the above mentioned studies simulated the SWS systems and analyzed the process performance. However, very few studies considered the tray efficiencies in their simulation with no details on the model validation. In addition, most of the studies were focused on how to achieve the desired stripped water composition with little attention to the process improvement. Also, to authors knowledge, no previous studies in the open literature have quoted the cost information required for the sour water stripping. The goal of this study is to utilize the process simulation tool for analyzing the sour water stripper process and improve the process performance by design modifications. A novel vapor compression design has been proposed in this study which is compared with other conventional designs reported in the literature. The effect of the design modifications are then evaluated economically in order to check the feasibility of the design.

2. Process Design

The design of the sour water stripping unit considered in this study is based on the refinery data processing a mixture of light and heavy Arabian crude oil. The sour water stripping simulation has been performed using the Aspen HYSYS. The feed specifications along with the major components in the system are shown in table 1. As recommended by previous studies (Nabgan et al., 2016), NRTL has been selected as the thermodynamic property package because the activity coefficient models are suitable in the presence of polar components and non-ideal system.

Table 1: Feed specifications used in the simulation model

Feed flow rate	t/h	185
Temperature	°C	40
Pressure	bar	4.9
Composition		
H_2S	mass fr.	0.0030
NH_3	mass fr.	0.0016
H_2O	mass fr.	0.9953
NaCl	mass fr.	0.0001

2.1. Base case design

Most of the new industrial stripper installations are similar to this design scheme. Figure 1 shows the process flow scheme for the base case design. The sour water feed is pre-heated with the stripped water to 60 °C before entering the stripper. The purity requirement of the stripped water is maintained by providing heat through the reboiler. Liquid phase side draw is withdrawn from the stage 6 which is then cooled down to 65 °C using an air-cooler and returned back to the top of the column. The vapor stream leaves at the top of the column mainly comprising of H₂S, NH₃ and water. This design as referred by its name is simple without a condenser that can save the cooling utility along with some capital cost while meeting the purity requirements of the stripped water.

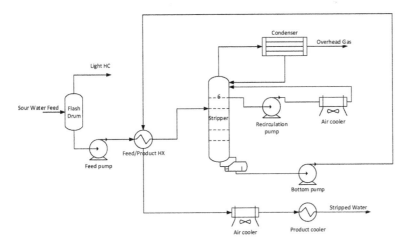

Figure 1: Process flow diagram of base case design

2.2. Bottom cycle vapor compression design

A new design is proposed in this study with the aim to reduce the energy requirements of the conventional sour water stripping process. The proposed design employs mechanical work using a compressor instead of hot and cold utilities. In this design, the stripped water stream leaving at the bottom of the column is flashed to a reduced pressure, whereby, some amount of vapours are generated. The produced vapours leave at the top of the flash drum and are fed to the two-stage compression train. A compression ratio of three is assumed in each compressor stage with an intercooler. The compressed vapor stream at 2.1 bar and 240.7 °C then heats up the incoming feed stream and is fed to the bottom of the column at 121.7 °C. The incoming feed stream is heated from 40 °C to 53.5 °C using the heat available from the compressed vapor. It is then heated to 60 °C using the hot utility before bring fed to the 7th stage in the stripper column. The advantage of this design is the elimination of stripper's condenser and reboiler which leads to a reduction in the utilities requirement. Since, the compression also increases the process stream temperature, the heat available from the compression work is supplied to the bottoms of the stripper. However, this design requires an additional compressor work to increase the stream pressure and subsequently the temperature. Figure 2 shows the process flow diagram for the vapor compression design. The reflux at the top of the column is provided in the same way as that of the simple stripper design by a circulation loop. A recirculation cooling loop withdraws some of the liquid from stage 6, cools it down to 60 °C and pump it back to the top of the column.

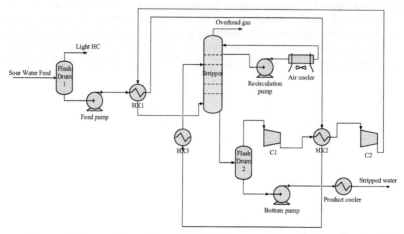

Figure 2: Process flow scheme for the bottom cycle vapor compression design

3. Results

3.1. Tray efficiency

The tray performance and its efficiency depends on the design, active area, weir length and height, down-comer area and so on. Since, no information regarding the tray efficiency was known from the plant data, the efficiency is estimated by fitting the simulation results with the plant data. The results show that the overall efficiency of the stripper trays is approximately 15 % which is a typical value for an industrial sour water strippers (Hatcher and Weiland, 2012; Nagpal, 2014).

3.2. Energy analysis

The stripped water stream is set to contain no more than 10 and 100 ppm of H_2S and NH_3 content respectively. The results show that the base case design consume more energy compared to the bottom cycle vapor compression design. Figure 3 shows the total energy and unit energy requirement per ton of water stripped. The novel design consumes approximately 53 % less energy compared to the base case design. This significant improvement has been made by cutting down the cold and hot utilities for the condenser and reboiler respectively. The largest energy consuming equipment in the base case is the reboiler which requires more than 70 % of the total energy. This hot utility requirement of the reboiler has been saved in the vapor compression design by using the mechanical energy instead of thermal energy. Cooling is the second highest energy consuming process in the base case which in most of the cases is provided by the cooling utility as shown in figure 4. In case of vapor compression design, cooling and compression are the main energy consuming steps accounting to around 48 % and 36 % respectively.

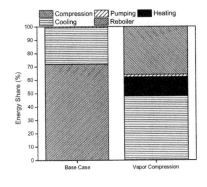

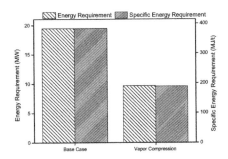

Figure 3: Comparative energy analysis sour water stripper designs

Figure 4: Percent energy share for the sour water stripper designs

Figure 5 shows the vapor phase composition profile of NH$_3$ and H$_2$S in the stripper. The results show that the removal of H$_2$S is accomplished easily and require less number of stages to achieve the desired stripped water purity specification. However, the removal of NH$_3$ from the sour water is more difficult and require more number of trays to satisfy the stripped water composition standards.

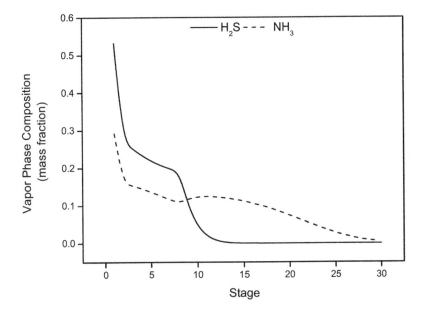

Figure 5: Vapor phase composition of H$_2$S and NH$_3$ in the stripper

4. Conclusions

In this study, Aspen HYSYS has been used to simulate the sour water stripping unit of a refinery. The base case design has been compared with a novel vapor compression design. Both the process designs were compared in terms of energy requirement while maintaining the stripped water purity of 10 ppm H_2S and 100 ppm NH_3 content. This study presents a novel design that can reduce the energy requirement of the stripping process significantly compared to the conventional designs. The results show that the proposed vapor recompression design can reduce the hot and cold utilities requirement by 90 % and 22 % respectively compared to the base case design.

Acknowledgment: The authors would like to acknowledge financial support from King Fahd University of Petroleum & Minerals (KFUPM).

References

Bellen, J., 2009. Design of Sour Water Stripping System, in: Proceedings of the 70th Philippine Institute of Chemical Engineers Annual National Convention.

Gai, H., Jiang, Y., Qian, Y., Kraslawski, A., 2008. Conceptual design and retrofitting of the coal-gasification wastewater treatment process. Chem. Eng. J. 138, 84–94.

Lieberman, N., 2013. Sour water strippers: Design and operation. Pet. Technol. Q. 18, 99–103.

Nabgan, B., Abdullah, T.A.T., Nabgan, W., Ahmad, A., Saeh, I., Moghadamian, K., 2016. Process simulation for removing impurities from wastewater using sour water 2-strippers Nagpal, S., 2014. Fine tune the design of sour-water strippers using rate-based simulation. Chem. Eng. (United States) 121, 42–46.

system via Aspen Hysys. Chem. Prod. Process Model. 11, 315–321.

Sharma, M.K., Nag, A., 2009. Process developed for enhanced H2S recovery from sour-water strippers. Oil Gas J. 107, 44–49.

Weiland, R.H., Hatcher, N. a, 2012. Sour water strippers exposed 285–298.

Anton A. Kiss, Edwin Zondervan, Richard Lakerveld, Leyla Özkan (Eds.)
Proceedings of the 29th European Symposium on Computer Aided Process Engineering
June 16th to 19th, 2019, Eindhoven, The Netherlands. © 2019 Elsevier B.V. All rights reserved.
http://dx.doi.org/10.1016/B978-0-128-18634-3.50089-8

Techno-economic Assessment of Future Generation IGCC Processes with Control on Greenhouse Gas Emissions

Usama Ahmed [a*], Umer Zahid [a]

[a] *Chemical Engineering Department, King Fahd University of Petroleum and Minerals, Dhahran, Saudi Arabia*

usama.ahmed@kfupm.edu.sa

Abstract

Integrated gasification and combined cycle (IGCC) is a pre-combustion carbon capture technology that can be used to generate electricity and hydrogen while reducing the green house gas emissions. In this study, three IGCC based process models are developed in Aspen Plus ® followed by their techno-economic evaluation. Case 1 is the conventional IGCC process which is considered as a reference model, whereas, case 2 and case 3 are the conceptual process models. In case 2, gasification unit in the conventional IGCC model is integrated with the reforming technology to utilize the steam produced in the gasification unit in the methane reforming process. This concept not only increased the overall yield of syngas but also the H_2 production capacity. On the other hand, the case 3 is modified to convert the conventional IGCC into oxy-fuel IGCC process keeping the reforming unit in place which nullifies the need of using standalone energy intensive water gas shift units and CO_2 capturing unit. The efficiencies calculated for case 1, case 2 and case 3 are 35.86%, 40.7% and 41.3%, respectively. The economic analysis showed that the cost required for each unit of energy generated is 2.93, 2.06 and 2.01 M€/MWe, respectively. The results also showed that the case 3 design not only offers highest process performance and economics but it offers least CO_2 specific emissions compared to the case 1 and case 2 designs.

Keywords: IGCC, SMR, Oxyfuel, CCS, LCOE.

1. Introduction

With the increase in population and industrialization during the last few decades have increased both the energy demand and pollution in the world. The power generation sectors mainly relies on the fossil fuels to compete the world energy demand and are held responsible for 35% of greenhouse gas (GHG) emissions where 75% of total emissions includes CO_2. Among various fossil fuels, coal and natural gas have been receiving a lot of attention for power generation due to their abundance in nature and already developed infrastructures. International Energy Agency (2014) statistics showed that almost 40.58% of electricity in 2010 was generated from only coal where its consumption is expected to increase by 33% in 2035 compared to 2009. Due to an ever increasing energy demand in future also, carbon capture and sequestration (CCS) technologies will play a vital role in controlling and abating GHG emissions. Natural gas combined cycle (NGCC), ultra-supercritical pulverized coal (USPC) and integrated gasification and combined cycle (IGCC) power plants are currently the main sources of electricity generation. However, the efficiency of power plants tremendously drops with the implementation of CCS technology. For instance, NGCC, USPC and IGCC power plants shows an efficiency drop of 7.1%, 11.4% and 9%, respectively with the CCS technology. Moreover, currently operating post combustion carbon capture processes from coal would nearly double the cost of electricity (COE) while decreasing the net output by 7-10%. On the other hand, pre-combustion processes have higher capital investments but they are more energy efficient if CCS is implemented on large scale. Although, NGCC processes offers higher process performances with CCS, however, the higher and fluctuating cost of natural gas limits its extensive utilization over coal based power plants. Therefore, the state of art technologies for power and H_2 generation can be integrated to enhance the overall process performance while abating the GHG emissions.

Process optimization and intensification techniques along with the better heat integration methods provides an opportunity to increase the reliability and sustainability of processes. Recently, Ahmed et al. (2016) and Cormos et al. (2015) explored the various design routes for enhancing the IGCC performance with CCS techniques. On the other hand, Yi et al. (2014) performed the studies for integrating IGCC and natural gas reforming processes to enhance the H_2/CO content in the syngas followed by their consequent use in various poly generation processes. Recently, Ahmed et al. (2017) presented the model for integrating the gasification and reforming technology that utilizes the in-process generated steam during coal slurry gasification process to assist the reforming process and makes the process more self-sustainable. This study has been performed in continuation of the previous work performed by Ahmed et al. (2016, 2017) with more promising results. In this study, the idea of integrating the available technologies (IGCC, Reforming and Oxyfuel) is presented to enhance the overall process sustainability. The results for the conventional and proposed processes will be compared in terms of both the process performance and economics to assess the design reliability.

2. Simulation Methodology and Process Description:

Three simulation models are developed in Aspen Plus ® using Peng Robinson equation of state as a thermodynamic package. Coal is an un-conventional compound and has been modeled based on proximate and ultimate analysis. The gasification, water gas shift and reformer reactors are modelled on the basis of RGibbs reactor models which are operated on the Gibbs free energy minimization laws to generate syngas reaction products as shown in Table 1.

Table 1: Design Assumptions for Model Development

Unit/Component/System	Modelling Unit	Parameter
Gasification Reactor	RGibbs (Reactor)	Coal flow rate= 38.51kg/s Temp/Press: 1550°C/32 bar
Reformer	RGibbs (Reactor)	NG flow rate: 2.47 kg/sec $H_2O:CH_4 = 3:1$ Temp/Press: 900-1050°C/ 32 bar
Air Separation Unit (ASU)	HeatX, Compr	Oxygen Purity 99.5% (vol) Energy: 245 kW/t
Shift Conversion (WGS)	RGibbs (Reactor)	(Co-Mo) Sour Catalyst Steam/CO: ~ 2.2
Acid Gas Removal H_2S and CO_2	RadFrac (Selexol Solvent)	H_2S/CO_2 Removal Percentage: 99.9 / 90

2.1. Conventional IGCC process (Case 1):

Case 1 is a conventional IGCC process which is taken as a base case model that sequentially integrates the gasification unit (GU), air separation unit (ASU), water gas shift reactor (WGS), heat recovery steam generation (HRSG), acid gas removal section (AGR), and combined cycle (CC) as shown in Figure 1. Coal water slurry is fed to the entrained flow gasification unit to generate syngas which is a mixture of CO, H_2, CO_2 and H_2O. Syngas leaves the gasification unit at a very high temperature (~1600 °C) and contains high concentration of H_2 and CO. The temperature of the syngas is reduced to 250-500 °C in the radiant and convective heat exchangers to carry out WGS reactions as shown in equation in Eq.(1).

$$CO + H_2O \leftrightarrow H_2 + CO_2 \qquad \Delta H = -41 \text{ KJ/mole} \qquad (1)$$

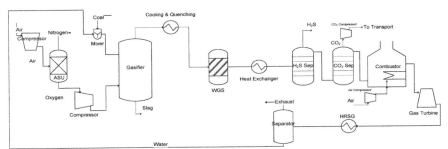

Figure 1: Case 1 – Conventional IGCC design for power generation with CO_2 capture

The syngas from WGS reactors is then passed through AGR section where most of the CO_2 and H_2S is removed and recovered by Selexol solvent. The separated CO_2 is than further processed and compressed to an elevated pressure for its transport and storage, whereas, H_2S is further treated in a Claus plant to recover elemental sulfur. The syngas leaving from AGR section contains high concentration of H_2 which is directed towards CC section to generate electricity and the process heat.

2.2. Integration of IGCC and SMR Process (Case 2):

Steam methane reforming (SMR) technology is extensively used for the commercial production of H_2 gas. SMR is an endothermic process which is carried out by reacting high pressure steam with the methane gas at a temperature range of 627-827°C as shown in equation (2). Reforming process is usually carried out in two sequential steps i.e. pre-reforming and reforming. Firstly, the compressed methane is heated and mixed with a high enthalpy steam in a pre-reforming section. Ahmed et al. (2017) and Lucero et al. (2015) demonstrated the reforming process over the nickel-based catalyst to generate H_2.

$$CH_4 + H_2O \leftrightarrow CO + 3H_2 \qquad \Delta H = 242 \text{ kJ/kmol} \qquad (2)$$

Conventional SMR processes requires an additional heat source for preheating the gas stream to assist the reforming process. However, in this case, the syngas generated during gasification process is cooled and mixed with the compressed natural gas where the inlet temperature of the reformer is maintained at 1150 °C. As the mixture passes through the reforming unit, the temperature reduces to 1040 °C due to an endothermic reforming reactions. The conceptual process flow diagram of case 2 can be seen from Figure 2. The syngas from the reforming section is then directed to the WGS reactors to generate additional H_2 and CO_2. The CO_2 and H_2S generated in the process is removed in the AGR section using Selexol process, whereas, the H_2 is sent to the CC section to generate electricity. As natural gas used in this case is an important utility, therefore, the corresponding net efficiency of NGCC power plants have been also incorporated for the fair evaluation of the analysis in the next section.

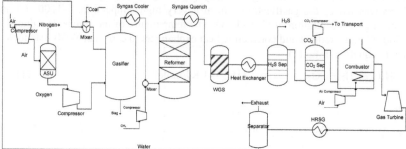

Figure 2: Case 2 – Integration of IGCC and methane reforming process with CO_2 capture

2.3. Integration of IGCC, SMR and Oxyfuel Processes (Case 3):

Oxyfuel combustion technology can be used for burning the fuel in the presence of high purity oxygen to generate more heat compared to air by avoiding its dilution with N_2. The flue gas generated from the oxyfuel combustion process contain high purity CO_2 and H_2O which do not requires any standalone chemical or physical sorbent process to capture CO_2. The temperature of the flue gas is reduced in multiple heat exchangers to condense the moisture and pure CO_2 is separated followed by its compressing in the multi-stage compression unit for further utilization. The case 3 design is an advanced version of case 2 in which we can integrate the oxyfuel combustion technology with the gasification and the reforming processes as shown in the Figure 3. The CO_2 generated in the combustion section is partially recycled to the combustion reactor to control both the combustion temperature and maintaining the inlet temperature of flue gas for gas turbine power generation unit. This integration will also nullify the need of installing additional WGS and CO_2 capture units compared to the case 1 and case 2 designs that will also improve both the process performance and economics of the overall process.

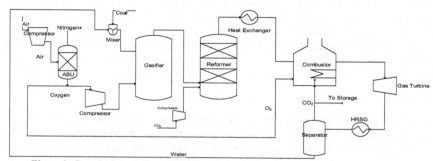

Figure 3: Case 3 - Integration of IGCC with the Reforming and Oxyfuel Technology

3. Results and Discussion

Case 1 is a conventional IGCC process design where the heating value of syngas typically depends on the operational conditions of the gasifier. The addition of reforming unit with the gasification unit in case 2 generates an additional syngas from SMR process. The SMR process utilizes high enthalpy steam from the syngas to convert CH_4 to H_2 while maintaining the reformer's temperature and pressure. Figure 4 provides the comparison of case 1 with the other two cases in terms of syngas composition and heating value at the outlet of the reforming unit. The case 2 and case 3 has the same configuration up to reforming unit so the syngas composition and heating value remained same at the reformer's outlet.

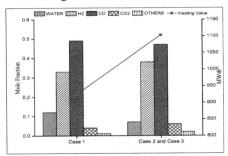

Figure 4: Syngas Composition & Heating Values at the Reformer's Outlet

The results showed that syngas production capacity for case 2 and case 3 has been increased compared to the case 1 design due to installation of the reforming unit. Due to the increase in H_2/CO ratio and heating value of the syngas in the case 2 and case 3 designs, the power generation capacity from both the steam cycle and the gas turbine section are also increased compared to the case 1 design. While comparing case 2 and case 3, it has been analyzed that case 3 generates more power in the steam cycle process due to an oxyfuel nature of the process and also due to an absence of WGS unit which requires steam to convert CO to H_2. However, the power generation from the gas turbine section for the case 3 is lower than the case 2 design as less flue gas passes through the gas turbine section due to syngas combustion with the high purity oxygen instead of excess air. The net power generated and process efficiency for case 1, case 2 and case 3 is calculated as (375.08, 472.92 and 495.01) MWe and (35.86, 40.7 and 41.3) % respectively. The breakup for power generation from the combined cycle processes is given in Figure 5.

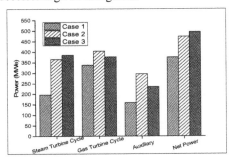

Figure 5: Comparison of process performance of all cases

The key purpose of any power plant is to produce electricity at an economical price. Some of the process performance and economic indicators are used to evaluate the LCOE (cost of electricity) with CCS technology, CO_2 specific emissions and CO_2 capture cost in terms of

CO_2 removal and avoidance cost for all the cases which are summarized in   Table 2. It has been seen from results that the case 3 design has a potential to reduce the LCOE by 11.6% and 6.2% compared to the case 1 and case 2 designs, respectively. Moreover, the case 3 design also offers a reduction in both the CO_2 specific emissions and CO_2 capture cost compared to the case 1 and case 2 designs.

Table 2: Comparison of some economic indicators for case 1, case 2 and case 3 designs

	Units	Case 1	Case 2	Case 3
LCOE	€/MW$_h$	70.57	66.47	62.35
CO_2 Specific emission	kg/MW$_h$	87.74	80.26	78.45
CO_2 avoidance/removal cost	€/t	36.23/26.99	27.97/20.45	25.66/18.35

4. Conclusions

In this study, three IGCC based process models have been developed and techno-economically compared. Case 1 is based on the conventional IGCC process, whereas, case 2 integrates the conventional IGCC with the reforming technology. Case 3 is a further modification of the case 2 design which converts the downstream process into oxyfuel technology which nullifies the utilization of standalone WGS and CO_2 capture units. It has been seen from results that the case 3 design offers higher process efficiency and economics compared to other cases which makes the overall process more reliable and sustainable.

Acknowledgement

The authors would like to acknowledge the support provided by the King Fahd University of Petroleum & Minerals (KFUPM) for funding this work through project No. SR181006.

References

International Energy Agency (IEA), World Energy Investment Outlook, 2014, France

Ahmed, U., Zahid, U., Jeong, Y.S., Lee, C. J., Han, C., 2016, IGCC process intensification for simultaneous power generation and CO_2 capture. Chemical Engineering and Processing: Process Intensification 101, 72-86.

Ahmed, U., Kim, C., Zahid, U., Lee, C. J., & Han, C., 2017, Integration of IGCC and methane reforming process for power generation with CO_2 capture. Chemical Engineering and Processing: Process Intensification, 111, 14-24.

Cormos, A.M., Dinca, C., Cormos, C.C., 2015, Multi-fuel multi-product operation of IGCC power plants with carbon capture and storage (CCS). Applied Thermal Engineering 74, 20-27.

Lucero, A. Goyal, J. Carroll, K. McCabe, and S. Gangwal. H_2S resistant steam reforming catalyst for upgrading coal derived syngas for coal to liquid production, https://www.netl.doe.gov/sites/default/files/2017-11/Lucero-Poster-for-DOE-Gasification-workshop.pdf

Yi, Q., Feng, J., Wu, Y., Li, W., 2014, 3E (energy, environmental, and economy) evaluation and assessment to an innovative dual-gas polygeneration system. Energy 66, 285-294.

Anton A. Kiss, Edwin Zondervan, Richard Lakerveld, Leyla Özkan (Eds.)
Proceedings of the 29th European Symposium on Computer Aided Process Engineering
June 16th to 19th, 2019, Eindhoven, The Netherlands. © 2019 Elsevier B.V. All rights reserved.
http://dx.doi.org/10.1016/B978-0-128-18634-3.50090-4

Synthesis of Solar Heat Network for Preheating of Industrial Process Streams

Ben Abikoye,[a,*] Lidija Čuček,[b,*] Adeniyi Isafiade,[a] Zdravko Kravanja[b]

[a]*Department of Chemical Engineering, University of Cape Town, Private Bag X3, Rondebosch 7701, Cape Town, South Africa*

[b]*Faculty of Chemistry and Chemical Engineering, University of Maribor, Smetanova ulica 17, 2000 Maribor, Slovenia*

abksem001@myuct.ac.za, lidija.cucek@um.si

Abstract

Industrial integration of solar for process heat applications with periodic heat storage and backup utility system ensures reliability and efficiency of renewable heat utilization, thus minimizing the dependence on fossil fuel and energy related emissions. Furthermore, by minimizing heat duty from backup utility, opportunities for matching solar thermal and solar heat storage could be fully explored. This study models the industrial application of solar thermal considering direct and indirect integration, periodic heat storage and backup utility. For the synthesis of the integrated design, a flowsheet superstructure is presented for multi-period heat supply network of industrial processes. The design and optimization of the integrated system is implemented and solved in GAMS with the objective of maximizing total heat output to the heat network. To demonstrate the performance of the model, the proposed solar heat network design for industrial utility retrofit is applied to an illustrative case study of preheating a cold industrial stream.

Keywords: Solar thermal, Solar heat, Thermal storage, Solar heat integration, Industrial solar integration.

1. Introduction

Over the past few decades, the global energy consumption has been on steady increase due to the rising of population and expanding economic activities. According to a recent report, heat consumption accounts for over 50 % of the annual global energy use (WEC, 2016) and analysis has revealed that as at 2014 about 75 % of this share of energy consumption (around 130 EJ) is currently sourced from fossil fuels (OECD/IEA, 2015) which negatively impacts the environment.

Solar thermal is a form of renewable energy with great potentials to substitute/ supplement the use of fossil fuels for various heating purposes because it is a low-carbon source of heat and power (electricity). Studies have shown that out of the total global industrial heat consumption of 85 EJ, 30 % is used for low temperature (<150 °C) heat operations (IEA, 2017). Due to the wide range of industrial processes with low temperature heat operations, industrial solar utilization is believed to have great potentials.

Solar industrial utility retrofit in combination with periodic heat storage (Abikoye et al. 2018) is a demonstration of how a renewable source of heat can be effectively planned for and harnessed with industrial heat networks. Due to supply variability and low thermal value of solar over some time periods, an important feature which could further improve thermal performance in such designs is the inclusion of an effective backup utility system in the design framework.

While a significant number of research works has been carried out on solar thermal utilization, not much has been done on the application and optimization of solar technologies for industrial processes (Kong et al. 2018). Even in some existing solar designs with thermal storage, managing the intermittent fluctuations of heat supply is still quite challenging due to the technical difficulties and large number of decision variables involved, especially when considering backup alternatives to circumvent the supply gaps in solar systems. In this study, an integrated design of a solar heat network is proposed for stream preheating in industrial processes in order to study attainable quantities of solar heat that can be harvested regardless of economics considerations which can vary significantly both temporarily and spatially. The design includes strategies that account for the multi-period variability in solar energy supply on hourly basis according to meteorological data obtained from EC-JRC PVGIS (2017) for the specific location considered. The synthesis method involves a balanced close-loop circuit of direct and indirect solar thermal system with periodic heat storage and backup utility.

2. Methodology

2.1. *Solar heat network design for industrial utility retrofit*

The framework for solar industrial preheating is outlined to demonstrate the flow of harvested solar thermal for direct and indirect (via heat storage tank) plant integration. Figure 1 consists of a closed-loop superstructure of industrial solar thermal utilization incorporated with a periodic heat storage and a backup boiler to form an integrated heat supply network. In the resulting structure, harvested solar thermal flows through the splitter which gives opportunities for both direct and indirect industrial integration of the captured solar heat where indirect integration through storage tank enables solar heat use in time periods when there is no solar irradiation.

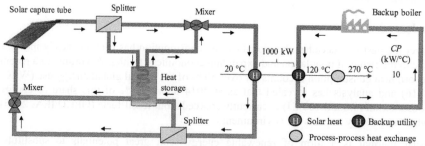

Figure 1: Integration of solar heat network for industrial stream preheating (modified from Abikoye et al. 2018)

The total solar heat available for integration is targeted for stream preheating across a specific heater for as much heat demand that could be satisfied while alternative heat source is provided to the network by the backup utility. The alternative heat source heats the cold stream to its final target temperature in cases where the captured solar heat is not sufficient. To ensure optimal and efficient solar heat use in the integrated system, another splitter is placed at the outlet from the process plant such that the heat transfer fluid can return to the solar collector or to the storage tank depending on whether the temperature level of return could be useful to buffer the heat in the storage tank.

2.2 Model development

The developed model comprises material and energy balances across the solar collector, splitters, mixers, heat storage tank, backup boiler and the plant (two heat exchangers) that is targeted for solar heat integration. It should also be noted that the operational features of a typical solar heating system are transient, therefore to account for the time dependencies, the model is formulated as a mixed-integer non-linear programming (MINLP) problem. Also, the synthesis is implemented simultaneously with the objective of maximizing the average solar heat output to the network ($Q^{solar}_{mp,dp,hp}$) shown in Eq. (1).

$$\max \sum_{mp \in MP} \sum_{dp \in DP} \sum_{hp \in HP} {}_{(dp,mp) \in DPM} Q^{solar}_{mp,dp,hp} \qquad (1)$$

where *hp*, *dp* and *mp* represent the hourly, daily and monthly periods and *DPM* stands for set of pairs of days and months.

The model takes into account variable flowrates, temperatures and energy flows across each unit within the entire system. Additionally, area of a solar thermal collector and its efficiency and storage tank volume are optimization variables. The data required to achieve this were retrieved as actual measured values of hourly global horizontal irradiation and ambient temperatures. Thermal energy provided by solar collector (in kWh/period) and the data for its calculation are based on the work by Isafiade et al. (2016), however in this work equality constraint is used and is multiplied by the number of hours for specific period.

The MINLP model consists of linear and nonlinear equality and inequality constraints and additionally it includes discrete or binary decisions. The binary variables ($y_{mp,dp,hp}$) are associated with the temperature of heat storage tank and the heat energy provided by heat transfer fluid from the solar collector. Eq. (2) shows such a constraint which states that the temperature in storage tank ($T^{storage\ tank}_{mp,dp,hp}$) should be lower than the difference between outlet temperature of the heat transfer fluid returning to solar collector ($T^{out-2,\ storage\ tank}_{mp,dp,hp}$) and the minimum temperature difference ($\Delta T_{\min}$), in a case the flow is non-zero. On the other hand, when there is no flow, there is no specific constraint on the temperature in storage tank.

$$T^{storage\ tank}_{mp,dp,hp} \leq T^{out-2,\ storage\ tank}_{mp,dp,hp} - \Delta T_{\min} + M \cdot (1 - y_{mp,dp,hp}),$$
$$\forall (mp \in MP, dp \in DP, hp \in HP) \qquad (2)$$

Eq. (2) represents big M constraint, *M* being big enough scalar, and binary variable $y_{mp,dp,hp}$ is connected to the flow from solar collector to the tank and back to the collector ($F^{in-1,storage\ tank}_{mp,dp,hp}$). If binary variable is 1, the flow should be between a minimum ($F^{\min}$) and a maximum value ($F^{\max}$), and 0 otherwise. Such constraints are shown in Eq. (3).

$$F^{\min} \cdot y_{mp,dp,hp} \leq F^{in-1,storage\ tank}_{mp,dp,hp} \leq F^{\max} \cdot y_{mp,dp,hp}, \quad \forall (mp \in MP, dp \in DP, hp \in HP) \qquad (3)$$

3. Case Study

The developed model is implemented and demonstrated on a specific location near Maribor, Slovenia as a case study, partly because low temperature industrial operations represent approximately 37 % of the total industrial heat demand in Slovenia (RSSO, 2017). This location was a reference point to obtain required meteorological data, such as hourly solar irradiation and ambient temperature. The data, which are based on the year 2016, were extracted from the EC JRC PVGIS (2017) using coordinates 46.552 N: 15.676 E Latitude and Longitude, and an elevation of 267 m above sea level.

In the case study, solar thermal is integrated with an industrial heat network for process stream preheating as shown in Figure 1. As a heat transfer fluid, 50/50 water-ethylene glycol is considered. For simplicity, only 1 cold process stream is considered in this demonstrative example while opportunities for using backup utility are accommodated within the framework of the model (see Figure 1).

To reduce computational time, mathematical model reduction techniques based on an earlier procedure presented by Egieya et al. (2018), which is a modification from presentation of Lam et al. (2011), is adopted. The 24 hours of each day are discretized into 4 periods of different durations: H1: 9 pm – 7 am, H2: 8 am – 10 am, H3: 11 am – 4 pm, H4: 5 pm – 8 pm. The 29 – 31 days of a month are discretized into just one period, while 12 months are considered in total. The input data on an hourly basis were averaged as previously done by Egieya et al. (2018). The model consists of 4,504 single equations, 4,755 single variables, and 48 binary variables. It was solved using SBB solver in GAMS with 1 % optimality gap in up to few hours on a personal computer with an Intel® Core™ i7-8750 H CPU @ 2.20 GHz processor with 8 GB RAM.

The results from the model show that the allowable volume of heat transfer fluid (V^{fluid}) in the storage tank and solar collector area (A_{panel}) have strong influence on the solution. Thus, the model has been solved considering different upper bounds for V^{fluid} and A_{panel}. Additionally, upper bound on flowrates of 100 t/h has been set. In almost all the solutions obtained (except for $A_{panel} = 100$ m², where V^{fluid} was 56.6 m³), both V^{fluid} and A_{panel} were set at their upper bounds. The graphs in Figure 2 show the relationship between the average heat load of solar thermal (Average DH^{solar}) exchanged with the cold process stream and the temperature of the stream achieved with solar (Average T^{solar}) for different values of A_{panel} between 100 and 10,000 m².

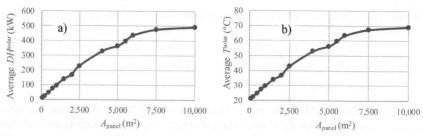

Figure 2: a) Average DH^{solar} and b) average T^{solar} with different sizes of solar collectors

From Figure 2, it could be seen that both DH^{solar} and T^{solar} significantly increase up to a A_{panel} value of 6,500 m³, DH^{solar} for 80.9 W/m² and T^{solar} for 0.008 °C/m² in average.

Beyond this A_{panel} value, the increase is lower, DH^{solar} is increased to about 16.7 W per additional m² of area and T^{solar} for 0.001 °C/m².

Figures 3 and 4 show the flow sheet values obtained for cases where the upper bound of the solar collector size is set to 1000 m³ and to 10,000 m³. Comparing these two figures, parameters such as the amount of heat captured by the solar collector, the amount of heat stored, and the quantity of heat that is ultimately exchanged between the solar heat transfer fluid and the cold process stream, are higher for the case where A^{UP}_{panel} is set as 10,000 m². It can also be noted that solar thermal achieves a higher preheating temperature of 69.2 °C for the 10,000 m³ case compared to the 1000 m³ case which only achieves a preheating temperature of 29.65 °C in average.

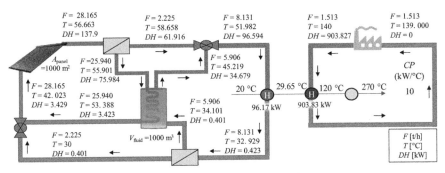

Figure 3: Average values of variables for the case $A^{UP}_{panel} = 1000$ m²

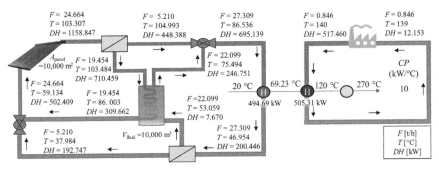

Figure 4: Average values of variables for the case $A^{UP}_{panel} = 10,000$ m²

4. Conclusions and Future Work

In this work, a simultaneous design and optimization procedure for integrating solar thermal with the heat network of an industrial plant has been developed. The new method which is based on an MINLP model, takes into consideration the time dependent variability in solar energy supply. It enables optimizing solar thermal utilization for industrial process pre-heating on hourly, daily and monthly time periods while also accommodating features that allow periodic storage of solar thermal and backup utility. Obtained results show the attainable quantities of solar heat that can be harvested for preheating of industrial process stream. The model demonstrates prospects of a good decision support tool for industrial utility planning. For the demonstrative case considered, the solution obtained shows the non-linear relationships between the area of solar collector (and volumes of thermal heat storage fluid) and the quantity of heat captured by the solar panel and thus temperatures achieved in the process. Both variables, A_{panel} and V^{fluid} were mostly set at their upper bounds. Future work will entail investigation of opportunities for inclusion of heat pump to increase thermal efficiency of both the direct and indirect integration. Processes involving a larger number of hot and cold streams, with multiple options of backup utilities, and economics-based objective function, will also be considered.

Acknowledgements

The authors wish to acknowledge the financial supports received from the National Research Foundation (NRF) of South Africa through the grant number 105780, Faculty of Engineering and the Built Environment at the University of Cape Town, South Africa, the Slovenian Research Agency (programs P2-0377 and P2-0032 and project L2-7633) and the Slovenia-Croatia bilateral project INTEGRES.

References

B. Abikoye, L. Čuček, A. Isafiade, A. Nemet, Z. Kravanja, 2018, Retrofitting of Industrial Utility Systems Considering Solar Thermal and Periodic Heat Storage, Proceedings of 1st International Conference on Technologies & Business Models for Circular Economy (TBMCE 2018), 253-261, doi: 10.18690/978-961-286-211-4.21

J.M. Egieya, L. Čuček, K. Zirngast, A.J. Isafiade, B. Pahor, Z. Kravanja, 2018, Biogas Supply Chain Optimization Considering Different Multi-Period Scenarios, Chemical Engineering Transactions, 70, 985-990 DOI: 10.3303/CET1870165

European Commission Joint Research Centre Photovoltaic Geographical Information System (EC JRC PVGIS), 2017, PVGIS tools. <re.jrc.ec.europa.eu/pvg_tools/en/tools.html> (accessed: August 2018)

International Energy Agency (OECD/IEA), 2015, World Energy Outlook <www.iea.org/publications/freepublications/publication/WEO2014.pdf> (accessed: November 2018)

International Energy Agency (IEA), 2017, New Report: Renewable Energy for Industry <www.solarpaces.org/new-iea-report> (accessed: February 2019)

A.J. Isafiade, Z. Kravanja, M. Bogataj, 2016, Design of integrated Solar Thermal Energy System for Multiperiod-Period Process Heat Demand, Chemical Engineering Transactions, 52, 1303-1308 DOI: 10.3303/CET1652218

C. Kong, L. Sing, J. Shiun, T.G. Walmsley, P. Y. Liew, 2018, Effect of Solar Utility temperature to Costing and Design Parameters of Integrated Solar Thermal System, Chemical Engineering Transactions, 70, 139-144, doi: 10.3303/CET1870024

H.L. Lam, J.J. Klemeš, Z. Kravanja, 2011, Model Size reduction Techniques for Large Scale Biomass Production and Supply Networks, Energy, 36, 4599-4608.

Republic of Slovenia Statistical Office (RSSO), 2017, Final Energy Consumption in Slovenia. <www.stat.si/StatWeb/en/News/Index/7722> (accessed: February 2019)

World Energy Council (WEC), 2016, World Energy Resources <www.worldenergy.org/wp-content/uploads/2016/10/World-Energy-Resources_Report_2016.pdf> (accessed: November 2018)

Anton A. Kiss, Edwin Zondervan, Richard Lakerveld, Leyla Özkan (Eds.)
Proceedings of the 29th European Symposium on Computer Aided Process Engineering
June 16th to 19th, 2019, Eindhoven, The Netherlands. © 2019 Elsevier B.V. All rights reserved.
http://dx.doi.org/10.1016/B978-0-128-18634-3.50091-6

On the implementation of generalized polynomial chaos in dynamic optimization under stochastic uncertainty: a user perspective

Satyajeet Bhonsale[a], Philippe Nimmegeers[a], Dries Telen[a], Joel A. Paulson[b], Ali Mesbah[b] and Jan Van Impe[a,*]

[a]*KU Leuven, Department of Chemical Engineering, BioTeC+ & OPTEC, Ghent, Belgium*
[b]*Department of Chemical and Biomolecular Engineering, University of California, Berkeley, USA*
jan.vanimpe@kuleuven.be

Abstract

Throughout the past century, numerous frameworks have been presented to address different types of uncertainty in model-based (dynamic) optimization. One of the most successful and promising frameworks to address uncertainty in dynamic optimization is generalized polynomial chaos (gPC). This framework is applicable to uncertainties modeled as random variables with generic (e.g., correlated and bimodal) probability distributions. An accurate and efficient approximation of the mean and variances of the model responses can then be readily computed from the coefficients of the gPC expansion. Two types of formulations exist to compute the gPC coefficients: intrusive and non-intrusive. In this paper, a tutorial and critical comparison are presented on the implementation of gPC. More specifically, an intrusive Galerkin approach and two non-intrusive approaches (probabilistic collocation and least-squares regression) have been implemented on a continuously stirred tank reactor case study.

Keywords: probabilistic uncertainty, generalized polynomial chaos, dynamic optimization

1. Introduction

Mathematical models are indispensable tools for the analysis, control and optimization of a wide range of complex technical systems. As models are only an approximate representation of reality, uncertainty is inherently present. This uncertainty can be structural, parametric or initial condition uncertainty as well as the impact of external disturbances and process variability which are typically present in the control and optimization of dynamic processes. In order to account for these sources of uncertainty systematically, two approaches can be followed, i.e., *stochastic* and *robust* optimization. In the former approach, the uncertainty is considered to be of a stochastic nature for which the probability distribution information is available. The latter assumes that the uncertainty is known to be fully contained within a given set and usually leads to the formulation where all constraints must be satisfied in the *worst case* scenario (Diehl et al., 2008). In this paper, stochastic uncertainty is considered in the model parameters and/or initial conditions. A key requirement to account for uncertainty in nonlinear optimization is accurate uncertainty propagation while maintaining a computationally tractable formulation.

This paper focuses on generalized polynomial chaos (Wiener, 1938) which exploits information on the distribution to approximate both mean and variance. To this extent a polynomial expansion is derived for which the coefficients need to be determined. A recent historical perspective on the use of polynomial chaos for optimization of dynamic systems has been presented by Kim et al. (2013) and a recent summary of the known theoretical results is provided in Paulson and Mesbah (2017). Two different approaches exist to determine the PCE coefficients: intrusive and non-intrusive formulations. The main contributions of this article, are a tutorial and critical comparison on the implementation of gPC formulations. In addition, an intrusive Galerkin formulation and two non-intrusive formulations (probabilistic collocation and least-squares regression) have been implemented on a continuously stirred tank reactor case study.

2. Dynamic optimization under stochastic uncertainty with gPC

2.1. Dynamic optimization under stochastic uncertainty

Consider the dynamic optimization problem under stochastic uncertainty in the interval $t \in [0, t_f]$:

$$\min_{u(\cdot)} \quad \mathbb{E}\{J(x, u, \theta)\} + \alpha_0 \text{Var}\{J(x, u, \theta)\},$$

$$\text{subject to:} \quad \dot{x} = f(x, u, \theta),$$

$$x(0) = x_0(\theta), \tag{1}$$

$$\mathbb{E}\{g_i(x, u, \theta)\} + \alpha_i \text{Var}\{g_i(x, u, \theta)\} \leq 0, \quad i = 1, \ldots, n_c,$$

$$\theta \sim p_\theta,$$

with $x \in \mathbb{R}^{n_x}$ the state vector, $u \in \mathbb{R}^{n_u}$ the control vector, $\theta \in \mathbb{R}^n$ the uncertain parameters, $x_0(\theta)$ is the initial condition, f the model equations, p_θ the parameter probability density function and $J(x, u, \theta)$ and $\{g_i(x, u, \theta)\}_{i=1}^{n_c}$ the optimization objective and constraints, respectively. The parameters $\boldsymbol{\alpha} = (\alpha_0, \alpha_1, \ldots, \alpha_{n_c})$ directly control the tradeoff between the mean and variance.

The main difficulty in solving (1), lies in the evaluation of the multidimensional integrals related to the expectation and variance operators $\mathbb{E}\{\cdot\}$ and $\text{Var}\{\cdot\}$ in the above formulation, since $\mathbb{E}\{R_k(\theta)\} = \int_{\theta \in \Theta} R_k(\theta) p_\theta(\theta) d\theta$ and $\text{Var}\{(R_k(\theta)\} = \mathbb{E}\{(R_k(\theta) - \mathbb{E}\{R_k(\theta)\})^2\}\}$ are generally defined in terms of a multidimensional integral for any function $R_k(\theta)$. Unless these integrals can be evaluated analytically as a function of the decision variables, these need to be approximated using a sampling-based method that can either be *deterministic* (e.g., Gauss quadrature) or *random* (e.g., Monte Carlo sampling) (Debusschere et al., 2004). Deterministic sampling methods result in $N = 100^n$, in case 100 points are spaced equally throughout the n uncertainty dimensions. Random sampling methods require less samples, but can still require a very large N to practically converge as e.g. in Monte Carlo where the convergence rate is quite low $O\left(1/\sqrt{N}\right)$.

2.2. Generalized polynomial chaos (gPC)

The gPC method approximates a model response y as a sum of orthogonal polynomials which are a function of the uncertain parameters for which stochastic information is avail-

On the implementation of generalized polynomial chaos in dynamic
optimization under stochastic uncertainty: a user perspective

543

able. The d-th order polynomial chaos expansion (PCE) of a model response y is defined as follows:

$$y_{\text{PCE}}(\theta) = \sum_{j=0}^{L} \hat{y}_j \Phi_j(\theta), \tag{2}$$

with $\hat{y}_j$ the unknown PCE coefficients and $\Phi_j(\theta)$ the multivariate orthogonal polynomials and j a term based index ($j = 0, \ldots, L$) and $L + 1 = (n_\theta + d)!/(n_\theta! d!)$.

These multivariate orthogonal polynomials can be written as a function of univariate orthogonal polynomials as it is typically assumed in polynomial chaos that the uncertain parameters are independent. In gPC, the uncertain parameters are written as a function of a standard distributed uncertain variable ξ. The Wiener-Askey can then be used to define generalized orthogonal polynomials as a function of ξ (Wiener, 1938; Xiu and Karniadakis, 2002). Recently, Paulson et al. (2017) proposed a further generalization, termed arbitrary polynomial chaos (aPC), to define the basis directly in terms of the *moments* of the uncertain variables.

The expected value and variance of R_y can be approximated with PCE as:

$$\mathbb{E}[y] \approx \hat{y}_0 \tag{3}$$

$$\mathbb{V}\text{ar}[y] \approx \sum_{j=1}^{L} (\hat{y}_j)^2 \mathbb{E}[\Phi_j^2(\theta)]. \tag{4}$$

Note that $\mathbb{E}[\Phi_j^2(\theta)]$ can be computed upfront and equals 1 for standard normalized polynomials.

3. Computing the PCE coefficients

Remark that up till now, it is not yet mentioned how the unknown PCE coefficients $\hat{y}_j$ can be computed. Two classes of methods exist to compute these unknown coefficients: *intrusive* and *non-intrusive* methods. The dynamic optimization problem formulations are presented in Table 1. In *intrusive methods* a deterministic set of equations is developed for the coefficients $\hat{y}$ based on a Galerkin projection of the approximation error between the model response function and its polynomial chaos expansion. For *intrusive* methods the model response needs to be explicitly known and preferably the explicit model response function is a polynomial function. More details on intrusive methods can be found in e.g., Ghanem and Spanos (1991), Debusschere et al. (2004). In *non-intrusive methods* the model is considered as a black box and exact expressions for the model response are not required. All *non-intrusive* methods can be considered as a weighted sum of model response evaluations in n_s sampling points. The non-intrusive Galerkin, probabilistic collocation and least squares regression differ in the number of sampling points n_s that are selected and the weighting matrices as indicated in Table 1.

Note that the intrusive gPC problem formulation no longer has any random variables appearing so that it can be solved using standard dynamic optimization methods. However, the complexity of evaluating the right-hand side inner products of the equations above

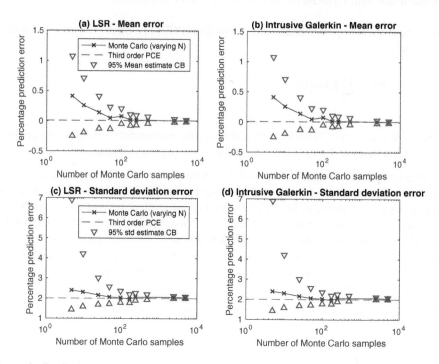

Figure 1: Prediction errors for mean and standard deviation for LSR (a,c) and intrusive Galerkin (b,d).

(which may not even have closed-form expressions) and the fact that there is no clear exploitable structure due to the strong correlation between all the variables. The fact that the number of terms in the right-hand side grows exponentially with order of the polynomial also implies gradient calculations will be very expensive, which is a key bottleneck in many optimization algorithms including interior point and active set methods.

4. Results for a CSTR case study

4.1. Case study

The continuously stirred tank reactor (CSTR) case study from Lucia et al. (2017) has been implemented to compare three different gPC implementations: intrusive Galerkin with non-intrusive probabilistic collocation (PCM) and least squares regression (LSR). In this CSTR the reactants A and B react to form a product C. The objective of the problem is to maximize the amount of C. The model consists of 7 differential equations, describing the change of the reactor volume with respect to time, the concentration mass balances of A, B and C, the dynamics of the reactor temperature and jacket temperature and the dynamics of the inlet jacket temperature. The controls are the reactor inflow and the setpoint of the thermostat. Two uncertain parameters have been considered to be uniformly distributed within the interval $[0.7\theta_{nom}, 1.3\theta_{nom}]$: the molar reaction enthalpy ΔH_R and the reaction constant k. The dynamic optimization problems have been discretized using an orthogonal collocation scheme.

On the implementation of generalized polynomial chaos in dynamic
optimization under stochastic uncertainty: a user perspective
545

4.2. Prediction error as function of order and method

As a measure the final temperature has been chosen and 10000 Monte Carlo (MC) samples have been taken as a benchmark for comparison with the prediction of mean and variance. Figure 1 indicates a minor effect on mean approximation while variance approximation improves with increasing order. The prediction error between MC and PCE has been plotted as a function of the number of parameter samples for both LSR as intrusive Galerkin.

Table 1: Dynamic optimization problem formulations for intrusive and non-intrusive gPC.

Intrusive Galerkin formulation

$$\min_{u(\cdot)} \hat{f}_0 + \alpha_0 \sum_{i=1}^{L} \hat{f}_i^2 \langle \Phi_i^2 \rangle$$
$$\text{subject to: } \hat{g}_{i,0} + \alpha_i \sum_{j=1}^{L} \hat{g}_{i,j}^2 \langle \Phi_j^2 \rangle \leq 0$$

$$
\begin{aligned}
\frac{d\hat{x}_k(t)}{dt} &= \frac{1}{\langle \Phi_k^2 \rangle} \left\langle f\left(\sum_{i=0}^{L} \hat{x}_i \Phi_i(\xi), u(t), \sum_{i=0}^{L} \hat{\theta}_i \Phi_i(\xi)\right), \Phi_k \right\rangle, \\
\hat{x}_k(0) &= \frac{\langle x_0, \Phi_k \rangle}{\langle \Phi_k^2 \rangle}, \\
\hat{f}_k &= \frac{1}{\langle \Phi_k^2 \rangle} \left\langle J\left(\sum_{i=0}^{L} \hat{x}_i \Phi_i(\xi), u(t), \sum_{i=0}^{L} \hat{\theta}_i \Phi_i(\xi)\right), \Phi_k \right\rangle, \\
\hat{g}_{i,k} &= \frac{1}{\langle \Phi_k^2 \rangle} \left\langle g\left(\sum_{i=0}^{L} \hat{x}_i \Phi_i(\xi), u(t), \sum_{i=0}^{L} \hat{\theta}_i \Phi_i(\xi)\right), \Phi_k \right\rangle, \\
\forall k &= 0, \ldots, L, \ \forall i = 1, \ldots, n_c.
\end{aligned}
$$

Non-intrusive formulations

$$\min_{u(\cdot)} \hat{f}_0 + \alpha_0 \sum_{i=1}^{L} \hat{f}_i^2 \langle \Phi_i^2 \rangle$$
$$\text{subject to: } \dot{x}^j = f(x^j, u, \theta^j), j = 1, \ldots, N,$$

$$
\begin{aligned}
x^j(0) &= x_0(\theta^j), j = 1, \ldots, N, \\
\hat{f}_k &= \sum_{j=1}^{N} w_{k,j} J(x^j, u, \theta^j), k = 0, \ldots, L, \\
\hat{g}_{i,k} &= \sum_{j=1}^{N} w_{k,j} g_i(x^j, u, \theta^j), i = 1, \ldots, n_c, \ k = 0, \ldots, L, \\
0 &\geq \hat{g}_{i,0} + \alpha_i \sum_{j=1}^{L} \hat{g}_{i,j}^2 \langle \Phi_j^2 \rangle, i = 1, \ldots, n_c, \\
\hat{\mathbf{y}} &= \mathbf{W} \mathbf{y} \text{ with } \mathbf{y} = \left[y\left(\theta^1\right), \ldots, y\left(\theta^N\right) \right]
\end{aligned}
$$

Non-intrusive Galerkin	Probabilistic collocation	Least squares regression
$\begin{bmatrix} \dfrac{q^1 \Phi_0(\theta^0)}{\langle \Phi_0^2 \rangle} & \cdots & \dfrac{q^N \Phi_0(\theta^{n_s-1})}{\langle \Phi_0^2 \rangle} \\ \vdots & \vdots & \\ \dfrac{q^1 \Phi_L(\theta^0)}{\langle \Phi_L^2 \rangle} & \cdots & \dfrac{q^N \Phi_L(\theta^{n_s-1})}{\langle \Phi_L^2 \rangle} \end{bmatrix}$	$\left(\left(\mathbf{\Lambda}^{(d)} \right)^{\mathsf{T}} \right)^{-1}$	$\left(\mathbf{\Lambda}^{(d)} \left(\mathbf{\Lambda}^{(d)} \right)^{\mathsf{T}} \right)^{-1} \mathbf{\Lambda}^{(d)}.$
with weights q^i from the quadrature rule	with $\mathbf{\Lambda}^{(d)} = \begin{bmatrix} \Phi_0(\theta^0) & \cdots & \Phi_0(\theta^{n_s-1}) \\ \vdots & \ddots & \vdots \\ \Phi_L(\theta^0) & \cdots & \Phi_L(\theta^{n_s-1}) \end{bmatrix}.$	with $\mathbf{\Lambda}^{(d)} = \begin{bmatrix} \Phi_0(\theta^0) & \cdots & \Phi_0(\theta^{n_s-1}) \\ \vdots & \ddots & \vdots \\ \Phi_L(\theta^0) & \cdots & \Phi_L(\theta^{n_s-1}) \end{bmatrix}.$

For the mean MC never seems to outperform the PCE accuracy. More than 1000 MC samples are required to outperform PCE.

4.3. CPU time

The IPOPT main loop times for the three different methods are displayed in Table 2 for different PCE orders. All states are initialized at a fixed value, not exploiting the advantage of non-intrusive approaches which can use the nominal state profiles as initialization. PCM outperforms LSR and intrusive Galerkin in all cases except for the first order PCE, where performance is similar. LSR and intrusive Galerkin have a similar performance, although intrusive Galerkin requires $\frac{(n+d)!}{n!d!} n_x$ states and LSR $n^{d+1} n_x$ states.

Table 2: CPU times in seconds for different orders obtained with LSR, PCM and intrusive Galerkin.

First order			Second order			Third order		
LSR	PCM	Galerkin	LSR	PCM	Galerkin	LSR	PCM	Galerkin
0.936	0.713	1.058	3.696	2.317	9.805	17.711	1.817	12.426

5. Conclusions

In this article a comparison between the different gPC formulations has been presented and an intrusive Galerkin, PCM and LSR have been implemented on a CSTR case study. Results indicate that non-intrusive formulations are preferred over intrusive due to the generally lower CPU time and potential further decrease in CPU time due to the parallelizable sampling-based structure of the dynamic optimization problem (Jiang et al., 2017).

Acknowledgements

The research is supported by: FWO-G.0863.18 and SB holds a Baekeland PhD grant from the Agency for Innovation through Science and Technology in Flanders.

References

B. Debusschere, H. Najm, P. Pébay, O. Knio, R. Ghanem, O. L. Maitre, 2004. Numerical challenges in the use of polynomial chaos representations for stochastic processes. SIAM Journal on Scientific Computing 26, 698–719.

M. Diehl, J. Gerhard, W. Marquardt, M. Mönnigmann, 2008. Numerical solution approaches for robust nonlinear optimal control problems. Computers and Chemical Engineering 32, 1287–1300.

R. Ghanem, P. Spanos, 1991. Stochastic Finite Elements A Spectral Approach. SpringerVerlag.

Y. Jiang, P. Nimmegeers, D. Telen, J. Van Impe, B. Houska, 2017. A distributed optimization algorithm for sampling-based stochastic optimal control. In: Proceedings of the 20th IFAC World Congress. pp. 11755–11760.

K.-K. Kim, D. Shen, Z. Nagy, R. Braatz, 2013. Wiener's polynomial chaos for the analysis and control of nonlinear dynamical systems with probabilistic uncertainties [historical perspectives]. IEEE Control Systems 33 (5), 58–67.

S. Lucia, A. Tătulea-Codrean, C. Schoppmeyer, S. Engell, 2017. Rapid development of modular and sustainable nonlinear model predictive control solutions. Control Engineering Practice 60, 51 – 62.

J. Paulson, E. Buehler, A. Mesbah, 2017. Arbitrary polynomial chaos for uncertainty propagation of correlated random variables in dynamic systems. Proceedings of the IFAC World Congress, 3607 – 3612.

J. A. Paulson, A. Mesbah, 2017. An efficient method for stochastic optimal control with joint chance constraints for nonlinear systems. International Journal of Robust and Nonlinear Control 21 (1).

N. Wiener, 1938. The homogeneous chaos. American Journal of Mathematics 60 (4), 897 – 936.

D. Xiu, E. Karniadakis, 2002. The Wiener-Askey polynomial chaos for stochastic differential equations. SIAM Journal of Scientific Computation 24, 619 – 644.

Anton A. Kiss, Edwin Zondervan, Richard Lakerveld, Leyla Özkan (Eds.)
Proceedings of the 29th European Symposium on Computer Aided Process Engineering
June 16th to 19th, 2019, Eindhoven, The Netherlands. © 2019 Elsevier B.V. All rights reserved.
http://dx.doi.org/10.1016/B978-0-128-18634-3.50092-8

Optimal dose administration of renally excreted drugs

Giuseppe Pesenti, Adriana Savoca, Davide Manca[*]

PSE-Lab, Dipartimento di Chimica, Materiali e Ingegneria Chimica "Giulio Natta" Politecnico di Milano, Piazza Leonardo da Vinci 32, Milano 20133, Italy

davide.manca@polimi.it

Abstract

The paper presents and discusses a basic pharmacokinetic model for vancomycin, an antibiotic that is principally excreted by kidneys. The model accounts for the degree of renal function by employing the CKD-EPI equation. Only one parameter of the model is identified by a nonlinear regression of experimental data, while the other parameters are evaluated *a priori* via correlations from the scientific literature.

We simulate the pharmacokinetic time-curves of vancomycin by accounting for different values of the glomerular filtration rate and show the strong influence of the degree of renal function on the drug pharmacokinetics. In addition, the model can be used to determine the optimal dose for patients featuring varying degrees of renal function. Results underline the importance of individualized treatment.

Keywords: pharmacokinetics, optimal dose, renal function, GFR, vancomycin.

1. Introduction

The assessment of the optimal dose for drug administration is a critical choice for clinical doctors and calls for considering the individual characteristics of patients. Since drugs are typically tested on healthy subjects, dosage guidelines and PK studies are often available for average healthy individuals. Conversely, in clinical practice, drugs are administered to ill and/or elderly patients, who often suffer from varying degrees of renal impairment. About 31% of administered drugs are mainly cleared by the kidneys (Varma et al., 2009). For these drugs, the patient's degree of renal function strongly affects the concentration profile of the drug and the administered dose is critical. The glomerular filtration rate (GFR) represents the volumetric flow of plasma that is filtered by the kidneys and is a useful measure to estimate the degree of renal function.

Renal function declines with age and may be further affected by renal diseases. Renal impairment is extremely common, even though a large fraction of people who suffer from it are unaware of their status (Girndt et al., 2016). Chronic kidney disease (CKD) at stages 3-5 is defined as a condition when GFR < 60 mL/min/1.73 m^2 for 3 months. This corresponds to the loss of more than half of the normal kidney function. According to Hill et al. (2016), 10.6% of the general world population suffers from CKD at stages 3-5. For patients with renal impairment, drug dosage is often suboptimal and drug dosing errors are common (Kim et al., 2016), which trigger adverse effects and reduce life quality and life expectancy.

We developed a pharmacokinetic (PK) model that can be applied as a tool to determine the optimal dose of a drug that is mainly cleared via renal filtration. The optimal dose is personalized according to the individual characteristics of the patients, *i.e.* age, sex, height, weight, and serum creatinine levels. These parameters, in particular, allow estimating GFR, and therefore the renal function, according to the CKD-EPI equation (Levey et al., 2009).

The PK model is applied to vancomycin, an antibiotic that is almost completely cleared by renal filtration and whose metabolism is negligible. Vancomycin is routinely administered in clinical settings especially to critically ill patients, who typically display heterogeneous characteristics and, in particular, an extremely wide range of degrees of renal function.

2. Methods

A rather simple PK model comprising only three compartments was developed to explicitly focus on renal function. The compartments (Figure 1) are (i) the global circulatory system, (ii) the renal circulatory system, and (iii) the other tissues.

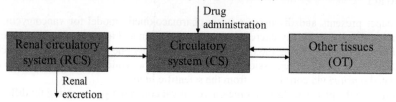

Figure 1 – Compartments of the PK model.

The global circulatory system (CS) involves the plasma contained in the whole circulatory system but the fraction that passes through the kidneys, which is described by the renal circulatory system (RCS) compartment. The third compartment lumps the other tissues and organs (OT) where the drug diffuses through the exchange between plasma and interstitial fluid at the capillaries.

The model consists of three ordinary differential equations (Eqs. 1-3) that quantify the material balances of vancomycin in each of the three compartments, including the exchange between them and the excretion due to renal filtration.

$$\frac{dm_{CS}}{dt} = \dot{m}_{IV} - \frac{Q_{CS\leftrightarrow RCS}}{V_{CS}} m_{CS} + \frac{Q_{CS\leftrightarrow RCS}}{V_{RCS}} m_{RCS} +$$
$$- \frac{K_{CS\leftrightarrow OT}}{V_{CS}} m_{CS} (1-R) + \frac{K_{CS\leftrightarrow OT}}{V_{OT}} m_{OT} \tag{1}$$

$$\frac{dm_{RCS}}{dt} = \frac{Q_{CS\leftrightarrow RCS}}{V_{CS}} m_{CS} - \frac{Q_{CS\leftrightarrow RCS}}{V_{RCS}} m_{RCS} - \frac{Q_{GFR}}{V_{RCS}} m_{RCS} (1-R) \tag{2}$$

$$\frac{dm_{OT}}{dt} = \frac{K_{CS\leftrightarrow OT}}{V_{CS}} m_{CS} (1-R) - \frac{K_{CS\leftrightarrow OT}}{V_{OT}} m_{OT} \tag{3}$$

m_{CS}, m_{RCS} and m_{OT} are the mass of drug (in mg) in the CS, RCS and OT compartments. $\dot{m}_{IV}$ is the intravenous (IV) infusion rate of vancomycin (in mg/h) administered to the patient, R is the fraction of vancomycin bound to blood proteins, $Q_{CS\leftrightarrow RCS}$ is the volumetric flow (mL/h) of plasma that reaches the kidneys, and $K_{CS\leftrightarrow OT}$ is a mass transfer coefficient (mL/h) related to capillary exchange. Finally, V_{CS}, V_{RCS}, and V_{OT} are the volumes (mL) of plasma or interstitial fluid in the corresponding compartments.

Q_{GFR} is the volumetric GFR and is estimated via the CKD-EPI equation (Levey et al., 2009) as a function of sex, age, serum creatinine, and body surface area (BSA), which in turn depends on the height and weight of the patient. The plasma flow to the kidneys $Q_{CS \leftrightarrow RCS}$ is calculated as 19% of the overall cardiac output, which is estimated as $3.5\,BSA$ (Cowles et al., 1971) multiplied by the average volumetric fraction of plasma in the blood, *i.e.* 0.53 for men and 0.58 for women.

The plasma volumes of CS and RCS are evaluated from the total mass of blood as a function of weight (Brown et al., 1997), its density (Vitello et al., 2014), and the fraction of blood that is contained in the RCS (Leggett et al., 1995). According to Butterfield et al. (2011), the average factor for vancomycin protein binding R is 0.415.

Since vancomycin poorly diffuses into bones, CNS, and lungs (Giuliano et al., 2010), these elements were excluded from the OT compartment. Following the approach of Abbiati et al. (2016), both mass and density of the overall OT compartment were estimated from Brown et al. (1997) as 70.3% of the total mass and 1.005 g/mL respectively. The OT compartment volume is estimated as their ratio.

The total flow exchanged at the capillaries is proportional to the global capillary exchange area and therefore to the number of capillaries in the body. Therefore, $K_{CS \leftrightarrow OT}$ is assumed to be proportional to the estimated OT compartment mass (Eq. 4).

$$K_{CS \leftrightarrow OT} = m_{OT} \cdot k^m_{CS \leftrightarrow OT} \tag{4}$$

For the sake of simplicity, we assume that $k^m_{CS \leftrightarrow OT}$ is constant for all the individuals and its value is identified via a nonlinear regression of clinical data. To minimize the distance between the simulated PK profiles and the measured values of vancomycin plasma concentration, the weighted sum of squared errors (SSE) between each experimental and simulated value j (over the N_i^{exp} values), for each patient i (over the N_P patients), is minimized (Eq. 5).

$$\min_{k^m_{CS \leftrightarrow OT}} SSE = \frac{1}{N_P} \min_{k^m_{CS \leftrightarrow OT}} \sum_{i=1}^{N_P} \left(\frac{1}{N_i^{exp}} \sum_{j=1}^{N_i^{exp}} \left(\frac{c_{CS,ij}^{sim} - c_{CS,ij}^{exp}}{c_{CS,ij}^{exp}} \right)^2 \right) \tag{5}$$

The proposed model is not a physiologically-based pharmacokinetic (PBPK) model, as it features a basic 3-compartment structure and lumps all the organs and tissues of the human body other than the kidneys in just one compartment. However, its description is consistent with the physiological processes in the human body and this allows determining quantitatively the whole set of model parameters but one, *i.e.* $k^m_{CS \leftrightarrow OT}$.

The experimental data were extracted from Turner et al. (2018), who published rich pharmacokinetic data of experimental vancomycin profiles for a heterogeneous population of critically ill patients in an intensive care unit (ICU). Vancomycin was administered with periodic infusions at a maximum rate of 1000 mg/h. Each patient received a different dose intravenously (in the range 500-1750 mg) over 0.7-2 h intervals. After a specific period (8, 12 or 24 h), a new cycle was repeated. The desired therapeutic target was to maintain vancomycin concentration above the 15-20 mg/L threshold for the whole time interval. This target, called trough concentration, can be achieved with periodic infusions (*e.g.*, 0.7-2 h) over long time intervals (*e.g.*, 8-24 h) as the elimination half-life of vancomycin is about 6-12 h (Rybak, 2006).

The initial values of CS concentration were linearly extrapolated from the two initial experimental points in Turner et al. (2018), and the initial RCS concentration was approximated with the CS one (due to the lack of further details in the experimental data). As far as the initial OT concentration values are concerned, the experimental points were collected from patients that had already received at least three successive vancomycin doses. To estimate the accumulation of vancomycin in the OT compartment, three consecutive cycles were simulated, each time using the final OT concentration as the next OT initial condition for the following simulation to achieve a plausible initial value.

3. Results

The regression was performed using the data of five patients from Turner et al. (2018) and yielded a value of 843.68 mL/h/kg for $k_{CS \leftrightarrow OT}^m$. For the sake of space, Figures 2 (a-c) show the simulated concentration profiles in CS, RCS, and OT and the experimental CS measures of three of the patients. As SSE (the average squared relative error for each experimental point, see also Eq. 5) is pretty low (0.1440), the regression is considered successful. Accordingly, Figures 2 (a-c) show a good fit of the experimental data. Figure 2 (d) shows the simulated time-profiles of drug mass over the three compartments for just one patient.

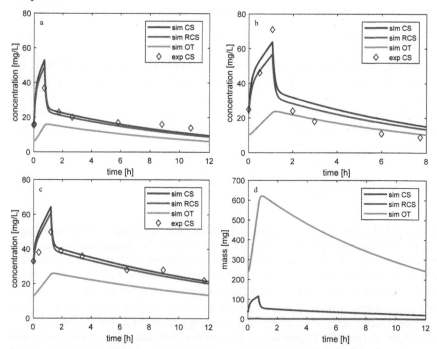

Figure 2 – (a-c) Simulated and experimental vancomycin concentration for patients #1-3. (d) Simulated mass profiles in the three compartments of the PK model for patient #1.

Once successfully identified, the model was employed to investigate the effect of the degree of renal function. Thus, we simulated the CS concentration dynamics of a specific virtual patient for a fixed vancomycin dose at different GFR degrees. The simulated individual was determined from the average characteristics of the abovementioned 5 patients: male, 57.8 years old, 85 kg, and 174 cm. This virtual patient received an infusion of 1000 mg over 1 h. The initial values of CS and RCS were assumed equal to 20 mg/L, whereas the initial OT concentration was estimated by simulating three previous cycles. The simulated GFR range (29-199 mL/min) is the same of patients from Turner et al. (2018), estimated according to the CKD-EPI equation. The results highlight simulated curves which vary widely for different values of GFR, as shown in Figure 3. In case of the highest GFR considered, for example, the peak and trough concentrations are 46.72 and 10.40 mg/L respectively, whereas in case of the lowest GFR they are 88.58 and 55.98 mg/L. It is worth observing that the simulated dose does not allow respecting the target trough concentration in case of the two highest GFR values, whereas it would lead to excessive vancomycin levels for the two patients with the lowest GFR. Horey et al. (2012) report a significant occurrence of nephrotoxicity (81.8%) when trough levels are higher than 35 mg/L.

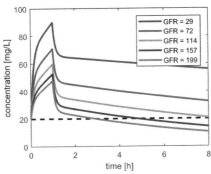

Figure 3 – Simulated plasma concentration of vancomycin for a virtual averaged patient as a function of their GFR (mL/min). The horizontal dashed line is the target trough concentration.

Finally, the PK model is used to find the optimal dose for the averaged individual, as a function of their GFR. A fixed infusion rate of 1000 mg/h is administered *in silico* for a varying time interval, with a period of 8 h between consecutive infusions. As in previous cases, we assume that the patient has already undergone three cycles and starts with an initial CS concentration of 20 mg/L. The dose is optimized individually so that the CS concentration at the end of the simulated interval is equal to 20 mg/L, which guarantees the target trough concentration. Table 1 reports the optimal doses, which display a marked difference (a ratio higher than 6) between the highest and lowest quantities of vancomycin to be administered. Over 24 h, the simulated doses cover the 924-5667 mg range, which is comparable with the 1000-5250 mg range reported in Turner et al. (2018).

Table 1 – Optimal vancomycin doses for a virtual averaged patient as a function of their renal function (estimated via GFR).

GFR [mL/min]	29	72	114	157	199
Optimal dose [mg]	308.0	593.9	964.6	1403.8	1889.0

4. Conclusions

Whenever renally-excreted drugs are concerned, the degree of renal function must be taken into account to determine the optimal dose for individual administration. In fact, as shown in Figure 3, the degree of renal function dramatically influences the drug concentration profile. The administered drug dosages can be optimized for each patient according to their bodily characteristics (*i.e.* sex, age, weight, and height) and serum creatinine, by employing suitable PK models, which can lead to improved compliance with therapeutic targets and reduced side effects by avoiding excessive drug concentrations. The proposed PK model allows medical doctors improving the design of personalized clinical treatments.

References

Abbiati, R.A., Lamberti, G., Grassi, M., Trotta, F., Manca, D. (2016). Definition and validation of a patient-individualized physiologically-based pharmacokinetic model. Comput. Chem. Eng. 1/4;84:394-408.

Brown, R.P., Delp, M.D., Lindstedt, S.L., Rhomberg, L.R., Beliles, R.P. (1997) Physiological parameter values for physiologically based pharmacokinetic models. Toxicol. Ind. Health 13(4):407-84.

Butterfield, J.M., Patel, N., Pai, M.P., Rosano, T.G., Drusano, G.L., Lodise, T.P. (2011). Refining Vancomycin Protein Binding Estimates: Identification of Clinical Factors That Influence Protein Binding. Antimicrob Agents Chemother. Sep; 55(9): 4277–4282.

Cowles, A.L., Borgstedt, H.H., Gillies, A.J. (1971). Tissue Weights and Rates of Blood Flow in Man for the Prediction of Anesthetic Uptake and Distribution. Anesthesiology. November 1;35(5):523-6.

Girndt, M., Trocchi, P., Scheidt-Nave, C., Markau, S., Stang, A. (2016). The Prevalence of Renal Failure. Results from the German Health Interview and Examination Survey for Adults, 2008-2011 (DEGS1). Dtsch Arztebl Int. Feb 12;113(6):85-91.

Giuliano, C., Haase, K.K., Hall, R. (2010). Use of vancomycin pharmacokinetic-pharmacodynamic properties in the treatment of MRSA infections. Expert Rev Anti Infect Ther. Jan;8(1):95-106.

Hill, N.R., Fatoba, S.T., Oke, J.L., Hirst, J.A., O'Callaghan, C.A., Lasserson, D.S., Lasserson, D.S. (2016). Global Prevalence of Chronic Kidney Disease – A Systematic Review and Meta-Analysis. PLoS ONE 11(7): e0158765.

Horey, A., Mergenhagen, K.A., Mattappallil, A. (2012). The Relationship of nephrotoxicity to vancomycin trough serum concentrations in a veteran's population: a retrospective analysis. Ann Pharmacother. Nov;46(11):1477-83.

Kim, G.J., Je, N.K., Kim, D.S., Lee, S. (2016). Adherence with renal dosing recommendations in outpatients undergoing haemodialysis. Journal of Clinical Pharmacy and Therapeutics, 41, 26–33.

Leggett, R., Williams, L., Eckerman, K. (1995). A Proposed Blood Circulation Model for Reference Man. Health Physics 69(2):187-201.

Levey, A.S., Stevens, L.A., Schmid, C.H., Zhang, Y.L., Castro, A.F., Feldman, H.I., Kusek, J.W., Eggers, P., Van Lente, F., Greene, T., Coresh, C. (2009). A New Equation to Estimate Glomerular Filtration Rate. Ann Intern Med. May 5; 150(9): 604–612.

Rybak, M.J. (2006). The Pharmacokinetic and Pharmacodynamic Properties of Vancomycin. Clinical Infectious Diseases; 42:S35–9.

Turner, R.B., Kojiro, K., Won, R., Chang, E., Chan, D., Elbarbry, F. (2018). Prospective evaluation of vancomycin pharmacokinetics in a heterogeneous critically ill population, Diagn. Microbiol. Infect. Dis., https://doi.org/10.1016/j.diagmicrobio.2018.06.022

Varma, M.V.S., Feng, B., Obach, R.S., Troutman, M.D., Chupka, J., Miller, H.R., El-Kattan, A. (2009). Physicochemical Determinants of Human Renal Clearance. J. Med. Chem. 52, 4844–4852.

Vitello, D.J., Ripper, R.M., Fettiplace, M.R., Weinberg, G.L., Vitello, J.M. (2014). Blood Density Is Nearly Equal to Water Density: A Validation Study of the Gravimetric Method of Measuring Intraoperative Blood Loss. Journal of veterinary medicine 12/01;2015:152730.

Anton A. Kiss, Edwin Zondervan, Richard Lakerveld, Leyla Özkan (Eds.)
Proceedings of the 29th European Symposium on Computer Aided Process Engineering
June 16th to 19th, 2019, Eindhoven, The Netherlands. © 2019 Elsevier B.V. All rights reserved.
http://dx.doi.org/10.1016/B978-0-128-18634-3.50093-X

Automating HAZOP studies using D-higraphs

Borja Martínez, [a] Manuel Rodríguez, [a*] Ismael Díaz, [a]

[a] Universidad Politécnica de Madrid, José Gutiérrez Abascal 2, 28006 Madrid, Spain

Abstract

In this paper we present a methodology to perform guided HAZOP studies using a functional modelling framework: D-higraphs. It is a formalism that gathers in a single model the functional as well as the structural information about the process considered of any given system. This tool uses an expert system to predict the behaviour of the modelled process in order to achieve a semi-automatic and systematic HAZOP analysis. In this paper it is applied to an industrial case showing the easy understanding of the proposed methodology and comparing the obtained results to those obtained conducting the HAZOP study in the conventional way.

Keywords: Functional modelling; HAZOP; Risk assessment.

1. Introduction

Throughout the history of the process industry there have been a lot of important aspects to be considered in the consequences of accidents: environmental impact, pollution, operators' occupational health and economy. This situation can involve lots of losses associated to shutdowns, reparations, compensations or fines, so avoiding accidents is not only a direct way to save money on losses, but also the incomes are increased because productivity does (De la Mata and Rodríguez, 2010).

According to the design stage of the process plant, Process Hazard Analyses (PHA) are carried out to identify the potential safety problems in order to provide possible solutions that enhance the safety of the plant, such as process changes, new control strategies or the use of safety instrumentation. There are a broad variety of methods but the most widely used is the Hazard and Operability Study (HAZOP) (Zhao et al., 2005). However, this technique consumes a lot of time an effort, so in the last decades a lot of work and resources have been put to develop tools and methodologies that automate this process.

Some of these tools are HAZOPExpert (Venkatasubramanian et al., 2000), PHASuite (Zhao et al., 2005), Functional HAZOP assistant (Rossing et al., 2010a, 2010b), Layered Digraph Model (Cui et al., 2008) and PetroHAZOP (Zhao et al., 2009).

In order to do this automation, expert systems (or production rule systems) are used to perform calculations functions of the causes and consequences due to a possible deviation that happened in the process, with a view to understand the severity of the situation.

In this work a new HAZOP assistant is developed based on a modelling technique called D-higraphs, which considers structural and functional information of the system under analysis. This methodology has been implemented using a production rule system called CLIPS (CLIPS, 2018). It has been applied to a standard scenario and its results are compared to those obtained doing the HAZOP study as usual.

2. D-higraphs: merging function and structure

2.1. Dualization: from Higraphs to D-higraphs

Higraphs are a general kind of diagramming objects well suited to specify the behavior of complex concurrent systems but not process system (Harel, 1987).

On the other hand, D-higraphs are an adaptation of Higraphs that consist of blobs, representing transitions, and edges, representing states. This adaptation of Higraphs was first presented in Rodríguez and Sanz (2009) as a modeling technique that merges functional and structural information of the system modeled.

It has to be noted that a D-higraphs is not a dual higraphs, obtained from changing blobs by edges and edges by blobs. The duality lies in their interpretation and properties.

2.2. Elements of a D-higraphs: Blobs and Edges

The two main elements of a D-higraphs are depicted in Figure 1, where the basic blob is represented in the left-hand-side, and the different types of edges are shown in the center. Blobs represent functions that are performed by an ACTOR producing state 2 if state 1 is enabled. Edges represent flows of mass, energy, or information, which are responsible of the interactions in a process system (Lind, 1994). The main properties of blobs and edges are described in De la Mata and Rodríguez (2010).

Figure 1. Basic blob and different types of edges.

2.3. Causal and qualitative reasoning

D-higraphs integrate a series of causation rules relating two events that allow us to track the evolution of failures across the system. These rules combined with sensor data of the plant enables the performance of Fault Detection and Isolation analysis using D-higraphs. However, certain analyses require the use of deviations and not only failures, like HAZOP studies. In a certain way, we need to simulate qualitatively the system in order to propagate these deviations. The description of a system is made in three different layers (Kuipers, 1984):

1. *Structural description*: described by variables, such as flow (F), pressure (P), temperature (T), composition (x), energy (E), information (I), level (L), valve opening (A), etc.

2. *Behavioral description*: potential behavior of the system as a network. The M^+ and M^- constraints (Kuipers, 1986) provide this information, but in some behaviors they need to be modified according to: M^{++}, M^{0+}, M^{-+}, M^{+0}, M^{00}, M^{-0}, M^{+-}, M^{0-} y M^{--}. The first sign shows the monotonicity for values under the expected one, and the other sign does for values above it. In Figure 2 some examples are shown.

3. *Functional description*: describes the purpose of a structural component and its connections provided by the D-higraphs layout.

The three layers of this representation are shown in the right-hand-side of Figure 1, where there is a physical device (DECANTER) whose main purpose is to *store liquid*. The decanter has two characteristic variables: level (Ld) and temperature (Td). Ld is affected by the inflow F3 with variations of the same sign (an increment of F3 increases Ld) and by the outflow F4 in the opposite way. In the same way, the flow F4 is affected by the level of the decanter in the same direction.

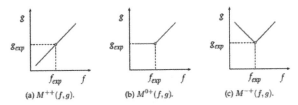

Figure 2. Some examples of the M constraints (De la Mata and Rodríguez, 2010).

3. D-higraphs and the CLIPS environment

The D-higraphs models are implemented using a graphic tool that has as input the P&ID of the process and it uses a D-higraphs built using a template (Álvarez, 2010). Once the model has been developed, it is loaded into the expert system that obtains the report of the deviation thanks to the rule database. The HAZOP study is performed feeding the deviations to the reasoning engine. The result of the analysis is provided to the user and it can be fed back in order to make changes into the process or D-higraphs.

CLIPS is the expert system that performs the analysis by entering the command "Assert" followed by the desired deviation, which is formed with a HAZOP guide word, and the process variable.

4. Case study

In this section, we present the oil vaporizer unit, which is designed to achieve superheated oil vapor from oil liquid, due to a furnace containing a heating coil and burners, where the natural gas combines with air to burn (BS IEC 61882:2001). To that end, this process uses two control loops: the first one has the goal to regulate the incoming oil flow, besides a low flow alarm of liquid oil, and the second one deals with the temperature of the outgoing vaporized oil flow manipulating the flow of natural gas to the burners. In addition to these control loops, there is an auto regulated valve that controls the pressure of the natural gas flow. A simplified P&ID of the unit is shown in Figure 3.

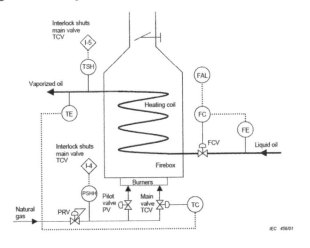

Figure 3. Oil vaporizer unit (BS IEC 61882:2001).

4.1. Functional decomposition

The main goal of the overall unit is to obtain oil vapor from the combustion between natural gas and external air, as said in the process description. To that end, the system can be decomposed into two subsystems that perform the necessary subgoals, in the following way: (1) Oil flow section: provide a constant feed of liquid oil and emerges vapor flow under operation conditions; (2) Burners section: provide through combustion the needed heat to vaporize the oil. This functional decomposition can be continued until the desired level of detail is obtained. Thanks to that and the P&ID, the D-higraphs can be developed. It is shown in Figure 4.

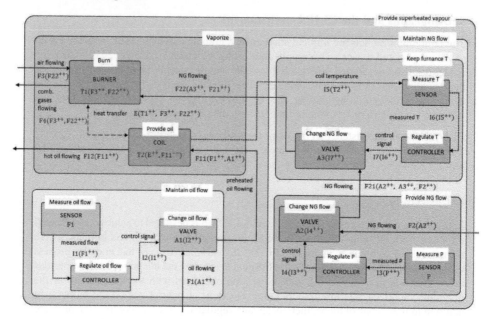

Figure 4. D-higraphs.

5. Hazop and D-higraphs results

In this section the results obtained for "No oil flow" deviation are shown. This deviation consists of the variable "oil flow" that passes through the heating coil and the HAZOP guide word "no". It should be noted that due to space constraints, only this deviation is shown, but the complete study has been conducted, applying all the HAZOP deviations.

5.1. HAZOP analysis

A modified table of the HAZOP report obtained for the case study is featured below in Table 1. It shows relevant details, such as the HAZOP team, the considered part of the process, the design intent and the deviation, which is where we focus on this paper. The HAZOP team points out that the main reasons for the lack of flow are due to a failure of the supply line, the flow control valve FCV or a failure of the vaporizer.

At the same time, the possible consequences of this deviation are reflected, where the overheating of the vaporizer is highlighted, as well as the safeguards and the actions required as preventive measures.

Table 1. Example HAZOP worksheet. No oil flow deviation (BS IEC 61882:2001).

STUDY TITLE: OIL VAPORIZER									
Drawing No. :					REVISION No.:			DATE:	
TEAM COMPOSITION: MG, NE, DH, EK, LB								MEETING DATE:	
PART CONSIDERED: Vaporizer coil from oil inlet (before flow measurement), to vapour exit to process (after temperature control)					DESIGN INTENT:	Inputs: Activities:	Oil flow from the feed line, heat from the furnace Vaporize, superheat and transfer oil vapour to the process		
No.	Guide word	Element	Deviation	Possible causes	Consequences	Safeguards	Comments	Actions required	Action by
1	No	Oil flow	No oil flow	– Supply failure – Flow control valve PCV closed	Vaporizer coil overheats and may fail	Low flow alarm FAL High temperature trip TSH	Safeguard depends on quick operator response	Consider low flow element FE to close main burner valve TCV	LB
				– Plugging of coil – Blockage down-stream of vaporizer	Oil in vaporizer will boil; Possible overheating and coking of heating coil	Low flow alarm FAL High temperature trip TSH		Check whether these safeguards are adequate and the ease with which the coil could be cleaned	NE

5.2. D-higraphs - CLIPS analysis

As it has been said before, once the topology and the rules of causes or consequences have been loaded, the analysis begins. For this, the "Assert" command is used, followed by the guide Word "No" ("Fail", in CLIPS) and the parameter "oil flow" ("hot_oil_flowing"). It is necessary to specify whether this variable belongs to an edge or blob. The CLIPS report is featured below.

```
CAUSES

CLIPS> (assert (Report))
<Fact-1>
CLIPS>    (assert    (Fail    edge
[hot_oil_flowing]))
<Fact-2>
CLIPS> (run)

The causative Edges are:
[preheated_oil_flowing]
[heat_transfer]
[air_flowing]
[NG_flowing]
[measured_T]
[NG_flowing]
[control_signal]
[NG_flowing]
[measured_P]
[control_signal]
[coil_temperature]
[control_signal]
[oil_flowing]
[measured_flow]

The causative Blobs are:
[PROVIDE_OIL]
[BURN]
[CHANGE_NG_FLOW]
[CHANGE_NG_FLOW]
[REGULATE_P]
[MEASURE_P]
[REGULATE_T]
[MEASURE_T]
[PROVIDE_OIL]
[CHANGE_OIL_FLOW]
[REGULATE_OIL_FLOW]
[MEASURE_OIL_FLOW]
```

```
CONSEQUENCES

CLIPS> (assert (Report))
<Fact-1>
CLIPS>    (assert    (Fail    edge
[hot_oil_flowing]))
<Fact-2>
CLIPS> (run)

The afected Edges are:
[hot_oil_flowing]
[coil_temperature]
[measured_T]
[control_signal]
[NG_flowing]
[comb_gases_flowing]
[heat_transfer]

The afected Blobs are:
[PROVIDE_OIL]
[VAPORIZE]
[MEASURE_T]
[REGULATE_T]
[KEEP_FURNACE_T]
[CHANGE_NG_FLOW]
[BURN]

There have been double fail in:
[PROVIDE_OIL]

There have been triple fail in:
[hot_oil_flowing]
[coil_temperature]
[MEASURE_T]
[PROVIDE_OIL]

There have been quadruple fail in:
[measured_T]
[hot_oil_flowing]
[coil_temperature]

The Hazard Level of this fail is: 14
```

5.3. Comparing the results

According to the results, CLIPS is useful to show all those edges and blobs that are involved in the contingency created and it also lists a series of devices that are not present in the HAZOP report. However, CLIPS does not go into much detail of the type of failure. That is why this methodology is only helpful to find possible sources, such as [BURN], where it warns that the cause can be due to a failure in the device that provides the energy to oil. In the same way it happens with the consequences, where it also highlights multiple failures in edges and blobs, implying that those devices have a high importance. This guided HAZOP can save a lot of time to the HAZOP team and avoid missing some causes or consequences as it follow every possible path in the process.

6. Conclusions and further work

In this paper we have presented a methodology to perform systematic guided HAZOP studies based on D-higraphs. It has been applied to an industrial process in order to show its applicability and compare a traditional HAZOP study with CLIPS. The results are easy to understand and helpful in order to broaden the field of analysis of the process, to make it more complete and deeper, increasing thus the security of the analysis. On the other hand, future work will be devoted to the implementation of a "translator", which will transform P&IDs models to D-higraphs, avoiding the text template that can be a human error source, hindering its quick implementation. In addition, the rules of causes and consequences should be analysed to give more depth in the analysis of each HAZOP guide word and to increase the level of detail in the CLIPS report.

References

Álvarez, M. E. 2010. Diagnosis de fallos en procesos químicos mediante modelos D-higraph. Final Project. Department of Chemical Engineering, Technical University of Madrid.

British Standard IEC 61882:2001. Hazard and operability studies (HAZOP studies) – Application guide, 52.

CLIPS. 2018. CLIPS, A Tool for Building Expert Systems. http://clipsrules.sourceforge.net

Cui, L., Zhao, J., Qiu, T., & Chen, B. 2008. Layered digraph model for HAZOP analysis of chemical processes. Process Safety Progress, 27(4), 293–305.

De la Mata, J. L., Rodríguez, M. 2010. Abnormal situation diagnosis using D-higraphs. Proc. of the 20th European Symposium on Computer Aided Process Engineering, pp. 1477-1482.

Harel, D. 1987. Statecharts: A visual formalism for complex systems. Sci. Comput. Program., 8.

Kuipers, B. 1984. Commonsense reasoning about causality. Artificial Intelligence, 24.

Kuipers, B. 1986. Qualitative simulation. Artifiial Intelligence, 29.

Lind, M. 1994. Modeling goals and functions of complex Industrial plant. Applied Artificial Intelligence, 8 (2).

Rodríguez, M., Sanz, R. 2009. Development of integrated functional-structural models. Computer Aided Process Engineering, 27.

Rossing, N. L., Lind, M., Jensen, N., Jorgensen, S. B. 2010a. A functional HAZOP methodology. Computers and Chemical Engineering, 34 (2).

Rossing, N. L., Lind, M., Jensen, N., & Jørgensen, S. B. 2010b. A goal based methodology for HAZOP analysis. Nuclear Safety and Simulation, 1(2).

Venkatasubramanian, V., Zhao, C., Viswanathan, S. 2000. Intelligent systems for HAZOP analysis of complex process plants. Computers and Chemical Engineering, 24 (9-10).

Zhao, C., Bhushan, M, & Venkatasubramanian, V. 2005. PHASuite: An Automated HAZOP Analysis Tool for Chemical Processes. Process Safety and Environment Protection, 83 (6).

Zhao, J., Cui, L., Zhao, L., Qiu, T., & Chen, B. 2009. Learning HAZOP expert system by case-based reasoning and ontology. Computers & Chemical Engineering, 33(1).

Anton A. Kiss, Edwin Zondervan, Richard Lakerveld, Leyla Özkan (Eds.)
Proceedings of the 29th European Symposium on Computer Aided Process Engineering
June 16th to 19th, 2019, Eindhoven, The Netherlands. © 2019 Elsevier B.V. All rights reserved.
http://dx.doi.org/10.1016/B978-0-128-18634-3.50094-1

A Novel Optimizable Inherent Safety Index Based on Fuzzy Logic

Daniel Vázquez[a*], Rubén Ruiz-Femenia[a], José A. Caballero[a]

[a]*Institute of Chemical Process Engineering, University of Alicante, PO 99, E-3080 Alicante, Spain*

vazquez.vazquez@ua.es

Abstract

In our days, the concept of inherent safety is gaining popularity thanks to its ability to assess the safety level of a plant at an early design stage. Hence, safety can be considered one of the core design principles, instead of a post-design add-on. In this work, we propose a novel index to assess the inherent safety level of a design. This index is based on the principles of fuzzy logic, which allow the user to shift the importance in the safety criteria easily, and its main objectives is to provide an optimizable framework. In order to achieve an optimizable fuzzy index, some concessions must be made in its methodology. As such, the presented index is not as quantitative as other safety indexes. However, this shortcoming is compensated with the comparative ability and modifiability that this index provides the decision maker with. As a conclusion, we showcase the ability of this novel index in assessing the inherent safety level of an example case.

Keywords: Inherent Safety, Fuzzy Logic, Optimization.

1. Introduction

In order to consider the design of a chemical process from a holistic point of view, it is necessary to have a method able to assess the safety level of a plant at an early design stage. The concept of inherent safety, coined by Kletz (Kletz & Amyotte, 2010), presents itself useful for this objective. The four main principles of inherent safety are: intensification, substitution, attenuation and limitation. The consideration of these principles allows the designer to give safety aspects the same importance as economic and environmental issues. Therefore, safety is considered a key design variable, instead of an afterthought once the main variables are fixed.

Safety analysis tend to be performed with the aid of safety indexes, such as Dow's (AICHE, 1994) and Safety Weighted Hazard Index (Khan et al., 2001). Some techniques, like the Hazard and Operability (HAZOP) method, consist in a committee of experts discussing the weak and hazardous points of a design. They use keywords, such as "high" and "low", which cannot be immediately quantified. This methodology resembles spoken language, and the use of fuzzy logic allows the designer to assemble spoken language with mathematical quantifiable rules (Zadeh, 1999). In this work, we use Mamdani's method (Mamdani & Assilian, 1975) in order to extract mathematical information from keywords. Mamdani's method comprises four steps: fuzzification of the inputs, establishment of the relationships among the inputs and outputs, aggregation of the conclusions and defuzzification of the output.

A problem that many safety indexes exhibit is that the mathematical expressions to compute them are nonconvex. Since they work with multiple variables at the same level, such as flows, temperatures, enthalpies and pressures, they must use nonlinear operators. More complex indexes that use dispersion models are highly nonlinear and nonconvex. Since this work has the objective of providing an optimizable index, the calculations must be maintained the most linear possible. The defuzzification step includes a nonlinear equation which is unavoidable, but the fuzzification and the relationships among fuzzy sets can be made completely linear with the inclusion of Generalized Disjunctive Programming (GDP).

Therefore, this work presents a novel optimizable (in the sense that it can be systematically optimized) inherent safety (in that it is calculated according to the principles of inherent safety) index based on fuzzy logic (which allows the user to connect keywords and establish relationships input-output maintaining a mostly linear model). The index is divided into sub-indices that account for each inherent safety principle. In this paper we present the sub-indices for intensification and attenuation. These are then part of a multi-objective optimization (MOO) problem.

2. Intensification sub-index

The intensification principle, also named minimization principle, is based on the core idea of diminishing the inventory inside a process unit. The inventory refers to both the amount of chemical in the unit (or exiting the unit in a period of time) and the amount of energy that these chemicals carry. The index is obtained as shown in Eq. (1).

$$II = (II_{energy} \wedge II_{inventory}) \tag{1}$$

Where II stands for Intensification Index, II_{energy} stands for the part of the sub-index that takes into account the energy in the unit, and $II_{inventory}$ stands for the part of the sub-index that takes into account the amount of mass in the unit, as well as the streams that go out of the unit.

Each of these parts is calculated by an equation, shown in Eq. (2).

$$II_{energy} = \sum_{i=1}^{C} \Delta Hc_i x_i + \Delta Hr$$

$$II_{inventory} = FE\,V \cdot \rho + \dot{m}_{t=10min} \tag{2}$$

Where:

- ΔHc_i stands for the combustion enthalpy of the chemical i of C components in the unit, in kJ/kg.

- ΔHr stands for the reaction enthalpy in the unit, if a reaction is happening, in kJ/kg

- x_i stands for the mass fraction of the chemical $i \in C$ inside the process unit.

- FE, V, ρ stand for the equipment factor, volume and density respectively. The equipment factor is a parameter that relates the volume of the unit with the amount of chemical inside. An example is 0.8 for reactors and tanks. If you are using the volume of chemical directly, its value is 1. The units of the volume and density are m^3 and kg/m^3 respectively.

- $\dot{m}_{t=10min}$ stands for the mass of chemical that leaves the process unit in a time interval of ten minutes, in kg.

In order to continue Mamdani's method, we have to fuzzify the input values for both parts of the index. As such, an interval must be fixed by the designer. Then, a fuzzification function is used to assign a membership value to each crisp input. It is recommended to use linear functions, such as the triangular or trapezoid functions. An example of fuzzification for both parts of the sub-index is shown in Table 1.

Table 1. Fuzzification of the input. Intensification index.

Semantic pointer	Range	Fuzzification function
Low (L)	0 – 60 % of the interval	Gaussian
Medium (M)	5 – 95 % of the interval	Triangular
High (H)	40 – 100 % of the interval	Gaussian

While the Gaussian function is nonlinear, it is chosen in this work as an example of how, the index is still able to provide a satisfactory result even when dealing with more nonlinearities than the one strictly needed. These intervals are examples. The safety experts of the plant must decide how many intervals are necessary and how wide they are in order to correctly classify the safety level of the design.

The experts must define as well the relationships between the two parts of the sub-index (Eq. (1)). Some decision making techniques, such as Analytical Hierarchy Process, can be useful to ensure that the relationships remain coherent. Each relationship has to be assigned to an output fuzzy set. For example, in order to illustrate this, in this work the relationships are shown in Table 2.

Table 2. Relationships among inputs

Output fuzzy set / Risk level	Implications ($II_{energy} \wedge II_{inventory}$)
Minimal	$(L \wedge L)$
Low	$(L \wedge M) \vee (M \wedge L)$
Medium	$(M \wedge M) \vee (L \wedge H) \vee (H \wedge L)$
Moderate	$(H \wedge M) \vee (M \wedge H)$
High	$(H \wedge H)$

In order to defuzzify the output, we need to know how these output fuzzy sets are created. The chosen outputs of the intensification index are fuzzified as shown in Table 3.

Table 3. Fuzzification of the output

Semantic Pointer	Value of the index	Fuzzification function
Minimal Risk	0 – ~10	Gaussian
Low Risk	4 – 15	Triangular
Medium Risk	15-35	Triangular
Moderate Risk	35-45	Triangular
High Risk	~40-50	Gaussian

After the step of aggregation, we obtain an aggregated output that can be defuzzified using a centroid.

3. Attenuation sub-index

The attenuation principle is based on the idea of diminishing the hazardous conditions during operation. As such, the main variables considered for its calculation are the operating temperature and the operating pressure, although these are not the only parameters that the index takes into account.

The methodology is analogous to the intensification sub-index one. As such, we present only the equations and example fuzzification intervals and relationships.

The equations are as shown in Eq. (3) and Eq. (4)

$$AI = (AI_T \wedge AI_P) \tag{3}$$

Where AI_T stands for the part of the index that depends on the temperature parameters and AI_P stands for the part of the index that depends on the pressure parameters.

$$AI_T = T_{op} + Pen_T \cdot \max(0, T_{op} - T_b) - Rw_T \cdot \max(0, T_b - T_{op})$$
$$AI_P = P_{op} + Pen_P \cdot \max(0, P_{vap} - P_{op}) \tag{4}$$

Where T_{op}, T_b stand for the operating temperature and the boiling temperature in ºC and P_{op}, P_{vap} stand for the operating pressure and vapour pressure in bar. Pen_T , Rw_T and Pen_P are penalization and reward parameters that reward the unit when working with subcooled liquids and penalize it when it works with overheated vapours. In this work, their values are set to 0.5, 0.1 and 0.5 respectively.

A possible fuzzification is shown in Table 4.

Table 4. Fuzzification of the input. Attenuation index.

Semantic Pointer	Range in temperature (ºC)	Range in pressure (bar)	Fuzzification function
Atmospheric (A)	~30	~1.5	Gaussian
Low (L)	10 – 50	1 – 6	Triangular
Medium (M)	40 – 80	4 – 10	Triangular
High (H)	70 - > 100	8 - > 12	Gaussian

A possible set of relationships is shown in Table 5.

Table 5. Relationships among inputs. Attenuation index

Output fuzzy set/ Risk level	Implications ($AI_T \wedge AI_P$)
Minimal	$(A \wedge A) \vee (A \wedge L)$
Low	$(L \wedge L) \vee (L \wedge A) \vee (A \wedge M) \vee (L \wedge M)$
Medium	$(M \wedge M) \vee (A \wedge H) \vee (M \wedge L) \vee (L \wedge H) \vee (M \wedge A)$
Moderate	$(H \wedge A) \vee (H \wedge L) \vee (M \wedge H)$
High	$(H \wedge H) \vee (H \wedge M)$

The fuzzification of the output is analogous to the one shown in Table 3.

4. Example and Results

We consider a number of units that work with certain operating conditions. No reaction is occurring inside these units. The properties of the chemicals inside the units are shown in Table 6.

Table 6. Data of the example case

Properties	Unit #01	Unit #02	Unit #03	Unit #04	Unit #05	Units
$\sum_{i=1}^{C} \Delta Hc_i x_i$	14.25	17.20	10.43	8.29	5.34	MJ/kg
$FE V \cdot \rho$	20000	15000	34000	10000	5000	kg
$\dot{m}_{t=10min}$	3000	2000	2000	1000	3000	kg
T_{op}, T_b	50, 50	30, 60	50, 30	40, 70	80,40	°C
P_{op}, P_{vap}	1, 1	3, 2	4, 6	8, 7	8, 12	bar
Inventory range			0 – 40			t
Energy range			0 – 20			MJ/kg
Temperature range			0 – 100			°C
Pressure range			0 – 12			Bar

We consider the global index as the aggregation of both the intensification and attenuation sub-indices. The resultant optimization model, based on Generalized Disjunctive Programming (GDP), is a Mixed Integer Non-Linear Programming (MINLP) problem. The nonlinearities are found in the defuzzification of the output step, which is performed using the centroid, and in the Gaussian fuzzification functions of the inputs. The rest of the calculations are linear. The results are shown in Table 7.

Table 7. Results of the optimization

Order from best to worst	Global Index	II	AI
Unit #02	39.86	29.98	9.88
Unit #04	43.40	20.22	23.18
Unit #03	52.74	32.74	20.00
Unit #01	53.10	28.11	24.99
Unit #05	66.26	16.27	49.99

It can be observed that the index is able to rank the different process units regarding its inherent safety level. In this example, an aggregation of both the intensification sub-index and the attenuation sub-index is performed. This is not the only option, since there are multiple possibilities to treat MOO problems. Another alternative is a weighted sum, giving more importance to one sub-index over the other. It is the duty of the decision maker to assign the correct importance to each sub-index.

An important remark is the case of Unit #05. Its attenuation sub-index has a value of practically 50, which is the highest value that the index achieves. If we look at the definition of the fuzzy sets for the input, Table 4, we can see that the high semantic pointer (H) starts at around 70 °C and 8 bar. If we apply Eq. (4), we obtain the values of $AI_T = 100$ °C and $AI_P = 10$ bar. While the temperature part of the attenuation index is indeed at its maximum allowed by the chosen range, the pressure part stills has room for an increment. However, any higher pressure, e.g., 11, 12 bar, will still result in an index of 50. This nuance shows that the decision maker must choose carefully the range of the intervals and the fuzzification functions of the inputs, as well as its ranges.

5. Conclusions

In this work we present the initial step in creating a novel inherent safety index based on fuzzy logic. The index is divided in sub-indices that refer to each main principle of inherent safety. The use of fuzzy logic allows the user to maintain a mostly linear model, which can be made strictly linear except for the objective function. It also allows the user to easily and quickly change parameters in order to fit the index to different problems. This is both an advantage and a disadvantage. While the modifiability of the index increases its versatility, it also forces the user to know the system of possibilities beforehand. Ranges must be chosen regarding the corresponding problem at hand, and so must be the relationships. The user has to know where to put more emphasis in the safety analysis. In some units, it may be better to give more importance to the pressure than to the temperature, and this must be reflected in the chosen relationships among input fuzzy sets.

The index proves its efficiency as an optimizable inherent safety index able to rank alternatives depending on their safety level. While its main use is comparative, due to the fact that each sub-index depends on a series of user-chosen parameters and ranges, with the appropriate considerations, i.e., relationships and ranges, it could be used as a global index for a process, with the advantage of being systematically optimizable and modifiable. For future works, it is intended to implement an analogous methodology to obtain an index for the substitution index, using the NFPA(2012) standard as the main variable.

Acknowledgments

The authors acknowledge financial support from the Spanish "Ministerio de Economía, Industria y Competitividad" (CTQ2016-77968-C3-02-P, FEDER, UE).

References

AICHE. (1994). Dow's Fire & Explosion Index Hazard Classification Guide. In.
Khan, F. I., Husain, T., & Abbasi, S. A. (2001). Safety Weighted Hazard Index (SWeHI). Process Safety and Environmental Protection, 79, 65-80.
Kletz, T., & Amyotte, P. (2010). A Handbook for Inherently Safer Design (Second Edition ed.).
Mamdani, E. H., & Assilian, S. (1975). An experiment in linguistic synthesis with a fuzzy logic controller. International Journal of Man-Machine Studies, 7, 1-13.
NFPA. (2012). NFPA 704: Standard System for the Identification of the Hazards of Materials for Emergency Response. In.
Zadeh, L. A. (1999). Fuzzy Sets as a Basis for a Theory of Possibility. Fuzzy Sets and Systems, 100.

Anton A. Kiss, Edwin Zondervan, Richard Lakerveld, Leyla Özkan (Eds.)
Proceedings of the 29th European Symposium on Computer Aided Process Engineering
June 16th to 19th, 2019, Eindhoven, The Netherlands. © 2019 Elsevier B.V. All rights reserved.
http://dx.doi.org/10.1016/B978-0-128-18634-3.50095-3

Optimization under uncertainty of melatonin dosing for critically ill patients

Adriana Savoca, Giuseppe Pesenti, Davide Manca[*]

*PSE-Lab, Dipartimento di Chimica, Materiali e Ingegneria Chimica "Giulio Natta"
Politecnico di Milano, Piazza Leonardo da Vinci 32, Milano 20133, Italy*

davide.manca@polimi.it

Abstract

Computer-aided modelling and simulation are effective tools to provide guidance in the design of clinical experiments and treatments. Simulations with physiologically-based pharmacokinetic (PBPK) models combine the drug material balances within the body to its real physiological and anatomical features and can be used to optimize drugs dosing and administration timing. We focus on melatonin administration to critically ill patients, a challenging population because of their high inter-individual variability in the pharmacokinetics (due to their heterogeneous and severe conditions). We show how the optimization problem can be suitably formulated to tackle this uncertainty, and compare the results obtained for critically ill patients and healthy individuals. The approach can be easily transferred to any other drug routinely administered in intensive care units whenever a desired pharmacokinetic profile is available.

Keywords: optimization, modelling, simulation, uncertainty, pharmacokinetics.

1. Introduction

Recent years have seen an increasing interest in melatonin. Although it is particularly well-known as a cure for sleep disturbances and restoration of circadian rhythms, researchers are investigating additional physiological and pathophysiological functions. Indeed, there is evidence of anti-cancer, anti-oxidative, anti-inflammatory, and analgesic properties (Brzezinski, 1997). Healthy individuals produce melatonin endogenously by means of the pineal gland according to the day-night rhythm. Melatonin production onsets with darkness (around 9-10 PM) and peaks at 2-4 AM. Healthy plasma peak levels are in between 60-100 pg/mL. After the peak, melatonin levels settle to the low daily baseline (5-10 pg/mL). Collaboration with Intensive Care Unit (ICU) of Ospedale San Paolo di Milano (Italy) allowed focusing on critically ill patients. Such patients exhibit disorders in melatonin secretion rhythm and/or lower levels compared to healthy individuals. This phenomenon is correlated to the lack of sleep, which likely increases both patients' morbidity and probability of mortality. There is evidence that exogenous melatonin has beneficial effects on these patients, mainly for treatment of sleep disorder, delirium, and oxidative stress (Bourne and Mills, 2006; Mistraletti et al., 2010). Several studies investigated the optimal dose with the purpose of reproducing the desired physiological levels of melatonin and proposed different doses (regimens) to restore the healthy endogenous rhythm. While physiological levels are desirable to restore circadian rhythms, pharmacological levels (*i.e.* supraphysiological levels, for instance about 3 orders of magnitude higher) are more suitable for anti-oxidant or anti-cancer purposes (Reiter et al., 2014). We show that computer simulation is an efficient tool to design and/or integrate such pharmacokinetic (PK) studies, with the advantage of reducing times and costs of the experiments. In addition, simulations using physiologically-based pharmacokinetic (PBPK) models allow comparing and evaluating the pharmacokinetics from not only different doses but also routes of administration. In fact, our first goal is to select the administration route that best mimics human physiological levels. Subsequently, we focus on that route and optimize dosing, also by comparing results for healthy individuals (by neglecting the endogenous contribution for the sake of clarity) and critically ill patients. The main issue with critically ill patients is that they are intrinsically rather heterogeneous, because of their different conditions (*e.g.*, age, dysfunctions, organs failure) (Mistraletti et al., 2010). This feature enhances inter-individual variability of melatonin pharmacokinetics. To deal with this problem, we propose a prospective approach to drug dosing optimization.

2. Methods

Figure 1 shows the structure of a multi-route compartmental PBPK model. The reference model for this work is Abbiati et al. (2016), where organs and tissues of the human body are represented by homogenous compartments. We complemented those compartments number and model structure to melatonin features and administration routes, by adding (i) the pineal gland, which is the source of endogenous melatonin, and (ii) the salivary glands (Savoca et al., 2018). A further equation accounts for the dynamics of main melatonin metabolite: 6-sulfatoxymelatonin (aMT6s) both in plasma and in urine. In case of oral administration (PO, *per os,* see also Figure 1), the model consists of material balances on either single or lumped homogenous compartments.

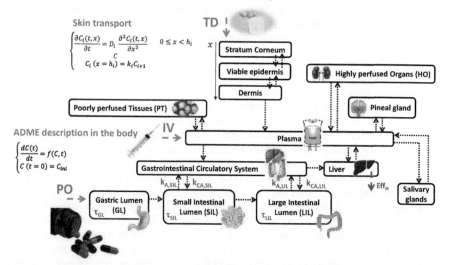

Figure 1 - Scheme of the PBPK model for description of melatonin ADME processes. Parameters in red are associated to the main processes responsible for inter-patient variability. While skin transport is described via PDEs discretized with respect to skin depth *x*, the other body compartments feature melatonin material balances in the form of ODEs.

These are the gastric lumen (GL), the small and large intestinal lumina (SIL and LIL), the gastrointestinal circulatory system (GICS), the plasma, the liver, the poorly perfused tissues (PT, lumping adipose tissue, skin, and muscles), and the highly perfused organs

(HO, lumping brain, lungs, and spleen). In case of intravenous (IV) route, the gastrointestinal compartments are neglected. Finally, in case of transdermal (TD) administration, skin is assumed as a separate compartment from PT and described by a set of partial differential equations (PDEs) with proper boundary conditions for skin TD absorption. The model features three skin layers: (i) stratum corneum, (ii) viable epidermis (also a metabolism site), and (iii) dermis, from which the drug is supposed to reach the systemic circulation. These PDEs are discretized with respect to the spatial coordinate (*i.e.* skin depth) and converted to ODEs and merged to those of the other compartments (Savoca et al., 2018). Model parameters include (i) individualized and assigned parameters that are either calculated as a function of patient's characteristics or found in the literature, and (ii) adaptive parameters (*e.g.,* diffusivities, transfer coefficients, metabolic constants) that are obtained via a non-linear regression of experimental data from the literature. Firstly, we use the multi-route PBPK simulations to compare levels resulting from PO, IV, and TD administration routes. Secondly, we perform an optimization based only on PO controlled release (CR), as it resulted the most suitable to mimic endogenous pharmacokinetics. Based on experimental release curves from the scientific literature, the optimal melatonin amount and time of administration are identified for three *in silico* individuals, (i) a healthy male, (ii) a healthy female, and (iii) an ICU patient. The PBPK model parameters for healthy individuals are identified with melatonin PK experimental data of healthy volunteers. Equally, the parameters that describe the PK of ICU patients are identified via regression with experimental data of the critically ill.

To account for considerable inter-individual variability, the optimization problem considers the uncertainty related to the (patho)physiological differences of such patients. The processes that most likely produce inter-subject variability are (i) absorption from the intestinal walls into gastrointestinal circulation (characterized by absorption constants $k_{A,SIL}$, $k_{A,LIL}$, $k_{CA,SIL}$, and $k_{CA,LIL}$ and residence times in gastrointestinal region τ_{GL}, τ_{SIL}, and τ_{LIL}) and (ii) hepatic metabolism (described by hepatic efficiency Eff_H). These model parameters are randomized within a proper range, which is chosen referring to physiology for the transit times, and model uncertainty for the others, to produce different PK profiles for the ICU virtual patient, VP. These additional NS "scenarios" embody the structure of the optimization problem in Eq. (1), where NM is the number of experimental data C_i^{ideal} that describe the healthy endogenous plasma concentration profile (Voultsios et al., 1997). The degrees of freedom are: *dose* and t_{adm} (*i.e.* timing of administration).

$$\min_{dose, t_{adm}} \sum_{k=1}^{NS} \left(\frac{\sum_{i=1}^{NM} \left(C_i^{ideal} - C_i^{VP,k} \right)^2}{NM} \right) \tag{1}$$

3. Results

3.1. Comparison of administration routes

The physiochemical properties of melatonin (*e.g.,* lipophilicity and low molecular weight) make it suitable for at least three administration routes, *i.e.* PO, IV, and TD. As far as the PO route is concerned, we consider both immediate and controlled release (CR) formulations. Figure 2 allows comparing the pharmacokinetics of these different routes under the same melatonin dose (1.5 mg in the left panel, 12 mg in the right panel). The characteristic slowness of TD absorption is particularly appropriate to mimic the sustained endogenous levels produced by the pineal gland. Equally, the PO (CR) formulation provides continued levels (T_{max} about 4 h), coupled with a steeper absorption.

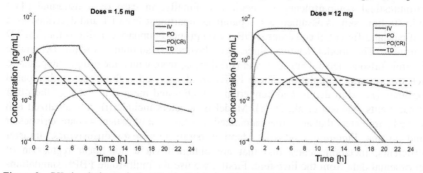

Figure 2 – PK simulations of a healthy individual with IV, PO (immediate release and controlled release (CR) formulations), and TD administrations of melatonin. Black dashed horizontal lines show the range of concentration peak after healthy endogenous production (60-100 pg/mL).

The difference in the velocity of early absorption affects the selection of the optimal administration timing as it affects the onset time of the pharmacological and physiological effects. Predictably, even low doses of continuous IV infusion produce the highest levels, thus it is probably the most appropriate to achieve prompt pharmacological (*i.e.* supraphysiological) levels. On the contrary, TD administration should be excluded for that purpose, even in case of higher doses. In case of PO immediate-release formulation, the melatonin concentration decreases rapidly after administration. However, even for low doses, this administration formulation allows reaching pharmacological levels, alternatively to IV infusion. This conclusion is in line with experimental studies where oral doses higher than 0.3 mg produce supra-physiological levels.

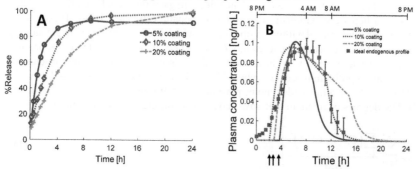

Figure 3 – (A) Experimental release curves for different formulations, as in Lee et al. (1995). (B) Optimized PK levels (continuous, dashed, and dotted lines) in ICU and ideal (experimental) healthy endogenous data (red squares). Black arrows indicate optimal timing of administration.

3.2. Optimization for PO CR route

Panel A of Figure 3 compares three PO (CR) formulations with different percentages of polymer coating (5-10-20%) that generate three different release curves as in Lee et al. (1995). Panel B of Figure 3 shows experimental data of the endogenous profile of an healthy individual (red squares, from Voultsios et al. (1997)), while continuous, dotted, and dashed lines are the optimized pharmacokinetics of an ICU patient who receives tablets featuring the three different release curves. The most suitable release curve corresponds to the 10%-coating tablet that best approaches the PK endogenous profile.

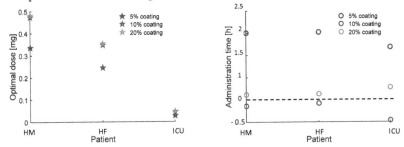

Figure 4 – Optimal melatonin dose (left panel) and timing of administration (right panel) for HM and HF (healthy male and female individuals) and ICU (critically ill patient). Dashed horizontal line (right panel) indicates the desired time of onset of melatonin effects.

Figure 4 shows the melatonin optimal doses and timing of administration. On the x-axis, HM and HF stand for the male and female healthy individuals, while ICU stands for the critically ill patient. It is worth noticing that the lowest dose is associated to the ICU patient. Indeed, for the same dose, PK studies show higher melatonin concentrations in critically ill patients, compared to healthy individuals. Probably, the continuous enteral nutrition of ICU patients facilitates melatonin absorption. Notably, PBPK model simulations are consistent with this behavior.

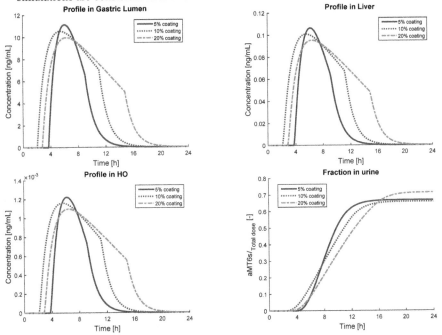

Figure 5 - PBPK model simulations for the critically ill patient in Gastric Lumen, Liver, HO (Highly perfused Organs), and aMT6s fraction in urine.

In addition, optimal dose values for the healthy individuals are in line with the results of experimental studies (as already mentioned, oral doses higher than 0.3 mg produce supraphysiological levels). Our results are not so far from this approximate value. Figure 4 (right panel) shows the optimal timing of administration in relation to the desired onset time for melatonin effects (see the horizontal dashed line at 0). In case of 10%-coating, the optimal administration timing for the ICU patient is about 30 min before the desired onset, while it is shorter for healthy individuals. This is consistent with the fact that critically ill patients exhibit higher levels of melatonin after exogenous administration. In all the other cases, to mimic the endogenous profile optimally, the administration timing should occur *after* the desired onset time, which evidently makes no sense. This confirms that the 10%-coating formulation is the most optimal to deliver physiological levels of melatonin. Finally, Figure 5 shows melatonin PK simulations in different compartments (*i.e.* Gastric Lumen, Liver, and HO, Highly perfused Organs) and the eliminated amount of melatonin metabolite, aMT6s, after the optimal administration of PO (CR) formulation to the ICU patient. Low levels in HO are consistent with the typical tissue hypoperfusion of critically ill patients. Experimentally, the eliminated melatonin is usually higher than 85%, while this threshold is not reached in our simulations. This may be related to two different reasons: (i) from the modeling point of view, our model underestimates aMT6s metabolic production as we consider (for simplicity) the liver contribution only, (ii) from the physical point of view, ICU patients may exhibit lower metabolism compared to healthy patients.

4. Conclusions

PBPK model simulations are an effective tool in melatonin optimal pharmacotherapy. We optimized melatonin dosing by comparing healthy individuals and critically ill patients. As the latter ones represent an extremely heterogeneous population, we proposed an approach that allows accounting for inter-subject variability generated by the gastrointestinal absorption and metabolic processes. Results are in line with conclusions from past experimental PK studies and can provide aid in future study for the challenging identification of melatonin optimal dose regimens in critically ill patients.

References

Abbiati, R.A., Depetri, V., Scotti, F., Manca, D. (2016). A new approach for pharmacokinetic model application towards personalized medicine, CACE, 38, 1611-1616.

Bourne, R.S., Mills, G.H. (2006). Melatonin: possible implications for the postoperative and critically ill patient. Intensive Care Med, 32, 371-379.

Brzezinski, A. (1997). Melatonin in humans. N Engl J Med, 336, 186-195.

Lee, B.J., Parrott, K.A., Ayres, J.W., Sack, R.L. (1995). Design and evaluation of an oral controlled release delivery system for melatonin in human subjects. Int J Pharm, 124, 119-127.

Mistraletti, G., Sabbatini, et al. (2010). Pharmacokinetics of orally administered melatonin in critically ill patients. J Pineal Res, 48, 142-147.

Reiter, R.J., Tan, D.X., Galano, A. (2014). Melatonin: exceeding expectations. Physiology (Bethesda), 29, 325-333.

Savoca, A., Mistraletti, G., Manca, D. (2018). A physiologically-based diffusion-compartment model for transdermal administration – The melatonin case study. Computers & Chemical Engineering, 113, 115-124.

Voultsios, A., Kennaway, D.J., Dawson, D. (1997). Salivary melatonin as a circadian phase marker: validation and comparison to plasma melatonin. J Biol Rhythms, 12, 457-466.

Anton A. Kiss, Edwin Zondervan, Richard Lakerveld, Leyla Özkan (Eds.)
Proceedings of the 29th European Symposium on Computer Aided Process Engineering
June 16th to 19th, 2019, Eindhoven, The Netherlands. © 2019 Elsevier B.V. All rights reserved.
http://dx.doi.org/10.1016/B978-0-128-18634-3.50096-5

Optimization of a shell-and-tube heat exchanger using the grey wolf algorithm

Oscar D. Lara-Montaño[a] and Fernando I. Gómez-Castro[a]

[a]*Departamento de Ingeniería Química, División de Ciencias Naturales y Exactas, Campus Guanajuato, Universidad de Guanajuato, Noria Alta S/N, Guanajuato, Guanajuato 36050, Mexico*
fgomez@ugto.mx

Abstract

Most chemical processes require heat exchangers to modify the temperatures of the streams involved in the production steps. Due to their many applications, the rigorous design of such exchangers is of interest, aiming to determine the physical characteristics required to obtain the desired variation in temperature. The mathematical models representing such devices have several degrees of freedom and non-lineal equations, thus robust optimization algorithms are required to obtain the optimal solution in a short time. In this work, the use of the grey wolf algorithm is proposed for the optimization of a shell-and-tube heat exchanger, modeled by the Bell-Delaware equations. With the proposed method, a minimum total annual cost of 3,978.2 USD was obtained, in a mean time of 0.7976 seconds.

Keywords: meta-heuristic optimization, shell-and-tube heat exchanger, grey wolf algorithm.

1. Introduction

Heat exchangers are among the most used auxiliary equipment in chemical industry, since cooling and heating are common operations which allow modifying the temperature, or even the phase, of process streams, according to the operational requirements. This implies that heat exchangers are necessary for almost any chemical process. Shell-and-tube exchangers are widely used in industry to obtain wide ranges of temperature variations for streams from low to high flow rates, with high heat transfer efficiency due to the turbulence occurring on the shell. The design of a shell-and-tube heat exchanger involves several variables, which are usually related through energy balances and empirical correlations. One of the most common strategies to design heat exchangers in the industry is the Bell-Delaware method, which considers the variations of the convective heat transfer coefficient with the baffle configuration and phenomena occurring in the baffles, as leakage, pass partition bypass, among others. Nevertheless, the equations which model the heat exchanger are highly non-lineal and non-convex, mainly due to the presence of fractional and logarithmic terms in the mathematical model. Moreover, some of the variables are integer, as the number of tubes, and other variables can be taken as continuous, but in practice they take discrete values, as the internal and external diameter of the tubes, which are constrained by the standard dimensions for commercial tubes. Thus, a robust method is necessary to obtain proper solutions to the optimal design problem of the heat exchanger. The use of meta-heuristic optimization strategies offers a viable alternative to the solution of such problem. In this work, a recently reported stochastic optimization method, namely, the grey wolf optimization algorithm, is proposed to solve the optimization problem for a shell-and-tube heat exchanger, represented by the Bell-Delaware model, aiming to the minimization of the total annual cost. The grey wolf optimization algorithm emulates the hunting mechanisms of grey wolves, and it has been reported that it possesses a superior exploitation capacity than other meta-heuristic algorithms, together with a high capacity to avoid local optima (Mirjalili et al., 2014)

2. Grey Wolf Optimizer

Grey Wolf Optimizer (GWO) emulates the hunting technic of wolves. It was modeled by Mirjalili et al. (2014). This optimization algorithm considers the wolves hierarchy; alpha (α), is not necessarily the strongest but is the one who makes important decisions that affect the whole group; beta (β) wolves help the alpha in decision making activity, these wolves respect the alpha but command the other lower level wolves; omega (ω) are the lowest ranked wolves in the hierarchy, although they are the least important, they help to maintain the structure of the pack; delta (δ) wolves are those that are not in any of the previous categories, they have a lower hierarchy than alpha and betas but higher than the omega.

The GWO algorithm takes into account different actions within the hunting process:

- Tracking, chasing, and approaching the prey.

- Pursuing, encircling, and harassing the prey until it stops moving.

- Attack towards the prey.

2.1. Mathematical model

The GWO algorithm defines the fitness solution as alpha α, the second and third best solutions are beta β and gamma γ, respectively. Other solutions are named omega ω. The optimization process is guided by α, β and γ. As mentioned before, wolves tend to encircle its prey. This behaviour is modeled with the equations 1 and 2.

$$\vec{D} = |\vec{C} \cdot \vec{X}_p(t) - \vec{X}(t)| \tag{1}$$

$$\vec{X}(t+1) = \vec{X}_p(t) - \vec{A} \cdot \vec{D} \tag{2}$$

$\vec{X}_p$ is the position vector of the prey, $\vec{X}$ is the position vector of a grey wolf, $\vec{A}$ and $\vec{C}$ are coefficient vectors , and t is the current iteration. The vectors $\vec{A}$ and $\vec{C}$ are calculated according to the equations 3 and 4

$$\vec{A} = 2\vec{a} \cdot \vec{r}_1 - \vec{a} \tag{3}$$

$$\vec{C} = 2 \cdot \vec{r}_2 \tag{4}$$

where components of the vector $\vec{a}$ are linearly decreased form 2 to 0 as the iterations pass, r_1 and r_2 are random vector with elements between 0 and 1.

In nature, grey wolves know where the prey is, however, in the mathematical framework we don't know where the optimum is (prey). To overcome this problem, it's supposed that the alpha, beta and delta wolves have a better idea about the position of the prey. Assumed this, the best three results are saved and oblige the other search agents to update their position. To simulate this, the equations 5-7 are used.

$$\vec{D}_\alpha = |\vec{C}_1 \cdot \vec{X}_\alpha - \vec{X}|, \ \vec{D}_\beta = |\vec{C}_2 \cdot \vec{X}_\beta - \vec{X}|, \ \vec{D}_\delta = |\vec{C}_3 \cdot \vec{X}_\delta - \vec{X}| \tag{5}$$

$$\vec{X}_1 = \vec{X}_\alpha - \vec{A}_1 \cdot \left(\vec{D}_\alpha\right), \ \vec{X}_2 = \vec{X}_\beta - \vec{A}_2 \cdot \left(\vec{D}_\beta\right), \ \vec{X}_3 = \vec{X}_\delta - \vec{A}_3 \cdot \left(\vec{D}_\delta\right) \tag{6}$$

$$\vec{X}(t+1) = \frac{\vec{X}_1 + \vec{X}_2 + \vec{X}_3}{3} \tag{7}$$

In summary, the population of wolves begins randomly within the search space. Each position of the wolves is a possible solution. The parameter $\vec{a}$ decreases in each iteration from 2 to 0, this parameter indicates the exploration and exploitation capacity of the GWO. If the value of $|A \geq 1|$, the wolf diverges from the prey, if $|A \leq 1|$ the wolf converges towards the prey.

3. Heat Exchanger Mathematical Model

3.1. Heat transfer of shell side

The Bell-Delaware mathematical model is used to predict the shell-side convective heat transfer coefficient h_s. This model considers different parameters and geometrical variables (Shah and Sekulic, 2003). An ideal convective heat transfer coefficient h_i is calculated and corrected using five parameters j according to the equation 8.

$$h_s = h_i j_c j_l j_b j_s j_t \tag{8}$$

h_i is evaluated as

$$h_i = j \frac{C_{ps} Pr_s^{-2/3}}{A_{o,cr}} \tag{9}$$

where C_{ps} is the fluid heat capacity, Pr_s is the Prandlt number, and j_c, j_l, j_b, j_s, j_t are correction factors for baffle configuration, shell to baffle and tube to baffle leakage effects, bundle pass and partition bypass, baffle spacing, and temperature gradient, respectively. $A_{o,cr}$ is the flow area near the shell center-line for one cross-flow section and j is the Colburn factor, it is calculated with the equation 10 (Wildi-Tremblay and Gosselin, 2007). The variable a is determined with 11. The parameters a_1, a_2, a_3 and a_4 are reported in Wildi-Tremblay and Gosselin (2007).

$$j = a_1 \left(\frac{1.33}{Pt/d_o} \right)^a (Re_s)^{a_2} \tag{10}$$

$$a = \frac{a_3}{1 + 0.14 Re_s^{a_4}} \tag{11}$$

$$\tag{12}$$

The Reynolds number Re_s is evaluated with equation 13, μ_s is fluid viscosity, m_s is the mass flow rate in shell-side and d_o is the tube external diameter.

$$Re_s = \frac{m_s d_o}{\mu_s A_{o,cr}} \tag{13}$$

The area of the heat exchanger area is calculated with the Equation 14.

$$A = \frac{Q}{U \Delta T_{ml} F_t} \tag{14}$$

where Q is the heat transfer rate, U is the global heat transfer coefficient, T_{LMDT} is the logarithmic mean temperature difference and F_t is a correction factor. The U coefficient depends of the convective heat transfer of shell and tube side as well as fouling resistance of both sides, it is calculated with the Equation 15

$$U = \frac{1}{\frac{1}{h_s} + R_{fs} + \frac{d_o \ln\left(\frac{d_o}{d_i}\right)}{2k_w} + R_{ft}\frac{d_o}{d_i} + \frac{1}{h_t}\frac{d_o}{d_i}} \tag{15}$$

h_t is convective heat transfer coefficients for tube side, k_w is the material thermal conductivity, R_{fs} and R_{ft} are the fouling factors for shell and tubes. The tube internal diameter, d_i, is calculates as $d_i = 0.8 d_o$.

3.2. Heat transfer in tube side

To calculate h_t, the equation 16 is used, this equation only works when the fluid in tubes is water (Sinnott and Towler, 2009). T_{Cm} is the medium fluid temperature and v_t is the fluid velocity in tubes that is calculated with the equation 17. Where ρ_t fluid density, m_t is the mass flow rate and N_t is the total number of tubes, is is calculated according the equation

$$h_t = \frac{4200\left(1.35 + 0.02 T_{Cm}\right) v_t^{0.8}}{d_i^{0.8}} \tag{16}$$

$$v_t = \frac{s}{N_t} \frac{m_t}{\pi \frac{di_t^2}{4} \rho_t} \tag{17}$$

3.3. Pressure drop calculations

The pressure drop in the tubes side is calculated with the equation 18, the friction factor, f, is evaluated as $f = 0.046 Re_t^{-0.2}$, s is the the pass number and L the length of tubes that is calculated using 19.

$$\Delta P_t = s\left(\frac{4fL}{d_i} + 2.5\right) \frac{\rho_t v_t}{2} \tag{18}$$

$$L = \frac{A}{\pi d_o N_t} \tag{19}$$

The expression 20 is used to calculate the pressure drop in shell-side

$$\Delta P_s = \left[\left(N_b - 1\right) \Delta P_{b,id} \zeta_b + N_b \Delta P_{w,id}\right] \zeta_l + 2\Delta P_{b,id}\left(1 + \frac{N_{r,cw}}{N_{r,cc}}\right) \zeta_b \zeta_s \tag{20}$$

where N_b is the number of baffles, $\Delta P_{b,id}$ is the ideal pressure drop in the central section, $N_{r,cw}$ is the effective tubes en the cross flow, $N_{r,cc}$ is the effective number of tubes rows crossed, ζ is a correction factor.

3.4. Cost estimation

In this study, the total annual cost (TAC) is used, this is the sum of fixed, C_f and operation cost C_{op}. To calculate the fixed cost the equation 22 is used (Smith, 2005). The purchase price C_p is corrected using the factors f_m, f_p and f_c for construction material, operating pressure and operation temperature, respectively. While the C_{op} is evaluated with equation 23.

$$C_p = 32800\left(\frac{A}{80}\right)^{0.68} \tag{21}$$

$$C_f = C_p f_m f_p f_c \tag{22}$$

$$C_{op} = \frac{\left(E_s + E_t\right) Ec H_r}{1000} \tag{23}$$

$$TAC = C_f \frac{r\left(1 + r\right)^n}{\left(1 + r\right)^n - 1} + C_f \tag{24}$$

where E_s and E_t is the pump power (Watts) used in shell and tube side, respectively. Ec is the energy cost (\$/kWh), Hr is the operational hours per year, n is the projected life time and r the interest rate per year. The optimization is performed using eleven parameters that can have a value between a given range, those are:

- Diameter of shell (D_s): 300mm -1000mm.

- Outer diameter of tube (d_o): 15.87mm 63.5mm.

- Tube pitch P_t: $[1.25do, 1.5do]$.

- Tube layout angle (TL): $[30°, 45°, 90°]$

- Baffle spacing at center (L_{bc}): $0.2D_s - 0.55D_s$

- Baffle spacing at the inlet and outlet ($L_{bo} = L_{bi}$): $L_{bc} - 1.6L_{bc}$

- Baffle cut (B_c): $[25\%, 30\%, 40\%, 45\%]$

- Number of tube passes (s): $[1, 2, 4]$

- Tube-to-baffle diametrical clearance (δ_{tb}): $0.01d_o - 0.1d_o$

- Diametrical clearance of shell-to-baffle (δ_{sb}): $0.01D_s - 0.1D_s$

- Outer diameter of tube bundle (D_otl): $0.8(D_s - d_{sb})$ - $0.95(D_s - d_{sb})$

The optimization process is subject to constrains for maximum allowed pressure drop in tube-side and shell-side, fluid velocity, and length to shell-diameter ratio, as follows:

$$\Delta P_s, \Delta P_t \leq \Delta P_a \tag{25}$$

$$1\text{m/s} \leq v_t \leq 3\text{m/s} \tag{26}$$

$$L/D_s < 15 \tag{27}$$

The equation 28 is the fitness function. The constants r_1, r_2, r_3 and r_4 are penalty values, if a constrain is violated a penalty value is activated.

$$FF = TAC + r_1 \, max[(\Delta P_s - \Delta P_a), \, 0] + r_2 \, max[(\Delta P_t - \Delta P_a), \, 0] +$$
$$r_3 [max\{(1 - v_t)\} + max\{(3 - v_t)\}, \, 0] + r_4 \, max[(L/D_s - 15), \, 0] \tag{28}$$

4. Case study

The case study is taken from Wildi-Tremblay and Gosselin (2007). It is required to design a heat exchanger with a flow rate of 18.8 kg/s of cooling water, the inlet temperature is 33 °C and the outlet temperature is 37.2 °C. The hot fluid is nafta, the inlet temperature is 114 °C and the outlet temperature is 40 °C. Water is placed in tube-side and nafta in shell-side. The construction material for tube and shell side is stainless steel and carbon steel, respectively.

Calculations are performed using a 5 % interest rate, 20 years life time period, 5000 operation hours per year, a pump efficiency of 0.85 and an electricity cost of 0.1 $/kWh. The maximum allowed pressure drop is 70,000 Pa. The factors to modify the purchase cost are $f_m = 1.7$, $f_t = 1.0$ and $f_p = 1.0$.

5. Results

MATLAB was used as codification environment for the heat exchanger mathematical model and GWO model. A population of 50 individuals was used with 50 iterations. To generate statistical information 30 runs where made. An average cost of 4,095.36 USD was found with a standard deviation of 103.57 USD. The minimum value was 3,977.76 USD. Particle swarm optimization (PSO) algorithm was also used to solve the problem as a comparison. With PSO an average cost of 4,197.56 USD with a standard deviation of 220.07 USD, the minimum value was 3,976.38 USD. The Table 1 shows the parameters value for both optimization methods. It can be seen that both method reached a similar solution. The computing time was 1.0161s for GWO and 2.1881s for PSO.

Table 1: Parameters for optimal heat exchanger configuration.

Parameter	D_s	d_o	N_t	A	L	P_t	TL	s	L_{bc}	L_{bo}	B_c
Unit	mm	mm		m^2	m	mm	°		mm	mm	%
GWO	302.36	15.87	144	32.35	4.50	19.83	90	1	60.47	60.47	25
PSO	301.90	15.87	143	32.30	4.53	19.83	90	1	60.38	60.38	25
Parameter	δ_{tb}	δ_{sb}	D_{otl}	N_b	v_t	L/D_s	ΔP_t	ΔP_s	C_{op}	C_f	TAC
Unit	mm	mm	mm		m/s		Pa	Pa	$/year	$/year	$/year
GWO	0.15	3.02	284.37	74	1.64	14.90	8938.76	12843.52	189.20	3789.08	3978.29
PSO	0.15	3.02	283.93	74	1.66	15.00	9028.80	12889.25	190.91	3784.94	3975.85

6. Conclusion

The Grey Wolf Optimizer has been proposed as a technique to solve the design and optimization of a shell-and-tube heat exchanger, modeled through the Bell-Delaware method. The optimization model is a MINLP, which is codified and solved in a MATLAB routine. The method has been proved to be efficient, reaching the optimal solution in a relatively low computing time. Moreover, the standard deviation between the obtained solutions in different tests is low, implying that the method tends to reach very similar optimal points for a number of runs.

References

S. Mirjalili, S. M. Mirjalili, A. Lewis, 2014. Grey wolf optimizer. Advances in engineering software 69, 46–61.

R. K. Shah, D. P. Sekulic, 2003. Fundamentals of heat exchanger design. John Wiley & Sons.

R. K. Sinnott, G. Towler, 2009. Chemical engineering design: SI Edition. Elsevier.

R. Smith, 2005. Chemical process: design and integration. John Wiley & Sons.

P. Wildi-Tremblay, L. Gosselin, 2007. Minimizing shell-and-tube heat exchanger cost with genetic algorithms and considering maintenance. International Journal of Energy Research 31 (9), 867–885.

Anton A. Kiss, Edwin Zondervan, Richard Lakerveld, Leyla Özkan (Eds.)
Proceedings of the 29th European Symposium on Computer Aided Process Engineering
June 16th to 19th, 2019, Eindhoven, The Netherlands. © 2019 Elsevier B.V. All rights reserved.
http://dx.doi.org/10.1016/B978-0-128-18634-3.50097-7

Optimization Under Uncertainty Based on a Data-driven Model for a Chloralkali Electrolyzer Cell

Erik Esche[a,*], Joris Weigert[a], Thomas Budiarto[a], Christian Hoffmann[a] and Jens-Uwe Repke[a]

[a]*Technische Universitaet Berlin, Process Dynamics and Operations Group, Sekr. KWT 9, Str. des 17. Juni 135, D-10623, Berlin, Germany*
erik.esche@tu-berlin.de

Abstract

Data-driven models are increasingly used to model chemical processes with the long-term goal of using them for real-time optimization. At the moment, the uncertainty contained in these models is scarcely modeled or mostly assumed to adhere to a multivariate normal distribution. In this contribution, we model both the input-output relation of a rigorous model as well as the uncertainty. During the training process of surrogate models, both accuracy as well as smoothness of the resulting models are ensured. For the case study of a Chloralkali electrolyzer cell, snapshots are generated based on a rigorous model. Surrogate models for input-output relationships and uncertainty are trained and compared regarding their fit, smoothness, and their applicability in chance-constrained optimization. Based on this methodology, a Gaussian process was developed for the input-output modeling and a functional covariance matrix with separate models for the entries using both artificial neural networks and linear regression for separate entries. The models were tested in a chance-constrained optimization framework showing excellent performance regarding speed of the computation and validity of the results.

Keywords: Data-driven modeling, surrogate, models, optimization under uncertainty

1. Introduction and Motivation

Data-driven models are increasingly used in chemical engineering applications for the support of optimal process operation. Examples of data-driven models recently used are linear regressions, artificial neural networks, support vector regression, gaussian process regression (also known as kriging), etc. Data to train and validate these models can stem from different sources, either experimental data or simulation snapshots from existing first principle models.

These sets of training data, of course, contain uncertainty: on the one hand through experimental measurement error or on the other hand through known uncertain parameters of an original model. This uncertainty information should be considered in the actual description of the data-driven model's output uncertainty.

Given the way how data-driven models are derived, it is well understood that their applicability is limited to the domain of the original data they are trained and validated upon. Beyond that, extrapolation and sometimes even interpolation between sparsely scattered data points becomes highly unreliable. There are a couple of techniques available to make sure that optimization solvers operating on data-driven models stay within the area of applicability, e.g. the implementation of inequality constraints regarding the domain of the model or the introduction of uncertainty maps as model elements.

In this contribution, we investigate possibilities to extend typical data-driven surrogate models by uncertainty models for the description of the uncertainty of each output variable, while standard data-driven techniques only provide static descriptions of the model's uncertainty. Furthermore, we evaluate these models regarding their performance in a framework for optimization under uncertainty.

2. Modeling of Input-Output Relationships and Uncertainty

To derive models for both input-output relationships as well as the uncertainty, we pursue a two-stage procedure. In the first stage, the input-output relationship is modeled, in the second stage the uncertainty of the outputs is then described. This is in contrast to most modeling strategies typically followed in machine-learning, wherein the assumptions for the input-output model often also contain the description of the uncertainty. However, this is then mostly limited to multi-variate normal distributions or discontinuous probability density models and only describes the uncertainty of the data-driven model.

For all further discussions here, a set of input and output data points is already given, which could stem from either experiments or sampling on a simulation model. Henceforth, a rigorous model will be taken as the basis.

2.1. Modeling of Input-Output Relationships

For modeling the input-output relationships, we assume that the input and output data have already been clustered, i.e. points in input space close to one another have been aggregated. Hence, clustering techniques will not be discussed here. Building upon existing implementations of various data-driven models in scikit-learn (Pedregosa et al., 2011), our python framework generates linear regression (LR), Gaussian process regression (GPR), and artifical neural networks (ANN) based on a wide selection of options for kernels, model parameters, optimization settings, and of course the ratio between the number of training data and test data.

After training the various models, they are evaluated with different statistical metrics describing their deviation to the testing data and the smoothness of the resulting surface functions for outputs plotted over inputs. The finally selected model is henceforth denoted as g with input variables u and output variables y, see Eq. (3).

2.2. Modeling of Uncertainty

Based on the chosen model for the input-output relationships, the deviations of all data points compared to that model are then computed and taken as the basis for modeling the uncertainty. For this purpose, we take two different approaches, which are sketched in Fig. 1. In the first approach, modeling the uncertainty is solely based on the deviations of the outputs and is independent of any input values. In the second approach, the input values are also considered, so that influences of the inputs on the uncertainty of the outputs may be incorporated.

As ansatz models for the uncertainty, multivariate normal distribution, Dirichlet distribution (multivariate beta distribution), and kernel density estimation are considered. Yet again, these models are trained/fitted to the present data and compared regarding their capabilities to describe the uncertainty. As above, the eventually selected uncertainty model is denoted as $\tilde{g}$, which describes the uncertain outputs $\tilde{y}$ depending on the outputs y generated by model g, some model parameters $\hat{p}$, and optionally the inputs u, see Eq. (4).

For the model generation, relevant uncertainty data for the respective ansatz is created at every input point. For a multivariate normal distribution, this would be the covariance of the outputs and for the Dirichlet distribution the model parameters α. Based on this data, the uncertainty model is trained and tested using the same python framework as for the input-output model generation.

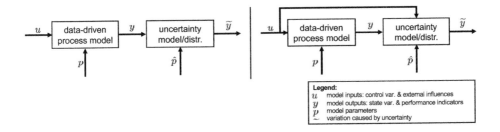

Figure 1: Two different modeling strategies pursued herein to accurately model the uncertainty contained in original data and induced by input-output model.

3. Framework for Optimization Under Uncertainty

The framework for optimization under uncertainty is fully implemented in python and builds upon the department's existing framework for chance-constrained optimization - the DoCCE (dynamically optimized chance constraint evaluator (Werk et al., 2012)). The extended framework developed for this contribution now supports systems as characterized by the following nonlinear programming problem (NLP) with objective function f, data-driven model g, uncertainty model $\widetilde{g}$, and the desired probability level α:

$$\min_{x} \quad f(x) \tag{1}$$

$$\text{s.t.} \quad \Pr\{h(x) \geq 0\} \geq \alpha \tag{2}$$

$$y = g(u) \tag{3}$$

$$y, u \subset x \quad \wedge \quad y \cap u = \emptyset$$

$$\widetilde{y} = \widetilde{g}(y, p) \quad \veebar \quad \widetilde{y} = \widetilde{g}(y, u, \hat{p}) \tag{4}$$

$$\widetilde{y} \subseteq y$$

For additional information on DoCCE's capabilities for mixed-integer nonlinear programming problems refer to (Esche et al., 2016).

4. Case Study - Chloralkali Electrolyzer Cell

To test the performance of input-output and uncertainty models inside the framework for optimization under uncertainty, a rigorous, steady-state model of the anolyte half cell of a Chloralkali electrolyzer cell (CEC) is used as a small-scale example.

The anolyte cell is modeled as a CSTR for a five component mixture (Na^+, Cl^-, OH^-, H_3O^+, H_2O). The model consists of 32 equations including descriptions for the chlorine production by the anode reaction, the autoprotolysis of water, the migration based sodium ion flux, and descriptions for water leaving by electroosmosis and with the chlorine gas stream.

4.1. Generation of Snapshots

The rigorous model is implemented in MOSAICmodeling (Esche et al., 2017) and from there exported to AMPL (Fourer et al., 2003) and solved as a simulation problem with IPOPT (Wächter and Biegler, 2005). For the case study, the input variables (feed volume flow and current density of CEC) are varied between a given set of bounds and the model parameters (feed temperature and electroosmosis factor) are assumed to follow a multivariate normal distribution. Samples for the output variables (outgoing liquid volume flow, mass fractions of all components) are generated by sampling 1 000 times from the input variables with a Latin Hypercube sampling and 20 times from the parameters following the normal distribution. Hence, 20 000 output samples are present, which can easily be clustered along the input samples. The output samples obtained from AMPL are then filtered to eliminate randomly appearing, non-converged solutions and the remainder is stored for subsequent training and testing.

4.2. Input-output Model

Based on the aforementioned number of samples, Gaussian process regression shows the best performance regarding match and smoothness of the resulting surface functions compared to the other tested model types. Randomly, 70 % of the generated snapshots are taken for training the Gaussian process with a squared exponential covariance function as kernel. The remaining data is used for testing and shows a mean squared error of 10^{-5}, an R^2 value of around 0.96, and a mean percentual deviation of around 2.7 %. The input-output model describes two inputs (feed volume flow, current density of CEC) and six outputs (outgoing liquid volume flow, mass fractions of all components). For the first two outputs (outgoing liquid volume flow, mass fraction of Na^+), the resulting surface functions are shown in Fig. 2 (plots (a) and (b)).

4.3. Uncertainty Model

For modeling the difference between data-driven model and original snapshot data, a number of different probability density functions were tested. The best fit was achieved with a functional covariance matrix describing all outputs of the data-driven model as follows:

$$\widetilde{y} = \widetilde{g}(y, Cov(u))) = y + \mathcal{N}(0, Cov(u)) \tag{5}$$

Every entry of the covariance matrix Cov is a function of the input variables u, which corresponds to the second approach sketched in Fig. 1. Depending on the form of variance and covariance of the respective output variables, either linear regression or gaussian process regression are used to describe the functional relationship between input and output uncertainty distribution. For the application here, all six output variables are taken as uncertain, resulting in a six-by-six covariance matrix. The surface function describing the relationship between the two inputs and the variance of output no. 2 and the covariance between outputs 1 and 2 are plotted in Fig. 2 (plots (c) and (d)). Of the 36 entries of the covariance matrix, eight entries are described with linear regression models, the remaining ones are described by individual ANNs.

To ensure that the reliability of the input-output model tends to zero outside of its training region, the models for the variance/diagonal entries in Cov are there set to the magnitude of the respective output y. This allows for an indirect hull formulation, which does not need to be added as an additional constraint and is adaptive to further training with new data.

4.4. Chance-constrained Optimization

To test the usability of the derived input-output and uncertainty models, a simple chance-constrained optimization problem is formulated based on the CEC example. As objective function, the outlet flow of sodium ions is minimized while a chance constraint is implemented to enforce an upper bound on the pH value of 2.88 (mass fraction of H_3O^+ equal to $2.5 \cdot 10^{-5}$) inside the cell. Always starting from the same initial point, the enforced probability level α of the chance constraint is steadily increased. The resulting increase in the objective function value is plotted over the probability level in Fig. 3. The objective function value shows the expected increase with the steadily increased constraint probability. The CPU seconds necessary for the computation appear independent of the enforced probability and are in a very reasonable range at below 25 seconds.

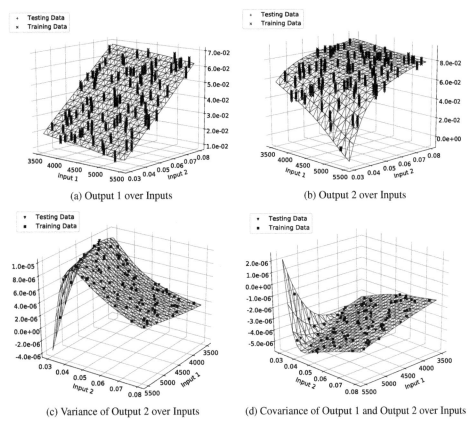

(a) Output 1 over Inputs

(b) Output 2 over Inputs

(c) Variance of Output 2 over Inputs

(d) Covariance of Output 1 and Output 2 over Inputs

Figure 2: Figures (a) and (b) showing outputs 1 and 2 plotted over the two input variables. Figures (c) and (d) showing variance of output 2 and covariance between output 1 and output 2 plotted over both inputs. x/square: training data, +/triangle: testing data; surface functions: predicted data and uncertainty models respectively.

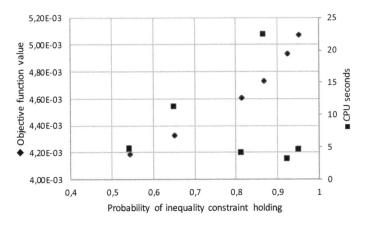

Figure 3: Objective function plotted over the enforced probability level. CPU seconds given on the secondary axis.

For the computation of the chance constraint's probability a five-dimensional sparse grid is used (first five outputs). For every single grid point the position is computed, at which the sixth output variable ensures the equality of the inner constraint ($h(x) = 0$; mass fraction of H_3O^+ equal to $2.5 \cdot 10^{-5}$). Given the variation of the covariance matrix over the input space, the sparse grid is adapted to the covariance matrix at every single iteration, i.e. at a probability computation.

The computation of the inner constraint is done by the secant method. The DoCCE framework by default uses Newton's or Haley's method in case first or even second derivatives are available. However, on using the data-driven input-output models, the framework falls back to the derivative-free approach. This is naturally highly inefficient, but given the speed of the input-output models the many function calls necessary for the secant method can be easily handled.

5. Conclusions & Outlook

Up to now, offline or even online application of optimization under uncertainty is still a major challenge with the time required for computing uncertain scenarios or integrating over the uncertainty space being the main hurdles. Using surrogate models to describe both input-output relations and uncertainty of an existing rigorous model or of plant data can be a building block to allow for the wide-spread fast application of optimization under uncertainty.

By initially comparing several different types of surrogate models for the input-output relationship, both a good match and sufficient smoothness can be ensured. Based on the hence obtained model, the uncertainty is then described with an additional model. Here, good results were obtained using a functional description of a covariance matrix of all the outputs of the input-output surrogate model. Using these two models together for optimization under uncertainty ensures both speed and reliability of the optimization results given their high accuracy in modeling the original data and their explicit model structures.

In future work, the derivatives will be added to both input-output as well as uncertainty models to further speed up the optimization run. In addition, the continuous retraining of both models will be exercised in online applications to continuously reduce the model uncertainty and extend the range of validity of these models while optimally running a plant. Furthermore, the minimally required training effort based on rigorous simulation snapshots will need to be discussed and hence also the design of computer experiments to limit the number of potentially expensive simulation runs.

6. Acknowledgements

The research project ChemEFlex (funding code 0350013A) is supported by the German Federal Ministry for Economic Affairs and Energy.

References

E. Esche, C. Hoffmann, M. Illner, D. Müller, S. Fillinger, G. Tolksdorf, H. Bonart, G. Wozny, J.-U. Repke, 2017. Mosaic - enabling large-scale equation-based flow sheet optimization. Chem. Ing. Tech. 89 (5), 620–635.

E. Esche, D. Müller, S. Werk, I. E. Grossmann, G. Wozny, 2016. Solution of chance-constrained mixed-integer nonlinear programming problems. In: Z. Kravanja, M. Bogataj (Eds.), Proceedings of the 26th European Symposium on Computer Aided Process Engineering - ESCAPE 26. No. 38. Elsevier, pp. 91–94.

R. Fourer, D. M. Gay, B. W. Kernighan, 2003. AMPL – A Modeling Language for Mathematical Programming, 2nd Edition. Broks/Cole – Thomson Learning.

F. Pedregosa, G. Varoquaux, A. Gramfort, V. Michel, B. Thirion, O. Grisel, M. Blondel, P. Prettenhofer, R. Weiss, V. Dubourg, J. Vanderplas, A. Passos, D. Cournapeau, M. Brucher, M. Perrot, E. Duchesnay, 2011. Scikit-learn: Machine learning in Python. Journal of Machine Learning Research 12, 2825–2830.

A. Wächter, L. Biegler, 2005. On the implementation of an interior-point filter line-search algorithm for large-scale nonlinear program. Math. Program. Ser. A.

S. Werk, T. Barz, H. Arellano-Garcia, G. Wozny, 2012. Performance analysis of shooting algorithms in chance-constrained optimization. In: I. A. Karimi, R. Srinivasan (Eds.), 11th International Symposium on Process Systems Engineering. Vol. 31 of Computer Aided Chemical Engineering. Elsevier, pp. 1512 – 1516.

Anton A. Kiss, Edwin Zondervan, Richard Lakerveld, Leyla Özkan (Eds.)
Proceedings of the 29th European Symposium on Computer Aided Process Engineering
June 16th to 19th, 2019, Eindhoven, The Netherlands. © 2019 Elsevier B.V. All rights reserved.
http://dx.doi.org/10.1016/B978-0-128-18634-3.50098-9

Parameter Estimation for Thermodynamic Models Using an Identifiability Analysis and Subset Selection

Christian Hoffmann[a,*], Joris Weigert[a], Erik Esche[a] and Jens-Uwe Repke[a]

[a]*Technische Universität Berlin, Process Dynamics and Operations Group, Sekr. KWT 9, Straße des 17. Juni 135, Berlin 10623, Germany*
*c.hoffmann@tu-berlin.de

Abstract

Parameter estimation problems are solved on a regular basis to fit thermodynamic models to experiments. However, conducting these experiments with a high accuracy is time-consuming. Hence, methods to identify parameters as fast as possible have to be used. In this contribution, subset selection is applied to parameter estimation problems with different datasets, such as VLE and excess enthalpy data. It is demonstrated that performing a subset selection with sensitivity analysis leads to an efficiently reduced set of estimated parameters. The results of the subset selection could additionally be used for an optimal design of experiments as the information gain of the different experimental datasets (VLE data, excess enthalpy) is different.

Keywords: Parameter estimation, Subset selection, Thermodynamic models

1. Introduction

Thermodynamics are a fundamental aspect of process design, modeling, simulation, and optimal operation in process engineering as evidenced by many publications on this subject in the past decades, e.g. (Hendriks et al., 2010). Many models have been suggested to describe the various phase equilibria appearing in multicomponent mixtures, such as activity models, (semi-)empirical cubic equations of state, and advanced equations of state (SAFT family, CPA, etc.).

Most thermodynamic models are highly nonlinear and hold several parameters, which are fitted to experimental data. At the same time, there is often little measurement data available and obtaining additional high-quality experimental data is time-consuming. By consequence, a number of issues can arise when performing parameter estimation on complex thermodynamic models: Noisy measurement data can be overfitted, identifiability of parameters cannot be ensured, and this in turn may lead to ill-conditioned parameter estimation problems, which show poor convergence and yield large variances of the estimated parameters. In addition, little can be found regarding parameter identifiability or their sensitivity with respect to the objective for thermodynamic applications, although there have been studies on parameter identifiability in general in the past few years, e.g. (Nogueira and Pontes, 2017).

Due to these shortcomings, this contribution investigates the identifiability of parameters in thermodynamic models in further detail. For this purpose, two parameter estimation problems were selected: the binary VLE of methanol and water and the dilution of sodium chloride in water. Both are described with appropriate activity models, which are briefly outlined in the next section. Activity models were selected because of their wide use in practical applications in the process industry. On top of that, they are preferred for low pressure applications for which the fugacity coefficient can usually be neglected. However, the approach is not limited to them and will certainly be extended to other property models in the future, especially equations of state.

2. Theoretical Fundamentals

In this section, the theoretical fundamentals of thermodynamic phase equilibria, the applied activity models and the parameter estimation framework are briefly discussed.

2.1. Thermodynamics

Thermodynamic equilibria can be described using the γ-φ-approach for the isofugacity criterion. Under low pressure assumptions, this yields Raoult's Law, extended by the activity coefficient in the liquid phase:

$$x_i \gamma_i P_{0,i}^{VL} = y_i P, \tag{1}$$

where x_i and y_i are the liquid and vapor mole fraction of component i, γ_i is the activity coefficient, $P_{0,i}^{VL}$ is the vapor pressure of the pure component and P is the pressure of the mixture. The activity coefficient is computed with the Wilson and the NRTL equation (Wilson, 1964; Renon and Prausnitz, 1968) for the methanol/water system and eNRTL (Chen and Evans, 1986) for the NaCl/water system.

Wilson: The expression for the activity coefficient is

$$\ln \gamma_i = 1 - \ln \left(\sum_{j=1} A_{ij} x_i \right) - \sum_{j=1} \frac{A_{ji} x_j}{\sum_k A_{jk} x_k}; \quad A_{ij} = \frac{v_j}{v_i} \exp\left(-\lambda_{ij}\right), A_{ii} = 1, \tag{2}$$

where v_i is the molar volume of component i. The binary interaction parameters λ_{ij} are the two parameters to be estimated. However, λ is often assumed to be temperature-dependent. This leads to a parameter estimation problem of up to ten parameters:

$$\lambda_{ij} = a_{ij} + \frac{b_{ij}}{T} + c_{ij} \ln T + d_{ij} T + e_{ij} T^2. \tag{3}$$

NRTL and eNRTL: The activity coefficient of the solvent is given by the product of the long-range contribution (LR) from the Debye-Hückel equation and the short-range contribution (SR) from the eNRTL equations. The equations for the LR term are not shown here because they do not hold any parameters for this estimation. The reader is referred to the literature (Chen and Evans, 1986). The equation for the SR term is (Chen and Evans, 1986):

$$\begin{aligned} \ln \gamma_{i=m}^{eNRTL} = {} & \frac{\sum_j X_j G_{jm} \tau_{jm}}{\sum_k X_k G_{km}} + \sum_{m'} \frac{X_{m'} G_{mm'}}{\sum_k X_k G_{km'}} \left(\tau_{mm'} - \frac{\sum_k X_k G_{km'} \tau_{km'}}{\sum_k X_k G_{km'}} \right) \\ & + \sum_c \sum_{a'} \frac{X_{a'}}{\sum_{a''} X_{a''}} \frac{X_c G_{mc,a'c}}{\sum_{k \neq c} X_k G_{kc,a'c}} \left(\tau_{mc,a'c} - \frac{\sum_{k \neq c} X_k G_{kc,a'c} \tau_{kc,a'c}}{\sum_{k \neq c} X_k G_{kc,a'c}} \right) \\ & + \sum_a \sum_{c'} \frac{X_{c'}}{\sum_{c''} X_{c''}} \frac{X_a G_{ma,c'a}}{\sum_{k \neq a} X_k G_{ka,c'a}} \left(\tau_{ma,c'a} - \frac{\sum_{k \neq a} X_k G_{ka,c'a} \tau_{ka,c'a}}{\sum_{k \neq a} X_k G_{ka,c'a}} \right), \end{aligned} \tag{4}$$

where m, c, and a stand for molecule, cation, and anion. The equations for the cations and anions are not shown here due to space limitations. In addition, $G_{ji,ki}$ is given by:

$$G_{ji,ki} = \exp\left(-\alpha_{ji,ki} \tau_{ji,ki}\right). \tag{5}$$

The binary interaction parameters $\tau_{ji,ki}$ and the non-randomness parameter $\alpha_{ji,ki}$ are the three parameters subject to the estimation. Again, τ and also α are however often assumed to be temperature-dependent. Here, we limit ourselves to the temperature dependence of τ. This leads to a parameter estimation problem of up to seven (eNRTL) or eleven (NRTL) parameters:

$$\tau_{ji,ki}^{eNRTL} = a_{ji,ki} + \frac{b_{ji,ki}}{T} + c_{ji,ki} \left[\frac{T^{ref} - T}{T} + \ln\left(\frac{T}{T^{ref}}\right) \right]; \quad \tau_{ji}^{NRTL} = a_{ji} + \frac{b_{ji}}{T} + c_{ji} \ln(T) + d_{ji} T^{e_{ji}}. \tag{6}$$

2.2. Parameter Estimation Framework with Subset Selection

The parameter estimation and identifiability analysis is carried out using the algorithm presented in (Müller et al., 2014). Its two main features are the regularization of the estimation problem via subset selection and an estimate of the covariance matrix of the parameters. First of all, data must be sampled, i.e. thermodynamic equilibrium data must be collected. Secondly, lower and upper bounds as well as initial guesses must be supplied. More details on this step are given below. Afterwards, a first parameter estimation is performed using the complete parameter set. Based on the results, the Fisher Information matrix (FIM) is approximated by

$$FIM \approx S^T \Sigma^{-1} S, \tag{7}$$

where S is the sensitivity matrix containing all derivatives of the model responses (temperatures, pressures, and vapor mole fractions) with respect to the parameters, and Σ is a matrix holding all variances of the measurements on its diagonal. In the following, the parameters are ranked according to their identifiability based on a singular value decomposition of the FIM. Parameters that cannot be identified are fixed to their current values and the parameter estimation is repeated until no changes in the active set take place. The lower bound of the standard deviation of the estimated parameters is estimated with the Cramér-Rao inequality. Hence, the standard deviations are the roots of the diagonal elements of the inverted FIM (Müller et al., 2014). The objective function f of the parameter estimation problem is

$$\min_p f = \sum_{DP} \sum_{DType} \left(\frac{DType_{DP}^{exp} - DType_{DP}^{calc}}{\sigma_{DType,DP}} \right)^2 \tag{8}$$

where the first sum ranges over all experimental isothermal and isobaric data points DP, the inner sum iterates all data types $DType$ (e.g. temperature, pressure, or mole fraction), and σ is the standard deviation of the measurement error. However, these are not always stated in the original datasets. In these cases, σ_P, σ_T, and σ_{y_i} were assumed to be 100 Pa, 0.1 K, and 0.01, respectively, which are typical values in the literature.

Table 1: Results of parameter estimation for methanol/water in step 1 (Wilson), experimental data at 328 K, taken from (Fu et al., 1989). Full-scale problem did not converge for 8 and 10 parameters.

Estimated parameters	Identifiable parameters	$\frac{\sigma_{a_{12}}^{PE,Full}}{\|a_{12}\|}$	$\frac{\sigma_{a_{21}}^{PE,Full}}{\|a_{21}\|}$	$\frac{\sigma_{b_{12}}^{PE,Full}}{\|b_{12}\|}$	$\frac{\sigma_{b_{21}}^{PE,Full}}{\|b_{21}\|}$	$\frac{\sigma_{c_{12}}^{PE,Full}}{\|c_{12}\|}$	$\frac{\sigma_{c_{21}}^{PE,Full}}{\|c_{21}\|}$
2	2	4.7E-7	1.5E-8	-	-	-	-
4	2	4.4E-1	1.1E-1	3.8E-1	9.9E-2	-	-
6	2	1.7E+0	1.1E+1	4.8E+2	8.4E+2	2.91E-1	1.78E+0

3. Results and Discussion

To analyze the behavior of the subset selection, the results are presented in three parts: In the first step, the parameter estimation is performed on equilibrium data only at a single constant temperature. In a second step, the number of different experimental temperatures is increased and typical temperature-dependent expressions for the parameters are introduced. Finally, additional data, such as excess enthalpies, are added to the parameter estimation problem. For all cases, the number of identifiable parameters and their variances are analyzed to demonstrate the merit of applying subset selection. Initial guesses for the parameters are always set to the arbitrary vectors $p_{init}^{NRTL} = [\alpha, a_{12}, a_{21}]^T = [0.2, 1, 2]^T$, $p_{init}^{Wilson} = [a_{12}, a_{21}]^T = [1, 2]^T$, and $p_{init}^{eNRTL} = [\alpha, a_{12}, a_{21}]^T = [0.2, 4, -8]^T$. Other parameters are initially set to zero. The algorithm has been implemented in Matlab 2017a using lsqnonlin.

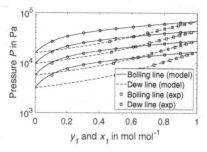

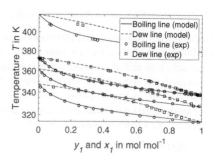

(a) Experimental data taken from (Fu et al., 1989) at 298, 308, 318, and 328 K.

(b) Experimental data taken from (Swami et al., 1956; Álvarez et al., 2011; Yang et al., 2011, 2012) at 0.4, 0.67, 1, and 4.3 bar.

Figure 1: P-x-y (a) and T-x-y (b) diagramm for methanol (1) and water, calculated with the NRTL equation; a_{12} = -0.01, a_{21} = 0.79, and α = 0.5.

3.1. Step 1: One dataset

In this first section, only one dataset at constant temperature is used. The results are shown in Tab. 1 for the methanol/water system and the Wilson equation. The algorithm determines that only two of up to ten parameters are identifiable. This is no surprise as the λ values are constants for a given temperature. These results can hence be seen as a plausibility check. Moreover, Tab. 1 shows the estimated standard deviation of the estimation divided by their expected value for the full-scale set (all parameters are active, first iteration of the algorithm) for 2, 4, and 6 estimated parameters. These values increase, the more parameters are added to the problem, until the standard deviation becomes larger than the expected value itself (last line in Tab. 1). Hence, the estimated parameters become more and more uncertain.

3.2. Step 2: Several datasets

In the next step, more experimental data are added to identify additional parameters in the temperature dependence of the interaction energies. The results of the parameter estimation are shown in Fig. 1 for the NRTL equation. The results for the Wilson equation are not shown here. Both activity models can accurately describe the VLE of methanol and water. However, only up to 4 parameters are identifiable for both models. The results for the parameter estimation of the full set (all parameters active, no subset selection) are given in Tab. 2 for NRTL. They show that adding additional data does not necessarily reduce the uncertainty of the parameters. For NRTL, the non-randomness factor α remains unidentifiable for all datasets. Secondly, it is observed that the number of identifiable parameters can decrease when more parameters are added to the problem. In addition to the larger dimensionality of the problem, this further complicates the parameter estimation as it leads to small gradients of the objective function hyperplane. Typically, the standard deviation of the parameter subset SsS0 is at least two orders of magnitude smaller than for the full set (see first line in Tab. 1 and 2). Thirdly, it must be noted that the excess enthalpy is poorly described if it is not considered in the parameter estimation problem (not shown here).

A second parameter estimation was performed for the water/NaCl system, for which total dissociation was assumed. The results are shown in Fig. 2a. Although the parameters are estimated over a temperature range from 298 to 423 K, only three parameters of seven (1 in 3) can be identified. All those three parameters describe the temperature dependence of the same binary interaction energy, meaning that the system can well be described by estimating only one binary interaction and set the other to an arbitrary value.

Table 2: Results of parameter estimation for methanol/water in step 2 (NRTL), experimental data as stated in Fig. 1.

Estimated parameters	Identifiable parameters	$\dfrac{\sigma_{a_{12}}^{PE,Full}}{|a_{12}|}$	$\dfrac{\sigma_{a_{21}}^{PE,Full}}{|a_{21}|}$	$\dfrac{\sigma_{b_{12}}^{PE,Full}}{|b_{12}|}$	$\dfrac{\sigma_{b_{21}}^{PE,Full}}{|b_{21}|}$	$\dfrac{\sigma_{c_{12}}^{PE,Full}}{|c_{12}|}$	$\dfrac{\sigma_{c_{21}}^{PE,Full}}{|c_{21}|}$
3	2	5.0E-6	9.5E-8	-	-	-	-
5	4	2.8E-6	2.7E-6	2.7E-6	5.8E-6	-	-
7	4	6.5E-6	8.4E-6	6.3E-6	9.0E-6	6.5E-6	8.7E-6
11	2	2.3E-2	2.8E-4	2.8E-2	6.0E-4	2.3E-2	2.0E-4

		$\dfrac{\sigma_{d_{12}}^{PE,Full}}{|d_{12}|}$	$\dfrac{\sigma_{d_{21}}^{PE,Full}}{|d_{21}|}$	$\dfrac{\sigma_{e_{12}}^{PE,Full}}{|e_{12}|}$	$\dfrac{\sigma_{e_{21}}^{PE,Full}}{|e_{21}|}$	$\dfrac{\sigma_{\alpha}^{PE,Full}}{|\alpha|}$
3	2	-	-	-	-	3.8E-4
5	2	-	-	-	-	4.0E-4
7	2	-	-	-	-	4.0E-4
11	2	8.4E-2	4.1E-6	3.8E-2	7.4E-6	1.6E-3

3.3. Step 3: Additional information

In this last step, additional information for the parameter estimation is given by including data of the excess enthalpy, which is correlated to the activity model by the Gibbs-Helmholtz equation. The results for the calculation of the excess enthalpy are displayed in Fig. 2b. Contrary to previous estimations, the excess enthalpy can now be well described without losing accuracy in the phase equilibria. Adding excess enthalpy data has a decisive effect on the parameter estimation problem as just one set of excess enthalpy data makes four of five parameters identifiable for the NRTL equation. This was not possible by using four different isothermal sets of VLE data in the parameter estimation and leads to an important message with respect to experimental investigations: If one excess enthalpy dataset yields more information gain than three additional VLE sets, significant costs and time can be saved by performing a subset selection with sensitivity analysis on a regular basis to plan the next experiments. As the measurement of thermodynamic equilibria is

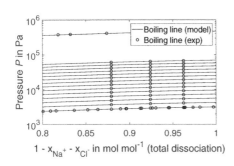

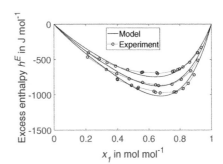

(a) calculated with the eNRTL equation, $a_{12} = 955.61$, $a_{21} = -1.12$, and $\alpha = 0.5$, experimental data at temperatures between 298 and 423 K from (Pepela and Dunlop, 1972; Mashovets et al., 1973; Berling et al., 1999; Nasirzadeh et al., 2004).

(b) calculated with the NRTL equation, $a_{12} = 0.98$, $a_{21} = 0.43$, $b_{12} = -321.95\,\text{K}$, $b_{21} = 95.12\,\text{K}$, and $\alpha = 0.5$, experimental data at 278.15, 298.15, and 323.15 K from (Tomaszkiewicz et al., 1986).

Figure 2: P-x-y diagramm for water and dissociated NaCl (a) and h^E-x diagramm for methanol and water (b). Only one parameter remains identifiable for the NaCl/water system.

quite time-consuming if done correctly, subset selection will be a valuable asset for optimal design of experiments in thermodynamic application.

4. Conclusion and Outlook

This contribution demonstrated the application of parameter estimation with subset selection for methanol/water and NaCl/water using different activity models. It was shown that thermodynamic models can contain unidentifiable parameters, e.g. the non-randomness parameter α in the NRTL model. This justifies the conventional suggestion to fix α in parameter estimations. The second major result concerns complex parameter estimation problem, for example in electrolyte chemistry. For these applications, the number of parameters could be drastically reduced by using a subset selection to simplify the parameter estimation problem. This may lead to more reliable thermodynamic models for gas treatment or electrolysis. The third important aspect is the improved parameter identifibiliy of activity models by using excess enthalpy data instead of additional VLE data. This could be related to the additional derivative information on the activity model that is introduced when using excess enthalpy data. In future work, the algorithm will be used for more complex phenomena, such as Vapor-Liquid-Liquid Equilibria, and more complex models, such as equations of state, to investigate its performance.

References

V. Álvarez, S. Mattedi, M. Iglesias, R. Gonzalez-Olmos, J. Resa, 2011. Phase equilibria of binary mixtures containing methyl acetate, water, methanol or ethanol at 101.3 kPa. Physics and Chemistry of Liquids 49 (1), 52–71.

D. Berling, B. Jönsson, G. Olofsson, 1999. The use of isothermal heat-conduction calorimetry in direct measurements of solvent vapor pressure. Journal of Solution Chemistry 28, 693–710.

C.-C. Chen, L. B. Evans, 1986. A local composition model for the excess gibbs energy of aqueous electrolyte systems. AIChE Journal 32 (3), 444–454.

J. Fu, K. Wang, Y. Hu, 1989. Studies on vapor-liquid and liquid-liquid vapor equilibria for the ternary system methanol-methyl methacrylate-water (I) three binary systems. Chinese Journal of Chemical Engineering.

E. Hendriks, G. M. Kontogeorgis, R. Dohrn, J.-C. de Hemptinne, I. G. Economou, L. F. Žilnik, V. Vesovic, 2010. Industrial requirements for thermodynamics and transport properties. Industrial & Engineering Chemistry Research 49 (22), 11131–11141.

V. Mashovets, V. Zarembo, M. Fedorov, 1973. Vapor pressure of aqueous NaCl, NaBr, and NaI at temperatures from 150-350 C. Zh. Prikl. Khim 46, 650–652.

D. Müller, E. Esche, D. C. López, G. Wozny, 2014. An algorithm for the identification and estimation of relevant parameters for optimization under uncertainty. Computers & Chemical Engineering 71, 94–103.

K. Nasirzadeh, D. Zimin, R. Neueder, W. Kunz, 2004. Vapor-pressure measurements of liquid solutions at different temperatures: apparatus for use over an extended temperature range and some new data. Journal of Chemical & Engineering Data 49 (3), 607–612.

I. B. Nogueira, K. V. Pontes, 2017. Parameter estimation with estimability analysis applied to an industrial scale polymerization process. Computers & Chemical Engineering 96, 75–86.

C. N. Pepela, P. J. Dunlop, 1972. A re-examination of the vapour pressures of aqueous sodium chloride solutions at 25 C. The Journal of Chemical Thermodynamics 4 (2), 255–258.

H. Renon, J. M. Prausnitz, 1968. Local compositions in thermodynamic excess functions for liquid mixtures. AIChE Journal 14 (1), 135–144.

D. Swami, V. K. Rao, N. N. Rao, 1956. Vapour-liquid equilibrium still for miscible liquids at atmospheric and subatmospheric pressures. Trans. Indian Inst. Chem. Eng 9, 32–46.

I. Tomaszkiewicz, S. Randzio, P. Gierycz, 1986. Excess enthalpy in the methanol-water system at 278.15, 298.15 and 323.15 K under pressures of 0.1, 20 and 39 MPa. II. experimental results and their analytical presentation. Thermochimica Acta 103 (2), 281–289.

G. M. Wilson, 1964. Vapor-liquid equilibrium. XI. a new expression for the excess free energy of mixing. Journal of the American Chemical Society 86 (2), 127–130.

C. Yang, S. Ma, X. Yin, 2011. Organic salt effect of tetramethylammonium bicarbonate on the vapor-liquid equilibrium of the methanol-water system. Journal of Chemical & Engineering Data 56 (10), 3747–3751.

C. Yang, F. Sun, S. Ma, X. Yin, H. Zeng, 2012. Organic salt effect on vapor-liquid equilibrium of the methanol + water system at subatmospheric pressure. Journal of Chemical & Engineering Data 57 (10), 2696–2701.

Anton A. Kiss, Edwin Zondervan, Richard Lakerveld, Leyla Özkan (Eds.)
Proceedings of the 29th European Symposium on Computer Aided Process Engineering
June 16th to 19th, 2019, Eindhoven, The Netherlands. © 2019 Elsevier B.V. All rights reserved.
http://dx.doi.org/10.1016/B978-0-128-18634-3.50099-0

Evaluation of Discretization Methods for Modeling the Chloralkali Membrane Process

Thomas Budiarto[a], Joris Weigert[a], Christian Hoffmann[a], Erik Esche[a] and Jens-Uwe Repke[a,*]

[a]*Technische Universität Berlin, Process Dynamics and Operation Group, Sekr. KWT 9, Str. des 17. Juni 135, Berlin 10623, Germany*
t.budiarto@campus.tu-berlin.de

Abstract

A chloralkali membrane cell process is modeled based on a macro-homogeneous approach. The Poisson-Nernst-Planck (PNP) equation is applied to model the multi-ion transport in the system. A steep gradient problem arises at the membrane's interfaces. The finite differences method, Hermite collocation on finite elements, and the Galerkin finite elements method are compared to determine the most efficient method to tackle the problem. A logarithmic reformulation is also investigated to evaluate its compatibility to solve the problem. The finite differences method and the Hermite collocation method turn out the best results, respectively in terms of the compuational time and accuracy. Afterwards, the finite differences method is applied to model a solution-membrane system based on the 1D PNP equation, whose results are discussed further regarding their subsequent applicability for extensive simulation studies.

Keywords: Hermite Collocation, Galerkin Finite Elements, The Poisson Nernst Planck equation, Chloralkali electrolysis

1. Introduction

The chloralkali membrane process is a potential energy buffer for demand-side management in the electricity market. Although this is an economically promising solution, the resulting dynamic operation is highly challenging. The chloralkali membrane electrolyzer is one among many critical apparatuses, which are fragile to dynamic load changes and also devalue considerably during dynamic operation. The total reaction in the electrolyzer is formulated as:

$$2\,NaCl + 2\,H_2O \longrightarrow Cl_2 + H_2 + 2\,NaOH$$

A model of a chloralkali membrane process is developed to enable further investigation of the dynamic characteristics of this equipment during flexible operation. The macro-homogeneous modeling approach introduced by Verbrugge and Hill (1990) and also validated by Verbrugge and Hill (1992) is considered to model the chloralkali process. It is already widely used to model electrochemical systems due to its reasonable accuracy and low computational cost, while it is adequately able to predict necessary phenomena for practical applications. This approach assumes that the modeled components are continuously distributed over the modeled spatial domain and can be represented by macroscopic variables, such as concentrations. Some authors (Moshtarikhah et al. (2017), Fíla and Bouzek (2003), Kodým et al. (2016)) have modeled the chloralkali membrane cell using this approach for a high current density regime. A numerical challenge in modeling such a system usually comes from the steep gradient at phase boundaries. Zheng and Wei (2011) successfully reduced the boundary layer complexity by incorporating the Boltzmann equation into the PNP system despite of the narrowed model validity under the overlimiting current regime. Various discretization methods have been applied in modeling the problem. However, the most suitable one remains a question. In the present contribution, a logarithmic reformulation and three well-known discretization methods: the finite differences method, the finite elements method with Hermite collocation, and the Galerkin finite elements method are benchmarked to justify the suitability in solving such problems.

2. Model Description

The modeled system depicted in Fig. 1 considers three main components in the chloralkali membrane cell, i.e. $Na^+(i = 1)$, Cl^- $(i = 2)$ and $OH^-(i = 3)$, which are assumed to have a continuous distributions in space. The domain is divided into three different parts: an anolyte diffusion layer (ADL), the cation exchange membrane (CM), and a catholyte diffusion layer (CDL).

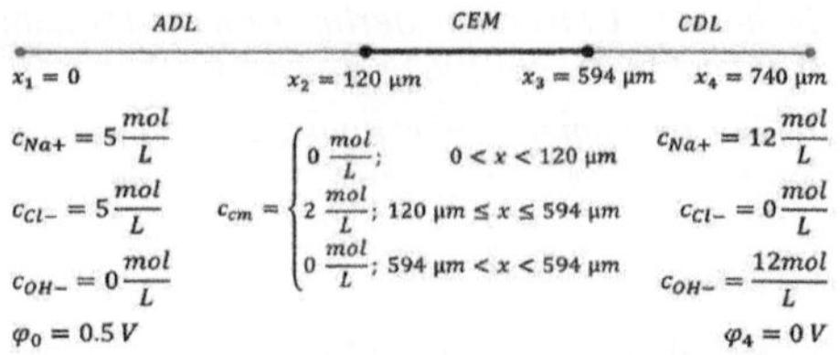

Figure 1: Schematic of the solution-membrane system

2.1. The Poisson Nernst Planck equation

The Poisson Nernst Planck (PNP) model considers the concentration of the three ionic components c_i and the electric potential φ in the modeled spatial domain. The 1D steady-state Poisson-Nernst-Planck system consists of:

$$D_i \left(\frac{d^2 c_i}{dx^2} + \frac{z_i F}{RT} \left(\frac{dc_i}{dx} \frac{d\varphi}{dx} + c_i \frac{d^2 \varphi}{dx^2} \right) \right) = 0 \tag{1}$$

$$\frac{d^2 \varphi}{dx^2} = -\frac{F}{\varepsilon} \left(z_m c_m + \sum_i^{Ni} z_i c_i \right) \tag{2}$$

D_i is the diffusion coefficient of component i. z_i, R, and T in Eq. (1) are the charge number of component i, the ideal gas constant ($8.314\,\mathrm{J\,K^{-1}\,mol^{-1}}$), and the temperature (K) of the modeled system, respectively. ε and F are the permittivity of the medium (assumed $\varepsilon \approx 3.9825 \times 10^{-10}\,\mathrm{F\,m^{-1}}$) and the Faraday constant ($96485\,\mathrm{C\,mol^{-1}}$). z_m and c_m denote the charge number of the fixed charges in the ion exchange membrane and their concentration.

2.2. The 1D linear model

To be able to benchmark the discretization methods, an analytical solution of a 1D linear model is derived and considered as a reference function. The linear differential system models an ionic liquid system in 1D space between two Dirichlet boundary conditions: $c_i(x = 0) = C_0$ and $c_i(x = L) = C_L$, wherein L is the length of the 1D space. The linear model assumes a linear electric potential distribution over the spatial domain. This assumption reduces the PNP equation into a second order homogeneous linear differential equation:

$$D_i \left(\frac{d^2 c_i}{dx^2} + \frac{z_i F}{RT} \beta \frac{dc_i}{dx} \right) = 0, \tag{3}$$

wherein β is the constant value of the electric potential gradient $\frac{d\varphi}{dx}$. An analytical solution has been derived for the linear model and leads to the following general solution: $c_i(x) = A_1 + A_2 e^{-k_i \beta x}$ with $k_i = \frac{z_i F}{RT}$. The coefficients A_1 and A_2 are determined by the spatial boundary conditions C_0 and C_L. These boundary conditions lead to a particular solution of the linear model:

$$c_i(x) = c_0 + \frac{C_0 - C_L}{1 - e^{-k_i \beta L}} \left(e^{-k_i \beta x} - 1 \right) \tag{4}$$

3. The Discretization Methods

We benchmarked the linear model using the three mentioned discretization techniques in comparison to the analytic solution. Space is discretized into $Nn - 1$ equidistant partitions, $0 = x_{n=1} < x_{n=2} < ... < x_{n=Nn} = L$. In the subsequent sections, the evaluated methods will only be briefly reviewed. Further details and fundamental background on these methods can be found in literature (Finlayson (1980)).

3.1. The finite differences method

For the first method, central finite differences are applied. The 1D space is divided into $Nn - 1$ partitions with an equal length of Δx. Eq. (5) shows the discretized form of Eq. (3). The equation system of the finite differences method holds $Nn - 2$ balance equations (Eq. (5)) and two boundary conditions C_0 and C_L.

$$D_i \left(\frac{c_{i,n+1} - 2c_{i,n} + c_{i,n-1}}{\Delta X^2} + \frac{z_i F}{RT} \beta \frac{c_{i,n+1} - c_{i,n-1}}{\Delta X} \right) = 0 \tag{5}$$

3.2. The finite elements method

In this contribution, Hermite collocation and Galerkin are applied on finite elements to approximate the solution. The approximation is carried out on $Nn - 1$ elements by a linear combination of basis functions. To simplify the discretization, the global variable x is transformed into local variable u by $u = \frac{x - x_n}{h_n}$. h_n is the length of the n-th element, given by $h_n = x_{n+1} - x_n$. Within each element, the solution is approximated by a linear combination of some basis function $N_j(u)$ shown in Eq. (6). The coefficients $a_{i,j,n}$ are then solved numerically to provide the approximated solution.

$$c_{i,n}(u) = \sum_{j=1}^{Nj} a_{i,j,n} N_{j,n}(u) \tag{6}$$

For Hermite collocation, four cubic Hermite polynomials are used as basis functions, which are $N_{j=1,n}(u) = (1-u)^2(1+2u)$, $N_{j=2,n}(u) = u(1-u)^2 h_n$, $N_{j=3,n}(u) = (u)^2(3-2u)$, and $N_{j=4,n}(u) = u^2(u-1)h_n$. As shown by Finlayson (1980) and Arora et al. (2006), it is convenient to choose the roots of shifted orthogonal Legendre polynomial ($P_2^{0,0}(u)$) as collocation points: $u_1 = 0$, $u_2 = \frac{1}{2}(1 + \frac{1}{\sqrt{3}})$, $u_3 = \frac{1}{2}(1 - \frac{1}{\sqrt{3}})$, $u_4 = 1$.

Eq. (6) is substituted into Eq. (3) resulting in the discretized form in Eq. (7). Eq. (7) is then evaluated at the inner collocation points, u_2 and u_3. The Hermite polynomials guarantee C^1 continuity at the element boundaries. Hence, only the two global boundary conditions $a_{i,n=1,j=1} = C_0$ at $x = 0$ and $a_{i,n=Nn-1,j=3} = C_L$ at $x = L$ need to be described. The equation system to be solved consists of $2(Nn - 1)$ balance equations (Eq. (7)) and the two overall boundary conditions.

$$D_{i,n} \left(\frac{1}{h_n^2} \sum_{j=1}^{Nj=4} a_{i,n,j} \frac{d^2 N_{j,n}(u)}{du^2} + \frac{z_i F}{RT} \frac{\beta}{h_n} \sum_{j=1}^{Nj=4} a_{i,n,j} \frac{dN_{j,n}(u)}{du} \right) = 0 \tag{7}$$

For the Galerkin method, three second order Lagrange polynomials are applied as basis functions ($N_j(u)$) of Eq. (6). Those polynomials are $N_{j=1} = 2(u-1)(u-1/2)$, $N_{j=2} = 4u(1-u)$, and $N_{j=3} = 2u(u-1/2)$. By substituting Eq. (6) into Eq. (3) and applying Galerkin'S method, the linear model turns into Eq. (8). Two additional boundary conditions in every element, $\frac{dc_{i,n}}{du} - \frac{dc_{i,n-1}}{du} = 0$ and $c_{i,n} - c_{i,n-1} = 0$ are added to the equation system to guarantee C^1 continuity at the element boundaries. C_0 and C_L are also added to the equation system as the outer boundary conditions of the spatial domain.

$$\int_0^L D_i \left(\frac{1}{h_n} \sum_{j=1}^{Nj=3} a_{i,n,j} \frac{d^2 N_{j,n}(u)}{du^2} + \frac{z_i F}{RT} \beta \sum_{j=1}^{Nj=3} a_{i,n,j} \frac{dN_{j,n}(u)}{du} \right) N_{j=2,n}(u) du = 0 \tag{8}$$

3.3. Logarithmic reformulation

In addition to the discretization, a logarithmic reformulation is applied to influence the scaling of the model. For this purpose, all concentrations are replaced by $c_i(x) = e^{\ln((c_i(x))} = e^{\bar{c}_i(x)}$ and the model is then solved in terms of $\bar{c}_i$. The assumption is that this scales better and also guarantees positivity of all concentration values. The reformulated model shown in Eq. (9) is then discretized with the central finite differences method to solve it numerically.

$$D_i e^{\bar{c}_i(x)} \left(\frac{d^2 \bar{c}(x)}{dx^2} + \left(\frac{d\bar{c}(x)}{dx} \right)^2 + \frac{z_i F}{RT} \beta \frac{d\bar{c}(x)}{dx} \right) = 0 \tag{9}$$

4. Comparison of the Methods

To benchmark the methods introduced in Section 3, a simulation study on the linear model is set up to determine concentrations of anions ($z_{i=1} = -1$) and cations ($z_{i=2} = +1$) in a solution system. The spatial domain L has a length of $10^{-3} m$ bounded by two Dirichlet boundary conditions for both ions, namely $C_0 = 12$ and $C_L = 10^{-7}$ $\text{mol}\,\text{m}^{-3}$, which represent the maximum concentration difference in the simulation of the electrolyzer model. The diffusion coefficients are $D_{i=1} = 10^{-11}$ and $D_{i=9} = 10^{-9}$ $\text{m}^2\,\text{s}^{-1}$, which represent the maximum and minimum values of diffusion coefficients in the electrolyzer model. The temperature is set to be 363 K, which is the typical operation temperature of the process. And the β is $-500\,\text{V}\,\text{m}^{-1}$, determined by the electric potential difference of 0.5 V devided by L. The condition number of the Jacobian matrix, the

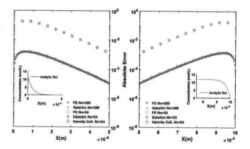

Figure 2: The comparison of the absolute error resulted by three discretization methods. The left side and the right side graphs show respectively the error profile of the negative component ($z_{i=1} = -1$) and the positive component ($z_{i=2} = +1$). The small graphs show the analytic solution of the corresponding model.

computation time and the maximum absolute error or deviation from the analytic solution are also presented in Table 1. The termination tolerance of 10^{-14} is set to end the computation. All equation systems are solved using fsolve of MATLAB with the Trust-Region-Dogleg algorithm.

4.1. The finite differences and the finite elements methods

As initial guesses, the concentrations of all components are set to 1 mol/L. The equation systems are discretized using the finite differences (FD) and both finite elements methods (FE). All simulation problems successfully converged with the absolute value of the function residuals smaller than the required termination tolerance. The simulation results plotted in Figure 2 show that the accuracies of the evaluated methods differ in regions of higher gradient values. The Hermite collocation method overall shows a higher accuracy compared to the other two. Tab. 1 shows that

Table 1: Numerical performance: Hermite collocation, finite differences, and Galerkin method

Parameters	Hermite Coll.(HC)	Finite Differences (FD)		Galerkin Method (GM)	
Nn	24	24	260	24	260
Condition number	$8.59 \cdot 10^7$	$7.38 \cdot 10^3$	$9.31 \cdot 10^5$	$4.68 \cdot 10^{13}$	$5.55 \cdot 10^{15}$
Computation time (s)	0.9958	0.2218	0.9974	0.4347	10.2488
Max.absolute error	0.0014	0.1781	0.0014	0.1781	0.0014

by increasing the number of discrete points/elements (Nn) to 260, the finite difference and the Galerkin method can achieve a similar accuracy resulted by the Hermite collocation method with 24 discrete elements. To achieve this accuracy, the finite differences method needs approximately similar computation time to that of the Hermite collocation.

4.2. The logartihmic reformulation

The logarithmically reformulated model is evaluated by comparing its performance to the non-reformulated model. The central finite differences is applied to discretize both models. Nn is set to 36, which is reasonably accurate for the finite differences method based on the previous results. The analytic solution is used as an initial guess. To investigate the convergence range of the reformulation method, four variations of boundary conditions (C_0 and C_L in $molL^{-1}$) are simulated: 24 and 2×10^{-1}, 12 and 2, 12×10^4 and 2, 12×10^{-4} and 2×10^{-9}. The other model parameters remain unchanged. The variation of the boundary conditions yields four different condition numbers for the reformulated model, which are 9.49×10^5, 9.06×10^3, 2.20×10^9

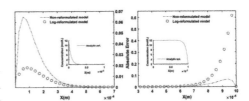

Figure 3: The comparison of the absolute error resulted by the log-reformulated model and the non-reformulated model. The left side and the right side graphs show respectively the error profile of the negative component ($z_{i=1} = -1$) and the positive component ($z_{i=2} = +1$). The small graphs show the analytic solution of the non-reformulated model for both components.

and 4.12×10^{12}, respectively. While the condition number of the non-reformulated model remains constant at 1.70×10^4 in all variations of the boundary conditions. Only for the second case of the logarithmic problem, the reformulated model successfully converged. The convergence of the reformulated method starts to breakdown as the solution value approaches one, because of the singularity of the log function as its value approaches zero. The reformulated model obtains higher accuracy only in the region with a concave upward profile as shown in Fig. 3. Since the aim of the current investigation is a selection of the discretization method, necessary further investigations to improve the reformulation method is not done here.

5. Modeling the Solution-Membrane System of the Chloralkali Electrolyzer

In this section, the application of the Poisson-Nernst-Planck equation to model a system of three ions in a membrane and two diffusion layers (shown by Figure 1) is presented. The model is an approximation of a chloralkali process in a segment of the membrane reactor. D_i and the size of the spatial domain are adopted from Kodým et al. (2016) and Fíla and Bouzek (2003). Continuity of the dependent variables and ion fluxes are applied at both solution-membrane interfaces (x_2 and x_3). Eq. (1) and Eq. (2) are discretized using the central finite differences method due to

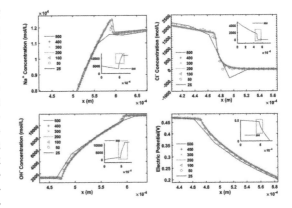

Figure 4: Profiles of the ions concentration and the electric-potential in the 1D PNP system (Fig. 1) resulted from simulations with various numbers of discrete points.

its relative simple initialization and low computational cost while preserving reasonable accuracy. The number of the discrete elements (Nn) was varied from 25 to 500 elements to justify the minimum number of elements necessary to obtain adequate accuracy. The simulations were converged with a tolerance of 10^{-14}. Fig. 4 shows the obtained profiles of the ion concentration and the electric-potential. Almost all of the discretization variants provide a similar overall profile. They only differ at the solution-membrane interface ($x = 474\mu m$ and $x = 594\mu m$), where the steepest gradient appears. Increasing the number of elements to more than 300 does not improve the accuracy significantly.

6. Conclusions and Outlook

Three discretization methods: the central finite differences, Hermite collocation on finite elements, and the Galerkin finite elements method have been evaluated using a 1D linear differential model. In comparison with its analytic solution, the Hermite collocation on finite elements method shows the highest accuracy, particularly in regions of steep gradients. However, with extra number of the discrete points the central finite differences method can also achieve the similar accuracy in an approxmiately similar computation time. A logarithmic reformulation was evaluated while using the central finite differences as the discretization method. The results show that this method makes the condition number of the Jacobian matrix more dependent on the actual solution range. Further investigation and modification of this method for tackling the dependency are necessary to make this method more applicable. The 1D Poisson-Nernst-Planck model has been adopted to model a solution-membrane system, approximating a chloralkali membrane process. The presented results show that the method is capable of being implemented in such a case by considering an appropriate number of elements to achieve a desired accuracy.

In future work, we will investigate non-equidistant discretizations. In regions of smaller gradient values, lower numbers of discrete points or finite elements could be applied and consequently the computational cost of the discretization techniques can be further reduced.

7. Acknowledgment

The LPDP (Indonesian Endowment Fund for Education) is gratefully acknowledged for supporting this research through the Ph.D. funding for the author. The German Federal Ministry for Economic Affairs and Energy is also gratefully acknowledged for supporting the research project ChemEFlex (funding code 0350013A).

References

Arora, S., Dhaliwal, S., Kukreja, V., 2006. Simulation of washing of packed bed of porous particles by orthogonal collocation on finite elements. Computers and Chemical Engineering 30, 1054–1060.

Fíla, V., Bouzek, K., 2003. A mathematical model of multiple ion transport across an ion-selective membrane under current load conditions. Journal of Applied Electrochemistry 33, 675–684.

Finlayson, B. A., 1980. Nonlinear Analysis in Chemical Engineering. McGraw-Hill.

Kodým, R., Fíla, V., Šnita, D., Bouzek, K., 2016. Poisson-Nernst-Planck model of multiple ion transport across an ion-selective membrane under conditions close to chlor-alkali electrolysis. Journal of Applied Electrochemistry 46, 679–694.

Moshtarikhah, S., Oppers, N., Groot, M., Keurentjes, J., Schouten, J., Schaaf, J. v. d., 2017. Nernst–Planck modeling of multicomponent ion transport in a Nafion membrane at high current density. Journal of Applied Electrochemistry 47, 51–62.

Verbrugge, M. W., Hill, R. F., 1990. Ion and Solvent Transport in Ion-Exchange Membranes: I. A Macrohomogeneous Mathematical Model. Journal of The Electrochemical Society 137, 886–893.

Verbrugge, M. W., Hill, R. F., 1992. Measurement of ionic concentration profiles in membranes during transport. Electrochimica Acta 37, 221–229.

Zheng, Q. and Wei,G.-W., 2011. Poisson–Boltzmann–Nernst–Planck Model. Journal of Chemical Physics 134, 194101.1-17.

Anton A. Kiss, Edwin Zondervan, Richard Lakerveld, Leyla Özkan (Eds.)
Proceedings of the 29th European Symposium on Computer Aided Process Engineering
June 16th to 19th, 2019, Eindhoven, The Netherlands. © 2019 Elsevier B.V. All rights reserved.
http://dx.doi.org/10.1016/B978-0-128-18634-3.50100-4

A steady-state and dynamic simulation tool for solid oxide fuel cell operation applications

Amirpiran Amiri,[a,*] Khaliq Ahmed,[b] Moses O. Tadé[b]

[a]*European Bioenergy Research Institute (EBRI), School of Engineering and Applied Science, Aston University, Birmingham, B4 7ET, United Kingdom*

[b]*Centre for Process Systems Computations, Department of Chemical Engineering, Curtin University, Kent Street, Bentley, WA 6102, Australia*

a.p.amiri@aston.ac.uk

Abstract

A modular simulator of dynamic behaviour of the Solid Oxide Fuel Cell (SOFC) system, suitable for use as a training tool is presented in this article, as an alternative to expensive practical tests. This simulator, developed in Aspen Custom Modeller (ACM), captures all of the processes in an SOFC module: mass, energy, and charge balances, overpotentials, ohmic losses and electrochemical reaction kinetics. The challenges relevant to programming and mathematical skills needed for models deployment are minimised. Application of the simulator is demonstrated through i) a basic steady-state simulation and 1D optimisatin followed by estimation of the stack's distributed variables and ii) illustration of the transient behaviour of the SOFC unit. Interpretation of SOFC operation dynamics, in particular, is emphasised to show the effectiveness of the simulator for training purposes and for laboratory demonstrations. The results show the key features of the SOFC module simulator for practical applications and for virtual laboratories. It also opens up opportunities for developing an in-built SOFC simulator module in a flowsheet simulation software such as Aspen Plus and Aspen HYSYS.

Keywords: SOFC, Simulator, Dynamic, Laboratory, ACM,

1. Introduction

Fuel cell, an emerging technology for future green energy production, is an active area of interest as a teaching unit and for research at chemical engineering departments at universities and industrial research and development (R&D) laboratories worldwide (Baker and Ağar, 2011). The expensive fuel cell test rigs have been used for cutting-edge research and occasionally for training purposes. However, lower cost, simplicity, safety, and speed are some of the advantages of numerical simulators compared to the experimental set-up. Moreover, convenient access to a computational tool, in contrast to the real-life experimental set-up, resolves the space and time limitations that are usually a hindrance to laboratory-based work (Aguiar et al., 2005, Lai et al., 2011). Since fuel cell is at its infancy stage, there is a shortage in existence of efficient and user-friendly simulators for it. Aspen Custom modeller (ACM) is used in this paper to develop a user-friendly SOFC simulator as depicted in Figure 1. The mathematical model that predicts the cell performance and behaviour has been demonstrated in our previous work (Amiri et al., 2015). The model provides user with the flexibility needed for an insightful simulation of an SOFC module, as dominant process variables and simulation parameters are conveniently accessible. The user first sets the main model parameters such as the SOFC configuration parameters. This involves the SOFC physical dimensions and the thermal and electrical properties of its material. Operating conditions such as the cell operating voltage, air and fuel flows and the temperatures at the cell inlet, are also among the user-specified information. The thermal and electrical metrics are the main output of the simulator. The module is modifiable, as its programming interface is readily accessible. In order to estimate the species and mixtures properties, *Aspen Properties* and *ACM* are integrated. Such a modelling framework–founded on the application of ACM for SOFC and other types of fuel cells – contributes to this new technology process taking advantage of the established in-built unit operations and the thermodynamical property estimation packages.

2. Demonstration of the capabilities of the Simulator

The simulator developed in this work is demonstrated by carrying out a number of case studies, which are presented below.

2.1. Case study I: Lumped parameter simulation of SOFC

Extraction of essential characteristic information including V-I data is always the preliminary step for the evaluation of fuel cell performance and for an assessment of the model's accuracy. In practice, it can be accomplished through ramping the operating voltage and recording the corresponding current. Normalisation of the estimated current, i.e., current/area, allows comparing cells/stacks with different sizes. Interpretation of the V-I characteristic curve and its connection to the underlying fundamental processes is critical in training and research applications. The V-I simulation results using the simulator developed in this work (Figure 1) is compared against experimental data as shown in Figure 2(a). The simulator is capable of generating V-I curves under various operating conditions as shown in Figure 2(b). Supporting data including detailed information for streams and cell internal variables allow further evaluation of the cell's performance. Figure 2(c) shows the variation of fuel utilisation, caused by a change in the operating current at constant voltage, when the inlet temperature is varying.

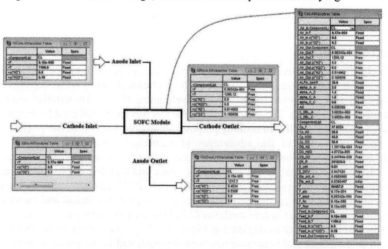

Figure 1: User-friendly SOFC simulator interface developed in ACM.

Since a lumped parameter analysis is presented in this section of the paper, the fuel-air flow configuration does not play a role in this case study. However, the flow pattern is important in the distributed parameter simulations that are presented in the following sections. In all of the cases presented in this work, the cell is assumed to operate adiabatically. Moreover, cell-to-cell and cell-to-surroundings heat transfer are ignored in this model, assuming a well-insulated stack.

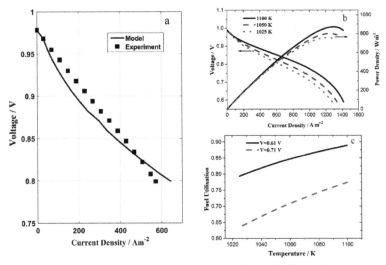

Figure 2: (a) Model validation using data from Tang et al. (2016); (b) Illustrative generation of V-I characteristics profile for different fuel temperatures

by using modular simulator capable of describing voltage losses regions; (c) cell's fuel utilisation for a range of fuel temperatures and under two operating voltages.

2.2. Case Study II: Distributed parameter simulation of SOFC

Visualisation of the distributed variables along the stack dimensions provides an illustrative tool to present the impact of system's variables on cell/stack performance homogeneity. This feature is of practical importance for process analysis of the entire system along with the stack's distributed variables. For 2D and 3D simulation, researchers have used CFD (Ni, 2013), COMSOL modelling facilities (Lai et al., 2011), finite volume model (Ma et al., 2015), and specifically developed tools (Khaleel, 2012). This type of analysis, however, still faces geometry complexity and calculation load challenges making their applications limited to the specific expertise and computational powers. This paper proposes an approach for capturing the stack's distributed variables in *Aspen Plus*, with drastically reduced computational time, approximately of the same order of magnitude of time needed for the simulation of other BoP components. Networking of 0D compartments allows simulating the SOFC as a more realistic reactor as internal spatial distributions of the state variables always exist. This is a straightforward task after exporting the developed module (Figure 1) from the *ACM* environment to the *Aspen Plus* environment. The number of compartments in series, however, must be estimated based on experimental Residence Time Distribution data (Amiri et al., 2015). The distributed parameter model is used to optimise the air (coolant) supply to each part of a cross flow SOFC to achieve a lower temperature variation across the cell. Optimum design and operation of SOFC needs to be examined against the performance characteristics measures including, durability, reliability and efficiency (Secanell et al., 2011). Some of these targets are to some extent mutually exclusive. For example, high efficiency necessitates operation at high fuel utilisation but may detrimentally impact on the SOFC lifetime, potentially due to the high rates of degradation at the higher levels of utilisation. Durability also depends on the reduction of thermal stresses. This can be achieved by using surplus coolant gas but the system efficiency will reduce as a consequence of the parasitic loss (Tang et al., 2016). From this viewpoint, the optimisation task for either the stack or the system as a whole is a multi-objective optimisation problem with some compromise in operational measures. The optimisation task in this article is an user-defined single objective function (Eq. (1)),

$$\min \ f = \frac{1}{\overline{T}} \sqrt{\sum_{i=1}^{n} \left(T_i - \overline{T}\right)^2}, \quad \overline{T} = \frac{1}{n} \sum_{i=1}^{n} T_i$$

(1)

with the constraint: each compartment must receive at least 5% of total air preventing oxygen starvation, where T_i and $\overline{T}$ stand for local and average temperature of the compartment, respectively. Figure 4 depicts the PEN (Positive electrode-Electrolyte-Negative electrode) temperature profile along the cell's length under different total excess air and with normal and optimised air flow distributions. As can be seen, this strategy is more influential at the lower range of the excess air flows. The wavy temperature profile in Figure 3(a) might be attributed to the discretisation method which is a limitation for developing the distributed models inside the flowsheeting platform. Either increasing the number of intervals or interpolating the values inside the intervals resolves such a flaw as can be seen in Figure 3(b). However, it must be noted that the profiles' trends suffice for schematically presenting the overall performance of the objective function and optimisation effort in a training task.

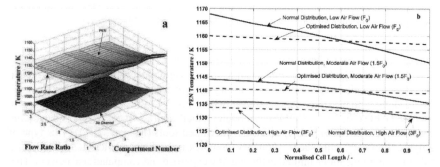

Figure 3. 3D and 2D presentations of the temperature gradient minimisation along the fuel flow path by coolant (air) distribution strategy and for different coolant's flow ratio (ratio of flow to basis-flow).

2.3. Case Study III: Transient simulation of SOFC

The open loop responses of current density, solid temperature, hydrogen concentration, voltage losses, and air/fuel utilisations, upon the inlet gas temperature changes in a stepwise pattern, are shown in Figure 4. Variation of ±20 K in the inlet gas temperature significantly impacts the cell's dynamics and also the final steady values of the state variables. The significant increase in the PEN temperature has its roots in two causes, namely the decline in cooling rate due to use of the hotter air, +20 K, and the extra heat released from the promoted exothermic electrochemical reaction. The rate of reaction increases as a result of the increase in the PEN temperature. A feature of the transient temperature behaviour is the equality of absolute value of the final temperature change (≈ 36K) and also the settling time (≈ 200s), for both, negative and positive inlet changes. From this viewpoint it might be concluded that the solid's temperature responses are almost linear. However, the average current shows under- and over-shoots which are not equal in absolute values. This is the case for the hydrogen concentration and OCV histories too. The trainee could explore and interpret the connection between these observations to understand how a non-linear system may behave in unstable circumstances. For instance, the presented scenario indicates the impact of the initial temperature in estimation of the current value at the moment of change implementation. In other words, the higher the difference between initial and final values of the temperature, the more significant is the under/over-shoots in current and other temperature-dependent profiles. Explanation of the dynamic observations based on the utilised empirical and physical correlations allows for the demonstration of the application of these predictive equations. As an example, one may focus on the OCV profile aiming to explain the connection between this voltage and the state variables' profiles based on the Nernst equation. OCV profile, Figure 4, is a strong function of temperature and the species concentration changes. Explanation of reaction rates by using the current profile along with the temperature and concentration histories is another learning practice. Analysis of the dynamic voltage losses will lead to a detailed understanding of the share of each term in the total voltage losses and thus the operating voltage dynamics. A stable operation requires the voltage fluctuations to be minimised. Since oscillations in the operating voltage are caused by instability in OCV and overpotentials, an insight of the time-dependent weight of each term of voltage equation (i.e., OCV, anode and cathode activation loss, concentration loss, ohmic loss) can help to understand the voltage element(s) that dominate(s) the operating voltage dynamics and to propose control strategies for steady operation of the SOFC.

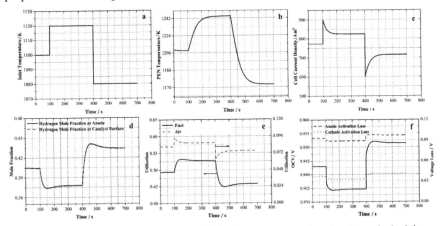

Figure 4. Dynamics of the SOFC state variables in response to a stepwise change in the inlet gases temperature.

3. Conclusions

This article provides an effective modelling simplification without compromising the dominant SOFC process phenomena. Complicated mathematics and the necessity of professional numerical skills make the application of academic models difficult particularly for non-academic users. This is an important motivation to develop simulators that reduces the demand of such skills for applied purposes. Compared to the literature, for instance the authors' previous publications (Amiri et al., 2015, 2016), the simulation approach presented in this work offers a considerable simplicity without sacrificing the model details. While the formers are beneficial for technical research purposes, the later, this work, is beneficial for both training and research. ACM further offers advanced applications including, but not limited to, model predictive control, process optimisation, knowledge based decision-making, model-based fault diagnosis, and process flowsheet simulation which makes it a very effective and convenient tool for intelligent automation of fuel cell process operations. The dynamic analysis presented in this article was to demonstrate this.

References

P. Aguiar, C.S. Adjiman, , N.P. Brandon, , 2005, Anode-supported intermediate-temperature direct internal reforming solid oxide fuel cell: II. Model-based dynamic performance and control, J. Power Sources, 147, 136-147.

A. Amiri, P. Vijay, M.O. Tadé, K. Ahmed, G.D. Ingram, V. Pareek, R. Utikar, 2015, Solid oxide fuel cell reactor analysis and optimisation through a novel multi-scale modelling strategy, Comput. Chem. Eng, 78, 10-23.

A. Amiri, P. Vijay, M.O. Tadé, K.Ahmed, , G.D. Ingram, V. Pareek, R. Utikar, 2016, Planar SOFC system modelling and simulation including a 3D stack module, Int. J. Hydrogen Energy, 41, 2919-2930.

D.K. Baker, E. Ağar, 2011, International Summer Engineering Program on fuel cells for undergraduate engineering students, Int. J. Hydrogen Energy, 36, 3712-3725.

M. Khaleel, 2012, Overview of SOFC Modeling and Simulation: Recent Progress, 13th Annual SECA Workshop, National Energy Technology Laboratory, Pittsburgh, PA.

K. Lai, B.J. Koeppel, K.S. Choi, K.P. Recknagle, X. Sun, L.A. Chick, V. Korolev, M. Khaleel, 2011, A quasi-two-dimensional electrochemistry modeling tool for planar solid oxide fuel cell stacks, J. Power Sources, 196, 3204-3222.

T. Ma, M. Yan, M. Zeng, J.-l. Yuan, Q.-y. Chen, B. Sundén, Q.-w. Wang, 2015, Parameter study of transient carbon deposition effect on the performance of a planar solid oxide fuel cell, Appl. Energy, 152, 217-228.

M.Ni, 2013, Modeling and parametric simulations of solid oxide fuel cells with methane carbon dioxide reforming, Energy Convers. Manage., 70, 116-129.

M. Secanell, J. Wishart, P. Dobson, 2011, Computational design and optimization of fuel cells and fuel cell systems: A review, J. Power Sources, 196, 3690-3704.

S. Tang, A. Amiri, P. Vijay, M.O. Tadé, 2016, Development and validation of a computationally efficient pseudo 3D model for planar SOFC integrated with a heating furnace, Chem. Eng. J., 290, 252-262.

Anton A. Kiss, Edwin Zondervan, Richard Lakerveld, Leyla Özkan (Eds.)
Proceedings of the 29th European Symposium on Computer Aided Process Engineering
June 16th to 19th, 2019, Eindhoven, The Netherlands. © 2019 Elsevier B.V. All rights reserved.
http://dx.doi.org/10.1016/B978-0-128-18634-3.50101-6

Thermal conductivity prediction of molten salt-based nanofluids for energy storage applications

B.H. Mahmoud[a*], L.F. Mortimer[a], M. Fairweather[a], H.P. Rice[a], J. Peakall[b], D. Harbottle[a]

[a]School of Chemical and Process Engineering, and [b]School of Earth and Environment, University of Leeds, Leeds LS2 9JT, UK

*bgy9bm@leeds.ac.uk

Abstract

Molten salt-based nanofluids (nano-salts) form an important class of thermal fluids that can act as both heat transfer and thermal energy storage media for high temperature applications, including solar thermal systems. Among these, the class of binary nitrate salts (60:40 wt. % $NaNO_3:KNO_3$) and their mixtures with metal oxide nanoparticles are the most prominent. This study evaluates the stability of nano-salts using a computational technique based on Lagrangian particle tracking, with the model considering the motion of solid nanoparticles suspended in a molten fluid. The technique enables various multiscale forces, with different characteristics, to be established. The system considered consists of 25-71 nm Al_2O_3 ceramic nanoparticles at volume fractions ranging from 1.0 to 5.0% suspended in fluids of different density ratios, with homogeneous temperature distributions from 250-600 °C. The simulation results demonstrate the effectiveness of the technique, with predictions elucidating the role of oscillatory structural, Brownian motion and particle collision forces, and their influence on the enhancement of thermal conductivity. The liquid structuring of salt melts around the embedded nanoparticles is found to play a key role in the nano-salts' thermal behaviour, with predictions in agreement with previous theoretical and experimental studies. The outcome of this research forms the basis for the potential use of nano-salts in solar thermal systems.

Keywords: Nanofluids, oscillatory structural force, thermal conductivity, energy storage.

1. Introduction

Binary mixtures of $NaNO_3:KNO_3$, like many other salts, contain ionic compounds such as sodium (Na^+), potassium (K^+) and nitrate (NO_3^-) ions and are, therefore, classified as alkali metal nitrates. When two nanoparticles (with smooth surfaces) are immersed in an ionic liquid such as molten nitrate salt, an oscillatory force exists between the particles due to the ordering of the confined liquid molecules in the thin film between the two surfaces. Theoretical predictions demonstrate that the ordering of liquid molecules reaches an energetic minimum at separations which correspond roughly to the diameter of a liquid molecule, as illustrated in Fig 1. At present, little is known about the thermal properties of this interfacial layer, however, theoretical analyses and numerical simulations predict that it acts as a thermal bridge, particularly in high temperature ionic fluids like molten salts. It is believed that these layered fluid molecules are in an intermediate physical state between that of the bulk fluid and the solid surfaces, thus forming a solid-like nanolayer of liquid molecules which leads to higher thermal conductivity than that of the bulk fluid (Choi, 2003).

In this study, a novel method is used to describe the oscillating layered structure of molten salt fluids (represented by the matrix of liquid molecules around the nanoparticles), and the influence of the interfacial layer thickness on the system conductivity. An explanation of this phenomenon was first given by Israelachvili (2011) who noted that the structural force arises once there is a change in the liquid density at the surface of nanoparticles, as they approach one other. This force may be thought of as the van der Waals force at small separations, with the molecular properties and density variations of the medium taken into account. This force is consequently dependent on the size, type and surface properties of the particles as well as the ionic concentration and density of the continuum.

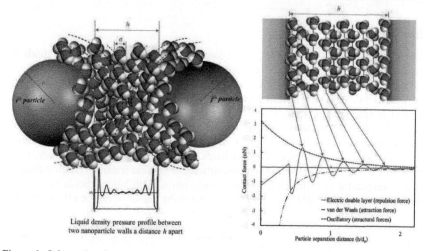

Figure 1. Schematic of structuring of molten nitrate molecules between two smooth spherical particles submerged in an ionic continuum (left); and period of force, i.e. diameter of small liquid molecules, causing oscillatory structural forces with monotonically decaying amplitude (right).

2. Computational Setup and Model Description

This work extends previous simulations (Mahmoud et al, 2018) performed using an in-house code embodying the multiscale numerical model. The model applies a Lagrangian particle tracking approach to investigate the dynamics of, and heat transfer mechanisms in, high temperature salt-based nanofluids. The three-dimensional computational region examined consists of a 1 μm cube filled with stagnant molten nitrate salt. This volume element is composed of a collection of 25-71 nm Al_2O_3 ceramic nanoparticles (50-1500 in number) that are injected uniformly across the domain. The motion of the embedded nanoparticles in the fluid is treated using an Eulerian-Lagrangian approach with fixed time stepping. The dynamic properties of both phases are coupled to the ambient temperature of the fluid suspension, that being molten nitrate salt at 250-600 °C.

The model describes the dynamic interactions between the i-th and j-th spherical nanoparticles in the normal unit direction, $\boldsymbol{n}_{ij}$, according to the approach of Fujita and Yamaguchi (2007). Particle collisions are resolved using a soft sphere approach as described by the Hertzian normal contact theory (Timoshenko and Goodier, 1970). The oscillatory structural force is considered by adding an extra term, $\boldsymbol{\Pi}^{os}$, to the classical DLVO expression for the disjoining pressure (Denkov and Kralchevsky, 1995):

$$\boldsymbol{\Pi}(h) = \boldsymbol{\Pi}^{vW}(h) + \boldsymbol{\Pi}^{el}(h) + \boldsymbol{\Pi}^{os}(h) \tag{1}$$

where $\boldsymbol{\Pi}^{vW}$ is the van der Waals attractive force:

$$\boldsymbol{\Pi}^{vW} = -\frac{A_H}{6\pi h_{ij}^3} \tag{2}$$

and h is the film thickness, A_H the Hamaker constant, and $\boldsymbol{\Pi}^{el}$ is the electric double layer repulsive force:

$$\boldsymbol{\Pi}^{el} = \frac{64\pi r n k_b T \Theta^2 e^{-\kappa h_{ij}}}{\kappa} \tag{3}$$

Here, r is the sphere radius, n the number density of electrolyte ions, k_b the Boltzmann constant, T the temperature of the suspension, Θ the polarisability factor, and κ the inverse of the Debye length.

The dependence of the oscillatory structural component of disjoining pressure on the film thickness can be specified using the formula of Denkov and Kralchevsky (1995):

$$\boldsymbol{\Pi}^{os}(h) = P_0 \cos\left(\frac{2\pi h}{d_1}\right) \exp\left(\frac{d^3}{d_1^2 d_2} - \frac{h}{d_2}\right), \; for \; h > d$$
$$\boldsymbol{\Pi}^{os}(h) = -P_0, \; for \; 0 < h < d \tag{4}$$

where σ is the diameter of the smaller fluid hard spheres (≈ 0.45 nm for molten salt molecules), d_1 the oscillatory period and d_2 the characteristic decay length, which are related to the particle volume fraction, φ, as follows:

$$\frac{d_1}{d} = \sqrt{\frac{2}{3} + a_1 \Delta\varphi + a_2(\Delta\varphi)^2}; \; \frac{d_2}{\sigma} = \frac{b_1}{\Delta\varphi} - b_2 \tag{5}$$

Here, $\Delta\varphi = \varphi_{max} - \varphi$, with $\varphi_{max} = \pi/3\sqrt{2}$ the value of φ at close packing, and $a_1, a_2,$ b_1 and b_2 are correlation coefficients determined theoretically with respect to φ. The particle osmotic pressure, P_0, is taken from the formula of Carnahan and Starling (1969):

$$P_0 = \rho_s k_b T \frac{1+\varphi+\varphi^2-\varphi^3}{(1-\varphi)^3} \tag{6}$$

in which ρ_s is the particle number density of the small fluid spheres given by $\rho_s = 6\varphi/\pi\sigma^3$. For $h > \sigma$ the structural disjoining pressure oscillates around P_0 as defined in Eq. (6). However, for $h < \sigma$ the small particles are expelled from the gap into the neighbouring bulk suspension by the depletion attraction, described by Eq. (4). When $h = \sigma$ there is a finite discontinuity as the interaction switches from an oscillatory to a depletion regime. The contribution of the interaction free energy per unit area of the film can be obtained by integrating the oscillatory structural forces:

$$f_{os}(h) = \int_h^\infty \boldsymbol{\Pi}^{os}(h') \, dh' \tag{7}$$

and from Eq. (4) and (7) one obtains:

$$f_{os}(h) = \boldsymbol{F}(h), \; for \; h \geq \sigma$$
$$f_{os}(h) = \boldsymbol{F}(\sigma) - P_0(\sigma - h), \; for \; 0 \leq h \leq \sigma \qquad (8)$$

where

$$\boldsymbol{F}(h) = \frac{P_0 \, d_1 \, exp(d^3/d_1^2 d_2 - h/d_2)}{4\pi^2 + (d_1/d_2)^2} \left[\frac{d_1}{d_2} \, cos\left(\frac{2\pi h}{d_1}\right) - 2\pi sin\left(\frac{2\pi h}{d_1}\right) \right] \qquad (9)$$

It should be noted that although soft sphere particle collisions are assumed, Eqs. (4) and (9) are applicable for hard sphere fluid molecules of diameter σ. However, the interparticle potential may still be 'soft' due to the actions of some long range forces.

3. Results and Discussion

Simulations were performed using the model, with results analysed to consider the forces and mechanisms responsible for nanoparticle dynamics, structural and surface property effects, and thermal conductivity enhancement. First, the spontaneous ordering process of nanoparticles in a suspension was examined, followed by the formation of a structured nanolayer (of liquid molecules around the seeded nanoparticles) and of percolation networks of nanostructures using a system under forced aggregation conditions.

A schematic diagram of the structural forces is given in Fig. 1 illustrating the dynamic properties of liquid films confined between two smooth particle surfaces. This shows the concentration dependence of the structural force in the oscillatory regime and how it is dominated by the decay length d_2, in line with Eqs. (4) and (9). The period of the force is equivalent to the diameter of the small liquid molecules σ, and shows an oscillatory nature close to the particle surface with an amplitude that decays monotonically with h (e.g. for a given h, the disjoining pressure increases almost five times for a 10% increase in the volume fraction φ of the liquid molecules). Furthermore, the model predicts the effect of temperature and nanoparticle size on the overall thermal conductivity of the system, with Fig. 2 giving model predictions (coloured) for pure molten salt which are in good agreement with experimental data (Ma and Banerjee, 2017). The figure also gives predictions of thermal conductivities of nanofluids for a fixed concentration of 1 vol. % and temperatures over the range shown. The results are compared with the theoretical work of Maxwell (1892), the data of Ma and Banerjee (2017) and other model predictions (Xuan and Li, 2000; Pang et al., 2016; Prasher et al., 2005), with good agreement found. It should be noted that the existing model showed more sensitivity to particle size in predicting conductivity than the other theoretical models illustrated in Fig. 2

Regarding size dependence, the model predicts that the conductivity of nanofluids containing 20nm Al$_2$O$_3$ particles is significantly greater than those containing 25nm and 71nm particles, by nearly 11% and 22%, respectively, although no systematic experimental investigation of size-dependant conductivities has been performed. Fig. 3 shows the thermal conductivity of the nanofluids, normalised by the conductivity of the base fluid, plotted as a function of the solid volume fraction, Φ, for the 71nm Al$_2$O$_3$ particles. The results show the contribution of the nanolayer and aggregation, and the nanolayer only, to the thermal conductivity, and how this increases with particle volume fraction. With regards to the effect of the nanolayer, at concentrations < 3 vol. % the majority of nanoparticles collide, although the formation of aggregates remains low. Hence, the thermal conductivity enhancement is dominated by the formation of nanolayers between particles. At $\Phi \geq 3$ vol. %, however, the combined effect curves show that the conductivity is enhanced by a factor of two to three, and at such concentrations aggregates (nanoclusters) form in addition to the nanolayers between them, although the interparticle distance is very small (0.5-1 nm). This leads to the conclusion that at high concentrations the effect of Brownian motion is dramatically reduced and instead percolation effects dominate due to reduced interparticle distances and increased particle nanolayering and aggregation.

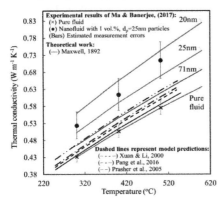

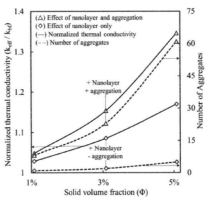

Figure 2. Comparison of model predictions of thermal conductivity with experimental measurements and analytical models for molten salt (Al₂O₃) nanofluids.

Figure 3. Nanoparticle concentration dependent thermal conductivities of nanofluids and effect of nanolayer and number of aggregates formed at 350 °C.

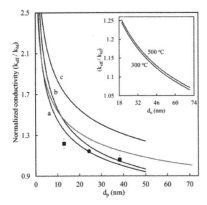

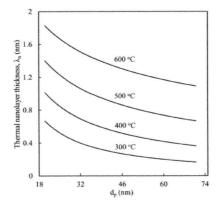

Figure 4. Effect of particle diameter d_p on thermal conductivity ratio. Insert shows conductivity ratio of nanolayer plotted as function of temperature.

Figure 5. Thermal conductivity ratio of nanolayer as function of particle diameter at fixed concentration of 1 vol. %.

Fig. 4 shows the effect of particle diameter on the thermal conductivity for $\Phi = 1$ vol. %. The predictions indicate that as the particle size is decreased, the interparticle distance decreases and, consequently, conduction-like effects become dominant, increasing the conductivity. The smaller the nanoparticles, therefore, the more the enhancement in the conductivity of nano-salts. Corresponding results for the effect of particle diameter on the nanolayer thickness are given in Fig. 5, with predicted values at different temperatures.

This demonstrates that the thickness of the nanolayer increases with reducing particle diameter, and with temperature due to Brownian motion effects. Hence both particle size and system temperature can be used to enhance the thermal conductivity of nanofluids.

4. Conclusions

Key variables related to the oscillatory structural force acting between two spherical nanoparticles, and the thermal conductivity of salt-based ionic nanofluids, have been examined using multiscale simulation. The thermal properties of nanofluids were found to be enhanced compared to those of the pure molten salt bulk fluid. The model has been found to perform well in comparison with similar studies, and provides confirmation of the effect of interparticle distance, particle concentration, temperature, and the formation of nanolayer and percolation networks, on the thermal conductivity of nano-salts. Future work will extend the current model's application to include the dynamic forces considered to be important in three-dimensional flows, as found in solar thermal heat storage systems, by coupling the tracking approach with direct numerical simulations.

Acknowledgements

BHM is grateful for the financial support of the Kuwait Institute for Scientific Research.

References

N.F. Carnahan, K.E. Starling, 1969, Equation of State for Nonattracting Rigid Spheres, J. Chem. Phys., 51, 635-637.

S.U.S. Choi, 2003, Thermal Conductivity of Nanofluids: Vision and Key Features, Thermal Conductivity 27/Thermal Expansion 15, 143-152.

N.D. Denkov, P.A. Kralchevsky, 1995, Colloid Structural Surface Forces in Thin Liquid Films, Prog. Colloid Polymer Sci., 98, 18-22.

M. Fujita, Y. Yamaguchi, 2007, Multiscale Simulation Method for Self-Organization of Nanoparticles in Dense Suspension, J. Comput. Phys., 223, 108-119.

J.N. Israelachvili, 1992, Intermolecular and Surface Forces, 2nd Edition, Academic Press, London.

B. Ma, D. Banerjee, 2017, Experimental Measurements of Thermal Conductivity of Alumina Nanofluid Synthesized in Salt Melt, AIP Advances 7, 115124.

B.H. Mahmoud, M. Fairweather, L.F. Mortimer, J. Peakall, H.P. Rice, D. Harbottle, 2018, Prediction of Stability and Thermal Conductivity of Nanofluids for Thermal Energy Storage Applications, Computer-Aided Chemical Engineering, 43, 61-66.

J.C. Maxwell, 1873, A Treatise on Electricity and Magnetism, Clarendon Press, Oxford.

C. Pang, J.W. Lee, Y.T. Kang, 2016, Enhanced Thermal Conductivity of Nanofluids by Nanoconvection and Percolation Network, Heat Mass Transfer 52, 511-520.

R. Prasher, P. Bhattacharya, P.E. Phelan, 2005, Thermal Conductivity of Nanoscale Colloidal Solutions (Nanofluids), Phys. Rev. Lett., 94, 025901.

S.P. Timoshenko, J.N. Goodier, 1970, Theory of Elasticity, McGraw-Hill, New York.

Y. Xuan, Q. Li, 2003, Investigation on Convective Heat Transfer and Flow Features of Nanofluids, J. Heat Transfer 125(1), 151-155.

Anton A. Kiss, Edwin Zondervan, Richard Lakerveld, Leyla Özkan (Eds.)
Proceedings of the 29th European Symposium on Computer Aided Process Engineering
June 16th to 19th, 2019, Eindhoven, The Netherlands. © 2019 Elsevier B.V. All rights reserved.
http://dx.doi.org/10.1016/B978-0-128-18634-3.50102-8

Nanoparticle behaviour in multiphase turbulent channel flow

B.H. Mahmoud[a]*, L.F. Mortimer[a], M. Fairweather[a], H.P. Rice[a], J. Peakall[b], D. Harbottle[a]

[a]School of Chemical and Process Engineering, and [b]School of Earth and Environment, University of Leeds, Leeds LS2 9JT, UK

*bgy9bm@leeds.ac.uk

Abstract

The behaviour of dispersed nanoparticles within a turbulent wall-bounded flow is investigated, with the fluid phase properties chosen to represent a thermofluid flow typical of those present in solar thermal power plants. The continuous phase is modelled using direct numerical simulation with the open source spectral element-based solver, Nek5000, with predictions of a statistically steady turbulent channel flow at shear Reynolds number $Re_\tau = 180$ first obtained and validated. A Lagrangian particle tracking routine is subsequently implemented to simulate the dispersed phase, and is capable of accommodating one-, two- and four-way coupling between the fluid and discrete phases. In order to investigate the effect that the turbulence field has on the dispersion properties of the solid nano-particulate phase, mean fluid and particle velocities, and turbulence statistics, are obtained and presented. Particle mean velocities are observed to lag behind the fluid flow in the outer layer for all coupling methods. Particle streamwise velocity fluctuations are lower than those of the fluid in the bulk region of the flow, but are greater than the latter in the buffer layer, with the addition of particle agglomeration augmenting this effect. Particle concentrations in the near-wall region are observed to increase over time due to turbophoresis.

Keywords: Direct numerical simulation, Lagrangian particle tracking, nanofluids, agglomeration, turbophoresis

1. Introduction

Particle-laden fluids have gained a lot of attention in recent years because of their existing and potential industrial applications. Of particular interest are nanofluids, which are dilute fluid suspensions of nanoparticles (1-100 nm) at relatively low concentrations (0.05-2.0% volume fraction) (Choi, 1995). They are prepared by dispersing nanoparticles with significantly higher thermal conductivity values (i.e. 10-430 $Wm^{-1}K^{-1}$ for pure elements) in conventional thermofluids with modest thermal conductivity (i.e. 0.1-0.6 $Wm^{-1}K^{-1}$ at 25°C) such as water, oil, molten salt or ethylene glycol. Unlike conventional fluids, the significant enhancement of thermal properties when solid nanoparticles are added presents new application opportunities, particularly in the energy sector. In this sector, the efficiency of heat removal and thermal management systems presents the greatest technological challenge. Hence, the heat transfer potential of nanofluids is now gaining interest by researchers and developers in the academic and industrial communities due to their advantageous thermal properties.

On the other hand, understanding transport phenomena such as the dispersion behaviour of particles in nanofluid flows is challenging, particularly in experimental studies where obvious difficulties occur. Hence, apart from constraints due to the size of nanoparticles and potentially difficult conditions (e.g. high temperatures), many other complications arise from the various forces acting on the particles at various magnitudes and time scales. In addition, there is currently a lack of a reliable theory capable of making accurate predictions of the flow and heat transfer behaviour of nanofluids (with relatively low solid volume fractions). A numerical approach is therefore proposed to investigate dispersion behaviour. More specifically, the work described develops a multi-scale computational model using Lagrangian particle tracking coupled with direct numerical simulation (DNS) to investigate the influence of dispersed nanoparticles on the surrounding carrier fluid, and the effect of the turbulence field on the dispersion and aggregation properties of the solid nano-particulate phase. The advantage of the model developed is its ability to study in detail phenomena such as interparticle collisions, turbophoresis and thermophoresis, with the approach also of value in investigations of the long-term stability of nanoparticle dispersions which as yet has not been considered in detail. It is also possible that the agglomeration of nanoparticles to form larger particles could lead to their deposition, surface impact and erosion, although evidence of this in the literature is contradictory (Buongiorno, 2009), with very few existing quantitative studies.

2. Computational Setup and Model Description

The simulations were performed using a numerical multi-scale model with the continuous phase predicted using the open source spectral element-based DNS code, Nek5000 (Fischer et al, 2008). This code was chosen based on its extensive testing, efficient parallelization capabilities and validation history. Within the code, the incompressible Navier-Stokes equations (mass and momentum conservation) are solved to high accuracy, with the code applied to a Cartesian grid consisting of $27 \times 18 \times 23$ 8th order elements (i.e. 5.7 M nodes) used to represent a turbulent channel flow at shear Reynolds number $Re_\tau = 180$. The elements were scaled such that those closest to the wall were distributed more densely. The geometry of the channel was $14\delta \times 2\delta \times 6\delta$, with $\delta = 0.1$ mm. For the purpose of this study, the computational coordinates (x, y, z) were used to represent the three-dimensional geometry of the channel, with x being the streamwise direction, y the wall-normal direction, and z the spanwise direction. Periodic boundary conditions were enforced in the streamwise and spanwise directions, while the wall-normal axis used no-slip conditions at $y = \pm\delta$. The flow was driven and maintained by a constant pressure gradient.

The dispersed phase was represented by 500k 100 nm diameter Al_2O_3 particles which were tracked through the fluid field. These were simulated using a Lagrangian particle tracking routine, which was developed for this work and implemented to interface concurrently with Nek5000. The motion of each nanoparticle is described using the Langevin equation (Sloan et al, 2012), where the translational velocity of the i-th particle is obtained from the principle of conservation of linear momentum. At each timestep, the force on each particle was calculated accounting for the particle contact force, the electric double layer repulsive force, the van der Waals attractive force, the fluid force and the random Brownian motion force. Other body forces such as gravity and buoyancy were found to be negligible for all length and time scales since their magnitudes are much smaller than the aforementioned surface forces. Further details can be found elsewhere (Mahmoud et al, 2018).

The model described was used to simulate the dynamics and mechanisms responsible for nanoparticle dispersion and aggregation using different levels of coupling. Consideration of solely fluid forces acting upon the particulate phase is known as one-way coupling. Two-way coupling was achieved by implementing the point-source-in-cell method whereby particle forces are fed back to the local fluid cells. Particle collisions (four-way coupling) were resolved using the soft sphere approach, as described by Hertzian normal contact theory (Timoshenko and Goodier, 1970). Finally, four-way coupled predictions were extended to include DLVO interparticle van der Waals attractive and electric double layer repulsive forces to allow the prediction of particle-particle agglomeration events (see Mahmoud et al, 2018). Chemical and mechanical properties were chosen to match Al_2O_3 in water, with the parameters used in the simulations provided in Table 1.

Table 1. Parameters used in the simulations.

Parameter	Carrier phase (water)	Particle phase (Al_2O_3)
Shear Reynolds number, Re_τ	180	-
Bulk Reynolds number, Re_B	2800	-
Particle diameter, d_p / nm	-	100
Number of particles, N_p	-	500,000
Volume, V / m^3	1.58×10^{-10}	4.07×10^{-13}
Volume fraction, Φ / vol %	-	0.26
Temperature, T / °C	25	25
Bulk velocity, U_B / m s^{-1}	25.67	25.68
Density, ρ / kg m^{-3}	997.1	3850
Viscosity, η_F / m^2 s^{-1}	0.917×10^{-6}	-

The simulations were first run as an unladen single-phase flow using a standard initial turbulence profile with added chaotic terms in the wall-normal and spanwise directions. Once turbulence was established, fluid statistics were monitored every 1.95 ns until the mean and fluctuating velocities reached a statistically steady state. Particles were then injected uniformly throughout the channel and given an initial velocity equal to that of the local fluid. Particle statistics in the wall-normal direction were obtained by splitting the domain into 120 equal volume cuboidal regions, and by averaging over all particles within each region. The statistics presented below represent those at a state where the near-wall particle concentration was approximately stationary with respect to time. From this steady state condition, two-way coupled runs were started, reducing the fluid and particle time step initially to avoid divergences in the flow field due to the impact of particle forces. Fluid and particle statistics were then recorded to determine when the system had finished responding to the addition of momentum-coupling. Once satisfied, statistics were determined as noted. This approach was repeated to obtain four-way coupled simulations, and results for four-way coupling plus particle agglomeration.

3. Results and Discussion

The results of each simulation were analysed to elucidate the behaviour of the fluid and the nanoparticles within the channel flow. The predictions demonstrated how particle concentrations increased with time in the near-wall regions due to turbophoresis, as illustrated in Fig 1. Preferential concentration of particles within low-speed streaks close to the walls was also noted.

Figures 2 and 3 compare the fluid streamwise mean velocity profile, and normal and shear stress profiles, for the single phase flow with those obtained by Moser et al. (1999) who also used DNS, with excellent agreement obtained.

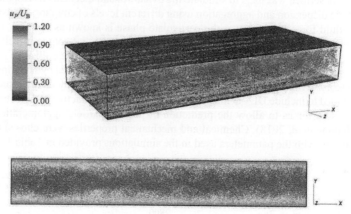

Figure 1. Particle distribution within $Re_\tau = 180$ channel flow, colours indicate particle to bulk velocity ratio, u_p/U_B (top); and snapshot of streamwise particle velocity on vertical plane (bottom).

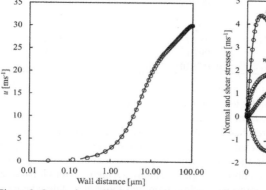

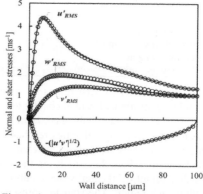

Figure 2. Comparison of fluid streamwise mean velocity profiles (— present, ○ Moser et al, 1999).

Figure 3. Comparison of fluid normal and shear stress profiles (— present, ○ Moser et al, 1999).

Figure 4 compares the particulate phase streamwise mean velocity against that of the unladen flow for each coupling mechanism considered. It is observed that for all the coupled cases, the particles lag slightly behind the unladen fluid flow between the turbulent region and the channel centre. This indicates that the coupling and interaction mechanisms all have a slight effect on the mean streamwise motion of the particles, albeit of the same order. However, Fig. 5 shows the root-mean-square of the velocity fluctuations, a measure of turbulence intensity, in each coordinate direction. In this case it is clear that for two-way and four-way coupling, the particulate phase exhibits similar velocity fluctuations in all three directions. More specifically, reduced turbulence fluctuations are observed compared to the single phase in the spanwise and wall normal directions, whilst the streamwise normal stress is greater in the turbulent region of the flow, but lower close to the channel centre. On introduction of the DLVO attractive and repulsive forces, a further slight increase in the streamwise normal stress is observed which is most significant in the turbulent region. This is likely due to the aggregation of particles in this region which leads to increased particle inertia due to their larger size, with such particles exhibiting greater decoupling from the local fluid velocities.

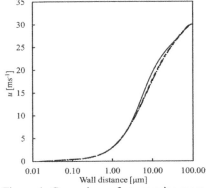

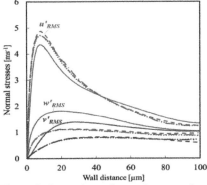

Figure 4. Comparison of streamwise mean velocity profiles (— unladen flow, — · — particles (two-way), · · · particles (four-way), — — particles (four-way + agglomeration).

Figure 5. Comparison of normal stresses (— unladen flow, — · — particles (two-way), · · · particles (four-way), — — particles (four-way + agglomeration).

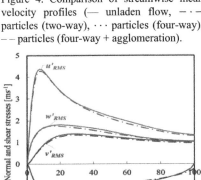

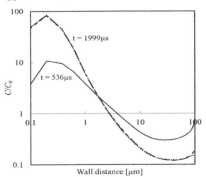

Figure 6. Fluid normal and shear stress profiles (— unladen flow, — · — two-way).

Figure 7. Particle concentration at 536 µs (— four-way + agglomeration), and 1999 µs (— · — two-way, · · · four-way, — — four-way + agglomeration).

Figure 6 considers the effect of two-way coupling on the fluid normal and shear stresses in order to determine how the particles modify the turbulence properties of the flow. The results demonstrate that two-way coupling has only a small influence on these statistics. Specifically, all three components of the normal stress and the Reynolds shear stress are attenuated, indicating that the presence of nanoparticles at the concentration considered reduces slightly the magnitude of turbulence in the flow. Since the effect is strongest in those regions which show greatest deviation between particle stresses and those of the unladen flow, this is likely due to greater slip velocities in those regions, meaning that the particles work to dampen the energy in the local turbulent eddies.

Finally, Fig. 7 compares the particle concentration distribution relative to the initial concentration, C_0, for each simulation. It is clear from the results that over the course of the simulations turbophoresis takes place, with a similar final behaviour observed for all cases considered. Over time this leads to a build-up of nano-particulate concentrations close to the walls. This has consequences for the agglomeration rate since the local concentration in these regions is nearly 100 times greater than the initial concentration once the system has reached a steady state. This also implies that, with time, particle deposition rates will likely increase due to the migration towards the walls. Interestingly, and despite the slight differences in particle velocity fluctuations for the different coupling mechanisms, there is very little difference in the eventual concentration distributions. This implies that the agglomerate structures do not, over the time studied, show preferential concentration in different regions of the channel when compared to the other particle flows considered.

4. Conclusions

The dispersion properties of a nanoparticle-laden channel flow have been studied using various coupling mechanisms between the particles and the fluid flow. The particles are found to be slightly decoupled from the fluid flow in that they lag behind the mean flow beyond the turbulent region for all coupling regimes. Velocity fluctuations indicate that the particles exhibit increased normal stresses in the streamwise direction in the turbulent region, but reduced values in the other coordinate directions. Interestingly, the inclusion of particle agglomeration increases the magnitude of this effect in the streamwise direction. Two-way coupling is shown to lead to a slight dampening effect on the flow turbulence. Concentration plots also indicate a time varying particle distribution, with a noticeable increase in particle concentration in the near-wall regions over the run times considered that is insensitive to the mode of coupling. Future work will further consider relating the effects observed to the rate of particle collision and agglomeration within the channel in order to better understand the dynamics which lead to the particle behaviour observed, and to allow conclusions to be reached regarding the implications for thermal energy storage systems using nanofluids.

Acknowledgements

BHM is grateful for the financial support of the Kuwait Institute for Scientific Research.

References

J. Buongiorno, L. Hu, 2009, Nanofluid Heat Transfer Enhancement for Nuclear Reactor Applications, Proc. ASME. 43918; Second International Conference on Micro/Nanoscale Heat and Mass Transfer, 3, 517-522.

S.U.S. Choi, 1995, Enhancing Thermal Conductivity of Fluids with Nanoparticles, in Developments and Applications of Non-Newtonian Flows, D.A. Siginer, H.P. Wang (Eds.), FED-V.231/MD-V.66, 99-105, ASME, New York.

P.F Fischer, J.W. Lottes, S.G. Kerkemeier, 2008, Nek5000 web page http://nek5000.mcs.anl.gov.

B.H. Mahmoud, M. Fairweather, L.F. Mortimer, J. Peakall, H.P. Rice, D. Harbottle, 2018, Prediction of Stability and Thermal Conductivity of Nanofluids for Thermal Energy Storage Applications, Computer-Aided Chemical Engineering, 43, 61-66.

R.D. Moser, J. Kim, N.N. Mansour, 1999, Direct Numerical Simulation of Turbulent Channel Flow up to Re_τ= 590, Phys. Fluids, 11, 943-945.

G. Sloan, Z.-G. Feng, K. Bhaganagar, D. Banerjee, 2012, Coupled Direct Numerical Simulation and Experimental Approach to Develop Framework for Nano Fluids, ASME International Mechanical Engineering Congress and Exposition, 7, 2877-2882.

S.P. Timoshenko, J.N. Goodier, 1970, Theory of Elasticity, McGraw-Hill, New York.

Anton A. Kiss, Edwin Zondervan, Richard Lakerveld, Leyla Özkan (Eds.)
Proceedings of the 29th European Symposium on Computer Aided Process Engineering
June 16th to 19th, 2019, Eindhoven, The Netherlands. © 2019 Elsevier B.V. All rights reserved.
http://dx.doi.org/10.1016/B978-0-128-18634-3.50103-X

Multi-objective optimisation of chemical processes via improved genetic algorithms: A novel trade-off and termination criterion

Viviane De Buck[a], Carlos André Muñoz López[a], Philippe Nimmegeers[a], Ihab Hashem[a] and Jan Van Impe[a,*]

[a]KU Leuven, Department of Chemical Engineering, BioTeC+ & OPTEC, Ghent, Belgium
*jan.vanimpe@kuleuven.be

Abstract

A sustainable chemical process operation often requires optimality with respect to multiple conflicting objectives as economic, societal and environmental aspects need to be addressed. Multi-objective optimisation aims at solving such problems. A single optimal solution for all objectives does not exist as one cannot improve with respect to one objective without worsening with respect to one of the other objectives. The result of a multi-objective optimisation algorithm is hence a Pareto set comprising equally optimal trade-off solutions. In this contribution an improved version of NSGA-II, one of the current state-of-the-art algorithms in evolutionary multi-objective optimisation, is presented and applied to the optimisation of an industrially relevant case. The proposed novel algorithm overcomes, amongst others, one of the major shortcomings of the currently used evolutionary multi-objective optimisation algorithms: the inability to distinguish between solutions based on their trade-off and distribution. This results in a Pareto front cluttered with irrelevant solutions. The performance of the improved algorithm has been evaluated for the multi-objective optimisation of a methane tri-reforming process for methanol production. Three objectives have been studied: (*i*) minimisation of the total energy demand, (*ii*) maximisation of the carbon efficiency and (*iii*) an economic profit function. For this INPROP, the recently developed interface between Matlab and Aspen Plus for multi-objective optimisation of chemical processes, is extended to perform multi-objective optimisation using the proposed method. Up till now, INPROP only exploited scalarisation-based multi-objective optimisation methods. Scalarisation methods convert the multi-objective optimisation problem (MOOP) in a sequence of single objective optimisation problems, which are solved separately using deterministic gradient-based methods. Evolutionary algorithms, like NSGA-II, are vector-based and tackle the MOOP in its entirety. The results obtained with the improved evolutionary algorithm are compared with earlier presented scalarisation-based multi-objective process optimisation results.

Keywords: Multi-objective optimisation, NSGA-II, Evolutionary algorithms, Trade-off, PIT-region, t-domination

1. Introduction

To maintain a competitive position in the current worldwide market, companies need to operate their processes as optimally as possible with respect to different, often conflicting, objectives (e.g. societal, environmental, and economical aspects). In such case, no one optimal solution exists, and decision makers need to resort to Pareto-optimal solutions. These optimisation problems are called multi-objective optimisation problems (MOOPs) and the solutions of such problems are a Pareto front, comprising all equally optimal trade-off solutions. The decision maker (DM) will choose one optimal solution from the Pareto front as the operating point. Computing (an approximation of) this Pareto front is the main goal when solving a MOOP. It is desirable to produce a diverse Pareto set in a minimal computing time. MOOPs are mathematically challenging problems and are generally solved via the use of dedicated algorithms. The two major algorithm categories are scalarisation methods and vectorisation methods. Since this contribution focuses on vectorisation methods, scalarisation methods will not be further discussed. The interested reader is referred to Das and Dennis (1997, 1998); Messac et al. (2003); Logist et al. (2010) for more information on this type of optimisation methods.

Vectorisation methods use stochastic algorithms to solve a MOOP and tackle the optimisation problem in its entirety (Deb et al., 2002). A sub-field of the stochastic algorithms are the evolutionary algorithms (EA), which are based on Darwin's evolution theory. EAs can generate multiple Pareto-optimal solutions in a single run, making them an excellent choice to solve MOOPs, especially if the decision maker is interested in a diverse set of solutions. Additionally, EAs have no need for derivative information which makes them suitable for black box optimisation. The considered evolutionary algorithm in this article is Non-dominated Sorting Genetic Algorithm-II (NSGA-II) (Deb et al., 2002). NSGA-II is an elitist evolutionary algorithm, equipped with a fast non-dominated sorting algorithm and a crowding distance parameter to obtain a diverse solution set.

The overall goal of this contribution is (*i*) to present a novel EA that overcomes the shortcomings of the NSGA-II algorithm, (*ii*) demonstrate its performance in the `INPROP` interface between `Matlab` and `Aspen Plus` and (*iii*) apply for the tri-objective optimisation of a methane tri-reforming process.

2. Multi-objective optimisation problems

2.1. Mathematical description of a MOOP

The following MOOP formulation is used throughout this article (Das and Dennis, 1997):

$$\min_{(\mathbf{u}) \in C} \mathbf{F}(\mathbf{x}, \mathbf{u}) = \{J_1(\mathbf{x}, \mathbf{u}) \dots J_M(\mathbf{x}, \mathbf{u})\} \tag{1}$$

with $\mathbf{u} \in \mathbb{R}^{n_u}$ the controls of the considered process, $\mathbf{x} \in \mathbb{R}^{n_x}$ the variables, $J_i(\mathbf{x}, \mathbf{u})$ the i-th objective function ($i \in \{1 \dots M\}$), and with C the constraint solution space:

$$C = \{(\mathbf{x}, \mathbf{u}) : \mathbf{h}(\mathbf{x}, \mathbf{u}) = 0; \mathbf{g}(\mathbf{x}, \mathbf{u}) \leq 0; \mathbf{a} \leq \mathbf{u} \leq \mathbf{b}\} \tag{2}$$

$$y = [\mathbf{u}^T, \mathbf{x}^T]^T \tag{3}$$

With $\mathbf{h}(\mathbf{x}, \mathbf{u}) : \mathbb{R}^{n_u + n_x} \mapsto \mathbb{R}^{ne}$ the *ne* equality constraints, $\mathbf{g}(\mathbf{x}, \mathbf{u}) : \mathbb{R}^{n_u + n_x} \mapsto \mathbb{R}^{ni}$ the *ni* inequality constraints and $\mathbf{a} \in \mathbb{R}^{n_u}$ and $\mathbf{b} \in \mathbb{R}^{n_u}$ the respectively lower and upper boundaries for the controls. A solution $\mathbf{y}^*$ of the MOOP is Pareto-optimal or non-dominated if there exists no other solution $\mathbf{y}$ for which $\mathbf{F}(\mathbf{y}) \leq \mathbf{F}(\mathbf{y}^*)$ and $\exists k : J_k(\mathbf{y}) < J_k(\mathbf{y}^*)$ with $k \in \{1 \dots M\}$ (Das and Dennis, 1997; Munoz Lopez et al., 2018).

2.2. Non-dominated sorting genetic algorithm II (NSGA-II)

NSGA-II is an evolutionary algorithm developed as an answer to the shortcomings of early evolutionary algorithms, which lacked elitism and used a sharing parameter in order to sustain a diverse Pareto set. NSGA-II uses a fast non-dominated sorting algorithm, sharing, elitism, and crowded comparison. Elitism implies that the best solutions of the previous iteration are kept unchanged in the current one. This significantly increases the convergence speed of the algorithm. Additionally, its use of a fast non-dominated sorting algorithm contributes to a significant reduction of its computational complexity. For more details, the interested reader is referred to Deb et al. (2002).

3. The tDOM-algorithm

Despite its significant improvement in comparison to its evolutionary predecessors, NSGA-II has two major shortcomings: (*i*) its inability to distinguish between solutions based on their trade-off, and (*ii*) its use of an arbitrary and problem-irrelevant stopping criterion. The presented novel tDOM-algorithm is based on the general framework of NSGA-II and is developed to remedy these shortcomings. To achieve this, the tDOM-algorithm employs t-domination instead of non-domination, via the introduction of a trade-off function and PIT-regions. This enables the tDOM-algorithm to distinguish between solutions based on their trade-off. Additionally, this allowed for the introduction of a non-arbitrary stopping criterion.

3.1. Preliminaries

PIT-region: Regions of practical insignificant trade-off (PIT-regions) are spatial structures which are constructed around the solutions in the objective space. The dimensions of the PIT-region are defined by a minimal trade-off Δt and distribution Δr. If two solutions are located in each others' PIT-region, both solutions are considered insignificantly different from one another by the DM and therefore one of these solutions can be filtered out of the population set (Mattson et al., 2004).

t-Domination: A solution $\mathbf{p}$ t-dominates solution $\mathbf{q}$ if $\mathbf{F}(\mathbf{p}) \leq \mathbf{F}(\mathbf{q})$, $\exists\, k : J_k(\mathbf{p}) < J_k(\mathbf{q})$, and $\mathbf{p} \notin PIT(\mathbf{q})$.

Trade-off function: The trade-off function determines the crowdedness of the PIT-regions of the obtained solutions. During the selection step, solutions are additionally sorted in ascending order according to crowdedness of their PIT-region, thus more emphasis is set on high trade-off solutions. Concurrently, the trade-off function establishes whether all the solutions of two subsequent generations are located within each others' PIT-regions. If this is the case, the `stop` Boolean is set to `true`, and the algorithm stops.

3.2. Algorithm description

The tDOM-algorithm uses the NSGA-II framework, but it is equipped with the multifunctional trade-off function that determines the trade-off between solutions and the algorithm's stopping criterion. Hashem et al. (2017) presented the idea of using the trade-off of solutions as a stopping criterion. In their divide and conquer scheme for deterministic algorithms, the exploration of a certain area of the Pareto front is ceased if the generated solutions no longer display the required trade-off or distribution. This idea is adapted for evolutionary algorithms via the PIT-regions in the tDOM-algorithm.

During the first iteration, N initial random solutions are generated in the parent set P_0, which is used to generate a first offspring set Q_1 ($|Q_1| = N$). Offspring solutions are obtained via crossovers and mutations of the parent solutions. At the t-th generation of the tDOM-algorithm, after offspring solutions are generated, the parent set P_{t-1} and offspring set Q_t are merged into a combined solution set R_t ($|R_t| = 2N$), enabling elitism. Subsequently, the solutions of R_t are sorted into their non-dominated front, and their crowding distance and trade-off are determined. Additionally, the stopping parameter `stop` is determined via the trade-off function. Based on the rank of their non-dominated front, their crowding distance, and their trade-off, only the best N solutions of R_t are retained. These solutions form the parent set P_t of the $(t+1)$-th iteration. The tDOM-algorithm is interrupted when the stopping parameter `stop` is set to `true` during the trade-off function.

4. Results and discussion

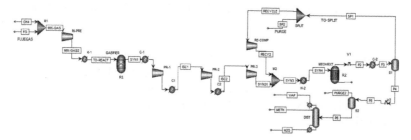

Figure 1: Methanol production via methane tri-reforming (Munoz Lopez et al., 2018).

A methane tri-reforming process converts flue gasses and a methane stream into methanol and water. This process was modelled by Munoz Lopez et al. (2018) in `Aspen Plus` (see Figure 1). To optimise this process the tDOM-algorithm is implemented in `Matlab 2018a`. The interface between the process simulator `Aspen Plus` and `Matlab` is referred to as INterface for PRocess OPtimisation (`INPROP`) (Munoz Lopez et al., 2018). During the optimisation, the controls **u** and variables **x** are transferred from `Aspen Plus` to `Matlab`. The controls **u** are subsequently optimised using the tDOM-algorithm and are send back to `Aspen Plus`, where the corresponding variables **x** are determined and send back to `Matlab`, continuing the optimisation procedure. This process repeats itself until the stopping criterion is satisfied. Three objectives were optimised, subject to a minimal required methanol purity of 98 % and a maximum methanol fraction of 85 % in the water stream (Munoz Lopez et al., 2018):

$$J_1(\mathbf{x},\mathbf{u}) = -\frac{[MEOH]_{METH}}{([CH_4]+[CO_2]_{FG})} \; [-] \quad (4) \qquad J_2(\mathbf{x},\mathbf{u}) = \frac{(|\dot{W}|+|\dot{Q}|)}{([MEOH]_{METH}/3600)} \left[\frac{MJ}{kmol}\right] \quad (5)$$

$$J_3(\mathbf{x},\mathbf{u}) = -\left(a_1[MEOH]_{METH} - (a_2[CH_4]+3600 \times a_3\,(|\dot{Q}|+|\dot{W}|)) - \frac{ann.cc}{8000}\right) \; [€/h] \quad (6)$$

subject to

$$0 < p_{S1} - p_{S2} \le 70 \qquad (7) \qquad 0 < p_{S2} - p_{DIST} \le 25 \qquad (8)$$
$$p_{PR-3} - p_{R2} = 0 \qquad (9) \qquad 0.98 - [MEOH]_{METH} \le 0 \qquad (10)$$
$$[MEOH]_{H2O} - 0.85 \le 0 \qquad (11)$$

Objective J_1 is the carbon efficiency of the process, with $[MEOH]_{METH}$ the methanol stream [kmol/h], $[CH_4]$ the methane stream [kmol/h], and $[CO_2]_{FG}$ the carbon dioxide in the flue gas stream [kmol/h]. Objective J_2 is the total energy demand required for the production of 1 kmol $MEOH$, with $|\dot{W}|$ the total amount of work [MW], and $|\dot{Q}|$ the total amount of thermal energy [MW]. Objective J_3 is the profit-cost balance with a_1 the unit price of $MEOH$, a_2 the unit price of CH_4, and a_3 the unit price of electricity. The obtained results and Pareto fronts are represented in Table 1 and Figure 2 respectively. For more information on the controls, the interested reader is referred to Munoz Lopez et al. (2018).

Table 1: Lower (**a**) and upper (**b**) boundaries of the controls **u**, anchor points of the Pareto front, and the original problem (adapted from Munoz Lopez et al. (2018)).

Results		a	b	Carbon effic. maximised	Total energy demand minimised	Profit maximised	Original process	Units
Controls	$[CH_4]$	200.00	800.00	345.93	378.80	366.23	400.00	kmol/h
	p_{R1}	1.05	5.00	1.00	3.74	2.44	1.00	MPa
	T_{R1}	400	980	980	943	974	850	K
	p_{R2}	50	300	300	174	52	50	MPa
	T_{R2}	200	300	200	200	204	220	K
	p_{S1}	25.00	40.00	40.00	31.80	39.40	24.00	MPa
	T_{S1}	25.00	50.00	25.00	31.62	26.00	25.00	K
	$[SP2]/[SP1]$	0.05	0.30	0.05	0.30	0.06	0.05	-
	p_{S2}	20.00	30.00	9.12	9.00	13.00	10	MPa
	p_{DIST}	9.00	20.00	9.00	9.00	13.00	10.00	MPa
	RR_{DIST}	1.5	3.0	3	1.5	1.5	1.5	-
	D/F_{DIST}	0.950	0.988	0.988	0.988	0.980	0.988	-
Objective	J_1	-	-	-0.9546	-0.8432	-0.8442	-0.7584	-
	J_2	-	-	1567.0	994.9	1189.5	1538.8	MJ/kmol
	J_3	-	-	-1078.0	-4244.0	-4407.5	-2537.2	€/h

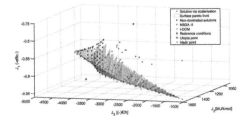

Figure 2: Pareto fronts generated via tDOM-algorithm, NSGA-II, and scalarisation method.

For all the objectives, Δt was defined as 10% and Δr as 15%. Note that in practical applications Δt and Δr can have different values for each objective. The values of Δt_i and Δr_i quantify the importance attached to the i-th objective. Visual analysis of the results displayed in Figure 2 raises two main observations. First, the results obtained via the scalarisation method (blue dots) and the surface interpolated from them seem to offer a well-defined approximation of the Pareto front for this MOOP. However, numerous solutions generated via the scalarisation method are non-Pareto-optimal, and therefore could be misleading for the DM. Logist et al. (2010) confirms this observation by stating that scalarisation methods can be prone to generate non-Pareto-optimal solutions, in contrast to EAs and the proposed tDOM-algorithm. Secondly, if the results generated by the tDOM-algorithm are compared with the results generated with the original NSGA-II algorithm, the tDOM-algorithm outperforms the NSGA-II algorithm. When the same conditions in terms of population size and number of generations were kept for both algorithms, the proposed algorithm converges to the actual Pareto front while the solutions from NSGA-II remain far from it. The normalised average distance to the Utopia point (i.e., all the individual objective minimisers) of the tDOM-solutions is 0.6914, while that of the NSGA-II solutions amounts to 1.0447, placing it significantly closer to the Nadir point (i.e., all the individual objective maximisers). This proves that the proposed tDOM-algorithm overcomes the limitations of the NSGA-II algorithm and produces a more informative Pareto front that is not affected with the presence of non-optimal solutions.

Finally, regarding the numerical results as presented in Table 1, the original process is non-optimal. All the generated solutions result in lower integral costs than those of the reference conditions. For instance, the most carbon efficient solution results in a gain of 20.55%. Strikingly, the energy consumption of this solution is only 1.80% higher than the original process. Despite this, a 57.51% loss in profit is displayed, compared to the original process, making the process economically infeasible. Again, note that the density of tDOM-solutions in this Pareto front area is sparser than in the more economically interesting knee of the Pareto front.

5. Conclusions

A sustainable process requires optimality with respect to multiple, often conflicting, objectives. In such cases, no single optimal solution exists, but instead multiple trade-off solutions. Determining the most optimal solutions is achieved via a multi-objective optimisation problem (MOOP). NSGA-II is a widely applied optimisation algorithm, used to solve MOOPs. However, it is unable to distinguish between solutions based on their trade-off, and it uses an arbitrary stopping criterion. To overcome these shortcomings, the tDOM-algorithm is presented. Via the introduction of regions of practically insignificant trade-off (PIT), solutions with a high trade-off are emphasised. Additionally, by applying the concept of t-domination, the tDOM-algorithm is equipped with a problem-relevant stopping criterion. The advantages of the tDOM-algorithm were demonstrated for the MOO of the methane tri-reforming process. Using the `INPROP` interface it was found that tDOM-algorithm is able of producing a diverse set of relevant Pareto-optimal solutions. This in strong contrast to solutions produced by NSGA-II, which do no converge to the Pareto front, and the solution set generated via a scalarisation method, which is populated with non-Pareto-optimal solutions.

Acknowledgements
This work was supported by KU Leuven Research Fund [PFV/10/002] Center-of-Excellence Optimization in Engineering (OPTEC). CAM holds a VLAIO-Baekeland [HBC.2017.0239] grant. IH is supported by FWO-SB grant 1S54217N.

References

Das, I., Dennis, J., 1997. A closer look at drawbacks of minimizing weighted sums of objectives for pareto set generation in multi-criteria optimization problems. Structural Optimization 14.

Das, I., Dennis, J., 1998. Normal-boundary intersection: A new method for generating the pareto surface in nonlinear multicriteria optimization problems. SIAM Journal on Optimization 8.

Deb, K., Pratap, A., Agarwal, S., Meyarivan, T., 2002. A fast and elitist multiobjective genetic algorithm: NSGA-II. Evolutionary Computation, IEEE Transactions on 6(2), 182–197.

Hashem, I., Telen, D., Nimmegeers, P., Logist, F., Van Impe, J., 2017. A novel algorithm for fast representation of a pareto front with adaptive resolution: Application to multi-objective optimisation of a chemical reactor. Computers and Chemical Engineering 106.

Logist, F., Houska, B., Diehl, M., Van Impe, J., 2010. Fast pareto set generation for nonlinear optimal control problems with multiple objectives. Structural and Multidisciplinary Optimization 42, 591–603.

Mattson, C., Mullur, A., Messac, A., 2004. Smart pareto filter: obtaining a minimal representation of multiobjective design space. Engineering Optimization 36(6), 721–740.

Messac, A., Ismail-Yahaya, A., Mattson, C., 2003. The normalized normal constraint method for generating the pareto frontier. Structural and Multidisciplinary Optimization 25.

Munoz Lopez, C., Telen, D., Nimmegeers, P., Cabianca, L., Logist, F., Van Impe, J., 2018. A process simulator interface for multiobjective optimization of chemical processes. Computers and Chemical Engineering 109, 119–137.

Anton A. Kiss, Edwin Zondervan, Richard Lakerveld, Leyla Özkan (Eds.)
Proceedings of the 29th European Symposium on Computer Aided Process Engineering
June 16th to 19th, 2019, Eindhoven, The Netherlands. © 2019 Elsevier B.V. All rights reserved.
http://dx.doi.org/10.1016/B978-0-128-18634-3.50104-1

DyOS - A Framework for Optimization of Large-Scale Differential Algebraic Equation Systems

A. Caspari[a], A. M. Bremen[a], J. M. M. Faust[a], F. Jung[a], C. D. Kappatou[a], S. Sass[a], Y. Vaupel[a], R. Hannemann-Tamás[a], A. Mhamdi[a] and A. Mitsos[a, b, c, *]

[a]*AVT Process Systems Engineering, RWTH Aachen University, 52056 Aachen, Germany*
[b]*JARA-CSD, RWTH Aachen University, 52056 Aachen, Germany*
[c]*IEK-10, Forschungszentrum Jülich, 52425 Jülich, Germany*
amitsos@alum.mit.edu

Abstract

Dynamic optimization problems arise in many fields of engineering. Typically, they are subject to models of differential-algebraic equations and further process constraints. To promote and investigate the application of methods based on dynamic optimization, an efficient and modular implementation of numerical algorithms for their solution is essential. We present the current status of the open-source software DyOS for the solution of large-scale dynamic optimization problems. DyOS has been applied to optimal operation, model-predictive control and process design problems in various case studies. DyOS is based on direct adaptive shooting algorithms and it allows for multi-stage problem formulations including binary decision making. Models can either be imported as standardized functional mock-up units, flat Modelica models, or C++ models. The modular implementation of DyOS enables the use of various open-source and commercial integrators and nonlinear programming solvers based on various numerical methods. DyOS can be accessed via Matlab or Python interfaces. As an illustrative large-scale application, we present the results of optimal operation of an air separation process under fluctuating electricity prices. An open-source version of DyOS including several parts of the framework presented is available at http://permalink.avt.rwth-aachen.de/?id=295232.

Keywords: dynamic optimization, direct adaptive shooting, open-source framework

1. Introduction

The solution of optimization problems constrained by differential algebraic equation systems (DAEs) is a common challenge in many fields. Among others, dynamic optimization of DAEs is used in process control, operation, and design. The direct optimization methods full discretization (Cuthrell and Biegler, 1987), single shooting (Brusch and Schapelle, 1973; Sargent and Sullivan, 1978; Kraft, 1985), and multiple shooting (Bock and Plitt, 1984) make use of discretization to treat the DAEs. There are already several software frameworks, which implement these methods. A list can be found in Nicholson et al. (2017). Open source implementations include pyomo:dae (Nicholson et al., 2017), ACADO (Houska et al., 2010), Optimica and JModelica (Åkesson et al., 2010), and TACO (Kirches and Leyffer, 2013). We present the current status of the open-source framework DyOS (Dynamic Optimization Software) for dynamic optimization based on direct adaptive shooting methods, which is tailored to large-scale DAEs. DyOS integrates several software packages including different integration and optimization methods, different nonlinear and linear equation solvers, and a graph coloring algorithm into a large framework for the efficient solution of dynamic optimization problems. Using the standardized modeling language Modelica and the standard Functional Mockup Unit (FMU), it allows straightforward model provision and optimization problem set-up. The remainder of the manuscript is structured as follows. The methods used, the implementation and the problems solved in the past are summarized in Section 2. A large-scale case study is shown in Section 3, before the work is concluded in Section 4.

2. Methods and Implementation

The optimization framework DyOS solves a multi-stage mixed-integer dynamic optimization problem of the form

$$\min_{\mathbf{u},\mathbf{z},\mathbf{p}} \sum_{i}^{N} \Phi(\mathbf{x}(t_i^-)) \tag{1a}$$

$$\text{s.t. } \mathbf{M}\dot{\mathbf{x}}(t) = \mathbf{f}_i(\mathbf{x}(t),\mathbf{y}(t),\mathbf{u}(t),\mathbf{p},\mathbf{z}), \qquad \forall t \in \mathscr{T}_i,\ 0 \leq i < N \tag{1b}$$

$$\mathbf{0} = \mathbf{g}_i(\mathbf{x}(t),\mathbf{y}(t),\mathbf{u}(t),\mathbf{p},\mathbf{z}), \qquad \forall t \in \mathscr{T}_i,\ 0 \leq i < N \tag{1c}$$

$$\mathbf{0} = \mathbf{h}_i(\mathbf{x}(t_i^+),\mathbf{x}(t_i^-),\mathbf{y}(t_i^-),\mathbf{p},\mathbf{z}), \qquad 1 \leq i < N \tag{1d}$$

$$\mathbf{0} \geq \mathbf{c}_i(\mathbf{x}(t),\mathbf{y}(t),\mathbf{u}(t),\mathbf{p},\mathbf{z}), \qquad \forall t \in \mathscr{T}_i,\ 0 \leq i < N \tag{1e}$$

on a finite time horizon $\mathscr{T} = \bigcup_{i=1}^{N} \mathscr{T}_i$, where N is the number of stages and $\mathscr{T}_i = [t_i, t_{i+1}]$ are the time horizons of the stage i, $\mathbf{f}_i : \mathbb{X} \to \mathbb{R}^{n_x}$ and $\mathbf{g}_i : \mathbb{X} \to \mathbb{R}^{n_y}$ define the semi-explicit differential-algebraic system of index 1 with the invertible matrix $\mathbf{M} \in \mathbb{R}^{n_x \times n_x}$, while $\mathbf{h}_i : \mathbb{R}^{n_x} \times \mathbb{R}^{n_x} \times \mathbb{R}^{n_y} \times \mathbb{R}^{n_p} \times \mathbb{R}^{n_z} \to \mathbb{R}^{n_x}$ indicates the initial conditions and $\mathbf{c}_i : \mathbb{X} \to \mathbb{R}^{n_c}$ the constraints, with $\mathbb{X} := \mathbb{R}^{n_x} \times \mathbb{R}^{n_y} \times \mathbb{R}^{n_u} \times \mathbb{R}^{n_p} \times \mathbb{R}^{n_z}$ Problem (1) aims at finding optimal control trajectories $\mathbf{u} : \mathscr{T} \to \mathbb{R}^{n_u}$, differential and algebraic state trajectories $\mathbf{x} : \mathscr{T} \to \mathbb{R}^{n_x}$ and $\mathbf{y} : \mathscr{T} \to \mathbb{R}^{n_y}$, respectively, for parameter values $\mathbf{p} \in \mathbb{R}^{n_p}$ and integer variables $\mathbf{z} \in \mathbb{N}^{n_z}$, that minimize an objective in Mayer form $\Phi : \mathbb{R}^{n_x} \to \mathbb{R}$. The superscripts $+$ and $-$ denote the upper and lower one-sided limits of t_i. The algorithms in DyOS are based on adaptive direct single- and multiple-shooting (Schlegel et al., 2004; Assassa and Marquardt, 2014), where the control variable profile discretization is automati-

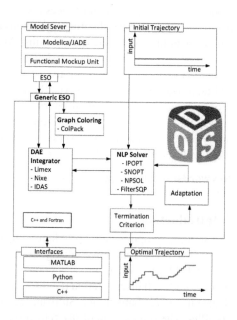

Figure 1: DyOS implementation structure.

cally adapted. Two types of grid adaptation methods can be selected: one based on the objective function improvement using wavelet analysis (Schlegel et al., 2004) and the other based on the necessary optimality conditions (Assassa and Marquardt, 2016). Grid adaptation allows the user to start the optimization using a coarse discretization grid and get a fine grid at the end of the optimization. Thus, grid adaptation can reduce the overall

CPU time by avoiding an abundant parameterization. This can be used to avoid over-parameterized solution, and the use of control structure detection can significantly reduce the granularity of the discretization without loosing information (Assassa and Marquardt, 2015). Using a branch-and-bound algorithm, DyOS can solve mixed-integer optimization problems (Oldenburg et al., 2003; Frankl et al., 2012). Moreover, a unique feature of DyOS are the special approaches to provide the Jacobian and the Hessian of the Lagrangian. The first- and second-order sensitivities can be provided by forward sensitivity integration and first-order adjoint equations. The Hessian can be provided using composite adjoints of the Lagrangian (Hannemann and Marquardt, 2007; Jorgensen, 2007). The modified discrete adjoint solver NIXE (Hannemann et al., 2010) serves as an integrator for the composite adjoint sensitivity system. The Jacobian of the models can be calculated in both forward and reverse mode, and the Hessian matrix can be calculated in reverse mode. A generic integrator interface implementation facilitates coupling of existing DAE integrator codes to DyOS. Wrappers for three different integrators are currently implemented: the semi-implicit extrapolation methods NIXE (Hannemann et al., 2010) and sLIMEX (Schlegel et al., 2004), as well as the backward differentiation formula IDAS (Serban et al., 2018). The architecture of DyOS is shown in Fig. 1. A generic optimizer interface enables coupling nonlinear programming codes to DyOS. Four different NLP solvers are currently available: SNOPT (Gill et al., 2005), NPSOL (Gill et al., 1986), IPOPT (Wächter and Biegler, 2005), and FilterSQP (Fletcher and Leyffer, 2002). A generic model interface is implemented, which allows to couple different models to DyOS. The model interface currently supports the functional mockup interface standard (FMI, 2014) and parsed Modelica models. In the latter case C++ code of the model residuals is generated and processed by the algorithmic differentiation tool dcc (Naumann, 2012) to generate first- and second-order derivatives. DyOS focuses on the solution of large-scale optimization problems by making use of adaptation strategies and the integration of efficient numerical software packages. Thus, several packages are used to support this purpose: the graph coloring package ColPack (Gebremedhin et al., 2013) for efficient Jacobian and Hessian calculation, nonlinear solver CMINPACK, as well as linear solvers KLU, SuperLu, and CSparse. Three front ends are implemented to access DyOS from C++, Matlab and Python. A minor limitation is the restriction to a constant matrix **M** and a system with a differential index of 1. However, every non-index-1 system can be reformulated to an index-1 system with constant matrix **M**, and, thus, this limitation is not severe. In the past, DyOS has been used for solving many challenging chemical engineering problems either as standalone solver, e.g., for dynamic optimization of batch recipes or as a subsolver embedded in an algorithm, e.g., in nonlinear model predictive control (NMPC) applications. Table 1 presents a non-exhaustive, yet exemplary, list of problems solved with DyOS which shows its wide range of applicability and its capability to handle large-scale DAE systems.

3. Dynamic Optimization of an Air Separation Process

Since air separation units (ASU) are electricity intensive processes, their flexible operation for demand-side management is economically promising due to the penetration of fluctuating renewable energy. In this section, an offline dynamic optimization of an ASU using DyOS is presented based on the work of Caspari et al. (2018). The flowsheet of the process is depicted in Fig. 4. Air is compressed from its ambient state at 1 bar to 10 bar and cooled down by a heat-exchanger and expansion in a turbine. It is separated into its components in a rectification column at a pressure of 6.6 bar comprising of an integrated

Table 1: Published contributions which make use of DyOS.

Reference	Problem Type	Problem Size
Caspari et al. (2018)	eNMPC	127 differential equations 2940 algebraic equations
Frankl et al. (2012)	Integrated Scheduling and Control	1500 equations 9 binary variables
Hartwich and Marquardt (2010)	DO	1752 differential equations 10779 algebraic equations
Kadam et al. (2007)	DO	200 differential equations 2500 algebraic equations
Oldenburg et al. (2003)	MIDO	330 DAEs 32 binary variables
Pontes et al. (2015)	DRTO	148 differential equations 2435 algebraic equations

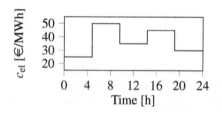 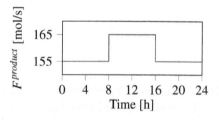

(a) Electricity price of the day ahead auction (Fraunhofer ISE, 2018).

(b) Assumed product demand rate.

Figure 2: Input parameters for the dynamic optimization.

reboiler and condenser. Nitrogen is withdrawn either from the storage tank or directly from the heat exchanger. The main energy consumers of the process are the feed air compressor and the nitrogen product liquefier. A nonlinear first-principle process model is used comprising of 127 differential and 2940 algebraic states and 5 input variables. The model is implemented in Modelica and connected via the Functional Mock-Up Interface. The economic objective function $L(t) = \int_{t_0}^{t_{end}} c_{el}(t)(P_{comp}(t) + P_{liq}(t) - P_{tur}(t))dt$ is minimized, where $P_{comp/liq/tur}$ is the power demand/supply of the compressor, liquefier, and turbine, respectively, and c_{el} is the fluctuating electricity price. t_0 and t_{end} are the initial and final time of the control horizon. The operational cost is compared to a constant operation benchmark. The electricity price profile used is shown in Fig. 2a. The profile of the product flowrate from the process is shown in Fig. 2b. The product purity is path-constrained to guarantee a predefined product quality. The storage tank holdup is endpoint-constrained to guarantee a minimum amount of product produced during the optimization horizon. The process operation is optimized over a time horizon of one day. We use wavelet-based grid adaptation with an adaptation of maximum five adaptation steps and an initial equidistant grid with eight piecewise constant control elements. SNOPT is used as NLP solver and sLIMEX as integrator with the tolerances set to 10^{-6}. The results of the dynamic optimization and of the benchmark operation strategy are shown in Fig. 3. We see that the tank is loaded when the electricity price is low and unloaded when it is

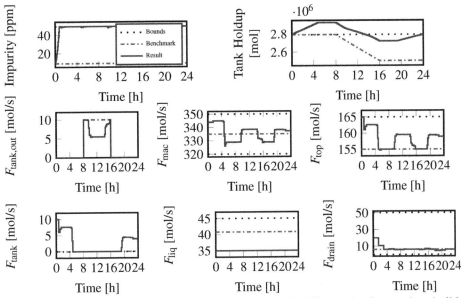

Figure 3: State and input trajectories of ASU case-study. The optimal operation (solid blue) is compared to a benchmark (dash-dotted red) corresponding to constant production rate. Top: Trajectories of selected constrained states. Rows 2 - 3: Trajectories of input variables.

high, as expected. The highest tank level is kept constant when the electricity price is at is maximum value, which is less intuitive. However, it can be explained by the increased product stream from 8 h on. In the benchmark operation the tank is unloaded due to the higher product demand. This difference is accounted for by the economic evaluation.

Moreover, the product impurity are at their bounds throughout the considered time horizon. The control variable profiles are shown in Fig. 3, where successful grid adaptation is demonstrated. They have a fine discretization where needed, e.g., for F_{mac}, and a coarse if not, e.g., for F_{liq}. The total runtime including the five grid adaptation steps took about 8 hours of CPU time. A Windows 7 computer is used with an Intel Core i3-6100 processor having 3.7 GHz and 8 GB RAM. The optimization results in a cost reduction of about 2 % with respect to the benchmark operation.

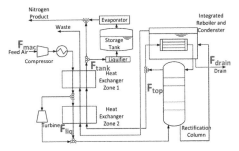

Figure 4: Air separation process flowsheet with control variables (bold red letters).

4. Conclusion

We present the dynamic optimization framework DyOS that is tailored to large-scale DAE systems. We review existing work which used DyOS for large-scale optimization problems. Finally, we demonstrate the application of the wavelet-based adaptation to an optimization of an air separation process.

Acknowledgement: The implementation of DyOS presented here is based on earlier versions that have been developed over many years by several researchers and programmers in the group of Wolfgang Marquardt. We thank him and them. We thank Uwe Naumann for allowing us to ship their algorithmic difffferentiation software dcc free of charge. We gratefully acknowledge the financial support of the Kopernikus project SynErgie by the Federal Ministry of Education and Research (BMBF) and the project supervision by the project management organization Projektttträger Jülich (PtJ), the Deutsche Forschungsgemeinschaft (DFG) in the Collaborative Research Center SFB 985 Functional Microgels and Microgel Systems within Project B4, the Federal Ministry of Education and Research (BMBF) for funding of the project CO2Min (FKZ: 033RC014), the European Union Horizon 2020 research and innovation programme under the Marie Sklodowska-Curie Grant Agreement No. 675251, and the Helmholtz Association under the Joint Initiative Energy System 2050 - A Contribution of the Research Field Energy".

References

J. Åkesson, K.-E. Årzén, M. Gäfvert, T. Bergdahl, H. Tummescheit, 2010. Comput. Chem. Eng. 34 (11), 1737–1749.

F. Assassa, W. Marquardt, 2014. Comput. Chem. Eng. 60, 242–259.

F. Assassa, W. Marquardt, 2015. Comput. Chem. Eng. 73, 82–101.

F. Assassa, W. Marquardt, 2016. problems. Comput. Chem. Eng. 92, 189–203.

H. Bock, K. Plitt, 1984. IFAC Proceedings Volumes 17 (2), 1603–1608.

R. G. Brusch, R. H. Schapelle, feb 1973. AIAA Journal 11 (2), 135–136.

A. Caspari, J. M. Faust, P. Schäfer, A. Mhamdi, A. Mitsos, 2018. IFAC-PapersOnLine 51 (20), 295 – 300.

J. E. Cuthrell, L. T. Biegler, 1987. AIChE J. 33 (8), 1257–1270.

R. Fletcher, S. Leyffer, 2002. Math. Program. 91 (2), 239–269.

FMI, 2014. http://fmi-standard.org.

K. Frankl, J. Brenner, W. Marquardt, 2012. ESCAPE-22 conference.

Fraunhofer ISE, 2018. https://www.energy-charts.de.

A. H. Gebremedhin, D. Nguyen, M. M. A. Patwary, A. Pothen, 2013. ACM Transactions on Mathematical Software 40 (1), 1–31.

P. E. Gill, W. Murray, M. A. Saunders, 2005. SIAM Review 47 (1), 99–131.

P. E. Gill, W. Murray, M. A. Saunders, M. H. Wright, 1986. NPSOL 5.0 User's Guide. Stanford University. Dept of Management Science and Engineering.

R. Hannemann, W. Marquardt, 2007. IFAC Proceedings Volumes 40 (5), 105–110.

R. Hannemann, W. Marquardt, U. Naumann, B. Gendler, 2010. Procedia Comput. Sci. 1 (1), 297–305.

A. Hartwich, W. Marquardt, 2010. Comput. Chem. Eng. 34 (11), 1873–1889.

B. Houska, H. J. Ferreau, M. Diehl, 2010. Optimal Control Applications and Methods 32 (3), 298–312.

J. B. Jorgensen, 2007. In: European Control Conference (ECC). IEEE, pp. 3649–3656.

J. V. Kadam, W. Marquardt, B. Srinivasan, D. Bonvin, 2007. AIChE J. 53 (3), 627–639.

C. Kirches, S. Leyffer, apr 2013. Mathematical Programming Computation 5 (3), 227–265.

D. Kraft, 1985. On converting optimal control problems into nonlinear programming problems. In: Computational Mathematical Programming. Springer Berlin Heidelberg, pp. 261–280.

U. Naumann, 2012. The Art of Differentiating Computer Programs. An Introduction to Algorithmic Differentiation. No. 24 in Software, Environments, and Tools. SIAM.

B. Nicholson, J. D. Siirola, J.-P. Watson, V. M. Zavala, L. T. Biegler, 2017. Mathematical Programming Computation 10 (2), 187–223.

J. Oldenburg, W. Marquardt, D. Heinz, D. B. Leineweber, 2003. AIChE J. 49 (11), 2900–2917.

K. V. Pontes, I. J. Wolf, M. Embiruçu, W. Marquardt, 2015. Ind. Eng. Chem. Res. 54 (47), 11881–11893.

R. W. H. Sargent, G. R. Sullivan, 1978. In: Optimization Techniques. Springer-Verlag, pp. 158–168.

M. Schlegel, W. Marquardt, R. Ehrig, U. Nowak, 2004. Appl. Numer. Math. 48 (1), 83–102.

M. Schlegel, K. Stockmann, T. Binder, W. Marquardt, 2005. Comput. Chem. Eng. 29 (8), 1731–1751.

R. Serban, C. Petra, A. C. Hindmarsh, 2018. User Documentation for IDAS v2.2.1. Center for Applied Scientic Computing, Lawrence Livermore National Laboratory.

A. Wächter, L. T. Biegler, 2005. Math. Program. 106 (1), 25–57.

Anton A. Kiss, Edwin Zondervan, Richard Lakerveld, Leyla Özkan (Eds.)
Proceedings of the 29th European Symposium on Computer Aided Process Engineering
June 16th to 19th, 2019, Eindhoven, The Netherlands.
http://dx.doi.org/10.1016/B978-0-128-18634-3.50105-3

Rate-based modelling and simulation of pilot scale distillation column

Mayra M. May-Vázquez, [a] Fernando I. Gómez-Castro, [a,*] Mario A. Rodríguez-Ángeles [b]

[a]*Departamento de Ingeniería Química, División de Ciencias Naturales y Exactas, Campus Guanajuato, Universidad de Guanajuato, Noria Alta S/N Noria Alta, Guanajuato, Guanajuato 36050, Mexico*

[b]*Departamento de Ingeniería en Plásticos, Universidad Politécnica de Juventino Rosas, Calle Hidalgo 102, Comunidad de Valencia, Santa Cruz de Juventino Rosas, Guanajuato 38253, Mexico*

fgomez@ugto.mx

Abstract

Batch distillation is perhaps the oldest operation used for separation of liquid mixtures. It is commonly used to produce fine chemicals and specialised products as alcoholic beverages, essential oils, perfume, pharmaceutical and petroleum products. Rigorous modelling of batch distillation can be developed by assuming phase equilibrium, or by rate-based approaches. The last approach represents in a more realistic way the phenomena occurring in the column, since it considers the heat and mass transfer rates for vapor and liquid phases. Due to the nature of their operation, batch distillation columns are modelled by a set of differential and algebraic equations (DAE). The present work concerns the simulation of a batch distillation column using the rate-based model, using a simplified approach for the calculation of the mass transfer rates. The pilot scale column modelled in this work has four trays, a total condenser and a pot. This column was used for separating a mixture of 75% mol methanol and 25% mol ethanol. As a first approach, mass transfer rates are obtained through rate-based simulations in Aspen Plus V8.8 for a pseudo-batch distillation column, using the Ideal thermodynamic model. The set of equations representing the rate-based batch column was solved using a specialized software (Polymath 6.0), taking the mass transfer rates as constant and equal to those obtained in the Aspen Plus simulation. The operating time of the batch column was 80 minutes, the thermal duty was kept as 500 W for the whole operation time, and the final composition in the pot was 72% mol methanol. The proposed strategy allows obtaining the composition and temperature profiles for the column, although it is still necessary to develop a proper mass transfer model to be included in the set of equations.

Keywords: batch distillation, rate-based modelling, mass transfer rates.

1. Introduction

Batch distillation is commonly used in the chemical, petroleum, polymers and pharmaceutic industries, and in the production of other fine chemicals. It is preferred over continuous distillation when the production is relatively small, when high added-value products are obtained, or it is required to produce different products in a single column.

For years the modelling and simulation of distillation columns has been the subject of several research. Several works have been presented for the modelling of the batch columns starting with the most elementary, as the one presented by Rayleigh, to the most robust formulation presented by Mujtaba (2004).

Two different approaches are available for the rigorous modelling of the interactions between phases in batch distillation columns, namely, equilibrium model and rate-based (nonequilibrium) model. The first one assumes vapor and liquid to be in thermodynamic equilibrium, using the efficiency of Murphree to describe the deviation from equilibrium. Thus, the accuracy of the predictions depends on the values assumed for this efficiency. The rate-based model doesn't require assuming the efficiency of Murphree, however, it requires good predictions of mass transfer coefficients, interfacial areas and diffusion coefficients (Sorensen, 2014).

In a trayed distillation column, the vapor from a lower stage is brought into contact with the liquid from an upper stage, allowing the two phases to exchange mass and energy across their common interface. Krishnamurthy and Taylor (1985) developed a nonequilibrium model based on general multicomponent mass and energy transport and using different correlations for the calculation of the binary mass transfer coefficient. A nonequilibrium or rate-based model employs the film model and equations based on transport phenomena to predict the mass transfer rates. This model is based on the MERSHQ equations, which consist of total and component material balances, energy balances, mass and energy rates of transfer across the interface, summation of mole fractions, hydraulic equation for pressure drop and equilibrium equations at vapor-liquid interface. The rate-based model is accurate (Taylor et al. 2000), but much more complicated than equilibrium model, therefore a more robust computing equipment is required to solve the system of equations. Ramesh et al. (2007) comments that an accurate mathematical model is necessary for the study of the dynamic characteristics and control of a distillation column, which is particularly important for batch distillation. López-Saucedo et al. (2016) presented the rigorous modelling for the simulation and optimization of a reactive batch distillation column. In the present work, a model for the representation of a pilot-scale batch distillation column is developed, taking as bases the model developed by López-Saucedo et al. (2016) but avoiding the reactive terms, and adding the mass and heat transfer contribution. As a first approach, mass transfer rates are assumed as constants, and a strategy to determine preliminary values for such rates is presented. The accuracy of such assumption is validated by comparison with experimental data.

2. Case of study

The present work concerns the modelling and simulation of a batch distillation column using the rate-based model. The work in divided in four stages: experimental, modelling of the pilot scale column, simulation in Aspen Plus V8.8 and solution of the obtained system of equations (DAE), using a specialized software (Polymath 6.0).

The experimental work was performed in a batch distillation column consisting of four sieve trays, a pot and a total condenser (Figure 1). This column was used to separate a mixture of alcohols with initial composition of 75% mol of methanol and 75% mol of ethanol, with initial charge of 0.196 kmol of the mixture. The characteristics of the column are shown in Table 1. The operating time of the batch column was 80 minutes, the thermal duty was kept as 500 W for the whole operation time. Samples were taken in each stage and then analysed in a gas chromatographer.

Figure 1.-Pilot scale column

Table 1.-Physical parameters of the batch column

Parameter	Value
Pot diameter	0.3 m
Pot height	0.27 m
Tray diameter	0.06 m
Tray Spacing	0.09 m

The rate-based mathematical model was developed for the column under study, with the following assumptions: the vapor-liquid interface reaches thermodynamic equilibrium, the trays are in mechanical equilibrium, the condenser operates at total condensation, the pot and the condenser are equilibrium stages, and the pressure along the column is constant. This last assumption is valid due to the small size of the column.

To obtain a preliminary estimate of the mass and heat transfer rates, a simulation of the pilot scale column was performed in Aspen Plus V8.8, representing the system a pseudo-batch column, by simulating a continuous column with feed on the bottoms and a reflux ratio of 1 and heat duty of 500 W. The column is represented with the RadFrac module, using the rate-based option. Thermodynamic equilibrium is modelled through the *Ideal* thermodynamic model.

The solution of the model for the batch column requires initial values for all the time-dependent variables. Such values are estimated by using the Aspen Batch Modeler V8.8, which assumes equilibrium for all the stages. The main specifications for this simulation are shown in Figure 2. Using the initial values obtained in this simulation for an initial condition of total reflux, the rate-based model is codified and solved in Polymath 6.0, aiming to obtain the liquid composition profile.

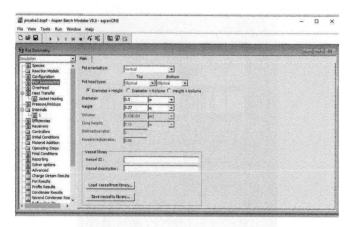

Figure 2.-Data for Aspen Batch Modeler

3. Results

The equations used to model the behaviour of the trays on the column are presented in this section. The total material balances for the vapor and liquid phases are:

$$\frac{dM_j^V}{dt} = V_{j-i} - V_j - N_{T,j} \tag{1}$$

$$\frac{dM_j^L}{dt} = V_{j+i} - V_j + N_{T,j} \tag{2}$$

The component material balances for component i in vapor and liquid phases on stage j are:

$$\frac{dy_{i,j}}{dt} = \frac{V_{j-1}}{M_j^V} y_{i,j-1} - \frac{V_j}{M_j^V} y_{i,j} - \frac{N_{i,j}^V}{M_j^V} \tag{3}$$

$$\frac{dx_{i,j}}{dt} = \frac{L_{j+1}}{M_j^L} x_{i,j+1} - \frac{L_j}{M_j^L} x_{i,j} + \frac{N_{i,j}^L}{M_j^L} \tag{4}$$

The energy balances of vapor and liquid phases on stage j are:

$$\frac{dH_i}{dt} = \frac{V_{j-1}}{M_j^V} H_{j-1} - \frac{V_j}{M_j^V} H_j - \frac{e_j^V}{M_j^V} \tag{5}$$

$$\frac{dh_i}{dt} = \frac{L_{j+1}}{M_j^L} h_{j+1} - \frac{L_j}{M_j^L} h_j + \frac{e_j^L}{M_j^L} \tag{6}$$

Rate of mass and energy transfer across interface is given by:

$$N_{i,j}^V = N_{i,j}^L \tag{7}$$

$$e_j^V = e_j^L \tag{8}$$

The mass and heat transfer rates in each stage are shown in Table 2. The stage 1 corresponds to the tray over the pot and the stage 4 corresponds to the tray below the condenser.

Table 2.-Mass and heat transfer rates (kmol/s)

Stage	Mass transfer rates (kmol/s)		Heat transfer rates (kJ/s)
	Methanol	Ethanol	Liquid
4	-3.30E-07	2.93E-07	-0.00211
3	-2.75E-07	2.44E-07	-0.00181
2	-2.23E-07	1.99E-07	-0.00151
1	-1.78E-07	1.59E-07	-0.00123

The trend of the composition in the pot is to increase because the amount of methanol in the reboiler decreases, while the distillate contains mostly methanol. As expected, the mol fractions of methanol tend to decrease from the upper to the lower stages for both, experimental and simulated results (Figure 3).

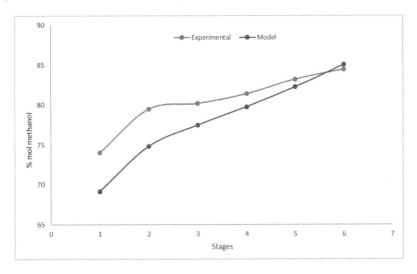

Figure 3.- Comparison of simulated and experimental profiles for liquid composition of methanol.

For the studied mixture, the composition of the pot changed from 75 mol% to a final composition of 74 mol% of methanol in the experimental system, while the model predicts a variation from 75 mol% to 69.13 mol% of methanol. This represents a difference of approximately 5.87 mol% between the experimental and the numerical results. This gap is reduced as the profile reaches the top of the column. The difference between experimental and numerical data is attributed to the assumption of constant mass transfer rates. Thus, as a part of our future work, a mass transfer model applicable to the studied system will be developed and validated.

4. Conclusions

A rate-based model has been developed to represent the separation of an alcohol mixture in a pilot scale batch column, assuming constant mass and heat transfer rates.

The mol compositions are similar between the experimental and simulation of the case of study. The experimental time was 80 minutes, while the simulation time was 53 minutes; in both case the same amount of distillate was obtained. The error between the experimental and simulated composition of methanol was 6% maximum and 1% minimum. The rate-based model developed provides a good approximation with the experimental results, although a reliable mass transfer model is still required.

Acknowledgements

The authors acknowledge the financial support provided by Universidad de Guanajuato and CONACYT, through the scholarship granted to M.M. May-Vázquez.

References

R. Krishnamurthy, R. Taylor, 1985, A Nonequilibrium Stage Model of Multicomponent Separation Processes. Part II: Comparision with Experiment, AIChE J., 31, 3, 456-465.

R. Taylor, R. Krishna, H. Kooijman, 2003, Real-World Modeling of Distillation, Chem. Eng. Prog., July, 28-39.

K. Ramesh, N. Aziz, S.R. Adb Shukor, M. Ramasamy, 2007, Dynamic Rate-Based and Equilibrium Model Approaches for Continuos Tray Distillation Column, J. Appl. Sci. Res., 3, 12, 2030-2041.

E. Sorensen, 2014, Design and Operation of Batch Distillation, in: Distillation Fundamentals and Principles, A. Górak and E. Sorensen (Eds.), Elsevier, UK, p. 187-224.

I. M. Mujtaba, 2004, Batch Distillation Design and Operation, Imperial College Press, UK, p. 56-115.

E. S. Lopez-Saucedo, I. E. Grossman, J. G. Segovia-Hernandez, S. Hernández, 2016, Rigorous modeling, simulation and optimization of a conventional batch reactive distillation column: A comparative study of dynamic optimization approaches, Chem. Eng. Res. Des., 111, July, 83-99.

Anton A. Kiss, Edwin Zondervan, Richard Lakerveld, Leyla Özkan (Eds.)
Proceedings of the 29th European Symposium on Computer Aided Process Engineering
June 16th to 19th, 2019, Eindhoven, The Netherlands. © 2019 Elsevier B.V. All rights reserved.
http://dx.doi.org/10.1016/B978-0-128-18634-3.50106-5

Computer-Assisted Experiments for the Identification of the Two-Phase Viscosity of Fluids

Xenia Gabrisch[a,*], Jens-Uwe Repke[a]

[a]Chair of Process Dynamics and Operation, Technical University of Berlin, Straße des 17. Juni 135, 10623 Berlin, Germany

xenia.gabrisch@tu-berlin.de

Abstract

The description of several transport phenomena requires the information about the viscosity of fluids. One application is a capillary tube that is operated as throttle device in the context of a heat pump. The two-phase pressure drop in the capillary tube can commonly be described using the homogenous flow model, which requires a valid correlation of the two-phase viscosity. Yet, no reliable correlation is available in literature, such that it is predictive for an extensive operation area. A lack of consistent and detailed experimental data as well as the lack of precise capillary specification complicates the matching of experimental and numerical results of the two-phase viscosity. For this reason, this work presents a systematic and comprehensive procedure in order to be able to identify a reliable two-phase viscosity. The procedure is a symbiosis of systematical numerical and experimental analysis of a two-phase refrigerant flow through a capillary tube. The numerical pre-analysis serves to identify sensitive parameters, which are experimentally refined afterwards. Comprehensive experimental investigations of the two-phase flow through the capillary provide understanding of different flow phenomena, which are inadequately described up to now. Numerical pre-analysis and extensive experimental investigations are the precondition for a computer-aided identification of the two-phase viscosity based on the experimental database.

Keywords: Computer-Assisted Experiments, Two-Phase Viscosity, Two-Phase Pressure Drop, Metastability, Hysteresis Effect

1. Introduction

Correlations of the two-phase viscosity of fluids are needed in order to describe various transport phenomena of fluids in process engineering. One application is the two-phase flow of a refrigerant through a capillary tube as a part of a heat pump system. The capillary serves as throttle device in rather smaller heat pump applications where it substantially determines the operation point. A predictive overall model of the heat pump is highly worth aspiring for, since it makes affordable a vast investigation of part components and their sensitivity towards the whole system. A precondition for this is a valid dynamic and predictive capillary model, i.e., the description of the two-phase flow through the capillary. The homogenous flow approach is a common assumption for the flow through a capillary tube. It requires the description of the two-phase viscosity of the considered refrigerant that is still an unsatisfactorily explored subject. Little data exists on natural and/or green refrigerants as statistics show (Dubba and Kumar, 2017). However, the latter are of growing importance in the context of the F-Gas Regulation. Sempértegui-Tapia and Ribatski (2017) stressed that a lot of the existing database on two-phase flow through capillaries goes along with imprecise data on the inner diameter and the absolute roughness of the inner surface of the capillary. Nevertheless, these parameters have a strong influence on the two-phase pressure drop in the capillary as numerical sensitivity investigations show. Imprecise parametrization of the according flow model leads to difficulties in validation and identification of an appropriate two-phase viscosity. The numerical results can hardly match the experimental data provided when only the viscosity correlation serves as adjusting screw.

Furthermore, experimental databases seldom provide information on metastability as well as the hysteresis effect on vaporization of the flow in a capillary tube. In fact, experimental investigations show that the impact of these effects on e.g. the measured pressure drop in a capillary tube are significant, hence, they need to be considered. Meyer and Dunn (1998) discussed the presence of a hysteresis curve that correlates with the metastability of the refrigerant flow. They proposed a coherent collection of experimental data since the experimental results depend on the history of previous measurements and conditions, respectively. Yet, little researchers followed the proposed experimental technique. Consequently, most experimental data is inconsistent in terms of the mentioned flow phenomena. Meyer and Dunn also advised to implement a memory function into the numerical capillary model that is able to capture the hysteresis effect. Especially, within the context of an overall heat pump model, the effect needs to be considered, as the hysteresis of the capillary is passed through within the operation of the heat pump. However, existing experimental data are insufficient to develop and implement a memory function that predicts a broad operation range, yet.

This work presents a computer-aided approach for a systematic gathering of experimental data that enables the identification of an appropriate correlation of the two-phase viscosity of fluids.

2. Homogenous Flow Model

The homogenous flow model is a common way to describe the pressure drop in a capillary tube. The total pressure drop Δp is simplified to the sum of the pressure drop of the liquid refrigerant Δp_{liq} and the two-phase pressure drop Δp_{tp}, see Eq. 1-3.

$$\Delta p = \Delta p_{liq} + \Delta p_{tp} \tag{1}$$

$$\Delta p_{liq} = \left(L_{liq} \cdot \frac{f}{2 \cdot d} + \xi \right) \cdot \frac{G^2}{\rho} \tag{2}$$

$$\Delta p_{tp} = \Delta \left\{ \frac{G^2 \cdot x^2}{\alpha \rho_v} + \frac{G^2 \cdot (1-x)^2}{(1-\alpha) \cdot \rho_v} \right\} + f \cdot \frac{G^2}{2 \cdot d \cdot \rho} \cdot L_{tp} \tag{3}$$

In Eq. 1-3 d is the inner diameter of the capillary tube. L_{liq} and L_{tp} mark the lengths inside the capillary that are occupied by liquid flow and two-phase flow, respectively. Further, ρ represents the density of the refrigerant and ξ the entrance pressure drop coefficient due to sudden contraction of the flow channel. The indices v and l denote the vapour and liquid density, respectively. G indicates the mass flux, α the void fraction and

x the vapour quality. The friction factor follows the correlation of Colebrook (1939), see Eq. 4.

$$\frac{1}{\sqrt{f}} = 1.14 - 2 \cdot \log\left(\frac{e}{d}\right) + \frac{9.3}{Re \cdot \sqrt{f}} \tag{4}$$

The calculation of the friction factor (Eq. 4) requires the inner diameter d, the absolute roughness of the inner surface of the capillary e, as well as the Reynolds-Number Re of the flow. However, the calculation of the Reynolds-Number depends on the dynamic viscosity μ alongside the inner diameter, the flow velocity v and the density of the refrigerant – see Eq. 5.

$$Re = \frac{v \cdot d \cdot \rho}{\mu} \tag{5}$$

Whereas the dynamic viscosity for the liquid phase of refrigerants is well determined, there is disagreement on the appropriate two-phase viscosity. As stated by Sempértegui-Tapia and Ribatski (2017), imprecise capillary parametrization in terms of diameter and roughness can shadow the actual influence of the viscosity correlation.

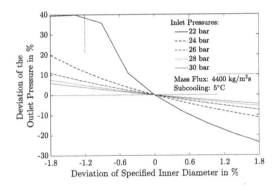

Figure 1: Impact of inner diameter uncertainty on the calculated outlet pressure

A sensitivity analysis (see Fig. 1) conducted with the given equation set (Eq. 1-5) shows how sensitive the calculated outlet pressure is towards a small degree of uncertainty of the inner diameter. The deviation of ±1.8 % corresponds to the manufacturer's specification of the tolerance of the inner diameter. It further becomes visible that the sensitivity increases for lower inlet pressures. An uncertainty of the inner diameter of only 1.2 % affects an uncertainty in the calculated outlet pressure of almost 40 %. Comprehensive studies show that the sensitivity increases for smaller degrees of subcooling and higher mass fluxes. It is only reasonable to identify any appropriate viscosity correlation if the uncertainty of the inner diameter is narrowed. The same applies for the absolute roughness. Within this work, the capillary diameter is determined by the means of a light microscope and the roughness by the means of a white light interferometry. Pre-investigations show that it is possible to narrow the tolerance of the inner diameter for capillaries of one production charge to at least ±0.9 %.

3. Experimental Investigations of the Two-Phase Pressure Drop

The experimental test rig presented in Fig. 1 serves for a comprehensive collection of two-phase pressure drop of propane for various conditions at the capillary inlet. The inlet condition of propane comprises the inlet pressure (PR-1), the inlet temperature (TR-1) and the mass flux (FIRC-1) of propane. The design of the experimental apparatus enables a wide operation range (PR-1: 10-30 bar, TR-1: 393-453 K, FIRC-1: 2-20 kg/h). The temperature is measured by thermocouples of type T providing a measuring error of ±0.5 K. The measuring error of the piezo-resistive pressure sensors is specified to ±0.7 %; the error of the Coriolis mass flow meter to ±0.3 %.

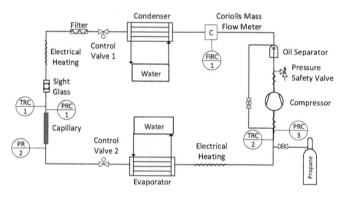

Figure 2: Experimental Apparatus

The capillary inside a heat pump is operated at flexible conditions depending on the application and outer circumstances of the operation. For a predictive and reliable capillary model, it is indispensable to validate the viscosity correlation against a wide range of operation conditions. However, the occurrence of hysteresis requires a coherent experimental data acquisition that drastically expands the original design of experiments. Hence, a systematic sensitivity analysis is conducted in order to understand whether the hysteresis effect is negligible for certain operation conditions. More precisely, the differences in pressure drop within hysteresis curves are examined for different inlet pressures, inlet temperatures and mass fluxes. Fig. 3 shows one exemplary hysteresis curve that depends on the increasing and decreasing of the subcooling. It makes clear that the different degrees of subcooling cannot be measured independently but depend on the previously performed subcooling. Furthermore, a discontinuity in the recorded pressure drops occurs at a subcooling of 7 °C and 5 °C. Although the operation conditions remained constant at this point, a sudden increase in pressure drop was recorded. Meyer and Dunn (1998) interpreted this phenomenon as the collapse of a metastable region.

Yet, understanding of how the metastable regions develop and what causes the collapse is still not well investigated and modelled (García-Valladares, 2007) (Dubba and Kumar,

2017). Little attention has been paid to explain the phenomenon of the hysteresis on vaporization as it appears in Fig. 3 since Meyer and Dunn presented their findings in 1998. However, knowledge and understanding of the hysteresis is crucial when modelling a capillary in the context of a heat pump.

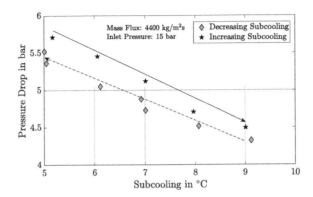

Figure 3: Hysteresis on vaporization depending on increasing and decreasing subcooling

4. Conclusions

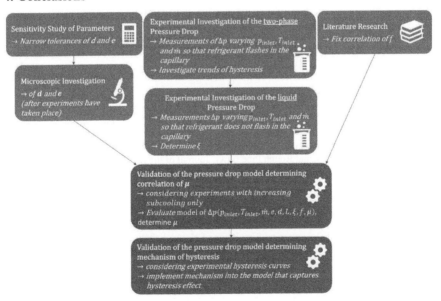

Figure 4: Systematic computer-aided approach for the validation of the pressure drop model

One reason for the fact that until today no satisfactory predictive two-phase correlation has been identified, is that the experimental database is not consistent and detailed enough. Because of that, this work aims for a systematic procedure to provide reliable data for the identification of the two-phase viscosity. For the systematic approach to obtain a predictive two-phase viscosity correlation, the presented experimental apparatus in Fig. 2 serves for extensive data gathering. A wide range of operation conditions is performed whereby hysteresis curves are recorded so that the influence of the inlet pressure, inlet temperature and mass flux through the capillary on the hysteresis becomes clear. Comprehensive data on hysteresis curves also serves to identify and mathematically describe the occurrence and possible correlation between hysteresis and metastability of the flow. This means, that the equation set of Eq. 1-5 needs to be complemented by the gathered understanding of both phenomena, e.g. by implementing a memory function that takes into account the history of simulated capillary inlet conditions. Liquid pressure drop experiments provide a base of validation data against which the entrance pressure drop coefficient is determined. Following the systematic concept for the model validation of the pressure drop in the capillary in Fig 4. and Eq. (2), only ξ is unknown at this point. Once, extensive data collection at the experimental apparatus is completed, the inner diameter and the absolute roughness of the considered capillary are investigated by the designated optical measurement techniques in order to provide a more precise parametrization of the capillary model. The numerical sensitivity analysis indicates that e.g. the diameter should at least be refined to an uncertainty of ± 0.5 % in order to have less than 10 % uncertainty in the calculated outlet pressure. The symbiosis of profound numerical and experimental analysis, thus, is necessary to reduce the overall degree of uncertainties of the capillary model in order to identify a predictive two-phase viscosity correlation of fluids. However, uncertainties still need to be considered when evaluating the viscosity correlation from the gathered experimental data, since any impacts cannot be captured by viscosity correlations. All in all, this work provides a systematic technique that, if followed by more researchers, delivers a reliable and precise data base in order to validate the two-phase pressure drop model of refrigerants.

References

Z.H. Chen, R.Y. Li, S. Lin, Z.Y. Chen, 1990, A Correlation for Metastable Flow of Refrigerant 12 Through Capillary Tubes, ASHRAE Transactions, Vol. 96, No. 1, pp. 550-554

C. F. Colebrook, 1939, Turbulent Flow in Pipes, with Particular Reference to the Transition Region between Smooth and Rough Pipe Laws, Journal of the Institution of Civil Engineers, Vol. 11, No. 4, pp. 133-156

S. K. Dubba and R. Kumar, 2017, Flow of Refrigerants Through Capillary Tubes: A State-of-the-Art, Experimental Thermal and Fluid Science, Vol. 81, pp. 370-381

O. García-Valladares, 2007, Numerical Simulation of Non-Adiabatic Capillary Tubes Considering Metastable Region. Part I: Mathematical Formulation and Numerical Model, International Journal of Refrigeration, Vol. 30, pp. 642-653

J. J. Meyer and W. E. Dunn, 1998, New Insights into the Behavior of the Metastable Region of an Operating Capillary Tube, HVAC & Research, Vol. 4, No. 1, pp. 105-115

D. F. Sempértegui-Tapia and G. Ribatski, 2017, Two-Phase Frictional Pressure Drop in Horizontal Micro-Scale Channels: Experimental Data Analysis and Prediction Method Development, International Journal of Refrigeration, Vol. 79, pp. 143-163

Anton A. Kiss, Edwin Zondervan, Richard Lakerveld, Leyla Özkan (Eds.)
Proceedings of the 29th European Symposium on Computer Aided Process Engineering
June 16th to 19th, 2019, Eindhoven, The Netherlands. © 2019 Elsevier B.V. All rights reserved.
http://dx.doi.org/10.1016/B978-0-128-18634-3.50107-7

Increasing the Reliability of Parameter Estimates by Iterative Model-based Design of Experiments Using a Flowsheet-Simulator

Maria Yliruka,[a] Norbert Asprion,[a] Roger Böttcher,[a] Johannes Höller,[b] Patrick Schwartz,[b] Jan Schwientek,[b] Michael Bortz[b,*]

[a] BASF SE, Chemical Process Modeling, Carl-Bosch-Str. 38, 67056 Ludwigshafen , Germany

[b] Fraunhofer Institute for Industrial Mathematics ITWM, Fraunhofer Platz 1, 67663 Kaiserslautern, Germany

michael.bortz@itwm.fraunhofer.de

Abstract

The reliability of flowsheet simulation results depends heavily on the knowledge of model parameters, among which are, for example, kinetic parameters of chemical reactions or substance property data describing thermodynamic behavior. These parameters are usually estimated by nonlinear regression with respect to data from a laboratory setup, mini-plant or operating data from a production process. Applying model-based design of experiments (DoE), operating conditions can be identified which maximize the information content of the resulting data for the regression problem. In this contribution, we present gradient-plots in order to make DoE-plans more transparent to the engineer. In a second step, we report on the implementation of an iterative DoE-scheme in a flowsheet-simulator. Thus, the interplay between estimating model parameters, planning experiments, adding resulting experimental data and re-adjusting the parameters is supported.

Keywords: process simulation, design of experiments, nonlinear regression, parameter estimation.

1. Introduction

To maximize the accuracy of least-square estimates of model parameters, model-based design-of-experiment-strategies have been established. Assuming a reasonable initial guess of the model parameters, these strategies yield a set of operating conditions by finding the optimal value of a scalar measure of the Fisher information matrix. After implementing the optimal set of operating conditions at the real plant, the model is adjusted to the measured responses in order to obtain more accurate model parameter estimations. The application of this approach to flowsheet simulations has previously been reported by Asprion et al. (2018).

In industrial applications, when implementing the optimal experimental plan, deviations from the proposed operating conditions might occur. A poor initial guess of the model parameters model-based design of experiments can lead to a poor experimental plan. Furthermore, in real experiments, generally deviations occur when applying the optimized experimental plan, i.e. realizing the different operating conditions.

To cope with these issues, we propose two extensions: In a first step, gradient plots are exploited to make the DoE-result more transparent to the planner. Together with the DoE-results for different criteria, these gradient plots, give an insight into how much the quality of an experimental plan depends on each of the experimental inputs.

In a second step, the following iterative approach is described in this contribution: Again, an initial estimate of the model parameters is assumed. A reduced experimental plan is then obtained from a Fisher information matrix that is calculated from derivatives. After the realization of the resulting reduced experimental plan at the plant, a new estimate of all model parameters is obtained. One then modifies the Fisher matrix of the previous step by including the already realized experiments and allowing a small number of additional experiments as new degrees of freedom. A new experimental plan is obtained and realized at the plant. This procedure can be repeated until some termination criterion is reached.

This article is organized as follows: In the next section, the formalism of iterative DoE is presented. Section three contains the concept of gradient plots, illustrated for the estimation of binary NRTL-parameters of different binary mixtures. Section four illustrates the iterative workflow. The article ends with a conclusion. Throughout, to generate the simulation results, the BASF inhouse flowsheet simulator Chemasim was used.

2. Iterative DoE approach

First, the notation required to formalize the iterative DoE-workflow is introduced.

In order to obtain a new estimate p_0^* of the model parameter vector p of length N_p, a weighted sum of squared residuals is minimized. Hereby, the deviation between the model predictions and the measured data is reduced.

$$p_0^* = \arg \min_p \sum_{i=1}^{N_e^0} \sum_{j=1}^{N_m} r_j(p, x_i)^2 \text{ with } r_j(p, x_i) = \sqrt{w_{i,j}} \left(\frac{\tilde{y}_{i,j} - y_j(p, x_i)}{\sigma_{\tilde{y}_{i,j}}} \right) \tag{1}$$

The j-th measured property in the i-th experiment is denoted by $\tilde{y}_{i,j}$. The corresponding model prediction $y_j(p, x_i)$ depends on the model parameter vector p and the design variable vector x_i of the i-th experiment. Additionally, weighting factors $w_{i,j}$ and standard deviations $\sigma_{\tilde{y}_{i,j}}$ of $\tilde{y}_{i,j}$ are included. N_e^0 corresponds to the number of experiments and the number of measured outputs is denoted by N_m.

The uncertainty of p_0^* stems from two sources (cf. Bates, Watts, 1990), namely the accuracy of the measurements (described by $\sigma_{\tilde{y}_{i,j}}$) and the correlation within x_i. This correlation is measured with respect to x_i's impact on the gradients of y_j with respect to p. On a more formal level, the Fisher information matrix (FIM) F (dimension $N_p \times N_p$) has to be calculated (cf. e.g. Schittkowski, 2007a) in order to estimate the covariance matrix of the p_0^*

$$F^0 = \sum_{i=1}^{N_e^0} \sum_{j=1}^{N_m} J_j(p_0^*, x_i)^T J_j(p_0^*, x_i) \tag{2}$$

with the Jacobians J_j (dimension $N_e^0 \times N_p$) consisting of column vectors

$$J_j(p_0^*, x_i) = \left(\left(\frac{\partial r_j}{\partial p_1}(p_0^*, x_i) \right)^T; ...; \left(\frac{\partial r_j}{\partial p_{N_p}}(p_0^*, x_i) \right)^T \right) \tag{3}$$

The covariance matrix C^0 corresponds to the inverse of the FIM F^0.

Let us now extend F^0 as follows: Apart from the x_i that defined the conditions of the already realized measurements $\tilde{y}_{i,j}$, additional $x_{i=N_e^0+1,...,N_e^0+N_e^1}$ are included. These additional x_i describe experiments still to be realized, on the basis of the estimates p_0^*. This extended Fisher matrix is called F^1. Well-known scalar DoE-criteria ϕ are considered as a function of $x_{i=N_e^0+1,...,N_e^0+N_e^1}$ and used to formulate an optimization problem to determine a new experimental plan:

$$\min \phi\left(x_{i=N_e^0+1,...,N_e^0+N_e^1}\right) \tag{4}$$

Possible DoE-criteria ϕ are , for example, for the A-criterion, $\phi = \text{trace}\left([F^1]^{-1}\right) = \sum_{i=1}^{N_p} \frac{1}{\lambda_i}$, or the D-criterion, $\phi = \det\left([F^1]^{-1}\right) = \prod_{i=1}^{N_p} \frac{1}{\lambda_i}$, where λ_i are the eigenvalues of F^1. The resulting x_i constitute the new experimental plan.

After the experiment, new parameter estimates p_1^* are found by minimizing a sum of squared residuals as in Eq. (1), now augmented by the additional experiments. Their covariance matrix can be estimated from the Fisher matrix F^1. New experiments follow from extending this matrix to a new F^2 by including $x_{i=N_e^0+N_e^1+1,...,N_e^0+N_e^1+N_e^2}$ as optimization variables, determined by solving a DoE task analogous to Eq. (4). This procedure is repeated until some termination criterion is fulfilled. A certain limit on the number of experiments or a threshold value for the accuracy of the estimates present suitable termination criteria.

In the following, a concrete example, namely a binary vapor-liquid flash, is used in order to illustrate the procedure described above. In a given experimental set up, the pressure P and the concentration of substance 1 in the liquid phase x_1 can be adjusted. The temperature T and the concentration of substance 1 in the vapor phase y_1 are measured as experimental outputs. The NRTL-parameters $A_{12}, A_{21}, B_{12}, B_{21}$ are to be estimated. Applying the procedure, P and x_1 should be chosen such that the reliability of the parameter estimates are maximized.

3. Gradient plots

First, $N_e^0 = 0$ is set and an experimental plan is to be designed from scratch.
To gain some intuitive insight, the gradients $\partial(w_{y_1} y_1)/\partial p'$ and $\partial(w_T T)/\partial p'$ with $p' = 5\frac{p-p_{min}}{p_{max}-p_{min}} + 5$, $p \in \{A_{12}, A_{21}, B_{12}, B_{21}\}$, $w_{y_1} = 100, w_T = 10$, are calculated for all x_1 at fixed P and for all P at fixed x_1. Using p' turned out to show favorable numerical results. For a mixture of methanol and water, these gradients are visualized in Figs. 1 and 2.

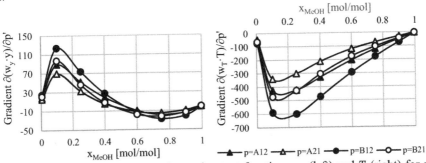

Figure 1: Gradient plots for experimental output functions y_1 (left) and T (right) for a mixture of water and methanol for constant $P = 1$ bar .

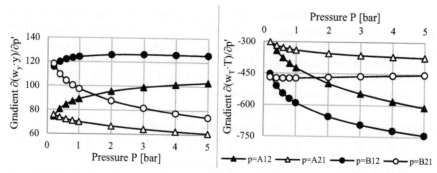

Figure 2: Gradient plots for experimental output functions y_1 (left) and T (right) for a mixture of water and methanol for constant $x_1 = 0.1$ mol/mol.

From Fig. 1 it follows that the highest dependence on the NRTL-parameters is observed for concentrations $x_1 < 0.4$.. The monotonic dependence of the gradients on the pressure at $x_1 = 0.1$ mol/mol is shown in Fig. 2. Hence, designs at the upper and lower boundary for the allowed pressure values are favored. Furthermore, the relative variation of the gradients with respect to the pressure at constant x_1 is much smaller than its variation with respect to x_1 at constant P(Fig. 1). Thus, we expect the optimal design points in the $x_1 - P$-plane to be located at P-values close to the bounds imposed by the experimental set up ($P = 0.1$ bar and $P = 5$ bar), and at x_1-values between 0 mol/mol and 0.4 mol/mol. Furthermore, it is to be expected that the parameter estimates will be highly correlated as the gradient plots show correlated behavior of the gradients over the entire P and x_1 ranges. These findings will be confirmed in section 4.

For a comparison, a binary azeotropic mixture of methanol and acetone is considered in an equivalent setup. The corresponding gradient plots are presented in Figure 3 and 4.

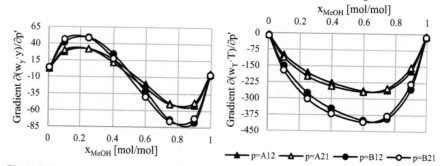

Figure 3: Gradient plots for experimental output functions y_1 (left) and T (right) for a mixture of methanol (1) and acetone (2) for constant $P = 1$ bar.

In contrast to the binary system of methanol-water, significant contributions to $\partial(w_{y_1} y_1)/\partial p$ now occur in two regions, namely for $0.1 < y_1 < 0.5$ and $0.5 < y_1 < 0.9$. But for the pressure, again a monotonic dependence is observed.

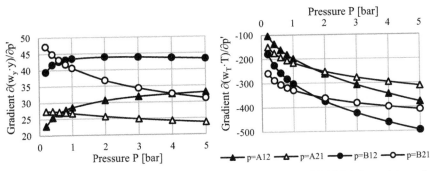

Figure 4: Gradient plots for experimental output functions y_1 (left) and T (right) for a mixture of methanol (1) and acteone (2) for constant $x_1 = 0.3$ mol/mol.

4. Illustration of iterative workflow

The gradient plots in the section 3 give some useful insights to how the optimal experimental plans will look like. In this section, the DoE-task in Eq. (4) is solved as a non-linear optimization problem for four experimental points from scratch, i.e. $N_e^0 = 0$, starting from different initial configurations. The results are presented in Fig. 5 which are in agreement with the gradient plots in section 3.

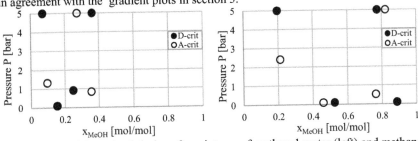

Figure 5: A- and D-optimal designs for mixtures of methanol-water (left) and methanol-acetone (right). These designs meet the expectations based on the gradient plots in section 3.

In the following, the discussion focuses on the binary mixture of methanol and water. In total, eight additional experiments should be realized after having performed the first experiments as shown in Fig. 5. Three different implementations of the additional experiments are considered:

I. $N_e^0 = 4$, $N_e^{1,2,3,4}=1$, that is, four additional iterations with one experiment in each iteration.

II. $N_e^0 = 4$, $N_e^1=4$, i.e., one additional iteration with four experiments

III. Four experiments at $P = 1$ bar and four experiments at $P = 5$ bar, each with $x_1 = 0.05, 0.35, 0.75, 0.95$ mol/mol.

The first $N_e^0 = 4$ experiments of alternatives I and II are shown in Fig. 5. Pseudo-measurements are generated by adding a random Gaussian error to the predictions of the true model in each iteration. The corresponding experimental plans are shown in Fig. 6. One observes that if model-based DoE-strategies are applied, the designs cluster in the regions where the gradients are highest, in agreement with the gradient plots shown in the previous section. In order to avoid the clustering, one could also imagine a hybrid DoE strategy, where the model-based approach is combined with a space-filling strategy, if a sufficient number of experiments are available. This is the subject of current research. To assess the quality of the plans, residual plots are shown in Fig. 7 for the differences between the measured and predicted values for T and y_1. From the values of these residuals, all of the three alternatives I-III seem to lead to comparable results.

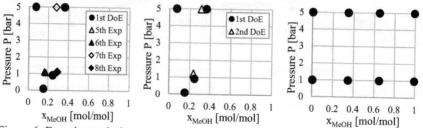

Figure 6: Experimental plans obtained for the three alternatives I-III (from left to right) described in the main text.

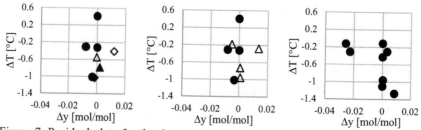

Figure 7: Residual plots for the three alternatives I-III, where the symbols in the plots have the same meaning as in Fig. 6. The axes show the residuals between measured and adjusted data for temperature (ΔT) and methanol concentration in the vapor phase (Δy).

5. Conclusion and outlook

Two extensions of the common DoE approach have been developed and implemented in BASF's inhouse flowsheet simulator Chemasim: The first extension consists in gradient plots which help to gain an intuitive insight into the correlations between parameter estimates and into promising regions for optimal experimental plans. The second extension supports an iterative workflow, where additional experiments are planned by fixing the ones already realized. The results suggest the development of a hybrid strategy, where a model-based DoE is combined with a space-filling strategy.

References

N. Asprion, J. Ritter, R. Böttcher, M. Bortz, 2018, Proceedings of the 28th European Symposium on Computer Aided Process Engineering, pp43-48

Bates, Watts, 1990, Nonlinear Regression Analysis and its Applications, John Wiley

K. Schittkowski, 2007a, Ind. Eng. Chem. Res., 46, 9137-9147.

Anton A. Kiss, Edwin Zondervan, Richard Lakerveld, Leyla Özkan (Eds.)
Proceedings of the 29th European Symposium on Computer Aided Process Engineering
June 16th to 19th, 2019, Eindhoven, The Netherlands. © 2019 Elsevier B.V. All rights reserved.
http://dx.doi.org/10.1016/B978-0-128-18634-3.50108-9

Estimating mixture properties from batch distillation using semi-rigorous and rigorous models

Michael Bortz,[a,*] Raoul Heese,[a] Alexander Scherrer,[a] Thomas Gerlach,[b] Thomas Runowski[b]

[a]*Fraunhofer Instistute for Industrial Mathematics, Fraunhofer Platz 1, 67663 Kaiserslautern, Germany*

[b]*Bayer AG, Engineering & Technology, 51368 Leverkusen, Germany*

*michael.bortz@itwm.fraunhofer.de

Abstract

Batch distillation experiments on laboratory scale are conducted in order to estimate NRTL parameters describing thermodynamic mixture properties. For this purpose, distillate composition and column temperatures are measured as functions of the batch hold-up and then used to fit model parameters with a non-linear regression approach. Two different models are presented, a semi-rigorous model relying on the assumption of constant molar overflow and a rigorous model from the commercial flowsheet simulator Aspen Custom Modeler. For both models, the NRTL parameters are estimated with good agreement to the experimental data. However, the semi-rigorous model is much simpler and therefore requires far less computational effort.

Keywords: batch distillation, constant molar overflow, non-linear regression, NRTL parameter estimation

1. Introduction

The knowledge of thermodynamic mixture properties is most relevant for reliable distillation process simulations. For many industrial applications, lab scale batch distillation experiments can be used to gain information about the separation behavior of complex multi-component mixtures. In this contribution, we address the question to which extent it is possible to estimate NRTL parameters reliably from this data. The estimation of such parameters from mixture properties is a numerically challenging problem as discussed by Gau et al (2000).

A detailed simulation of a distillation process based on a rigorous model requires expert knowledge for the fine-tuning of the model and is often computationally demanding. In order to reduce the complexity of the problem, a semi-rigorous model is set up based on the equilibrium stage model assuming constant molar overflows within the column and empty column hold-ups. This leads to decoupled mass and energy balances and therefore to considerable simplifications of the MESH equations, and allows for a product stream composition parametrized by the batch hold-up. Such a simplification has already been discussed by Doherty and Perkins (1978) in detail and has been applied to batch distillation column models by Dongen and Doherty (1985), however, with an additional simplification of the column profile.

Both semi-rigorous and rigorous model are used to estimate NRTL parameters from minimizing the sum of squared residuals between calculated and experimentally measured compositions and temperatures. For this purpose, the semi-rigorous model makes use of Matlab's native Levenberg-Marquardt optimizer. The rigorous model is realized in a prototypic software framework, which combines numerical simulation with Aspen Custom Modeler based on an implementation in its specific modeling language with a gradient-based optimization routine, see Schittkowski (2009). This software feeds NRTL parameters into a simulation instance and obtains simulation results from there, computes function values and numerical gradients for the optimization routine and obtains updated NRTL parameters from there, see Figure 1.

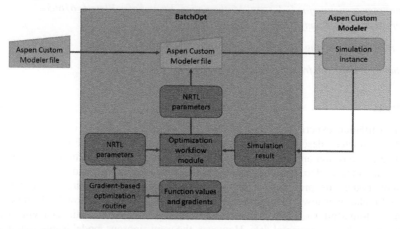

Figure 1: Software framework BatchOpt with its interfaces to Aspen Custom Modeler and gradient-based optimization routine.

This paper is organized as follows: Section 2 presents the semi-rigorous model and derives the equations used for the numerical simulation. Section 3 contains a short account on the experimental setup in the laboratory and compares measured data with simulated data from the two models using NRTL parameters from literature. Section 4 contains the results obtained from solving the corresponding regression problem. The paper ends with a conclusion.

2. Semi-rigorous model

The rigorous model used to model a batch distillation is based on coupled theoretical equilibrium stages within the MESH equation framework, see Stichlmair and Fair (1998). This means that each equilibrium stage i is described by variables H_i (liquid hold-up in kmol), V_i (vapour stream leaving stage i, in kmol/h), L_i (liquid stream leaving stage i, in kmol/h), $\boldsymbol{x}_i$ (composition of L_i in mol/mol), $\boldsymbol{y}_i$ (composition of V_i in mol/mol), temperature T_i (in K) and pressure p_i (in bar). The stages are numbered such that $i = 0$ corresponds to the batch, and $i = N$ corresponds to the topmost stage. Above the topmost stage a total condenser ($i = N + 1$) is fed with the vapor stream V_N and a liquid distillate stream D with composition $\boldsymbol{x}_{N+1} = \boldsymbol{x}_D$ is withdrawn in addition to the liquid backflow L_{N+1} to the topmost stage. The reflux ratio $R = L_{N+1}/D$ describes the relation of these streams. To model the hold-up in each equilibrium stage as a function of time, the

MESH-equations must be combined with a suitable hydrodynamic model. For a detailed discussion of the rigorous model, we refer to the aforementioned literature.

For the semi-rigorous model the stage hold-ups in the packed column are neglected based on the assumption of a comparatively small packing hold-up in comparison to the pot. Therefore, the $H_{i>0}$ are dropped such that no further model of the column hydraulics is required. Component Mole balances then read

$$\frac{d}{dt}(x_0 H_0) = -Dx_D$$

$$V_i y(x_i) = L_{i+1} x_{i+1} + Dy(x_N), i = 0, \dots, N-1$$

$$Dx_D = V_N y(x_N) - L_{N+1} x_D$$

The first equation contains the total balance, the second the balances for the intermediate stages and the last for the top stage. Here the VLE relation $y = y(x)$ has been used. Dependence on the constant pressure $p_i = p$ and stage temperatures T_i have not been included in order to keep the notation simple. The total condenser enforces $y(x_N) = x_{N+1} = x_D$. In the next step, the approximation of constant molar overflows is made, which eliminates the stage dependence of internal streams, resulting in constant streams $V_i \equiv V$ and $L_i \equiv L$. Furthermore, a new pseudo-time variable $\tau = \ln \frac{H_0(t=0)}{H_0(t)}$ is introduced in order to parametrize the complete solution in terms of the relative batch hold-up. Time dependence is therefore completely eliminated, which means that energy balance is decoupled from mass balances.

These steps yield

$$(R+1)y(x_i) - Rx_{i+1} = x_0 - \frac{d}{d\tau}x_0, i = 0, \dots, N-1$$

$$y(x_N) = x_0 - \frac{d}{d\tau}x_0$$

This differential-algebraic system of equations constitutes the semi-rigorous model. It is completely determined once R and $x_0(t = 0)$ are given.

3. Experimental setup

The experimental data is obtained from a real experiment in an industrial lab. The batch distillation column that was used for the experiment is a DN 50 column with 1.3 m of random packing (glass rings, 4 mm diameter, 4 mm length). Approximately 2 kg of the initial solvent mixture was prepared for the experiment. The mixture consisted of 30 wt% acetone, 30 wt% methanol, and 40 wt% butanone. The distillation was performed at 1 bar. During the start-up at the beginning of the experiment and after an intermediate shut-down the column was initialized at infinite reflux ratio R, otherwise a constant reflux ratio of 5 was applied. The medium temperature of the sump heat bath was continuously adjusted to ensure a constant pressure drop within the expected limits of the packing. The head temperature as well as the pot vapor and liquid temperatures were continuously logged. The distillate was fractionated into approximately 40 separate samples, which were further analyzed using GC analyses with an FID-detector. Additional analyses were performed of the pot content before and after the distillation to ensure agreement with the mass balance. Feeding the semi-rigorous and the rigorous model with NRTL parameters from the Aspen data base yields good accordance with the measured data, see Figure 2.

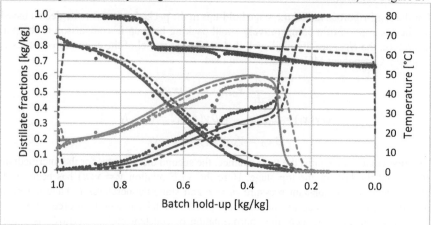

Figure 2: Distillate concentrations and head temperatures (violet) for initial NRTL parameters from experiment (dots), semi-rigorous model (solid lines) and rigorous model (dashed lines) for Acetone (blue), Methanol (green) and MEK (red).

The semi-rigorous model clearly achieves a better prediction of the experimental data than the rigorous model. The reason for this surprising behaviour is unknown to the authors, but might be an interesting starting point for further studies. Nevertheless, both models appear suitable for a fitting of NRTL parameters. This presumption will be confirmed in the next section.

4. Fitting of NRTL parameters

We exemplarily fit the two NRTL parameters B_{12} and B_{21} describing the mutual interactions between Acetone and Methanol and use fixed literature values for all other NRTL parameters. Thus, the joint fitting parameter $\Theta = (B_{12}, B_{21})$ is two-dimensional and the regression problem can be formulated as

$$\widehat{\Theta} = \text{argmin}_\Theta \sum_n w_n |d_n - m_n(\Theta)|^2$$

Here $\widehat{\Theta}$ denotes the optimal NRTL parameters, d_n describes the measured data point n and $m_n(\Theta)$ the corresponding calculated data point obtained from the chosen model (semi-rigorous or rigorous) for a specific choice of Θ. The sum index n over all measured mixture concentrations in distillate x_D and measured head temperatures T_N. The non-negative weights w_n allow for a tuning of the influence of different measurement points on the fitting result.

An appropriate pre-processing of the measurement data has been performed in such a way that outliers are omitted and all data points operate on the same scale. The weights w_n have been defined proportional to the inverse density of the neighboring data points. This choice compensates the varying density of the data with respect to the batch hold-up and therefore avoids an overfitting of densely measured regions. As an initial guess for the fitting parameters we choose deliberately displaced values $\Theta_{guess} = (-50, -500)$ in relation to the Aspen values $\Theta_{Aspen} = (102, 114)$. In case of the rigorous model fit we have neglected the initial data points d_n in the sum of squared residuals so that the transient behavior of the simulation has no effect on the fitting. Moreover, we also reduced the total number of data points in order to reduce the influence of numerical noise on numerical gradient computation and thereby improve the convergence of the optimization process. Such a data-dependent noise arises because the Aspen simulation has a relatively low numerical accuracy which can accumulate with an increasing number of sampling points in the regression problem. To suppress this effect we have excluded all temperature data and used only about one sixth of the measured concentrations suitably distributed over the hold-up. A major benefit of our semi-rigorous model becomes apparent: Although the rigorous model might in principle lead to simulations which are closer to the physical reality, its numerical evaluation can still be less precise for practical purposes than a simplified model.

The fitting results are shown in Figures 3 and 4. We find that both the semi-rigorous and the rigorous model lead to a reasonably good fit.

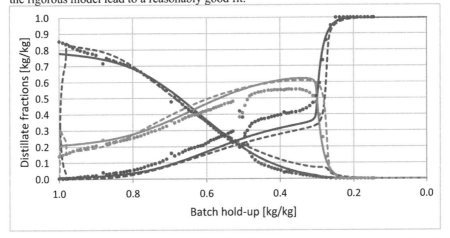

Figure 3: Distillate concentrations for fitted NRTL parameters from experiment (dots), semi-rigorous model (solid lines) and rigorous model (dashed lines) for Acetone (blue), Methanol (green) and MEK (red).

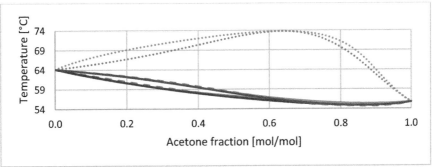

Figure 4: Phase diagram with liquid (blue) and vapour (orange) Acetone fractions for initial (dotted lines) and literature (solid lines in dark color) NRTL parameters and NRTL parameters fitted with semi-rigorous (solid lines) and rigorous model (dashed lines).

Summarized, starting from the initially chosen parameters $\Theta_{guess} = (-50, -500)$ we have recovered two different sets of optimal parameters $\hat{\Theta}_{semi-rigorous} = (-57, 284)$ and $\hat{\Theta}_{rigorous} = (272, -36)$, respectively, from the two different models by numerically solving a regression problem with data from a real experiment. Despite the quality of the fits, it is interesting to mention that the two resulting sets of parameters are different and do both not correspond to the original values from the Aspen data base $\Theta_{Aspen} = (102, 114)$. This ambiguity of the NRTL parameters is well-known and poses a major challenge for their estimation, see Gau et al. (2000). Further research would be required to analyze in detail to which extend the resulting parameters depend on the chosen models or the formulation of the regression problem.

5. Conclusions

Using the approximation of constant molar overflow we have derived a semi-rigorous batch distillation model for which energy balances are decoupled from mass balances. This approach yields a simplified system of differential-algebraic equations, where distillation time is replaced by the relative batch hold-up. We have shown that although evaluations of this semi-rigorous model require far less computational effort than evaluations of a rigorous model from a commercial flowsheet simulator, it is still able to predict the experimental data from an industrial lab with equally good precision. Furthermore, we have used both semi-rigorous and rigorous model to successfully fit NRTL parameters to the experimental data by means of a non-linear regression approach as a proof of concept. Our results highlight the ambiguity of the NRTL parameters and show that our semi-rigorous model can in practice be superior to the rigorous model despite its simplifications.

In conclusion, the semi-rigorous model approach presented herein allows for estimation of thermodynamic mixture properties based on experimental data from batch distillations using a packed column with multiple stages.

References

M. F. Doherty, J. D. Perkins, 1978, On the Dynamics of Distillation Processes – I, Chem. Eng. Science, 33, 281-301

D. Van Dongen, M.F. Doherty, (1985), Design and synthesis of homogeneous azeotropic distillations. 1. Problem formulation for a single column. Industrial & Eng. Chem. Fund. 24

C.-Y. Gau, J.F. Brennecke, M. A. Stadtherr, 2000, Reliable nonlinear parameter estimation in VLE modeling, Fluid Phase Equilibria 168, 1-18

H.Z. Kister, 1992: Distillation Design, McGraw-Hill Education, 510-512

K. Schittkowski, 2009, NLPQLP: A Fortran implementation of a sequential quadratic programming algorithm with distributed and non-monotone line Search - User's guide, Version 3.1, Technical report, Dep. of Comp. Science, University of Bayreuth

J. G. Stichlmair and J. R. Fair, 1998, Multistage Batch Distillation in Distillation – Principles and Practices, 284-327

E. F. Wijn, 1999, Weir flow and liquid height on sieve and valve trays, Chem. Eng. Journal 73, 191-204

Anton A. Kiss, Edwin Zondervan, Richard Lakerveld, Leyla Özkan (Eds.)
Proceedings of the 29th European Symposium on Computer Aided Process Engineering
June 16th to 19th, 2019, Eindhoven, The Netherlands. © 2019 Elsevier B.V. All rights reserved.
http://dx.doi.org/10.1016/B978-0-128-18634-3.50109-0

An MILP Approach for Short-term Scheduling of Batch Operations

Hossein Mostafaei[a], Iiro Harjunkoski[a,b,*]

[a]*Process Control and Automation, School of Chemical Engineering, Aalto University, Espoo 02150, Finland*

[b]*ABB AG, Corporate Research Center, Ladenburg, Germany*

iiro.harjunkoski@de.abb.com

Abstract

In this paper, we address the short-term scheduling of multipurpose batch plants, a challenging problem that has received growing attention in the past few years. We present a new mixed integer linear programming (MILP) framework based on the state-task network (STN), which employs a multi-grid continuous-time approach. Compared to other formulations in the literature, the proposed model leads to smaller and simpler mathematical models with strong LP-relaxations, which is reflected in the ability to find the optimal solutions in shorter CPU times. We demonstrate the performance of our model with a complex and comprehensive case study from the literature.

Keywords: Batch plant, Scheduling, MILP, Mathematical modeling.

1. Introduction

Short-term scheduling of batch processes has received growing attention over the past two decades. It consists of allocating limited resources to activities over time to optimize the plant operation in terms of some specific performance criteria such as maximum profit or minimum makespan. Earlier work in this area can be found in Vaselenak et al. (1987). Research on the short-term scheduling of multipurpose batch plants has used mixed integer linear programming (MILP) considering the time representation within the planning horizon as either discrete or continuous. Discrete-time representations divide the time horizon into slots of equal and fixed duration, whereas continuous- time representations relax such assumption. Extensive reviews can be found in Floudas and Lin (2004) and Harjunkoski et al. (2014). Continuous-time models can be further classified into two: single-grid (Castro et al., 2004; Maravelias and Grossmann, 2003; Sundaramoorthy and Karimi, 2005) and multi-grid (Ierapetritou and Floudas, 1998, Shaik and co-workers 2009; 2012). In the former, time slots are common for all units, while the latter provides each unit to have its own set of time intervals, which is not shared with other units.

Kondili et al. (1993) were the first to develop a discrete-time MILP based on the state-task network (STN) representation. In this model, the length of the time slots are determined from the greatest common factor among the processing times involved in the problem. For the same problem, Ierapetritou and Floudas (1998) developed an efficient multi-grid continuous-time MILP formulation that defines the duration of tasks by the optimization. The model needs less number of events (or time slots) compared to the single-grid models (Castro et al., 2004; Maravelias and Grossmann, 2003; Sundaramoorthy and Karimi, 2005). Based on the model by Ierapetritou and Floudas (1998), Shaik and Floudas (2009) presented an MILP formulation that can be utilized in both batch and continuous plants. In this paper, we propose a new multi-grid continuous-time MILP scheduling model for multipurpose batch plants, based on the STN representation. Compared to other models in the literature, the proposed model is very tight and does not use any tightening constraint to generate a small integrality gap. We define a new set of sequencing constraints, which result in fewer continuous variables and constraints compared to previous multi-grid approaches. Furthermore, compared to literature, the proposed model leads to the same number of binary variables without decoupling tasks from units.

2. Problem statement

We focus on short-term scheduling of multipurpose batch plants, where a set of products are manufactured using a number of shared production units. Given the processing time data and the state-task network (STN) representation for the plant, we aim to optimally define the sequencing and timing of tasks in each units in order to maximize the total profit during a specific time horizon or minimize the total time required to meet demands. To sequence tasks in units, we use the concept of run $r \in R$; run r should start after the completion of $r-1$ in unit j. If run r is executed in unit j, one of tasks $i \in I_j$ (set of tasks that can be processed in unit j) is being processed in this unit.

3. Scheduling model

3.1. Task allocation, batch size and processing time

If binary variable $X_{i,j,r} = 1$, a certain volume of task i is being processed in unit j during run r $(V_{i,j,r})$. The processing time of task i in unit j at run r is assumed to be given by a constant plus a term proportional to the related batch size, where $cp_{i,j}$ and $vp_{i,j}$ are the constant and variable processing times of task i in unit j, respectively. In turn, $X_{j,r}^{\text{no task}} = true$ means that task i is not allocated to unit j and so the continuous variables $LR_{i,j,r}$ and $V_{i,j,r}$ are set to zero. We have thus the following disjunction (Mostafaei and Castro 2017; Castro and Mostafaei 2017; Castro et al. 2018):

$$\bigvee_{i \in I_j} \begin{bmatrix} X_{i,j,r} \\ v_{i,j}^{\min} \leq V_{i,j,r} \leq v_{i,j}^{\max} \\ LR_{i,j,r} = cp_{i,j} + vp_{i,j}V_{i,j,r} \end{bmatrix} \vee \begin{bmatrix} X_{j,r}^{\text{no task}} \\ V_{i,j,r} = 0 \ \forall i \in I_j \\ LR_{i,j,r} = 0 \ \forall i \in I_j \end{bmatrix} \ \forall j,r \tag{1}$$

The MILP format of the above disjunction is described through eqs. (2)-(4).

$$\sum_{i \in I_j} X_{i,j,r} \leq 1 \quad \forall j,r \tag{2}$$

$$v_{i,j}^{\min} X_{i,j,r} \leq V_{i,j,r} \leq v_{i,j}^{\max} X_{i,j,r} \quad \forall i \in I_j, j,r \tag{3}$$

$$LR_{i,j,r} = cp_{i,j} X_{i,j,r} + vp_{i,j}V_{i,j,r} \quad \forall i \in I_j, j,r \tag{4}$$

3.2. Material balance

The excess amount of state s at the start of run r ($F_{s,r}$) is computed through eq. (5), where f_s^{initial} is the initial inventory of state s. In eq. (5), $\rho_{i,s}^p$ and $\rho_{i,s}^c$ are the proportion of state s produced or consumed from task i, respectively.

$$F_{s,r} = f_s^{\text{initial}} + \sum_{r'<r}\sum_{i\in(I_s^p\cap I_j)} \rho_{i,s}^p \sum_j V_{i,j,r'} - \sum_{r'\le r}\sum_{i\in(I_s^c\cap I_j)} \rho_{i,s}^c \sum_j V_{i,j,r'} \quad \forall s,r \tag{5}$$

3.3. Sequencing process runs

Process run r in unit j should not start before the end of run $r-1$ in the same unit. Besides, the start of run r in unit j consuming state s should be after the end of process run $r-1$ in unit j' feeding the same state. The sets J_s^p and J_s^c in (7) include units that feed and consume state s, respectively.

$$SR_{j,r} \ge SR_{j,r-1} + \sum_{i\in I_j} LR_{i,j,r-1} \quad \forall j, r\ge 2 \tag{6}$$

$$SR_{j,r} \ge SR_{j',r-1} + \sum_{i\in I_{j'}} LR_{i,j',r-1} \quad \forall j\in J_s^c, j'\in J_s^p (j\ne j'), s\in S, r\ge 2 \tag{7}$$

The completion time of the last process run in each unit should not surpass the horizon length, $h_{\max}$.

$$SR_{j,r} + \sum_{i\in I_j} LR_{i,j,r} \le h_{\max} \quad \forall j, r\ge |R| \tag{8}$$

3.4. Sequence-dependent changeovers

If tasks i' and i are processed in unit j during runs $r-1$ and r respectively, there will be a constant changeover time of $\tau_{i',i,j}$ associated to the start of run r in unit j.

$$X_{i,j,r} \wedge X_{i',j,r'} \wedge \neg(\bigcup_{r''=r'+1}^{r-1}\bigcup_{i''\in I_j} X_{i'',j,r''}) \Rightarrow X_{i,i',j,r',r}^{\text{changeover}} \quad \forall i,i'\in I_j (i\ne i'), j\in J, r\ge r' \tag{9}$$

$$\bigvee_{i\in I_j}\bigvee_{i'\in I_j}\left[\begin{array}{c} X_{i,i',j,r',r}^{\text{changeover}} \\ SR_{j,r} - (SR_{j,r-1} + LR_{i',j,r-1}) \ge \tau_{i',i,j} \end{array}\right] \quad \forall j, r>r' \tag{10}$$

We can now eliminate variable $X_{i,i',j,r',r}^{\text{changeover}}$ from the formulation by combining the constraints derived from form Eqs. (9-10), giving rise to the following equation:

$$SR_{j,r} - (SR_{j,r-1} + LR_{i',j,r-1}) \ge \tau_{i',i,j}(X_{i,j,r} + X_{i',j,r'} - \sum_{r''=r'+1}^{r-1}\sum_{i''\in I_j} X_{i'',j,r''} - 1) \tag{11}$$

$$\forall i,i'\in I_j (i\ne i'), j\in J, r\ge r'$$

3.5. Meeting demand

Demands at states $s\in SM\subset S$ storing final products are enforced as a hard constraint in eq (14).

$$\sum_r \sum_{i\in I_s^p} \rho_{i,s}^p \sum_{j\in J_i} V_{i,j,r} \ge d_s \quad \forall s\in SM \tag{12}$$

3.6. Objective function

Two alternative objectives are considered. They are:

(1) The maximization of profit given in eq (13), where the parameter vs_s is the value of state s :

$$\max z = \sum_s vs_s \sum_r \sum_{i \in I_s^p} \rho_{i,s}^p \sum_{j \in J_i} V_{i,j,r} \tag{13}$$

The model for profit maximization consists of eqs. (2)-(8),(11) and (13).

(2) The minimum makespan given in (14):

$$\min \ z = H \tag{14}$$

where the continuous variable H is an upper bound on the completion time of last run in each unit:

$$SR_{j,r} + \sum_{i \in I_j} LR_{i,j,r} \le H \ \ \forall j, r \ge |R| \tag{15}$$

The model for makespan minimization consists of eqs. (2)- (7), (11)-(12), (14) and (15).

Remarks: Eq (16) below, the so-called *tightening* constraint, is a common constraint used e.g. in Shaik and co-workers (2009, 2012) and Marvelias and Grossmann (2003) and leads to strong LP-relaxations. It helps speed up the branch and bound solution search, and consequently decrease the solution CPU times. When minimizing the makespan the time horizon parameter in (16) needs to be replaced by the continuous variable H. We will show that our proposed model does not need the tightening constraint.

$$\sum_r \sum_{i \in I_j} LR_{i,j,r} \le h_{\max} \ \ \forall j \tag{16}$$

4. Case Study: A complex and comprehensive problem in the literature

The performance of our model is compared to a similar previous work by Shaik and Floudas (2006), hereafter referred to as SF. We consider a complex and comprehensive case study (Example 3) in Sundaramoorthy and Karimi (2005). Since our model does not allow tasks to span over multiple events and for the sake of a fair comparison, we only consider $\Delta n = 0$ in SF model and remove the big-M term in constraint (16), which makes it exactly equivalent to the model by Vooradi and Shaik (2012). Both the proposed model and SF model were implemented in GAMS/ CPLEX 12.7.1 (using 4 threads in parallel) on an Intel Core i5-7300U (3.33 GHz and 8 GB of RAM).

The model statistics and computational results when maximizing the total profit for two different time horizons are given in Table 1. From this table, both approaches need the same number of runs (events) to confirm the optimum and perform equally well. However, our model has fewer continuous variables and constraints and exhibits strong LP-relaxations with 6 runs for the first scenario and with 8 runs for the second scenario. Table 1 also summarizes the results for both models without the tightening constraint (16). As can be observed, the LP-relaxations (RMILP) do not change without the tightening constraint for the purposed model, which is not the case for the SF model.

Table 1: Results for the case study when maximizing total profit

	$|R|$	CPU (s)	Nodes	Binary variables	Total variables	Eqs	MILP ($)	RMILP[a] ($)
				($h_{\max} = 8$ h)				
SF	5	0.43	304	55	286	457	1583.4	2100.0

	5*	0.34	340	55	286	451	1583.4	2100.0
	6	0.87	5744	66	343	551	1583.4	2750.9
	6*	0.82	4878	66	343	545	1583.4	2826.7
Our	5	0.34	428	55	261	365	1583.4	2100.0
	5*	0.28	309	55	261	359	1583.4	2100.0
	6	0.53	2827	66	313	440	1583.4	2563.2
	6*	0.71	3276	66	313	434	1583.4	2563.2
			$(h_{max} = 12\ h)$					
SF	7	0.50	619	77	400	645	3041.2	3465.6
	7*	0.35	299	77	400	639	3041.2	3465.6
	8	1.29	2017	88	457	739	3041.2	3988.4
	8*	0.67	1066	88	457	733	3041.2	4059.3
Our	7	0.43	492	77	365	515	3041.2	3463.9
	7*	0.31	192	77	365	509	3041.2	3463.9
	8	0.59	1245	88	417	590	3041.2	3846.0
	8*	0.73	1088	88	417	584	3041.2	3846.0

*Results without the tightening constraint (16), [a]Relaxed Solution of MILP

Table 2 shows the results for the case study when minimizing the makespan for two different demand scenarios. In the first scenario i.e., $d_{S12} = d_{S13} = 250$ mass unit (mu), both models work equally well, but our model again leads to smaller and tighter mathematical models. For the second scenario and with the tightening constraint, our purposed model finds the optimum in just 2.95s and confirms it in 44.54 s. This represents a one-order-of-magnitude time saving compared to the SF's model, which takes 1567.2 s to confirm the optimality of solution confronted with 26 events. Without the tightening constraint, the purposed model again exhibits the same LP-relaxation and can confirm the optimality just in few seconds (12.92s). This is not the case for the SF model, which exhibits week LP-relaxations and takes minutes to prove the optimality.

Table 2: Results for the case study when minimizing the makespan

	$|R|$	CPU (s)	Nodes	Binary variables	Total variables	Eqs	MILP (h)	RMILP (h)
			$(d_{S12} = d_{S13} = 250$ mu$)$					
SF	10	0.39	167	110	572	918	17.02	14.27
	10*	0.58	187	110	572	912	17.02	12.76
	11	0.87	824	121	629	1012	17.02	14.27
	11*	1.04	755	121	629	1006	17.02	12.62
Our	10	0.32	0	110	522	742	17.02	14.53
	10*	0.31	181	110	522	736	17.02	14.53
	11	0.92	967	121	574	817	17.02	14.39
	11*	0.76	746	121	574	811	17.02	14.39
			$(d_{S12} = d_{S13} = 750$ mu$)$					
SF	26	144.9	158743	286	1484	2422	47.01	44.48
	26*	139.1	86100	286	1484	2416	47.01	37.86
	27	1567.2	1701164	297	1541	2516	47.01	44.48
	27*	1368.5	880148	297	1541	2510	47.01	37.66

Our	26	2.95	2468	286	1354	1942	47.01	44.84
	26*	3.75	3591	286	1354	1936	47.01	44.84
	27	44.54	67710	297	1406	2017	47.01	44.64
	27*	12.92	12883	297	1406	2011	47.01	44.64

*Results without the tightening constraint (18)

5. Conclusions

A multi-grid continuous-time MILP formulation for the short term scheduling of multipurpose batch plants has been developed. We relied on the STN representation to derive the problem constraints. It has been shown that the proposed model exhibits the same LP-relaxation with and without the tightening constraint frequently used in the literature. We validated the proposed model using a complex and comprehensive case study from the literature. The results demonstrated that the proposed model is smaller and significantly faster than previous similar work.

Acknowledgements

Financial support is gratefully acknowledged from the Academy of Finland project "SINGPRO", Decision No. 313466.

References

J.A.Vaselenak, I.E. Grossmann, A.W. Westerberg, 1987, An embedding formulation for the optimal scheduling and design of multipurpose batch plants, End. Eng. Chem. Res, 26, 139-148.

C.A. Floudas, X. Lin, 2004, Continuous-time versus discrete-time approaches for scheduling of chemical processes: A review, Comput. Chem. Eng, 28: 2109-2129.

I. Harjunkoski et al., 2014, Scope for industrial applications of production scheduling models and solution methods Comput. Chem. Eng, 62, 161-193.

E. Kondili, C.C. Pantelides, R. Sargent, 1993, A general algorithm for short-term scheduling of batch operations-I. MILP formulation Comput. Chem. Eng, 17, 211-227.

M.G. Ierapetritou, C.A. Floudas, 1998, Effective continuous-time formulation for short-term scheduling. 1. multipurpose batch processes, Ind. Eng. Chem. Res, 37, 4341-4359.

P. M. Castro, A.P Barbosa-Povoa, H. Matos, A. Novais, 2004, Simple continuous-time formulation for short-term scheduling of batch and continuous processes, Ind. Eng. Chem. Res, 43, 105-118.

C.T. Maravelias, I.E. Grossmann, 2003, New general continuous-time state-task network formulation for short-term scheduling of multipurpose batch plants Ind. Eng. Chem. Res, 42, 3056-3074.

A. Sundaramoorthy, I.A. Karimi, 2005, A simpler better slot-based continuous time formulation for short-term scheduling in multipurpose batch plants Chem. Eng. Sci, 60, 2679-2702.

M.A. Shaik, C.A. Floudas, 2009, Novel unified modeling approach for short-term scheduling Ind. Eng. Chem. Res, 48 6, 2947-2964.

R. Vooradi, M. Shaik, 2012, Improved three-index unit-specific event-based model for short-term scheduling of batch plants, Comput. Chem. Eng, 43, 148-172.

H. Mostafaei, P.M. Castro, 2017, Continuous- time scheduling formulation for straight pipelines AIChE, 63, 1923-1936.

P.M. Castro, H. Mostafaei, 2017, Product-centric continuous-time formulation for pipeline scheduling. Computers and Chemical Engineering, 104, 283-295.

P.M. Castro, I.E. Grossmann, Q. Zhang, 2018, Expanding scope and computational challenges in process scheduling Comput. Chem. Eng, 114, 14-42.

Anton A. Kiss, Edwin Zondervan, Richard Lakerveld, Leyla Özkan (Eds.)
Proceedings of the 29th European Symposium on Computer Aided Process Engineering
June 16th to 19th, 2019, Eindhoven, The Netherlands. © 2019 Elsevier B.V. All rights reserved.
http://dx.doi.org/10.1016/B978-0-128-18634-3.50110-7

Synthesis and optimization of refinery hydrogen network using surrogate models

Shihui Wang[a], Li Zhou[a,*], Xu Ji[a] and Yagu Dang[a]

[a]*School of Chemical Engineering, Sichuan University, No.24 South Section 1, Yihuan Road, Chengdu, 610065, P. R. China*
chezli@scu.edu.cn

Abstract

Previous works have developed methodologies for hydrogen network optimization, with a simplistic assumption of constant equilibrium distribution coefficient (K-value) for separation process, which leads to an inaccuracy of the solution. To address this problem, a surrogate-assisted modeling and optimization method for the design of refinery hydrogen network has been developed. The established models fully considered the changing characteristics of K-value in flash units, as well as the chemical processes happened in hydrotreaters, such as property of the processed crude oil (mainly the sulfide and 3+ring core aromatic content), formation of H_2S and light hydrocarbons (C1-C5). These process characteristics were reflected through the employment of surrogate modelling technique, which can be employed to compensate the computationally time-consuming nature of the corresponding first-principles-based models, due to its versatility. Polynomial surrogate model can be easily built using the least square method, and low order models are sufficient to approximate equipment models. A case study involving four hydrogen consumers is solved to indicate the efficacy of the proposed approach, and an NLP model is formulated. Compared to the result obtained by method proposed by the literature, the proposed method suggests more of gas flow to fuel system, since the calculated H_2S content in the product flow is comparatively high. Therefore, it can be concluded that the proposed method can deliver a more realistic result.

Keywords: Hydrogen network, Surrogate model, Design, Optimization

1. Introduction

The methodologies for the synthesis and optimization of refinery hydrogen networks can be divided into two categories: pinch analysis and mathematical programming. The latter shows more advantages because it takes into account some underlying constraints. It was originally developed by Hallale and Liu (2001). The research was continued by Kumar et al. (2010), considering several practical constraints (such as pressure constraints and hydrogen purity constraints) to obtain realistic solutions. Jia and Zhang (2011) proposed an improved modeling approach which defined the K-values in the flash separation units and incorporated the flash units into hydrogen consumer models. Umana et al. (2014) introduced an empirical model to predict the hydrogen consumption and the formulation of light hydrocarbons, and modeled the new hydrogen networks synthesis problem as an NLP (nonlinear programming).

Simplified equipment models were employed in the superstructure of optimization models in the previous works. In order to capture a more realistic behavior of the system, more accurate models should be used to represent equipments. However, the use of realistic models would be difficult due to high computational time in solution of the hydrogen network synthesis problem in an optimization algorithm.

This work proposes the use of surrogate modelling technique for hydrogen networks synthesis problems. It can capture the complicated chemical and physical processes involved in the hydrotreating and flash process, in the meanwhile, it requires less computation effort. Hence, more realistic solutions can be obtained in a reasonable time by applying the proposed methodology. This paper is structured as follows. Section 2 describes the methodology of building surrogate models. Section 3 provides a case study and shows a methodology to solve the hydrogen network synthesis problem by using surrogate models to represent equipment models, while Section 4 presents some conclusions.

2. Surrogate modeling and optimization: steps and strategies

The use of surrogate models in synthesis and optimization problems has been reported in many cases, e.g. Graciano and Le Roux (2013) and Sikorski et al. (2016). A surrogate model can be used to approximate the behaviors of a complicated system by only taking into account nature of the input-ouput relationship. Due to the simplicity of forms, a surrogate model can usually be solved with much lower computational efforts, compared to the original model. The steps of surrogate-assisted modeling and optimization used in this study are summarized below:

1. Selecting a set of input-output variables that are independent, as the characteristic indicators for the concerned processes.
2. Generating a set of sampling data for the selected input variables within the respective operational ranges (as described in Section 2.2).
3. Producing output values for each sampling point, by employing first principle models or commercial software packages.
4. Training the selected surrogate models with a portion (80% in this case) of the generated input-output data sets. The selection of a preferable surrogate model will be described later in Section 2.1.
5. Validating the obtained surrogate model with the remaining portion (20% in this case) of the generated input-output data sets.
6. Integrating the established surrogate models into the hydrogen network optimization problem.

2.1. Selection of surrogate models

There are several types of surrogate models such as polynomial, kriging, support vectors machine and artificial neural network. Polynomial can be built easily by using least square method and are sufficient to fit most models or data. In this work, polynomial surrogate model was employed to approximate hydrotreaters and flash unit models, due to its simplicity of forms and accuracy. For more detailed information about the selected surrogate models, the readers are referred to Forrester et al. (2008).

2.2. Sampling and validating plans

The sample sets were generated using Sobol sequences, developed by Sobol (1967), a type of quasi-random and low-discrepancy sequences which can achieve faster space-filling over other sequences. A number of accuracy measures were used including R^2, root-mean-square-error (*RMSE*) and residual plot.

3. Case Study

The case study was taken from Umana et al. (2014), it consists of two possible hydrogen producers and four consumers, which again contains one hydrotreater and one flash unit.

3.1. Surrogate model fitting for flash units and hydrotreaters

3.1.1. Flash units

In order to overcome the drawback of constant K-value assumption in the previous works, Aspen Plus was used to model the flash separation units based on the operation conditions given in Jia and Zhang (2011). The model then served as a data generator for surrogate model fitting. In this case, ten indicators for the reaction effluent were chosen as the input variables, and eight were chosen for the gaseous stream, which is given in 1.

Figure 1: Flash unit model indicating input variables and output variables.

where T_{fin} is temperature, P_{fin} is pressure, Fin_{H2} is inlet hydrogen flow rate, Fin_{HC} is inlet light hydrocarbons flow rate, Fin_{H2S} is inlet H_2S flow rate, $Fout_{H2}$ is outlet hydrogen flow rate, $Fout_{H2S}$ is outlet H_2S flow rate, $Fout_{Ci}$ is outlet light hydrocarbons flow rate and $Fout_{gas}$ is outlet gas flow rate of the flash unit.

The results are represented in Table 1 and residual plots are illustrated in Fig 2. The R^2 is close to 1 and RMSE are relatively minor, indicating a good correlation by the surrogate models. Meanwhile, residual plots show that residuals are in random distribution.

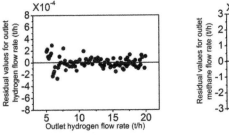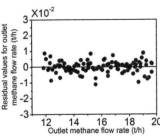

Figure 2: Plot of residuals for polynomial fit.

Table 1: Indicators for the flash unit model fitting results.

Output variables (t/h)	Polynomial RMSE	Polynomial R^2
$Fout_{H2}$	9.18×10^{-5}	
$Fout_{C1}$	3.78×10^{-3}	
$Fout_{C2}$	3.20×10^{-3}	
$Fout_{C3}$	5.24×10^{-3}	
$Fout_{C4}$	1.12×10^{-3}	0.999997
$Fout_{C5}$	4.85×10^{-4}	
$Fout_{H2S}$	1.40×10^{-2}	
$Fout_{gas}$	1.25×10^{-2}	

3.1.2. Hydrotreaters

The empirical model for the hydrotreaters provided by Umana et al. (2014) was reformulated into a much simpler form. For the hydrotreater, six input variables and eight output variables were chosen which is illustrated in Fig 3.

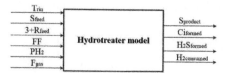

Figure 3: Hydrotreater model with input variables and output variables.

where T_{rin} is temperature, S_{feed} is sulphur content in the feed flow, $3+R_{feed}$ is 3+ring core aromatic content in the feed flow, FF is inlet oil flow rate, P_{H2} is hydrogen partial pressure, F_{gas} is inlet gas flow rate, $S_{product}$ is sulphur content in the product, C_{formed} is amount of light hydrocarbons formed, Ci=C1-C5, H_2S_{formed} is amount of H_2S formed, and $H_{2consumed}$ is hydrogen consumption of the hydrotreater.

Table 2: Indicators for the hydrotreater model fitting results.

Output variables	Polynomial RMSE	Polynomial R^2
$S_{product}$ (ppwm)	9.88×10^{-2}	
$C1_{formed}$ (t/h)	2.09×10^{-6}	
$C2_{formed}$ (t/h)	3.90×10^{-6}	
$C3_{formed}$ (t/h)	1.27×10^{-5}	
$C4_{formed}$ (t/h)	1.40×10^{-5}	0.999986
$C5_{formed}$ (t/h)	4.86×10^{-6}	
H_2S_{formed} (t/h)	8.53×10^{-4}	
$H_{2consumed}$ (t/h)	7.17×10^{-5}	

Table 2 and Fig. 4 give the results for the hydrotreater surrogate model fitting. The indictors and residual plots all suggest good fitting.

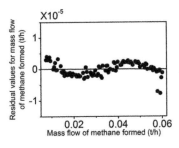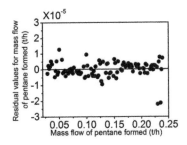

Figure 4: Plot of residuals for polynomial fit.

3.2. Synthesis and optimization of the hydrogen network

As noticed, the use of first-principles-based models in an optimization platform would be unfeasible due to high computational time and technical difficulties. Surrogate models developed in Section 3.1 can be employed in the solution of the synthesis problem, due to their great versatility. The objective function is to minimize the operating cost that accounts for the hydrogen production cost and fuel gas value. Operation conditions (T and P) for the flash units were set as fixed, constraint for sulphur content in oil product were imposed and the required hydrogen consumption for each hydrotreater were optimization variables for this problem. It was solved in GAMS which takes 0.172 s to give a result. The result is shown in Figure 5. For the flash unit, the established surrogate models fully consider the changing characteristics of K-value along with the conditions of feed flow. The details of inlet conditions were provided by Umana et al. (2014). When compared with the previous work (Table 3), it indicates a comparatively higher production rate of H_2S in the outlet of the flash unit which may cause more H_2S in the recycle stream sent to the reactor. As a result, more of the purge gas from DHT unit was suggested to be sent to the fuel system.In other words, the necessary constraint for H_2S accumulation in the system prevented further reuse of the DHT purge gas. Thus, it can be concluded that a more accurate model for the flash process is necessary in obtaining a more accurate simulation result for the hydrotreating process.

Table 3: Results comparison between the proposed method and the literature.

		Outlet of DHT flash units	
		This study	Previous study
Flowrate (t/h)		42.905	46.811
	H_2	0.1404	0.3939
	C_1	0.3842	0.5895
	C_2	0.0048	0.0053
Compositions(mass fraction)	C_3	0.0082	0.0034
	C_4	0.0037	0.0017
	C_5	0.0005	0.0007
	H_2S	0.4582	0.0055

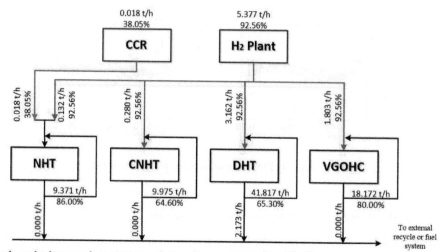

H₂ plant: hydrogen plant. CCR: catalytic reformer. DHT: diesel hydrotreater. NHT: naphtha hydrotreater. CNHT: cracked naphtha hydrotreater. VGOHC: vacuum gas oil hydrocracker.

Figure 5: Integrated hydrogen network under varying hydrogen consumption

4. Conclusion

This paper introduces a methodology to optimize the design of refinery hydrogen network by using surrogate models to reflect the chemical and physical process in the hydrotreaters and flash units. When applied in a case study, the established surrogate models achieved reasonable fit, and the synthesis problem can be solved efficiently. Compared with results provided in the previous work, it was notice that necessary constraints of inlet H_2S flow rate should be considered, causing by a large amount of outlet H_2S flow of the DHT flash unit. This difference can be attributed to the consideration of the changing separation efficiency of flash units along with the feed flow conditions. As a result, more realistic results can be obtained by using the proposed models.

References

A. I. J. Forrester, A. Sobester, A. J. Keane, 2008. Engineering Design via Surrogate Modelling: A Practical Guide. Wiley , .

J. E. A. Graciano, G. A. C. Le Roux, 2013. Improvements in surrogate models for process synthesis. Application to water network system design. Computers and Chemical Engineering 59, 197–210.

N. Hallale, F. Liu, 2001. Refinery hydrogen management for clean fuels production. Advances in Environmental Research 6, 81–98.

N. Jia, N. Zhang, 2011. Multi-component optimization for refinery hydrogen networks. Energy 36, 4663–4670.

A. Kumar, G. Gautami, S. Khanam, 2010. Hydrogen distribution in the refinery using mathematical modelling. Energy 35, 3763–3772.

J. Sikorski, G. Brownbridge, S. Mosbach, M. Kraft, 2016. Parameterisation of a biodiesel plant process flow sheet model. Computers and Chemical Engineering 95, 108–122.

I. M. Sobol, 1967. Distribution of points in a cube and approximate evaluation of integrals. Ussr Computational Mathematics and Mathematical Physics 7, 86–112.

B. Umana, A. Shoaib, N. Zhang, R. Smith, 2014. Integrating hydroprocessors in refinery hydrogen network optimization. Applied Energy 133, 169–182.

Anton A. Kiss, Edwin Zondervan, Richard Lakerveld, Leyla Özkan (Eds.)
Proceedings of the 29th European Symposium on Computer Aided Process Engineering
June 16th to 19th, 2019, Eindhoven, The Netherlands. © 2019 Elsevier B.V. All rights reserved.
http://dx.doi.org/10.1016/B978-0-128-18634-3.50111-9

Real-time design space description in pharmaceutical manufacturing

Gabriele Bano,[a] Pierantonio Facco,[a] Marianthi Ierapetritou,[b] Fabrizio Bezzo,[a] Massimiliano Barolo[a*]

[a]CAPE-Lab, Department of Industrial Engineering, University of Padova, Italy

[b]Rutgers University, 98 Brett Road, Piscataway, NJ, 08854, USA

max.barolo@unipd.it

Abstract

In this paper, we present a methodology to assist the offline description and online maintenance of the design space of a pharmaceutical product. The methodology is intended as a proactive risk-management tool to be included in a design space submission. First, classical feasibility analysis is exploited to obtain an offline model-based description of the design space (e.g., at the process development stage). Then, a dynamic state estimator is used to continuously adapt the model during plant operation, using measurements available from plant sensors. Surrogate-based feasibility analysis is used to continuously update the model-based description of the design space based on the up-to-date model returned by the state estimator. The tracking effectiveness of the methodology is shown for a co-milling process of a pharmaceutical production.

Keywords: quality by design, design space, state estimation, pharmaceutical manufacturing, model maintenance

1. Introduction

Following the recent FDA ICH Q12 draft guideline (ICH, 2018), the design space (DS) of a pharmaceutical product represents a set of established conditions (raw material properties and critical process parameters, CPPs) that guarantee to fulfill predefined specifications on the product critical quality attributes (CQAs).

The DS is typically obtained at the product/process development stage by exploiting a process model (either mechanistic or data-driven) and targeted laboratory experimentation. In principle, if all disturbances and sources of uncertainty that may affect the model predictions were accounted for at this stage, working within the resulting model-based representation of the DS would guarantee the desired product quality. In practice, however, there is no guarantee that the prediction fidelity of the model will remain unchanged as process operation progresses (Pantelides and Renfro, 2013). Process-model mismatch may in fact arise from parameter drifts (e.g., a heat exchange coefficient may change due to fouling), or insufficient/inappropriate description of the underlying physical phenomena driving the process (e.g., unmodeled physical phenomena that could not be observed at the laboratory scale, such as the effect of downstream/upstream units or of environmental factors). The fact that, along a plant lifecycle, the model may not be able to accurately reproduce the actual plant behavior, questions the appropriateness of the operating conditions selected by using the DS description obtained at the development stage. In this regard, the recent ICH Q12 draft guideline (ICH, 2018) acknowledges that "(…) it may be necessary to change approved established conditions as a result of knowledge gained during product lifecycle…" and aims at providing a comprehensive regulatory framework on how to perform this in practice.

In this study, we propose a methodology to perform two sequential tasks: *i*) obtain an offline model-based description of the design space at the development stage; *ii*) obtain an up-to-date description of the design space as process operation progresses, by continuously reconciling the model predictions with the observed plant behavior. We intend the two activities (offline DS description and online DS maintenance) as complementary, making them appealing for a joint inclusion in a design space submission (i.e., for regulatory approval), in such a way as to reduce the burden of post-approval revision processes. We discuss the ability of the methodology to track the DS of a simulated de-lumping process of a pharmaceutical production using a conical miller.

2. Proposed methodology

Let us consider a dynamic system for the production of a pharmaceutical drug. The state-space representation of a pharmaceutical unit (or process) is typically given by a system of nonlinear differential-algebraic equations (DAEs) of the form:

$$\begin{bmatrix} \dot{\mathbf{x}}_1(t) \\ \mathbf{0} \end{bmatrix} = \begin{bmatrix} \mathbf{f}_1(\mathbf{x}_1(t), \mathbf{x}_2(t), \mathbf{q}(t), t) \\ \mathbf{f}_2(\mathbf{x}_1(t), \mathbf{x}_2(t), \mathbf{q}(t), t) \end{bmatrix} + \begin{bmatrix} \mathbf{w}_1(t) \\ \mathbf{w}_2(t) \end{bmatrix} \tag{1}$$

subject to initial conditions:

$$\mathbf{x}_1(0) = \mathbf{x}_{1,0} + \mathbf{w}_1(0) \tag{2}$$

where $\mathbf{x}_1(t)[N_1 \times 1]$ is the differential state vector, $\mathbf{x}_2(t)[N_2 \times 1]$ is the algebraic state vector, $\mathbf{w}_1(t)[N_1 \times 1]$ and $\mathbf{w}_2(t)[N_2 \times 1]$ are zero-mean random processes with unknown statistics representing the model error related to the differential and algebraic states respectively, and $\mathbf{q}(t) [M \times 1]$ is the vector collecting the raw material properties and CPPs (i.e., process parameters that have a strong effect on the product critical quality attributes). Formulation (1) assumes that there are no control variables (i.e., an open-loop scenario is considered). The model equations can also be concisely expressed in the implicit form:

$$\mathbf{F}(\dot{\mathbf{x}}_1(t), \dot{\mathbf{x}}_2(t), \mathbf{x}_1(t), \mathbf{x}_2(t), \mathbf{q}(t), t) = \mathbf{0} \ . \tag{3}$$

We assume the availability of measurements from plant sensors at each time step t_k. The L-dimensional measurement vector at time t_k is denoted as $\mathbf{y}(t_k)$, and its relation $\mathbf{h}(\cdot)$ with the state vector is given by:

$$\mathbf{y}(t_k) = \mathbf{h}(\mathbf{x}_1(t_k), \mathbf{x}_2(t_k), t_k) + \mathbf{v}(t_k); \ k = 1,2, \dots, K \quad , \tag{4}$$

where $\mathbf{v}(t_k) [L \times 1]$ is the measurement noise.

The proposed methodology can be summarized in four steps.

Step #1: offline DS description. This activity is typically performed at the development stage. Given the process model (3), we define the feasibility function $\boldsymbol{\Psi} (\mathbf{q}(t), \mathbf{x}_1(t), \mathbf{x}_2(t), t)$ as the maximum value of the I quality constraints imposed on the product CQAs:

$$\Psi(\mathbf{q}(t), \mathbf{x}_1(t), \mathbf{x}_2(t), t) = \max_{i \in I} g_i(\mathbf{q}(t), \mathbf{x}_1(t), \mathbf{x}_2(t), t), \quad i = 1, \dots, I \tag{5}$$

where $g_i(\mathbf{q}(t), \mathbf{x}_1(t), \mathbf{x}_2(t), t), i = 1, \dots, I$ is the set of quality constraints.. Based on this definition, the model-based description $\widehat{DS}$ of the design space (i.e. the set of CPPs and raw material properties that allow satisfying all quality constraints) is obtained by exploiting classical feasibility analysis (Halemane and Grossmann, 1983) according to:

$$\widehat{DS} = \{\mathbf{q}(t) | \Psi(\mathbf{q}(t), \mathbf{x}_1(t), \mathbf{x}_2(t), t) \leq 0\}. \tag{6}$$

The description of the DS as expressed by Eq. (6) requires the solution of the following bilevel optimization problem (also called flexibility test problem (Halemane and Grossmann, 1983)):

$$\chi = \max_{\mathbf{q}(t) \in \mathbf{Q}(t)} \Psi(\mathbf{q}(t), \mathbf{x}_1(t), \mathbf{x}_2(t), t) \qquad \text{subject to} \tag{7}$$

$$\mathbf{F}(\dot{\mathbf{x}}_1(t), \mathbf{x}_1(t), \mathbf{x}_2(t), \mathbf{q}(t), t) = \mathbf{0}; \quad \mathbf{x}_1(0) = \mathbf{x}_{1,0} \tag{8}$$

$$\mathbf{Q}(t) = \{\mathbf{q}(t) | \mathbf{q}^{lo}(t) \leq \mathbf{q}(t) \leq \mathbf{q}^{up}(t)\} \quad .$$

The DS description obtained according to Eq. (6) through the solution of (7)-(8) represents the best representation of the DS that can be obtained with the available process model and with the best estimate of the model parameters obtained at the laboratory scale.

Step #2: uncertain model parameters determination. The underlying assumptions that we make is that process-model mismatch can be compensated for by continuously updating the system state and recalibrating some of the original model parameters. The parameters that should be recalibrated online can be chosen according to two criteria:

a) if prior knowledge on the uncertainty or disturbances that may affect plant operation is available, the parameters are determined by preliminary qualitative diagnosis of the model structure;

b) if condition a) does not hold true, sensitivity analysis can be used to determine the parameters that most affect the product CQAs. Only these parameters will be continuously adjusted during plant operation, as they are strongly related with the accuracy of the model-based description of the DS.

The set of parameters that are recalibrated online is denoted as $\mathbf{p}(t)[V \times 1]$, with $V \leq L$.

Step #3: state estimation and online parameter recalibration. The state estimator proposed by Cheng *et al.* (1997) is exploited to obtain the current system state and to perform the parameter recalibration at each time step t_k. The peculiarity of this state estimator is that, despite the traditional extended Kalman filter (EKF), its derivation is directly obtained from the DAE formulation (1) and does not require any assumptions on the form of the distributions of the state vector and measurement vector (which are assumed as normally distributed in the standard EKF formulation). The ability of this state estimator to handle large nonlinear DAE systems (involving more than 200 differential equations and 14,000 algebraic equations) has been discussed recently (Pantelides *et al.*, 2016). The mathematical formulation of this estimator can be found in the cited reference.

The online parameter recalibration is obtained through a state augmentation procedure (Ricker and Lee, 1995), by augmenting the differential state vector $\mathbf{x}_1(t)$ with the set of uncertain parameters $\mathbf{p}(t)$. At each time step t_k, the state estimator returns the up-to-date values of $\mathbf{x}_1(t_k)$, $\mathbf{x}_2(t_k)$ and $\mathbf{p}(t_k)$.

Step #4: online DS maintenance. The up-to-date system state and parameter values returned by the state estimator are used to update the model-based description of the DS. The DS can be updated with the same measurement interval Δt_k at which measurements are collected from the plant or with a user-defined time interval Δt_m, provided that $\Delta t_m \geq \Delta t_k$. At each time t_m, the up-to-date DS representation is obtained according to:

$$\widehat{DS}_m = \{\mathbf{q}(t_m) | \Psi_m(\mathbf{q}(t_m), \mathbf{x}_1(t_m), \mathbf{x}_2(t_m), \mathbf{p}(t_m), t_m) \leq 0\} \tag{9}$$

by solving the flexibility test problem. The computational time required for the solution of the flexibility test problem must be smaller than the DS update interval Δt_m. If this condition does not hold true, surrogate-based feasibility analysis using a kriging or radial-basis function (RBF) surrogate can be used to make the online implementation viable. Mathematical details on this approach are discussed in Wang et al. (2017). For multidimensional design spaces (i.e., when the number of CPPs and raw material properties is greater than two), the joint projection to latent structures/RBF feasibility analysis approach proposed by Bano et al. (2018) can be exploited to reduce the problem dimensionality.

3. Test example

The application of the proposed methodology is illustrated for a simulated de-lumping operation of a pharmaceutical powder using a conical miller. The model proposed by Wang et al. (2017) is used to simulate the system behaviour. The model equations are given by Eq. (10)-(13) with the initial conditions and nominal values of the parameters reported in Table 1. The three state variables to be collected in vector $\mathbf{x}_1(t)$ are the mass holdup $M(t)$ in the co-mill, the outlet mass fraction $w_{API}(t)$ of the active pharmaceutical ingredient (API), and the outlet mass fraction $w_{ex}(t)$ of the excipient. The only algebraic state variable is the 90% D-value of the particle size distribution of the bulk material at the outlet $d_{90}^b(t)$, i.e. the diameter at which 90% of the bulk mass is comprised of smaller particles. Following the regulatory parlance, d_{90}^b is the product CQA, the impeller blade speed ω is a CPP, and the 90% D-value of the API at the inlet $d_{90,API}^{in}$ is a raw material property affecting the product CQA. Both ω and $d_{90,API}^{in}$ are considered as time-invariant.

4. Simulation set-up and results

It is desired to obtain a bulk material that satisfies the condition $222.5 \leq d_{90}^b \leq 224 \ [\mu m]$ within 100s of co-milling operation. The design space for this process is defined as the set of combinations of $(\omega, d_{90,API}^{in})$ that guarantee to obtain the desired specifications for $d_{90}^b(t)$ within the desired time frame.

Table 1. Initial conditions for the differential state variables and nominal values of the parameters of model (10)-(13).

Variable/ parameter	Units	Value
M_0	[kg]	0.19
$w_{API,0}$	[-]	0
$w_{ex,0}$	[-]	1
τ_{max}	[s]	40
ω_{min}	[rad/s]	104.62
a	[rad/s]	10.47
b	[m³/s]	1

$$\bar{\tau}\frac{dM(t)}{dt} + M(t) = \bar{\tau}F^{in}; \qquad (10)$$

$$\frac{d(w_i^{out}M(t))}{dt} = w_i^{in}F^{in} - \frac{w_i^{out}M(t)}{\bar{\tau}} \quad i = \text{API,ex}; \qquad (11)$$

$$\bar{\tau} = \tau_{max}\left[1 - \exp\left(-\frac{a}{\omega-\omega_{min}} - \frac{b}{F^{in}}\right)\right]; \qquad (12)$$

$$d_{90}^b(t) = w_{API}(t)d_{90,API}^{in} + w_{ex}(t)d_{90,API}^{in} \qquad (13)$$

The empirical relation (12) for the mean residence time is obtained from residence time distribution (RTD) experiments performed at the laboratory scale, and the regression parameters (τ_{max}, a, b) are therefore subject to a high degree of uncertainty when used to simulate a full-scale operation. Moreover, obtaining accurate initial values for the mass holdup and mass fractions (which both depend on upstream units) can be cumbersome.

In order to test the DS tracking performance of the proposed methodology, a situation was investigated where the model structure was correct, but erroneous values of the model parameters were used as well as an incorrect initial estimate of the system state. Specifically, a +10% deviation on the initial state estimate M_0 and a +35% deviation on the nominal value of parameter τ_{max} were enforced. The choice of enforcing a parametric mismatch on τ_{max} was dictated by the fact that its effect on the product CQA is considerably stronger than the other two regression parameters (a, b). Synthetic measurements of mass holdup to be fed to the estimator were generated at a frequency of 1 Hz; noise was simulated by adding the random error $v(t_k) \sim N(0,0.01^2)$ to the simulation results. The covariance for the model error $\mathbf{w}_1 \sim (0, \mathbf{Q})$ state estimator was set by trial and error to the value $\mathbf{Q} = \text{diag}(0.05^2; 0.001^2; 0.001^2)$ for each time step t_k

The DS that can be obtained from model (10)-(13) with the correct initial state and nominal values of τ_{max} of Table 1 is denoted as the actual DS of the process. On the other hand, the DS as predicted by the estimator is denoted as the estimated DS. The actual DS is shown in the contour plot of Fig. 1a (i.e., the portion of the input domain within which the feasibility function is smaller than 0). Fig. 1b shows the discrepancy between the actual DS and the estimated DS that would be obtained at the development stage with a wrong estimate of the initial state of the system and of the parameter τ_{max}. Fig. 1c-1f show the tracking ability of the proposed methodology after 5,10,15 and 20 s of process operation (i.e., $\Delta t_m = 5s$). A RBF surrogate was exploited to reconstruct the boundary of the DS given the up-to-date model returned by the state estimator. The actual DS is recovered after ~20 s of operation, i.e., in less than 1/5 of the total co-milling operation.

5. Conclusions

The aim of this study was to propose a systematic methodology to assist the offline description and online maintenance of the design space of a pharmaceutical product. First,

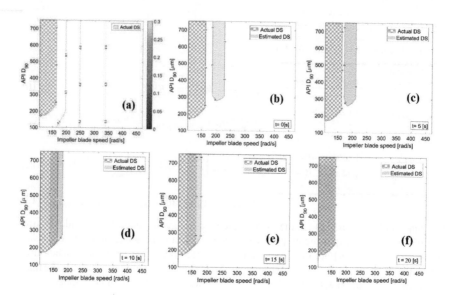

Figure 1. (a) Actual design space, (b) Estimated DS and actual DS at the development stage; estimated DS and actual DS after (c) 5s, (d) 10s, (e) 15s and (f) 20s of plant operation.

surrogate-based feasibility analysis was exploited to obtain an initial offline description of the design space using the available process model. Then, given few online measurements made available by plant sensors, an automatic strategy was proposed to continuously update the design space as plant operation progresses. The ability of the proposed approach to track a 35% parametric mismatch and a 10% error on the initial state estimate for a co-mill process of a pharmaceutical powder was shown. Applications of the proposed DS maintenance tool include open-loop decision support, real-time optimization, definition of optimal set-points or set-point trajectories within the boundary of the up-to-date design space.

References

Bano, G., Wang Z., Facco, P., Bezzo, F., Barolo, M., Ierapetritou M. (2018) A novel and systematic approach to identify the design space of pharmaceutical processes. *Comput. Chem. Eng.* **115**, 309-322.

Cheng, Y.S., Mongkhonsi, T., Kershenbaum, L.S (1997) Sequential estimation for nonlinear differential and algebraic systems- theoretical development and application. *Comput. Chem. Eng.* **21**,1051-1067.

Halemane, K. P., Grossmann, I. E. (1983) Optimal process design under uncertainty. *AIChE J.*, **29**: 425-433.

ICH (2018) Q12 - Technical and regulatory considerations for pharmaceutical product lifecycle management. Core guideline for industry.

Pantelides, C. C., Renfro, J. G. (2013) The online use of first-principles models in process operations: Review, current status and future needs. *Comput. Chem. Eng.* **51**, 136-148

Pantelides, C.C., Bano, G., Cheng Y.S., Spatenka S., Matzopoulos M., *Model-based real time monitoring of ethylene cracking furnaces*, 2016 AIChE Spring Meeting & 12th Global congress on process safety: Houston, TX; paper 444934

Ricker, N. L., and Lee, J. H. (1995). Nonlinear modeling and state estimation for the Tennessee Eastman challenge process. *Comput. Chem. Eng*, **19**, 983-1005

Wang, Z., Escotet-Espinoza, M. S., & Ierapetritou, M. (2017). Process analysis and optimization of continuous pharmaceutical manufacturing using flowsheet models. *Comput. Chem. Eng.*, **107**, 77-91.

Anton A. Kiss, Edwin Zondervan, Richard Lakerveld, Leyla Özkan (Eds.)
Proceedings of the 29th European Symposium on Computer Aided Process Engineering
June 16th to 19th, 2019, Eindhoven, The Netherlands. © 2019 Elsevier B.V. All rights reserved.
http://dx.doi.org/10.1016/B978-0-128-18634-3.50112-0

Flexibility Assessment of a Distillation Train: Nominal vs Perturbated Conditions Optimal Design

Alessandro Di Pretoro[a,b], Ludovic Montastruc[a*], Flavio Manenti[b], Xavier Joulia[a]

[a]Laboratoire de Génie Chimique, Université de Toulouse, CNRS/INP/UPS, Toulouse, France

[b]Politecnico di Milano, Dipartimento di Chimica, Materiali e Ingegneria Chimica "Giulio Natta", Piazza Leonardo da Vinci 32, 20133 Milano, Italia

ludovic.montastruc@ensiacet.fr

Abstract

Multicomponent mixtures can be separated into their single components by mean of different distillation train configurations. The standard design procedure consists of the assessment of the optimal columns configuration according to the economic and operational aspects. Anyway this optimal design is strictly related to the operating conditions, i.e. perturbations, when present, can seriously turn the tables. In these cases a flexibility analysis could be of critical importance to assess the operating conditions range of better performance for a system configuration with respect to another one.

This is the typical case of biorefineries (and bio-processes in general) where the composition perturbations downstream the fermenter across the year's seasons are completely normal due to the floating nature of the feedstock. Since no similar studies have been found in literature, a brand new ABE/W (acetone, n-butanol, ethanol, water) mixture separation case study has been set up; this mixture derives from an upstream microbial conversion process and the successful recovery of at least biobutanol and acetone is crucial for the profitability of the operation.

Therefore the purpose of this paper is the comparison between the possible distillation train configurations from a flexibility point of view. We are interested in particular in highlighting the differences, if present, between the economic optimal solution and flexibility optimal configuration that sometimes could not be the same, causing this way a very profitable design to be much less performant under perturbated conditions.

The flexibility assessment has been performed with an established procedure introduced in previous papers; all the flexibility indexes proposed in literature have been used both of simple and most complex usage in order to refine the analysis and a flexibility economic assessment has been carried out as well. Finally the two different configurations as well as the two different procedures (operating conditions based vs perturbated conditions based) have been compared both from a design and an economic point of view; then analogies and differences as well as their consequences from a decision making point of view have been highlighted and discussed.

Keywords: flexibility analysis, design optimization, distillation, column trains

1. Introduction

In refinery operations distillation has always been the leading separation process. In designing a distillation column, given the inlet streams (T, P, partial flowrates), column top pressure, type of condenser (total or partial) and two design (separation) specifications, one degree of freedom stays unfilled. Either reflux ratio R (or ratio R/R_{min}) or number of stages N should be fixed in order to univocally determine the unit design, anyway no physical constraints can help us to make a choice.

The standard decision making process to select the number of stages is indeed an economic-based optimization. Capital and operating costs for given specifications are calculated at different number of stages N (i.e. reflux ratios); due to the increasing CAPEX and the decreasing OPEX trends with respect to N, the total cost function shows a minimum for the R and N values corresponding to the most profitable column design. However it is worth selecting less profitable solutions whether the optimum point is located close to R_{min} or N_{min} conditions.

When multicomponent mixtures have to be treated, distillation trains need to be designed. Several distillation train configurations are possible according to the amount of components present in the feed and how many of them are worth to be recovered. For instance the simplest configurations for a multicomponent mixture with two components recovery required are shown in Figure 1. They're namely defined as:

    A) indirect configuration (sequential recovery from the heaviest to the lightest component);

    B) direct configuration (sequential recovery from the lightest to the heaviest component);

    C) midsplit configuration (a preliminary split between heaviest and lightest components is performed, then the separation is refined to achieve specification).

Each single column (and related equipment) is then designed on the basis of the lowest total cost and the cheapest train configuration is selected.

This procedure is well established and it has always worked well so far, anyway it has a main limitation: the economic assessment and equipment design are strictly related to the nominal operating conditions, i.e. they don't take into account feedstock or operating conditions perturbations that could occur. This means that, whether a feed composition perturbation occurs, the system could not be able to achieve the separation specifications or at least a relevant increase of operating costs can be detected causing the most profitable design not to be as profitable as expected.

In refinery's operation these problem are less appreciable since long-term contracts for crude oil supplying and blending processes ensure an almost constant and stable feedstock quality. However, during last 15 years there has been an increasing interest for the production of chemicals and fuels from renewable resources because of growing concerns about global warming and climatic change, increasing crude oil price and existing legislations restricting the use of non-renewable energy sources. The direct consequence of this trend results in an even more increasing demand for bio-based fuels and raw materials, i.e. bio-refinery processes. Anyway bio-processes are highly subjected to composition perturbations downstream the fermenter across the year's seasons due to the floating nature of the feedstock.

Being fermentation usually carried out as a batch process, in order to ensure the desired daily productivity, several fermenters working at the same time are required. On the other hand, even when continuous fermenters are used, their scale up and then the feed flowrate that can be processed have a limit. These conditions cause the fermentation process section to be very expensive, therefore a constantly good performance of the products recovery section is of critical importance for the profitability of the plant.

In the light of the above an a priori flexibility analysis of the different distillation train configurations is non-optional for this kind of separation in order to allow the decision maker to make a multi-criteria-based choice about the optimal design to be selected.

2. Objectives and methodology

The purpose of the paper is the economic and flexibility based comparison between different distillation train configurations aimed to the same separation specifications.

As already mentioned, the economic optimal design provided was determined by mean of the usual procedure; capital and operating costs have been estimated using Guthrie (1969) – Ulrich (1984) - Navarrete (2001) correlations.

Flexibility analysis has been performed both from a deterministic (Swaney & Grossmann, 1985; Saboo and Morari, 1985) and a stochastic (Pistikopoulos & Mazzuchi, 1990) point of view and coupled with economics according to the procedure shown by Di Pretoro et al. (2019).

ProSim Plus® process simulator has been used to assess the feasibility of the separation as well as to estimate all process parameters.

Since no former application of flexibility analysis to distillation trains has been found in literature, a new case study referring to the separation of an ABE/W mixture, coming from a fermentation process and a preliminary dewatering operation, has been proposed. The feed composition is listed in Table 1.

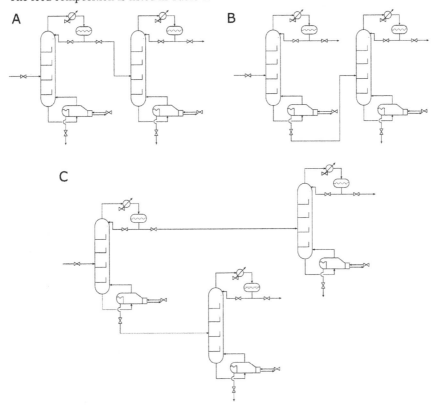

Figure 1 - Distillation train configurations for two components recovery

Table 1 - Feed components partial flowrates

Component	Partial flowrate (mol/s)
Acetone	12.030
Ethanol	3.839
n-Butanol	61.328
Water	12.428

The successful recovery of at least biobutanol and acetone is considered crucial for the profitability of the operation. In order to do this, a minimum of two distillation columns are required and three configurations are possible as previously shown in Figure 1. Midsplit configuration specifications are as follows:

1. Split column:
   1.1. Acetone recovery ratio in the distillate: 0.995;
   1.2. n-Butanol recovery ratio in the bottom: 0.98;
2. Acetone recovery column (top column):
   2.1. Acetone recovery ratio in the distillate: 0.995;
   2.2. Distillate acetone mass fraction: 0.995;
3. n-Butanol recovery column (bottom column):
   3.1. n-Butanol recovery ratio in the bottom: 0.98;
   3.2. Bottom n-butanol mass fraction: 0.99.

Specifications for direct and indirect configuration can be easily deducted from the midsplit ones. The direct configuration has resulted to be highly unfeasible since we should recover in the first column a highly acetone concentrated stream from a feed with a very low acetone molar fraction. Therefore only indirect and midsplit configurations will be compared.

3. Optimal design and flexibility assessment

As already mentioned, the standard design procedure has been conducted as usual; optimal number of stages and relative annual total cost for each column are listed in Table 2. With an overall annual cost of 933,509 $/y vs 1,084,082 the indirect configuration results to be the most convenient with respect to the midsplit one.

The addition of a preliminary column indeed does not substantially affect the acetone column utilities consumption.

Table 2 - Distillation train optimal design

	1st column		2nd column		3rd column	
	N (feed)	Cost ($/y)	N (feed)	Cost ($/y)	N (feed)	Cost ($/y)
Indirect	16 (10)	580,016	50 (46)	353,493	/	/
Midsplit	35 (9)	455,493	50 (47)	352,224	16 (8)	276,365

First of all a flexibility analysis based only on the actual feasibility of the separation (i.e. without taking into account equipment sizing) has been performed. The most critical parameters, as well as the most likely to change, are water and butanol fractions; therefore water and butanol partial flowrates were then considered the uncertain parameters for the analysis.

Despite what usually happens in these situations and what we expected, the midsplit configuration, i.e. the one with one column more, doesn't result to be more flexible than the indirect one as shown in Figure 2. On the contrary it is slightly less performant. For a water vs. n-butanol ratio higher than 0.23 (0.22 for the midsplit) indeed the separation is not feasible at all.

According to the Swaney & Grossmann index (F_{SG}), that assesses the highest simultaneous perturbation of all uncertain parameters that the system is able to withstand, the indirect configuration flexibility is about 5% (midsplit about 4%). According to Saboo & Morari the Resilience Index (RI), that defines the largest total disturbance load a system is able to withstand independently of the direction of the disturbance, stays around 8% (midsplit about 7%). Finally, according to the Pistikopoulos & Mazzuchi stochastic flexibility index, evaluating the probability that the system could absorb the disturbance, we find SF=77.86% (75.85% for the midsplit) in case of a normal probability perturbation distribution with a 10% variance. These values don't take into account the equipment sizing but thermodynamics only; it means no matter how much we pay for a bigger reboiler or a larger column, no higher flexibility value can be achieved. The same feasibility region has been obtained by changing the columns number of stages between approximately 0.75 and 1.5 times N_{opt}.

Flexibility analysis and economic assessment have then been coupled as shown in Di Pretoro et al. (2019). Total annual costs vs. partial flowrates perturbations have been plotted for the indirect configuration in Figure 3.a. An analogous trend has been obtained for the midsplit configuration.

However, the three columns configuration keeps being more expensive than the two column one, i.e. even under perturbated condition the external duties overconsumption is not compensated by the additional equipment despite what usually happens in standard distillation cases.

Costs result to be higher whether a bigger oversizing is necessary, i.e. positive deviation for both water and butanol flowrates, and along the operating conditions close to the feasibility boundary.

Moreover, the additional cost vs. flexibility plot for the deterministic indexes is reported in Figure 3.b as well; since F_{SG} represents the flexibility related to the simultaneous deviation of all uncertain variables, it implies a higher cost compared to the same RI value.

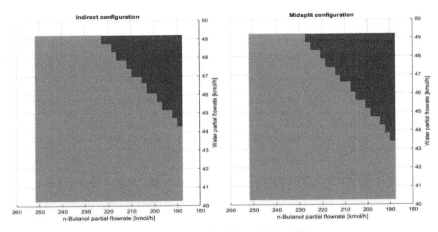

Figure 2 - Feasibility diagrams (Green = Feasible, Blue = Unfeasible)

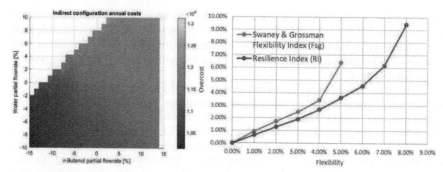

Figure 3 - Economic assessment (Indirect configuration): a. Costs vs. partial flowrates; b. Costs vs. flexibility

4. Conclusions

This paper introduces the comparison of distillation trains configurations both on a flexibility and economical basis. Flexibility assessment of distillation trains (involving both series and parallel columns) have been successfully performed with deterministic as well as stochastic indexes. Results have then been coupled with an economic assessment in order to obtain the overcost vs. flexibility analysis plot providing a critical tool to the decision maker.

The indirect configuration, that was the cheapest one, resulted to be also a little bit more flexible than the midsplit configuration, despite the expectation. The economic gap due to the additional column is conserved also under uncertain conditions as well as non-optimal column design. Moreover we can state that beyond a $F_{SG}=4\%$ or RI=7% it is less worth investing since the additional costs line becomes steeper.

However, beside the numerical results that are case-specific, the outcome of general validity is that, in thermodynamically constrained system, the feasibility and flexibility boundaries cannot go over a certain value by adding separation stages to the distillation column or, in general, investing more. An a priori flexibility analysis and economic assessment could then be crucial for making the best design choice and to know the limitation of our system if perturbations are likely to occur.

References

[1] K. M. Guthrie, 1969, 'Capital Cost Estimating', Chemical Engineering, 76.3, 114-142.
[2] G. D. Ulrich, 1984, 'A Guide to Chemical Engineering Process Design and Economics', Wily.
[3] P. F. Navarrete and W. C. Cole, 2001, 'Planning, Estimating, and Control of Chemical Construction Projects', 2nd Edition, CRC Press.
[4] R.E. Swaney and I.E. Grossmann, 1985, 'An Index for Operational Flexibility in Chemical Process Design. Part I: Formulation and Theory', AIChE Journal, 31, 621-630.
[5] Ak Saboo, M. Morari, and Dc Woodcock, 1985, 'Design of Resilient Processing Plants .8. a Resilience Index for Heat-Exchanger Networks', Chemical Engineering Science, 40.8, 1553-1565.
[6] E. N. Pistikopoulos and T. A. Mazzuchi, 1990, 'A Novel Flexibility Analysis Approach for Processes with Stochastic Parameters', Computers & Chemical Engineering, 14.9, 991_1000.
[7] A. Di Pretoro , L. Montastruc, F. Manenti, X. Joulia, 2019, 'Flexibility analysis of a distillation column: indexes comparison and economic assessment', Accepted by Computers and Chemical Engineering the 2nd February 2019.

Anton A. Kiss, Edwin Zondervan, Richard Lakerveld, Leyla Özkan (Eds.)
Proceedings of the 29th European Symposium on Computer Aided Process Engineering
June 16th to 19th, 2019, Eindhoven, The Netherlands. © 2019 Elsevier B.V. All rights reserved.
http://dx.doi.org/10.1016/B978-0-128-18634-3.50113-2

Dynamic Modelling and Simulation of Chinese Hamster Ovary (CHO) Cell Fermentation for Advanced Biopharmaceutical Manufacturing

Haruku Shirahata,[a] Samir Diab,[b] Hirokazu Sugiyama,[a] Dimitrios I. Gerogiorgis[b*]

[a] *Department of Chemical System Engineering, University of Tokyo, 113-8656, Japan*

[b] *School of Engineering (IMP), University of Edinburgh, Edinburgh, EH9 3FB, UK*

D.Gerogiorgis@ed.ac.uk

Abstract

Chinese hamster ovary (CHO) cells are widely used in fermentation processes towards biopharmaceutical manufacturing of monoclonal antibodies (mAbs). This work presents dynamic models of two different fermentation modes: batch mode to produce interferon (IFN)-γ and perfusion mode to produce mAbs. The models predict concentration profiles of cells, substrate, by-product and product, which are validated versus experimental results from the literature. Sensitivity analyses were conducted to establish important parameters for dynamic states that can be investigated in process design. Time and operating costs were evaluated using dynamic models for batch and perfusion modes. Varying initial cell concentration shows a trade-off between production time and cost towards modelling and optimisation of advanced biopharmaceutical manufacturing.

Keywords: Chinese hamster ovary (CHO) cells; Fermentation; Process design.

1. Introduction

The biopharmaceuticals market is growing rapidly compared to that of conventional pharmaceuticals (Otto, Santagostino and Schrader, 2014). Typical manufacturing processes comprise of drug substance manufacturing, including fermentation and purification to produce active pharmaceutical ingredients (APIs), and drug product manufacturing for formulation (Fig. 1). Fermentation of mammalian cells is widely implemented in different operation modes for biopharmaceuticals; batch and fed-batch modes are commonly implemented, and perfusion operations are developed towards continuous manufacturing (Bielser et al., 2018). Dynamic modelling of fermentation processes can be implemented for quantitative comparative evaluation of different designs prior to expensive and laborious experimental campaigns and pilot plant studies.

Chinese hamster ovary (CHO) cell fermentation is often implemented for the production of monoclonal antibodies (mAbs), a class of biopharmaceuticals produced in high sales volumes (Ecker, Jones and Levine, 2015). Different fermentation modes are implemented in the literature for the production of various mAbs (Kelley, 2009). This work implements dynamic modelling incorporating CHO cell fermentation kinetics for two different culture modes (batch and perfusion) for advanced biopharmaceutical manufacturing process design. Model validation versus experimental results is implemented to establish which biological phenomena are well represented by the models. Parametric sensitivity analyses are then implemented to elucidate critical kinetic and design parameters in the models. Process design and economic evaluation under varying assumptions are then presented.

2. Dynamic Process Modelling of Fermentation Processes

Biopharmaceutical products from fermentation are synthesised as metabolites of biological cells following substrate consumption and accompanied by cell growth and waste generation. Fermentation processes are typically operated in either batch, fed-batch of perfusion modes prior to purification and formulation of the final drug product, as shown in Fig. 1. Batch operation begins with all cells and culture media in the bioreactor, and solution containing products is removed at the end of the run. Fed-batch mode feeds substrate intermittently to control nutrient concentrations throughout the batch cycle. Perfusion mode fermentation constantly feeds and harvests the bioreactor, with bleeding to control cell concentrations, in an effort towards attaining the operational benefits of continuous manufacturing, which is being adopted for certain APIs in conventional pharmaceutical manufacturing. This work considers batch fermentation for interferon (IFN)-γ production and perfusion fermentation to produce fully-humanised mAb.

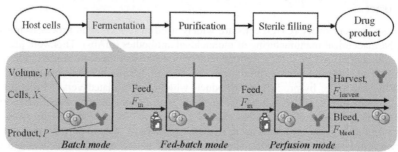

Figure 1: Typical biopharmaceutical manufacturing process and different culture modes.

2.1. Batch Mode Fermentation

Fox et al. (2004) developed a dynamic model for the batch CHO cell fermentation to produce IFN-γ, described by Eqs. 1–5. The model describes concentration profiles of cells (X), substrate (glucose, S), and product (IFN-γ, P) as a function of time (t). The specific cell growth (μ) and substrate consumption (q_S) are explicitly considered via Monod kinetics; the specific product formation rate (q_P), maximum specific growth rate (μ_{max}), maximum specific substrate consumption rate (q_{max}), Monod constant (K) and substrate consumption rate (K_S) are defined in the literature. The value of μ depends on S with respect to the threshold substrate concentration (S_t) (Fox et al., 2004).

$$\frac{dX}{dt} = \mu X \tag{1}$$

$$\frac{dS}{dt} = -q_S X \tag{2}$$

$$\frac{dP}{dt} = q_P X \tag{3}$$

$$q_S = \frac{q_{max} S}{K_S + S} \tag{4}$$

$$\mu = \frac{\mu_{max} S}{K + S} \ (S \geq S_t); \ \mu = 0 \ (S < S_t) \tag{5}$$

2.2. Perfusion Mode Fermentation

Karst et al. (2017) developed a dynamic model for the perfusion mode fermentation of CHO cells to produce fully-humanised mAb, described by Eqs. 6–10. In addition to concentration profiles of cells (X), substrate (S) and product (mAb, P), the perfusion model also describes concentration profile of waste product ammonia (A), which requires a value for the specific ammonia production rate (q_{amm}), defined in the literature (Karst et al., 2017), as well as the working volume variation (V). Steady-state operation and constant working volume are assumed by controlling the feed (F_{in}) and product (F_{out}) stream flowrates of the perfusion reactor; thus the time differential of the working volume (Eq. 9) is equal to zero. The outlet flowrate is controlled via the harvest ($F_{harvest}$) and bleed (F_{bleed}) rates, which depends on the working volume and the specific growth rate (μ). Bleed and harvest rates are calculated via Eq. 9. Monod kinetics describe μ, μ_{max} and the ammonia growth inhibition constant ($K_{\mu,amm}$) available in the literature (Karst et al., 2017).

$$\frac{\mathrm{d}(VX)}{\mathrm{d}t} = \mu VX - F_{bleed}X \tag{6}$$

$$\frac{\mathrm{d}(VP)}{\mathrm{d}t} = q_{p}VX - F_{harvest}P \tag{7}$$

$$\frac{\mathrm{d}(VA)}{\mathrm{d}t} = q_{amm}VX - F_{out}A \tag{8}$$

$$\frac{\mathrm{d}V}{\mathrm{d}t} = F_{in} - F_{out} = 0;\ F_{out} = F_{harvest} + F_{bleed}\ ;\ F_{bleed} = \mu V \tag{9}$$

$$\mu = \frac{\mu_{max}\ K_{\mu,amm}}{K_{\mu,amm} + A} \tag{10}$$

The implemented models for batch (Fox et al., 2004) and perfusion (Karst et al., 2017) mode fermentations do not account for cell death or the production or consumption of other compounds, e.g. lactate produced during the reaction due to the lack of parameters available for such phenomena. Development of these models to account for concentration profiles of additional species should be implemented given sufficient experimental data.

3. Results and Discussion

3.1. Dynamic Model Sensitivity Analysis

Sensitivity analyses were conducted for dynamic states for different fermentation modes to establish design and operating parameters for investigation during process design. Model parameters are perturbed individually by ±20% from their base values. The sensitivity of dynamic states on various design and operating parameters is measured by:

$$R = \frac{i_{0,perturbed} - i_{end,perturbed}}{i_{0,basecase} - i_{end,basecase}} - 1 \tag{11}$$

Here, R is the sensitivity ratio, $i_{0,perturbed}$ and $i_{0,basecase}$ are initial dynamic states with and without perturbations, respectively, while $i_{end,perturbed}$ and $i_{end,basecase}$ are the equivalent final dynamic states. The sensitivity of product concentration, P, to various kinetic and operating parameters is considered for both batch and perfusion fermentation processes.

Fig. 2 shows the sensitivity of product concentration (R_P) to various kinetic and operational parametric perturbations. For the batch fermentation, kinetic parameters K, K_S, q_{max}, q_P and μ_{max} have the greatest effect on product concentration, while S_t has a lesser effect. The batch fermentation initial cell and substrate concentrations (X_0 and S_0, respectively) affect product concentration more than initial product concentration (P_0). For the perfusion mode fermentation, product concentration is very sensitive to the value of q_P compared to other model kinetic parameters. The perfusion mode values for $F_{harvest}$, X_0 and V_0 have the most significant effect on product concentration compared to A_0 and P_0. Sensitivity analyses on dynamic models are important to elucidate key kinetic parameters that must be fit to a high degree of accuracy during parameter regression from experimental data as well as operating parameters that can be tuned during process design.

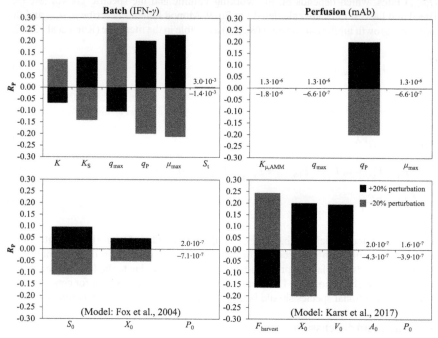

Figure 2: Product concentration sensitivity to different kinetic and operating parameters.

3.2. Dynamic Model Validation

The implemented dynamic models for batch and perfusion fermentation modes were compared versus published experimental data for model validation purposes. Fig. 3 shows profiles of X, S, A, P, and V for the batch and perfusion fermentation modes. The models were validated by t-testing, which showed good reproducibility with a significance level of 0.05 for both modes. The batch model reproduces the data well until $t = 98$ hr, after which cell concentration profiles significantly deviate due to the lack of cell death expressions in the model. For process design purposes, the maximum batch run time is assumed to equal 98 hr to ensure the model is viable. The perfusion model generally reproduces the experimental data well, with a slight over-prediction of P. Consideration of cell death in the model as well as concentration profiles of other significant biological compounds will enhance our understanding of the kinetic behaviour of this process.

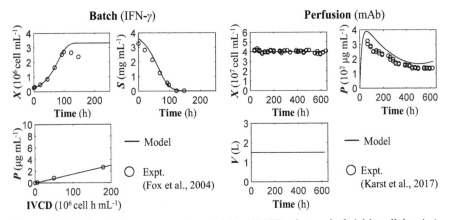

Figure 3: Model validation vs. experimental data (IVCD = integral of viable cell density).

3.3. Process Design Space Investigation and Economic Analysis

Economic evaluation of different process designs is imperative to elucidate promising cost-effective configurations. The current analysis investigates the effect of varying initial cell concentration on required production time and the corresponding normalised operating costs with respect to mass of product and bioreactor working volume. Operating costs (C_{OpEx}) are composed of cell (C_{cells}), media (C_{media}) and agitation ($C_{agitation}$) costs.

$$C_{OpEx} = C_{cells} + C_{media} + C_{agitation} \tag{12}$$

Fig. 4 shows production time and operating costs per unit product mass per unit bioreactor working volume for both batch and perfusion fermentation processes. In both cases, there is a trade-off between the processing time and the operating cost with varying initial cell concentration; as cell concentration increases, production time decreases, but a corresponding increase in cost is observed associated with increased cell quantities present in the fermentation broth. Cost calculations do not account for optimal batch numbers, sizes and scheduling, which will allow for improved costs and provide further insight into optimal design of the considered batch fermentation. Provision of production requirements, product sales prices and additional economic data for these particular processes will elucidate absolute cost components for clarification of economic viability.

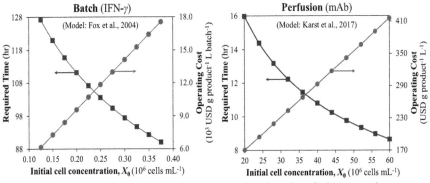

Figure 4: Production time and operating costs for batch and perfusion operations.

Consideration of perfusion downtimes and numbering-out/up of unit operations is another important consideration. Incorporation of detailed capital expenditure calculations into the total costs requires reliable cost-capacity correlations for specific biopharmaceutical manufacturing unit operations in order to gain insight into forecasted total costs. Provided accurate economic parameters, unit cost correlations and reduced model discrepancies with respect to experimental data, a dynamic optimisation problem formulation incorporating the kinetic models described in this work can allow elucidation of optimal control strategies of different dynamic parameters to meet specific economic objectives.

4. Conclusions

Dynamic models of different modes of fermentation of CHO cells were developed for manufacturing of different biopharmaceutical products: batch mode to produce IFN-γ and perfusion mode to produce fully-humanised mAb. The models were validated with experimental values from the literature, with the models for batch and perfusion modes showing good reproducibility. Sensitivity analyses of different operating parameters' effects on product concentrations established initial cell and substrate concentrations as important design variables for batch and perfusion modes. A trade-off between the production time and costs is observed for both fermentation modes. This work is the first to implement the described dynamic models for batch (Fox et al., 2004) and perfusion (Karst et al., 2017) CHO cell fermentation for process design and economic analysis of different biopharmaceutical manufacturing routes. Future work will implement the models into a dynamic optimisation problem formulation to establish optimal operating and design parameters for advanced biopharmaceutical manufacturing from CHO cells.

5. Acknowledgements

Ms. Haruku Shirahata acknowleges the support of the Global Leader Program for Social Design and Management and a Grant-in-Aid for JSPS Research Fellowship. Mr. Samir Diab acknowledges the support of the Engineering and Physical Sciences Research Council (EPSRC) via a Doctoral Training Partnership PhD Fellowship. Dr. Hirokazu Sugiyama acknowledges a Grant-in-Aid for Young Scientists Fellowship. All authors acknowledge the financial support of the Nagai and Great Britain Sasakawa Foundations.

References

J.M. Bielser, M. Wolf, J. Souquet, H. Broly and M. Morbidelli, 2018, Perfusion mammalian cell culture for recombinant protein manufacturing – a critical review, *Biotechnol. Adv.*, 36, 1328–1340.

D.M. Ecker, S.D. Jones and H.L. Levine, 2015, The therapeutic mAb market, *mAbs*, 7, 1, 9–14.

S.R. Fox, U.A. Patel, M.G.S.Yap and D.I.C. Wang, 2004, Maximizing IFN-γ production by chinese hamster ovary cells through temperature shift optimization, *Biotechnol. Bioeng.*, 85, 2, 177–184.

D.J. Karst, E. Scibona, E. Serra, J.M. Bielser, J. Souquet, M. Stettler, H. Broly, M. Soos, M. Morbidelli and T.K.Villiger, 2017, Modulation and modeling of monoclonal antibody N-linked glycosylation in mammalian cell perfusion reactor, *Biotechnol. Bioeng.*, 114, 9, 1978–1990.

B. Kelley, 2009, Industrialization of mAb production technology: the bioprocessing industry at a crossroads, *mAbs*, 1, 5, 443–452.

R. Otto, A. Santagostino and U. Schrader, 2014, The beauty and the beast: a perspective on biopharmaceuticals, McKinsey&Company, 9–18.

Anton A. Kiss, Edwin Zondervan, Richard Lakerveld, Leyla Özkan (Eds.)
Proceedings of the 29th European Symposium on Computer Aided Process Engineering
June 16th to 19th, 2019, Eindhoven, The Netherlands. © 2019 Elsevier B.V. All rights reserved.
http://dx.doi.org/10.1016/B978-0-128-18634-3.50114-4

Statistical diagnosis of process-model mismatch by means of the Lagrange multiplier test

Marco Quaglio[a], Eric S. Fraga[a] and Federico Galvanin[a,*]

[a]*Department of Chemical Engineering, University College London (UCL), Torrington Place, WC1E 7JE London, United Kingdom*

*f.galvanin@ucl.ac.uk

Abstract

Modelling chemical processes frequently requires the construction of complex systems of differential and algebraic equations involving a high number of state variables and parameters. Whenever a model structure is proposed, its adequacy is checked with a goodness-of-fit test. The goodness-of-fit test is capable of detecting the presence of over-fitting or under-fitting. However, when some modelling error is detected, the test does not provide guidance on how to modify the model equations to match the behaviour of the physical system under analysis. In this work, a test statistic is derived from a tailored Lagrange multiplier test with the aim of diagnosing potential sources of process-model mismatch and to provide guidance on how to evolve approximated model structures towards a higher level of complexity. The proposed test is applied on a simulated case study of a yeast growth model in a fed-batch bioreactor.

Keywords: model misspecification, model building, Lagrange multiplier, maximum likelihood, Fisher information

1. Introduction

The construction of a parametric model from observations of process behaviour generally requires significant effort both for i) building an opportune functional form for the model equations and ii) for precisely estimating its parameters. The former aspect frequently leads to the formulation of approximate model structures. A classical approach for assessing the adequacy of a process model is the goodness-of-fit test, which compares the model residuals against their expected distribution under the null hypothesis that the model structure is exact (Silvey, 1975). Two types of modelling errors can be detected with a two-tailed goodness-of-fit test:

- Over-fitting. The model involves an excessive number of free parameters, i.e. a simpler model structure shall be preferred to describe the process behaviour.

- Under-fitting. The model is neglecting relevant parameters and/or variables, i.e. the model structure is not sufficiently complex to capture the process behaviour. When the model is under-fitting there is a significant discrepancy between process observations and model predictions, i.e. a process-model (PM) mismatch.

Systematic approaches are available to amend the structure of an over-fitting model. One may perform further tests, e.g. the Wald test (Wald, 1943) or the univariate *t*-test for parameter significance (Asprey and Naka, 1999), with the aim of testing the hypothesis that some model parameters satisfy certain constraints. As an example, one may test the null hypothesis that some parameters equal zero. If there is not enough evidence to disprove this hypothesis, one shall favour the constrained model and fix those parameters to zero. This is frequently equivalent to excluding parameters (and the variables whose presence is controlled by those parameters) from the model structure. In the under-fitting case, the amendment of the model structure generally poses substantial challenges to the modeller. In fact, there may be significant uncertainty on which model components are correlated to the PM mismatch and on how to evolve the model structure for reducing and eventually eliminating the mismatch.

The importance of diagnosing the sources of PM mismatch is recognised in the literature on process monitoring (Wang et al., 2012; Badwe et al., 2009), but the problem is considered only in the context of linear, black-box models for control applications. An approach for diagnosing PM mismatch in first principle models was proposed by Meneghetti et al. (2014), where a latent variable model is used to highlight differences between process and model in the distribution of some auxiliary variables. These auxiliary variables represent user-defined combinations of variables and parameters appearing in the model. However, defining opportune auxiliary variables may not be obvious and the diagnosis is sensitive to their definition. A superstructure-based approach was suggested by Engle (1982), where the under-fitting model is regarded as a constrained instance of one or multiple alternative superstructures. A Lagrange multiplier test (Silvey, 1959) is then employed to challenge the model against the more complex alternatives. A limitation of this approach is that the definition of the superstructures relies entirely on the intuition of the modeller.

In this work, a model building approach is proposed where a Lagrange multiplier test is used to diagnose PM mismatch. The test does not require the definition of alternative model structures or the use of superstructures. Instead, the test aims at falsifying the hypothesis that a given model parameter is a state-independent constant. The test involves the computation of a score statistic which is proportional to the marginal fitting cost associated to the aforementioned hypothesis. It is shown that the score provides a useful index for guiding the evolution of the model towards a higher level of complexity. A high score associated to a parameter indicates strong evidence for justifying the evolution of the parameter into a state-dependent function.

2. Methodology

A model structure is proposed in Eq. (1) to describe a physical process of interest. In Eq. (1), $\mathbf{f}$ is a $N_f \times 1$ array of model functions, $\mathbf{x}$ is a $N_x \times 1$ array of state variables, $\dot{\mathbf{x}}$ is a $N_x \times 1$ array of time derivatives for the state variables, $\mathbf{u}$ is a $N_u \times 1$ array of manipulable system inputs, t is time and $\theta \in \Theta$ is a $N_\theta \times 1$ array of model parameters $\theta_1, ..., \theta_{N_\theta}$. In Eq. (1), $\hat{\mathbf{y}}$ is a $N_y \times 1$ array of model predictions for N_y measurable system states $\mathbf{y}$. Model predictions are expressed as a $N_y \times 1$ array of functions $\mathbf{h}$.

$$\mathbf{f}(\dot{\mathbf{x}}, \mathbf{x}, \mathbf{u}, t, \theta) = \mathbf{0}; \quad \hat{\mathbf{y}} = \mathbf{h}(\mathbf{x}, \mathbf{u}, t, \theta) \tag{1}$$

A dataset Y is available to estimate the parameters θ. The dataset Y consists of N samples of $\mathbf{y}$ where the i-th sample $\mathbf{y}_i$ is collected setting the system inputs to $\mathbf{u}_i$ and sampling at time t_i, i.e. $Y = \{(\mathbf{u}_i, t_i, \mathbf{y}_i) \text{ with } i = 1, ..., N\}$. Measurements for $\mathbf{y}$ are affected by Gaussian

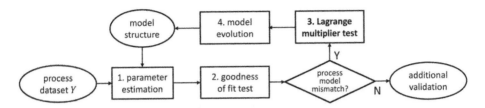

Figure 1: Simplified diagram showing the proposed model building approach.

noise with covariance matrix Σ. A model building framework implementing a step of PM mismatch diagnosis is introduced in Figure 1. The procedure involves the following steps:

1. A parameter estimation step. At this stage the model parameters θ are fitted to the available dataset Y employing a maximum likelihood approach.

2. A goodness-of-fit test. A test on the goodness-of-fit is performed to detect the presence of PM mismatch.

3. A Lagrange multiplier test. If PM mismatch is detected, a Lagrange multiplier test is performed to test the hypotheses that model parameters are state-independent constants by computing a likelihood-based score statistic.

4. A model evolution step. Parameters with the highest score statistic are evolved into state-dependent functions and the procedure is repeated from Step 1.

The iterative process interrupts when no PM mismatch is detected. One shall then proceed with additional model validation procedures, e.g. improving the precision of parameter estimates. Steps 1-3 in the procedure are further detailed in the following subsections. It is recognised that the convergence of the proposed approach relies on the selection of appropriate functional forms to evolve model parameters in the model evolution step. This aspect is going to be the focus in future research activities.

2.1. Parameter estimation

Let $\Phi(\theta|Y)$ be the log-likelihood function (Bard, 1974). The maximum likelihood estimate $\hat{\theta}$ is obtained solving the N_θ unconstrained likelihood equations Eq. (2).

$$\nabla\Phi(\hat{\theta}|Y) = \mathbf{0} \tag{2}$$

2.2. Goodness-of-fit test

The goodness-of-fit is evaluated with a 95% χ^2 test. The critical value χ^2_{ref} is computed from the χ^2 distribution with degree of freedom $N \cdot N_y - N_\theta$. If the test fails, PM mismatch is diagnosed by means of the Lagrange multiplier test illustrated in the following section.

2.3. Lagrange multiplier test

It is assumed that the elimination of the mismatch requires the replacement of a certain parameter with an opportune state-dependent function. A statistical test for diagnosing PM mismatch is now introduced with the aim of testing the hypothesis that a certain parameter θ_i is a state-independent constant. The competing hypotheses under test are:

- Null hypothesis: θ_i and θ_j, with $j \neq i$, are all state-independent constants.

- Alternative hypothesis: θ_i is a state-dependent quantity and θ_j, with $j \neq i$, are state-independent constants.

Without loss of generality, it is assumed that the parameter under analysis is $\theta_i = \theta_1$. The log-likelihood function is written assuming that θ_1 is a state-dependent quantity, i.e. $\theta_1 = g(\mathbf{x}, \mathbf{u}, t)$ (knowledge of the functional form of g is not required in the test). The parameter set θ is extended to the $(N + N_\theta - 1) \times 1$ array of parameters $\theta_E = [\theta_{11}, \theta_{12}, ..., \theta_{1N}, \theta_2, \theta_3, ..., \theta_{N_\theta}]$. In θ_E, parameter $\theta_{1i} = g(\mathbf{x}, \mathbf{u}_i, t_i)$ represents the value of function g at experimental conditions $\mathbf{u}_i$ and sampling time t_i. Let $\Phi_E(\theta_E | Y)$ be the log-likelihood function written for dataset Y under parametrisation θ_E.

$$\Phi_E(\theta_E | Y) = -\frac{N}{2} [N_y \ln(2\pi) + \ln(\det(\Sigma))]$$
$$-\frac{1}{2} \sum_{i=1}^{N} [\mathbf{y}_i - \hat{\mathbf{y}}(\mathbf{u}_i, t_i, \theta_{1i}, \theta_2, ..., \theta_{N_\theta})]^T \Sigma^{-1} [\mathbf{y}_i - \hat{\mathbf{y}}(\mathbf{u}_i, t_i, \theta_{1i}, \theta_2, ..., \theta_{N_\theta})] \tag{3}$$

Under parametrisation θ_E, the i-th element in the sum in Eq. (3) is a function of parameters $\theta_{1i}, \theta_2, ..., \theta_{N_\theta}$. The set of $N - 1$ constraints $\mathbf{s} = (\theta_{11} - \theta_{12}, ..., \theta_{1N-1} - \theta_{1N}) = \mathbf{0}$ is defined. The imposition of constraints $\mathbf{s} = \mathbf{0}$ is equivalent to assuming that g is a parameter, i.e. the functional form g is constant and independent from the states. The constrained maximum likelihood estimate $\hat{\theta}_E$ is obtained solving the constrained likelihood equations.

$$\nabla \Phi_E(\hat{\theta}_E | Y) + \nabla \mathbf{s} \hat{\alpha} = \mathbf{0}$$
$$\mathbf{s} = \mathbf{0} \tag{4}$$

In Eq. (4), $\hat{\alpha}$ is the estimate for the $N - 1 \times 1$ array of Lagrange multipliers. Notice that $\hat{\theta}_{1i} = \hat{\theta}_1 \ \forall i = 1, ..., N$ because of the constraints $\mathbf{s} = \mathbf{0}$. As shown by Silvey (1959); Engle (1982), if the null hypothesis is true, the score statistic ξ_1 in Eq. (5) (subscript 1 refers to the parameter θ_1 under diagnosis) is distributed as a χ^2 distribution with degree of freedom equal to the number of imposed constraints, i.e. $N - 1$.

$$\xi_1 = \hat{\alpha}^T \nabla \mathbf{s}^T \mathbf{H}^{-1} \nabla \mathbf{s} \hat{\alpha} \sim \chi^2 \tag{5}$$

In Eq. (5), $\mathbf{H}$ is the $(N + N_\theta - 1) \times (N + N_\theta - 1)$ Fisher information matrix associated to the estimates $\hat{\theta}_E$ (Bard, 1974). The critical value for the test ξ_{ref} is calculated from a χ^2 distribution with $N - 1$ degrees of freedom and 95% of significance. A $\xi_1 > \xi_{ref}$ shall be interpreted as evidence of θ_1 being a state-dependent quantity given that $\theta_2, ..., \theta_{N_\theta}$ are state-independent parameters. The score ξ_i may be computed for the generic i-th parameter following the above procedure. If $\xi_i > \xi_{ref}$ and $\xi_j > \xi_{ref}$, the fitting quality is expected to increase by relaxing the constraints either on θ_i or on θ_j. However, a $\xi_i > \xi_j > \xi_{ref}$ suggests that the evidence for justifying the evolution of parameters into state-dependent functions is stronger for parameter θ_i than for parameter θ_j.

3. Case study and results

The illustrated Lagrange multiplier test is demonstrated with a case study on a fed-batch bio-reactor system simulated in silico (Asprey and Macchietto, 2000). The process behaviour is described by the set of equations Eq. (6) with a Cantois-type kinetic Eq. (7).

$$\frac{dx_1}{dt} = (r - u_1 - \theta_4)x_1; \quad \frac{dx_2}{dt} = -\frac{rx_1}{\theta_3} + u_1(u_2 - x_2); \quad \frac{dx_3}{dt} = \theta_5 u_2 \tag{6}$$

$$\text{"true" process rate: Cantois} \rightarrow r = \frac{\theta_1 x_2}{\theta_2 x_1 + x_2} \tag{7}$$

In Eq. (6) and Eq. (7), $x_1(t)$ is the biomass concentration [g/L], $x_2(t)$ is the substrate concentration [g/L], $u_1(t)$ is the dilution factor [h^{-1}], $u_2(t)$ is the substrate concentration in the feed [g/L] and x_3 is a dummy process variable with no physical meaning. The set of equations involves a set of five parameters $\theta = [\theta_1, \theta_2, \theta_3, \theta_4, \theta_5]$. The candidate model structure involves the set of equations Eq. (6) with a Monod-type kinetic Eq. (8).

$$\text{assumed rate: Monod} \rightarrow r = \frac{\theta_1 x_2}{\theta_2 + x_2} \tag{8}$$

Experimental data are generated in-silico by integrating the model equations with the "true" Cantois-type rate law. The parameter set assumed to simulate the experiments is $\theta^* = [0.310, 0.180, 0.550, 0.050, 0.200]$. The dataset Y consists of $N = 28$ samples of $y = [x_1, x_2, x_3]$ collected in four dynamic experiments performed at different combinations of dilution factor and substrate concentration in the feed considering two levels for each variable $u_1 = \{0.050, 0.20\}$ and $u_2 = \{5.0, 35.0\}$. In each experiment, seven samples are collected at intervals of 3.0 hours. Initial conditions are fixed at $x_1(0) = 1.0$, $x_2(0) = 0.01$ and $x_3(0) = 0.1$. Measurements are affected by uncorrelated Gaussian noise with standard deviation $5 \cdot 10^{-2}$ [various units].

The estimate $\hat{\theta} = [0.305, 0.288, 0.524, 0.047, 0.199]$ for the candidate model parameters is obtained fitting the dataset Y. Subsequently, a 95% goodness-of-fit test is performed. A sum of squared residuals of 2301.6, larger than $\chi^2_{ref} = 100.7$, highlights the presence of PM mismatch.

The mismatch is diagnosed using the proposed Lagrange multiplier test. The critical value used in the test is $\xi_{ref} = 40.1$. Score statistics are reported in the radar chart in Figure 2a. As one can see from Figure 2a, the smallest score is associated to θ_5, i.e. $\xi_5 = 21$. The score suggests that parameter θ_5 is the least correlated to the root of the PM mismatch. Since $\xi_5 < \xi_{ref}$, the replacement of θ_5 with a function of the states is not expected to significantly improve the fitting quality. The scores associated to parameters $\theta_1 - \theta_4$ are higher than the reference value, i.e. $\xi_i > \xi_{ref} \ \forall i = 1, ..., 4$. The highest scores are $\xi_2 = 2245$ and $\xi_1 = 2218$, suggesting that parameters θ_2 and θ_1, which appear in the misspecified Eq. (8), are the most correlated to the source of PM mismatch. Also the scores associated to θ_3 and θ_4, i.e. $\xi_3 = 684$ and $\xi_4 = 1829$, are significantly higher than $\xi_{ref} = 40.1$. However, since $\xi_2 > \xi_1 > \xi_4 > \xi_3$, the evidence for justifying the replacement of a parameter with a state-dependent function is stronger for θ_2 and θ_1 when compared to the evidence associated to parameters θ_4 and θ_3. The scores can be interpreted as indexes for driving parameter evolution into functions, as represented in Figure 2b.

The modelling activity may proceed by evolving the parameters with the highest score into state-dependent functions. The PM mismatch can be eliminated by evolving θ_2 into the function $\theta_2 x_1$, but also by evolving θ_1 into $\theta_1(\theta_2 + x_2)/(\theta_2 x_1 + x_2)$. In future research activities, further tests will be formulated for evolving parameters into functions by supporting the construction of appropriate functional forms of the process variables.

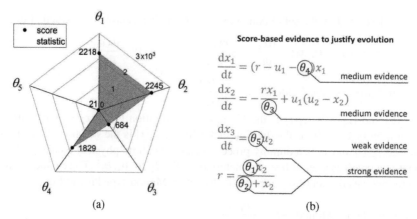

Figure 2: (a) Score statistics for parameters in the candidate model. (b) Score-based evidence for justifying the evolution of parameters into state-dependent functions.

4. Conclusions

When under-fitting is detected by challenging a parametric model against process data, model complexity shall be increased. The lack of systematic approaches to increase model complexity frequently leads to the full rejection of the model and the formulation of alternative model structures from scratch. A statistical test is proposed in this work to diagnose process-model mismatch which could inform the evolution of the model. The proposed score statistic is proportional to the marginal fitting cost associated to the assumption that a given parameter is a state-independent constant. A high score indicates strong evidence for expecting an improvement on the fitting quality if the parameter were evolved into a state-dependent function. Future work will focus on developing tests for unravelling functional relationships between state variables and the parameters selected for evolution.

References

Asprey, S. P., Macchietto, S., 2000. Statistical tools for optimal dynamic model building. Computers & Chemical Engineering 24 (2), 1261–1267.

Asprey, S. P., Naka, Y., 1999. Mathematical Problems in Fitting Kinetic Models - Some New Perspectives. Journal of Chemical Engineering of Japan 32 (3), 328–337.

Badwe, A. S., Gudi, R. D., Patwardhan, R. S., Shah, S. L., Patwardhan, S. C., 2009. Detection of model-plant mismatch in MPC applications. Journal of Process Control 19 (8), 1305–1313.

Bard, Y., 1974. Nonlinear Parameter Estimation. Academic Press.

Engle, R. F., 1982. A general approach to lagrange multiplier model diagnostics. Journal of Econometrics 20 (1), 83–104.

Meneghetti, N., Facco, P., Bezzo, F., Barolo, M., 2014. A Methodology to Diagnose Process/Model Mismatch in First-Principles Models. Industrial & Engineering Chemistry Research 53 (36), 14002–14013.

Silvey, S. D., 1959. The Lagrangian Multiplier Test. The Annals of Mathematical Statistics 30 (2), 389–407.

Silvey, S. D., 1975. Statistical Inference. CRC Press.

Wald, A., 1943. Tests of statistical hypotheses concerning several parameters when the number of observations is large. Transactions of the American Mathematical Society 54 (3), 426–482.

Wang, H., Xie, L., Song, Z., 2012. A Review for Model Plant Mismatch Measures in Process Monitoring. Chinese Journal of Chemical Engineering 20 (6), 1039–1046.

Anton A. Kiss, Edwin Zondervan, Richard Lakerveld, Leyla Özkan (Eds.)
Proceedings of the 29th European Symposium on Computer Aided Process Engineering
June 16th to 19th, 2019, Eindhoven, The Netherlands. © 2019 Elsevier B.V. All rights reserved.
http://dx.doi.org/10.1016/B978-0-128-18634-3.50115-6

Optimal design of experiments for the identification of kinetic models of 5-hydroxymethylfurfural hydrogenation

Andrea Bortoli[a,b], Fabrizio Bezzo[a] and Federico Galvanin[b,*]

[a]*CAPE-Lab - Computer-Aided Process Engineering Laboratory, Department of Industrial Engineering, University of Padova, via Marzolo 9, 35131 Padova (PD), Italy*

[b]*Department of Chemical Engineering, University College London (UCL), Gower St., WC1E 7JE London, United Kingdomd*

corresponding author: f.galvanin@ucl.ac.uk

Abstract

The increasing issues about the use of fossil raw materials advocate for an expanding utilization of biomass-based fuels and chemicals. Among the bio-based furan compounds, the 5-hydroxymethylfurfural (HMF) has received considerable attention in the chemical industry since it can be hydrogenated to 2,5-dimethylfuran (DMF) that is a valuable alternative fuel. The identification of a suitable kinetic model, where all the non-measurable kinetic parameters can be reliably estimated, is crucial to pursue the process optimization. In this work, the kinetic models currently available in literature for the HMF hydrogenation process are investigated to underline their strengths and weaknesses using a sensitivity-based identifiability analysis. The application of identifiability analysis techniques allows to define a set of fully identifiable kinetic models to be used for statistically reliable predictions. Furthermore, the use of design of experiments techniques leads to the characterization of design space regions that maximize the quality of the statistics related to the different estimates.

Keywords: 5-hydroxymethylfurfural, identifiability analysis, kinetic models

1. Introduction

Diminishing fossil fuel reserves and growing concerns about global warming indicate that sustainable sources of energy are needed in the near future (Roman-Leshkov et al. (2007)). Thus, the interest toward *renewable fuels* is rapidly growing and the new biomass-derived fuels seem to be an alternative suitable solution, clean and environmental safe, to fossil fuels (Demirbas (2010)) used for vehicles. However, for fuels to be useful in transportation sector, they must have specific physical properties that allow for efficient distribution, storage and combustion. While these properties are fulfilled by non-renewable petroleum-derived liquid fuels, the low energy density, high volatility and tendency to absorb water, are the reasons that bring the researchers to keep looking for a more efficient substitute to currently existent alternative fuels. The catalytic production of 2,5-dimethylfuran (DMF) from 5-hydroxymethylfurfural (HMF) seems to be a potential answer. The use of a catalytic process leads indeed to the identification of a route for transforming abun-

dant carbon-neutral renewable biomass resources into a liquid fuel suitable for the transportation sector (Parikka (2004)), with the final result of a diminished reliance of world's
economy on petroleum derivatives and an increased environmental safety. Since HMF hydrogenation is a relatively new process, a well validated kinetic model capable of giving
reliable predictions of the process, has not been defined yet: the identification procedure
is complex and, in the full range of expected process conditions, a structural identifiability analysis on the existing kinetic models available in literature has never been proposed. Different assumptions and mechanisms lead to different kinetic model structures
and determine the overall model complexity: from the simple power law to more complex structures involving adsorption coefficients (Gawade et al. (2016); Gyngazova et al.
(2017); Luo et al. (2015); Jain and Vaidya (2016), Grilc et al. (2014)). In this paper an
identification analysis is carried out on one of the aforementioned kinetic models, and
a correlation study is carried out to underline potential parametric identifiability issues.
Finally, model-based design of experiments (MBDoE) techniques are employed to define
the most informative experiments to be performed in a batch reactor system.

2. Methodology

2.1. Procedure for the identification of HMF hydrogenation kinetic models

The block flow diagram of the proposed procedure for the study of the HMF hydrogenation kinetic models, is given in Figure 1. As a first step, a set of candidate kinetic models

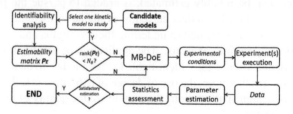

Figure 1: General procedure for the model identification.

is retrieved from the literature available. On each candidate, the identifiability analysis
based on the study of the correlation between parameters is conduced by exploiting the
local sensitivities. Once a set of identifiable kinetic models is found, MBDoE is applied to
generate the optimal experimental conditions meant to maximize the Fisher Information
Matrix (FIM) trace (Fisher (1935)). The results of the two analyses determine whether the
kinetic models gathered at the beginning are affected by structural or practical unidentifia-
bility issues. Moreover, they allow to define the most suitable regions of the experimental
design space in which experiment must be carried out to maximize the quality of the
statistics related to each estimate.

2.2. Identifiability analysis and MBDoE

Model identifiability procedures are used to recognize in advance structural and practical weaknesses related to models structure and application conditions. Structural identifiability is a property of the model structure and depends on the specific form of the
differential-algebraic equations used to describe the phenomenon. Once an identifiable

model is available, the problem moves to the reliable estimation of its non-measurable parameters: to reduce the weight of this procedure, in terms of time and resources, MB-DoE techniques can be used to select the best experiments to be performed among a set of possible conditions (Galvanin et al. (2016)). With the sensitivity analysis, the local sensitivities for any m-th measurable output are evaluated perturbing one-at-time each N_θ non-measurable parameter and the result is a $n_m \times N_\theta$ sensitivity matrix. By repeating the analysis for each sampling time, it is possible to build a $n_{sp}n_m \times N_\theta$ *estimability matrix* and it can be used as an index of the model identifiability condition. A model can be classified as structurally identifiable if $rank(\mathbf{P}_E) < N_\theta$ (Shaw, 1999). This condition is satisfied when each column of the matrix $\mathbf{P}_E$ is independent on the others. Once the identifiability study has been performed, the sensitivities can be used to calculate the FIM trace and assess the amount of information available for each parameter that requires estimation (see (4.3)).

$$Tr\left[\mathbf{H}\right]_{kl} = Tr\left[\sum_{k=1}^{N_\theta}\sum_{i=1}^{N_{exp}}\sum_{j=1}^{N_m}\left[\frac{1}{\sigma_{ij}^2}\left(\frac{\partial \hat{y}_{ij}}{\partial \theta_k}\frac{\partial \hat{y}_{ij}}{\partial \theta_l}\right)\right]\right] \cong Tr\left[\mathbf{V}_\theta^{-1}\right] \tag{1}$$

where $Tr\left[\mathbf{H}\right]_{kl}$ represents the kl-th element of a metric function (trace) of the FIM and $\mathbf{V}_\theta$ is the variance-covariance matrix. Notice that, once the FIM is available for a kinetic model, according to Bard (1974) the variance-covariance matrix can be approximated to the FIM inverse. While the FIM does not take into account the correlation between parameters, the variance-covariance matrix does and allows to figure out the best experimental conditions capable of maximizing the estimates quality. It is possible to demonstrate that by improving the fitting of the model, the quality of the approximation improves as well. The expected correlation between model parameters can be computed from the elements of $\mathbf{V}_\theta$ through the correlation matrix $\mathbf{C}$, whose elements are:

$$c_{ij} = \frac{\mathbf{V}_{\theta,ij}}{\sqrt{\mathbf{V}_{\theta,ii}\mathbf{V}_{\theta,jj}}} \tag{2}$$

Notice that the correlation matrix is a function of the experimental conditions: by perturbing the design variables also the correlation, hence the model identifiability, changes.

3. Case study: kinetic model and design space

For lack of space, only the study of one among kinetic model of Gawade et al. (2016), among the most promising and complex, is reported. In this kinetic model, from now on called M1, the dual-site Langmuir-Hinshelwood-Hougen-Watson (LHHW) theory is used to describe the adsorption and desorption mechanisms of the various species. The differential balances for the species are shown in the following. A = HMF, B = bis-hydroxymethylfuran, D = DMF, E = 2,5dimethyltetrahydrofuran, W = water.

$$-\frac{dC_A}{dt} = \frac{k_1 K_A C_A \sqrt{K_{H_2}p_{H_2}}w}{[1+K_A C_A + K_B C_B + K_D C_D + K_E C_E][1+\sqrt{K_{H_2}p_{H_2}}+K_W C_W]} \tag{3}$$

$$\frac{dC_B}{dt} = \frac{[k_1 K_A C_A - k_2 K_B C_B]\sqrt{K_{H_2}p_{H_2}}w}{[1+K_A C_A + K_B C_B + K_D C_D + K_E C_E][1+\sqrt{K_{H_2}p_{H_2}}+K_W C_W]} \tag{4}$$

$$\frac{dC_D}{dt} = \frac{[k_2 K_B C_B - k_3 K_D C_D]\sqrt{K_{H_2}p_{H_2}}w}{[1+K_A C_A + K_B C_B + K_D C_D + K_E C_E][1+\sqrt{K_{H_2}p_{H_2}}+K_W C_W]} \tag{5}$$

$$\frac{dC_E}{dt} = \frac{k_3 K_D C_D \sqrt{K_{H_2} p_{H_2}} w}{[1 + K_A C_A + K_B C_B + K_D C_D + K_E C_E][1 + \sqrt{K_{H_2} p_{H_2}} + K_W C_W]} \tag{6}$$

where C_i are the concentrations and K_i are the adsorption coefficients of the various species, k_i are the kinetic constants of the different reactions, w is the catalyst loading in g/L and p_{H_2} is the hydrogen partial pressure in atm.

3.1. Definition of design space

For the study of this transformation in a batch system, initial concentrations of HMF and DMF are considered as the most meaningful design variables to be investigated. To the aim of reducing the computational expenditure of the study, the Latin Hypercube Sampling is used to select 10 couplets of initial concentrations uniformly distributed in the entire range of concentrations (see Table 1). To study the effect of a limited number of measurements on the collected information, hence on the quality of the estimates, only 10 samplings are simulated and their allocation is evenly spaced along the experiment duration.

Table 1: Values of HMF and DMF initial concentrations.

Exp.	1	2	3	4	5	6	7	8	9	10
C_{HMF}^0 [M]	0.1556	0.0667	0.0000	0.1333	0.0889	0.2000	0.0222	0.1778	0.1111	0.0444
C_{DMF}^0 [M]	0.0667	0.0222	0.0444	0.0000	0.0889	0.2000	0.1111	0.1333	0.1556	0.1778

4. Kinetic model identification results

4.1. Identifiability analysis results

In Table 2 it is possible to appreciate that at least three couples of parameters are totally correlated and rank$(\mathbf{P}_E) = 6 < 9 = N_\theta$. Moreover, although some minor changes, by varying the sampling points schedule adopted, the three total correlations do not disappear and the kinetic model remains structurally unidentifiable. To solve the correlation problem,

Table 2: Correlation matrix for the kinetic model M1 based on the sampling distribution S1: values and colormap.

R	k_1	k_2	k_3	K_A	K_B	K_D	K_E	K_{H_2}	K_W
k_1	1.000								
k_2	0.703	1.000							
k_3	-0.020	-0.058	1.000						
K_A	**0.999***	0.687	-0.020	1.000					
K_B	0.700	**1.000***	-0.059	0.685	1.000				
K_D	-0.027	-0.070	**1.000***	-0.027	-0.071	1.000			
K_E	-0.679	-0.860	-0.008	-0.664	-0.858	0.003	1.000		
K_{H_2}	0.782	**0.991**	0.008	0.769	**0.990**	-0.004	-0.868	1.000	
K_W	-0.563	**-0.904**	-0.062	-0.553	**-0.904**	-0.049	0.841	-0.891	1.000
r_{crit}	1	3	1	0	2	0	0	0	-

| -1.00 | -0.75 | -0.50 | -0.25 | 0 | +0.25 | +0.50 | +0.75 | +1.00 |

since the non-linearity of the system is high, a simplified version of the kinetic model is proposed.

4.2. Simplified version of the kinetic model M1 (M1.2)

The purpose of this simplified version is to by-pass the identifiability issues previously highlighted in order to end up with a simpler version whose non-measurable parameters would be easier to estimate in a statistically reliable way. The new kinetic model is:

$$-\frac{dC_A}{dt} = \frac{k_1 \, C_A \, \sqrt{K_{H_2} p_{H_2}} \, w}{1 + \sqrt{K_{H_2} p_{H_2}}} \tag{7}$$

$$\frac{dC_B}{dt} = \frac{[k_1 \, C_A - k_2 \, C_B] \sqrt{K_{H_2} p_{H_2}} \, w}{1 + \sqrt{K_{H_2} p_{H_2}}} \tag{8}$$

$$\frac{dC_D}{dt} = \frac{[k_2 \, C_B - k_3 \, C_D] \sqrt{K_{H_2} p_{H_2}} \, w}{1 + \sqrt{K_{H_2} p_{H_2}}} \tag{9}$$

$$\frac{dC_E}{dt} = \frac{k_3 \, C_D \, \sqrt{K_{H_2} p_{H_2}} \, w}{1 + \sqrt{K_{H_2} p_{H_2}}} \tag{10}$$

where the nomenclature is analogous to the one used with M1. The comparison of the concentration profiles obtained from the process simulation using the original kinetic model M1 and the simplified version M1.2, allows to quantify the magnitude of the approximation. No substantial differences are present such that the two kinetic models are equivalent: a simpler kinetic model, whose parameters are not affected by correlation issues, can still represent accurately the hydrogenation process.

4.3. Model-based information analysis

In Figure 2 the information and covariance analysis results are illustrated for a sequence of 10 experiments to be performed. The figure shows the cumulative information as given by the trace of FIM and the trace of the variance-covariance matrix $\mathbf{V}_\theta$ for 10 in-silico experiments. The conclusions are that conditions of simulations 2 and 4 lead to the high-

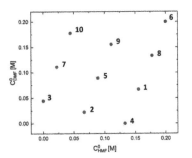
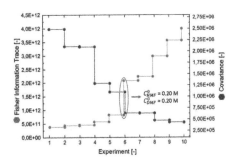

Figure 2: Profiles of Fisher information trace and variance-covariance matrix trace for the kinetic model M1.2 (T = 383 K, P_{H_2} = 5 atm)

est covariance reduction while conditions of simulation 6 allow to obtain the greatest increment in the information content.

5. Conclusions

In this paper a sensitivity-based identifiability analysis has been applied to kinetic models of HMF hydrogenation developed from batch reaction data. Through the study of the correlation matrix and its evolution for different values of the design variables, it has been possible to detect and classify the presence of identifiability issues for the kinetic models. Given the high complexity of the kinetic model proposed by Gawade et al. (2016), a simplified version of the same model has been suggested to overcome the impossibility to estimate the full set of kinetic parameters for this model. On the newly proposed model, the information analysis results highlighted that high initial concentrations of HMF and DMF lead to higher amounts of information while low initial concentrations lead to a greater covariance reduction. To conclude, the work presented here represents a first step toward the identification of a more complete kinetic model that contemplate the explicit dependency of reaction rates on both temperature and pressure. It highlights how to obtain reliable predictions on concentration, an extremely complex representation of the chemistry at the basis of the process is not required: kinetic models with many parameters are likely to be unidentifiable and not suitable to be validated through simple kinetic experiments.

References

Bard, Y., 1974. Nonlinear Parameter Estimation. Academic Press.

Demirbas, A., 2010. Fuels from Biomass. In: Biorefineries. Green Energy and Technology. Springer, London, pp. 33–73.

Fisher, R. A., 1935. The design of experiments. Oliver & Boyd, Oxford, England.

Galvanin, F., Cao, E., Al-Rifai, N., Gavriilidis, A., 2016. A joint model-based experimental design approach for the identification of kinetic models in continuous flow laboratory reactors. Computers and Chemical Engineering 95, 202 – 215.

Gawade, A. B., Tiwari, M. S., Yadav, G. D., 2016. Biobased Green Process: Selective Hydrogenation of 5-hydroxymethylfurfural to 2,5-dimethylfuran under Mild Conditions Using Pd-Cs2.5h0.5pw12o40/K-10 Clay. Acs Sustainable Chemistry & Engineering 4 (8), 4113–4123.

Grilc, M., Likozar, B., Levec, J., 2014. Hydrodeoxygenation and hydrocracking of solvolysed lignocellulosic biomass by oxide, reduced and sulphide form of NiMo, Ni, Mo and Pd catalysts. Applied Catalysis B: Environmental 150-151, 275–287.

Gyngazova, M. S., Negahdar, L., Blumenthal, L. C., Palkovits, R., 2017. Experimental and kinetic analysis of the liquid phase hydrodeoxygenation of 5-hydroxymethylfurfural to 2,5-dimethylfuran over carbon-supported nickel catalysts. Chemical Engineering Science 173, 455–464.

Jain, A. B., Vaidya, P. D., 2016. Kinetics of Catalytic Hydrogenation of 5-Hydroxymethylfurfural to 2,5-bis-hydroxymethylfuran in Aqueous Solution over Ru/C. International Journal of Chemical Kinetics 48 (6), 318–328.

Luo, J., Arroyo-Ramirez, L., Wei, J., Yun, H., 2015. Comparison of HMF hydrodeoxygenation over different metal catalysts in a continuous flow reactor. Applied Catalysis a-General 508, 86–93.

Parikka, M., 2004. Global biomass fuel resources. Biomass and Bioenergy 27 (6), 613–620.

Roman-Leshkov, Y., J Barrett, C., Y Liu, Z., A Dumesic, J., 2007. Production of Dimethylfuran for Liquid Fuels from Biomass-Derived Carbohydrates. Nature 447, 982–5.

Anton A. Kiss, Edwin Zondervan, Richard Lakerveld, Leyla Özkan (Eds.)
Proceedings of the 29th European Symposium on Computer Aided Process Engineering
June 16th to 19th, 2019, Eindhoven, The Netherlands. © 2019 Elsevier B.V. All rights reserved.
http://dx.doi.org/10.1016/B978-0-128-18634-3.50116-8

On the Solution of the Smoluchowski Coagulation Equation Using a Conservative Discretization Approach (CDA)

Menwer Attarakih[a,b,*] and Hans-Jörg Bart[b,c]

[a]The University of Jordan, Scjool of Engineering, Department of Chemical Engineering, 11942 Amman, Jordan

[b]Chair of Separation Sciences and Technology, The University of Kaiserslautern, 67653 Kaiserslautern, Germany

attarakih@yahoo.com

Abstract

The continuous Smoluchowski coagulation equation, which is known as the population balance equation (PBE) for particle coagulation, is a nonlinear integro-partial differential equation with no general analytical solution. In this work, we are concerned with extending our discrete formulation of the PBE for particle breakage using a Conservative Discretization Approach (CDA) (Attarakih et al., 2004) to solve the Smoluchowski coagulation equation coupled with particle growth. The method is based on introducing auxiliary functions to modify the discrete loss and formation terms in the discrete PBE. These are then uniquely determined by exactly reproducing two arbitrary chosen integral quantities from the continuous PBE. The CDA is validated using many test cases with known analytical solutions including coupled particle coagulation and growth dynamics as a simplified model for a batch crystallizer. The discrete approximate solutions for the number concentration function is found to converge with an order $O(1/M)$ where M is the number of grid points.

Keywords: CDA, Population Balances, Coagulation, Smoluchowski.

1. Introduction

The continuous nonlinear Smoluchowski coagulation equation (also known as the population balance equation for particle coagulation) is an integro-partial differential equation with no general analytical solution. It finds many applications in process system engineering and on individual unit operation level in pharmaceutical and chemical processes with mono and multivariate number density functions. This equation can describe the system behaviour up to any degree of detail which is necessary for understanding many single processing units such as crystallizers, turbulent flame reactors, polymerization reactors, bubble phase reactors, and extraction columns (Attarakih and Bart, 2014, Ramkrishna, 2014, Ferreira et al., 2017). In spite of the intensive research in the last decades, which is concerned with fast numerical solvers based on the moment methods, numerical solutions which are able to conserve particle integral properties suffer from losing the particle size distribution. The latter is required in industrial particulate systems where it is used to determine mechanical and physiochemical system properties, for online control purposes (Attarakih et al., 2012, Attarakih and Bart, 2014), to evaluate the negative particle fluxes at zero particle size as in the case of droplet evaporation (Vie et al., 2013) and to accommodate time varying boundary conditions in age-structured models of hematological disease (Foley and

Mackey, 2009). When numerical solutions are concerned, our successful discrete formulation of the population balance equation for particle breakage using a Conservative Discretization Approach (CDA) (Attarakih et al., 2004) laid down a solid foundation for the solution of the highly nonlinear and stretched (w.r.t. particle property space) Smoluchowski coagulation equation. The discrete set of equations is derived by treating the number of particles in each size subdomain as a single particle with known fixed position. Starting from a discrete and consistent initial number density, these particles are allowed to coagulate with a given probability and frequency to produce particles of large sizes. Prior to coagulations events, the newly born particles are allowed to adjust their local positions within each subdomain such that two selected integral properties are conserved. This is called internal consistency of the discrete Smoluchowski coagulation equation w.r.t the continuous one. Similar to our CDA for particle breakage, this internal consistency is enforced by introducing a set of two unique and general auxiliary functions (formation and loss auxiliary functions) that are uniquely determined by matching the integral properties obtainable from the discrete set against those from the continuous Smoluchowski equation. These auxiliary discrete functions are converted into matrices which are computed offline and thus placing no new computational burden during the time evolution of the particle-particle coagulation events. The computed matrices depend on the particle grid structure and are functions only of the arithmetic mean volume (mass) of the coagulating pair of particles and the representative volume in which the coagulated pair falls.

2. Discretization of Smoluchowski Equation using the CDA

The Conservative Discretization Approach (CDA) for droplet breakage (Attarakih et al., 2004) when applied to the Smoluchowski coagulation equation with particle growth provides not only the discrete number concentration function, but also its zero and third moments (or any two prior selected population integral properties). The key idea behind the CDA is to constraint the integral particle properties derived from the discrete Smoluchowski coagulation by those derived from its continuous counterpart. This not only reduces the number of ODEs to be solved, but also increases the accuracy of both the calculated particle size distribution and its desired moments. Following these lines, one can introduce auxiliary functions to the formation and loss terms in a hope to force the discrete Smoluchowski coagulation to conserve two desired integral properties of the particle size distribution:

$$\frac{dN_i(x;t)}{dt} = \sum_{k=0}^{i}\sum_{j=k}^{i} \left[\alpha_{k,j}\Psi_{k,j}^i \right](1 - \tfrac{1}{2}\delta_{k,j})\omega_{k,j}N_kN_j - N_i\sum_{j=0}^{M-1}\eta_{i,j}\omega_{i,j}N_j + S_i \qquad (1)$$

In this equation N_i is the total number concentration in the ith subdomain that is defined as $V_i = [v_{i-1/2}, v_{i+1/2})$, $i = 0,1...M$ with a representative particle diameter $d_i^* = \sqrt[3]{v_i^*}$ where v^* is the arithmetic mean of the V_i. subdomain boundaries and M is the total number of subdomains. The coagulation binary interaction matrix (Ψ^i) records the occurrence of successful coagulation events between pair of particles from two subdomains of labels (k and j). The summation $\Sigma (\Psi^i) = 1$, $\forall i$ is required to conserve the mass of the newly born particles by coagulation. The physical meaning of this constraint is that no newly born particle by coagulation can exist at the same time in more than one subdomain. The definition of the elements of this matrix are similar to that presented in Attarakih et al. (2009). The two new auxiliary functions α and η are introduced in the respective formation and loss terms to conserve exactly any two targeted population integral properties. For the conservation of zero and third moments w.r.t. particle diameter, these functions are given by:

$$\alpha_{k,j} = \frac{1}{2\chi_{k,j}-1}, \ \ \eta_{i,j} = \frac{\chi_{i,j}}{2\chi_{i,j}-1}, \ \ \chi_{k,j} = \frac{\sum_{i=1}^{M} v_{i-1}^* \Psi_{k,j}^i}{v_k^* + v_j^*} \tag{2}$$

Note that $\chi_{k,j}$ is in the order of one and can be smaller than one if the summation of the volumes of the coagulating particles from the subdomains (k,j) is greater than v^* in the *i*th subdomain, equals to one when their volume is exactly the same as v^* in the *i*th subdomain or greater than one otherwise. These functions do not depend on the particle coagulation frequency and probability but depend only on the grid structure. For example, when the grid is linear in terms of particle diameter $\chi_{k,j} = 1$ and hence both α and η are unity. In this case the discrete Smoluchowski coagulation equation is reduced to the special case of Hidy (1965) where all the integral particle properties are correctly predicted; however, at the expense of drastic increase of the number of ODEs.

The discrete term S_i on the r.h.s of Eq.(1) takes into account the discrete particle breakage which conserves total number and volume concentrations (Attarakih et al., 2004) plus the discrete growth term which is derived using the same concept used in deriving Eq.(1). This derivation is constrained by the conservation of total number and volume concentrations and is given by:

$$S_i^g = H_i(d_i^*, r)(g(d_i^*)N_i - rg(d_{i-1}^*)N_{i-1}) \tag{3}$$

Where $g(d)$ is the particle growth rate, r is the ratio between two consecutive discrete particle diameters (r = $[d_{max}/d_{min}]^{(1/M)}$ for geometric grid spanning the domain d $\in [d_{min}, d_{max}]$) and the function H is a simple function of d* and r. The convective flux (w.r.t. particle diameter) in Eq.(3) is a conservative modified first-order upwind scheme which conserves exactly total volume and number concentrations and guarantees the positivity of the reconstructed number concentration function. To this end, the system of Eqs.(1 to 3) presents a consistent discrete model for the numerical solution of the Smoluchowski coagulation equation coupled to particle breakage and growth. To the best of the authors' knowledge, this is the first complete and consistent discrete model for the solution of the population balance equation which takes into account all the possible particle mechanisms including particle nucleation which can be easily added as a birth source term in the first subdomain.

3. Numerical Results and Discussion

3.1. Numerical Analysis

The proposed CDA for Smoluchowski coagulation equation is validated in the first step against well-known analytical solutions. These solutions depend on the coagulation frequency where particle coagulation in a suspension may occur through variety of mechanisms such as Brownian motion, turbulent diffusion and laminar shear (Hidy and Brock, 1970). From physical and analytical point of view, the Brownian motion and turbulent diffusion are the two popular mechanisms. For Brownian coagulation, ω depends on the sizes of the two coagulating particles. When one particle is in the continuum regime, the coagulation frequency is given by the Smoluchowski kernel:

$$\omega(v, v') = \omega_0 (v + v')\left(v^{-1} + v'^{-1}\right) \tag{4}$$

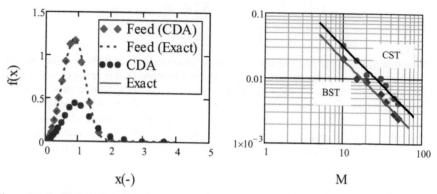

$$x(-) \qquad\qquad\qquad\qquad M$$

Figure (1): (Left). Solution of Smoluchowski equation with constant kernel particle aggregation (ω_0) in CST using the CDA. (Right). Convergence of the CDA based on the RMSE using $\omega = \omega_0$ in batch and continuous stirred tanks. $d_{min} = 0.01$, $d_{max} = 4$, $\tau = 4$, $M = 30$, the feed PSD is $3x^2\exp(-x^3)$ and the I.C. is zero.

In the initial stage of coagulation of a monodispersed suspension the coagulation frequency is essentially size independent. It has been suggested that ω_0 is a good approximation to ω if the Knudsen numbers ($Kn = 2\lambda/d$) of both coagulating particles are less than 0.1 even for the case of polydispersed suspension. On the other hand, for turbulent diffusion particle coagulation, ω can be approximated by $\omega = \omega_0(v + v')$. These are obviously the only two physically realistic kernels for which analytical solutions of the Smoluchowski equation were derived.

Figure (1, Left) shows the CDA solution as compared to the analytical one (Hounslow, 1990) for constant particle coagulation in a CST (Continuous Stirred Tank) with residence time $\tau = 4$ (dimensionless). Using only 30 subdomains (evolved on a geometric grid) and using AdamsBDF (Adams method with backward differentiation formulas) as an ODE solver, the system of ODEs (Eq.(1)) were integrated from zero initial condition until steady state. As can be seen from this figure, the numerical solution is very accurate with a very high precision reproduction of the first and third moments of the particle size distribution, thanks to the auxiliary functions ($\alpha_{k,j}$, $\eta_{k,j}$).

This convergence of the CDA was tested for both CST and BST as shown in in Figure (1, Right) using uniform grids ($d_{min} = 0$ and $d_{max} = 4$) and the RMSE (Root Mean Squared Error) based on the difference between the CDA and the analytical solutions using the same discrete predefined grid points where a 10-point grid solution results in less than 0.1 RMSE and still conserves total volume and number concentrations. It is clear that the convergence of the CDA is in the O(1/M) for both cases. When the geometric grid was used ($d_{min} = 0$ and $d_{max} = 4$)), the CDA is more accurate than that of the uniform grid with even faster rate of convergence. This increased accuracy is expected since the geometric grid results in new born particles with volumes that are very close to the representative volumes in each subdomain. This hypothesis is elucidated by careful examination of the $\chi_{k,j}$ elements which were very close to unity.

3.2. Batch Crystallizer: Coupled size dependent growth and coagulation

In this section, particle growth and coagulation in a batch stirred tank (BST) is used as a simplified model for a batch crystallizer where the particle size distribution (PSD) depends on time and particle size. In a batch crystallizer, the initial seeds used are carried by the evolution of the PSD and becomes part of it.

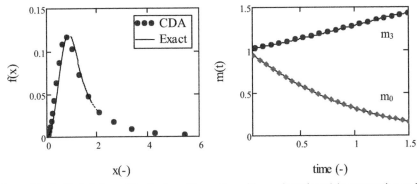

Figure (2): (Left). Solution of Smoluchowski equation with sum kernel particle aggregation and linear particle growth in BST using the CDA. (Right). Prediction of the zero and third moments of PSD using CDA. dmin = 0.005, dmax = 6, τ = 1.5, M = 30, initial condition $f(x) = 3x^2\exp(-x^3)$.

The growth rate of crystals $g(x)$ expresses the rate of change of particle volume due to deposition of material on the particle surface. When the Knudsen number (Kn = $2\lambda/d$) is less than 0.1, the rate of deposition is predicted by the classical continuum diffusion theory (Hidy and Brock, 1970). In this regime the growth rate is given by $g(x)$ = $(1/3)g_0x^\gamma$ where γ = 3. The rate determining step for deposition, based on this growth rate, is the chemical reaction that takes place throughout the volume of the particle. In this case study, we confined our attention to the case when γ = 1 where the growth is linearly proportional to particle diameter. By combining linear particle growth and sum kernel ($\omega = \omega_0(v + v')$ particle coagulation, which is induced by turbulent diffusion, one can use the analytical solution of Ramabhadran et al. (1976). This analytical solution is challenging and is complicated by the product of exponential function and modified Bessel function of the first kind. The exponential part is a manifestation of the exponential initial condition ($f(x) = 3x^2\exp(-x^3)$). Figure (2, Left) shows the predicted PSD using our CDA with 30 subdomains using a geometric grid w.r.t. particle diameter where $\Lambda = g_0/\omega_0 = 0.25$ and $\tau = 1.5$. This means that the dominant mechanism in this example is particle coagulation. This results in a reduction of particle number concentration with little volume growth as shown in Figure (2, Right). In this figure, not only the PSD was accurately predicted, but also the total number and volume concentrations. The conservation of the zero and third moments of the source term is not affected by the number of grid points, but by the discrete form of the initial condition or the inlet feed distribution. This shows the advantage of the CDA when compared to other discrete methods which require very fine grids. The computational time of the CDA is less than that of the fixed-pivot technique which support our previous CPU time analysis for the case of particle breakage (Attarakih et al, 2004).

4. Summary and Conclusions

The numerical analyses of the present CDA show two desirable properties: Firstly, the simplicity of the source term structure (composed of simple summations) which can be easily programmed thanks to the explicit form of the two auxiliary functions and the interaction matrix in which the footprint of the successful coagulation events is saved. Secondly, the two selected conserved integral quantities (e.g total number and volume concentrations) are exactly conserved irrespective of the number of discrete equations. This presents a major advantage over the existing consistent discrete methods (e.g. Fixed-pivot technique). Accordingly, the reconstructed number concentration function converges to the exact solution with exponential decay in terms of the RMSE as function of grid points. As a final conclusion, the CDA is a general discrete formulation framework not only for the Smoluchowski coagulation equation, but also for other deterministic integral equations including simultaneous particle breakage, growth and nucleation in batch and continuous particulate systems and can be easily extended to bivariate population balances.

References

M. Attarakih and H.-J. Bart, 2014, Solution of the population balance equation using the differential maximum entropy method (DMaxEntM): An application to liquid extraction columns. Chem. Eng. Sci, 108, 123-133.

M. Attarakih, H. B. Jildeh, M. Mickler and H. J. Bart, 2012, The OPOSPM as a nonlinear autocorrelation population balance model for dynamic simulation of liquid extraction columns. Comp. Aided Chem. Eng., 31, 1216-1220.

M. Attarakih, C. Drumm snd H.-J. Bart, 2009, Solution of the population balance equation using the sectional quadrature method of moments(SQMOM). Chem. Eng. Sci., 64, 742--752.

M. Attarakih, H.-J. Bart and N. M. Faqir, 2004, Solution of the droplet breakage equation for interacting liquid-liquid dispersions: A conservative discretization approach. Chemical Engineering Science,12, 2547-2565.

G. G. S. Ferreira, P.L. Lage and L. F. L. R. Silva, 2017, Extension and convergence analysis of the univariate direct quadrature spanning tree method. Powder Tech., 322, 301-313.

C. Foley and M. C. Mackey, 2009, Dynamic hematological disease: A review. J. Math. Biol., 58, 285-322.

G. M. Hidy, 1965, On the theory of the coagulation of noninteracting particles in brownian motion. J. Coll. Sci., 20, 123-144.

G. M. Hidy and J. R. Brock, 1970, The Dynamics of Aerocolloidal Systems, Pergamon Press, Oxford, England.

M. J. Hounslow, 1990, A discretized population balance for continuous systems at steady sate. AIChE J., 36, 106-116.

T. E. Ramabhadran, T. W. Peterson and J. H. Seinfeld (1976). Dynamics of aerosol coagulation and condensation. AIChE Journal, 22, 840-851.

D. Ramkrishna and M. R. Singh, 2014, Population Balance Modeling: Current Status and Future Prospects, Annu. Rev. Chem. Biomol. Eng., 5, 123-146.

A. Vie, F. Laurent and M. Massot, 2013, Size-velocity correlations in hybrid high order moment/multi-fluid methods for polydisperse evaporating sprays: Modeling and numerical issues. J. Comp. Phys., 237, 177-210.

Anton A. Kiss, Edwin Zondervan, Richard Lakerveld, Leyla Özkan (Eds.)
Proceedings of the 29th European Symposium on Computer Aided Process Engineering
June 16th to 19th, 2019, Eindhoven, The Netherlands. © 2019 Elsevier B.V. All rights reserved.
http://dx.doi.org/10.1016/B978-0-128-18634-3.50117-X

Coordination of multiple production and utility systems in a multi-leader multi-follower Stackelberg game

Ludger Leenders[a], Kirstin Ganz[a], Björn Bahl[a], Maike Hennen[a] and André Bardow[a,b,*]

[a]*Institute of Technical Thermodynamics, RWTH Aachen University, Aachen, Germany*
[b]*Institute of Energy and Climate Research - Energy Systems Engineering (IEK-10), Forschungszentrum Jülich GmbH, Jülich, Germany*
andre.bardow@ltt.rwth-aachen.de

Abstract

Large industrial sites typically consists of multiple production and utility systems. To minimize overall cost, these systems need to coordinate the operation. The problem resulting can be stated as a multi-leader multi-follower Stackelberg game. Thus, we propose a method which coordinates the operation across multiple production systems (leaders) and on-site utility systems (followers). The proposed method performs iterative feedback loops between production and utility systems. The coordination between the production and utility systems is performed by load- and time-dependent energy costs. The proposed method is applied to a case study with two production systems and two utility systems. The proposed mathod saves 7.3 % in total cost compared to the common separated and unidirectional optimization between each production system and the corresponding utility system. Thus, in summary, we provide an efficient method to enable cost optimization across multiple production and utility systems to reduce site-wide energy cost.

Keywords: Utility System, Production System, Multi-Leader Multi-Follower

1. Motivation

In large industrial sites, multiple production and utility systems are operated on-site. Usually, these systems are operated by different companies or business units. Thus, operational optimization is commonly performed individually and sequentially: First, the production systems schedule their production plan and determine the corresponding energy demand. Subsequently, the energy demand is supplied by the utility system corresponding to each production system. Consequently, there is no feedback between the systems and suboptimal overall cost arise. In this paper, we assume that operation for minimal overall cost is desired.

In principle, operation for minimal overall cost can be achieved by an integrated optimization problem of all production and utility systems. Such an integrated optimization has already been proposed for one production and utility system (Agha et al., 2010). The integrated optimization led to significant cost savings compared to sequential optimization. However, an integrated optimization is often practically prohibited, if the systems are operated by different companies. In such cases, the systems are not allowed to exchange their system knowledge. Maxeiner et al. (2017) therefore allocate shared resources by a central site manager. The problem is solved by an iterative solution approach via price-based coordination. In their case study, a production system with 3 semi-batch reactors is considered. However, the starting times of the reactors are predefined and not scheduled. In the iterations, the degrees of freedom are the inputs and number of intervals. A central coordinator can be avoided by a multi-leader multi-follower Stackelberg game, where the production systems are the leaders and the utility systems are the followers.

A single-leader multi-follower Stackelberg game has been solved iteratively by Yu and Hong (2016) for a smart grid with one utility company (leader) and multiple customers (follower). Besides profit maximization of the leader and cost minimization of the followers, the method flattens the load profile. Maharjan et al. (2013) solve a multi-leader multi-follower Stackelberg game of a smart grid also by an iterative solution approach for a single time step. The exchanged information between leader and follower are the energy price and the energy demand. Ramos et al. (2018) solve a multi-leader single-follower and a single-leader multi-follower Stackelberg game for design of eco-industrial parks with continuous production systems. Thus, no production scheduling is required. The Stackelberg games are formulated as bilevel problems which are solved by replacing the followers' optimization problem by the Karush-Kuhn-Tucker reformulation. Yue and You (2017) propose an algorithm to solve a mixed-integer linear bilevel problem for the design and operation of supply chains in single-leader single-follower Stackelberg games. The above reviewed literature consider continuously operated or pre-scheduled production systems and shows the benefits of coordination by Stackelberg games. In an earlier publication, the authors therefore proposed a coordination method for a single batch production and a single utility system in a single-leader single-follower Stackelberg game (Holters et al., 2018). This paper extends the coordination method to multiple production and utility systems in a multi-leader multi-follower Stackelberg game. This extension allows to capture the complexity of actual industrial sites.

2. Coordination of multiple production and utility systems

In this section, we present a coordination method for multiple production and utility systems in a multi-leader multi-follower Stackelberg game. The method aims at minimizing energy and production cost for all production systems. In the method, all systems optimize themselve and the results are coordinated. The coordination uses only public information. Thus, the coordinating authority can be any participating production or utility system. A central site-manager or authority to handle non-public information is not required.

The method consists of 4 steps to optimize and to coordinate production and utility systems (Figure 1). In step ①, each production system schedules its production, assuming constant energy prices. The resulting energy demand is used as input for step ②. In step ②, the utility systems are scheduled. The utility systems coordinate the amount of energy provided by each utility system (Section 2.1). In step ②, load- and time-dependent energy costs are calculated (Holters et al., 2018) and passed to the production systems. The load- and time-dependent energy costs are the input for step ③. In step ③, the production systems re-schedule their production now using the load- and time-dependent energy costs (Section 2.2). The resulting energy demand is passed to the utility systems to finally schedule the utility systems (step ④). Thus, in step ④, the utility systems schedule their final operation to calculate the final energy cost. Step ④ performs the same computations as step ②. Steps ②, ③ and ④ use inner algorithms, which are explained in the following Sections 2.1 and 2.2.

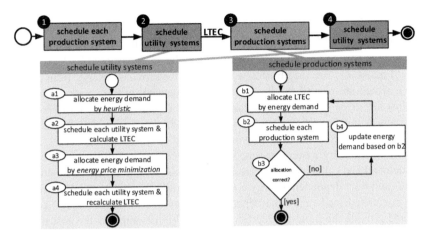

Figure 1: Method to solve the multi-leader multi-follower Stackelberg game by coordination between multiple production and utility systems. Two inner algorithms are employed to schedule utility systems (step ②+④) and schedule production systems (step ③). LTEC: load- and time-dependent energy costs

2.1. Schedule utility systems, step ②+④

In step ② and step ④, the utility systems are scheduled to fulfill the energy demand of the production systems. The amount of energy supplied by each utility system is determined by minimizing the energy price of each energy form e. The coordination of the utility systems is performed in four steps (Figure 1; a1-a4): In step a1, the energy demand of each energy form is allocated to all utility systems based on the maximum capacity of each utility system (=heuristic). An energy price minimization is not possible here, because load- and time-dependent energy costs are not calculated before. In step a2, the utility systems schedule their operation for the allocated energy demand from step a1 and each utility system calculates its load- and time-dependent energy costs. The load- and time-dependent energy costs approximate for each time step the resulting energy costs for changes in the energy demand. For this approximation, the operation of each utility system is scheduled for 2 selected increased energy demands and 2 selected decreased energy demands. The selected energy demands represent loads, at which the supply structure of the utility system needs to change, i.e., an additional unit needs to be switched on or a running unit can be switched off. Between these energy demands, the corresponding energy costs are interpolated to calculate the load- and time-dependent energy costs.

In step a3, the energy price of each energy form e is minimized (Eq. 1) using the load- and time-dependent energy costs of each utility system to allocate the energy demand to the utility systems. This optimization problem is performed by the coordinating authority:

$$\min_{V_{i,e}, C_{i,e}, x} c_e^{min} \tag{1}$$

$$\text{s.t.} \quad \sum_{i \in US} V_{i,e}^{supply} = V_e^{demand} \tag{2}$$

$$c_e^{min} \geq \frac{C_{i,e}}{V_{i,e}}, \forall i \in US \tag{3}$$

$$A(V_{i,e}, C_{i,e}, x)^T \leq b \tag{4}$$

The objective (Eq. 1) is to minimize the energy price c_e^{min} of each energy form e. The energy supply $V_{i,e}^{supply}$ of the utility systems i needs to fulfill the energy demand V_e^{demand} (Eq. 2). The energy price c_e^{min} is the maximum of the energy prices $C_{i,e}/V_{i,e}$ of all utility systems (Eq. 3). $C_{i,e}$ are the absolute energy cost for provided energy form e by utility system i, which are part of the load- and time-dependent energy costs. All additional constraints are given in Eq. 4, i.e., calculation of $C_{i,e}$ from load- and time-dependent energy costs as function of $V_{i,e}$. x summarizes all additional variables. The energy price minimization allocates the energy demand to the utility systems.

In step a4, each utility system re-schedules its operation to fulfill the newly allocated energy demand and calculates the corresponding load- and time-dependent energy costs. The load- and time-dependent energy costs of all utility systems are cumulated. For step ②, the cumulated load- and time-dependent energy costs and the energy cost are the output and provide the input of step ③. For step ④, the output is the cost to fulfill the final energy demand.

2.2. Schedule production systems, step ③

In step ③, the scheduling of the production systems is coordinated. The scheduling of the production systems is coordinated in 4 steps (Figure 1; b1-b4):

In step b1, the cumulated load- and time-dependent energy costs from step ② are allocated to the production systems. In the allocation of load- and time-dependent energy costs, each section of the piecewise linear load- and time-dependent energy costs (Section 2.1) is split and allocated to the production systems. In the first iteration of the inner algorithm, the load- and time-dependent energy costs are allocated equally to the productions systems. In further iterations, the energy demand from the previous iteration is used for allocation to the production systems. In step b2, each production system uses the allocated load- and time-dependent energy costs from step b1 to schedule its production and calculate the energy demand. In step b3, the allocation of cumulated load- and time-dependent energy costs in step b1 is checked by the coordinating authority. If the sum of all energy cost calculated by each production system with the allocated load- and time-dependent energy costs is not equal to the energy cost for the overall energy demand calculated by the cumulated load- and time-dependent energy costs, the algorithm is repeated. If the energy costs are equal, the algorithm terminates. The output of step ③ is the energy demand of all production systems.

3. Case study

3.1. Description

In the case study, an industrial site is considered with 2 production systems and 2 utility systems. The production systems are based on literature examples from Kondili et al. (1993) and Kallrath (2002). Here, we added electricity and heat demands. The product demand is fixed at the time horizon of 30 h. The utility systems are based on the model by Voll et al. (2013). The utility system for the production system from Kondili et al. (1993) has 3 boilers (4000 kW, 1500 kW, 500 kW) and 2 identical combined-heat-and-power engines (1500 kW). The utility system for the production system from Kallrath (2002) has 2 boilers (3000 kW, 1000 kW) and 1 combined-heat-and-power engine (3000 kW). For both utility systems equal prices are assumed to buy (0.16 €/kWh) and purchase (0.1 €/kWh) electricity and buy gas (0.06 €/kWh) from the public grid. All optimization

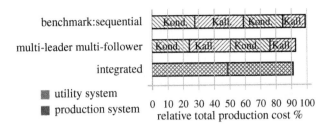

benchmark:sequential

multi-leader multi-follower

integrated

■ utility system
■ production system

0 10 20 30 40 50 60 70 80 90 100
relative total production cost %

Figure 2: Cost in the case study for the different approaches: The common sequential approach between each production system and the corresponding utility system (benchmark: sequential = 100 %), the multi-leader multi-follower Stackelberg game solved by the proposed coordination method (multi-leader multi-follower) and the integrated optimization of all systems (integrated). Kond.:Kondili; Kall.:Kallrath

problems are formulated in GAMS 24.7.3. The scheduling problems of production and utility systems (MILP) are solved with CPLEX 12.6.3.0, the energy price minimization problems (MINLP) (Eq. 1-4) are solved with DICOPT and CONOPT 3.17A.

3.2. Results

The case study is solved using the proposed method to coordinate multiple production and utility systems in a multi-leader multi-follower Stackelberg game. The results of the method are compared with the common practice to optimize sequentially each production system and the corresponding utility system, and the ideal benchmark, integrated optimization of all systems (Holters et al., 2017). The integrated optimization is solved in 728 s, the proposed method solves the problem in 1477 s.

The proposed method saves 7.3 % of the total production cost compared to the sequential approach (Figure 2). Compared to the integrated optimization, the method increases the cost by only 1.8 % (Figure 2). Thus, the costs from the proposed method are close to the costs from the ideal benchmark. Costs are saved for energy (14.8 %) while production cost increase slightly (3.4 %, Figure 2). However, overall, the production systems as the leaders still benefit, because they have to cover all cost for the energy supply.

In the proposed method, the energy demand of the production systems changes compared to the sequential approach (Figure 3): The peak demands are reduced for electricity (-25.1 %) and increased for heat (+8.5 %). The overall electricity demand also decreases (-17.7 %) and the heat demand increases (+8.0 %). Thus, the production schedules switched to processes with heat demand, because heat can be generated cheaper than electricity. Furthermore, the share of electricity from the public grid decreases (sequential 31.9 %; multi-leader multi-follower 8.2 %). Thus, utilization of on-site utility systems is increased by better coordination between production and utility system scheduling.

Uncertainty in energy demands, electricity prices and gas prices is not considered in the proposed method, but would be an important extension for practical adaption. To explore the sensitivity of the approach to data, we generated 10 instances with variations of ±20 % around the original energy demands of the production systems by latin-hypercube sampling. For the instances, the proposed method reduces cost by 9.2 % compared to the sequential optimization and is again close to the integrated optimization which saves 10.2 % . Thus, the proposed method saves even more cost than in the nominal case study. In general, the cost savings depend on the actual energy demand of production systems.

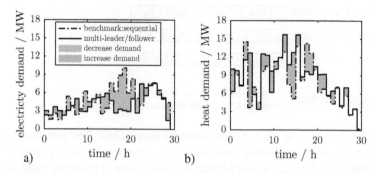

Figure 3: Energy demand of the production systems for the sequential approach and for the proposed method to coordinate the multi-leader multi-follower Stackelberg game.

4. Conclusion

A coordination method is proposed to reduce the overall cost of multiple production and utility systems in a multi-leader multi-follower Stackelberg game. The coordination method employs load- and time-dependent energy costs in one feedback iteration.

In a case study, the coordination method reduces overall cost by 7.3 % compared to the common sequential approach. These cost savings are obtained by a revised production schedule, leading to slightly increased production cost (3.4 %), but significantly decreased energy cost (14.8 %). A computational study of 10 instances shows the general benefit of the proposed method.

Acknowledgments
This study was funded by the 'Europäischer Fond für regionale Entwicklung (EFRE)' (EFRE-0800289). The support is gratefully acknowledged.

References

M. H. Agha, R. Thery, G. Hetreux, A. Hait, J. M. L. Lann, 2010. Integrated production and utility system approach for optimizing industrial unit operations. Energy 35 (2), 611–627.

L. Holters, B. Bahl, M. Hennen, A. Bardow, 2018. Playing Stackelberg games for minimal cost for production and utilities. In: Proceedings of ECOS 2018.

L. Holters, B. Bahl, M. Lampe, M. Hennen, A. Bardow, 2017. Integrated synthesis of batch plants and utility systems. Comp. Aided Chem. Eng. 40, 625 – 630.

J. Kallrath, Aug 2002. Planning and scheduling in the process industry. OR Spectrum 24 (3), 219–250.

E. Kondili, C. Pantelides, R. Sargent, 1993. A general algorithm for short-term scheduling of batch operations - I. MILP formulation. Comp. & Chem. Eng. 17 (2), 211–227.

S. Maharjan, Q. Zhu, Y. Zhang, S. Gjessing, T. Basar, 2013. Dependable Demand Response Management in the Smart Grid: A Stackelberg Game Approach. IEEE Transactions on Smart Grid 4 (1), 120–132.

L. S. Maxeiner, S. Wenzel, S. Engell, 2017. Shared resource allocation in the process industries via price-based coordination for systems with discrete decisions. Comp. Aided Chem. Eng. 40, 1897 – 1902.

M. A. Ramos, M. Rocafull, M. Boix, D. Aussel, L. Montastruc, S. Domenech, 2018. Utility network optimization in eco-industrial parks by a multi-leader follower game methodology. Comp. & Chem. Eng. 112, 132 – 153.

P. Voll, C. Klaffke, M. Hennen, A. Bardow, 2013. Automated superstructure-based synthesis and optimization of distributed energy supply systems. Energy 50, 374–388.

M. Yu, S. H. Hong, 2016. Supply-demand balancing for power management in smart grid: A stackelberg game approach. Applied Energy 164, 702 – 710.

D. Yue, F. You, 2017. Stackelberg-game-based modeling and optimization for supply chain design and operations: A mixed integer bilevel programming framework. Comp. & Chem. Eng. 102, 81 – 95.

Anton A. Kiss, Edwin Zondervan, Richard Lakerveld, Leyla Özkan (Eds.)
Proceedings of the 29th European Symposium on Computer Aided Process Engineering
June 16th to 19th, 2019, Eindhoven, The Netherlands. © 2019 Elsevier B.V. All rights reserved.
http://dx.doi.org/10.1016/B978-0-128-18634-3.50118-1

From peak power prices to seasonal storage:
Long-term operational optimization of energy systems by time-series decomposition

Nils Baumgärtner[a], David Shu[b], Björn Bahl[a], Maike Hennen[a] and André Bardow[a,b,*]

[a]*Institute of Technical Thermodynamics, RWTH Aachen University, Aachen, Germany*
[b]*Institute of Energy and Climate Research - Energy Systems Engineering (IEK-10), Forschungszentrum Jülich, Jülich, Germany*
andre.bardow@ltt.rwth-aachen.de

Abstract

Long-term operation of energy systems is a complex optimization task. Often, such long-term operational optimizations are solved by direct decomposing the problem into smaller subproblems. However, direct decomposition is not possible for problems with time-coupling constraints and variables. Such time-coupling is common in energy systems, e.g., due to peak power prices and (seasonal) energy storage. To efficiently solve coupled long-term operational optimization problems, we propose a time-series decomposition method. The proposed method calculates lower and upper bounds to obtain a feasible solution of the original problem with known quality. We compute lower bounds by the Branch-and-Cut algorithm. For the upper bound, we decompose complicating constraints and variables into smaller subproblems. The solution of these subproblems are recombined to obtain a feasible solution for the long-term operational optimization. To tighten the upper bound, we iteratively decrease the number of subproblems. In a case study for an industrial energy system, we show that the proposed time-series decomposition method converges fast, outperforming a commercial state-of-the-art solver.

Keywords: large-scale MILP, seasonal storage, network charges, emission targets

1. Introduction

In industry, energy is often supplied by on-site energy systems. The efficiency of on-site energy systems can be significantly improved by optimizing operation. Operational optimization typically results in mixed-integer linear programming (MILP) problems. These MILP problems are proven to be weakly NP-hard, and thus computationally challenging for for large problems sizes (Goderbauer et al., 2019).

In the operation of energy systems, the number of variables results directly from the number of considered time steps, and thus long-term operational optimization leads to many variables. An intuitive solution approach is to solve the time steps independently, i.e., use direct decomposition. However, such direct decomposition is only possible without time-coupling constraints and variables (Bradley et al., 1992). In practice, time-coupling constraints and variables are common for energy systems, e.g., by peak power prices, seasonal storage systems, annual emission limits or net connection fees. To cope with time-coupling constraints in the optimization of energy systems, various solution methods have been proposed (Tab.1). A first class of methods is based on simplification of

Table 1: Solution methods for long-term operational optimizations of energy systems with time-coupling constraints and variables

Approach/Idea	Literature	Strengths (+) / Limits (−)
Model simplifications	(Piacentino and Cardona, 2008), (Yokoyama, 2013)	+ easily applicable − limited model scope
Non-deterministic	(Eglese, 1990), (Kavvadias and Maroulis, 2010)	+ allow parallelization + generic − no quality measure
Decomposition	(Yokoyama and Ito, 1996), (Al-Agtash and Su, 1998), (Rong et al., 2008), (Nasrolahpour et al., 2016), (Wang et al., 2016)	+ allow parallelization + generic + provide quality measure − slow convergence − complex formulation

component models to reduce the complexity of the optimization, rendering the full optimization problem solvable even with time-coupling constraints and variables. However, model simplification limits the accuracy of the results. Second, non-deterministic methods, such as genetic algorithms, are therefore employed to solve large-scale problems. While these non-deterministic approaches can generate good solutions for difficult problems and often allow for parallelization, they are unable to evaluate the quality of the proposed solution (Hanne and Dornberger, 2017). Therefore, mathematical decomposition methods have been nested to treat both time-coupling constraints and variables in MILP optimizations, e.g., column generation, Lagrangian, and Benders (Wang et al., 2016). However, despite the successful application of mathematical decomposition methods to energy system problems, some challenges remain: Column generation often suffers from slow convergence in practice (Desrosiers and Lübbecke, 2011a). The formulation and implementation of Branch-and-Price is complex (Desrosiers and Lübbecke, 2011b). Lagrangian methods require a good choice of multipliers for fast convergence. However, the selection of Lagrangian multipliers is difficult leading to a large variety of methods (Conejo et al., 2006). Benders decomposition suffers from slow convergence due to a high number of slow iterations. Improvements for the convergence of Benders decomposition have been proposed but their formulation and implementation is complex (Rahmaniani et al., 2017).

In this work, we propose a time-series decomposition-based solution algorithm for solving long-term operational optimization problems. The proposed time-series decomposition handles both time-coupling constraints and variables in the operational optimization. The method combines the strengths of the approaches in literature (Tab.1) using an exact model, is easily applicable, allows for parallelization and shows fast convergence.

2. Time-coupling constraints and variables in operational optimization

To illustrate the complexity of operation optimization problems with time-coupling constraints and variables, we state a generic operational problem for energy systems as mixed-integer linear programming (MILP) problem.

$$\min_{\dot{V}_{n,t}, \delta_{n,t}, \dot{V}_{\text{grid}}^{\max}, \dot{V}_{n,t}, x} OPEX = \sum_{t \in \mathcal{T}} \left(\Delta t_t \sum_{n \in \mathcal{C}} c_{n,t}^{\text{o}} \frac{\dot{V}_{n,t}}{\eta_n} \right) + c_p \cdot \dot{V}_{\text{grid}}^{\max} + c_{\text{net}} \cdot \sum_{t \in \mathcal{T}} \dot{V}_{\text{grid},t} \qquad (1)$$

$$\text{s.t.} \quad \sum_{n\in\mathscr{C}\setminus\mathscr{C}_{\text{stor}}} \dot{V}_{n,t} + \sum_{n\in\mathscr{C}_{\text{stor}}} (\dot{V}_{n,t}^{\text{out}} - \dot{V}_{n,t}^{\text{in}}) = \dot{E}_t, \qquad \forall t\in\mathscr{T}, \qquad (2)$$

$$A_1\dot{V}_{n,t} + \tilde{A}_1\delta_{n,t} \le b_1, \qquad \forall t\in\mathscr{T}, \forall n\in\mathscr{C}, \qquad (3)$$

$$A_2\left(\dot{V}_{n,t}, \delta_{n,t}, x\right)^{\text{T}} \le b_2, \qquad \forall t\in\mathscr{T}, \forall n\in\mathscr{C}, \qquad (4)$$

$$V_{n,t} + \Delta t_t \cdot (\dot{V}_{n,t}^{\text{in}} - \dot{V}_{n,t}^{\text{out}}) = V_{n,t+1}, \qquad \forall t\in\mathscr{T}, \forall n\in\mathscr{C}_{\text{stor}}, \qquad (5)$$

$$|\dot{V}_{\text{grid},t}| \le \dot{V}_{\text{grid}}^{\text{max}}, \qquad \forall t\in\mathscr{T}, \qquad (6)$$

$$c_i = \begin{cases} c_i^{\text{high}} & ,\text{if } \frac{\sum_{t\in\mathscr{T}} \dot{V}_{\text{grid},t}\cdot\Delta t_t}{\dot{V}_{\text{grid}}^{\text{max}}} \le 2500h \\ c_i^{\text{low}} & ,\text{otherwise} \end{cases} \qquad \text{for i} = \{\text{net},\text{p}\} \qquad (7)$$

$$\sum_{t\in\mathscr{T}}\left[(\dot{V}_{\text{grid},t}\cdot c_{t,el}^{\text{CO2}}) + \sum_{n\in\mathscr{C}}(\frac{\dot{V}_{n,t}}{\eta_n}\cdot c_{t,gas}^{\text{CO2}})\right] \le C_{\text{CO2}}^{\text{max}}, \qquad (8)$$

$$\delta_{n,t}\in\{0,1\}; x\in\mathbb{R}^a\times\{0,1\}^{\tilde{a}}; \dot{V}_{n,t}\in\mathbb{R}; V_{n,t}, \dot{V}_{\text{grid}}^{\text{max}}\in\mathbb{R}^+.$$

Operational expenses *OPEX* are defined as the sum of the output power $\dot{V}_{n,t}$ of every component $n\in\mathscr{C}$ in every time step t divided by the efficiency η_n and multiplied by the specific operation cost $c_{n,t}^{\text{o}}$ and the duration Δt_t of a time step (Eq.1). A further contribution to *OPEX* (Eq.1) are the network charges C_{net}, which result from the electricity consumption $\sum_{t\in\mathscr{T}} \dot{V}_{\text{grid},t}$ multiplied by network charges $c_{\text{net}}^{(\text{low/high})}$ that depend on the utilization time. The peak power $\dot{V}_{\text{grid}}^{\text{max}}$ multiplied by a peak power price c_{p} results in additional *OPEX* (Eq.1). As constraint, the component's output power $\dot{V}_{n,t}$ plus the net energy output of the storage units $\dot{V}_{n,t}^{\text{out}} - \dot{V}_{n,t}^{\text{in}}$ has to meet the energy demand $\dot{E}_t$ at every time step t (Eq.2). Further (in)equalities with the coefficient matrices A_1, $\tilde{A}_1$, and the vector b_1 determine the component's binary on/off status $\delta_{n,t}$ and the current part-load performance (Eq.3). Additional constraints are summarized in the surrogate coefficient matrix A_2, including all other variables of the original problem represented by the vector x (Eq.4). The future storage level $V_{n,t+1}$ is coupled to the current storage level $V_{n,t}$ by the net energy input of the storage units $\dot{V}_{n,t}^{\text{in}} - \dot{V}_{n,t}^{\text{out}}$. Thus, the storage balance equation couples the entire time series (Eq.5). The peak power $\dot{V}_{\text{grid}}^{\text{max}}$ is the maximum electricity exchanged with the grid. Thus, $\dot{V}_{\text{grid}}^{\text{max}}$ is a time-coupling variable for the entire time series (Eq.6). The dependency of prices $c_i^{(\text{low/high})}$ on the utilization time is both a of coupling constraint and variable for the entire time series (Eq.7). Often, annual emission limits $C_{\text{CO2}}^{\text{max}}$ have to be obeyed. Emission limits represent a coupling constraint for the entire time series (Eq.8). To solve such long-term operational problems despite time-coupling (Eq. 5-8), we propose a time-series decomposition method.

3. Time-series decomposition for long-term operational optimization

A time-series decomposition method is proposed to generate feasible solutions of long-term operational optimization problems with known solution quality. The decomposition method provides lower and upper bounds in a parallel computing mode.

For the lower bound, we relax all binary variables ($\delta_{n,t}, x\in\{0,1\}$) of the operational problem (Eq.1-8), thereby converting the complex MILP into an LP, which can be solved efficiently. This solution of the relaxed problem serves as first lower bound. Subsequently, the Branch-and-Cut procedure starts by branching on binary variables and cutting off branches which cannot improve the solution (IBM Cooperation, 2016).

The upper bound is obtained by four steps (Fig. 1):

(i)   Initial heuristic to initialize the number of subproblems
(ii) Decomposition of time-coupling constraints and variables
(iii) Optimizing subproblems in parallel computing mode
(iv) Combining subsolutions to upper bound

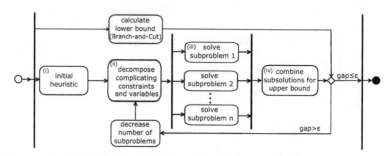

Figure 1: Overview of the proposed time-series decomposition method to create feasible solutions of operational optimization problems with known solution quality.

Using the lower and upper bound, we calculate a solution quality ε and check if the desired optimality gap is satisfied.

$$\varepsilon = \frac{\text{upper bound} - \text{lower bound}}{\text{upper bound}}. \tag{9}$$

If the optimality gap is not satisfied, we iteratively decrease the number of subproblems. In the following, we present the details of steps (i), (ii), and (iv) of the proposed time-series decomposition.

Step (i): Initial heuristic

Initialization of the decomposition method requires an initial number of subproblems. To identify a good estimate for this initial number, a heuristic is employed, aiming at minimal calculation time for the first decomposition.In the heuristic, we consider a wide range for the possible number of subproblems. For each number , we decompose the problem but solve only the first subproblem. The decomposition and solution time is recorded and extrapolated to the full number of subproblems. The number of subproblems resulting in the minimum extrapolated solution time is selected as the initial number of subproblems.

Step (ii): Decomposition of time-coupling constraints and variables

We decompose complicating constraints and variables into smaller subproblems. The decomposition is generic and conducted automatically based on the type of time-coupling constraint or variable:

(1)   For storage-like constraints (Eq. 5), we fix start and end values for each subproblem to ensure feasibility. The fixed values are adapted in the next iteration.
(2)   Time-coupling variables like (Eq. 6-7) are replaced by independent copies in every subproblem, resulting in independent subproblems, e.g., net connection fees and peak power prices are calculated for each subproblem independently.
(3)   For time-coupling constraints like the emission limits in Eq. (8), a fraction of the limit is allocated to each subproblem. This fraction is computed for each subproblem by independent minimization of the emissions within each subproblem.

From peak power prices to seasonal storage: Long-term operational
optimization of energy systems by time-series decomposition

707

(4) To improve performance, we extend each subproblem by aggregated time steps and the peak demands of all other subproblems. Thus, in each subproblem, a small part of the long-term operational optimization is solved with the full accuracy of the time series and the rest with low accuracy.

Step (iv): Combining subsolutions to upper bound

The solutions of the subproblems are combined to a feasible solution for the original problem. For this, the independent copies of variables in the subproblems (2) are resubstituted and the added aggregated time steps (4) are deleted. The solution of the final iteration is used to warmstart the original problem to further enhance solution quality.

4. Case study

The proposed decomposition method is applied to a long-term operational problem based on Baumgärtner et al. (2018). We investigate an industrial energy system with three units of each boilers, compression chillers, absorption chillers, and heat exchangers, one combined heat and power engine, a photovoltaic system, an inverter station, a battery, and one storage tank for each hot and cold water. We consider one year of operation with a two-hourly resolution for demands of process heat, hot and cold water, electricity, as well as solar radiation, and electricity grid prices. The original operational problem contains $1.2 \cdot 10^6$ equations and $6 \cdot 10^5$ variables (incl. $2 \cdot 10^5$ binaries) with $3 \cdot 10^6$ nonzero elements. The resulting long-term operational problem is highly coupled due to the storage and battery systems, an annual emission limit, peak power prices and net connection fees (Eq.1-8). To validate the computational results, we repeat the calculation for 5 instances generated by statistical noise ($\pm 5\%$) on the data. As benchmark, we solve the original synthesis problem directly with CPLEX without any decomposition.

In the initial heuristic (step (i)), the original problem is decomposed into 219 subproblems. The size of the subproblems is iteratively increased until the desired optimality gap of 2 % is satisfied with a decomposition into 20 subproblems.

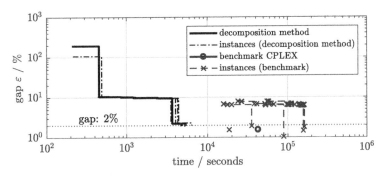

Figure 2: Gap ε of the proposed decomposition method and the benchmark CPLEX as function of the solution time. The required optimality gap of 2 % is marked in dotted red.

The decomposition method finds a feasible solution, with cost deciating less than 2 % from optimality, in 5,207 s on average (Fig. 2). The average computational time of the benchmark is 16 times larger (83,952 s) to obtain solutions of equal quality. On average, after 203 s, the proposed time-series decomposition method generates a first feasible solution, whereas on average the benchmark requires 175 times longer (35,617

s) to provide a feasible solution. Thus, the proposed decomposition method outperforms the benchmark in all instances by over an order of magnitude.

5. Conclusions

The long-term operational optimization of energy systems leads to computationally challenging optimization problems. In this paper, we propose a time-series decomposition method providing feasible solutions with known quality. The method decomposes the original problem into smaller subproblems, which are efficiently solved in parallel.

The proposed method requires only simple problem reformulations for creating subproblems and recombines their solutions to a feasible solution of the complete problem while still representing a rigorous decomposition. The proposed method is applied to a long-term industrial operational problem, including time-coupling constraints and variables due to storage systems, emission limits, peak power prices, and net connection fees. The proposed method provides fast convergence, outperforming commercial solvers by more than an order of magnitude.

References

S. Al-Agtash, R. Su, 1998. Augmented Lagrangian approach to hydro-thermal scheduling. IEEE Trans. Power Syst. 13 (4), 1392–1400.

N. Baumgärtner, R. Delorme, M. Hennen, A. Bardow, 2018. Design of low-carbon utility systems: Exploiting time-dependent grid emissions for climate-friendly demand-side management. submitted to a journal.

S. P. Bradley, A. C. Hax, T. L. Magnanti, 1992. Applied mathematical programming, 19th Edition. Addison-Wesley, Reading, Mass.

A. J. Conejo, E. Castillo, R. García-Bertrand, R. Mínguez, 2006. Decomposition techniques in mathematical programming: Engineering and Science Applications. Springer-Verlag, Berlin, Heidelberg.

J. Desrosiers, M. Lübbecke, 2011a. Branch-Price-and-Cut Algorithms. John Wiley & Sons.

J. Desrosiers, M. E. Lübbecke, 2011b. Branch-price-and-cut algorithms. Wiley Interscience, Hoboken, NJ.

R. W. Eglese, 1990. Simulated annealing: A tool for operational research. Eur. J. Oper. Res. 46 (3), 271–281.

S. Goderbauer, M. Comis, F. J. Willamowski, 2019. The synthesis problem of decentralized energy systems is strongly NP-hard. Comput. Chem. Eng., doi.org/10.1016/j.compchemeng.2019.02.002.

T. Hanne, R. Dornberger, 2017. Computational intelligence in logistics and supply chain management. Vol. 244 of Internat. Ser. Oper. Res. Management Sci. Springer, Switzerland.

IBM Cooperation, 2016. IBM ILOG and CPLEX Optimization and Studio and CPLEX User's and Manual and Version 12 and Release 7.

K. C. Kavvadias, Z. B. Maroulis, 2010. Multi-objective optimization of a trigeneration plant. Energy Policy 38 (2), 945–954.

E. Nasrolahpour, S. J. Kazempour, H. Zareipour, W. D. Rosehart, 2016. Strategic sizing of energy storage facilities in electricity markets. IEEE Trans. Sustain Energy 7 (4), 1462–1472.

A. Piacentino, F. Cardona, 2008. EABOT – Energetic analysis as a basis for robust optimization of trigeneration systems by linear programming. Energy Convers. Manag. 49 (11), 3006–3016.

R. Rahmaniani, T. G. Crainic, M. Gendreau, W. Rei, 2017. The Benders decomposition algorithm: A literature review. Eur. J. Oper. Res. 259 (3), 801–817.

A. Rong, R. Lahdelma, P. B. Luh, 2008. Lagrangian relaxation based algorithm for trigeneration planning with storages. Eur. J. Oper. Res. 188 (1), 240 – 257.

Q. Wang, J. D. McCalley, T. Zheng, E. Litvinov, 2016. Solving corrective risk-based security-constrained optimal power flow with Lagrangian relaxation and Benders decomposition. Inz. J. Eelc. Power. 75, 255–264.

R. Yokoyama, 2013. Optimal operation of a gas turbine cogeneration plant in consideration of equipment minimum up and down times. J. Eng. Gas. Turbine Power 135 (7), 071801.

R. Yokoyama, K. Ito, 1996. A revised decomposition method for MILP problems and its application to operational planning of thermal storage systems. J. Energ. Resour. 118 (4), 277–284.

Anton A. Kiss, Edwin Zondervan, Richard Lakerveld, Leyla Özkan (Eds.)
Proceedings of the 29th European Symposium on Computer Aided Process Engineering
June 16th to 19th, 2019, Eindhoven, The Netherlands. © 2019 Elsevier B.V. All rights reserved.
http://dx.doi.org/10.1016/B978-0-128-18634-3.50119-3

Scale-up Modeling of a Pharmaceutical Antisolvent Crystallization via a Hybrid Method of Computational Fluid Dynamics and Compartmental Modeling

Merve Öner,[a] Stuart M. Stocks,[b] Jens Abildskov,[a] Gürkan Sin,[a*]

[a]*Process and Systems Engineering Center, Department of Chemical and Biochemical Engineering, Technical University of Denmark, 2800 Kgs. Lyngby, Denmark*

[b]*LEO Pharma A/S, Industriparken 55, 2750 Ballerup, Denmark*

gsi@kt.dtu.dk

Abstract

In this work, a model of a 218 L scale pharmaceutical antisolvent crystallization process was developed. The model is based on a hybrid method of computational fluid dynamics (CFD) and compartmental modeling. In the model, the mixing behaviour of the bulk fluid at two different impeller speeds was obtained from CFD simulations. The compartmental map of the crystallizer was extracted from CFD results based on a hypothesis driven compartmentalization approach. A novel dynamic compartment model was developed to capture the fluid dynamics during the feeding of the antisolvent into the crystallizer and implemented in MATLAB/Simulink environment. Developed model takes into account the changes in compartmental volume, solvent concentrations and density and it assumes a dynamic flow between compartments during the filling. Dynamic compartment model can be also applied in other areas of modeling practices in chemical engineering instead of steady-state compartment models such as fed batch fermentation.

Keywords: Pharmaceutical crystallization, dynamic compartmental modeling, scale-up, computational fluid dynamics (CFD)

1. Introduction

The performance of crystallization process changes significantly dependent on the scale. Upon scale-up, the influence of the fluid dynamics and mixing on the process kinetics becomes important and variations in the crystal size distribution (CSD), purity and morphology often occur and that impacts the product quality and the performance of further downstream processes (Wei, 2010). Several experimental studies on the antisolvent crystallization system demonstrated the strong dependency of obtained CSD on the operation conditions such as crystallizer scale, impeller speed (mixing intensity), antisolvent addition rate and mode of addition such as direct or reverse. Often variations in these operating conditions directly effects the mixing of the solvent with antisolvent, so called the composition of the solvent mixtures (Woo et al., 2006). Homogeneous mixing in a short time is difficult to achieve in the large-scale crystallizer by making no concessions to the cost of the operation or product stability e.g. high impeller speed to promote mixing increases power input and leads to crystal attrition. When the mixing is inhomogeneous, it leads to local variations of important process variables such as solute and antisolvent concentration, supersaturation, particle concentration in the large scale geometry (Woo et al., 2006, Green, 2002). Since the crystallization kinetics such as nucleation and growth are strongly influenced by those process variables, the crystallization occurs at different kinetic rates in the vessel depending on the local variation profile. Many published studies that focused on aiding the optimization and control of crystallization processes are based on a well-mixed assumption (Nagy et al., 2008). Even though an optimum operation condition is determined after several experiments at well-mixed laboratory scale, this might not be valid for the scaled-up system, since the mixing behaviour and related local variation can be significantly different. Therefore, understanding and predicting the mixing behaviour in the large scale crystallizers is an effective strategy and crucial for the improvement of the process performance. Fluid dynamics of the large scale and related limitations of the chemical system should be always taken into account in tandem with the interactions of thermodynamics and kinetics between solute-solvent system in modeling of large-scale crystallizers, in order to support reliable design, optimization and control.

This study presents an approach to develop a predictive model for an antisolvent crystallization process scale-up of an active pharmaceutical ingredient (API) that is based on a hybrid method of computational fluid dynamics (CFD) and dynamic compartment modeling. Reliable and detailed mixing information of the fluid system obtained from non-reactive CFD simulations is used as a guidance to build up compartments. The mixing dynamics of the antisolvent addition into the solution is modelled with a dynamic compartment model in which the volumes of the compartments and fluxes in-between changes over time. The compartmental model, where crystallization kinetics are coupled with fluid dynamics, is implemented in MATLAB/Simulink. While compartmental modeling is a well applied technique in many areas of modeling practices in chemical engineering, there is no known application on the pharmaceutical antisolvent crystallization process. Besides, developed compartmental models in the literature always assume the volume of the compartments as constant, which is not the reality during addition of a second liquid into the solution as in the antisolvent crystallization. Therefore, this work presents also a pioneer approach for the dynamic compartmentalization method based on author's knowledge. Additionally, developed model can be applied to other processes where the volume changes can not be ignored e.g. fed batch fermentation.

2. Hybrid Model Development

2.1. Crystallizer geometry

A 218 L crystallizer vessel from a previous work was used for the model development of the large scale antisolvent crystallization system. The vessel has 0.640 m of internal diameter and 0.740 m height. A three-blade marine type impeller of 0.300 m diameter is placed in the vessel with a 0.270 m clearance from the vessel bottom. The diameter of the impeller shaft is 0.040 m. Four baffles are located with 0.009 m distance from the vessel wall (Öner et al., 2018). The initial liquid height in the crystallizer before antisolvent addition is 0.455 m, which equals to 126.1 L of the liquid volume.

2.2. Mixing characterization via CFD simulations

The mixing behaviour of the single-phase liquid in the crystallizer was predicted by solving the representative Navier-Stokes equations through transient CFD simulations performed with a commercial CFD software ANSYS CFX release 17.1. A turbulent fluid flow in the crystallizer was created by the impeller rotation at a speed of 40 rpm and 100 rpm. The standard k-ε turbulence model was used. The crystallizer volume was divided into two domains: a rotating domain and a stationary domain. The rotating domain is a cylindrical zone with 0.330 m diameter and 0.100 m height that contains the impeller and rotates at the impeller speed. The stationary domain contains the remaining zone. The frozen rotor approach was chosen to model the rotation of the impeller in terms of frame change model between the intersections of the two domains. The rotating and the stationary domains were discretized into 118,895 elements of tetrahedron mesh and 1,037,970 elements of hexahedron mesh, respectively (Öner et al., 2018). Several monitor points at different locations in the crystallizer were placed to monitor the time evolution of the fluid velocity. When the fluid velocity remained constant at all these monitor points (reached the steady state), the simulation was ended and the transient average value of the flow velocity components was used in further compartmentalization procedure.

2.3. Compartmentalization

The aim of the compartmentalization approach is to describe the imperfect mixing by defining the large scale fluid system as a network of finite-number interconnected ideally-mixed sub-volumes that contain no or negligible gradients (Wells and Ray, 2006, Nauha et al., 2018). The compartmental zones can be decided based on several criteria such as flow pattern, gradients of temperature and concentration, solid distribution or local energy dissipation (Kougoulos et al., 2006). In the last decade, CFD has been immensely utilized as a standard tool to study the mixing behaviour and its limitations on the chemical systems in detail. A coarser mesh of CFD cells can be created through compartmental models that facilitates the prediction of fluid dynamics and can be coupled with complex reaction kinetics in a simplified simulation environment in a computational cost efficient manner (Nauha et al., 2018, Nørregaard et al., 2018). The compartmental zones can be identified by processing the fluid dynamics information obtained from CFD simulations using a manual or automatic zoning technique (Bezzo and Macchietto, 2004). In this work, the mixing behavior in the crystallizer volume was firstly predicted by means of CFD simulations. The compartmental zones were identified based on a novel hypothesis-driven compartmental model approach that includes the analyzing of axial and radial bulk flow velocities at different locations in the crystallizer. The boundaries of the compartments were defined at the locations, where there is a change in the flow direction in radial and axial components of the velocity. A unidirectional flow was considered for each surface of compartments (Nørregaard et al., 2018).

2.4. Modeling and simulation of antisolvent crystallization process

Antisolvent crystallization of acetylsalicylic acid (aspirin) from ethanol (solvent) and water (antisolvent) was chosen as a case study. Previously published solubility and kinetic data in the literature were used (Lindenberg et al., 2009). The initial solution in the crystallizer has a volume of 126.1 L and contains the weight fraction of 0.25 w/w water and 0.75 w/w ethanol at 35 °C. The initial supersaturation was 1.05. After addition of the seed, the crystallization started with feeding the antisolvent, water into the solution at a rate of $2.3 \cdot 10^{-5}$ m^3/s for 4000 s. When the antisolvent addition is completed, the final volume in the crystallizer is 218 L and contains 0.60 w/w water. The density change of the liquid mixture upon addition of the antisolvent was also taken into account and dynamically calculated during the simulation.

3. Results and Discussion

3.1. Mixing simulation via CFD and compartmentalization

The mixing characteristics of 218 L liquid flow at two different impeller speeds of 40 rpm and 100 rpm were studied with CFD simulations and is shown in Figure 1 (right). The obtained results show that there is much higher liquid flow circulation around the impeller region and the bottom of the vessel compared to top region in the vessel. After analyzing the three components of the bulk flow velocities at different locations in the vessel, total six compartments were detected and the compartmental map is illustrated in Figure 1 (left). The volume of each compartments (at t = t_{final}) and the volumetric flow rate between compartments (at t = t_{final}) are listed in Table 1. It should be noted that at the beginning of the antisolvent crystallization, while compartment 5 and 6 were completely full, compartment 3 and 4 were empty, and compartment 1 and 2 contained some amount of liquid. As the antisolvent was added to the vessel, firstly the empty volumes were filled in time. During the filling. It was assumed that the volumetric flow rate between compartment 1 and compartment 2 was constant until the compartments were full with liquid, then it started to increase dynamically up to final volumetric flow rate, during the filling of the compartment 3 and compartment 4, since additional flow, $Q_{4 \to 1}(t)$ entered to the system. The volumetric flow rates between empty compartments were activated after the volume of the compartments below was full. The volumetric flowrate between compartment 3 and 4, $Q_{3 \to 4}(t)$ as well as between compartment 2 and 3, $Q_{2 \to 3}(t)$ was also increased dynamically as filling of top zones started. These fluid data were used as input in the compartmental modeling of the antisolvent crystallization in the next section.

3.2. Compartmental model simulation

Antisolvent crystallization kinetics coupled with the fluid dynamics was simulated by means of compartmental modeling. The dynamics of the compartment volumes and accumulated antisolvent amounts in each compartment during the addition of antisolvent into the crystallizer at an impeller speed of 40 rpm are illustrated in Fig. 2 (top). During the antisolvent addition, it was assumed that antisolvent feed was entered from top of the vessel into both compartment 1 and compartment 2 with a volumetric flow rate proportional to their volumes, since the compartments are open volume systems and added liquid will increase the the liquid height at the same amount.

Table 1. Volumetric flow rates between compartments and the volume of the compartments.

Impeller speed	Volumetric Flow Rate [m³/s]						
	$Q_{1 \to 2}$	$Q_{2 \to 3}$	$Q_{3 \to 4}$	$Q_{4 \to 1}$	$Q_{2 \to 5}$	$Q_{5 \to 6}$	$Q_{6 \to 1}$
40 rpm							
t = t_0	0.0101	0	0	0	0.0101	0.0101	0.0101
t = t_{final}	0.0127	0.0026	0.0026	0.0026	0.0101	0.0101	0.0101
100 rpm							
t = t_0	0.0326	0	0	0	0.0326	0.0326	0.0326
t = t_{final}	0.0400	0.0074	0.0074	0.0074	0.0326	0.0326	0.0326
	Volume [m³]						
Time	**C1**	**C2**	**C3**	**C4**	**C5**	**C6**	
t = t_0	0.0351	0.0270	0	0	0.0200	0.0440	
t = t_{final}	0.0560	0.0430	0.0240	0.0310	0.0200	0.0440	

When these compartments were filled, the antisolvent was fed into the top compartments of 3 and 4. However, the filling of compartment 3 and 4 introduced the new flow from compartment 4 into 1, and increased flow ware between the compartment 1 and 2 that explains the increasing mass of antisolvent as illustrated in the Fig. 2 (top). Local variations of the antisolvent fraction shown in Fig. 2 (bottom) affect locally the crystallization growth and nucleation kinetics due to the differences in the supersaturation profiles.

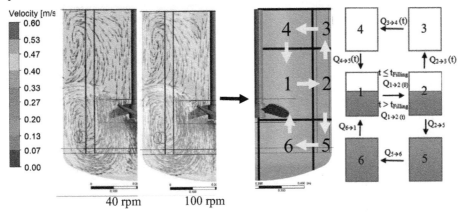

40 rpm   100 rpm

Figure 1. Flow velocity and the mixing behavior at different impeller speed (left) and compartmental map (right).

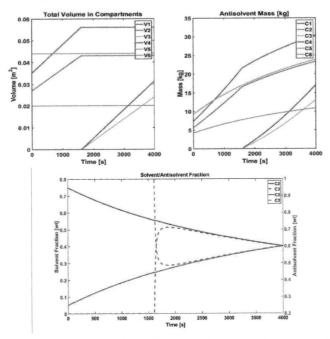

Figure 2. Compartment volumes (top-left), accumulated antisolvent amounts (top-right) and solvent fractions (bottom) during addition of antisolvent into the crystallizer.

4. Conclusions

A model of a large scale pharmaceutical antisolvent crystallization process was developed based on a hybrid approach of computational fluid dynamics and compartmental modeling. Fluid dynamics of bulk fluid mixing at two different impeller speeds were studied via CFD simulations. Compartmental zones were determined based on the flow velocities obtained from CFD simulation through a hypothesis driven compartmentalization approach. A dynamic model was incorporated for predicting the volume changes of the compartments and dynamic exchange flows in-between. The crystallization of aspirin from ethanol (solvent) and water (antisolvent) was simulated for each compartment that interchanges liquid flows and related properties such as density, solvent/antisolvent weight fraction as well as particles. Future work will focus on the refinement of the compartmental map in two ways. First, analyzing the third component of flow velocity in circumferential direction will enable the addition of the antisolvent from a more specific feed point. Second, CFD simulations with different bulk fluid volumes will be performed in order to study the fluid dynamics of antisolvent addition and evolution of the compartmental map in more detail.

References

F. Bezzo and S. Macchietto, 2004, A general methodology for hybrid multizonal/CFD models, Part II: Automatic zoning, *Computers & Chemical Engineering*, 28, 513-525.

D. Green. In *Handbook of Industrial Crystallization*, 2nd ed.; A. S. Myerson, Ed.; Butterwoorth-Heinemann: Boston, 2002; pp 181-200.

C. Lindenberg, M. Krättli, J. Cornel and M. Mazotti, 2009, Design and optimization of a combined cooling/antisolvent crystallization process, *Crystal Growth & Design*, 9, 2, 1124-1136.

E. Kougoulos, A.G. Jones and M. Wood-Kaczmar, 2006, A hybrid CFD compartmentalization modeling framework for the scaleup of batch cooling crystallization process, *Chem. Eng. Comm.*, 193, 1008-1023.

E. K. Nauha, Z. Kálal, J. M. Ali, V. Alopaeus, 2018 Compartmental modeling of large stirred tank bioreactors with high gas volume fractions, *Chemical Engineering Journal*, 334, 2319-2334.

A. Nørregaard, C. Bach, U. Krühne, U. Borgbjerg, K. V. Gernaey, 2018, Hypothesis-driven compartment model for stirred bioreactors utilizing computational fluid dynamics and multiple pH sensors, *Chemical Engineering Journal*, 356, 161-169.

M. Öner, C. Bach, T. Tajsoleiman, G. S. Molla, M. F. Freitag, S. M. Stocks, J. Abildskov, U. Krühne, G. Sin, 2018. Scale-up modeling of a pharmaceutical crystallization process via compartmentalization approach, *Computer Aided Chemical Engineering*, 44, 181-186.

Z. K. Nagy, M. Fujiwara, R. D. Braatz, 2008, Modeling and control of combined cooling and antisolvent crystallization processes, *Journal of Process Control*, 18, 856-864.

G. J. Wells, W. H. Ray, 2006, Methodology for modeling detailed imperfect mixing effects in complex reactors, *AIChE Journal*, 51, 1508-1520.

H. Y. Wei, 2010, Computer-aided design and scale-up of crystallization process: Integrating approaches and case studies, *Chemical Engineering Research and Design*, 88, 1377-1380.

X. Y. Woo, R. B. H. Tan, P. S. Chow, R. D. Braatz, 2006, Simulation of mixing effects in antisolvent crystallization using a coupled CFD-PDF-PBE approach, *Crystal Growth & Design*, 6, 6, 1291-1303.

Anton A. Kiss, Edwin Zondervan, Richard Lakerveld, Leyla Özkan (Eds.)
Proceedings of the 29th European Symposium on Computer Aided Process Engineering
June 16th to 19th, 2019, Eindhoven, The Netherlands. © 2019 Elsevier B.V. All rights reserved.
http://dx.doi.org/10.1016/B978-0-128-18634-3.50120-X

Modelling of bubble column hydrodynamics using CFD and SQMOM as a population balance solver

Jan Schäfer[a], Mark W. Hlawitschka[a], Menwer Attarakih[a,b*] and Hans-Jörg Bart[a]

[a]*Chair of Separation Science and Technology, TU Kaiserslautern, 67663 Kaiserslautern, Germany*
[b]*School of Engineering, Chem. Eng. Dept., The University of Jordan, 11942-Amman, Jordan*
jan.schaefer@mv.uni-kl.de

Abstract

The complex interactions between the turbulent flow field, bubble size distribution, mass transfer and chemical reactions make the design of bubble column reactors a challenging task. Especially at broad bubble size distributions the commonly used QMOM is not able to track the different velocities of small and large bubbles, while the classes methods are limited due to a high computational load. In this work, we extended our CFD-Sectional QMOM (SQMOM) (Drumm et al., 2008) to model and simulate bubbly gas flow in a rectangular column. For this purpose, we established a setup to measure, in 18 different zones of a rectangular bubble column, the bubble size distribution, the bubble velocity and bubble orientation. The coalescence and breakage model parameters are extracted in a parameter study using the software Dakota for a single case. A satisfactory agreement between local values of three experimentally investigated flow rates and simulations are found without further adjustment of the parameters. This work enables therefore a characterization of heterogeneous bubbly regimes including breakage and coalescence as found in industrial reactive bubble columns.

Keywords: Bubble movement, Local bubble size distribution, Sectional Quadrature Method of Moments, Population balance equation

1. Introduction

In many process engineering fields, dispersed systems are used to enhance momentum, heat and mass transport in either liquid-liquid, gas-liquid, solid-liquid or solid-gas phases. The generation of mono or multivariate size distributions depends not only on the particle generation and the internals of the apparatus, but also on the operational conditions. These include throughput and energy input. Among these multiphase apparatuses is the bubble column reactor, which is used in chemical and biochemical processes to bring a gas phase in contact with a fluid phase to enhance mass transfer and chemical reactions through maximizing the available interfacial area concentration. The complex interactions between the turbulent flow field, bubble size distribution, mass transfer and chemical reactions make the design of the reactors a challenging task (Hlawitschka et al., 2016). In this regard, population balance models coupled to computational fluid dynamics (CFD) have become a suitable tool to investigate bubbly gas flows where the evolution of full bubble size distribution can be modelled. This is because the experimental evidence shows that broad distributions developed along bubble column reactors due to bubble breakage, coalescence and growth which could not be ignored (Hlawitschka et al., 2016). Unfortunately, the main population balance CFD modelling tools are based, on the one hand, on the Quadrature Method Of Moments (QMOM) which fail to predict the bubble column hydrodynamics due to averaging the whole distribution. On the other hand, classes methods which can follow the full bubble size distribution are inaccurate, especially when a small number of classes are used to reduce the expensive computer computational cost. For this reason, the Sectional Quadrature Method of Moments (SQMOM) (Attarakih et al., 2009) is used, which is a combination of both approaches (discrete and moment methods) to overcome these drawbacks and enable the simulation of BSD with difficult shapes, like a bimodal distribution.

1.1. Numerical framework

The SQMOM is implemented to the multiphaseEulerFoam solver of the toolbox Open-FOAM (version 4.1). The solver is an Euler-Euler multiphase approach and treats each phase as interpenetrating continua. The multiphase approach enables a direct implementation of the primary and the secondary particle concept of the SQMOM, where the primary particles represent the discrete sections and the secondary particles are responsible to account for the interactions between the sections.

The hydrodynamics inside the bubble column is basically simulated using the Navier-Stokes equations for each phase:

$$\frac{\partial \alpha_n}{\partial t} + \vec{u}_n \cdot \nabla \alpha_n + \nabla \cdot (\vec{u}_{comp}(1 - \alpha_n)) = \alpha_n S_\alpha \tag{1}$$

$$\frac{\partial}{\partial t}(\alpha_n \rho_n \vec{u}_n) + \nabla \cdot (\rho_n \alpha_n \vec{u}_n \vec{u}_n) = -\alpha_n \nabla p - \nabla \cdot (\alpha_n \tau_n) + \alpha_n \rho_n \vec{g} + \vec{F}_{D,n} + \vec{F}_{VM,n} \tag{2}$$

The phase fraction of a phase n is denoted by α, the density of each phase by ρ, and the velocity $\vec{u}$. In addition, the solver multiphaseEulerFoam includes an interface sharpening term, which includes the interface compression velocity:

$$\vec{u}_{comp} = C_\alpha |\vec{u}| \frac{\nabla \alpha}{|\nabla \alpha|} \tag{3}$$

A value of C_α enables the reconstruction of the interface of large bubbles. However, the dynamic switching between particles accounted by PBM and resolved particles is not resolved until now and we apply a value of $C_\alpha = 0$.

The hydrodynamic interactions between the phases like drag, lift, virtual mass, etc. are accounted by the respective forces. The drag force $F_{D,n}$ is determined by the equation of Tomiyama et al. (1998):

$$C_D = max\left(min\left(\frac{16}{Re}(1 + 0.15Re^{0.687}), \frac{48}{Re}\right), \frac{8}{3}\frac{Eo}{(Eo+4)}\right) \tag{4}$$

The Reynolds number *Re* and the Eötvos number *Eo* are calculated by:

$$Re = \frac{\rho_c d_{32} |\vec{u}_c - \vec{u}_d|}{\mu_c} \text{ and } Eo = \frac{g(\rho_c - \rho_d)d_{32}^2}{\sigma_c} \tag{5}$$

The virtual mass force $\vec{F}_{VM,n}$ uses a constant value of $C_{VM} = 0$:

$$\vec{F}_{VM,n} = \alpha_{n^*} \rho_n C_{VM} \left(\frac{Du_n^*}{Dt} - \frac{Du_n}{Dt} \right) \tag{6}$$

The superscript $*$ describes the interacting other phase.

As turbulence model, the model Smagorinsky turbulence model is applied. For the calculation of the energy dissipation, the following equation is applied:

$$\varepsilon = \frac{\mu_{eff,c}^3}{\rho_c^3 (C_S \Delta)^4} \tag{7}$$

C_S is a model constant with a value of 0.167. The cubic root of the cell volume is Δ.

1.1.1. SQMOM

The Sectional Quadrature Method of Moments (SQMOM) and its variants was introduced by Attarakih et al. (2009). The SQMOM calculates the change of the moments using the primary and secondary particle based concept. The primary particles correspond to the classes of a distribution, the secondary particles involve the interactions such as coalescence and breakage, based on the Quadrature Method of Moments concept. The moment of order k of the primary particle i, falling in the bubble size interval $[L_{i-1/2}, L_{i+1/2}]$, can be calculated as follows:

$$m_k i = \int_{L_{i-1/2}}^{L_{i+1/2}} (L_i)^k n(L,x,t) dL \approx \sum_{j=1}^{N_s p} (w_{ji}(x,t) L_{ji}^k(x,t)) \tag{8}$$

Four moments are sufficient to represent each section. Thereby, each section moves with its own velocity. The two equal weights and abscissas can be calculated by the moments m_0, m_1 and m_3:

$$L_{1,2} = m_1 \pm \frac{1}{\sqrt{3}} \sqrt{\frac{m_3}{m_1} - m_1^2} \tag{9}$$

$$w_{1,2} = \frac{1}{2} m_0 \tag{10}$$

The transport equation for each section can therefore be calculated as:

$$\frac{\partial}{\partial t} (\alpha_i \rho_i m_k^{<i>}) + \nabla \cdot (\alpha_i \rho_i m_k^{<i>} \vec{u}_i) = \alpha_i \rho_i S_k^{<i>} \tag{11}$$

The source terms *S* for breakage and coalescence are described in Drumm et al. (2008). In this work, the breakage from Alopaeus et al. (2002) and coelescence from Coulaloglou and Tavlarides (1977) and Prince and Blanch (1990) are applied. The breakage frequency is:

$$g(L) = C_1 \varepsilon^{1/3} erfc \left(\left[C_2 \frac{\sigma}{\rho_c \varepsilon^{2/3} L^{5/3}} + C_3 \frac{\mu_d}{(\rho_d \rho_c)^{1/2} \varepsilon^{1/3} L^{4/3}} \right]^{1/2} \right) \tag{12}$$

and the coalescence frequency is given by:

$$a(L, L^*) = C_4 \varepsilon^{1/3} (L + L^*)^2 (L^{2/3} + L^{*2/3})^{1/2} \eta(L, L^*) \tag{13}$$

The coalescence efficiency is:

$$\eta(L, L^*) = exp \left(-C_5 \frac{\mu_c \rho_c \varepsilon}{\sigma_c^2} \left(\frac{L L^*}{L + L^*} \right) \right) \tag{14}$$

The parameters described in literature are $C_1 = 6$, $C_2 = 0.04$ and $C_3 = 0.01$, $C_4 = 0.88$ and $C_5 = 6 \cdot 10^9$ (Buffo et al., 2013). There every system shows slight influences to coalescence and breakage, the model parameters were optimized using the optimization toolbox Dakota.

2. Experimental and numerical setup

A pseudo rectangular bubble column with a dimension of 0.18x0.04x1 m is filled with water up to a level of 0.6 *m*. Gas is introduced at the center of the column through a needle sparger with 5 needles in a row. The pitch of each needle is 1.5 *cm* and needle inner diameter is 1 *mm*. The gas superficial velocity was adjusted to 6 and 10 *mm/s*. A high speed camera (Imaging Solutions, IDT NX-8 S2) was placed in front of the column to track the bubbles in 18 sections of the column. Images were taken at a frame rate of 500 images per second, which in general allows a detection of bubble movement. The images were automatically analysed in regard to bubble size, bubble shape and orientation using the Opencv toolbox. The inlet diameter was determined from these experiments, by determine the diameter distribution close to the inlet. For the case of 6 *mm/s*, the inlet diameter was 6.7 *mm/s* in average and for the case of 10 *mm/s*, the inlet diameter is 6.3 *mm*. The numerical representation of the bubble column (1) consists of a hexahedral mesh with 28x5x120 cells. The dispersers is simplified by a planar surface with an area of 50 *mm* x 6 *mm*. Also in the simulation, the air phase above the water level is accounted for.

3. Results

For the case the superficial velocity of 6 *mm/s*, the model parameters were optimized to obtain a good fit of the bubble size distributions (Figure 2), while for symmetry reasons, only the left zones and middle zones of the bubble column are presented. The optimization resulted in parameters for $C_1 = 2$ and $C_4 = 0.1$. The other parameters were kept equal to the values, described in the numerical framework section. The average diameter obtained from experiments is 6.0 *mm* and the simulation results in an average diameter of 6.0 *mm*. The bubble regime is breakage dominated. In a second step, we applied the parameters to the case of higher superficial velocity of 10 *mm/s*. It can be seen, that the simulation fits well to the experimental results (Figure 3). The bubble size changes from 6.3 *mm* to

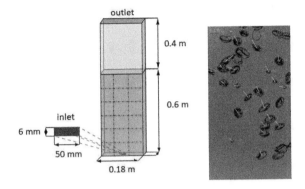

Figure 1: Numerical representation of the experimental setup with the 18 measurement zone for the bubble size detection (left) and example of the bubble size detecion (right).

5.7 *mm* in average. The simulation predicts a diameter of 5.9 *mm* in average. A clear shift to smaller bubble sizes can be seen from the sections. Especially close to the wall, the smaller sized bubbles dominate the flow regime, while in the center of the column, larger bubbles can be seen. This effect is enhanced at higher velocities.

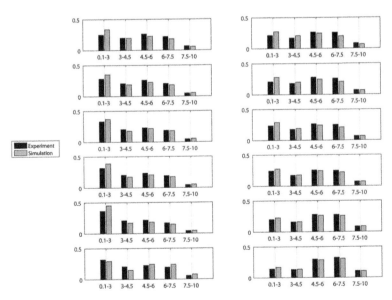

Figure 2: Bubble size distribution in each section at a superficial velocity of 6 *mm/s*.

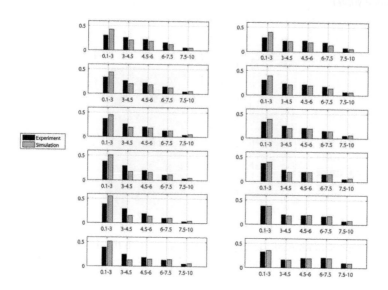

Figure 3: Bubble size distribution in each section at a superficial velocity of 10 mm/s.

4. Conclusion

In this work, we presented a method to model polydisperse systems coupled with an open source toolbox (OpenFOAM) to predict the local size distribution in a pseudo rectangular bubble column. We validated the SQMOM population balance solver to experimental data obtained by a high speed camera and automated data processing. The SQMOM is able to track the bubble size distribution by combining the advantages of the classes method with the ones of the quadrature method of moments. For the still inevitable calibration of the coalescence and breakage parameters, the toolbox Dakota was successfully applied. The computational performance can be flexibly adapted by adding or removing primary particles, leading in the second case to a reduced order model (OPOSPM).

References

V. Alopaeus, J. Koskinen, K. I. Keskinen, J. Majander, 2002. Simulation of the population balances for liquidŰliquid systems in a nonideal stirred tank. Part 2Űparameter fitting and the use of the multiblock model for dense dispersions. Chem Eng Sci 57, 1815–1825.

M. M. Attarakih, C. Drumm, H.-J. Bart, 2009. Solution of the population balance equation using the sectional quadrature method of moments (SQMOM). Chem Eng Sci 64, 742–752.

A. Buffo, D. L. Marchisio, M. Vanni, P. Renze, 2013. Simulation of polydisperse multiphase systems using population balances and example application to bubbly flows. Chem Eng Res Des 91, 1859–1875.

C. A. Coulaloglou, L. L. Tavlarides, 1977. Description of interaction processes in agitated liquid-liquid dispersions. Chem Eng Sci 32, 1289–1297.

C. Drumm, M. Attarakih, S. Tiwari, J. Kuhnert, H.-J. Bart, 2008. Implementation of the sectional quadrature method of moments in a CFD code. 6th International Conference on CFD in Oil & Gas, Metallurgical and Process Industries, SINTEF/NTNU, Trondheim, Norway, 10-12 June 2008.

M. W. Hlawitschka, J. Schäfer, M. Hummel, C. Garth, H.-J. Bart, 2016. Populationsbilanzmodellierung mit einem Mehrphasen-CFD-Code und vergleichende Visualisierung. Chem Ing Tech 88, 1480–1491.

M. J. Prince, H. W. Blanch, 1990. Bubble coalescence and break-up in air-sparged bubble columns. AIChE J. 36, 1485–1499.

A. Tomiyama, I. Kataoka, I. Zun, T. Sakaguchi, 1998. Drag Coefficients of Single Bubbles under Normal and Micro Gravity Conditions. JSME international journal. Ser. B, Fluids Therm Eng 41, 472–479.

Anton A. Kiss, Edwin Zondervan, Richard Lakerveld, Leyla Özkan (Eds.)
Proceedings of the 29th European Symposium on Computer Aided Process Engineering
June 16th to 19th, 2019, Eindhoven, The Netherlands. © 2019 Elsevier B.V. All rights reserved.
http://dx.doi.org/10.1016/B978-0-128-18634-3.50121-1

Single-shooting optimization of an industrial process through co-simulation of a modularized Aspen Plus Dynamics model

Mikael Yamanee-Nolin[a,*], Anton Löfgren[a], Niklas Andersson[a], Bernt Nilsson[a], Mark Max-Hansen[b] and Oleg Pajalic[b]

[a]*Lund University, Naturvetarvägen 14, 221 00 Lund, Sweden*
[b]*Perstorp AB, Industriparken, 284 80 Perstorp, Sweden*
mikael.yamanee-nolin@chemeng.lth.se

Abstract

The Python Module Coupler (PyMoC) is a tool for co-simulation of Aspen Plus Dynamics modules that together make up an overall process flowsheet. The tool requires only user input in the form of file paths to Aspen Plus Dynamics modules, and it is able to automatically make the required connections there between, and keep track of the simulation whilst updating the streams regularly. This contribution briefly discusses the implementation and mechanisms of PyMoC, and then applies it to a multi-module, single-shooting constrained optimization problem, where an industrial set-up consisting of an evaporator system coupled to a distillation column is studied. This serves as a showcase of PyMoC's functionality and usability, as well as its potential in serving as a helpful tool for practitioners of model-based studies who could benefit from modularizing their models. Utilizing PyMoC for this purpose, the optimization results indicate that the operating costs induced from the steam consumption can be reduced by 54% compared to a nominal operating case, but a holistic, full-process study is necessary to understand the full set of possibilities, causes, and effects.

Keywords: Python, Aspen Plus Dynamics, co-simulation, optimization, PyMoC

1. Introduction

Model-based studies have a wide range of important uses, and can help practitioners save both time and money, whilst improving quality and safety of a process (Oppelt et al., 2015). Especially dynamic model-based studies have many different applications due to their capabilities of investigating not only steady-state conditions but also transient patterns (Skorych et al., 2017). Thus, performing such studies, e.g. single-shooting optimization, plays an important role in improving production processes in order to satisfy demands regarding e.g. environmental aspects whilst increasing production capacity.

When modeling and simulating large, complex flowsheets, there are advantages to be found in dividing the overall model into smaller sub-modules (i.e. modularization), such as simplifying the addition of complementing models and opening up possibilities for parallel work-flows (Felippa et al., 2001). It also makes overview easier if the models would follow existing P&IDs. Modularization is furthermore a solution to convergence issues that large-scale complex process flowsheet models may suffer from (Lin et al., 2017), which would otherwise obstruct model-based studies.

However, modularization comes with its own challenges, as there will thus be a need to connect and co-simulate the modules, which poses a challenge in itself (Andersson, 2016). Doing so manually is obviously not feasible considering the sheer number of spatial and temporal connections necessary for continuous simulation. Commercially available tools such as the AspenTech Operator Training Simulator (OTS) could be used, but the lack of publications utilizing the OTS for model-based studies (Ahmad et al., 2016) supports the conclusion that this tool may not be appropriate to use for such studies. To this end, a tool called the Python Module Coupler (PyMoC) has been developed to help practitioners with co-simulation of modules developed in Aspen Plus Dynamics (APD), utilizing the process flowsheeting software as the engine for calculations. The Python implementation of PyMoC allows for advanced model-based studies by automating connections and data transfer through the application of a naming convention and a zero-order hold analogy (ZOHA), respectively.

In this contribution, PyMoC has been used to optimize a multi-module model of an oscillating polyalcohol separation process, consisting of a two-stage evaporator system and a methanol distillation column. PyMoC will first be introduced briefly, before the modules and the optimization problem is presented, followed by results and conclusions.

2. The Python Module Coupler - PyMoC

PyMoC is based on the COM enabled interface first presented in Nolin et al. (2017), and works by taking as input the paths of the APD files that are to be co-simulated, and then automatically connects these and co-simulates them. The nature of its Python implementation further simplifies customizing model-based studies and applying useful 3rd party software. In this section, two of the main mechanisms behind the function of PyMoC are briefly explained; (i) the naming convention, and (ii) how the transfer of data between modules is performed during runtime.

2.1. The naming convention

In order to minimize the amount of work required by the user, connections between modules are made automatically. This is based on a naming convention, i.e. streams with identical stream names are connected. PyMoC automatically recognizes which stream is the source and the destination, based on the 'Fixed'/'Free' stream variable property used within APD. This means that the user only needs to make sure that the streams to be connected are named identically during modeling.See figure 1 for an illustrative, where the streams 'FEED' will be connected with the algorithm recognizing that the Module A stream is the source to the destination in Module B. The naming convention is also used for deciding which results that are to be presented. The user may provide an *interesting stream-name prefix*, which the algorithm will use to recognize for which streams the user wants results. This is practical especially for large systems, as the user can name the interesting streams with that prefix instead of naming specific streams, and the stream results will be extracted automatically for all interesting streams. Using figure 1 as an example again with e.g. "I-" as the prefix, streams I-IN, I-V, and I-L will have their results extracted automatically.

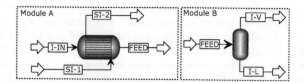

Figure 1: An illustrative example for the naming convention.

Single-shooting optimization of an industrial process through co-simulation of a
modularized Aspen Plus Dynamics model
723

2.2. Data transfer using zero-order hold

A zero-order hold (ZOH) strategy, which has recently been successfully applied for the control of chromatographic separation (Sellberg et al., 2017), is utilized to transfer data between modules, and is essentially a piece-wise constant method. It works by taking the output of the source stream and setting that as the input of a destination stream, keeping this constant over a simulation time horizon, τ. The length of the simulation time horizon is chosen by the user, who should consider the trade-off between accuracy and speed - a smaller τ gives more frequently updated modules, increased accuracy since modules can work with fresher data, as well as longer run-times. The main advantage is the simple implementation, and the main disadvantage is that the sudden step-changes to a variable may introduce discontinuities, something of which the user needs to be aware.

3. Optimization of a modularized model using PyMoC

The problem entails optimizing the two parts of the polyalcohol separation system modeled in two independent flowsheets in order to grant the aforementioned advantages of modularization. The modules are described here, followed by the formulation of the optimization problem.

3.1. The models

The modularized process is presented schematically in figure 2. The evaporator system module has been presented in Nolin et al. (2018). The methanol distillation column was modeled using standard blocks of *RADFRAC*, *MHEX*, and *FLASH*2 in Aspen Plus and then converted to Aspen Plus Dynamics, since the evaporator system was oscillating with propagations into the distillation system. The default controllers added during the conversion to an APD model were kept. An important aspect to note of both processes is that the separation was driven by steam at different pressures, inducing different process costs. Furthermore, of special interest are the streams named PROD and MEOH in figure 2, representing the target product stream of the main component in each module.

The distillation module shares four connections with the evaporator module, all of which drawn from the top of process units in the evaporator module, thus containing the most volatile components at each instance. These streams are passed through a 'translation module' (TM in figure 2) since the evaporation and distillation modules do not share identical Aspen Property Definition files. The difference there-between, c.p., is that formaldehyde was excluded from the distillation module component/property sets during modeling (and subsequently also the Maurer reactions (Hasse and Maurer, 1991) of the evaporator system), as its presence was assumed to be negligible. Essentially, this means that the distillation module cannot handle formaldehyde since its component/property sets do not contain the component. The translation module makes sure that formaldehyde is bypassed, but that the rest of the stream states (in terms of temperatures, pressures, mass flows, and compositions) are transferred from the evaporation to the distillation module. The translation module consists of one *SEP* block per stream, with the singular task of separating formaldehyde into a bypass stream, available for use if necessary later on.

3.2. The optimization problem

The steam consumption was one of the major cost-drivers in a nominal operating case of the overall, oscillating process. Thus, the goal of the optimization was to minimize the steam consumption cost incurred during daily operation while managing process and product demands (which are averaged due to the process oscillations captured in the modules). These demands entail the evaporation module product stream (PROD in figure 2) purity and mass flow, as well as the mass flow and methanol concentration in the top stream of the distillation column (MEOH in figure 2). In addition to these constraints, another constraint on the minimum mass flow rate from the top of the distillation column was set at half of the nominal run mean value, to keep the column from running dry. This gives a total of five inequality constraint functions. Furthermore, each simulation included a pre-processing simulation period of 12 simulation hours to have any potential (cyclic) steady-state established before the optimization run. The problem was approached by employing a single-shooting strategy with $\tau = 0.1h$, and formulated as unbounded optimization subject to non-linear constraints:

$$\underset{u}{\text{minimize}} \quad \phi(u) = \sum_{i=1}^{2} \frac{c_i}{u_{i,nom}} \cdot u_i$$

w.r.t. $u_1 = w_{steam,\, evap} \in \mathbb{R}$

$u_2 = w_{steam,\, dist} \in \mathbb{R}$

s.t.   Modularized flowsheet model

$C_1 = \overline{w}_{PROD} - C_{w_{PROD}} \geq 0$ $\qquad$ $C_2 = \overline{P}_{PROD} - C_{P_{PROD}} \geq 0$

$C_3 = \overline{w}_{MEOH} - C_{w_{MEOH}} \geq 0$ $\qquad$ $C_4 = \overline{P}_{MEOH} - C_{P_{MEOH}} \geq 0$

$C_5 = w_{MEOH,\, min} - C_{w_{MEOH,\, min}} \geq 0$

where w is mass flow rate, P is purity, $\overline{x}$ denotes the average of a variable over the time period, subscripts *PROD* and *MEOH* refer to the streams thus named (figure 2) $u_{i,nom}$ is the decision variable values , and c_i is a price factor relating the mass flow of steam to the incurred cost thereof; $c_1 = 1$ and $c_2 = 0.7$, reflecting the cost ratio between the two steam pressure levels. C_{ij}, $i = (w,P)$, $j = (PROD, MEOH)$ denote the respective values of the *mean constraints*, while $C_{w_{MEOH,\, min}}$ denotes the constraint value for the minimum flow rate in the MEOH stream. The problem was solved by utilizing the scientific computing package *SciPy*'s implementation of the optimization algorithm Constrained Optimization By Linear Approximation (COBYLA), using the nominal point of the simulation as initial values for the decision variables, and running the model as part of the constraint function rather than the objective function.

4. Results and discussion

The objective value for the nominal run, $\phi(u_{nom}) = 1.7$, represents a normalized hourly steam consumption cost. By reducing u_1 by 69% and u_2 by 33%, the optimization was able to reduce the objective value by 54% to $\phi(u_{opt}) = 0.78$, whilst successfully satisfying the constraints. The

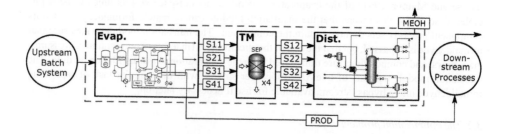

Figure 2: A schematic of the modularized process model, marked by the dashed box; the evaporator system ("Evap.") is described in Nolin et al. (2018), whilst the translation module ("TM") and the distillation column ("Dist.") are introduced in this contribution. Note the target product streams PROD and MEOH. The decision variables, i.e. the steam streams, are fully embedded in each module.

latter can be seen in figures 3 and 4, as the mean of variables in the optimal run is greater than the respective mean constraint; the same is true for the minimum flow constraint regarding $\overline{w}_{MEOH}$.

To gain insight into the dynamic behavior of the process, the PROD and MEOH stream results (i.e. w and P) of the nominal run as well as the optimal run are presented together with their mean values and the relevant constraints in figures 3 and 4, respectively. The results have been scaled to be centered around the mean constraint for each variable, rendering the results as dimensionless quantities. Neither graph show sudden, discontinuous responses at the start/end of the simulation time horizons, suggesting that the ZOHA strategy has not created any significant discontinuities.

As can be seen in figure 3, the mass flow and purity for the product stream vary somewhat during the nominal run, as previously reported in Nolin et al. (2018), and such is still the case for the optimal run. The size (i.e. difference between minumum and maximum) of the oscillations in the mass flow have been reduced by 27%, which should lead to simplified control and mitigated effects downstream. Furthermore, the optimal solution will effectively lower the purity by almost 2 percentage units. Together, the increased production rate as measured by w_{prod} and the decreased purity as measured by P_{prod} indicate that the optimal solution essentially produces more of a less concentrated product stream. It is therefore possible that increased costs will be incurred downstream to evaporate any excess water. Exactly how these interact with each other and how they in combination will affect downstream processes may require further studies.

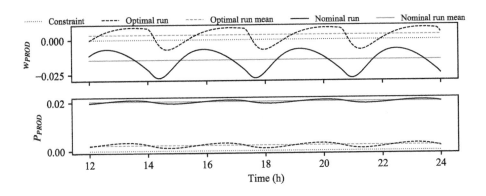

Figure 3: The PROD stream results from the nominal and optimal runs.

The mass flow results for the MEOH stream presented in figure 4 show that the optimal run yields massive oscillations over cycles, with a "jittery" model response, the latter of which presumably caused by the fast dynamics of a pressure controller at the top of the distillation column. The content of this stream is primarily used as fuel for the process, and the effects of propagations here will thus presumably not propagate to the same extent as will oscillations in the PROD stream, even though they are relatively large. Furthermore, the purity of the MEOH was increased significantly in the optimal run. This, combined with the reduced steam consumption for both modules, is further support for the natural conclusion that less water is evaporated in the evaporator module, and subsequently less water is passed on to the distillation column via the top-drawn streams.

5. Conclusions

The optimization shows that it is possible to reduce steam costs by 54 % compared to the nominal case whilst adhering to process demands. However, this may be a globally suboptimal solution

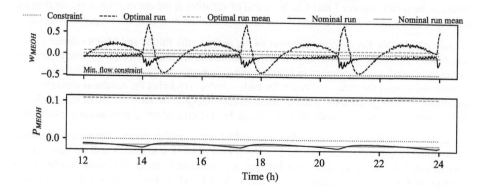

Figure 4: The MEOH stream results from the nominal and optimal runs; note the additional constraint regarding minimal mass flow rate.

when looking at the full process, since less water is evaporated in the investigated modules. This leads to as of now uncertain consequences downstream, but it is possible that the savings in the evaporator and distillation modules presented in the current work may be negated by increased costs downstream. As such, it is imperative to perform a holistic investigation of the full process to prepare for improved decision-making. However, the current work shows that, for the investigated systems, reducing the steam consumption whilst still adhering to production and product demands is indeed possible. Furthermore, oscillatory propagations from any module to other parts of the process need to be studied further. Negative effects thereof are especially necessary to study, and these can potentially be mitigated through an optimal control trajectory optimization possibly combined with improved tuning of the relevant controllers. PyMoC should be a useful tool to use for the former, due to the nature of its Python implementation as well as the implementation of the ZOHA strategy for data transfer.

References

Ahmad, Z., Patle, D. S., Rangaiah, G., 2016. Operator training simulator for biodiesel synthesis from waste cooking oil. Process Safety and Environmental Protection 99, 55 – 68.

Andersson, C., 2016. Methods and tools for co-simulation of dynamic systems with the functional mock-up interface. Ph.D. thesis, Lund University.

Felippa, C. A., Park, K., Farhat, C., 2001. Partitioned analysis of coupled mechanical systems. Computer Methods in Applied Mechanics and Engineering 190 (24), 3247 – 3270, advances in Computational Methods for Fluid-Structure Interaction.

Hasse, H., Maurer, G., 1991. Vaporliquid equilibrium of formaldehyde-containing mixtures at temperatures below 320 k. Fluid Phase Equilibria 64, 185 – 199.

Lin, Z., Wang, J., Nikolakis, V., Ierapetritou, M., 2017. Process flowsheet optimization of chemicals production from biomass derived glucose solutions. Computers & Chemical Engineering 102, 258 – 267.

Nolin, M., Andersson, N., Nilsson, B., Max-Hansen, M., Pajalic, O., 2017. Unbiased selection of decision variables for optimization. In: Espuña, A., Graells, M., Puigjaner, L. (Eds.), 27th European Symposium on Computer Aided Process Engineering. Vol. 40 of Computer Aided Chemical Engineering. Elsevier, pp. 253 – 258.

Nolin, M., Andersson, N., Nilsson, B., Max-Hansen, M., Pajalic, O., 2018. Analysis of an oscillating two-stage evaporator system through modelling and simulation: An industrial case study. Accepted for publication in Chemical Engineering Transactions, vol. 69.

Oppelt, M., Wolf, G., Urbas, L., 2015. Life cycle simulation for a process plant based on a two-dimensional co-simulation approach. Vol. 37 of Computer Aided Chemical Engineering. Elsevier, pp. 935 – 940.

Sellberg, A., Holmqvist, A., Magnusson, F., Andersson, C., Nilsson, B., 2017. Discretized multi-level elution trajectory: A proof-of-concept demonstration. Journal of Chromatography A 1481, 73 – 81.

Skorych, V., Dosta, M., Hartge, E.-U., Heinrich, S., 2017. Novel system for dynamic flowsheet simulation of solids processes. Powder Technology 314, 665 – 679, special Issue on Simulation and Modelling of Particulate Systems.

Anton A. Kiss, Edwin Zondervan, Richard Lakerveld, Leyla Özkan (Eds.)
Proceedings of the 29th European Symposium on Computer Aided Process Engineering
June 16th to 19th, 2019, Eindhoven, The Netherlands. © 2019 Elsevier B.V. All rights reserved.
http://dx.doi.org/10.1016/B978-0-128-18634-3.50122-3

A Discrete-time MILP Formulation for the Optimal Scheduling of Maintenance Tasks on Oil and Gas Wells and Surface Facilities

Victoria G. Achkar[a,b], Vanina G. Cafaro[a,b*], Carlos A. Méndez[a,b], Diego C. Cafaro[a,b]

[a]INTEC (UNL-CONICET), Güemes 3450, 3000 Santa Fe, Argentina

[b]Facultad de Ingeniería Química (UNL), Santiago del Estero 2829, 3000 Santa Fe, Argentina

vcafaro@fiq.unl.edu.ar

Abstract

Onshore oil and gas exploitation areas are usually composed of a numerous set of wells geographically distributed. The extraction of oil and gas requires complex and expensive equipment, including production devices and surface facilities. To keep efficiency sufficiently high, wells need regular maintenance. In this work, we address the scheduling of maintenance tasks on oil and gas wells and surface facilities. The main challenge is to determine the assignment and sequencing of operations combined with vehicle routing decisions, also accounting for preemption and precedence constraints. The goal is to maximize the use of available resources and also minimize both the production loss and the risk of failure in every well, using a mixed integer linear programming (MILP) formulation. We solve three case studies with increasing complexity to finally assess the model performance in real-size problems of the Argentine oil and gas industry.

Keywords: oil and gas wells, maintenance tasks, optimization, scheduling.

1. Introduction

Maintenance operations over oil and gas fields are usually performed by a specialized fleet of heterogeneous vehicles and crews. These activities comprise safety, environmental protection and regulatory tasks; as well as preventive, predictive and corrective maintenance. Sometimes, depending on the task to be performed, the production of the well needs to be interrupted yielding losses of profits. In practice, tasks are grouped into workorders, and there are many costs associated to the length of an order, related to the production loss and the risk of failure of the well. The more extended the order over the time horizon, the higher the costs of this order. Also, delays on the start time of interventions may cause substantial production losses.

The challenge of this problem is twofold. On the one hand, maintenance tasks should be assigned to crews, each of them having its own capabilities. A task can only be performed by certain crews, and the shifts of the crews widely vary, requiring time coordination. Crews have to travel from well to well and sometimes this time can be relevant (e.g., hours). On the other hand, every task should be precisely scheduled to account for precedence constraints, over a short-term time horizon. A task does not need to be scheduled immediately after the preceding one, but it certainly cannot be scheduled earlier. There are also both preemptive and non-preemptive tasks. A preemptive task can be interrupted once the shift is over and be continued later. In contrast, a non-preemptive task must necessarily be started and completed within the same day. Complex tasks usually do not allow for interruptions.

To the best of our knowledge, very few works in the literature have focused on the optimal operation of onshore oil and gas wells using multiple heterogeneous resources. Several works have tackled the maintenance planning problem, but most of them are just focused on the most expensive resource: the workover rig (Aloise et al., 2006; Duhamel et al., 2012; Fernández Pérez et al., 2018). The rig planning problem can be seen as the scheduling of jobs (workovers) on parallel heterogeneous machines (rigs), including routing decisions to move the equipment from well to well. However, these problems do not address the whole set of operations, nor preemption and precedence constraints. On the other hand, continuous-time and precedence-based models have proved to be an effective choice when sequence-dependent changeovers are to be considered (Méndez et al., 2006; Castro et al., 2018). However, they would present severe difficulties to manage crews with different shifts. As a result, we propose a discrete-time formulation (Kondili et al., 1993) distinguishing between active and idle periods for every crew. The main contribution of this work is the development of an efficient discrete-time formulation that is able to manage: a) oil and gas well maintenance tasks; b) heterogeneous resources; c) different work shifts; d) preemptive and non-preemptive tasks; e) precedence constraints; f) risk of failure and production losses; and g) crew's travelling time.

2. Problem Statement and Mathematical Model

Our mathematical formulation is based on Kondili's discrete-time approach with predefined fix-size time periods. We introduce six major sets, being I: operations, O: orders, J: crews, T: time periods, D: days and C: locations. The model solution generates a maintenance schedule for every active crew over the planning horizon minimizing operating costs. Figure 1 summarizes the main components of the model and their features.

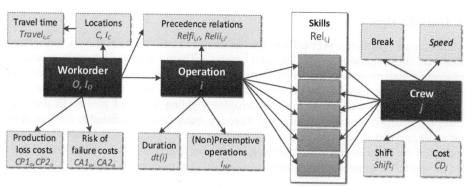

Figure 1: Graphical description of the model

As seen in Figure 1, a maintenance workorder o consists on the set of operations i included in the subset I_o. Each operation $i \in I_o$ requires specific skills and equipment, thus being necessary to assign a crew that is capable of performing that task. Crews are heterogeneous: their specific skills are derived from matching technical capabilities of

*A Discrete-time MILP Formulation for the Optimal Scheduling of Maintenance
Tasks on Oil and Gas Wells and Surface Facilities*

729

the crew and technical requirements of the operations. We define the subset $Crew_i$ to represent the crews with the skills to perform operation i ($j \in Crew_i \subset J$) and the subset $Task_j$ for the operations that can be performed by crew j ($i \in Task_j \subset I$). The binary parameter $Rel_{i,j}$ is equal to one if $j \in Crew_i$, and zero otherwise. Additionally, the subset $Shift_j$ includes the periods within the work shift of crew j ($t \in Shift_j \subset T$). Crews have different work shifts and breaks. Shifts are difficult to manage because they widely vary for every crew (not only the start and end times but also the number of working days per week).

The binary variable $W_{i,j,t}$ takes value 1 if operation i is assigned to crew j and starts on time period t. Eq. (1) states that every task should be accomplished by a single crew over the time horizon.

$$\sum_{j \in Crew_i} \sum_{t \in Shift_j} W_{i,j,t} = 1 \quad \forall i \in I \tag{1}$$

In turn, no operation can start until the assigned crew has finished its previous task. This implies that, if the crew starts performing a given operation i at period $t' < t$, the start time of any other operation is forbidden in any time t for at least dt units of time after the start of the task i. This requirement is expressed by Eq. (2).

$$\sum_{i \in Task_j} \sum_{\substack{t' = t - dt_i + 1 \\ t' \in Shift_j}}^{t} W_{i,j,t'} \leq 1 \quad \forall j \in J, t \in Shift_j \tag{2}$$

Note that constraint (2) is only binding for operations assigned to the same crew j and evaluates just the active periods of that crew, i.e. $\{t-dt_i+1, t-dt_i+2,\ldots, t\} \in Shift_j$.

Moreover, Eq. (3) determines the value of variable $WF_{i,j,t}$, stating that the end of the operation i occurs just when the time given by its length (dt_i) has gone, that is dt_i-1 periods after it has started. Note that no operation can be completed after the end of the time horizon.

$$W_{i,j,t} = WF_{i,j,t+dt_i-1} \quad \forall i \in I, j \in Crew_i, t \in Shift_j, t \leq |T| - dt_i + 1 \tag{3}$$

Precedence and concurrence constraints determine that a task cannot start until the previous one has finished (end-start relation), or that a task cannot start until the previous one has started (start-start relation). These relations are represented using two binary matrices $Relfi_{i,i'}$ and $Relii_{i,i'}$, respectively. Their elements are equal to one in case the relationship between i and i' is enforced. Eq. (4) accounts for such relations, usually by linking tasks within the same order.

$$TI_{i'} \geq TF_i \quad \forall (i,i')|Relfi_{i,i'} = 1 \qquad TI_{i'} \geq TI_i \quad \forall (i,i')|Relii_{i,i'} = 1 \tag{4}$$

$$TI_i = \sum_{j \in Crew_i} \sum_{t \in Shift_j} W_{i,j,t} * (t-1) * slot \qquad TF_i = \sum_{j \in Crew_i} \sum_{t \in Shift_j} WF_{i,j,t} * t * slot$$

Finally, we introduce the notion of preemptive tasks within the equations developed by Kondili et al. (1993). Preemption allows for task splitting when there is a break. Castro et al. (2018) and Peteghem et al. (2010) introduced this concept into their model formulations by making modifications in some constraints. Instead, we propose to simply reduce the time domain to a subset, which only includes the available periods for each crew, as shown in Figure 2. In this figure, each cell is a time period. Striped cells are unavailable periods, grey cells represent ongoing operations, and white cells are idle periods.

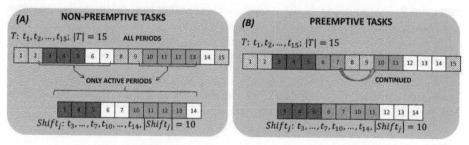

Figure 2: Shifts, preemptive and non-preemptive tasks definition.

As mentioned in the introduction section, non-preemptive constraints enforce that a task must start and end within the same day, mainly due to safety issues. I_{NP} represents the subset of non-preemptive operations. Variables $X_{i,j,d}$ and $XF_{i,j,d}$ in Eq. (5) are equivalent to $W_{i,j,t}$ and $WF_{i,j,t}$ but considering days instead of single time periods.

$$X_{i,j,d} = XF_{i,j,d} \quad \forall i \in I_{NP}, j \in Crew_i, d \in D \tag{5}$$

Following the changeover time concept introduced by Kondili et al. (1993), a travelling matrix is here proposed. We assume that the operations set I can be partitioned into disjoint sets I_c according to the locations c where each task is to be performed. The travelling time between location c and c' is represented by the parameter $travel_{c,c'}$. Thus we introduce a mathematical constraint stating that if two operations i' and i located in different sites c' and c are assigned to the same crew in the same day, and i' is scheduled earlier than i, then the end of operation i' cannot be distanced from the start of i less than $travel_{c',c}$ periods. This can be written in terms of the following linear inequality (6).

$$W_{i,j,t} + \sum_{\substack{t'=t-travel_{c',c} \\ t' \in Shift_j \cup T_d}}^{t-1} WF_{i',j,t'} \leq 1 \tag{6}$$

$$\forall j \in J, d \in D, t \in Shift_j \cup T_d, c \neq c', (i \neq i') \in Task_j, i \in I_c, i$$

The MILP problem goal is given by Eq. (7), where important cost components are to be minimized. Variable MK is the completion time of the last task over the planning horizon, CD_j is the hourly fixed cost for crew j, $CP1_o$ and $CP2_o$ are production losses, $CA1_o$ and $CA2_o$ are risks-of-failure costs (in USD per hour), while $TIOT_o$ and $TFOT_o$ are the initial and completion times of order o. Note that the crew cost CD_j is paid even if the crew is not used by the scheduler. Since crews are outsourced, these costs must be paid until the end of the last operation.

$$Min \quad z = MK \sum_{j \in J} CD_j + \sum_{o \in O} CA1_o * TIOT_o + \sum_{o \in O} CA2_o * (TFOT_o - TIOT_o)$$
$$+ \sum_{o \in O} CP1_o * TFOT_o + \sum_{o \in O} CP2_o * (TFOT_o - TIOT_o) \tag{7}$$

A Discrete-time MILP Formulation for the Optimal Scheduling of Maintenance
Tasks on Oil and Gas Wells and Surface Facilities

731

3. Case Studies and Results

To evaluate the computational performance of the proposed model we solve three real-world case studies with increasing complexity from the Argentine oil and gas industry. Table 1 summarizes the model size and total operating cost in the solution of every case study. The MILP is implemented in GAMS using the solver CPLEX 24.6.1, on an Intel® XEON® CPU.

Table 1: Model size and optimization results for every case study

Case Study	$|I|$	$|O|$	$|J|$	$|T|$	CPU time (s)	Makespan (h)	Total Cost (USD)
1	28	4	24	96	1.8	33.5	102,939.3
2	45	6	24	96	4.8	34.5	109,936.5
3	73	19	34	96	16.6	42.0	154,947.0

The three cases comprise the same exploitation area and a planning horizon of two days. Note that the first example involves a total of 28 tasks (4 orders) and 24 crews, and takes less than 2 CPU seconds to be solved. The second example includes 45 tasks (6 orders) with the same number of crews, and is solved to optimality in less than 5 CPU seconds. Finally, the third case study comprises 73 tasks (19 orders) taking more than 3 times the CPU time consumed by the second case study. Figure 3 depicts the Gantt chart of the optimal solution to Case Study 1, in which tasks within the same order have the same colour. It comprises 4 workorders for repairing leaks in aqueducts and pipelines. For this purpose, specialized crews with skills to dig and weld, among other more general tasks, are needed. We can easily observe precedence and concurrence relations such as in the workorder o_3 starting with task i_{15}, assigned to crew j_{19}. Tasks i_{16} and i_{17} have end-start relations with task i_{15}, and a start-start relation among themselves. At noon, crews stop for lunch break. In fact, tasks i_4, i_{23} and i_{24} are interrupted for lunch and resumed later. After lunch, crew j_{11} starts performing task i_{18} (end-start relation with i_{17}) and when i_{18} is completed, i_{19} and i_{20} can also be executed. Once crew j_9 completes task i_{20}, crew j_{18} can perform task i_{21}. Furthermore, workorder o_2 (starting with task i_8) is the only one associated to production losses since the beginning of the time horizon. For that reason, task i_8 starts as soon as possible. In contrast, workorder o_1 (starting with i_1) yields production losses while it is being executed. Hence, once started, it is forced to end as soon as possible. Note that tasks i_{28} and i_7 must be performed during the second day, by crews j_{18} and j_{19}, respectively. Finally, i_8, i_{18} and i_{25} are non-preemptive tasks.

4. Conclusion

A novel discrete-time MILP model for planning general maintenance tasks on oil and gas wells and surface facilities has been proposed to simultaneously optimize scheduling and routing decisions. The main contribution of our work is the inclusion of travelling times, precedence and concurrence relations, preemptive and non-preemptive operations, different work shifts and heterogeneous crews. Real-world case studies from the Argentine oil and gas industry have been efficiently solved in reasonable computational times. The optimal solutions yield the allocation of up to 34 resources to 73 operations, in less than 20 seconds. Future work will focus on the development of solution strategies to manage the exponential complexity of larger size problems, including more tasks, crews and locations, over longer time horizons.

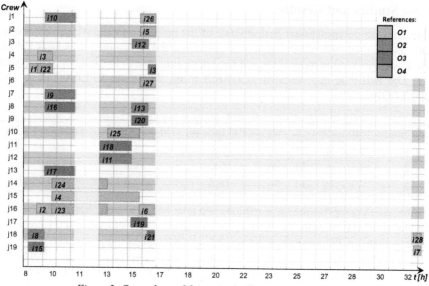

Figure 3: Gantt chart of the optimal solution for Case Study 1

References

DJ. Aloise, D. Aloise, CTM. Rocha, CC. Ribeirob, JC. Ribeiro Filhoc, LSS. Moura, 2006, Scheduling workover rigs for onshore oil production, Discrete Applied Mathematics, 154(5), 695–702. doi: 10.1016/j.dam.2004.09.021.

PM. Castro, IE. Grossmann, Q. Zhang, 2018, Expanding scope and computational challenges in process scheduling, Computers & Chemical Engineering, 114, pp. 4–42. doi: 10.1016/j.compchemeng.2018.01.020.

PM. Castro, I. Harjunkoski, IE. Grossmann, 2018 Expanding RTN discrete-time scheduling formulations to preemptive tasks, Computer Aided Chemical Engineering, 1225–1230. doi: 10.1016/B978-0-444-64241-7.50199-3.

C. Duhamel, A. Cynthia Santos, L. Moreira Guedes, 2012, Models and hybrid methods for the onshore wells maintenance problem, Computers & Operations Research, 39(12), 2944–2953. doi: 10.1016/j.cor.2012.02.026.

MA. Fernández Pérez, F. Oliveira, S. Hamacher, 2018, Optimizing Workover Rig Fleet Sizing and Scheduling Using Deterministic and Stochastic Programming Models, Industrial & Engineering Chemistry Research, 57(22), 7544–7554. doi: 10.1021/acs.iecr.7b04500.

E. Kondili, CC. Pantelides, RWH Sargent, 1993, A general algorithm for short-term scheduling of batch operations—I. MILP formulation, Computers & Chemical Engineering, 17(2), 211–227. doi: 10.1016/0098-1354(93)80015-F.

CA. Méndez, J. Cerdá, IE. Grossmann, I. Harjunkoski, M. Fahl, 2006, State-of-the-art review of optimization methods for short-term scheduling of batch processes, Computers & Chemical Engineering, 30(6–7), 913–946. doi: 10.1016/j.compchemeng.2006.02.008.

V. Peteghem, M. Van and Vanhoucke, 2010, A genetic algorithm for the preemptive and non-preemptive multi-mode resource-constrained project scheduling problem, European Journal of Operational Research. Elsevier B.V., 201(2), 409–418. doi: 10.1016/j.ejor.2009.03.034.

Anton A. Kiss, Edwin Zondervan, Richard Lakerveld, Leyla Özkan (Eds.)
Proceedings of the 29th European Symposium on Computer Aided Process Engineering
June 16th to 19th, 2019, Eindhoven, The Netherlands. © 2019 Elsevier B.V. All rights reserved.
http://dx.doi.org/10.1016/B978-0-128-18634-3.50123-5

Optimal design of multi-stage depressurization systems using dynamic modelling

Juan Quattordio[a], Sander Groenendijk[a], Robert Kedzierski[a], Hans Göebel[a,*]

[a] Fluor, Taurusavenue 155, Hoofddorp 2132 LS, The Netherlands

hans.goebel@fluor.com

Abstract

High pressure process facilities like hydrocrackers and solvent deasphalting units in most cases are equipped with a system to quickly discharge the inventory in case of an emergency, and by doing so reduce the pressure to safe values in a short amount of time. Multi-stage depressurization is usually applied to cope with additional boundary conditions, such as high reliability and the limited capacity of the downstream flare system. In this paper, a design development is described using detailed dynamic simulation studies to come to an optimal design of such a system. The result of the work described is a structured design procedure for use on large scale design projects.

Keywords: depressurization, dynamic simulation, solvent deasphalting unit, hydrocracker

1. Introduction

Process facilities handling vapor or LPG at high pressures are in most cases equipped with a system to quickly discharge the inventory in case of an emergency in order to reduce the pressure and by doing so reducing the risk of fire and explosion and consequential damages.

Typical examples of this are: Hydrotreaters, Hydrocrackers and LPG plants.

The example presented in this study is related to an Solvent Deasphalting Unit, which uses LPG as solvent for the liquid-liquid extraction of the asphalt components in the crude oil vacuum distillation residue. [Sattarin, 2006]

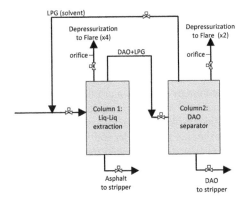

Figure 1: block flow diagram of SDA unit

The target of the system depressurization design is typically to reduce the pressure to 8 bar or 50% of the operating pressure, whichever lower in a period of 15 minutes time. [API, 2014]

For some designs this can be solved with readily available tools like the Aspen HYSYS depressurization module, or the HYSYS blowdown module [AspenTech, 2018]. An example of this is the depressurization of a hydrocracker: for this unit the depressurization calculations can be solved in a relatively simple way by means of the standard utilities. A typical hydrocracker example is shown on figures 2A and 2B.

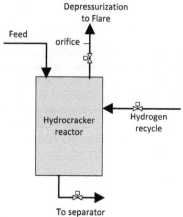

Figure 2A

Figure 2B

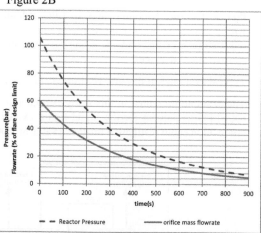

Figure 2A: the figure shows a typical block flow diagram of a Hydrocracker unit reactor Figure 2B: a typical depressurization curve for a hydrocracker reactor is shown. The fluid is depressurized from an initial pressure of 105 barg to a final pressure of 7 barg in 15 minutes. As can be observed, this can be achieved in one step, via a single valve. The calculation has been done with the HYSYS blowdown module.

The depressurization calculation of the system becomes more difficult when, as in the case of SDA process, dealing with liquid LPG at supercritical conditions, since a single valve design would imply a too high initial peak, which in turn would have a significant economic impact in the flare system design i.e. flare header and flare stack will increase in size. In the case of connecting to existing flares, it would imply to exceed the flare system capacity.

In order to cope with this constraint, multistage depressurization is applied.

2. A dynamic simulation study applied to a depressurization system

The design procedure of the SDA unit multistage depressurization system is discussed when using HYSYS dynamic simulation. Additionally, the benefits of this method compared with the standard HYSYS depressurizing utilities are highlighted.

2.1 Definition of the system

The evaluated system consists of two columns containing liquid LPG at high pressure (see Figure 1), which will be depressurised in parallel. In order to reduce the peak flowrate released to the flare, multiple valves are installed i.e. 4 on-off valves for the first column and 2 on-off valves for the second. The depressurized fluid is sent to flare via the flare header and knock out drum, which allows the liquid LPG collected during the depressurization case.

2.2 Staggered Depressurization Scenarios (multistage depressurization)

In industrial plants, the flare has a maximum capacity of gas that it can burn off. Exceeding this capacity can result in incomplete combustion and high pressure built-up exceeding the design conditions of the system. The soot produced in incomplete combustion could potentially block the flare. Hence, the flow of flammable gases to the flare needs to be limited below the maximum capacity.

In a standard depressurizing setup, peak flow is reached at the start, when the pressure is highest.

To reduce the peak flow, pressure is often relieved from a vessel stepwise: multiple valves, with smaller openings than the original single valve, are connected to the vessel. These valves are opened at different times. In this way, the initial peak flow that would be present in the original single valve setup, is distributed over several peaks. Consequently, the pressure can be decreased by the same amount in the same time as in the non-staggered case, without exceeding the maximum flare capacity. This is called staggered depressurization.

This method is also applied to plants with a high amount of equipment, where multiple units are usually connected to the same flare. This can create a high total flow to the flare. This total flow can be reduced by using a stepwise method, similar as described above for a single vessel. A staggered pressure relief scenario is created for the multiple vessel system by opening the valves of the several units at different times.

2.3 Sectionalizing

Sectionalizing is applied in order to limit the inventory release in the case of leakage, e.g. if only one column needs to be depressurized. This can reduce for some design cases the required capacity of the emergency depressurization system, considering that the case of all sections depressurizing at once is not a case for flare header sizing.

However, the study case is a particular case in which the flare capacity is limited since an existing flare is considered, and additionally the case of both sections depressurizing at the same time has to be considered.

One major drawback is the greatly increased number of valves required for this setup. More valves require higher investment cost, more maintenance and more chance of leakage to the flare. However, for this case increasing the amount of valves cannot be avoided, in order not to exceed the flare design limit constraint.

2.4 Control valve versus restriction orifice

There are typically two alternatives to control the emergency depressurization i.e. via a control valve or by means of a combination of on-off valve and a restriction orifice.

This study has been performed considering a combination of on-off valves and restriction orifices.

The benefit of this configuration is to avoid the risk of freezing because of low temperatures (as low as -40°C), caused by LPG depressurization. That may cause malfunctioning of closing the control valve that has been opened for depressurization.

With the proposed scheme the on-off valve will be able to close since the low temperatures will occur downstream the RO. The restriction orifice is installed at a safe distance downstream the on-off valve, so that the low temperature can dissipate without risk of freezing in the on-off valve.

2.5 Computational setup

This study is executed in Aspen HYSYS, using the full dynamic simulation capabilities. HYSYS also offers two other methods to simulate depressurization, the Depressuring Utility and the Blowdown Module, which are easier to use, but allow less detail in the model.

The thermodynamic model used in each depressuring case is the Peng-Robinson equation of state. Being HYSYS' most enhanced model, Peng-Robinson is especially suitable for the fluid considered in this study, with a wide range of T and P applicability and its extensive binary coefficients database.

For the modelling of the system, adiabatic vessels are considered.

2.6 Valve characteristics and hydraulics

2.6.1 On-off valves

On-off valves opening time is included in the simulation. A valve model was used with a cv-percentage opening characteristic taken from vendor information. For the actuator, a linear characteristic was taken with different values for the time to fully open the valve for individual valves. Note that in the HYSYS depressurization and blowdown utilities (and many other simplified calculation modules), on-off valves are considered instantaneously opened, which is a simplification of the method which leads to a higher peak than actual flow, and to a shorter depressurization time than actual.

2.6.2 **Flare system**

A level control was implemented for flare knock-out drum in the model. Having the level control keeps a low level to minimize evaporation in the KO vessel in the model. In reality, the KO vessel does not have a level control, but a quick evaporation is unlikely because of the limited surface area between gas and liquid. In the depressurization curves, the mass flow in and out of the KO vessel is shown.

Hydraulic restrictions were added to the system in order to model the hydraulics of the downstream system. The input to these restrictions was based on the detailed hydraulic calculations available for the existing system.

2.7 **Simulation results**

The main results of the depressurization study done with HYSYS dynamic simulation can be observed in Figure 3. In Figure 4, the results of the depressurizing tool are shown.

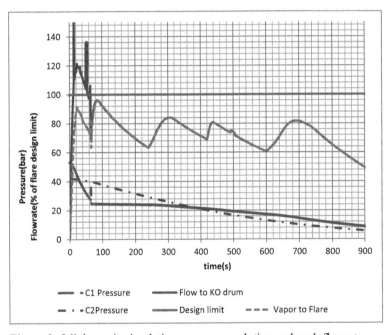

Figure 3: full dynamic simulation, pressure evolution and peak flowrate

As can be observed in the Figure 3, the C1 and C2 pressures are reduced to recommended levels while the depressurizing flowrate is within the capacity of the flare system.

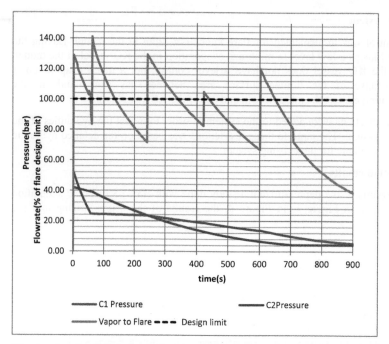

Figure 4: simplified dynamic simulation using depressurization utility, pressure evolution and peak flowrate

Figure 4 shows that, when applying the depressuring utility, the design of the flare system is exceeded when the same orifice sizes and opening times are considered respect to the full dynamic simulation approach. The main reason for such a discrepancy is that depressurization utility does not take into account limitations like hydraulics, opening time of on-off valves and positive impact of a flare knock-out drum.

3. Conclusions

When dealing with complex depressurization systems with additional constraints respect to standard designs, a full dynamic simulation is a tool to be considered since, despite being more time consuming to build if compared with the HYSYS depressurization utility and blowdown module, its results are more accurate, take into account the influence of more parameters and can better represent the actual system behaviour, leading to an optimal design of the depressurization system.

4. References

Sattarin, Manzar & Modarresi, Hassan & Talachi, Hossaien & Teymori, Mohammad. (2006). Solvent deasphalting of vacuum residue in a bench-scale unit. Petroleum & Coal. 48. 14-19.

API recommended practice 521, sixth edition, January 2014, Guide for Pressure-Relieving and Depressuring Systems.

AspenTech (2018): www.aspentech.com

Anton A. Kiss, Edwin Zondervan, Richard Lakerveld, Leyla Özkan (Eds.)
Proceedings of the 29th European Symposium on Computer Aided Process Engineering
June 16th to 19th, 2019, Eindhoven, The Netherlands. © 2019 Elsevier B.V. All rights reserved.
http://dx.doi.org/10.1016/B978-0-128-18634-3.50124-7

Innovative mapping method for screening reactive distillation designs

Rahma Muthia,[a] Megan Jobson,[a] Anton A. Kiss[a,b*]

[a]School of Chemical Engineering and Analytical Science, The University of Manchester, Sackville Street, Manchester, M13 9PL, United Kingdom

[b]Sustainable Process Technology, Faculty of Science and Technology, University of Twente, PO Box 217, 7500 AE Enschede, The Netherlands

tony.kiss@manchester.ac.uk

Abstract

Reactive distillation (RD) technology offers key benefits in many chemical processes, including energy savings and costs reduction. Prior to its application in industry, screening, addressing technical feasibility and economic viability, must be performed at the conceptual design level. But these tasks can be challenging and time-consuming since detailed models are usually needed. To overcome this complexity, we provide a mapping method to quickly assess the applicability of RD. The mapping method overlays key parameters of a real system, i.e. relative volatilities (α) and chemical equilibrium constant (K_{eq}), onto pre-calculated graphs indicating the RD performance, i.e. the reflux ratio (RR) vs number of theoretical stages (NTS) based on generic cases. The mapping method focuses on quaternary systems ($A + B \rightleftharpoons C + D$). A case study (methyl lactate hydrolysis) is used to demonstrate the approach. Three scenarios are presented, applying different characteristic volatility values; each scenario gives rise to a different RD applicability map for equilibrium constants in the range 0.01 to 10. The findings are validated against results of rigorous process simulation and optimisation. The most accurate scenario is that in which α sets are calculated for mixtures with molar compositions 99% C / 1% A, 50% A / 50% B, 1% B / 99% D, respectively. The results show that the mapping approach allows the prediction of number of theoretical stages and reflux ratio to be estimated within 10% of the optimum values.

Keywords: reactive distillation, mapping method, applicability graph.

1. Introduction

Reactive distillation (RD) is an important intensification technology that offers multiple advantages: 1. an improved chemical process (i.e. higher conversion and selectivity), 2. energy savings, 3. costs reduction, and 4. inherently safer designs (Shah et al., 2012). This technology has received industrial interest for over 30 years; and for example the production of methyl acetate and ethers using RD is commercially well established (Stankiewicz, 2003). Within the same time frame, studies have been performed to intensify operation of a wider range of chemical processes, such as (trans-)esterification, hydrolysis, (de-)hydration and alkylation (Kiss, 2017).

In spite of the promising applications offered by RD, the complexity of designing RD columns has hindered industrial application of the technology. Simpler approaches are needed to guide design engineers and support design decision making as to whether RD is an applicable unit (Segovia-Hernández et al., 2015). Recent work has aimed to provide such guidance, via a mapping approach that facilitates screening of RD application (Muthia, Reijneveld, et al., 2018). The method uses RD applicability graphs which plot reflux ratio (RR) vs number of theoretical stages (NTS) and aid go/no-go screening of proposed RD operations considering the maximum acceptable values for NTS and RR. The mapping method is currently limited to use in quaternary reactions (Muthia, van der Ham and Kiss, 2018). This paper presents an extended development of the method and highlights the importance of using appropriate characterisation of the relative volatilities in the column to predict RD applicability.

2. Mapping method

Figure 1 (left) shows the RD configuration used in this study. The column is assumed to operate at atmospheric pressure, with negligible pressure drop, and to achieve vapour-liquid and reaction equilibria at each stage. The reactive section is located between the inlets of the lighter and heavier reactants; reaction and separation occur simultaneously in this section. Further separation takes place in the rectifying and stripping sections, to achieve the targeted product purities. It is assumed that equal molar flows of the reactants are fed to the column as saturated liquids.

The RD column, with any configuration, is simulated using Aspen Plus v8.6. For a given NTS, a sensitivity analysis is carried out in which the number of stages in the rectifying, reactive and stripping sections is varied. A generic case is defined, in which the boiling order of the reactants and products and the type of reaction are defined (e.g. $A + B \rightleftharpoons C + D$). The method assumes that the generic cases have ideal vapour-liquid equilibrium behaviour (neither azeotropes formation nor liquid split) and constant key parameters, i.e. all relative volatilities (α) and chemical equilibrium constant (K_{eq}). The optimisation tool within Aspen Plus is used in order to minimize the reflux ratio, where the purity of both products is specified as a constraint. Multiple (flat) optimal solutions are obtained for each choice of NTS which correspond to multiple column designs that can meet the specifications. For a given number of theoretical stages, the lowest value of the reflux ratio defines a boundary to the region in which RD is feasible – this is known as the applicability area, as shown in Figure 1 (right).

Figure 1 (right) depicts the boundary lines of two RD applicability areas, corresponding to two different K_{eq}s. Only on and above each boundary line, the RD technology is applicable, i.e. the targeted product purities are achieved. The two dashed curves are the lower bounds belonging to two generic cases, i.e. with K_{eq}s equal to 1 and 2.

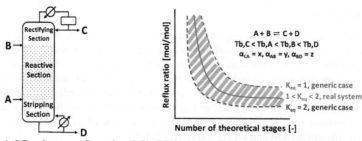

Figure 1. RD column configuration (left); RD boundary lines of generic and real systems (right)

The boundary lines of the generic cases are used to predict the RD applicability of a specific, real system. Firstly, key process parameters are calculated (a set of α values and the value of K_{eq}) for the real system. Then the user seeks the two boundary lines, one with a higher K_{eq} value and one with a lower K_{eq}. This allows the user to estimate the position of the boundary line for the real system. For example, for a real system with $1 < K_{eq} < 2$, its boundary line is predicted to lie between the two generic boundary lines, within the shaded area shown in Figure 1 (right). Later, rigorous simulations will be carried out to confirm that the actual boundary line of the real system – indicated by the solid line – is indeed well predicted by the neighbouring generic boundary lines.

In classic distillation, short-cut methods, such as the Fenske and Underwood methods, are used to estimate the minimum number of theoretical stages (NTS_{min}) and minimum reflux ratio (RR_{min}). The α value may be that of the feed or considered as an average α along the column based on the composition of the top and the bottom streams, and the results of the Fenske and Underwood design calculations can be relatively sensitive to which approach is adopted. The approximation quality is significantly affected by the nonideality of the mixtures involved. Greater errors are in general obtained in more nonideal systems (Smith, 2016). Therefore, it is crucial to use an appropriate representation of the set of α values in the column when applying simple distillation design methods. In the context of RD, this study evaluates different representations of α sets in the development of the mapping method. The work assumes that the characteristic value of the equilibrium constant, K_{eq}, should be calculated at the average boiling point (T_b) of the two reactants, as the temperature profile in the reactive section is typically confined to the within the range of the reactant boiling temperatures.

The generic boundaries are created by extensive series of calculations. The vast number of possible combinations of α sets and K_{eq} values implies that an infinite number of boundary lines for generic cases can be obtained. Therefore, the range of K_{eq} is limited to a pragmatic range from 0.01 to 10 (i.e. 0.01, 0.02, 0.05, 0.1, 0.2, 0.5, 1, 2, 5, 10) that aims to cover the range of reactions with potential for practical RD application. In addition, the lower bound is chosen to the set of results corresponding to a number of theoretical stages that is twice the minimum ($NTS = 2 \cdot NTS_{min}$), in which the reflux ratio is up to 10% higher than the lowest reflux ratio on the boundary line. These choices are based on heuristics for estimating the optimal number of stages for classic distillation.

3. Case study

This study focuses on the quaternary reaction ($A + B \rightleftarrows C + D$), where $T_{b,C} < T_{b,A} < T_{b,B} < T_{b,D}$), which has been explored widely for RD applications. Due to space limitations, only the case study of methyl lactate hydrolysis is presented, as shown in Eq. (1).

$$\text{Water (A)} + \text{Methyl lactate (B)} \rightleftarrows \text{Methanol (C)} + \text{Lactic acid (D)} \tag{1}$$

| T_b | 100 °C | 144.8 °C | 64.7 °C | 216.85 °C $\Delta H_r = +33.6$ kJ.mol^{-1} |

The activity coefficients are calculated by UNIFAC-HOC and a correlation between temperature and chemical equilibrium constant is shown in Eq. (2), where T is in K (Sanz et al., 2004). An azeotrope exists at 99.8°C with a molar composition of 97% water and 3% methyl lactate. In this study, the targeted purity of products $\geq$ 99 mol%.

$$\ln\left(K_{eq}\right) = 2.6 - (1954.2 / T) \tag{2}$$

4. Method development and validation

Table 1 presents three scenarios, applying different definitions for the characteristic α sets. For all scenarios, α_{AB} is for a 50/50 mol% mixture of the reactants, corresponding to the equimolar feed of reactants. In Scenario 1 (S1), α_{CA} and α_{BD} are calculated using the compositions of the top and the bottom streams, respectively. Scenario S2 aims to consider volatilities within the column, and not just at its extremities; therefore, the characteristic α_{CA} and α_{BD} are calculated 50/50 mol% binary mixtures. Scenario S3 calculates α_{CA} and α_{BD} at compositions (1/99% CA and 99/1% BD mixtures) that are only expected to occur if K_{eq} is very low, leading to very low conversion. In this case, a single RD column is unlikely to be appropriate.

Table 1. Characterisation of α sets

Scenario	Representation of α set		
	α_{CA}	α_{AB}	α_{BD}
S1	2.5 (99/1 mol%)		6.5 (1/99 mol%)
S2	3.6 (50/50 mol%)	5.5 (50/50 mol%)	11.7 (50/50 mol%)
S3	7.5 (1/99 mol%)		14 (99/1 mol%)

The dashed boundary lines in Figure 2, Figure 3 and Figure 4 (left) represent generic cases for S1, S2 and S3, respectively. Note that the solid line in each graph, which is the actual boundary line for the case study, is added later, after performing rigorous simulation for validation purposes.

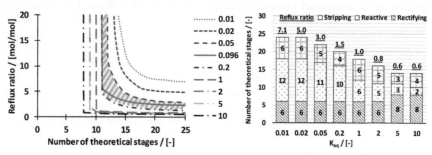

Figure 2. RD applicability areas (left); their RD configurations at NTS=2·NTS$_{min}$ (right) for S1

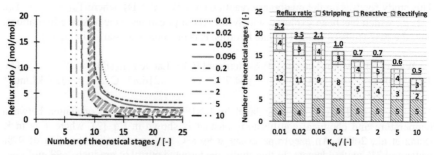

Figure 3. RD applicability areas (left); their RD configurations at NTS=2·NTS$_{min}$ (right) for S2

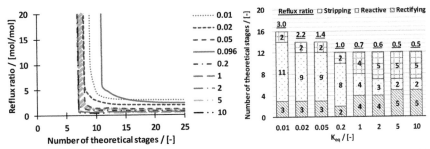

Figure 4. RD applicability areas (left); their RD configurations at NTS=2·NTS$_{min}$ (right) for S3

The size of RD applicability areas of the generic cases increases from S1, S2, to S3, respectively: the increasing ease of separation between reactants and products (shown in Table 1), leads to lower reflux ratios for any number of stages. This observation is in agreement with the resulting RD configurations, presented in Figures 2, 3 and 4 (right). In each system, fewer reactive stages are needed for higher K$_{eq}$ values, since the reaction performance is improved. Conversely, more separation stages are needed because fewer reactive stages achieve less simultaneous separation.

For the particular conditions of the case study, K$_{eq}$ is 0.096, calculated using Eq. (2). A premise of the mapping method is that the actual boundary line will lie between neighbouring generic boundary lines, i.e. within the shaded areas in Figure 2, Figure 3 and Figure 4 (left). Rigorous simulations of the case study provide the actual boundary line, indicated by the solid line. It may be seen that the generic boundary lines predict its location well only in S1, i.e. the effectiveness of the mapping method is sensitive to the approach used to characterise volatilities in the column.

Figure 5 (left) illustrates how the generic results can be used to design a particular RD column using linear interpolation to estimate number of theoretical stages and reflux ratio, for K$_{eq}$ = 0.096. The number of rectifying, reactive and stripping sections can be estimated using the same approach. Multiple designs configurations exist; two RD configurations of neighbouring generic cases (with K$_{eq}$ values close to the actual value) are considered, i.e. K$_{eq}$ values of 0.05 and 0.2. Figure 5 (right) shows the actual (simulated) RD configuration and configurations predicted using linear interpolation for S1, S2 and S3. Table 2 quantifies the goodness of fit in terms of the differences in NTS and RR, relative to that of the actual case. S1 is in good agreement with the generic results, with deviations below 10%.

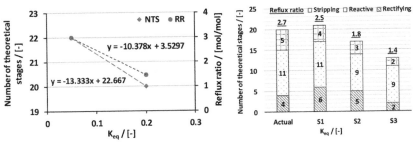

Figure 5. NTS and RR predictions for S1 (left); Predicted and actual RD configurations (right)

Table 2. Comparison of linearly interpolated and actual NTS and RR values

Scenario	NTS			RR		
	Actual	Predicted	Deviation	Actual	Predicted	Deviation
S1	20	21	5%	2.7	2.5	8%
S2	20	17	15%	2.7	1.8	33%
S3	20	13	35%	2.7	1.4	48%

5. Conclusions

The mapping method aims to help engineers to carry out relatively quick initial evaluation of potential RD applications. The approach uses characteristic relative volatilities and chemical equilibrium constant of a real system to screen the RD designs based on generic RD applicability graphs. This study highlights the importance of having the appropriate characterisation of relative volatilities sets to predict the RD applicability and validates the approach by comparing predictions to rigorous simulation results. The relative volatilities sets should be calculated for total feed, top product and bottom product conditions. The approach enabled prediction of NTS and RR for the case study with deviations of less than 10%.

Acknowledgements

RM gratefully acknowledges full fund support from LPDP (Indonesia Endowment Fund for Education). AAK is thankful for the Royal Society Wolfson Research Merit Award.

References

A. A. Kiss, 2017, Process intensification by reactive distillation, Process Synthesis and Process Intensification: Methodological Approaches, 143-181, Boston, De Gruyter.

R. Muthia, A. G. T. Reijneveld, A. G. J. van der Ham, A. J. B. ten Kate, G. Bargeman, S. R. A. Kersten, A. A. Kiss, 2018, Novel method for mapping the applicability of reactive distillation, Chemical Engineering and Processing: Process Intensification, 128, 263-275.

R. Muthia, A. G. J. van der Ham, A. A. Kiss, 2018, Preliminary economic ranking of reactive distillation processes using a navigation method, Computer Aided Chemical Engineering, 43, 827-832.

M. T. Sanz, R. Murga, S. Beltrán, J. L. Cabezas, J. Coca, 2004, Kinetic study for the reactive system of lactic acid esterification with methanol: methyl lactate hydrolysis reaction, Industrial & Engineering Chemistry Research, 43, 2049-2053.

J. G. Segovia-Hernández, S. Hernández, A. B. Petriciolet, 2015, Reactive distillation: A review of optimal design using deterministic and stochastic techniques. Chemical Engineering and Processing: Process Intensification, 97, 134-143.

M. Shah, A. A. Kiss, E. Zondervan, A. B. de-Haan, 2012, A systematic framework for the feasibility and technical evaluation of reactive distillation processes, Chemical Engineering and Processing: Process Intensification, 60, 55-64.

R. Smith, 2016, Separation of Homogeneous Fluid Mixtures I – Distillation, Chemical Process Design and Integration, 155-158, United Kingdom, John Wiley & Sons Ltd.

A. Stankiewicz, 2003, Reactive separation for process intensification: an industrial perspective, Chemical Engineering and Processing, 42, 137-144.

Anton A. Kiss, Edwin Zondervan, Richard Lakerveld, Leyla Özkan (Eds.)
Proceedings of the 29th European Symposium on Computer Aided Process Engineering
June 16th to 19th, 2019, Eindhoven, The Netherlands. © 2019 Elsevier B.V. All rights reserved.
http://dx.doi.org/10.1016/B978-0-128-18634-3.50125-9

Integrated Process and Controller Design Software Tool – ProCACD

Jialiang Wang[a], Peng Ji[a], Xi Chen[a,b,*], Anjan Tula[c], Rafiqul Gani[a,c]

[a] College of Control Science and Engineering, Zhejiang University, Hangzhou, China
[b] National Center for International Research on Quality-targeted Process Optimization and Control, China
[c] PSE for SPEED, Skyttemosen 6, Allerod, DK-3450, Denmark
*: xi_chen@zju.edu.cn

Abstract

The field of Process system engineering (PSE) is constantly developing with the availability of advanced computational resources. Since 1960s, process simulation has been one of the most successful story in using computer aided methods and tools in the field of chemical engineering. Nowadays, several software tools are available for process simulation, process optimization, process synthesis and design. However, the current software in PSE is mainly focussed on processes without consideration of controller design or validation. The gap between process design and controller design seems to be increasing, which may lead to suboptimal solutions especially for closed-loop systems. Therefore, there is always a demand for integrating the process design with consideration of the controller design; even though the development of such software tool has not been well addressed so far, or are industry specific. In this paper, a model-based integrated process and controller design software tool called ProCACD (computer aided controller design) is presented along with a case study to design controllers and optimize controller parameters for a system of three-tanks-in-series with recycle.
Keywords: computer aided controller design, process simulation, PID tuning.

1. Introduction

Nowadays sustainable and efficient processes are needed in chemical industry to address the grand challenges of resource depletion, energy consumption and environmental impacts (Roh et al., 2016). Therefore, identification, design and development of appropriate processes are important for the industry to remain competitive. During the last decades, many researchers have developed computer aided software tools to address different aspects of process development, including Aspen for process simulation and control, ProCAFD (Tula et al., 2017) for process synthesis, GAMS (Biegler, 2018) for process optimization, etc. However, it seems that not much work has been done in the area of software development of simultaneous process design and control, though a trend towards considering process design and control aspects simultaneously has been proposed. Several methodologies have been developed for addressing the interactions between process design and process control (Mansouri et al., 2015). At first, researchers focus on the controllability of process systems. Controllability metrics based on open and closed-loop stability analysis were developed (Yi & Luyben, 1997). However, controllability metrics are used mostly in either steady state or linear dynamic models, and the uncertain link between the value of the measure and the plant design may cause trouble. Thus, methods to overcome the limitation of controllability metrics appeared. These methods can be classified into two types. One type is based on multi-objective optimization (Gebreslassie et al., 2012). The other type is based on dynamic optimization (Diangelakis et al., 2017). Lagging behind the advance of method development for integration of process design and control, the software development is quite scarce. The objective of process design is to identify the types of tasks/operations that need to be performed, the corresponding design of the operation/equipment, their configuration, mass/energy flows, etc. (Tula et al., 2015). And the main objective of process control is to design control system to achieve optimal closed-loop dynamic performance (Yuan et al., 2012). Solving these two problems independently may lead to suboptimal solutions. A key to integrating the process design and controller design is to model them in a unified structure. Embedded with the previously developed modelling tool-box MoT (Fedorova et al., 2015), an integrated controller design software tool, ProCACD, is proposed in this work.

2. Architecture of ProCACD

2.1. MoT based Model-objects

ProCACD is a c# based software tool developed in Visual Studio. The process and control models are generated in ProCACD through the modelling tool-box MoT, where model developers define equations and set necessary variable values. In this work, a generic model object approach is implemented where a unified model is used to represent both open-loop and closed-loop processes for all possible pairings and all controller types (P, PI, PID, etc). As shown in Figure 1, one model-object can have several different configurations in ProCACD. While using the model-objects, the user should select the manipulated variables (MVs) and controlled variables (CVs) according to the real process, and then select the controller type and pairing based on his system. 'MVi' and 'CVi' are used to name the ith selected MVs and CVs, respectively.

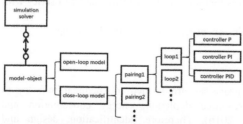

Figure 1: Different configurations of model-object

The controller equations part is the most essential part for model developers to establish a model-object with different kinds of controller configurations. Keywords '*ol*', '*clp*', '*clpi*', and '*clpid*' are kept to denote logic configurations of open-loop control, closed-loop P control, closed-loop PI control, and closed-loop PID control, respectively. Additionally, to denote the pairing between MVs and CVs, another keyword, "*Pairm_n*" is adopted to denote if a pairing exists between the mth MV and n[th] CV. An example template is given as follows to describe the controller equations of a process containing two MVs and two CVs.

$$Error1 = CV1 - CV1SP \tag{1}$$

$$Error2 = CV2 - CV2SP \tag{2}$$

$$\frac{dAE1}{dt} = Error1 \tag{3}$$

$$\frac{dAE2}{dt} = Error2 \tag{4}$$

$$
\begin{aligned}
MV1 = MV1 * o11 + \\
[(P1 * Error1 + MV1Star) * clp1 + (P1 * Error1 + I1 * AE1 + MV1Star) * clpi1] * Pair1\_1 \\
+ [(P1 * Error2 + MV1Star) * clp1 + (P1 * Error2 + I1 * AE2 + MV1Star) * clpi1] * Pair1\_2
\end{aligned} \tag{5}
$$

$$
\begin{aligned}
MV2 = MV2 * o12 + \\
[(P2 * Error1 + MV2Star) * clp2 + (P2 * Error1 + I2 * AE1 + MV2Star) * clpi2] * Pair2\_1 \\
+ [(P2 * Error2 + MV2Star) * clp2 + (P2 * Error2 + I2 * AE2 + MV2Star) * clpi2] * Pair2\_2
\end{aligned} \tag{6}
$$

By properly setting the logic variables, this template can represent different controller type and the pairing structure between MVs and CVs. It should be noted that the need for process understanding is very essential for an efficient design. The process model together with the controller model template, called as MoT based model-object in this project, can be used to design, analyze and verify controller design and application.

2.2. Process Analysis and Controller Design

An overview of the 5-staged method is presented in Figure 2, which describes the main architecture of the ProCACD software as follows.

1.Problem Definition	2.View Model Variable	3.Open-Loop Run	4.Controller Configuration	5.Closed-Loop Run
Inputs: Generic MoT model-object *Outputs:* Configured process model	*Inputs:* Configured process model *Outputs:* Detailed variable information of the model	*Inputs:* Configured open-loop process model Data of initial variable values *Outputs:* Data of model simulation results	*Inputs:* Configured open-loop process model *Outputs:* Best pairing of the model Tuned Controller parameters results	*Inputs:* Tuned Controller parameters results *Outputs:* Data of configured closed-loop model simulation results

Figure 2: Process Analysis and Controller Design Method (in ProCACD)

<u>Problem Definition</u>: The main objective of this step is to define the configuration of the loaded generic MoT model-object. Configuration includes open-loop or closed-loop model, number of closed-loops as well as the pairing status and the selection of controller type (P, PI, or PID) for each loop.

<u>View Model Variable</u>: In this step, the configured process model defined in Problem Definition is elaborated through a table showing all the model variable details. If closed-loop option is chosen in Problem Definition step, an additional table showing the pairing of each loop is added.

<u>Open-Loop Run</u>: This step is used for the open-loop option in Problem Definition, where the configured open-loop process model variable details are listed in a table allowing users to set the initial input variable values so that open-loop simulations can be performed.

<u>Controller Configuration</u>: This is an essential step for finding the best pairing structure and tuning of the controller parameters for a closed loop process model. Here we connect Tai-ji PID tuning system through a web-API deployed in public cloud (www.taijipid.com). This web-based technology can conduct system identification and PID parameter tuning based on supplied simulation data. Additionally, the relative gain is calculated to find the best pairing by using the identified transfer function model. Once the best pairing is found, it is possible to tune the PID controller parameters. The related flow-diagram is shown in Figure 3. The MoT first generates open-loop data

through simulations. The generated simulation data is transformed to equal time interval data using the cubic spline interpolation algorithm embedded in ProCACD. Then the transformed simulation data is exported to Tai-ji PID tuning system, which analyses the process through transformed simulation data and conducts system identification as well as tuning of the controller parameters.

Closed-Loop Run: In this step, the tuned controller parameters are used for the configured close loop process model simulation. The software also allows the user to modify the controller parameters and add disturbances in this step. Eventually, the software provides a graph, in which, different closed-loop simulations are compared.

The integration of process and controller design is achieved through model analysis in terms of sensitivity of process variables to controller variables.

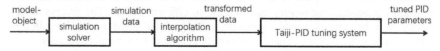

Figure 3: Flowsheet of Controller Tuning step

3. Case Study

The application of ProCACD is highlighted using a recycled three-tanks-in-series process model stored in a MoT-based model-object. The process is shown in Figure 4(a). Variables A1, A2 and A3 represent the cross-sectional area of the three tanks. Variables h1, h2 and h3 represent the liquid level of three tanks. Variables alpha1, alpha2 and alpha3 represent the valve opening values. Variables Fin, F1, F2 and Fout represent the inlet and outlet flowrate of the tanks. Variable purge represents the outlet flowrate of the whole system. The candidate control variables and manipulated variables are also marked in the figure with bracked CV and MV, respectively. ProCACD helps users to find the best pairing, design controllers for the process, and tune controller parameters.

In the first step, Problem Definition, a user starts from introducing the MoT model, followed by a selecting options between open-loop or closed-loop analysis. If open-loop option is choosen in Problem Definition step, then in step 2, View Model Variable, a table will be automatically generated to list all the variables in this model; there follows an Open-Loop Run step, where the user can conduct open-loop simulations through the tank model. While if the closed-loop option is choosen in Problem Definition, further an initial configuration among CVs and MVs and selection of controller type will be prompted. Then in the second step, View Model Variable, ProCACD automatically creates another table listing the user's configuration information. Afterwards, the Open-Loop Run step is skipped and ProCACD goes straight to the Controller Configuration option, where the best pairing between CVs and MVs is found and the controller parameters are tuned accordingly.

The recycled three-tanks-in-series process model consists of 3 CVs and 3 MVs. Thus, there is a total of 6 different pairings if a user wants to control all the three liquid levels. It also means that the model has 6 different closed-loop configurations. ProCACD can find the best configuration using relative gain method through three steps. First, transfer function matrix is obtained with the generated open-loop simulation data. Then, relative gain matrix is calculated according to the transfer function matrix. Last, the best pairing is obtained by analysing the relative gain matrix. In this case, the best configuration is shown in Figure 4(b), where valve opening of the outlet stream of each tank is used to control each tank level, which agrees with the process understanding.

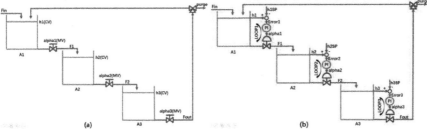

(a)   (b)

Figure 4: A case study of recycled three-tanks-in-series
(a) The original process flowsheet; (b) The process flowsheet with best pairing controller design.

Based on this closed-loop configuration, ProCACD further tunes the PID controller parameters in Controller Configuration step. After finishing Controller Configuration step, the data, including the tuned controller parameters, is stored and transferred to the Closed Loop Run step, where users can conduct closed-loop simulations. Figure 5 shows the comparison of the simulation results of CVs with the tuned controller parameters and the initial controller parameters which were obtained manually accodring to experiences. The simulation results indicate that the controllers perform well both in disturbance rejection and set point tracking using the tuned controller parameters. Here, the value of the integral time square error (ITSE) is used to quantitatively analyze control performance. At time 0, users give a set point step change of h1 from 1 to 2. The ITSE value of h1 using the tuned parameters is 0.31, much less than the ITSE value 0.62 using initial parameters. From the simulation result of h1, we can also see that the tuned parameters perform both less overshoot and less adjusting time, indicating a better set point tracking. As for h2 and h3, the step change of h1 could be regarded as a disturbance to them. The ITSE values of h2 and h3 using the tuned parameters are 0.19 and 0.23, respectively, less than the ITSE values of 0.26 and 0.33 with initial parameters. From the simulation results of h2 and h3, it can also be seen that the tuned parameters bring less oscillation amplitude and less adjusting time, thus a better disturbance rejection. At 10 second time, a disturbance step change of Fin from 0.1 to 0.2 is introduced. The ITSE values of h1, h2 and h3 using the tuned parameters are 0.15, 0.26 and 0.31, respectively, less than the ITSE values of 0.28, 0.31 and 0.37 with the initial parameters. As shown in Figure 5, the tuned parameters perform less oscillation amplitude and less adjusting time than the initial setting, which again demonstrates better disturbance rejection. Further integration of the process design and controller design can be achieved through analyzing the sensitivity of process variables to controller variables, e.g., how the recycle ratio from the final tank outlet to the first tank affects the process dynamics and what the optimal recycle ratio should be designed.

4. Conclusions

In this work, a computer-aided method and associated software is developed to integrate modelling-simulation tools with controller design, analysis and verification tools. Interfacing with the modelling toolbox MoT, ProCACD helps users to design controllers from an open-loop process model with designated candidate CVs and MVs. The best pairing among the CVs and MVs can be detected. PID controller parameters can be well tuned. Good performance in disturbance rejection and set point tracking is demonstrated through a case study involving control of liquid levels of a recycled three-tanks-in-series process model. As a summary, the model-based analysis tool provides a good understanding of the process and through it, a good design of the controller configuration and the controller parameter tuning can be achieved. In the future, an extensive library of process models and control strategy such as model predictive control (MPC) will also be implemented. On the basis of this work, a simultaneous process and controller design will be developed.

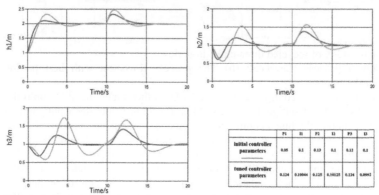

Figure 5: Comparison simulation results using different controller parameters

Acknowledgements

The authors gratefully acknowledge the financial support of NSFC-Zhejiang Joint Fund for the Integration of Industrialization and Informatization (No. U1509209).

References

L. T. Biegler, 2018, New directions for nonlinear process optimization, Current Opinion in Chemical Engineering, 21, 32-40.

N. A. Diangelakis, B. Burnak, J. P. Katz, E. N. Pistikopoulos, 2017, Process Design and Control optimization: A simultaneous approach by multi-parametric programming, AIChE J, 63(11), 4827-4846.

M. Fedorova, G. Sin, R. Gani, 2015, Computer-aided modelling template: Concept and application, 83, Computers & Chemical Engineering, 232-247.

B. H. Gebreslassie, Y. Yao, F. You, 2012, Design under uncertainty of hydrocarbon biorefinery supply chains: multiobjective stochastic programming models, decomposition algorithm, and a comparison between cvar and downside risk, AIChE J, 58(7), 2155–2179.

S. S. Mansouri, M. Sales-Cruz, J. K. Huusom, J. M. Woodley, R. Gani, 2015, Integrated Process Design and Control of Reactive Distillation Processes, IFAC-PapersOnLine, 48, 8, 1120-1125.

K. Roh, R. Frauzem, R. Gani, J. H. Lee, 2016, Process systems engineering issues and applications towards reducing carbon dioxide emissions through conversion technologies, Chemical Engineering Research and Design, 116, 27-47.

Tai-ji PID. http://www.taijipid.com.

A. K. Tula, M. R. Eden, R. Gani, 2015, Process synthesis, design and analysis using a process-group contribution method, Computers & Chemical Engineering, 81, 245-259.

A. K. Tula, R. Gani, M. R. Eden, 2017, New Method and Software for Computer-Aided Flowsheet Design and Analysis, Computer Aided Chemical Engineering, 40, 649-654.

C. K. Yi, W. L. Luyben, 1997, Design and control of coupled reactor/column systems—Part 1. A binary coupled reactor/rectifier system, Computers & Chemical Engineering, 21, 1, 25-46.

Z. Yuan, B. Chen, G. Sin, R. Gani, 2012, State-of-the-art and progress in the optimization-based simultaneous design and control for chemical processes, AIChE J, 58(6), 1640–1659.

Anton A. Kiss, Edwin Zondervan, Richard Lakerveld, Leyla Özkan (Eds.)
Proceedings of the 29th European Symposium on Computer Aided Process Engineering
June 16th to 19th, 2019, Eindhoven, The Netherlands. © 2019 Elsevier B.V. All rights reserved.
http://dx.doi.org/10.1016/B978-0-128-18634-3.50126-0

Computational Fluid Dynamics of Rectangular Monolith Reactor vs. Packed-Bed Column for Sorption-Enhanced Water-Gas Shift

Vlad C. Sandu[a,*], Ionela Dumbrava[a], Ana-Maria Cormos[a], Arpad Imre-Lucaci[a], Calin C. Cormos[a], Paul D. Cobden[b], Robert de Boer[b]

[a]Faculty of Chemistry and Chemical Engineering, Babeş-Bolyai University, Arany Janos 11, Cluj-Napoca RO-400028, Romania

[b]ECN part of TNO, Westerduinweg 3, Petten 1755 LE, The Netherlands

vcrsandu@chem.ubbcluj.ro.

Abstract

Sorption-enhanced water-gas shift (SEWGS) process is very attractive for an energy efficient pre-combustion CO_2 capture, as it enables direct conversion of syngas into separate streams of H_2 and CO_2 at high temperatures and pressures. Using advanced computational fluid dynamics (CFD) methods, quantitative performance differences were assessed for rectangular channel monolith structures versus regular packed-bed structures when used for pre-combustion CO_2 capture. Published data of breakthrough capacities at different pressures for CO_2 and H_2O were used to validate a multicomponent adsorption isotherm. A COMSOL 1D model was developed to describe CO_2 adsorption in a fixed-bed reactor, filled with adsorbent pellets, to confirm the accuracy of the results compared to the existing studies, after which a 2D model was built simulating the adsorption step of a SEWGS process inside of a monolith reactor channel. Model predictions display an increase in productivity of adsorption in the case of monolith structures versus conventional packed-bed columns. Results will be used to improve the performance of experimental monolith structures undergoing SEWGS.

Keywords: CFD, CO_2 adsorption, isotherm, SEWGS

1. Introduction

Developing energy efficient low carbon applications is of great importance today as an active way of combating the climate change (IPCC, 2014). Sorption-enhanced water-gas shift (SEWGS) is a pre-combustion carbon capture and storage (CCS) process which combines the water-gas shift (WGS) reaction (Eq. (1)) with in situ adsorption of CO_2 (Eq. (2)) at 300-500 °C and 10-40 bar. Steam can also be adsorbed (Eq. (3)).

$$CO + H_2O \leftrightarrow CO_2 + H_2 \tag{1}$$

$$CO_2 + \bullet \leftrightarrow CO_2 - \bullet \tag{2}$$

$$H_2O + \bullet \leftrightarrow H_2O - \bullet \tag{3}$$

A SEWGS process consists of a series of reactors capable of CO_2 adsorption, operated in pressure cycles, similar to the cycles of a PSA, as to enable the periodic loading and regeneration of the sorbent. By using multiple reactors, the process can be characterized as a continuous one, allowing the constant production of separate H_2 and CO_2 streams. In the adsorption step of the cycle, syngas is fed into a reactor where the CO and steam react to produce CO_2 and H_2. The sorbent material takes up the CO_2 and a hot high pressure, H_2 rich product stream is directly produced, ready to be used as gas turbine fuel for power generation. SEWGS enables a direct conversion of syngas into separate hot streams of H_2 at feed pressure and CO_2 at regeneration pressure, making the process attractive for pre-combustion CCS and reduction of GHG emissions (van Selow et al., 2009).

Hydrotalcite based adsorbents are valuable for SEWGS, as they demonstrate high thermal stability, fast sorption kinetics and high CO_2 selectivity. The clay layered structure collapses at high temperatures, transitioning to a well dispersed mixed metal oxide with a higher surface area because of porosity formation. The impregnation of the oxide with K_2CO_3 increases the sorbent's capability to adsorb basic species. The potassium-promoted hydrotalcite (K-HTC) has two roles in SEWGS, catalyzer for the WGS reaction and sorbent for reversibly adsorbing CO_2. After adsorption, during K-HTC regeneration, the CO_2 released is sufficiently pure to be stored (Sikander et al., 2017).

Traditionally, columns filled with granulated adsorbent pellets are used in a SEWGS process, however, in this work, the columns are replaced with innovative 3D printed monolith reactors built of K-HTC material, as packed-bed reactors show significant bottleneck due to the restrictions regarding flow-rate inside the reactor, pressure drops and adsorption kinetics (Govender and Friedrich, 2017). A graphical representation of a monolith structure with square channels is presented in Figure 1.

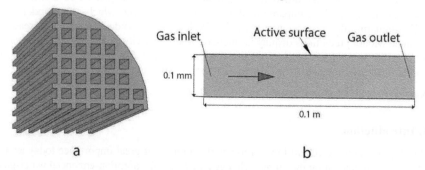

Figure 1. a – 3D schematic representation of a monolith reactor with square channels; b – 2D representation of the channel geometry used in the monolith reactor model.

Models simulated in COMSOL Multiphysics are used in order to further add improvements to experimental monolith structures. If successful, a significant size reduction of SEWGS for syngas processing with CO_2 capture will be possible while maintaining the same productivity.

CFD of Rectangular Channel Monolith Reactor vs. Packed-Bed Column for SEWGS

753

2. Model development

This paper is evaluating the high-temperature, high-pressure adsorption step of a SEWGS process in which the columns, normally filled with K-HTC pellets that act as sorbents, are replaced by monolith reactors that are made entirely of adsorbent K-HTC material. Using COMSOL Multiphysics, a 1D model was developed to simulate, in space and time, the adsorption process of CO_2 in a packed-bed reactor. A reactor model published by Reijers et al. (2009) was used for validation. Following, a 2D COMSOL Multiphysics model was developed to simulate the adsorption step of SEWGS for CO_2 inside a single rectangular channel of a monolith reactor.

2.1. Adsorption isotherms

Adsorption isotherms are used to describe the quantity of adsorbate on the surface as a function of its pressure at constant temperature. Boon et al. (2014) used experimentally obtained breakthrough data to fit a multicomponent adsorption isotherm for the system and obtained good results with two double isotherms, deriving a model that takes into account surface and nanopores contributions for the adsorption of CO_2 and H_2O at high pressures.

2.2. Model parameters and assumptions

For the 1D fixed-bed reactor model, process parameters are taken from literature (Reijers et al., 2009), so as to add validity to the predictions and enable proper comparison. Although the monolith structure contains around 500 channels, the 2D model simulates the adsorption of CO_2 inside a single rectangular channel, in order to reduce hardware computation requirements. The geometry of the model is seen in Figure 1b. The parameters for the fixed-bed reactor model and the rectangular channel reactor model are presented in Table 1.

Table 1. Model specific parameters

Parameter	Fixed-bed model	Monolith model	Parameter	Common values	
Length	0.2 m	0.1 m	Bed density	533	kg m^{-3}
Tube diameter	0.016 m	-	Particle density	922	kg m^{-3}
Bed height	0.02 m	-	Feed temperature	673.15	K
Width	-	1e-4 m	k_{LDF}	0.1	s^{-1}
Feed velocity	0.0056 m s^{-1}	0.035 m s^{-1}			
Feed pressure	101,325 Pa	25e5 Pa			
Porosity	0.4	0.44			

Simplifying assumptions are common for both models. These include a uniform distribution of sorbent activity, laminar fluid flow, dispersion does not occur, heat transfer is not considered and the LDF mass transfer coefficient is constant.

2.3. Process phenomena

For the fixed-bed model, the phenomena occurring are convection-diffusion of the bulk phase and diffusion-adsorption of CO_2, which are solved with a convection-diffusion equation (Eq. (5)) and a porous media transport equation (Eq. (6)).

$$\frac{\partial c_i}{\partial t} + \nabla \cdot (-D_i \nabla c_i) + u \cdot \nabla c_i = R_i \tag{5}$$

$$(\varepsilon_p + \rho k_{p,i}) \cdot \frac{\partial c_i}{\partial t} + \left(c_i - \frac{\rho}{(1 - \varepsilon_p)} \cdot c_{p,i} \right) \frac{\partial \varepsilon_p}{\partial t} + \nabla \cdot \Gamma_i + u \cdot \nabla c_i \tag{6}$$

For the 2D monolith reactor channel model, mass transport in the bulk is solved by using Eq. (5), while adsorption of CO_2 is solved through the material balance on the active surface of the walls inside the channel (Eq. (7)). The surface concentration of CO_2, c_s, is described using Eq. (8) with terms for the linear driving force mass transfer coefficient and adsorption isotherm. The way through which mass transport and surface adsorption are coupled is by setting the adsorption rate as an outward flux in the boundary condition for Eq. (5).

$$\frac{\partial c_s}{\partial t} + \nabla \cdot (-D_s \nabla c_s) = r_{ads} \tag{7}$$

$$\frac{\partial q_{CO_2}}{\partial t} = k_{LDF} \cdot \left(q_{CO_2}^* - q_{CO_2} \right) \tag{8}$$

3. Results and discussions

3.1. Breakthrough capacities for CO_2 and H_2O

For validation of the adsorption isotherms, published data (Boon et al., 2014) regarding breakthrough capacities for CO_2 and H_2O were plotted as a function of pressure, with pressure values of up to 24 bar. The data points in Figure 2 show pure component breakthrough capacities measured for CO_2, while Figure 3 shows the capacities for steam. The lines are drawn based on the isotherm developed from the full dataset and the symbols are the measured data.

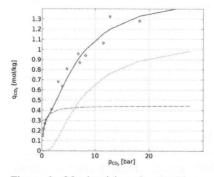
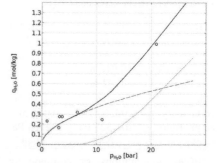

Figure 2. CO_2 breakthrough capacities vs CO_2 partial pressure (diamonds), predicted capacity (line), surface contribution (dashed line), nanopore contribution (dotted line).

Figure 3. Pure H_2O breakthrough capacities versus H_2O partial pressure (circles), predicted capacity (line), surface contribution (dashed), nanopore contribution (dotted line).

The capacities for CO_2 seen in Figure 2 follow a two-step adsorption mechanism. The first step is due to surface sites and adds contribution up to 0.4 mol kg^{-1}, while the additional adsorption at partial pressures over 3 bar is attributed to nanopores. Steam behaves similarly to CO_2. In Figure 3, at partial pressures under 12 bar, the experimental capacities show a surface contribution of about 0.3 mol kg^{-1}, while the point above 20 bar might indicate an additional nanopore adsorption mechanism.

3.2. Fixed-bed reactor model describing CO_2 adsorption

In regards to the validation of the fixed-bed reactor model, Figure 4 shows the breakthrough curve calculated by the COMSOL 1D model compared to existing published data (Reijers et al., 2009). The results seem to be in agreement with their predictions, as the breakthrough times are within close range and the curves present similar profiles for identical process parameters.

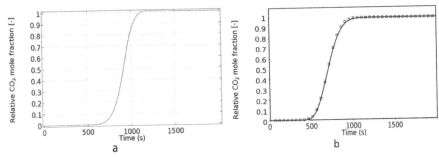

Figure 4. CO_2 mole fraction at the reactor outlet relative to CO_2 mole fraction of the feed gas calculated by the COMSOL 1D. a – breakthrough curve calculated by the COMSOL Multiphysics model; b – breakthrough curves calculated by the MATLAB model (line) and from the analytical solution (symbols) (Reijers et al., 2009).

3.3. Monolith reactor model describing CO_2 adsorption in a single rectangular channel

The breakthrough curve predicted by the 2D monolith reactor model, in which the adsorption of CO_2 takes places at the surface of the walls inside the rectangular channel, can be seen in Figure 5. Comparing the time of breakthrough and its profile with existing data predicted by fixed-bed reactor models, it can be assumed that a monolith reactor would provide a better adsorption of CO_2.

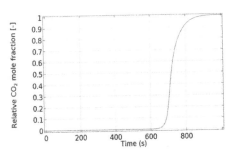

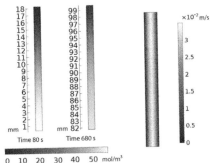

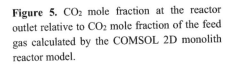

Figure 5. CO_2 mole fraction at the reactor outlet relative to CO_2 mole fraction of the feed gas calculated by the COMSOL 2D monolith reactor model.

Figure 6. CO_2 surface concentration at different times calculated by the COMSOL 2D monolith reactor model and surface velocity profile along the reactor.

4. Conclusions

Using the published data regarding breakthrough capacities of CO_2 and H_2O, a multicomponent adsorption isotherm has been successfully validated. The isotherm accounts for surface adsorption at lower partial pressures and nanopore contributions at higher values of partial pressures.

A 1D model of a fixed-bed reactor has been developed using COMSOL Multiphysics, with the purpose of validation based on published data. Using the multicomponent isotherm and the linear driving force approximation, the adsorption of CO_2 was successfully simulated, as breakthrough predictions agree with other predictions found in literature.

Finally, a 2D monolith reactor model describing adsorption of CO_2 occurring at the surface of a single channel's walls was developed. Although validation is not possible at the moment due to lack of experimental data, assessing the time of breakthrough and its profile leads to the conclusion that a monolith structure would provide better adsorption.

Acknowledgements

This work was supported by a grant of the Romanian National Authority for Scientific Research and Innovation, CCCDI - UEFISCDI, project number COFUND-ACT ERANET – 3D-CAPS (contract number: 87/2017): "Three Dimensional Printed Capture Materials for Productivity Step-Change", within PNCDI III.

References

J. Boon, P.D. Cobden, H.A.J. van Dijk, C. Hoogland, E.R. van Selow and M. van Sint Annaland, 2014, Isotherm model for high-temperature, high-pressure adsorption of CO_2 and H_2O on K-promoted hydrotalcite, Chem. Eng. J., 248, 406-414.

S. Govender and H.B. Friedrich, 2017, Monoliths: a review of the basics, preparation methods and their relevance to oxidation, Catalysts, 7, 2, 62.

IPCC, 2014, Climate change 2014: Synthesis report. Contribution of working groups I, II and III to the Fifth Assessment Report of the Intergovernmental Panel on Climate Change, IPCC: Geneva, Switzerland.

H.T. Reijers, J. Boon, G.D. Elzinga, P.D. Cobden, W.G. Haije and R.W. van den Brink, 2009, Modelling study of the sorption-enhanced reaction process for CO2 capture. I. Model development and validation, Ind. Eng. Chem. Res., 48, 15, 6966-6974.

E.R. van Selow, P.D. Cobden, P.A. Verbraeken, J.R. Hufton and R.W. van den Brink, 2009, Carbon capture by sorption-enhanced water–gas shift reaction process using hydrotalcite-based material, Ind. Eng. Chem. Res. 48, 9, 4184-4193.

U. Sikander, S. Sufian and M.A. Salam, 2017, A review of hydrotalcite based catalysts for hydrogen production systems, Int. J. Hydrogen Energy, 42, 31, 19851-19868.

Anton A. Kiss, Edwin Zondervan, Richard Lakerveld, Leyla Özkan (Eds.)
Proceedings of the 29th European Symposium on Computer Aided Process Engineering
June 16th to 19th, 2019, Eindhoven, The Netherlands. © 2019 Elsevier B.V. All rights reserved.
http://dx.doi.org/10.1016/B978-0-128-18634-3.50127-2

A novel process monitoring approach based on Feature Points Distance Dynamic Autoencoder

Feifan Cheng[a] and Jinsong Zhao[a,b,*]

[a]State Key Laboratory of Chemical Engineering, Department of Chemical Engineering, Tsinghua University, Beijing 100084, China
[b]Beijing Key Laboratory of Industrial Big Data System and Application, Tsinghua University, Beijing 100084, China
jinsongzhao@tsinghua.edu.cn

Abstract

For chemical industry, safety is always primary. A safe and reliable systems are required to ensure the safety of chemical plants. Many data-driven process monitoring methods have been developed and successfully applied to various processes. Autoenocoder is an unsupervised learning algorithm, which can extract the features automatically from the unlabelled data. However, one limitation of autoencoder is that it does not consider any temporal dependency of the data. And autoencoder can not be ensured to get various meaningful features from the raw data. In this work, we proposed Feature Points Distance Dynamic Autoencoder (FPDDAE) to capture the temporal dependency and encourage the autoencoder to get meaningful features. The FPDDAE is constructed by the recurrent neural network (RNN), RNN can capture the time dependency of the process by adding a recurrent hidden state whose activation at each time is dependent on that of the previous time. To make the data points as near as possible in feature space, we define a penalty term $\mathcal{FPD}$ that measures the average distance between any two points in feature space. The penalty term $\mathcal{FPD}$ is a constraint to encourage the FPDDAE to learn meaningful features. A simple nonlinear simulation example is used to illustrate how the proposed method works. The proposed method is applied to the Tennessee Eastman process (TEP) to demonstrate its performance.

Keywords: Process monitoring; Dynamics; Deep learning; Alarm management.

1. Introduction

For chemical industry, safety is always primary. Names like Bhopal or Piper Alpha, are well-known not only for causing a lot of death but also for the damage to the environment (Drysdale and Sylvester-Evans, 1998; Sen and Egelhoff, 1991). A safe and reliable systems are required to ensure the safety of chemical plants. With the wide application of distributed control system (DCS) and large number of variables are measured and stored, many data-driven process monitoring methods have been developed and successfully applied to various processes.

Data-driven process monitoring methods can be roughly divided into statistical methods and artificial intelligent methods, although there are many connections between them. Some typical statistical methods include principal component analysis (PCA) (Wise et al., 1990), partial least squares (PLS) (Kruger and Dimitriadis, 2008),independent component analysis (ICA) (Lee et al., 2004), Fisher discriminant analysis (FDA) (He et al., 2005), statistics pattern analysis (SPA) (He and Wang, 2011) and their variations. Due to the dynamics and nonlinearity of the chemical process data, statistical methods have a lot of limitations when they are applied to the process monitoring.

For artificial intelligent based process monitoring methods, significant progress has been made in recent years, especially for the deep learning (DL) methods. DL methods were originally proposed as feature selection and classification methods. There is one limitation of most deep learning methods that they need large amount of labelled data and usually they do not perform well with limited data(Zhang and Zhao, 2017; Wu and Zhao, 2018). Autoenocoder is an unsupervised learning algorithm, which can extract the features automatically from the unlabelled data. However, one limitation of autoencoder is that it does not consider any temporal dependency of the data. And autoencoder can not be ensured to get various meaningful features from the raw data (Jia et al., 2018). The feature extraction process of an autoencoder can be regarded as the dot produce results between its weight matrix composed by a set of basis vectors and raw data. In this paper, we proposed Feature Points Distance Dynamic Autoencoder (FPDDAE) to solve the above problems. We use the recurrent neural network (RNN) to construct the autoencoder. RNN can capture the time dependency of the process by adding a recurrent hidden state whose activation at each time is dependent on that of the previous time. To make the data points as near as possible in feature space, we define a penalty term $\mathcal{FPD}$ that measures the average distance between any two points in feature space. The penalty term $\mathcal{FPD}$ is a constraint to encourage an autoencoder to learn meaningful features.

The remainder of the paper is organized as follows. In section 2, the autoencoder and RNN are briefly reviewed. Section 3 introduces the proposed FPDDAE method. In addition, a simple nonlinear simulation example is used to demonstrate how the proposed method work. In section 4, the proposed method is applied to the TEP model to demonstrate its performance. Conclusions are given in section 5.

2. Autoencoder and recurrent neural network

2.1. Autoencoder

An autoencoder consists of encoder and decoder. Given unlabeled data $\{\mathbf{x}_m\}_{m=1}^{M}$, the function $\mathbf{f}$ is called encoder and will calculate a feature vector $\mathbf{h}_m$ from $\mathbf{x}_m$:

$$\mathbf{h}_m = \mathbf{f}(\mathbf{x}_m) \tag{1}$$

The decoder reconstructs $\hat{\mathbf{x}}_m$ from the feature vector $\mathbf{h}_m$ by a mapping function $\mathbf{g}$:

$$\hat{\mathbf{x}}_m = \mathbf{g}(\mathbf{h}_m) \tag{2}$$

The set of parameter θ of the encoder and decoder are learned simultaneously on the task of reconstructing as well as possible the original input data. The aim of an autoencoder is to minimize the reconstruction error. This minimization is usually carried out by stochastic gradient descent in the training of Multi-Layer-Perceptrons (MLPs). The reconstruction error is as followed:

$$\mathcal{L}_{AE} = \frac{1}{2M} \sum_{m=1}^{M} ||\hat{\mathbf{x}}_m - \mathbf{x}_m||_2^2 \tag{3}$$

2.2. Recurrent neural network

A recurrent neural network (RNN) is an extension of a conventional feedforward neural network, which is able to handle a variable-length sequence input. The reason that RNN can handle time series is that RNN has a recurrent hidden state whose activation at each time is dependent on that of the previous time. Long short-term memory units (LSTMs) are one type of RNN, which make each recurrent unit to adaptively capture dependencies of different time scales. LSTMs have cell and forget gate to modulate the flow of information. The structure of LSTMs is showed in figure 1.

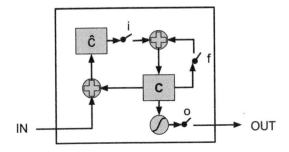

Figure 1: The structure of LSTMs.

3. Feature Points Distance Dynamic Autoencoder

We use $\mathbf{X}_t$ to denote a window (with window width w) of process measurements of n variables as below:

$$\mathbf{X}_t = [\mathbf{x}_{t-w+1}, \mathbf{x}_{t-w+2}, \cdots, \mathbf{x}_t]^T = \begin{bmatrix} x^{(1)}(t-w+1) & x^{(2)}(t-w+1) & \cdots & x^{(n)}(t-w+1) \\ x^{(1)}(t-w+2) & x^{(2)}(t-w+2) & \cdots & x^{(n)}(t-w+2) \\ \vdots & \vdots & \ddots & \vdots \\ x^{(1)}(t) & x^{(2)}(t) & \cdots & x^{(n)}(t) \end{bmatrix} \quad (4)$$

LSTMs are used as the neural network layers of FPDDAE to capture the time dependency among the process variables. The encoder $\mathbf{f_L}$ consists of two layers of LSTMs and calculates the feature vector $\mathbf{h}_t$ from $\mathbf{X}_t$:

$$\mathbf{h}_t = \mathbf{f_L}(\mathbf{X}_t) \quad (5)$$

The decoder reconstructs $\hat{\mathbf{X}}_t$ from the feature vector $\mathbf{h}_t$ by a mapping function $\mathbf{g_L}$:

$$\hat{\mathbf{X}}_t = \mathbf{g_L}(\mathbf{h}_t) \quad (6)$$

The penalty term $\mathcal{FPD}$ is the measure of the average distance between any two points in feature space. The historical data of normal operation is easily obtained in the industry. The process monitoring model is often built from the data at normal state. Therefore, it is meaningful to make points in feature space as near as possible when training the model. The penalty term $\mathcal{FPD}$ is defined as followed:

$$\mathcal{FPD} = \frac{1}{M-w} \sum_{i=1}^{M-w} \sum_{j=1}^{i} ||\mathbf{h}_i - \mathbf{h}_j||_2^2 \quad (7)$$

The cost function of FPDDAE is made up of reconstruction error and $\mathcal{FPD}$. The β regular parameter controlling the weight between the reconstruction error and the penalty term $\mathcal{FPD}$. The cost function is as followed:

$$\mathcal{L}_F = \frac{1}{2(M-w)} \sum_{t=1}^{M-w} ||\hat{\mathbf{X}}_t - \mathbf{X}_t||_2^2 + \beta \frac{1}{M-w} \sum_{i=1}^{M-w} \sum_{j=1}^{i} ||\mathbf{h}_i - \mathbf{h}_j||_2^2 \quad (8)$$

The FPDDAE is trained by minimizing the cost function $\mathcal{L}_F$. The structure of FPDDAE is showed at figure 2. The $\mathcal{L}_F$ is used as the monitoring scores. A threshold of monitoring scores is estimated by the empirical method. If test samples are faulty, when they are projected onto the FPDDAE model, which was trained using normal samples, the resulted monitoring scores would be higher than the threshold.

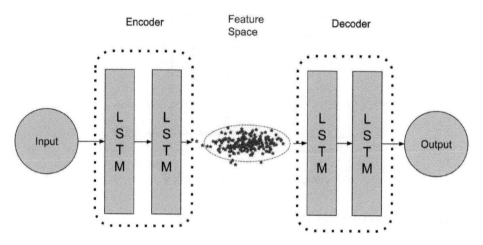

Figure 2: Structure of FPDDAE.

3.1. A simple nonlinear example

A simple nonlinear simulation example is as followed:

$$x_2 = x_1^2 + e \tag{9}$$

where x_1 is a random variable that follows a uniform distribution between [-0.5, 0.5], and e is a random variable that follows a normal distribution with variance 0.02. A total of 15000 normal samples is simulated with 10000 samples for training and 5000 samples for validation. Two groups of testing samples (faults A and B) are simulated, each group with 5000 samples. Figure 1 shows the scatter plot of the normal and faulty samples. Both autoencoder and FPDDAE are trained by normal data. The results of autoencoder and FPDDAE at training process are compared in figure 3. From the figure 3 (b)-(d), the average distance of data points decreases in the FPDDAE method. The normal data and faulty data are clearly separated in the feature space. However, as showed at figure 3 (e)-(f), the normal data and faulty data can not be separated clearly by using an autoencoder. The proposed method FPDDAE can deal with the nonlinearity and capture the meaningful features.

4. Case study

In this section, the benchmark Tennessee Eastman model process simulator is used to demonstrate the performance of the proposed method. Compared with the small nonlinear simulation model in the previous section, the TEP is a much larger nonlinear system. The model consists of five major units: a reactor, condenser, compressor, separator, and stripper (Downs and Vogel, 1993). The process contains 12 manipulated variables and 41 measured variables. The measured variables contain 22 process variables sampled every 3min, and 19 quality variables sampled with dead time and time delays. In this case study, 22 process variables and 12 manipulated variables are used for the process monitoring. Here we compare PCA, DPCA, KPCA, autoencoder and FPDDAE. For all the methods, 960 samples of normal state is used as the training data set. The validation data set is made up of 480 samples of normal state. Each fault consists of 960 samples, and the fault is introduced at 161 samples. The upper control limits correspond to the 99% confidence level for all the methods.

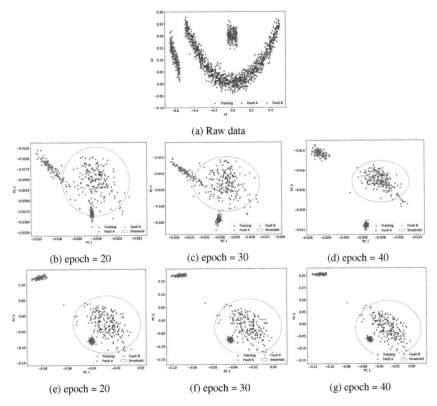

(a) Raw data

(b) epoch = 20   (c) epoch = 30   (d) epoch = 40

(e) epoch = 20   (f) epoch = 30   (g) epoch = 40

Figure 3: Scatter plot of normal and faulty data. Raw data: (a). FPDDAE: (b) , (c) , (d) . Autoencoder: (e) ,(f) , (g).

The fault detection rates of different methods for all faults are listed in Table 1. It is suggested that faults 3,9 and 15 are difficult to detect and may have been corrected by the control mechanism, so they are not consider here (Lee et al., 2006). In the case study, PCA, KPCA and DPCA don't perform well on six faults (Fault 5, 10, 16, 19, 20, 21). In comparison, the proposed FPDDAE method have a higher detection rate than other methods.

5. Conclusion

In this paper, we proposed a new cost function to make the points in the feature space as near as possible. Based on this new cost function, we proposed FPDDAE for the process monitoring. FPDDAE can capture the temporal dependency and encourage the autoencoder to get meaningful features. Compared with the traditional methods like PCA, FPDDAE can deal with nonlinearity and dynamics. The performance of the proposed FPDDAE is compared with other methods on a small nonlinear example and the benchmark Tennessee Eastman process. The results show that FPDDAE can detect the faults more efficiently than other methods. The temporal dependency is captured by the LSTMs.

This work highlights that the unsupervised deep learning methods can be adapted for process monitoring. Various meaningful features can be captured by using the different cost functions. For

Table 1: Fault Detection Rates of PCA, DPCA, KPCA, AE and FPDDAE for TEP

Fault	PCA		DPCA		KPCA		AE	FPDDAE
	T^2	SPE	T^2	SPE	T^2	SPE	SPE	scores
1	99.1	99.6	99.1	99.6	99.2	99.8	99.0	99.3
2	98.5	98.5	98.5	98.4	98.2	98.8	97.8	98.4
4	5.2	97.2	3.8	100.0	7.8	99.1	99.4	99.9
5	**23.5**	**26.0**	**23.4**	**32.5**	**23.1**	**25.0**	**60.6**	**88.5**
6	98.8	100.0	98.6	100.0	18.6	99.5	99.4	99.6
7	39.2	100.0	61.0	100.0	99.0	100.0	99.8	99.8
8	96.2	96.9	96.9	97.5	96.9	96.1	98.5	97.8
10	**30.5**	**21.8**	**25.9**	**34.9**	**36.0**	**22.2**	**79.5**	**91.3**
11	19.9	68.6	17.0	85.2	32.0	58.4	98.8	99.0
12	97.6	96.0	98.6	97.2	98.0	92.5	99.6	100.0
13	93.2	95.2	93.9	95.5	94.0	94.8	94.1	94.3
14	79.5	100.0	91.6	100.0	97.8	99.9	99.6	99.8
16	**12.5**	**16.6**	**9.5**	**30.2**	**18.2**	**17.6**	**73.1**	**94.3**
17	72.8	91.2	74.1	95.6	74.4	93.5	96.8	98.3
18	89.1	90.0	88.5	90.4	23.6	90.6	89.0	95.9
19	**0.2**	**20.4**	**0.4**	**48.5**	**0.4**	**6.9**	**90.9**	**97.6**
20	**28.6**	**43.8**	**27.6**	**57.4**	**29.4**	**44.9**	**88.6**	**89.1**
21	31.0	43.2	34.5	47.2	31.5	44.4	50.4	70.6

future work, determining the value β regular parameter needs further research.

References

J. J. Downs, E. F. Vogel, 1993. A plant-wide industrial process control problem. Computers & chemical engineering 17 (3), 245–255.

D. Drysdale, R. Sylvester-Evans, 1998. The explosion and fire on the piper alpha platform, 6 july 1988. a case study. Philosophical Transactions Mathematical Physical and Engineering Sciences 356 (1748), 2929–2951.

Q. P. He, S. J. Qin, J. Wang, 2005. A new fault diagnosis method using fault directions in fisher discriminant analysis. AIChE journal 51 (2), 555–571.

Q. P. He, J. Wang, 2011. Statistics pattern analysis: A new process monitoring framework and its application to semiconductor batch processes. AIChE journal 57 (1), 107–121.

F. Jia, Y. Lei, L. Guo, J. Lin, S. Xing, 2018. A neural network constructed by deep learning technique and its application to intelligent fault diagnosis of machines. Neurocomputing 272, 619–628.

U. Kruger, G. Dimitriadis, 2008. Diagnosis of process faults in chemical systems using a local partial least squares approach. AIChE Journal 54 (10), 2581–2596.

J.-M. Lee, S. J. Qin, I.-B. Lee, 2006. Fault detection and diagnosis based on modified independent component analysis. AIChE journal 52 (10), 3501–3514.

J.-M. Lee, C. Yoo, I.-B. Lee, 2004. Statistical process monitoring with independent component analysis. Journal of Process Control 14 (5), 467–485.

F. Sen, W. G. Egelhoff, 1991. Six years and counting: Learning from crisis management at bhopal. Public Relations Review 17 (1), 69–83.

B. M. Wise, N. Ricker, D. Veltkamp, B. R. Kowalski, 1990. A theoretical basis for the use of principal component models for monitoring multivariate processes. Process control and quality 1 (1), 41–51.

H. Wu, J. Zhao, 2018. Deep convolutional neural network model based chemical process fault diagnosis. Computers & Chemical Engineering 115, 185–197.

Z. Zhang, J. Zhao, 2017. A deep belief network based fault diagnosis model for complex chemical processes. Computers & Chemical Engineering 107, 395–407.

Anton A. Kiss, Edwin Zondervan, Richard Lakerveld, Leyla Özkan (Eds.)
Proceedings of the 29th European Symposium on Computer Aided Process Engineering
June 16th to 19th, 2019, Eindhoven, The Netherlands. © 2019 Elsevier B.V. All rights reserved.
http://dx.doi.org/10.1016/B978-0-128-18634-3.50128-4

A Framework for Multi-level Life Cycle Analysis of the Energy System

Emre Gençer,[a,*] Francis M. O'Sullivan [a]

[a]*MIT Energy Initiative, Massachussetts Institute of Technology, 77 Massachussetts Avenue, Cambridge, MA, 02139, USA*

emregencer@mit.edu

Abstract

The energy sector is undergoing a major transformation that is characterized by greater convergence of power, transportation, and industrial sectors and inter-sectoral integration. The existing techniques and tools are unable to accurately estimate the environmental impact of this paradigm shift. To develop a realistic understanding of these dynamics, we have developed a modeling framework that is designed to explore the emissions impacts of all relevant technological, operational, temporal, and geospatial characteristics of the evolving energy system. The tool is built as a MATLAB app that encapsulates MATLAB models, databases, and integrated process simulations. A modular framework constitutes the underlying analytical engine that covers all the life stages of major energy conversion pathways. The current version of the tool contains more than 900 individual pathways, which are responsible for ~80% of US greenhouse gas (GHG) emissions. Here we present an overview of the tool, the modeling approach and example results of case studies investigating electric power system.

Keywords: Life cycle analysis, multi-level analysis, energy systems modeling, computational tool, process simulation

1. Introduction

The global energy sector faces the grand challenge of meeting the increasing demand while profoundly reducing greenhouse gas emissions. Today's energy sector is responsible for approximately 80% of the world's total GHG emissions, and the electricity sector is the largest single emitting sector with 33% share. Industrial processes constitute 22% of emissions, while the transportation sector is responsible for 16% (Annual Energy Outlook 2018, 2018). Moving forward, the evolution of energy systems is characterized by greater convergence of power, transportation, and industrial sectors and inter-sectoral integration. Existing techniques and tools are unable to accurately estimate the environmental consequences of this paradigm shift. Understanding the implications of these dynamics requires novel tools that provide deep systems-level insights (Majumdar and Deutch, 2018). To address this pressing need, we have developed a modeling framework that is specifically designed to explore the emissions impacts of all relevant technological, operational, temporal, and geospatial characteristics of the evolving energy system.

The tool is built as a MATLAB app that encapsulates MATLAB models, databases, and integrated process simulations. A modular framework constitutes the underlying analytical engine that covers all the life stages of major energy conversion pathways. The

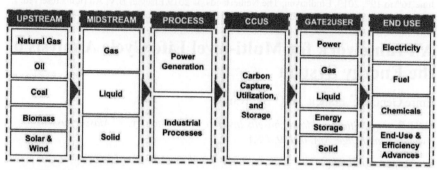

Figure 1 Summary of the contents of the tool. All major conventional and renewable energy pathways with their associated end-uses covering more than 85% of GHG emission sources in the US are represented.

first version of the tool contains more than 900 individual pathways (Figure 1), which are responsible for ~80% of US greenhouse gas (GHG) emissions. For the GHG emission hot spots, such as power plants and some chemical conversion pathways, detailed process simulation capabilities have been incorporated for in-depth analysis. In addition to performing pathway-level life cycle analysis (LCA), a central aspect of this analytical framework is the ability to assess key systems interactions and couplings. The system-level analysis is enabled by the embedded power systems and vehicle fleet models that captures market dynamics and explore dynamics of technology adoption and usage.

This paper focuses on the overview of the tool, the modeling approach as well as the results of case studies investigating electric power system. We demonstrate how the changes in the operational variability of natural-gas fired power plants impacts the system-wide emissions. Specifically, the operation of NG power plants in the evolving power system that significantly reduces plant performance and increases the emissions footprint of NG power generation. Example results of analysis of power plant dispatch profiles and detailed life cycle analysis of the US power grid using high resolution plant level simulation models and incorporation of publicly available US-wide generation and emissions data are presented (U.S. EPA, 2018a, 2018b).

2. Methodology

A crucial aspect of this analytical framework is the ability to assess key systems interactions and couplings. This allows transition options to be comprehensively assessed on the same basis. To allow performing such comprehensive analyses, we have built a flexible and modular programming architecture specifically designed to evolve as the complex energy system restructures.

The modular approach composed of four main compartments at the very high-level: User input, Control panel, Life stage modules, and Model output. To initiate the computation the necessary input parameters such as selection of complete value chain, specifications of power grid mix, geographical location, and temporal resolution should be provided by user. Control panel module constitutes the core of the tool that takes user inputs and communicates with relevant life stage modules to send and receive information as shown in Figure 2(a). The results from each life stage module are adjusted and combined in accord with the user selections given by Eq. (1). The energy consumption by fuel type is used as the basis for calculations. The efficiency of each stage is accounted for in the overall calculation denoted by ℓ. EF$_i$ represents the emission factor from each stage given in the stage specific unit and χ is the conversion factor to adjust to the final unit. The results calculated as the sum of contribution from each stage is returned as output in desired unit and format.

$$EF = \sum_{i=1}^{6}(EF_i \times \chi_i)\prod_{j=1}^{i}1_j \qquad (1)$$

Each life stage module consists of sub-modules. Depending on options selected, different sets of submodules are activated in parallel with the real-world operation. For example, the bituminous coal upstream operation includes all steps of extraction described by the processes involved coupled with fuels and electricity consumed. The midstream and gate2user stages are characterized by the phase of the flow. Process step is represented with high resolution to include all feedstocks and energy flows. The detailed information and data are collected from published LCA literature, reports, publicly available tools and life cyle inventory databases such as technology baselines reports (DOE NETL, 2015), GREET model (Wang, 2011), ecoinvent database.

2.1. Modeling Approach

The described programming architecture and linked modules are implemented in MATLAB. We have augmented MATLAB's capabilities by integrating with Aspen Plus process simulation software (Gençer and Agrawal, 2017a). This approach allows complementing life cycle analysis with process simulation capabilities to capture the performance and emission changes arising from technological and operational variations. It is computationally very expensive and unnecessary to simulate every process for all potential conditions. However, the developed architecture provides a platform to implement simulations of process units with high emission rates, critical for the system design, or sensitive to externalities.

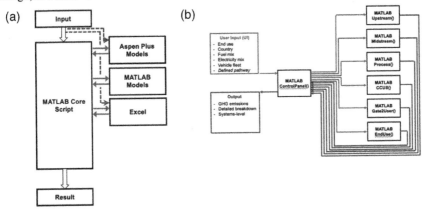

Figure 2 (a) The tool is developed in MATLAB with the added capabilities of communicating with various modeling programs such as Aspen Plus. (b) The modular structure: control panel connecting to primary life stage modules.

Figure 2(a) depicts the communication between MATLAB Core Script and auxiliary components: MATLAB Models, Aspen Plus Models, and Excel models and databases.

As needed, the tool can be equipped with more programming platforms. MATLAB is used to develop life stage modules, each one of which has its unique structure. Each module is composed of numerous custom developed MATLAB functions. Functions are designed to minimize the repetition of same scripts and framed clearly separate different tasks.

Natural gas fired power plants play a critical role in the evolving electric power system

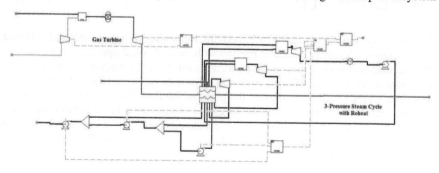

Figure 3 Process flow diagram of natural gas combined cycle unit simulated in Aspen Plus to match the performance of GE's 7FA model.

both as a lower carbon intensity alternative to coal power plants, and as balancing capacity for variable renewable energy sources. Power plant performance is sensitive to parameters such as percent loading, ambient temperature and relative humidity. To have a representative characterization of power generation units, we have developed Aspen Plus simulations for the most widely used combined cycle and gas turbine units. The performance of models is validated using the manufacturer's catalogs (Chase and Kehoe, 2013). Simulations represents steady-state operation at various conditions including percent loading (Gençer and Agrawal, 2017b).

3. System Boundaries

Pathway level analysis constitutes the backbone of the computation engine. The platform is capable of calculating all the combinations of modules, presented in Figure 1, that form a meaningful pathway. The individual pathways can be further expanded with the addition of new modules. Cradle-to-grave system boundary for every complete pathway is set and the selections are limited to allowed components. System boundary for coal-to-electricity pathway is shown

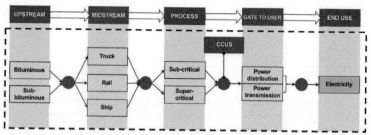

Figure 4 Coal-to-electricity pathway system boundary.

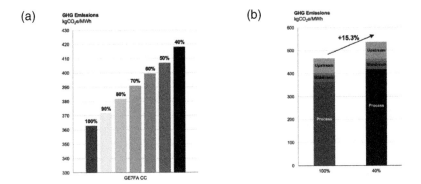

Figure 5 (a) GHG emissions from the flue gas of NGCC for varying loadings. (b) Cradle-to-grave life cycle emissions of shale gas-to-power pathway for 100 % and 40 % of the nameplate capacity of NGCC unit.

in Figure 4. For every life stage, there are multiple options that can be selected such as the coal type (bituminous or subbituminous), the transportation method of coal (truck, rail, or ship). Combination of these alternatives can also be specified.

3.1. Representation of Systems

Pathway-level analysis provides valuable insights however, understanding system wide emissions impact is critical. The presented modular framework is designed to perform systems-level calculations. A system is defined as a collection of individual pathways. This approach allows performing high resolution LCA based upon detailed individual pathways embedded. System can be as small as two pathways and as large as a city or a region. To determine the minimum emission option, the problem can be optimized using genetic algorithm (Gençer et al., 2015; Liu and Bakshi, 2018).

4. Results

The model can be run in pathway level or systems-level modes. The pathway level calculations are performed to estimate the life cycle GHG emissions in a given system boundary. The impact of cycling for NGCC plants is explored. Simulation results for 40 % to 100 % loading relative to nameplate capacity for a NGCC unit is shown in Figure 5(a). The emission rate increases from 362 kgCO$_2$/MWh to 419 kgCO$_2$/MWh when the power output is reduced to 40 %. The emission impact of this variation is propagated to

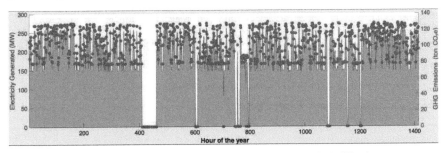

Figure 6 Hourly LCA based on observed load profile of a NGCC unit in California.

all life cycle stages of the supply chain. Cradle-to-grave life cycle analysis for the two extreme cases are performed and results are summarized in Figure 5(b). The emission intensity increases by 15.3 % relative to operation at peak efficiency. Using the embedded hourly generation profiles of thermal generation units a life cycle emissions of generators in the US has been calculated. Results for a combined cycle unit in California (Dynegy Moss Landing Power Plant Unit 1A) is shown in Figure 6, the area graph shows the hourly electricity generation and dots are the calculated full life cycle emissions in tCO_2e. For this particular unit, we observe more than 40% fluctuations in total emissions. While one reason for this change is the lower net generation, the other reason is higher emission intensity operation due to operation at off peak mode.

5. Conclusions

The adoption of a holistic approach is increasingly important to accurately characterize the energy system. Here, we have demonstrated a novel tool to integrate the systems aspect for the conventional life cycle analysis. The underlying analytic engine constitutes of numerous individual energy pathways. The developed tool provides a consistent platform to estimate LCA of all components of the energy sector. Furthermore, the system representation is embedded into the tool for power and transportation sectors. LCA of power generation at hourly generator level resolution is estimated by integrating calculated performances from process simulations.

6. References

Annual Energy Outlook 2018. 2018.

Chase DL, Kehoe PT. GER-3574G - GE Combined-Cycle Product Line and Performance. Schenectady, NY: 2013.

DOE NETL. Cost and Performance Baseline for Fossil Energy Plants. vol. 1a. 2015.

Gençer E, Agrawal R. Strategy to synthesize integrated solar energy coproduction processes with optimal process intensification. Case study: Efficient solar thermal hydrogen production. Comput Chem Eng 2017a;105:328–47. doi:10.1016/j.compchemeng.2017.01.038.

Gençer E, Agrawal R. Synthesis of efficient solar thermal power cycles for baseload power supply. Energy Convers Manag 2017b;133:486–97. doi:10.1016/j.enconman.2016.10.068.

Gençer E, Tawarmalani M, Agrawal R. Integrated Solar Thermal Hydrogen and Power Coproduction Process for Continuous Power Supply and Production of Chemicals. vol. 37. 2015. doi:10.1016/B978-0-444-63576-1.50076-5.

Liu X, Bakshi BR. Extracting Heuristics for Designing Sustainable Built Environments by Coupling Multiobjective Evolutionary Optimization and Machine Learning. Comput Aided Chem Eng 2018;44:2539–44. doi:10.1016/B978-0-444-64241-7.50418-3.

Majumdar A, Deutch J. Research Opportunities for CO2Utilization and Negative Emissions at the Gigatonne Scale. Joule 2018;2:805–9. doi:10.1016/j.joule.2018.04.018.

U.S. EPA. Emissions & Generation Resource Integrated Database (eGRID) 2018a.

U.S. EPA. Air Markets Program Data 2018b.

Wang M. GREET Model: The Greenhouse Gases, Regulated Emissions, and Energy Use in Transportation Model. 2011.

Anton A. Kiss, Edwin Zondervan, Richard Lakerveld, Leyla Özkan (Eds.)
Proceedings of the 29th European Symposium on Computer Aided Process Engineering
June 16th to 19th, 2019, Eindhoven, The Netherlands. © 2019 Elsevier B.V. All rights reserved.
http://dx.doi.org/10.1016/B978-0-128-18634-3.50129-6

Nonlinear dynamic analysis of chemical engineering processes described by differential-algebraic equations systems

Ataíde S. Andrade Neto[a,*], Argimiro R. Secchi[a] and Príamo A. Melo[a]

[a]*Chemical Engineering Program, COPPE, Universidade Federal do Rio de Janeiro, Brazil*
ataide@peq.coppe.ufrj.br

Abstract

Chemical processes are subject to parametric variation due to, among others things, desired changes in process conditions, instrumentation malfunction or unpredicted disturbances. The outcome of these adversities is plural, the entire system may collapse or the output variables might not be affected at all. Thus, the theoretical analysis of processes prone to nonlinear responses plays a key role in design and operation of chemical plants either for safety or economic purposes. Because of the widespread use in the last couple decades of the differential-algebraic equations (DAE) approach in chemical processes modeling, the development of computational algorithms and tools specifically designed for the analysis of DAE systems becomes necessary, specially for high-index cases. In this work, we present a novel and index-free approach for the nonlinear dynamic analysis of mathematical models based on DAEs. A methodology for the direct detection of Hopf bifurcation points based on an optimization procedure, in which we rewrite the necessary condition for the Hopf bifurcation point occurrence as a constrained optimization problem was developed. In this approach, we do not compute the generalized eigenvalues of the system, but their Hurtwitz determinants using a new algorithm for the computation of characteristic polynomials of matrix pencils based on the La Budde's method. The resulting optimization problem was solved with a hybrid global optimization technique, coupling particle swarm (PSA) and active-set (ASA) algorithms. The parametric continuation of steady-state branches was conducted with the pseudo arc-length method and the stability analysis based on the spectral theory for linear matrix pencils. As an illustrative example we evaluate the dynamic behavior of a reactive flash drum formulated as an index-2 DAE system. The results show that the proposed methodology can handle DAE systems of high index in a fast and accurate way.

Keywords: Hopf bifurcation, differential-algebraic equations, stability analysis.

1. Introduction

Since the advent of calculus, the mathematical modeling of dynamic physicochemical processes has been based on ordinary and partial differential equations, with a very few exceptions (notably, the works of Lagrange on constrained mechanics dated from 1788 and Kirchhoff on electric circuits from 1847). However, with the growing studies on the differential-algebraic equations systems, started in the early 1970s, and also because their vast applicability this paradigm has been changing. Several authors have already pointed out numerous advantages of working directly with DAE; but we reinforce that formulating differential-algebraic models in many practical applications occurs naturally, specially in chemical engineering, as thermodynamic and equilibrium constraints, which are all imposed by algebraic equations, may be directly incorporated in the process modeling. Because of this feature, the DAE approach is largely exploited by the majority of dynamic simulation software used in the context of Computer Aided Process Engineering (CAPE).

Regarding the dynamic analysis of chemical processes, we can safely say that it is a well-developed field for systems governed by ordinary differential equations (ODE) or discrete maps, specially the bifurcation theory which contemplates the study of dynamic systems under variation in their evolution laws. From a historical point of view, it is possible to recognize the importance of the bifurcation theory developed for ODE as a fundamental tool for nonlinear analysis. Unfortunately, for systems described by DAE, the same is not true. Because it is a rather new topic compared to ODE systems, computational algorithms and tools specifically designed for DAE have not evolved so steadily yet. It is noticed, nevertheless, that some works in the literature have already addressed the bifurcation analysis for DAE systems using either classical algorithms for differential equations or extensions of them for index-1 systems (Clausbruch et al., 2006), which are far much simpler than high-index DAE.

Although it is possible to reduce some high-index DAE to index-1 systems, this can be a tedious error-prone procedure and, in many cases, the solution of the reduced system may significantly differ from that of the original problem due to the well-known drift-off effect. Additionally, Harney et al. (2013) showed that the stability analysis of the reduced system may not represent the stability of the higher-index system from which it is derived, often being necessary to apply some stabilization methodologies, which has been developed for DAEs in Hessenberg form of size 2.

Knowing beforehand the precise location where nonlinear phenomena, such as bifurcation points, occur is of great importance in real-life applications, as not only safety but also economic issues may be avoided. Also, because the DAE approach is the current paradigm in the theoretical analysis of chemical processes, computational methods that efficiently handle DAE systems becomes necessary. Driven by this, we present, in this work, a novel and index-free approach for the direct computation of Hopf bifurcation points (HBPs), without the necessity of applying index reduction algorithms or stabilization procedures.

2. Theoretical framework

2.1. Linearization of differential-algebraic equations systems

The core of bifurcation theory of nonlinear system inevitably falls back to the dynamic analysis of linear ones. Because of that, the fundamental question one may ask is if there exist a linearized DAE system with the same qualitative behavior around fixed points of its nonlinear counterpart. Reich (1995) proved that the existence of such systems depends on some conditions which will be presented in the sequence.

Consider the nonlinear index-ν DAE system in the fully implicit form

$$f(x(t), \dot{x}(t); p) = 0 \tag{1}$$

with $f : \mathbb{R}^n \times \mathbb{R}^n \times \mathbb{R}^m \mapsto \mathbb{R}^n$ and $p \in \mathbb{R}^m$ a vector of time-invariant parameters. A linearization of f around a fixed point x_e in the form

$$B(p)\dot{y}(t) = A(p)y(t) \tag{2}$$

where $A = \nabla_x f^T(x_e, 0; p)$, $B = \nabla_{\dot{x}} f^T(x_e, 0; p)$ and $y = x - x_e$, will exist only if the original DAE in Eq. (1) is regular (or solvable) and fulfill the following conditions:

$$\text{rank}\left[\nabla_{\dot{x}} f^T(x, \dot{x}; p)\right] = \text{constant for all } t \tag{3a}$$

$$\text{rank}\left[\nabla_x f^T(x_e, 0; p)\right] = n \tag{3b}$$

$$\text{rank}\left[\nabla_x g_\nu^T(x_e, 0; p)\right] = n \tag{3c}$$

in which $g_V(x,\dot{x};p)$ is a derivative-array obtained by stacking the vector f with all the equations that arise in an index reduction procedure. According to Campbell (1995), those conditions are simple to evaluate and often observed in physical systems.

2.2. Stability in DAE systems

Several authors have shown that the stability of a linear DAE is closely related to the spectrum, $\sigma(A,B)$, of the matrix pair (A,B) as defined in Eq. (2) (see Reich (1995) for a detailed overview on this subject). The spectrum of a DAE have exactly n_d finite values; the other $n - n_d$ values is said to be at the infinity. Here, n_d represent the number of Dynamics Degree of Freedom (DDoF) and n the dimension of the system. If all the finite values in $\sigma(A,B)$ lie in the left complex half-plane, then, the fixed point is stable.

2.3. Detection of Hopf bifurcation points

Hopf bifurcation points can be detected by an indirect method by tracing a branch of steady state solutions of an ODE system, usually done by homotopy continuation methods, while monitoring the eigenvalues of Jacobian matrix at the fixed points. When a single pair of eigenvalues crosses the imaginary axis a trapping method, such as the bisection or the secant method, can be used to refine the HBP. This procedure, despite being effective and easily extended to handle DAE systems, has a high computational cost. Alternatively, HBPs can be calculated directly. The first successful algorithm for the direct computation of Hopf bifurcation points in ODE systems was presented by Griewank and Reddien (1983) by formulating a set of $3n + 2$ equations that algebraically determines these points. Later, Reich (1995) extended this algorithm to the DAE systems.

We present a different approach in which instead of an augmented algebraic system, we solve a constrained nonlinear optimization problem. The main advantage of this method is that we do not restrict the Hopf bifurcation points search to a single parameter of the model. In fact, our algorithm works for any number of parameters. Also, we do not compute the spectrum of the DAE system, but its $n_d - 1$ Hurwitz determinants, D_k.

The Hurwitz determinants can be calculated from the normalized characteristic polynomial:

$$P(\lambda;p) = \det(\lambda B - A)/\bar{a}_{n_d}(p) = a_0(p) + a_1(p)\lambda + a_2(p)\lambda^2 + \cdots + \lambda^{n_d} \tag{4}$$

by building the Hurwitz matrix:

$$L(p) = \begin{bmatrix} a_1(p) & a_0(p) & 0 & \cdots & 0 \\ a_3(p) & a_2(p) & a_1(p) & \cdots & 0 \\ a_5(p) & a_4(p) & a_3(p) & \cdots & 0 \\ \vdots & \vdots & \vdots & \ddots & \vdots \\ 0 & 0 & 0 & \cdots & 1 \end{bmatrix} \tag{5}$$

then, evaluating its first $n_d - 1$ principal subdeterminants:

$$D_k(p) = \det(L_k) = \det \begin{bmatrix} l_{1,1} & \cdots & l_{1,k} \\ \vdots & \ddots & \vdots \\ l_{k,1} & \cdots & l_{k,k} \end{bmatrix} \tag{6}$$

where $a_i = \bar{a}_i/\bar{a}_{n_d}$ and $\bar{a}_i(p)$ are the coefficients of $\bar{P}(\lambda;p) = \det(\lambda B - A)$; $L \in \mathbb{R}^{n_d \times n_d}$, $L_k \in \mathbb{R}^{k \times k}$, $D_k \in \mathbb{R}$ and $k = 1,2,3,\ldots,n_d - 1$.

Extending the theorem of Liu (1994) for DAE systems, a Hopf bifurcation point arises when:

$$a_0 > 0,\ D_1 > 0,\ D_2 > 0,\ldots,\ D_{n_d-2} > 0,\ D_{n_d-1} = 0 \tag{7}$$

This allows us to formulate the following constrained optimization problem:

$$\min_{p \in \mathbb{P}^m, \, x \in \mathbb{R}^n} S(p) = D_{n_d-1}^2 \quad \text{subject to:}$$

$$a_0 > 0, \, D_1 > 0, \ldots, D_{n_d-2} > 0 \tag{8}$$

$$f(x, \dot{x}; p) = 0$$

where $\mathbb{P}^m \subseteq \mathbb{R}^m$ is a selected parametric space and $S : \mathbb{P}^m \mapsto \mathbb{R}$. The global minimum of this problem $(S(p) = 0)$ is always a Hopf bifurcation point.

2.4. Characteristic polynomials of matrix pencils

A general matrix pair (A, B) can be decomposed by Householder reflections into the form $A = QHZ$ and $B = QTZ$ where Q and Z are orthogonal, H upper Hessenberg and T upper triangular $n \times n$ matrices. Then,

$$\lambda B - A = \lambda QTZ - QHZ \Rightarrow \lambda Q^T QTZZ^T - Q^T QHZZ^T = \lambda T - H \tag{9}$$

Solving $\det(\lambda T - H)$ is numerically more efficient than solving $\det(\lambda B - A)$, because it can be rapidly evaluated by the following recursion formula derived from the La Budde method (Rehman and Ipsen, 2011):

$$\bar{P}_i(\lambda; p) = (\gamma_i \lambda - \alpha_i) \bar{P}_{i-1}(\lambda; p) + \sum_{k=1}^{i-1} \left[(t_{i-k,i}\lambda - h_{i-k,i}) \bar{P}_{i-k-1}(\lambda; p) \prod_{m=i-k}^{i-1} \beta_m \right] \tag{10}$$

with $\bar{P}_0(\lambda; p) = 1$ and $\bar{P}_1(\lambda; p) = \gamma_1 \lambda - \alpha_1$; $i = 2, 3, \ldots, n$. The coefficients α_i and β_i are, respectively, the diagonal and the subdiagonal of H; γ_i the diagonal of T; $t_{i,j}$ and $h_{i,j}$ are the (i, j)-elements of T and H; $\bar{P}_n(\lambda; p) = \bar{P}(\lambda; p) = \det(\lambda T - H) = \det(\lambda B - A)$.

3. Results

In order to evaluate the proposed methodology, it was applied to a benchmark model in chemical engineering. Consider the index-2 system describing the chemical reaction $A \rightarrow B \rightarrow C$ conducted in reactive flash drum:

$$f(x, \dot{x}; p) = \begin{bmatrix} \dot{x}_A - x_{Af} + x_A \left[\ell + K_A \phi + D_{a1} \exp\left(\frac{-g_1}{u+1}\right) \right] \\ \dot{x}_B - x_{Bf} + x_B \left[\ell + K_B \phi + D_{a2} \exp\left(\frac{-g_2}{u+1}\right) \right] - x_A D_{a1} \exp\left(\frac{-g_1}{u+1}\right) \\ \dot{u} - 1 + u + \phi \delta - Q - H_1 D_{a1} x_A \exp\left(\frac{-g_1}{u+1}\right) - H_2 D_{a2} x_B \exp\left(\frac{-g_2}{u+1}\right) \\ K_A x_A + K_B x_B + K_C x_C - 1 \\ x_A + x_B + x_C - 1 \\ \ell + \phi - 1 \end{bmatrix} = 0 \tag{11}$$

where x_A, x_B and x_C are molar fractions, u the dimensionless temperature and ϕ and ℓ the vapor and liquid fractions; the vector of search parameters is $p^T = [D_{a1}, D_{a2}, g_1, g_2, \delta, Q, H_1, H_2]$. The feeding compositions x_{Af} and x_{Bf} were set to 0.8 and 0.2, respectively, and the equilibrium constants $K_i = P_i^{sat}/P_{ref}$. The saturation pressure was modeled by the Antoine equation

$$P_i^{sat} = \exp\left[\alpha_i + \frac{\beta_i}{(u+1)T_{ref} - \gamma_i} \right] \tag{12}$$

for some reference chemical species with the following parameters: $\alpha^T : [21.3, 23.2, 25.1]$; $\beta^T : [-2428.2, -3835.2, -6022.2]$; $\gamma^T = [35.4, 45.3, 25.3]$. The reference temperature and pressure were set to 298 K and 101,325 Pa.

The optimization problem in Eq. (8) for the model described by Eq. (11) was solved using a hybrid approach by coupling the particle swarm (PSA) and active-set (ASA) algorithms. The PSA was applied at the start of the optimization procedure until a predetermined value of the objective function was reached, $S(p_m) = \varepsilon_m$. Then, the ASA was called to refine the solution to $S(p_f) = \varepsilon_f$, where ε_f is a predefined tolerance. This technique can be more efficient and effective for non convex problems with high number of optimization variables. In Table 1, we present a comparison between the hybrid approach and the standalone algorithms in terms of number of successful attempts and spent computational time that support this assertion. All simulations were done with Matlab on a 8GB RAM, Intel CORE-i7 laptop running Linux. With the exception of the standalone ASA, the PSA and the hybrid approaches were able to attain the global minimum in every scenario.

Table 1: Average performance of optimization algorithms[†].

Parameters	PSA[††]	ASA[††]	Hybrid[††]
all	129.0/4	$-/10$	12.1/0
D_{a1}, Q	53.1/0	1.9/0	13.6/0
D_{a1}, δ	56.6/0	1.9/0	12.9/0
Q	51.1/0	1.8/0	11.5/0

[†] $\varepsilon_m = 0.099$; $\varepsilon_f = 10^{-8}$; random initial guess;
[††] Time (s) / Number of failures in 10 attempts.

An appropriated selection of $\mathbb{P}^m$ is necessary for the success of the optimization. The vectors $L^T = [0,0,0,0,0,0,0,0]$ and $U^T = [10,10,10,10,100,10,100,100]$ represent feasible values for all the parameters, as they are dimensionless groupings resulting from the combination of physical properties and operating conditions, therefore, they were chosen to bound the set $\mathbb{P}^m$. As a result of the optimization problem, we found that a Hopf bifurcation point occurs at:

$$x^T = [0.2920,\ 0.3469,\ 0.0681,\ 0.7466,\ 0.3611,\ 0.2534]$$
$$p^T = [8.6807,\ 9.9707,\ 6.7821,\ 3.8784,\ 15.5261,\ 1.3430,\ 35.9778,\ 99.8517]$$

The periodic solutions arising at this HBP are stable, as can be seen in the phase diagram and the time series in Fig. 1. Another HBP was found at $Q = 2.1741$, using Q as the single search parameter while fixing all other parameters. In this case, the arising periodic solutions were found to be unstable.

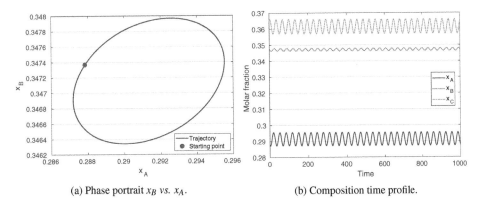

(a) Phase portrait x_B vs. x_A.   (b) Composition time profile.

Figure 1: Simulation in the neighborhood of Hopf bifurcation point at $Q = 1.3430$, the stable case. Total simulation time $t = 1000$.

The pseudo arc-length method was applied in order to make the one-parameter steady-state continuation of the model in Eq. (11). The resulting bifurcation diagram of this procedure is presented in Fig. 2.

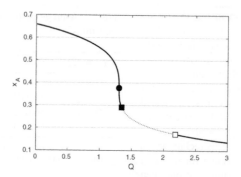

Figure 2: Bifurcation digram for the model in Eq. (11) using Q as the continuation parameter. Solid line: stable branch; dotted line: unstable branch; ■: HBP around stable periodic solutions; □: HBP around unstable periodic solutions; •: bifurcation point.

4. Conclusion

A novel methodology for the direct computation of Hopf bifurcation points in differential-algebraic equations systems was presented. This strategy is based on the formulation of the constrained optimization problem in Eq. (8) with multiple search parameters. With the proposed methodology, we were able to find the occurrence of HBPs in a benchmark model with up to eight search parameters in a fast and accurate manner.

Acknowledgments

This work was supported by the National Council for Scientific and Technological Development (CNPq) grant numbers 302893/2013-0 and 152572/2016-3. This study was financed in part by the Coordenação de Aperfeiçoamento de Pessoal de Nível Superior - Brasil (CAPES) - Finance Code 001.

References

K. E. Brenan, S. L. Campbell, L. R. Petzold, 1996. Numerical Solution of Initial-Value Problems in Differential-Algebraic Equations. Society for Industrial and Applied Mathematics (SIAM), Philadelphia, PA.

S. L. Campbell, 1995. Linearization of daes along trajectories. Zeitschrift für angewandte Mathematik und Physik ZAMP 46 (1), 70–84.

B. C. Clausbruch, E. C. Biscaia, P. A. Melo, 2006. Stability analysis of differential-algebraic equations in AUTO_DAE. Vol. 21 of Computer Aided Chemical Engineering. Elsevier, pp. 297 – 302.

A. Griewank, G. Reddien, 1983. The calculation of hopf points by a direct method. IMA Journal of Numerical Analysis 3 (3), 295–303.

D. Harney, T. Mills, N. Book, 2013. Numerical evaluation of the stability of stationary points of index-2 differential-algebraic equations: Applications to reactive flash and reactive distillation systems. Computers & Chemical Engineering 49, 61 – 69.

I. Hyanek, J. Zacca, F. Teymour, W. H. Ray, 1995. Dynamics and stability of polymerization process flow sheets. Industrial & Engineering Chemistry Research 34 (11), 3872–3877.

W. Liu, 1994. Criterion of hopf bifurcations without using eigenvalues. Journal of Mathematical Analysis and Applications 182 (1), 250 – 256.

M. Mangold, A. Kienle, E. Gilles, K. Mohl, 2000. Nonlinear computation in diva — methods and applications. Chemical Engineering Science 55 (2), 441 – 454.

R. Rehman, I. C. F. Ipsen, 2011. La Budde's Method for Computing Characteristic Polynomials. ArXiv e-prints.

S. Reich, 1995. On the local qualitative behavior of differential-algebraic equations. Circuits, Systems and Signal Processing 14 (4), 427–443.

B. Simeon, 2017. On the History of Differential-Algebraic Equations. Springer International Publishing, Cham, pp. 1–39.

R. P. Soares, A. R. Secchi, 2005. Direct initialisation and solution of high-index DAE systems. Vol. 20 of Computer Aided Chemical Engineering. Elsevier, pp. 157 – 162.

Anton A. Kiss, Edwin Zondervan, Richard Lakerveld, Leyla Özkan (Eds.)
Proceedings of the 29th European Symposium on Computer Aided Process Engineering
June 16th to 19th, 2019, Eindhoven, The Netherlands. © 2019 Elsevier B.V. All rights reserved.
http://dx.doi.org/10.1016/B978-0-128-18634-3.50130-2

Parameter Estimation for Thermal Runaway of Li-ion cells: a Gaussian Process approach

Robert Milton[a], Peter Bugryniec [a] and Solomon Brown[a,*]

[a]*Department of Chemical and Biological Engineering, University of Sheffield, Sheffield, S1 3JD, United Kingdom*
s.f.brown@sheffield.ac.uk

Abstract

Lithium ion (Li-ion) cells are the most prominent electrochemical energy storage device in todays world as they are utilised in many applications across many scales. However, Li-ion cells can suffer from a severe safety issue known as thermal runaway (TR). This process is due to exothermic chemical decomposition of a cells components. Being able to understand and model this process is essential for the development of safer batteries. Lithium iron phosphate (LFP) cells are known to have the safest chemistry of Li-ion cells. However, TR models developed for LFP cells have not been validated and when compared to new experimental work are shown to be inaccurate. Hence, the development of an accurate and validated LFP TR model is the focus of present research.

Classical TR modelling of Li-ion cells utilises four Arrhenius equations to predict the reaction rate of these reactions and in turn the heat generated. However, the development of a TR model (via parameter estimation) is difficult due to 1) the large range some of the parameters of the Arrhenius equation can take i.e. several 10s order of magnitude between literature values for a given reaction, 2) the complex interaction between different parameters within an Arrhenius equation, and 3) the effect of the heat generated by each reaction on the others. Given this, direct minimisation of the root mean squared error (RMSE) between simulated and experimental results has proven to be difficult, with optimized parameters unable to represent important experimental features.

As such, an approach is developed in which the viable parameter space is defined and sampled using a pseudo-random sampling. The error of the heuristic fit (RMSE) is then emulated by a Gaussian Process, further refined by Global Sensitivity Analysis. The result is an emulator providing predictions (with attached uncertainties a part of the process) as a function of a reduced number of combined parameters. This is a reduction in model order achieved by a novel, optimal rotation of input basis.

Keywords: Li-ion, thermal runaway, Gaussian Processes, parameter estimation

1. Introduction

Lithium ion (Li-ion) cells are a prominent electrochemical energy storage device, being utilised in many applications across many scales from mobile phones, to electric vehicles and grid scale energy storage (Placke et al., 2017). However, Li-ion cells can suffer from a severe safety issue known as thermal runaway (TR) (Wang et al., 2012). The hazard of TR is one of an uncontrollable temperature rise of a cell, due to heat generation from the exothermic chemical decomposition of a cell's components (Melcher et al., 2016), that can lead to catastrophic failure and result in fire and explosion. Hence, understanding the TR process is essential for the development of safer batteries.

Significant research has gone into studying the safety of Li-ion cells of various chemistries under various abuse methods, which has shown that the Lithium iron phosphate (LFP) cathode is the safest (Liu et al., 2016; MacNeil et al., 2002). Additionally, much research has gone into modelling the TR of cells (e.g. Hatchard et al., 2001; Coman et al., 2017), as this is more cost effective and safer than iterating cell and battery design experimentally. Previous work utilises Accelerating Rate Calorimetry (ARC) to determine the initial reaction kinetics of the SEI and cathode reactions (Richard and Dahn, 1999a) and inverse modelling techniques for parameter estimation of reaction kinetics for cell components (Richard and Dahn, 1999b) and full cells (Ren et al., 2018; Liu et al., 2018). Ren et al. (2018) determine parameters values through Kissinger and nonlinear fitting methods of DSC data. Fundamental thermal abuse experiments of ARC, DSC and oven exposure are used to validate such models. However, TR models developed for LFP cells (Peng and Jiang, 2016) have not been validated and when compared to new experimental work (Bugryniec et al., 2018) are shown to be inaccurate. Hence, the development of an accurate and validated LFP TR model is the focus of present research.

The classical theory of TR attributes the heat generation to four chemical reactions, the solid electrolyte interphase, negative electrode, positive electrode and electrolyte reactions (Richard and Dahn, 1999a). The heat generation of these reactions is commonly modelled utilising Arrhenius equations (Hatchard et al., 2001), characterized by the activation energy, frequency factor and heat of reaction, which we refer to here as the "reaction parameters" (12 parameters in total, 3 for each of the 4 individual reactions). However, preliminary work has shown that direct minimisation of the root mean squared error (RMSE) between simulated and experimental results is difficult, with optimized parameters unable to represent important experimental features.

In order to address this, in this paper we develop an approach for estimating the parameters through the development of a Gaussian Process (GP) emulator. To increase the efficiency of the optimization the dimensionality reduction method is applied, which utilises both an appropriate kernel and a Global Sensitivity Analysis (GSA).

This work is organised as follows: Section 2 presents a description of the full model that is applied to simulate TR. Section 3 describes the approach to model order reduction using GPs and GSA, while Section 4 presents the application of this approach to estimating the parameters of TR in fully charged 18650 LFP cells. Section 5 presents the conclusions drawn.

2. Full Order Model

The full order model is constructed in *COMSOL Muiltiphysics 5.2a* (https://uk.comsol.com/) and simulates the thermal runaway behaviour of an 18650 LFP cell under an ARC heat-wait-seek (HWS) test. ARC is considered as it operates in such a manner that the cell experiences near adiabatic conditions. Hence, with no heat exchange to or from the ARC, the temperature rise of a cell is entirely due to self-heating and can be entirely attributed to the decomposition reactions, while the model can be simplified to a zero heat loss simulation, reducing the amount of uncertainty by eliminating the variable for heat transfer between the cell and its surroundings.

The cell is modelled by a 1 dimensional asymmetric line along the radius of the cell comprised of 102 finite elements. The geometry is simplified by considering the multilayer jelly roll (i.e the electrodes, separators and current collectors) as a single homogeneous material with averaged thermo-physical properties. Heat transfer in the model assumes a solid body throughout and considers conduction within the cell and convection at the cell's surface. Convection is only considered during the HWS part of the ARC simulation, upon self-heating detection the heat transfer coefficient is set to zero to simulate adiabatic conditions.

The governing equations for the heat generated by the decomposition reactions follows that outlined by Kim et al. (2007). Wherein the rate of each reaction follows an Arrhenius relation, while the power generated by each reaction is the product of the specific heat of reaction, specific weight and reaction rate. In this work, the model geometry simulates a single domain for the jelly roll, with each decomposition reaction applied over the entire jelly roll domain, there would result in an over-estimate of heat generated. As such, to take account of this fact, the heat generated by each decomposition equation is scaled by a factor equal to the proportion of jelly roll that the reaction actually occurs in.

3. Model Order Reduction

To describe the dependence of RMSE on the reaction parameters we adopt the notation

$$y \propto \text{RMSE}$$
$$\mathbf{x} \propto (A_{ne}, A_{pe}, E_{a,ne}, E_{a,pe}, H_{ne}, H_{pe})$$

(1)

where each variable is offset and scaled to have zero mean and unit variance. Without loss of generality RMSE is represented as the scalar response f to input vector $\mathbf{x}$ plus independent noise e of zero mean

$$y(\mathbf{x}) = f(\mathbf{x}) + e$$

(2)

Our first assumption is that y and e are normally distributed at any fixed $\mathbf{x}$, rendering this model as a GP, which is a cheap and versatile emulator.

The significance of each input dimension to the GP is readily discerned by an Automated Relevance Determination (ARD) kernel. However, this restricts the orientation of relevant dimensions to the fixed axes of $\mathbf{x}$. As an alternative, we develop an approach employing the GP simply as an emulator facilitating global sensitivity analysis (GSA) via the Sobol' indices (Sobol', 2001). Using an arbitrary basis to calculate the Sobol' indices furnishes a very practical method for optimizing the rotation of input dimensions.

Essentially, optimization is then a two-stage process: 1) a GP emulator is optimized, then GSA using the emulator rotates the input basis; 2) this rotated basis is then used in a new emulator. Ultimately this yields an emulator that only significantly depends on a dimensionally reduced basis.

3.1. Gaussian Process Emulator

The emulator takes a $(1 \times M)$ row vector $\mathbf{x}$ and returns a Gaussian random variable

$$y(\mathbf{x}) \sim \text{N}\left[\bar{f}(\mathbf{x}), \Sigma_y\right] \quad \text{where} \quad \bar{f}(\mathbf{x}) = k(\mathbf{x}, \mathbf{X})(k(\mathbf{X}, \mathbf{X}) + \sigma_e^2 \mathbf{I})^{-1} \mathbf{y} =: \sigma_f^{-2} k(\mathbf{x}, \mathbf{X}) \tilde{\mathbf{y}}$$

(3)

whose mean $\bar{f}(\mathbf{x})$ is learned from training data $\mathbf{y} = f(\mathbf{X}) + \mathbf{e}$. Standard Bayesian inference has been used to express the mean prediction in terms of the $(N \times 1)$ observed responses $\mathbf{y}$ to $(N \times M)$ training inputs $\mathbf{X}$. At the heart of this lies the kernel function $k \colon \mathbb{R}^{I+M} \times \mathbb{R}^{J+M} \to \mathbb{R}^I \times \mathbb{R}^J$, expressing the correlation between responses to input samples of sizes $(I \times M)$ and $(J \times M)$. In this paper, of course, the number of input dimensions is $M = 6$ throughout. This work exclusively uses the ARD kernel (Wipf and Nagarajan, 2007):

$$k(\mathbf{x}', \mathbf{x}) := \sigma_f^2 \exp\left(-\frac{(\mathbf{x} - \mathbf{x}')\Lambda^{-2}(\mathbf{x} - \mathbf{x}')^\top}{2}\right)$$

(4)

where Λ is an $(M \times M)$ *diagonal* positive definite lengthscale matrix. The work which follows would be vastly complicated by any other kernel. However, this choice can be entirely justified from the assumption that the similarity function $k(\mathbf{x}', \mathbf{x})$ is differentiable at $\mathbf{x} = \mathbf{x}'$, together with original assumption that RMSE is normal (see Rasmussen and Williams, 2005, for further standard details).

3.2. Global Sensitivity Analysis

In this section an $(M \times 1)$ sample datum $\mathbf{u}$ is drawn from a standardized normal test distribution

$$\mathbf{u} \sim \mathsf{N}[(\mathbf{0})_M, (\mathbf{I})_{M \times M}] \quad \text{where} \quad (\mathbf{I})_{M \times M} \text{ is the } (M \times M) \text{ identity matrix.} \tag{5}$$

This provides input to the emulator upon rotation by row orthogonal matrix Θ

$$\mathbf{x} =: \mathbf{u}^\mathsf{T} \Theta \quad \text{eliciting response} \quad \bar{f}(\mathbf{x}) = \bar{f}(\mathbf{u}^\mathsf{T} \Theta) \tag{6}$$

GSA proceeds by conditioning on several fixed components of rotated input $\mathbf{u}$. The variance of $\bar{f}(\mathbf{u}^\mathsf{T} \Theta)$ due to the first m components of $\mathbf{u}$ is

$$D_{\mathbf{m}} := \mathsf{E}\left[\mathsf{E}\left[\bar{f}(\mathbf{u}^\mathsf{T}\Theta)|(\mathbf{u})_{\mathbf{m}}\right]^2\right] - \mathsf{E}\left[\bar{f}(\mathbf{u}^\mathsf{T}\Theta)\right]^2 \tag{7}$$

The ARD kernel affords analytic expressions for these quantities, after some algebra. Firstly

$$\mathsf{E}\left[\bar{f}(\mathbf{u}^\mathsf{T}\Theta)\right] = \mathbf{g}\,(\mathbf{1})_N \tag{8}$$

where $\mathbf{1}$ is a vector of ones, and $\mathbf{g}$ is the $(1 \times N)$ (Θ-independent) row vector

$$\mathbf{g} := \left|\Lambda^{-2} + \mathbf{I}\right|^{-1/2} \sum_{n=1}^{N} (\tilde{\mathbf{y}})_n\,(\mathbf{I})_{n \times N} \exp\left(-\frac{(\mathbf{X})_{n \times M}\left(\Lambda^2 + \mathbf{I}\right)^{-1}(\mathbf{X})_{n \times M}^\mathsf{T}}{2}\right) \tag{9}$$

the modulus of a matrix signifying, as usual, its determinant. Then

$$D_{\mathbf{m}} = \frac{\mathbf{g}\,\mathbf{W_m}\,\mathbf{g}^\mathsf{T}}{\left|2(\Sigma)_{\mathbf{m} \times \mathbf{m}} - (\Sigma)_{\mathbf{m} \times \mathbf{m}}^2\right|^{1/2}} - \mathbf{g}\,(\mathbf{1})_{N \times N}\,\mathbf{g}^\mathsf{T} \tag{10}$$

where $\mathbf{W_m}$ is the $(N \times N)$ symmetric matrix with components

$$(\mathbf{W_m})_{n \times o} := \exp\left(\frac{-(\mathbf{T})_{n \times \mathbf{m}}(\Sigma)_{\mathbf{m} \times \mathbf{m}}^{-1}(\mathbf{T})_{n \times \mathbf{m}}^\mathsf{T} - (\mathbf{T})_{o \times \mathbf{m}}(\Sigma)_{\mathbf{m} \times \mathbf{m}}^{-1}(\mathbf{T})_{o \times \mathbf{m}}^\mathsf{T}}{2}\right)$$

$$\exp\left(\frac{+((\mathbf{T})_{n \times \mathbf{m}} + (\mathbf{T})_{o \times \mathbf{m}})(\Phi)_{\mathbf{m} \times \mathbf{m}}^{-1}(\Sigma)_{\mathbf{m} \times \mathbf{m}}^{-1}((\mathbf{T})_{n \times \mathbf{m}}^\mathsf{T} + (\mathbf{T})_{o \times \mathbf{m}}^\mathsf{T})}{2}\right) \tag{11}$$

and

$$\mathbf{T} := \mathbf{X}\left(\Lambda^2 + \mathbf{I}\right)^{-1}\Theta^\mathsf{T}$$
$$\Sigma := \Theta\left(\Lambda^{-2} + \mathbf{I}\right)^{-1}\Theta^\mathsf{T} \tag{12}$$
$$\Phi := \Theta\left(\Lambda^{-2} + \mathbf{I}\right)^{-1}\left(2\Lambda^{-2} + \mathbf{I}\right)\Theta^\mathsf{T}$$

These $D_{\mathbf{m}}$ are then maximized using gradient descent, for $m = 1, 2, \ldots$ in turn.

4. Results

In this section, the methodology developed above is applied to the estimation of the reaction parameters described in Section 2 for experimental ARC data of fully charged 18650 LFP cells during HWS testing. In order to provide the input data for applying the GP approach the parameter space is sampled using a standard Latin hypercube method. These inputs are then filtered for simulations in which physically incorrect reaction initiation temperatures are obtained.

Optimization of the Sobol' indices via GPs reveals that two directions account for less than 0.15% of RMSE variance in total. There is also a clear principal direction, composed mainly of H_{pe}, which accounts for at least 35% of RMSE variance on its own. The variance is therefore (almost) entirely captured in four dimensions, which could potentially be reduced to just two dimensions by accepting some loss of fidelity.

The optimal two-dimensional parameter subspace is shown as a contour plot in Fig. 1, alongside the least relevant two-dimensional parameter subspace. Fragmentation or noise in these plots indicates uncaptured variance in RMSE. Ideally, the optimal subspace exhibits a smooth contour plot. By the Bayesian measure of fit (log likelihood), the Sobol' optimized GP model improves 19% over an unrotated ARD kernel, and 37% over the optimal isotropic one.

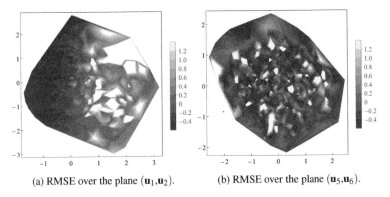

(a) RMSE over the plane $(\mathbf{u}_1, \mathbf{u}_2)$. (b) RMSE over the plane $(\mathbf{u}_5, \mathbf{u}_6)$.

Figure 1: Contour plots of normalized RMSE over (a) the two most significant directions and (b) the two least significant directions.

A GP has been fit to the two most relevant directions $(\mathbf{u}_1, \mathbf{u}_2)$ alone, selecting a somewhat regularized local optimum with noise variance of 0.36. This GP was searched for minimum predicted RMSE, and combined with mean values for the irrelevant coordinates to produce a set of optimal reaction parameters (ROM).

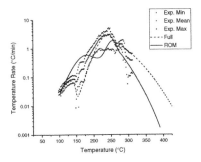

Figure 2: Comparison of predictions obtained with reaction parameters selected by reduced model (ROM) optimization, heuristic full model optimization, and experimental data.

Fig. 2 presents the variation of the temperature rate with temperature according to simulation and experiment. The reaction parameters used for simulation have been optimized by ROM, and independently by a costly heuristic full model optimization. Clearly the ROM optimized model is no substitute for full optimization at this stage, but it does lie within experimental range over most of the domain, and reflects the gross features of the experimental plots reasonably well.

5. Conclusions

In this work a GP approach for the estimation of reaction parameters for the simulation of thermal runaway in Li-ion batteries was presented. The method uses a GSA-based dimensionality reduction to increase the efficiency of the optimization process.

When applied to data obtained from the experimental testing of 18650 LFP cells, comparison of the reduced-dimension GP emulators showed that the difference in predictions between the four- and six-dimensional emulators was negligible. For optimization purposes nearly all the useful information resides in just two-dimensions. Future work will investigate less robust, but potentially more precise, high variance (low noise) GP solutions, and analyze the robustness of the reduced approach.

6. Acknowledgements

This work is financially supported by the Engineering and Physical Sciences Research Council (EPSRC) under grant number (EP/P026214/1) and in the form of the Energy Storage and its Applications Centre for Doctoral Training (EP/L016818/1).

References

P. J. Bugryniec, J. N. Davidson, D. J. Cumming, S. F. Brown, 2018. Pursuing safer batteries: thermal abuse of lifepo$_4$ cells, manuscript submitted for publication.

P. T. Coman, E. C. Darcy, C. T. Veje, R. E. White, 2017. Modelling Li-Ion Cell Thermal Runaway Triggered by an Internal Short Circuit Device Using an Efficiency Factor and Arrhenius Formulations. Journal of The Electrochemical Society 164 (4), A587–A593.

T. D. Hatchard, D. D. MacNeil, A. Basu, J. R. Dahn, 2001. Thermal Model of Cylindrical and Prismatic Lithium-Ion Cells. Journal of The Electrochemical Society 148 (7), A755–A761.

G. H. Kim, A. Pesaran, R. Spotnitz, 2007. A three-dimensional thermal abuse model for lithium-ion cells. Journal of Power Sources 170 (2), 476–489.

X. Liu, Z. Wu, S. I. Stoliarov, M. Denlinger, A. Masias, K. Snyder, 2016. Heat release during thermally-induced failure of a lithium ion battery: Impact of cathode composition. Fire Safety Journal 85, 10–22.

X. Liu, Z. Wu, S. I. Stoliarov, M. Denlinger, A. Masias, K. Snyder, 2018. A Thermo-Kinetic Model of Thermally-Induced Failure of a Lithium Ion Battery: Development, Validation and Application. Journal of Electroanalytical Society 165 (11), A2909–A2918.

D. D. MacNeil, Z. Lu, Z. Chen, J. R. Dahn, 2002. A comparison of the electrode/electrolyte reaction at elevated temperatures for various Li-ion battery cathodes. Journal of Power Sources 108 (1-2), 8–14.

A. Melcher, C. Ziebert, M. Rohde, H. J. Seifert, 2016. Modeling and simulation of the thermal runaway behavior of cylindrical Li-ion cells-computing of critical parameters. Energies 9 (4), 1–19.

P. Peng, F. Jiang, 2016. Thermal safety of lithium-ion batteries with various cathode materials: A numerical study. International Journal of Heat and Mass Transfer 103, 1008–1016.

T. Placke, R. Kloepsch, S. Dühnen, M. Winter, 2017. Lithium ion, lithium metal, and alternative rechargeable battery technologies: the odyssey for high energy density. Journal of Solid State Electrochemistry 21 (7), 1939–1964.

C. E. Rasmussen, C. K. I. Williams, 2005. Gaussian Processes for Machine Learning (Adaptive Computation and Machine Learning series). The MIT Press.

D. Ren, X. Liu, X. Feng, L. Lu, M. Ouyang, J. Li, X. He, 2018. Model-based thermal runaway prediction of lithium-ion batteries from kinetics analysis of cell components. Applied Energy 228, 633–644.

M. N. Richard, J. R. Dahn, 1999a. Accelerating Rate Calorimetry Study on the Thermal Stability of Lithium Intercalated Graphite in Electrolyte I. Experimental. Journal of The Electrochemical Society 146 (6), 2068–2077.

M. N. Richard, J. R. Dahn, 1999b. Accelerating Rate Calorimetry Study on the Thermal Stability of Lithium Intercalated Graphite in Electrolyte. II. Modeling the Results and Predicting Differential Scanning Calorimeter Curves. Journal of The Electrochemical Society 146 (6), 2078–2084.

I. M. Sobol', 2001. Global sensitivity indices for nonlinear mathematical models and their monte carlo estimates. Mathematics and Computers in Simulation 55, 271–280.

Q. Wang, P. Ping, X. Zhao, G. Chu, J. Sun, C. Chen, 2012. Thermal runaway caused fire and explosion of lithium ion battery. Journal of Power Sources 208, 210–224.

D. Wipf, S. Nagarajan, 2007. A new view of automatic relevance determination. In: Proceedings of the 20th International Conference on Neural Information Processing Systems. NIPS'07. Curran Associates Inc., USA, pp. 1625–1632.

Anton A. Kiss, Edwin Zondervan, Richard Lakerveld, Leyla Özkan (Eds.)
Proceedings of the 29th European Symposium on Computer Aided Process Engineering
June 16th to 19th, 2019, Eindhoven, The Netherlands. © 2019 Elsevier B.V. All rights reserved.
http://dx.doi.org/10.1016/B978-0-128-18634-3.50131-4

Improved Design of Experiments for Identification of MIMO Systems

Kurt E. Häggblom

Åbo Akademi University, Faculty of Science and Engineering, Biskopsgatan 8, Turku FI–20500, Finland

khaggblom@abo.fi

Abstract

A problem in the identification of MIMO systems is that the system outputs in an identification experiment may be strongly correlated if the inputs are perturbed by uncorrelated signals, as is standard practice. Such a correlation reduces identifiability.

A set of methods to design input perturbations that minimize the sample correlation between the outputs has previously been proposed. These methods require an initial model for the design. In this paper, a data-based design method is proposed. Data are obtained from preliminary experiments with the system to be identified. Besides being preferable from a practical point of view, the data-based approach makes it easier to handle some numerical issues that gave problems in the model-based approach.

A design method that minimizes the input or output peak value subject to desired output variances with no output correlation is presented. A model of an ill-conditioned distillation column is used to illustrate the method.

Keywords: System identification, Multivariable systems, Ill-conditioned systems, Experiment design, Data-based design.

1. Introduction

The quality of the data is of utmost importance in the identification of multiple-input multiple-output (MIMO) systems. The standard approach of perturbing all inputs simultaneously by uncorrelated signals tends to produce correlated outputs. For ill-conditioned systems this correlation is very strong. Such data may jeopardize identifiability (Koung and MacGregor, 1992).

A design method that addresses the output distribution was proposed by Häggblom (2017a, 2018b). The method can produce uncorrelated outputs, which is considered good for identifiability. A drawback of the method is that it requires an initial model of the system. A short overview of related design methods is given in Häggblom (2017a).

In this paper, a completely data-based method is introduced for the same purpose of obtaining uncorrelated outputs. Data are obtained from one or more preliminary experiments with the system to be identified. It is possible, for example, to use the data from a standard identification experiment with uncorrelated inputs to design a better experiment. Additional properties such as input and output peak values can be minimized in addition to correlation handling.

An ill-conditioned distillation column model is used for illustration of the methods.

2. Problem formulation

Experiment design for identification of MIMO systems is considered. The system has n inputs $u(k)$ and n outputs $y(k)$, sampled at time instants $k = 1, \ldots, n_s$, where n_s is the total number of sample points. The variables are related by a dynamic relationship

$$y(k) = G(\mathrm{q})u(k),\tag{1}$$

where $G(\mathrm{q})$ is a matrix of pulse transfer operators defined through the shift operator q. This relationship is assumed to be initially unknown. It is not implied that a model of this form is to be identified.

The input design for the identification experiment is facilitated by the use of an n-dimensional perturbation signal $\xi(k)$. This signal is typically a random binary signal (RBS), a pseudo random signal (PRBS), or a multi-sinusoidal signal (MSS). The correlation between the individual signals $\xi_i(k)$, $i = 1, \ldots, n$, should preferably be small (ideally non-existent). In practice, this is achieved by constructing each ξ_i from a base sequence ξ_0, of length N, by shifting it (approximately) $(i-1)N/n$ positions in a circular way. As suggested by Ljung (1999), more than one period of the sequences may be used to give a total sequence length $n_s = n_p N$, where n_p is the number of periods.

The input $u(k)$ to be applied in the identification experiment is given by a linear transformation

$$u(k) = T\xi(k),\tag{2}$$

where T is a constant matrix determined in the input design with the aim of making the output samples $y_i(k)$, $k = 1, \ldots, n_s$, $i = 1, \ldots, n$, uncorrelated with $y_j(k)$, $j \neq i$.

The output correlation depends on the output covariance matrix, which for an $n \times n$ system is defined by $n(n+1)/2$ parameters. This suggests that the same number of adjustable elements of T is sufficient to produce uncorrelated outputs. Thus, T can be a triangular or symmetric matrix, for example. If more elements are used, it is possible to optimize some quantity besides output correlation. In this paper, minimization of the peak values $\max_{i,k}|y_i(k)|$ and $\max_{i,k}|u_i(k)|$ is considered.

3. Input design

Applying the input $u(k)$, $k = 1, \ldots, n_s$, to a system yields an $n_s \times n$ matrix of sampled outputs Y, where the kth row and ith column of Y holds the sample $y_i(k)$. Given the perturbation sequence $\xi(k)$, $k = 1, \ldots, n_s$, it is desired to choose T in Eq. (2) to give Y specified properties. In particular, the covariance matrix $P = \mathrm{cov}(Y)$ is desired to be diagonal, which means no correlation between the outputs. Assuming the variances $\mathrm{var}\, y_i = 1$ are desired, the objective is to obtain $P = I$.

Assume it is known that the single input $u_i(k) = \xi_j(k)$ produces an output matrix Y_ℓ, $\ell = i + (j-1)n$. If the system is linear, applying an input $u_i(k) = T_{ij}\xi_j(k)$ would then produce the output matrix $T_{ij}Y_\ell$. If Y_ℓ is known for every combination of $u_i(k)$ and $\xi_j(k)$, applying the input $u(k)$ given by Eq. (2) would then produce the output

$$Y = \sum_{i=1}^{n}\sum_{j=1}^{n}T_{ij}Y_\ell , \quad \ell = i+(j-1)n ,\tag{3}$$

where T_{ij} is the element of T in row i and column j.

To streamline the notation needed further below, the vector

$$x = \text{vec}(T)\tag{4}$$

is introduced. The vectorization results in $x_\ell = T_{ij}$, where $\ell = i+(j-1)n$. Equation (3) is then replaced by

$$Y = \sum_{\ell=1}^{n^2}x_\ell Y_\ell .\tag{5}$$

The output covariance matrix becomes

$$P = \sum_{\ell_1=1}^{n^2}\sum_{\ell_2=1}^{n^2}x_{\ell_1}x_{\ell_2}P_{\ell_1\ell_2} ,\tag{6}$$

where $P_{\ell_1\ell_2} = \text{cov}(Y_{\ell_1},Y_{\ell_2})$ is the matrix of covariances between Y_{ℓ_1} and Y_{ℓ_2}. Thus, $P_{\ell_1\ell_2}$ can be calculated when Y_{ℓ_1} and Y_{ℓ_2} are known.

The task of the input design is now to determine the vector x to obtain $P = I$. The nonlinearity of Eq. (6) is a difficulty, however. To overcome this, Eq. (6) can be linearized and solved iteratively. The linearization is

$$P = \sum_{\ell_1=1}^{n^2}\sum_{\ell_2=1}^{n^2}\left(\tilde{x}_{\ell_1}x_{\ell_2} + x_{\ell_1}\tilde{x}_{\ell_2} - \tilde{x}_{\ell_1}\tilde{x}_{\ell_2}\right)P_{\ell_1\ell_2} ,\tag{7}$$

where $\tilde{x}$ is the previous value of x in the iteration procedure.

4. Obtaining data

Data for the design is generated by one or more experiments with the system to be identified. The most reliable method is to make an experiment with every combination $u_i(k) = \xi_j(k)$, $i = 1,\ldots,n$, $j = 1,\ldots,n$, one at a time. This results in n^2 experiments, each one yielding a matrix of sampled outputs Y_ℓ, $\ell = i+(j-1)n$, needed in the input design.

For $n > 2$, this is a lot of experiments, and even for $n = 2$, four experiments might be undesirable. An alternative is to make just n experiments with $u_i = \xi_j$, $i = 1,\ldots,n$ and j arbitrary (e.g., $j = i$ or $j = 1$). For each experiment, a pulse-response model $G(q)$ satisfying Eq. (1) can be determined in a simple way. This makes it possible to simulate all combinations $u_i = \xi_j$ to obtain the required output data matrices.

It is possible to take this one step further, and make only one experiment with $u(k) = \xi(k)$. Here, all inputs are perturbed simultaneously. If the components $\xi_i(k)$, $i = 1,\ldots,n$, are essentially uncorrelated with one another, it is possible to determine the n pulse-response models above and proceed in the same way. This kind of experiment is the standard identification experiment recommended in textbooks (e.g., Ljung 1999; Isermann and Münchhof, 2011), but here the data is used to design a better experiment.

5. Solution procedures

In the case of a structurally constrained T (which is a user choice) with $n(n+1)/2$ free elements such that T is not structurally singular, Eq. (6) can be solved directly to obtain a solution that yields $P = I$. However, there are multiple solutions because of the quadratic nature of Eq. (6). Moreover, various column and row permutations of T can be applied. For a triangular structure, there are $(n!)^2$ permutations; for a symmetric or skew-symmetric structure, there are $n!$ permutations of each.

To avoid the nonlinearity of Eq. (6), an iterative application of Eq. (7) can be used. It is then convenient to use an optimization framework to obtain a solution. Using the YALMIP toolbox (Löfberg, 2004) in conjunction with MATLAB makes it easy to formulate the problem as

$$\max_{x \in X} \lambda \text{ , s.t. (7) and } \lambda I \le P \le I , \tag{8}$$

where X denotes the allowed structures of x (and T). This procedure does not eliminate multiple solutions. Generally, the solution depends on the starting value $\tilde{x}$ in Eq. (7).

If T is constrained to a lesser degree, an unconstrained T being the typical case, Eq. (6) and (7), with $P = I$, are underdetermined with respect to x. This makes it possible to optimize some other property besides correlation. Minimization of the peak values $\max_{i,k} |y_i(k)|$ and $\max_{i,k} |u_i(k)|$ are very relevant choices.

Minimization of $\max_{i,k} |y_i(k)|$, later referred to as $\min Y_{max}$, can be formulated as

$$\min_{x \in X} r \text{ , s.t. (5), (7), } P = I \text{, and } -r \le Y \le r . \tag{9}$$

In the case of perturbation signals that switch between two levels, as e.g. PRBS inputs, minimization of $\max_{i,k} |u_i(k)|$ can be accomplished by minimization of T_∞ (Häggblom, 2018a, 2018b). This minimization can be formulated as

$$\min_{x \in X} r \text{ , s.t. (7), } P = I \text{, and } \sum_{j=1}^{n} |T_{ij}| \le r \text{ , } i = 1,\ldots,n . \tag{10}$$

Because these optimizations are completely data based, they are also non-convex. This means that there is no guarantee that the obtained solution is a global optimum. Hence, many starting values $\tilde{x}$ should be tried. Fortunately, the differences between the best local optima tend to be small.

6. Case study

An ill-conditioned distillation column model introduced by Skogestad and Morari (1988) is used to illustrate the input design methods. This model was also used for input design in Häggblom (2017b, 2018b). The model is a state-space model

$$\begin{matrix} \dot{x}(t) = Ax(t) + Bu(t) \\ y(t) = Cx(t) \end{matrix}, \quad A = \begin{bmatrix} -\frac{1}{194} & 0 \\ 0 & -\frac{1}{15} \end{bmatrix}, \quad B = \begin{bmatrix} 1 & -1 \\ 0 & 1 \end{bmatrix}, \quad C = \begin{bmatrix} \frac{87.8}{194} & \frac{1.4}{15} \\ \frac{108.2}{194} & -\frac{1.4}{15} \end{bmatrix}. \quad (11)$$

In this case study, the sampling time is $T_s = 1$ and a PRBS with minimum switching time $T_{sw} = 4$ and sequence length $N = 255$ is used as perturbation.

For a triangular T structure, including all permutations of columns and rows, eight solutions were found (two for each permutation) by the optimization in Eq. (8). The ones with the smallest peak values $\max|y| \equiv \max_{i,k}|y_i(k)|$ and $\max|u| \equiv \max_{i,k}|u_i(k)|$ are

$$\min Y_{max}: \quad T = \begin{bmatrix} 1.4863 & 0 \\ 1.4652 & 0.0866 \end{bmatrix} \Rightarrow \max|y| = 2.5940, \ \max|u| = 1.5567 \quad (12)$$

$$\min T_\infty: \quad T = \begin{bmatrix} 0 & 1.5012 \\ -0.0820 & 1.4646 \end{bmatrix} \Rightarrow \max|y| = 2.9594, \ \max|u| = 1.5466 \quad (13)$$

For a symmetric or skew-symmetric T, including all permutations, eight solutions were found (two for each permutation). The ones with the smallest peak values are

$$\min Y_{max}: \quad T = \begin{bmatrix} 1.0439 & 1.0875 \\ 1.0875 & 1.0179 \end{bmatrix} \Rightarrow \max|y| = 2.7250, \ \max|u| = 2.1315 \quad (14)$$

$$\min T_\infty: \quad T = \begin{bmatrix} 1.0628 & -0.9897 \\ 0.9897 & -1.0542 \end{bmatrix} \Rightarrow \max|y| = 2.7367, \ \max|u| = 2.0525 \quad (15)$$

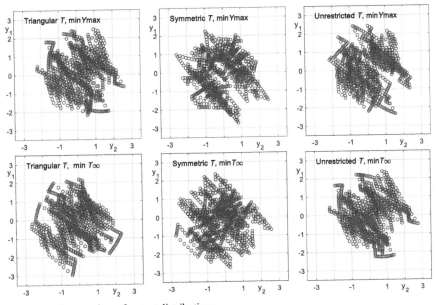

Figure 1. Scatter plots of output distributions.

Minimization of the peak values with an unrestricted T matrix using the formulations in Eqs (9) and (10) gave the following results:

$$\min Y_{max} : \quad T = \begin{bmatrix} 1.4568 & 0.3367 \\ 1.4189 & 0.4116 \end{bmatrix} \Rightarrow \max|y| = 2.4079, \ \max|u| = 1.8305 \tag{16}$$

$$\min T_\infty : \quad T = \begin{bmatrix} -0.0363 & 1.4769 \\ 0.0432 & 1.4700 \end{bmatrix} \Rightarrow \max|y| = 2.7726, \ \max|u| = 1.5132 \tag{17}$$

As can be seen, a triangular type of T matrix is a good choice for obtaining a small input peak value, whereas a symmetric type of T matrix is not good. A small output peak value requires minimization of Y_{max} with an unrestricted T matrix.

Figure 1 shows scatter plots of the output distributions of the various designs.

7. Conclusions

A data-based method for design of experiments for identification of MIMO systems was described. The required data can be obtained from some preliminary experiment(s) with the system. The input design, which is easy to carry out with standard optimization software, yields uncorrelated outputs. This is considered good for identifiability. In addition, input and output peak values can be minimized subject to desired output variances with no output correlation. It is an advantage in process operation to obtain desired output variances with input and output peaks as small as possible. The method works with any kind of standard perturbation signals used in system identification.

References

K.E. Häggblom, 2017a, A new optimization-based approach to experiment design for dynamic MIMO identification, IFAC PapersOnline, 50 (1), 7582–7587.

K.E. Häggblom, 2017b, Design of optimal experiments for dynamic MIMO identification, Proc. 27th European Symp. on Computer Aided Process Design — ESCAPE 27, Barcelona, Spain, 319–324.

K.E. Häggblom, 2018a, Input designs to obtain uncorrelated outputs in MIMO system identification, Proc. 13th Int. Symp. on Process systems Engineering — PSE 2018, San Diego, CA, USA, 637–642.

K.E. Häggblom, 2018b, Easy ways to design inputs to obtain uncorrelated outputs in MIMO system identification, IFAC PapersOnline, 51 (15), 227–232.

R. Isermann and M. Münchhof, 2011, Identification of Dynamic Systems, Springer: Berlin and Heidelberg, Germany.

C.-W. Koung and J.F. MacGregor, 1992, Design of identification experiments for robust control. A geometric approach for bivariate processes, Ind. Eng. Chem. Res., 32 (8), 1658–1666.

L. Ljung, 1999, System Identification: Theory for the User, Prentice Hall: Upper Saddle River, NJ, USA.

J. Löfberg, 2004, YALMIP, A toolbox for modeling and optimization in MATLAB, Proc. IEEE Int. Symp. on Computer Aided Control Systems (CACSD), Taipei, Taiwan, 284–289.

S. Skogestad and M. Morari, 1988, Understanding the dynamic behavior of distillation columns, Ind. Eng. Chem. Res., 27 (10), 1848–1862.

Anton A. Kiss, Edwin Zondervan, Richard Lakerveld, Leyla Özkan (Eds.)
Proceedings of the 29th European Symposium on Computer Aided Process Engineering
June 16th to 19th, 2019, Eindhoven, The Netherlands. © 2019 Elsevier B.V. All rights reserved.
http://dx.doi.org/10.1016/B978-0-128-18634-3.50132-6

Machine Learning of Molecular Classification and Quantum Mechanical Calculations

Jie-Jiun Chang[1], Jia-Lin Kang[2*], David Shan-Hill Wong[1*], Cheng-Hung Chou[1], Hsuan-Hao Hsu3, Chen-Hsuan Huang3 and Shang-Tai Lin[3*]

1 Department of Chemical Engineering, National Tsing Hua University, Hsinchu, Taiwan

2 Department of Chemical and Material Engineering, Tam Kang University, New Taipei City, Taiwan 30013

3 Department of Chemical Engineering, National Taiwan University, Taipei, Taiwan

e-mail: conlinkang@gmail.com, dshwong@che.nthu.edu.tw, stlin@ntu.edu.tw

Abstract

In this paper, a machine learning method is proposed to extract molecular features as floating-point numbers in a high dimensional space from the language-like description Simplified Molecular Input Line Entry Specification (SMILES). Principle component analysis showed that this method can successfully classify alkanes and alcohols and also the chain lengths of the molecular by their location in a three-dimensional feature space. A neural network model is build using the location of a compound in this high dimensional space as input to predict the "sigma-profile", the charge distribution of the molecule near a perfect infinite conductor, which is calculated by quantum mechanics. The sigma-profile can be used in the COSMOSAC model for predicting thermodynamic properties such as activity coefficient. Preliminary results showed that an accurate neural work model with generalization ability can be developed.
Keywords: Machine Learning, Word embedding, COSMO-SAC, Sigma profile..

1. Introduction

One of the popular ways of generalized correlations of thermodynamic properties, developed over four decades ago, is the use of group contribution methods (Joback and Reid 1987, Fredenslund et al. 1975). Such methods required expert suggestions of the functional dependence of the predicted properties and regression of binary interaction parameters using large amount of data. In the last two decades, a priori, or first principle approach that used quantum mechanical calculations to predict thermodynamic properties has been developed (Klamt 1995, Lin and Sandler 2002). In the COSMO method, quantum mechanical calculations is used to predict the charge distribution of a molecule near an infinite conductor, known as the sigma σ-profile, which can be used to predict thermodynamic properties of mixtures (e.g. COSMO-SAC). Substantial effort needs to be expended in producing the σ-profile. Database of σ-profiles of a limited number of compounds was provided 0. Yet it is desirable that a fast surrogate generation method be developed to alleviate the load of first principle calculations.

Machine learning (ML) is the use of computer and statistics to learn from data with minimum human intervention. In other words, ML tries to identify the functional relation between an input and an output from a set of data, given that such afunctional relation exists. Sigma profile can be considered as a function of molecular structure since it is uniquely defined. Yet there are many ways to represent molecular structure ranging from aforementioned group contribution method to text-based description such as Simplified Molecular Input Line Entry Specification (SMILES, Weininger, 1998) or .mol file 0) or even three dimensional representation (Humphrey et al. 1996). Recent development in machine learning has been able to convert word-based content into vector space (Mikolov et al 2013). In this paper, a machine learning method is proposed to convert word-based molecular features from SMILES into a floating-point vector space representation, and used it to develop a neural network to generate σ-profiles.

2. Method

2.1. Molecular recognition using SMILES and word embedding

The SMILES format encoded molecular structure clearly with a short ASCII string. It is able to read the structures like chain length, double bond (=), triple bond (#) and aromatic ring (c1ccccc1) easily. With this link between molecules and nature language, we can use machine learning language model to extract molecular features.

The SMILES format is presented as word, which is not readable by machine. To translate the word to inputs of network, i.e. vectors, we build a "dictionary". In this dictionary, every elements and symbols can be transformed to a specific number. Then we can translate the SMILES format data to sequences of numbers. However, these number sequences are just encoding, and do not represent "characteristic" or feature of the molecules. Word embedding solve this problem by projecting translated sequence into a high-dimensional vector using a neural network.

In order to that the transformation is able to truly recognize molecule features, the high dimensional output of the embedding layer is collapsed by a dense-layer with 1 output. About 1372 true compounds are used and tagged 0, or "true-compound". Another 1372 compounds with randomly created SMILES file are tagged 1 as "false" or "fake-compound". Supervised learning are used until the recognizer network can accurately distinguish between the two classes. 274 true compounds and the same amount of fake-compound are used as test set.

2.2. Sigma profile predictor

The high dimensional output of are then used as input into a Long short-term memory (LSTM), which is commonly used in nature language recognition is used (), with hyperbolic tangent activation function and 4-layer back-propagation network with rectified linear unit (RELU) activation function. It is trained with 1096 compounds while 279 were used as test data. The overall network structure is shown in Figure 1.

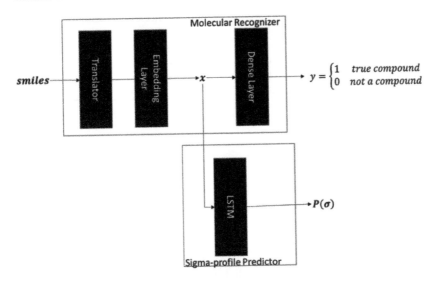

Figure 1 : Overall network structure

3. Results

3.1. Recognizer and Molecular Classification

Table 1 showed the training performance of our recognizer. There is a limited number of false positive, i.e. fake compound recognized as true, are found because we may have 2 accidentally generated a true compound. There is no "false negative", i.e. true compound recognized as fake.

Table 1: Performance of the Recognizer

	True Compound	Fake Compound
Training Data		
Output 0	1372	1
Output 1	0	1371
Test Data		
Output 0	274	1
Output 1	0	273

Hence principle component analysis (PCA) (Joliffe 2011) was performed to help visualize how molecules are distributed in the high dimensional space. Figure 2(a) showed that the first 3 PCs account for about 80% of the variation. Furthermore Figure 2 (b) to 2(d) if we locate homologues of normal paraffins, straight chain alcohols and acids, they are arranged in an orderly manner, indicating that the embedment is able to transform the text-based SMILES input into a distance-relevant high dimensional space that can be used for molecular recognition and classification.

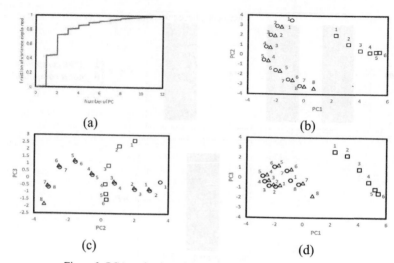

(a) (b)

(c) (d)

Figure 2: PCA projection of the high dimensional feature space

3.2. Sigma-profile prediction

Figure 3 showed the best model we obtained with different training set. Out of 274 test data, the average R^2 is 0.96, 179 has a R^2 of over 0.95, the worst R^2 is 0.79. Figure 4a and 4b showed ML predictions sigma profile for two compounds with R^2=0.99 0.79 respectively. Even when the actual agreement is inferior, the trend of the sigma-profile is consistent.

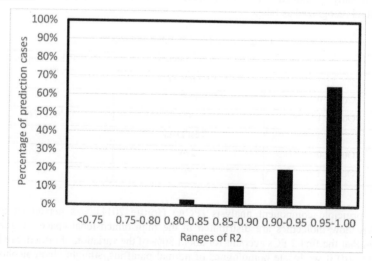

Figure 3 Distribution of prediction accuracy

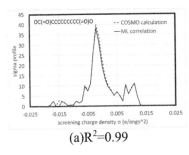
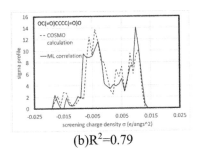

(a)R^2=0.99   (b)R^2=0.79

Figure 4: Sigma profile correlations of (a) OC(=O)CCCCCCCCC(=O)O, R2=0.99

3.3. Prediction of infinite dilution coefficients

Figure 5a and 5b compare the infinite dilution coefficients obtained using sigma profiles predicted by ML and sigma profiles using quantum mechanical calculations in water and n-hexane respectively. Fair agreements were obtained between two types of sigma profiles. However, it was found that the ML model over-predicts the infinite dilution activity coefficient in water when they are much less than 1; and under-predicts the infinite dilution activity coefficient in n-hexane when is much greater than 1. This indicates that ML correlation is biased towards non-polar compounds. Improvement of model can be achieved by refined sampling of training data.

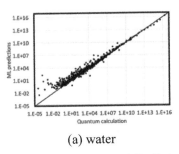
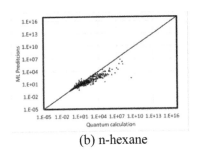

(a) water   (b) n-hexane

Figure 5: Prediction of infinite dilution coefficients

4. Conclusion

The above results serve as a preliminary demonstration that molecular classification and prediction of sigma-profile, results of quantum calculations, using text-based molecular description is possible. A recognizer was trained using word-embedment network, and a LSTM transformation network. The network gave no false negative and very few false positive. PCA analysis showed that the transformed space can be used as for molecular feature representation and classification. Use this space as input, we showed that fairly accurate prediction of sigma-profile can be developed. Optimization of network structure have not yet been considered. The promising results suggest that extension of this approach to a more extensive data base should be a valuable for a priori property prediction and molecular design. Refinement of neural network structure, better sampling of data and the use of other molecular representation should also be investigated.

References

Dalby, A., Nourse, J. G., Hounshell, W. D., Gushurst, A. K., Grier, D. L., Leland, B. A., & Laufer, J. (1992). Description of several chemical structure file formats used by computer programs developed at Molecular Design Limited. *Journal of Chemical Information and Computer Sciences,* 32(3), 244-255.

Fredenslund, A., Jones, R. L., & Prausnitz, J. M. (1975). Group-contribution estimation of activity coefficients in nonideal liquid mixtures. *AIChE Journal*, 21(6), 1086-1099.

Hochreiter S.and Schmidhuber J.. (1997) Long short-term memory. *Neural Computation*, 9(8):1735–1780.

Humphrey, W., Dalke, A., & Schulten, K. (1996). VMD: visual molecular dynamics. *Journal of Molecular Graphics*, 14(1), 33-38.

Joback, K. G., & Reid, R. C. (1987). Estimation of pure-component properties from group-contributions. *Chemical Engineering Communications*, 57(1-6), 233-243.

Jolliffe, I. (2011). Principal component analysis. In International encyclopedia of statistical science (pp. 1094-1096). Springer, Berlin, Heidelberg.

Klamt, A. (1995). Conductor-like screening model for real solvents: a new approach to the quantitative calculation of solvation phenomena. *The Journal of Physical Chemistry*, 99(7), 2224-2235.

Lin, S. T., & Sandler, S. I. (2002). A priori phase equilibrium prediction from a segment contribution solvation model. Industrial & engineering chemistry research, 41(5), 899-913.

Mikolov, T., Chen, K., Corrado, G., & Dean, J. (2013). Efficient estimation of word representations in vector space. *arXiv preprint arXiv*:1301.3781.

Mullins, E., Oldland, R., Liu, Y. A., Wang, S., Sandler, S. I., Chen, C. C., ... & Seavey, K. C. (2006). Sigma-profile database for using COSMO-based thermodynamic methods. Industrial & engineering chemistry research, 45(12), 4389-4415.

Weininger D. SMILES, a chemical language and information system. 1. Introduction to methodology and encoding rules. Journal of Chemical Information and Modeling. 1998, 28, 31–36.

Anton A. Kiss, Edwin Zondervan, Richard Lakerveld, Leyla Özkan (Eds.)
Proceedings of the 29th European Symposium on Computer Aided Process Engineering
June 16th to 19th, 2019, Eindhoven, The Netherlands. © 2019 Elsevier B.V. All rights reserved.
http://dx.doi.org/10.1016/B978-0-128-18634-3.50133-8

Comparative CFD analysis of thermal energy storage materials in photovoltaic/thermal panels

Aya Al-Hmoud[a], Daniel Sebastia-Saez[a], Harvey Arellano-Garcia[a,b,*]

[a]*Department of Chemical and Process Engineering, University of Surrey, Guildford GU2 7XH, United Kingdom*

[b]*LS Prozess- und Anlagentechnik, Brandenburgische Technische Universität Cottbus-Senftenberg, D-03046 Cottbus, Germany*

h.arellano-garcia@surrey.ac.uk

Abstract

Photovoltaic/thermal systems are a novel renewable energy approach to transform incident radiation into electricity and simultaneously store the excess thermal energy produced. Both sensible and latent heat storage materials have been investigated in the past for thermal storage; with desert sand having been recently considered as an efficient and inexpensive alternative. In this work, we use a transient Computational Fluid Dynamics simulation to compare the performance of desert sand to that of well-established phase-change materials used in photovoltaic/thermal systems. The simulation gives as a result the temperature profiles within the device as well as the time evolution of the charge/discharge cycles when using PCMs. The results show the suitability of desert sand as a thermal storage material to be used in photovoltaic/thermal systems.

Keywords: photovoltaic/thermal system, phase change material, thermal energy storage, CFD, charge/discharge cycle.

1. Introduction

Amongst the different renewable energy technologies available, photovoltaic systems are currently one of the best positioned to be fully implemented in order to tackle the global carbon mitigation challenge. An important drawback however is their low efficiency, which results in only a fraction of the incident energy being converted into electricity, while the rest of the incident energy is lost to the surroundings in the form of heat (Preet, 2018). Nonetheless, this energy loss may lead to a temperature rise which can jeopardy the structure of the photovoltaic (PV) cell, ultimately causing a decrease in its lifetime. With the cooling of the PV panel being crucial, an alternative technology called photovoltaic thermal (PV/T) systems has emerged to allow for co-generation of both electricity and thermal energy. In PV/T systems, the heat loss can be stored by increasing the temperature of a material layer, i.e. a thermal energy storage (TES) medium, placed underneath the absorber. The thermal energy stored in this manner can subsequently be passed on to a liquid or gas stream. PV/T systems give way thus to increased general efficiency relative to photovoltaic cells cooled by natural convection (Preet, 2018). It is necessary then to determine the best material for the TES module to maximise the performance of the PV/T configuration. Sensible heat TES media and phase change materials (PCM) are the options available.

Sensible TES media store sensible heat as a function of their specific heat capacity, whereas PCMs allow for extra energy storage by undergoing phase change. PCMs can therefore pave the way to increased efficiencies and overnight use thanks to slow energy release after the external source of heat ceases to be applied. Moreover, the use of PCMs in conjunction with PV cells allows for effective control of the working temperature of the cell by damping any fluctuations (Alva et al., 2017; Sardarabadi et al., 2017; Ma et al., 2017). Regarding sensible heat storage, silicon carbide (SiC) and natural desert sand have also received attention recently because their particulate material gives way to enhanced heat transfer. Desert sand has also the advantage of presenting high availability and extraordinary resistance to agglomeration, being capable of withstanding temperatures of up to 1000 °C.

Research on the use of desert sand as a TES medium began in the 1980s (Flamant, 1982), and has been taken up recently because the use of costless local materials is considered a key factor to reduce the levellised energy cost of CSP systems (Schlipf et al., 2015). A comprehensive assessment of the thermal and morphological properties of different types of desert sand from the United Arab Emirates was reported in the literature (Diago et al., 2018; Iniesta et al., 2015). They used these data to further develop a combined solar receiver/storage system (similar to that proposed by Flamant et al., 2013) using desert sand as TES medium.

The scope of the work presented here is to further develop the use of desert sand by presenting a transient CFD approach to compare the performance of sand and some well-established PCMs (including capric/palmitic acid, salt hydrate, and n-octacosane) in a PV/T configuration. A similar configuration has been reported by Mousavi et al. (2018), who run a steady-state 2-D CFD model to carry out a parametric study and exergy analysis of the system including different PCMs. The objective of this work, in contrast, is to assess the performance of desert sand in the same PV/T configuration by using a transient 3-D approach, and establish a comparison with various PCMs. The thermal efficiency of the system, temperature distributions within both the water channel and the surrounding thermal storage matrix, and the heating-cooling cycles of both n-octacosane and sand-based systems are simulated to quantify the suitability of desert sand as an effective material to be used in PV/T systems. As of today, to the best of our knowledge the use of desert sand in PV/T systems remains unexplored, and thus this article presents the first steps in that direction. The article begins with the description of the computational methodology employed (Section 2), and follows with a systematic grid convergence assessment for the main output variables from the simulation, i.e. temperature and density of the phase change material, before discussing the results in section 3 and presenting the concluding remarks in section 4.

2. Modelling methodology and grid convergence study

The computational domain is depicted in Figure 1, and consists of a copper pipe containing a water stream embedded in a rectangular PCM block exposed to the radiation from the sun. An additional layer, placed on top of the PCM, is included in the model in order to represent the absorber layer. The computational domain mimics, then, the configuration presented by Browne et al. (Browne et al., 2015; 2016), but only one of the copper pipes has been considered here for computational economy reasons. The schematic illustration showcases the dimensions and the different layers of the three-dimensional computational domain used in this work. The top wall of the absorber layer (the one which is not in contact with the PCM layer) is modelled as a constant heat source wall in order to mimic the incident sunrays. A PCM matrix is placed directly underneath. A granular material is defined in the PCM matrix in those cases where desert sand was considered. Water enters the copper pipe with a specific mass flow rate and temperature (mass flow inlet boundary condition with 0.002 kg/s) and abandons the domain through a pressure outlet boundary. Adiabatic walls are specified as boundary conditions on the rest of the boundaries. The simulations were performed using the commercial software ANSYS Fluent v19.1. The options Solidification/Melting and Energy were switched on along with the laminar option for turbulence. The steady state solver was implemented to obtain the results in Figures 2, 3 and 4. Under-relaxation factors were kept at default values. Further simulations were run by using the transient solver, in order to monitor the time evolution of temperature difference between the water inlet and outlet. To do so, the heat flux wall boundary condition was switched on and off each other 4,000 s flow time in order to mimic the charge/discharge cycles of the PCM matrix.

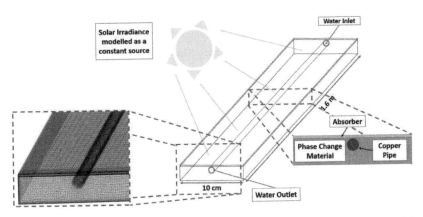

Figure 1: Schematic illustration of the computational domain including boundary conditions, dimensions and a detail of the numerical grid.

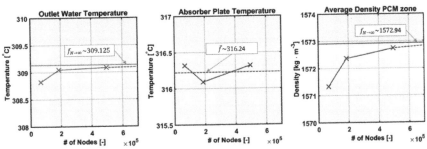

Figure 2: Results of the grid convergence test.

A systematic grid convergence assessment has been performed by applying the Richardson extrapolation method (Roache, 1994), which allows to quantify the numerical error caused by the space discretization relative to the estimated solution of the conservation equations at zero grid spacing. A coarse (67,488 nodes), medium (186,951), and a fine mesh (496,824) were used to perform the grid convergence study. The results are reported in Figure 2, where the extrapolated value at zero grid spacing is also represented in those cases that showed convergence (outlet water temperature and the density of the PCM zone). Oscillatory behaviour is observed for the average absorber plate temperature; this possibility is also covered in the literature (Ali et al., 2009). The order of magnitude of the maximum value observed for the grid convergence index (see its definition in Roache, 1994) using the fine and the medium mesh was 10^{-4}. This means a deviation obtained with the different grids of up to 0.01%.

3. Results and discussion

The steady state solver was initially used to check the temperature fields across the device upon a range of solar irradiance values (from 150 to 1,200 W/m^2) and using different options as PCM. The two plots on the top part of Figure 3 depict the temperature difference between the average temperature at successive cross-sections along the pipe and the temperature at inlet conditions (25°C). Similar values are obtained for n-octacosane and desert sand, proving the latter as a valid material in order to harvest the excess energy produced in the PV/T panel and transfer it to a working fluid. The colour maps on the bottom part of Figure 3 shows the temperature distribution in a plane parallel to the absorber and containing the symmetry axis of the pipe upon a solar irradiance of 1,200 W/m^2. The results show that the temperature attained by the liquid at the outlet boundary and the maximum temperature of the TES matrix do not match (~315 K against ~366 K) when using n-octacosane (a PCM). A longer domain would therefore be needed in order to fully avail the energy stored by the PCM. Conversely, they are close when using sand as TES medium (~315 K against ~319 K). This suggests that there is an advantage in using desert sand instead of n-octacosane because a smaller quantity of TES medium is required to fully avail the incident solar irradiance.

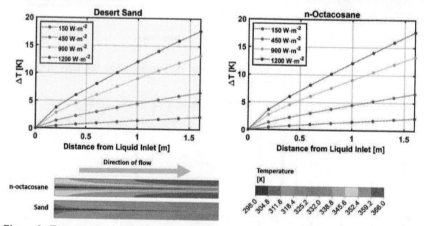

Figure 3: Temperature profiles in the symmetry axis of the copper pipe (top two graphs) and colour maps of the temperature distribution within the PCM matrix (bottom part of the figure) for n-octacosane and sand.

Figure 4 on the other hand shows the effect of the solar irradiance on the PCM solid fraction (left-hand side graph) for several materials. A visualization of the boundary delimiting the liquid and the solid fraction is included (right-hand side plot) for the case of n-octacosane. The graph on the left-hand side allows the reader to establish which PCM is more advantageous depending on the solar irradiance. Among the materials used in our simulations, n-octacosane needed a solar irradiance of 600 W/m^2 to begin melting (subsequently storing latent heat), whereas capric-palmitic acid underwent full phase change for the entire range of solar irradiances tested in the present study. The results contained in Figure 4 allow the user of the present model to calculate the amount of latent heat that a given PCM can store for solar irradiances between 150 and 1,200 W/m^2 and different materials.

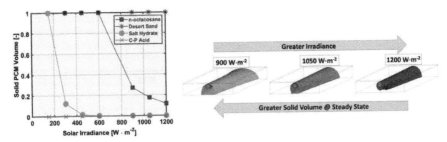

Figure 4: Relationship between the PCM solid fraction and the solar irradiance (left-hand side graph). Visualization of the PCM n-octacosane melted volume at steady state as a function of the solar irradiance (right-hand side). In the latter, the water outlet is visible, whereas the inlet is hidden by the solid portion of the PCM.

Finally, Figure 5 shows the transient charge/discharge cycle of the PCM material n-octacosane relative to the behavior of desert sand, which does not undergo phase change. This transient solution was obtained by using the results at steady-state as the initial values. In the beginning the heat flux was switched off, mimicking the conditions that the panel would have at night. In the case of desert sand, one can observe that heat has been retained during approximately 4,500 s (1.25 hours), after which there is no water temperature difference between inlet and outlet. The PCM, however, retains heat during more time by virtue of the phase change process. The results in Figure 5, however, prove as expected that the use of a PCM is more convenient than granular desert sand in those applications where heat needs to be released overnight.

4. Final remarks

A 3-D CFD model has been developed in order to compare the suitability of different materials to be used as thermal energy storage (TES) media in photovoltaic/thermal panels, including desert sand and different phase change materials (PCM).
Better heat transfer to the water stream occurs at steady state with desert sand than with n-octacosane (one of the PCMs studied), leading to a reduction on the volume of TES needed to fully avail the thermal energy excess. Moreover, since the 3-D model presented here calculates the solid volume fraction of PCM upon given conditions, the user can determine which PCM is best to be used for a particular value of the solar irradiance and to estimate the latent heat stored. The transient configuration proves as a useful tool to study the charge/discharge cycles of the thermal energy storage materials, and thus provides a value of the energy a particular TES medium can release and for how long.

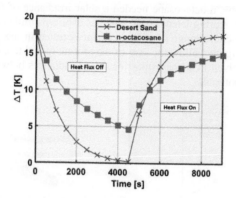

Figure 5: Time evolution of the inlet-outlet water temperature difference.

References

M.S.M. Ali, C.J. Doolan, V. Whitley. 7th International Conference on CFD in the minerals and process industries (CSIRO), Melbourne, Australia, December 2009.

G. Alva, L. Liu, X. Huang, G. Fang, 2017, Thermal energy storage materials and systems for solar energy applications, Renew. Sust. Energ. Rev., 68(1), 693–706.

M.C. Browne, K. Lawlor, A. Kelly, B. Norton, S. J. McCormack, 2015, Indoor characterisation of a photovoltaic/thermal phase change material system, Energ. Proced., 70, 163–171.

M.C. Browne, D. Quigley, H.R. Hard, S. Gilligan, N.C.C. Ribeiro, N. Almeida, S.J. McCormack, 2016, Assessing the thermal performance of phase change material in a photovoltaic/thermal system, Energ. Proced., 91, 113–121.

M. Diago, A.C. Iniesta, A. Soum-Glaude, N. Calvet, 2018, Characterization of desert sand to be used as a high-temperature thermal energy storage medium in particle solar receiver technology, Appl. Energ., 216, 402–413.

G. Flamant, 1982, Theoretical and experimental study of radiant heat in a solar fluidized-bed receiver, AIChE J., 28(4), 529–535.

G. Flamant, D. Gauthier, H. Benoit, J.-L. Sans, R. Garcia, B. Boissiere, R. Ansart, M. Hemati, 2013, Dense suspension of solid particles as a new heat transfer fluid for concentrated solar thermal plants: On-sun proof of concept, Chem. Eng. Sci., 102, 567–576.

A.C. Iniesta, M. Diago, T. Delclos, Q. Falcoz, T. Shamim, N. Calvet, 2015, Gravity-fed combined solar receiver/storage system using sand par- ticles as heat collector, heat transfer and thermal energy storage media, Energ. Proc., 69, 802–811.

T. Ma, J. Zhao, J. Han, 2017, A parametric study about the potential to integrate phase change material into photovoltaic panels, Energ. Proced., 142, 648–654.

S. Mousavi, A. Kasaeian, M. Behshad, S. Mohammad, H. Jahangir, 2018, Numerical investigation of the effects of a copper foam filled with phase change materials in a water-cooled photovoltaic/thermal system, Energ. Convers. Manage. 163, 187–195.

S. Preet, 2018, Water and phase change material based photovoltaic thermal management systems: A review, Renew. Sust. Energ. Rev., 82(1), 791–807.

P.J. Roache, 1994, Perpective: A method for uniform reporting of grid refinement studies. J. Fluids Eng., 116(3), 405–413.

M. Sardarabadi, M. Passandideh-Fard, M.-J. Maghrebi, M. Ghazikhani, 2017, Experimental study of using both ZnO/ water nanofluid and phase change material (PCM) in photovoltaic thermal systems, Sol. Energ. Mat. Sol. C., 161, 62–69.

D. Schlipf, P. Schicktanz, H. Maier, G. Schneider, 2015, Using sand and other small grained materials as heat storage medium in a packed bed HTTESS, Energ. Proced., 69, 1029–1038.

Anton A. Kiss, Edwin Zondervan, Richard Lakerveld, Leyla Özkan (Eds.)
Proceedings of the 29th European Symposium on Computer Aided Process Engineering
June 16th to 19th, 2019, Eindhoven, The Netherlands. © 2019 Elsevier B.V. All rights reserved.
http://dx.doi.org/10.1016/B978-0-128-18634-3.50134-X

DEM Study of a Mixer for Core Manufacturing System

Jiwon. Roh,[a,b] Junghwan. Kim,[a,*] Man Sig. Lee,[a] Il. Moon,[b]

[a]*Korea Institute of Industrial Technology, 55 Jongga-ro, Jung-gu, Ulsan 44413, South Korea*

[b]*Yonsei University, 50 Yonsei-ro, Seodaemun-gu, Seoul 03722, South Korea*

kjh31@kitech.re.kr

Abstract

A core is a special, preformed part of a casting which is essential for complex and delicate shapes in the casting process. Around 95% of sand and 5% of binder are mixed as the raw material for manufacturing the core. Organic binders exhibit a high performance but generate contaminants and toxic gases since they are composed of toxic chemicals, and therefore, the trend in popular types of binder is evolving from organic to inorganic. In this context, we focus on the development of a discrete element model (DEM) model for the mixer in the core manufacturing process using an inorganic binder. We validate the developed model by comparing it with an actual horizontal mixer system. The actual mixer has dimensions of 1.36 m in length and 0.17 m in diameter. When the process is simulated once under the same operating conditions, the actual process run time is the same as the simulation run time. Based on this model, we carry out case studies by varying conditions such as the length of the mixer, and location of injection nozzle. As per our DEM study, the mixer length can be reduced by more than 20% relative to the existing design. We also suggest alternative mixer designs by optimizing the location of the injection nozzle.

Keywords: Core, Inorganic Binder, DEM, Mixer.

1. Introduction

Casting is a manufacturing process in which molten metal is poured into a mould of desired shape and allowed to solidify. The core is the part of the mould which fills the empty space of the mould forming internal cavities in the casting process. Most moulds are made of sand. To fix the mould, a binder is added to the sand. In this regard, although organic binders are currently prevalent worldwide, they generate harmful gases such as benzene and formaldehyde. Further, air bubbles form when the molten metal solidifies, thereby deteriorating the quality of the product. In addition, since an organic binder is for single use only, a considerable amount of waste is discharged. However inorganic binders are eco-friendly because they can be reused and they do not emit harmful substances.

Despite industrial research on inorganic binders, very few manufactures have attempted to address the issue of core manufacturing based on inorganic binders. For core manufacture, it is important to mix a minimum amount of inorganic binder evenly with sand mould and simultaneously ensure excellent fluidity in the mixed state. Existing core manufacturing has relied on empirical manipulation. In order to produce a high quality core, it is necessary to optimize the core manufacture process and analyse whether the process has led to appropriate mixing. Against this backdrop, in this study, we developed a computational fluid dynamics (CFD) mixing model and carried out simulations using the discrete element method (DEM) for core manufacturing. The DEM computes the flow of segmented fluid based on molecular dynamics. It is a numerical analysis method suitable for micro-mechanical behaviour calculations of particles or granular materials. Further, based on an intuitive representation of how individual particles collide with each other, contact stiffness can be used to express the interaction between the grid and the particles. Our simulation results were validated through experiment and the results can be applied directly to improve the actual process.

2. Experiments

The experimental horizontal mixer system used for our investigations consisted of a hopper with a pile of sand and a steel cylindrical vessel with a length of 1.36 m, and diameter of 0.17 m. Paddle impellers were positioned along a rotating shaft which was aligned along the centre of the stationary vessel. This shaft-impeller was connected to a motor. The paddle impellers on the shaft were arranged in various angled patterns as shown in Figure 1. Figure 2 illustrates the dimensions of the mixer considered in the study. In all our experiments, spherical sand particles with an average particle size of 0.15 mm and density of 550 kg/m³ were used. This mixer operated at a rotational speed of 50 RPM. The inorganic binder used in the experiments comprised a mixture of silica calcium and sodium oxide.

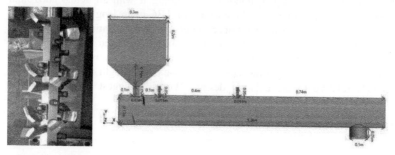

Figure 1. Paddle Impeller shaft in mixer   Figure 2. Geometry and dimensions of mixer

2.1. Mixing quality of Mixer

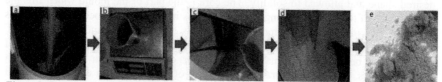

Figure 3. Experiment process (a)Cleaning of mixer (b)Measurement of red dye (c)Pouring of dye into the mixer (d)Mixing with sand and binder (e)Estimating on experiment result

Figure 3. indicates the experimental procedures for mixing quality test. Red coloured particles were stacked in the hopper, to evaluate the mixing performance. We note from the figure that the red colour is hardly visible in the mixture after mixing; i.e. the mixer affords an even mix

2.2. Fluidity test results

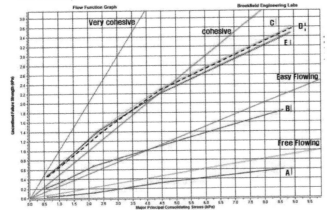

Figure 4. Fluidity graph of mixture for various binder content values

Table 1. Binder content of corresponding to each curve in Figure 4

Data name	Binder content
A	0%
B	1%
C	2%
D	3%
E	4%

In order to determine the optimal binder ratio for the mixing process, we examined the fluidity of the mixture as a function of the binder content.

In Figure 4, curves A, B and C lying curves between the cohesive curve and the easy flowing ranges satisfy the appropriate fluidity condition. Among the three corresponding binder content values, we chose the binder with the lowest content (Curve C, 2%) in our experiments.

3. Simulations

Next, we constructed the simulation model using the experimental data. All the DEM and CFD simulations were performed with the use of STAR CCM+ (SIEMENS).

3.1. Numerical approach

In general, CFD simulations are based on continuum models. However, DEM is a discrete approach which accurately models the micromechanics of granular material. Further, the continuum model considers the entire material as one mass, whereas each particle is a unique quantity in DEM. The governing equations of the particle translational and rotational motions can be expressed as the following Newton's equations.

$$m\frac{dv}{dt} = \sum F_g + F_c + F_{fluid} \tag{1}$$

$$I\frac{d\omega}{dt} = \sum (M^T + M^r) \tag{2}$$

Here, m, v, I, ω represent the mass, velocity, moment and angular velocity of a particle, respectively. Further, $F_g, F_c, F_{fluid}, M^T, M^r$ denote the force due to gravity, contact force between particles, fluid force, torque produced at the point of contact, and rolling friction force corresponding to particle-particle and particle-wall contacts, respectively. Here, we note that the choice of the time step is critical in DEM simulations. The time step has to be set to sufficiently small value to ensure numerical stability and accuracy, and it is limited by the time taken for a Rayleigh wave to propagate across the surface of the sphere from one pole to the opposite pole.

$$\tau = \pi \frac{R_{min}}{v_{Rayleigh}} \tag{3}$$

In the above equation, $\tau, R_{min}, v_{Rayleigh}$ represent the time-step, minimum particle radius and surface wave speed, respectively. The τ value is set to 30%. The Rayleigh velocity is solved internally, however, it depends on the material properties, particularly the Poisson's ratio and Young's modulus. Thus, we have

$$\tau_2 = 2.94 \left(\frac{5\sqrt{2}\pi\rho}{4} \frac{1-u^2}{E} \right)^{0.4} \frac{R_{Particle}}{\sqrt[5]{v_{impact}}} \tag{4}$$

Here, $\rho, u, E, V_{impact}, R_{particle}$ denote the particle density, Poisson's ratio, Young's modulus, impact velocity and particle radius, respectively. Upon assumption of the Hertzian contact theory, the duration of impact of two perfectly elastic spheres needs to be equal to a minimum of 10time-steps to estimate the collision accurately.

3.2. Model setup

Our simulation geometry was the same as that shown in Figure 2. The material properties of the particle were set as follows; Poisson's ratio = 0.35 and Young's modulus =5MPa. The simulation consisted of more than 2 million polyhedral meshes. The

Figure 5. Simulation using The field function

Lagrangian multiphase interaction was used in this model. To simulate the mixing of the binder with the sand, we set the field function assuming that the binder is coated on the particle surface. The field function was declared such that the particle size after coating was 5% larger than that before coating. The field function was applied to the particles which existed in the area lying in the angular range of 0.3° below the injector, as depicted in Figure 5.

3.3. Simulation Results

We analysed the mixing results in 20 internal regions in the mixer. Figure 6 shows the model wherein the injector position is changed from 0 to 0.5 along the x-axis. Figure 7, shows the analysed regions of the mixer. In order for the blue region in Figure 7 to be distinguished in the grayscale mode, the blue area corresponding to coating degree = 0 was indicated by X.

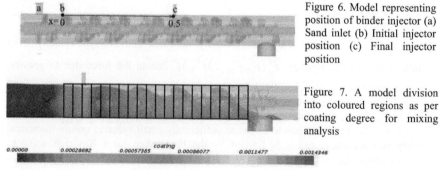

Figure 6. Model representing position of binder injector (a) Sand inlet (b) Initial injector position (c) Final injector position

Figure 7. A model division into coloured regions as per coating degree for mixing analysis

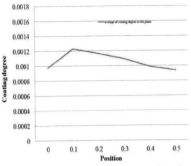

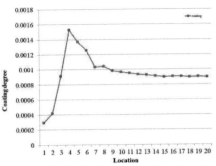

Figure 8. Coating degree as function of injector position

Figure 9. Coating degree as per location along mixer length

Figure 8 depicts the coating degree at the outlet as a function of the injector position Figure 6. When the injector is located at the zero point, the particle velocity tends to become low, thus leading to poor coating. Otherwise, the coating degree is satisfactory when the injector is close to the zero. The curve indicates that the overall coating difference is not large with change in the injector position. Therefore, the location of the injector is not a main consideration in the mixing process. Figure 9 shows the degree of coating obtained at each of the 20 segments shown in Figure 7. The coating degree increase up to location # 5, which is directly under the binder injection nozzle. However, the slope of curve is nearly zero beyond location #15, which indicates that the coating is well mixed and exhibits uniform distribution, and thus, further mixing is not necessary.

The coating degree was determined as the average particle data along the vertical cross section of the mixer Figure 11. The data were calculated as per Figure 8 at and each position shown in Figure 9.

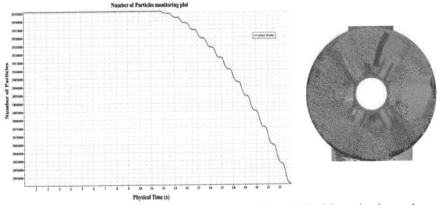

Figure 10. Number particles in mixer as function of time

Figure 11. Particle coating degree along vertical cross section of mixer

The residence time in the mixer was defined as the start time at which the particle number began decreasing due to particles exiting the outlet. The residence time in this simulation was 12 seconds Figure 10. This value is the same as the corresponding experimental values, which result validates the reliability of the simulation.

4. Conclusions

We investigated the mixing performance of a horizontal mixer via experiments and DEM simulations. The results of the simulations and experiments were found to be in good agreement. The performance of the mixer was subsequently evaluated as a function of the mixer length and injection nozzle position. In addition, the flow pattern of particles was examined based on the particle size, and coating degree.

Our findings indicate that, the total length of the cylindrical vessel can be reduced to 70% of the original length; the particles were already uniformly distributed inside the mixer at a position 1.09 m away from the particle inlet along the x axis of Figure 2. When the injector of the binder nozzle was located close to the inlet along the x-axis, the mixing quality tended to improve, but the difference in the mixing quality as a function of the subsequent nozzle position was not large. When the particles were mixed with the binder close to the inlet, there was increased stacking and adhering of particles to the impeller. Further, we determined that minimized cleaning load improves the process operating conditions, while ensuring high mixing quality. Therefore, the injector should be located in the midpoint of the mixer along the x-axis.

We plan to focus on varying the vessel fill level, increasing the impeller rotational speed, and the DEM solving time in our follow up studies. We believe that our findings will significantly contribute to industrial manufacturing processes.

Acknowledgement

This study has been conducted with the support of the Korea Institute of Industrial Technology as "Development of Global Optimization System for Energy Process (kitech EE-18-0017)".

References

A. Yaraghi, M. Ebrahimi, F. Ein-Mozaffari, A. Lohi, 2018, Mixing assessment of non-cohesive particles in a paddle mixer through experiments and discrete element method (DEM), Advanced Powder Technology, 29, 11, 2693-2706

C. J. Coetzee, 2014, Discrete and continuum modelling of soil cutting, Computational Particle Mechanics, 1, 4, 409-423

A. Mariotti, C. Galletti, R. Mauri, M. V. Salvetti, E. Brunazzi, 2018, Steady and unsteady regimes in a T-shaped micro-mixer: Synergic experimental and numerical investigation, Chemical Engineering Journal, 341, 414-431

W. Cai, G. R. McDowell, G. D. Airey, 2013, Discrete element modelling of uniaxial constant strain rate tests on asphalt mixtures, Granular Matter, 15, 163-174

Z. You, M. ASCE, W. G. Buttlar, 2004, Discrete Element Modeling to Predict the Modulus of Asphalt Concrete Mixtures, J. Mater. Civ. Eng, 16, 2, 140-146

Z. You, 2003, development of a micromechnical modeling approach to predict asphalt mixture stiffness using the discrete element method, Doctoral Thesis

SIEMENS product lifecycle management software, 2016, Introduction to particle modeling using the discrete element method

EDEM, 2018, What is dem- an introduction to the discrete element method, webinar

Anton A. Kiss, Edwin Zondervan, Richard Lakerveld, Leyla Özkan (Eds.)
Proceedings of the 29th European Symposium on Computer Aided Process Engineering
June 16th to 19th, 2019, Eindhoven, The Netherlands. © 2019 Elsevier B.V. All rights reserved.
http://dx.doi.org/10.1016/B978-0-128-18634-3.50135-1

Global Uncertainty and Sensitivity Analysis for Robust Design of a Rotary Kiln Process

Thomas B. Iversen,[a] Gürkan Sin,[a,*]

[a]*Process and Systems Engineering Center (PROSYS), Department of Chemical and Biochemical Engineering, Technical University of Denmark, Søltofts Plads Building 229, 2800 Kgs. Lyngby, Denmark*

*gsi@kt.dtu.dk

Abstract

In this contribution, we present and evaluate a systematic framework for comprehensive uncertainty and sensitivity analysis of a model used for design of Rotary Kiln processes. We consider two sources of uncertainties, namely operational (such as measurement errors, feedstock composition, etc.) and model (key assumptions in the model used for design equations) parameter uncertainty. As model outputs for evaluation we considered the impacts of these uncertainties on key process design metrics, specifically the minimum required rotary kiln length and the conversion degree of limestone. The results revealed that the operational sources of uncertainty lead to a higher uncertainty in process design metric (e.g. standard deviation of the computed length is 6.1 m) compared to the model parameter uncertainty (standard deviation of the computed length is 4.5 m). In order to achieve a robust process design, one needs to dimension the length of the reactor with 187 m so that all particles will be converted with 100 % efficiency with 95 % confidence. Ignoring these sources of uncertainty will lead to suboptimal process performance with the degree of conversion of limestone reduced to 97 %. Among input uncertainty considered, the global sensitivity analysis revealed measurement errors of temperature sensors as the most influential parameters. Overall the results encourage application of comprehensive sensitivity and uncertainty analysis methods for robust design of rotary kiln processes.

Keywords: Uncertainty, Sensitivity, Rotary Kiln, Monte Carlo simulation, Morris Screening, Sobol's method.

1. Introduction

A rotary kiln is a physically large process unit used in cement production where limestone is decomposed into calcium oxide which forms the basis of cement clinker particles under high temperatures. The modelling of rotary kilns are well documented in literature. Mujumdar et al. 2007 developed an iteration based rotary kiln simulator (RoCKS), which integrates models for a pre-heater, calciner, kiln and clinker cooling that agreed well with observations in industry. The model takes complexities in reactions and heat transfers with different sections into account by coupling multiple models with common boundaries regarding heat and mass communications. Other work (Ngadi and Lahlaouti, 2017) neatly demonstrates an experimentally proven kiln model being applied for screening of combustion fuel used for kilns, and how it may impact the production. This contribution coupled modelling of reactions and heat transfer in the bed region and another model for combustion and heat transfer in the freeboard region.

While modelling of these processes with varying degree of complexity has been performed, proper uncertainty and sensitivity analysis of these models have not been given due importance/consideration. As the use of computer aided process engineering tools increases, the need for robust uncertainty and sensitivity analysis frameworks becomes more important. There are several frameworks of uncertainty and sensitivity analysis applied for different problems, from good modelling practice (Sin et al, 2009) to process design and product design (Frutiger et al 2016). These frameworks typically include the following steps (0) problem statement, (i) identification of input sources of uncertainties, (ii) sampling (iii) Monte Carlo simulations and (vi) sensitivity analysis. The purpose of this work is to perform a systematic uncertainty and sensitivity analysis of rotary kiln process design in order to address the following: (1) Given a certain base case design, what is the impact of uncertainties in the model and measurements on the key process design metrics (minimum required reactor length and degree of conversion), and, (2) given a certain source of uncertainties, what is the robust design to ensure process performance with 95 % confidence.

2. Modelling of the Physical System

The overall goal of the rotary kiln model evaluated here is to determine the minimum required rotary kiln length to process 115,000 tons of limestone annually. The design model is built on a number of mechanisms and processes (Mujumdar et al., 2007), including a spherical particle model, a shrinking core model with three resistances (gas film, ash layer, and reaction at core), a steady state energy balance, and a counter-current gas-particle flow in kiln. The model accounts for changes in flue gas compositions, which affects the heat transfer coefficient and the particle core temperature.

Table 1: Summary of equations used in rotary kiln. Parameters marked up red are used in uncertainty analysis.

Equation	Description
$\dfrac{dX_i}{dt} = -\dfrac{3h_p}{\Delta H \rho R_i}$ $\left(\dfrac{\lambda(1-X_i)^{1/3}(T_g - T_c)}{h_p R_i (1-(1-X_i)^{1/3}) + \lambda(1-X_i)^{1/3}} \right)$	Conversion rate (X) of particle size i. h_p is the energy transfer coefficient, R is the particle radius, λ is the heat diffusion coefficient, and T_c is the particle core temperature. This is used to find the conversion for the drying and calcination, which uses enthalpies (ΔH), densities (ρ) and heat diffusion coefficients. Heat of reaction is used for calcination and the heat of vaporization is used for drying.
$h_p = 23.7 G^{0.67} \left(\dfrac{A_{KW}}{A_P} \right)$	The heat transfer coefficient is dependent on the gas mass velocity (G) and the fraction of particles consuming heat.
$\log_{10}(P_i) = A - \dfrac{B}{C + T_c}$	Antoine's equation is used to find the temperature at the unreacted core of the particle.
$\left(\dfrac{A_{KW}}{A_P} \right) = \begin{cases} 0.0686 & for \quad t < \tau_1 \\ 0.1744 & for \quad \tau_1 < t < \tau_2 \\ 0.5194 & for \quad \tau_2 < t \end{cases}$	Increased effective area when particles are fully reacted. τ_i is the time required to fully convert a particle size i. A represents the area of the kiln wall (denoted KW) and particles (denoted P).
$G_1(X) = G_0 + m_K[(1-X_1) + (1-X_2) + (1-X_3)]$	A measure of the gas mass velocity. Throughout the kiln, the amount of gas changes accordingly to the calcination and drying.
$L = \dfrac{NDSt}{0.19}$	Used to find total kiln length, L. t is the residence time of the particles, D is kiln diameter, S is the inclination, and N is the rotational speed.

The model also accounts for discrete particle distributions, where fully reacted particles are assumed to no longer consume heat (Dam-Johansen K, 2018). The conceptual model is shown in Figure 1 and the equations are shown in Table 1 (Levenspiel, O., 1999). The model and the framework for the sensitivity and uncertainty analysis have been implemented in Matlab ® (Mathworks) while additional sensitivity analysis has been performed using Polynomial Chaos Expansion (PCE) with UQlab (ETH Zurich).

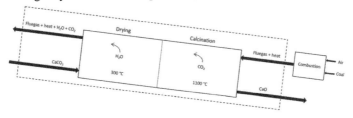

Figure 1: Defined rotary kiln system that have been modelled (stippled lines). Heat is produced through combustion of coal, which flows counter-current of the limestone. The wet limestone is first dried, where water vapor is added to the flue gas composition. Thereafter, the calcination reaction forms calcium oxide particles and carbon dioxide gas. The gas is added to the flue gas composition.

3. Methodology for Uncertainty and Sensitivity Analysis

The framework for uncertainty and sensitivity analysis (Sin et al, 2009) used here is illustrated in Figure 2. Input uncertainty is first determined (Table 2), which is used to make a sample based on the input data (Figure 3a). Each parameter set in this sample is then used in the model to create a set of output data (Figure 3b). The output data can be evaluated accordingly to ambitions (uncertainty/sensitivity metrics etc.), which can be visualized and/or ranked to draw conclusions. In this work, input uncertainty in operational (Table 2) and model (highlighted in bold and red in Table 1) parameters are evaluated.

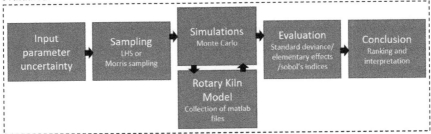

Figure 2: Overview of framework for uncertainty/sensitivity analysis according to Sin et al., 2009.

Table 2: Input uncertainty for operational parameters used in uncertainty and sensitivity analysis.

Parameter	Description	(Mean) μ	Unit	(Std.dev) σ
$T_{g,d}$	Temperature in drying section	573	K	12.76
$T_{g,c}$	Temperature in calcination section	1,373	K	12.76
m_{CaCO3}	Mass feed of limestone	115,000	t/yr	293.37
m_{Coal}	Mass feed of coal	9,547	t/yr	24.35
N	Rotational speed of kiln	1/3	1/min	1.70E-4
S	Inclination of rotary kiln	52.6	mm/m	8.06E-4

4. Results and Discussion

4.1. Uncertainty Analysis

The model output uncertainty is based on input uncertainty of parameters relevant for controlling the kiln operation, as shown in Table 2. Input space was sampled using Latin Hypercube Sampling (LHS) to generate 4,000 samples shown in Figure 3a. These samples are simulated using the model through Monte Carlo simulations (Figure 3b). Thereafter, the uncertainty related to the model output data were evaluated. Figure 3c and 3d present the model output results in cumulative distribution functions (CDF) of the kiln length and conversion rate for a fixed length. The figure shows that the operational uncertainty gives the highest output uncertainty. Therefore, taking the input uncertainties into account, to ensure a robust design, one needs to dimension the length of the reactor with 187 meters so that in 95 % of uncertainty realization (hence confidence) that all particles will be converted with 100 % efficiency.

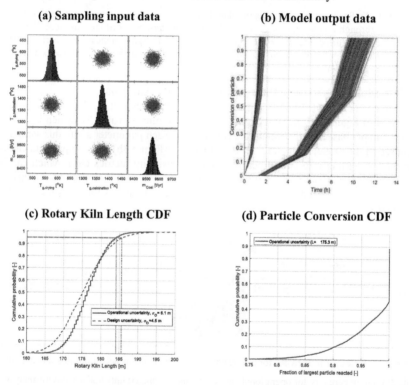

Figure 3: Input (a) and output (b) data using operational input uncertainty accordingly to Table 2. Cumulative distribution function (CDF) of length (c) and average conversion with a fixed length (d) from uncertainty analysis. For the length, both operational and design uncertainty is included.

If the length is kept at 175 meters (base case design obtained by assuming no uncertainty), all but the largest particle in the particle distribution would be 100 % converted. However, it was found that the largest particle would on average be 97.15 %

(Figure 3d) converted. The latter particle consists of 35 w% of the limestone fed to the kiln, which amounts to roughly 1,147 tons of unreacted limestone annually wasted.

4.2. Sensitivity Analysis

Given that the output uncertainty is highest with operational sources of uncertainty, a global sensitivity analysis is performed on 6 operational parameters. To this end, two global sensitivity analysis techniques are used: Morris screening (Sin et al. 2009) and Sobol's method through Monte Carlo sampling and PCE-based method (Al et al. 2018).

4.3. Morris Screening

Morris Screening is a global sensitivity method that systematically varies one parameter at a time at randomly selected points in the input space. The input parameter change is then evaluated based on how much is changes the output, and stored as Elementary Effects (EE). By doing a sufficient amount of these local sensitivity measures, the mean value and standard deviance of the elementary effects provides a global context to the sensitivity analysis (Sin et al, 2009). Figure 4 show EE of the operational parameters, where high frequency at low values represents a non-influential parameter (low mean and standard deviance). Conclusions from this Morris screening is that N and S are insignificant, and the temperature is the most influential parameter.

4.4. Sobol's Method

Sobol's method determines the sensitivity of parameters on model output based on the decomposition of variance. Sobol's method produces two sensitivity measures, main effect (S_i) and total effect (S_{Ti}) respectively. Thus, S_i describes how much, on average, the model output variance could be reduced by if parameter i could be fixed. S_{Ti} is the expected variance when all parameters except i are fixed. While S_i is used to prioritize parameters relative to each other, S_{Ti} is used as a measure to

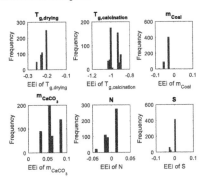

Figure 4: Morris screening result. High frequency of EE near 0 corresponds to low sensitivity.

determine non-important parameters. Table 3 show the results from Sobol's method. The table show which of the parameters are most influential for this model, where the parameter with rank 1 is the most sensitive. Notably, the results are well in accordance with the Morris screening results. All values should be positive, where negative numbers can be described as a consequence of numerical approximation.

Table 3: Sobol indices for sensitivity analysis of operational parameters on the model output.

Parameter	S_i	S_{Ti}	$S_{i,PCE}$	$S_{Ti,PCE}$	Rank
Temperature in drying section	0.0463	0.0487	0.0490	0.0491	2
Temperature in calcination section	0.9470	0.9447	0.9467	0.9468	1
Mass feed of limestone	0.0001	0.0018	0.0011	0.0012	4
Mass feed of coal	0.0030	0.0040	0.0030	0.0031	3
Rotational speed of kiln	-0.0027	0.0005	0.0000	0.0000	5
Inclination of rotary kiln	-0.0014	0.0002	0.0000	0.0000	6
SUM	0.9924	0.9998	0.9999	1.0001	N.A.

5. Conclusions

This work demonstrates successful application of uncertainty and sensitivity analysis in the model-based design and analysis of a rotary kiln process. The results showed that there are significant uncertainties, and that the uncertainty attached to operational uncertainty (standard deviation equal to 6.1 m) gives higher model length output uncertainty compared to the design uncertainty (standard deviation equal to 4.5 m). This means that in order to counter the effect of the operational uncertainty, one needs to dimension the length of the reactor with 187 m so that in 95 % of confidence one can ensure that all particles will be converted with 100 % efficiency. If the length is kept at 175 m which corresponds to the base case design, the largest particle would on average be 97.15 % converted. Taking the annual capacity into account (115,000 t limestone/y), this amounts to 1,147 t of unreacted limestone wasted annually.

Moreover, global sensitivity analysis indicated the following as the most influential parameters from the operational uncertainty (in descending order): temperature in calcination zone (1) and drying zone (2), the mass flow of limestone (3) and coal (4), the kiln rotational speed (5), and inclination of the kiln (6). Based on the input uncertainty, the four latter parameters can be seen as non-influential for the model output variance. Overall, the results show a high model output based on the input uncertainty, which highlights the importance of including detailed uncertainty and sensitivity analysis in model development. The results encourage application of comprehensive sensitivity and uncertainty analysis to improve robustness of rotary kiln process design.

References

K.S. Mujumdar, K.V. Ganesh, S.B. Kulkarni, and V.V. Ranade. Rotary cement kiln simulator (rocks): Integrated modeling of pre-heater, calciner, kiln and clinker cooler. Chemical Engineering Science, 62:2590–2607, 2007.

Levenspiel, O. (1999) Chemical Reaction Engineering. 3rd Edition. John Wiley & Sons, New York, 54.

Dam-Johansen, K (2018), Lecture notes Industrial reaction engineering, DTU Chemical Engineering, spring 2018 semester, Lygnby, Denmark.

Sin G, Gernaey KV, Lantz AE. Good modeling practice for PAT applications: Propagation of input uncertainty and sensitivity analysis. Biotechnology progress. 2009 Jul;25(4):1043-53.

Ngadi, Z., & Lahlaouti, M. L. (2017). Impact of Using Alternative Fuels on Cement Rotary Kilns: Experimental Study and Modeling. Procedia Engineering, 181, 777–784.

Frutiger, J., Andreasen, J., Liu, W., Spliethoff, H., Haglind, F., Abildskov, J. and Sin, G., 2016. Working fluid selection for organic Rankine cycles–Impact of uncertainty of fluid properties. Energy, 109, pp.987-997.

Al, R., Behera, C. R., Zubov, A., & Sin, G. (2018). Systematic framework development for the construction of surrogate models for wastewater treatment plants. In Computer Aided Chemical Engineering (Vol. 44, pp. 1909-1914). Elsevier.

Anton A. Kiss, Edwin Zondervan, Richard Lakerveld, Leyla Özkan (Eds.)
Proceedings of the 29th European Symposium on Computer Aided Process Engineering
June 16th to 19th, 2019, Eindhoven, The Netherlands. © 2019 Elsevier B.V. All rights reserved.
http://dx.doi.org/10.1016/B978-0-128-18634-3.50136-3

A novel scenario aggregation framework based on network community detection methods

Sergio Medina-González, Ioannis Gkioulekas, Vivek Dua, Lazaros G. Papageorgiou[*]

Centre for Process Systems Engineering, Department of Chemical Engineering, University College London, Torrington Place, London WC1E 7JE, United Kingdom.

l.papageorgiou@ucl.ac.uk

Abstract

Development of fast, robust and reliable computational tools capable of addressing the process management under uncertain conditions, is an active topic in the current process systems engineering literature. In fact, scenario reduction strategies (for example SCENRED and OSCAR) have acquired a lot of attention to overcome the traditional issues associated to large-scale scenario-based problems. Thus, this work proposes a novel scenario-reduction alternative (henceforth known as SCANCODE approach) by combining Graph Theory to construct a network and community detection methods to identify the clusters within the network. The capabilities and limitations of the proposed approach were tested through the two-stage MILP optimisation of a bio-based energy network under raw material availability and energy demand uncertainties. For comparison purposes, the same problem was solved using the sets of scenarios obtained with SCENRED and OSCAR. This comparison demonstrates the quality of SCANCODE approach while states the potential benefits of the proposed approach over the current alternatives.

Keywords: Scenario aggregation, Graph Theory, Community detection.

1. Introduction

The explicit consideration of the inherent uncertainty in a process system is becoming a key aspect for improving system performance and guaranteeing feasible operation. Two-stage programming and robust optimisation are the most used mathematical formulations/techniques to solve problems affected by uncertain conditions in which the conditions are modelled through a sufficiently large set of scenarios with their associated probability. Even though these formulations aid to effectively represent the whole uncertainty space, they are highly demanding in terms of computational effort. In order to address this critical challenge, scenario reduction strategies such as SCENRED and OSCAR have been successfully and extensively used during the recent past (Feng and Ryan, 2013; Li and Floudas, 2016). Essentially, both approaches identify a small amount of scenarios that minimise the total distance between them and the original uncertainty space; however, in the case of OSCAR, the effect of the input disturbances over the output performance is also considered. Despite being very effective, proximity might not be the best criterion to define clusters and more importantly, cluster centroids, since a lot of information associated to the pairwise relations is lost. Such information could be used as a metric to define and evaluate the quality of the clusters centroids.

Consequently, in this work an integrated framework of Graph Theory and network community detection methods is proposed. On one hand, Graph Theory is used to construct a network out of a large set of data using the pairwise information to determine connections. Disregarding the high-dimensionality or different distribution of the raw data set, the obtained network is composed essentially by a set of vertices (representing the scenarios) connected by edges if and only if the correlation of those vertices is equal to or higher than a desired value (threshold). On the other hand, any suitable algorithm can be used to extract a set of communities out of the network using a modularity function as quality metric (Xu et al., 2007). Several community detection methods are available in the literature including Girvan-Newman, Tyler-Wilkinson and Louvain algorithms among others (Javed et al, 2018). Individually, Graph Theory and community detection methods have been applied to different data management applications such as the worldwide web, collaboration networks and biological systems (Newman and Girvan, 2004). However, to the best authors' knowledge, they have never been used together in a scenario reduction framework.

The capabilities of the proposed approach were tested by comparing its performance against the ones obtained by the traditional SCENRED and OSCAR approaches, while using the two-stage MILP bio-based energy management problem described in Medina-González et al., (2017) as a comparison test bed.

2. Solution strategy

The proposed approach consists of four parts: Parameter initialisation/declaration, network construction, cluster generation and centroid identification. A detailed explanation of these elements is presented.

2.1. Parameter initialisation.

In this step, a sufficiently large set of scenarios is defined to represent the process's uncertainties. In order to create an interconnected structure out of this data set (i.e. a network), the pairwise relationship between vertices are modelled and collected in an adjacency matrix ($A_{i,j}$) using any suitable correlation metric. Finally, in order to reduce the network complexity, the connections quality might be assess using a tolerance value (threshold that lies between 0 and 1).

2.2. Network construction.

Using the above defined parameters, the quality of the network connectivity ($A_{i,j}$) is adjusted, by replacing any connectivity values that do not satisfy the minimum threshold condition by zero (non-connection state), hence obtaining a strongly connected network. Notice that even though the threshold definition is independent of the correlation value, it affects the network density, which might lead to an impractical solution. For example, low threshold values lead to "perfectly connected" networks and therefore the whole system is considered as a unique cluster, while large threshold values produce nodes that are considered as isolated clusters. Thus, a systematic threshold definition rule is vital.

2.3. Cluster/community generation.

This part of the algorithm aims to identify the communities that lead to the most efficient network division. Essentially, a community is a local area/group of vertices densely connected between them and loosely (or not at all) connected with other groups. In order to assess the quality of these communities, the modularity metric (Q) can be used which represents the number of edges that fall within communities/modules minus the expected number of edges that should fall into communities in an equivalent network configuration with edges being placed randomly (Newman and Girvan, 2004). The general formulation of the community detection problem is presented in Eq. (1), where the partition that yields the maximum modularity for a target network is sought.

$$Q = \sum_m \left[\frac{L_m}{L} - \left(\frac{D_m}{2L} \right)^2 \right]$$

(1)

From Eq. (1), the first term $\frac{L_m}{L}$ represents the ratio of edges that fall into module m in relation with the total number of links in the network (L), while the second one represents the expected fraction of links that would fall in module m if they were randomly generated. Particularly, D_m is the total random degree in each module m and the difference in these terms indicate how "non-random" cluster m is.

2.4. Centroid identification.

For each one of the obtained communities/clusters, their centroids are identified by selecting the vertex with the highest centrality criteria value. For simplicity, three different criteria are suggested, however more options might be found in the literature:

- *Degree*. Represents the number of connections of each vertex.
- *Betweeness*. Accounts for the paths passing through a vertex.
- *Closeness*. Distance of a vertex against all the others within a cluster.

The general SCANCODE algorithm is presented next:

0. Initialise a defined amount of scenarios that represent the process uncertainties as well as a threshold value ($Th= [0, 1]$) in order to establish the connections between vertices.
    a. Generate the adjacency matrix (A_{ij}) by calculating the correlation between each pair of vertices.
1. Let the value in A_{ij} be zero if the correlation value is below the defined threshold ($A_{ij} < Th$) and create the network by using the new data in the adjacency matrix.
2. Identify the community arrangement that maximises the modularity metric using any available algorithm/method.
3. For each cluster, identify the scenario with the highest value in the desired centrality metric.

3. Illustrative example

Due to space limitations and since the scope of the paper is to describe and test the proposed approach, the mathematical formulation of the case study is omitted and the interested readers are referred to Medina-González et al., (2017). However, for continuity purposes a brief description of the case study is included. The problem was formulated as a MILP problem that maximises the economic benefit of a biomass-based energy SC system through the management of its design and operations. The model considers nine districts (fc), and all of them can be simultaneously biomass suppliers, energy generation and market sites. 40 different biomass states (s), six available technologies (tec) and 79 activities (act) were considered across a monthly discretization (t) of a year horizon. Cassava Rhizome (CR) was used as a raw material for energy production, while its availability and the total energy demand ($As(s,fc,t)$ and $dem(s,fc,t)$ respectively) were considered as uncertainty sources. A total of 153 uncertain parameters are considered since As and dem are defined only for the first and last raw material state respectively while for As, only five time periods are considered (length of the CR production season). Without loss of generality, 100 equiprobable scenarios were randomly generated for each uncertain parameter using a normal distribution with the average values presented in Table 1 and a 30% standard deviation.

Table.1. Mean values for uncertainty conditions at each district.

District	fc_1	fc_2	fc_3	fc_4	fc_5	fc_6	fc_7	fc_8	fc_9
Demand (MJ)	1942	4055	15250	19363	2684	3198	913	3884	4169
Availability (kg)	12.75	24.38	81.1	122.18	16.22	22.07	5.27	21.08	28.15

4. Results and discussion

Using the Pearson correlation and three thresholds values (0.91; 0.92 and 0.93) the adjacency matrices and the associated networks were constructed as described in section 2. Then, the Louvain algorithm was used to detect the communities within each network. Essentially, Louvain is a two-step algorithm that maximises the modularity metric, in which for a given network, the first step assigns nodes into clusters only if that increases the modularity value, whereas the second step creates a new network where each node represents a cluster from the previous step. These two steps are iterated until no further modularity improvement is possible (Blondel et al., 2008). After applying the Louvain algorithm for this problem, a total of 9, 13 and 31 communities were identified for each threshold respectively. Analysing the obtained networks (Figure 1), it is evident that the density is inversely proportional to the threshold value. Particularly, the larger the threshold values, the more isolated scenario clusters are produced, whereas for small values a very densely connected network is obtained which compromises the definition of cluster centroids. Such a behaviour confirms the undesirable properties in the reduced set of scenarios for the extreme threshold points and stresses the need for a metric that represents a balanced rate between number of clusters and network density.

For the three generated networks, their centroids were identified using degree as centrality metric. The probability of each cluster centroid is represented by the aggregation of the original probabilities of all the elements within their respective cluster, while the original uncertainty parameters information was kept. Finally, the MILP problem was implemented in GAMS 24.7 and solved for each one of the reduced sets of scenarios using CEPLEX 12.6.3 to a relative optimality gap of 5%.

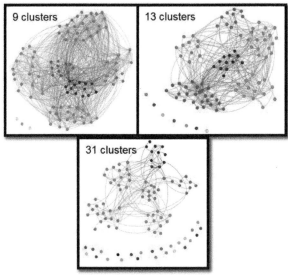

Figure 1. Networks and clusters for different thresholds values.

In order to illustrate the effectiveness of the proposed approach, SCENRED and OSCAR (the two most used scenario reduction approaches) were used as a comparison reference. The resulting set of scenarios from the three methods represent the input data to solve the MILP problem. Table 2 shows the optimal results for each case.

Table.2. Results for the optimisation of MILP problem.

	Size/modules(m)	ExpProfit (€)	PostProcess Profit (€)	Gap (%)	CPUtime (s)
FULL-SPACE	100	345,198	---	--	131,607
	Th= 0.91		*Modularity (Q=0.205214)*		
OSCAR	9	346,642	345,231	0.4085	1,101
SCENRED	9	348,304	342,374	1.7322	1,193
SCANCODE	9	357,655	345,500	3.5183	1,137
	Th= 0.92		*Modularity (Q=0.32264)*		
OSCAR	13	343,475	345,115	0.4752	1,459
SCENRED	13	349,373	345,500	1.1211	1,512
SCANCODE	13	348,142	345,115	0.8771	1,495
	Th= 0.93		*Modularity (Q=0.43473)*		
OSCAR	31	346,051	345,115	0.2711	7,765
SCENRED	31	348,562	345,115	0.9987	7,812
SCANCODE	31	344,156	343,545	0.1779	7,818

Table 2, displays a significant dispersion between the expected performances (*ExpProfit*) for the reduced set of scenarios and the full-space (no reduction), since the scenarios in the reduced set may be different for each cluster and strategy. Therefore, a post-process analysis was performed in order to promote a fair comparison (*PostProcessProfit*). To derive those values, the first stage decisions obtained after optimising the MILP problem using the reduced set, were fixed for the full-space problem. The gap between the expected value and its associated post-process outcome was also calculated, confirming that the three approaches approximate the profit (variation <4%) and proving that SCANCODE is a feasible alternative to the current scenario reduction approaches. Despite this small gap, the approximation error for SCENRED and SCANCODE increases as a function of the reduction degree while in the case of OSCAR, a relatively steady gap was obtained despite the level of reduction. Such a behaviour is due to the consideration of both, the original uncertain parameters and their effect over the expected performance. Nonetheless, obtaining such information implies a pre-processing task, which hinders its application to large-scale problems. In any case, further research seeking the reduction of the approximation gap in SCANCODE is crucial for its further application in real-life problems with large sized scenario sets.

5. Conclusions

This paper proposes a novel scenario reduction/aggregation framework that integrates Graph Theory and community detection methods. Numerical results demonstrate that the proposed strategy is as efficient as other well-studied techniques for identifying a reduced and representative set of scenarios. Additionally, the well-structured cluster definition used in the proposed approach justifies its potential applications to large-scale networks considering many uncertainty scenarios (of several orders of magnitude). Despite the efficiency of SCANCODE, some opportunity areas have been identified that will improve its performance. Particularly, further work is focused on combining this strategy with other data-management techniques to identify the most efficient relation between the number of clusters and the quality of the uncertainty space.

Acknowledgements

The authors would like to thank the financial support received from the UK Engineering and Physical Sciences Research Council (under the project EP/M027856/1) as well as the UK Leverhulme Trust under grant number RPG-2015-240.

References

Blondel, V. D., Guillaume, J.L., Lambiotte, R. and Lefebvre, E. 2008. Fast unfolding of communities in large networks, Journal of Statistical Mechanics: Theory and Experiment, (10).

Feng, Y. and Ryan, S.M. 2013. Scenario construction and reduction applied to stochastic power generation expansion planning. Computers & Operations Research, 40, 9-23.

Javed, M.A., Younis, M.S., Latif, S., Qadir, J. and Baig, A. 2018. Community detection in networks: A multidisciplinary review. Journal of Network and Computer Applications, 108, 87-111.

Li, Z. and Floudas, C.A. 2016. Optimal scenario reduction framework based on distance of uncertainty distribution and output performance: II. Sequential reduction, Computers & Chemical Engineering, 84, 599-610.

Medina-González, S., Graells, M., Guillén-Gosálbez, G., Espuña, A., and Puigjaner, L. 2017. Systematic approach for the design of sustainable supply chains under quality uncertainty, Energy Conversion and Management, 149, 722-737.

Newman, M.E.J. and Girvan, M. 2004. Finding and evaluating community structure in networks. Physical Review, 69, 1-15.

Xu, G., Tsoka, S., and Papageorgiou, L.G. 2007. Finding community structures in complex networks using mixed integer optimisation, The European Physical Journal B, 60, 231-239.

Anton A. Kiss, Edwin Zondervan, Richard Lakerveld, Leyla Özkan (Eds.)
Proceedings of the 29th European Symposium on Computer Aided Process Engineering
June 16th to 19th, 2019, Eindhoven, The Netherlands. © 2019 Elsevier B.V. All rights reserved.
http://dx.doi.org/10.1016/B978-0-128-18634-3.50137-5

A Fuzzy Analytic Hierarchy Process (FAHP) Approach to Multi-Objective Optimisation of Oil Palm Value Chains

John Frederick Tapia, Sheila Samsatli[*]

Department of Chemical Engineering, University of Bath, Claverton Down, Bath, United Kingdom, BA2 7AY

[*]S.M.C.Samsatli@bath.ac.uk

Abstract

The economic potential of palm oil and palm-based biomass can be realised through oil palm's very high vegetable oil yield and the wide variety of high-value products that can be derived from it. This potential can be maximised through streamlined oil palm value chains (OPVCs) which involve considering different environmental impacts alongside the economic benefits. Multi-objective optimisation aids in the development of a strong value chain by generating valuable planning insights based on the most appropriate set of impact weights. However, a typical approach in assigning impact weights is arbitrary or based on rough estimates. This study develops a decision framework to support planning and designing OPVCs. The decision framework is a novel approach of integrating a fuzzy analytic hierarchy process (FAHP) to the multi-objective optimisation of OPVCs. This enables descriptive judgments to be converted into numerical weights. An optimal design is then generated based on these weights. A case study based on Malaysian palm oil biomass scenario is presented to illustrate the decision tool. This could help develop better policies in the future through a systematic approach in dealing with sustainability issues in the palm oil industry.

Keywords: Value chain modelling, fuzzy analytic hierarchy process, palm oil biomass, environment-food-energy-water (EFEW) nexus.

1. Introduction

Palm oil is regarded as the world's main source of vegetable oil due to its excellent yield and low land requirement (Corley, 2003). The current status of vegetable oil industry is such that the replacement of palm oil is economically infeasible as alternative crops would likely require more land to produce the same yield as oil palm. However, several issues arise with palm oil plantations such as negative impacts of land use change, biodiversity losses and waste generation. In a typical palm oil mill, around four tons of waste materials are generated for every ton of palm oil produced. Bio-conversion technologies can transform these wastes into high-value products such as energy, fuels and other valuable products. To maximize the benefits from these transformations, a strong value chain is required. It is formed by a network of conversion technologies, logistical infrastructures and associated activities to convert low-value waste materials into high-value products (Jarvis and Samsatli, 2018). The development of a strong value chain requires rigorous planning and design considering the presence of multiple sustainability factors and the guidance of expert recommendations. In this study, a systematic decision framework based on multi-objective optimisation and multi-criteria decision analysis (MCDA) approaches are developed to address these barriers in planning and design of oil palm value chains (OPVCs).

Recent PSE works on palm oil and palm-based systems presented methods to aid planning and designing systems such as integrated biorefineries and supply chains (Ng and Ng, 2013). Optimisation models on large-scale palm oil systems have been developed considering plantation management (Foong et al., 2019) and EFB valorisation (Abdulrazik et al., 2017). These models addressed specific problems focusing on maximising economic gains. None of the recent and relevant studies focused on large-scale palm oil systems addressed multi-objective and multi-criteria decision making simultaneously. Thus, in this paper a fuzzy analytic hierarchy process (FAHP) approach is integrated with a multi-objective mixed integer linear program (MOMILP) for OPVCs considering environmental and economic impacts weighted through expert judgement. Using FAHP to quantify verbal judgements as numerical weights has been demonstrated in a wide range of applications in sustainable technologies (Promentilla et al., 2018) and in multi-objective molecular design (Ooi et al., 2017). The rest of this paper is organised as follows. Section 2 gives a brief description of the decision framework and the models used are described in Section 3. Then, the framework is illustrated using the Malaysian palm oil industry case with results given in Section 4. Finally, conclusions and future works are given in Section 5.

2. Decision Framework

The FAHP approach to multi-objective optimisation of OPVCs is summarised in Figure 1. First, the optimal solution of the value chain based on the best economic potential, the minimum climate change impact and the minimum water impact are determined. This is to identify the factor to normalise the objectives when aggregated into a single objective. Then, the weights of each impact are obtained using FAHP approach based on four criteria, namely, short-term benefit, long-term benefit, policy development and social acceptance. Finally, an optimal solution based on the weights generated by FAHP is obtained.

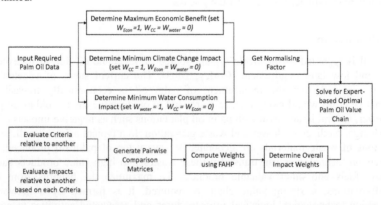

Figure 1: Decision framework for multi-objective optimization of OPVCs with FAHP. The weights of each impact objective are determined based on a decision structure with four criteria.

3. Optimisation Models

3.1. Multi-Objective Oil Palm Value Chains

The MOMILP model is summarized below with an aggregated objective function subject to the following key constraints:

$$\min \sum_{i,p} W_i(NF_i)(IU_{i,p} + FIP_{i,p}^{OM} + VIP_{i,p}^{OM} + IP_{i,p}^{Cap} + IT_{i,p}^{OM} + II_{i,p}^{OM}) \tag{1}$$

$$RU_{r,z,s,y,p} + RP_{r,z,s,y,p} + RT_{r,z,s,y,p} + RI_{r,z,s,y,p} \geq D_{r,z,s,y,p}(D_r^{\min}) \tag{2}$$

$$RU_{b,z,s,y,p} \leq AE_{b,z}YFE_p Y_{b,z,s,y} + Y_{b,z,s,y}\sum_{p'} YF_{p,p'}.AI_{b,z,p'} \tag{3}$$

$$RP_{r,z,s,y,p} = \sum_c (PROD_{c,z,s,y,p})(CONV_{r,c,p}) \tag{4}$$

$$RT_{r,z,s,y,p} = \sum_{t,z'} TR_{t,r,z,z',s,y,p} - \sum_{t,z'} TR_{t,r,z',z,s,y,p} \tag{5}$$

Eq. (1) defines the weighted objective function, including impacts from utilization, production, transportation and import of resources. Eq. (2) ensures the satisfaction of demands by balancing net resource utilisation, production, transportation and import. The constraint on the available oil palm biomass (Eq. (3)) is based on the area available for plantation, the biomass yield and the expansion of land at each time period. Resources are produced through conversion technologies with rates and conversion factors given in Eq. (4). Finally, the net rate of transportation of resources is denoted by Eq. (5). For brevity, only these main constraints in the model are shown. More details on how the impacts are defined and the other constraints in the model can be found in related works (Samsatli and Samsatli, 2018; Samsatli et al., 2015).

3.2. Fuzzy Analytic Hierarchy Process (FAHP)

The outline of the procedure to determine the impact weights to be used for the multi-objective optimization model is as follows:

1. The decision structure is developed based on a hierarchical structure in which three impacts are evaluated using four criteria. For each criterion, the relative importance of each impact is determined by qualitative expert judgment. Qualitative judgements are given as either "equally", "slightly more", "moderately more", "strongly more" or "very strongly more" important than the other with equivalent triangular fuzzy number (TFN) of <1, **1**, 1>, <1.2, **2**, 3.2>, <1.5, **3**, 5.6>, <3.0, **5**, 7.9> and <6.0, **8**, 9.5>, respectively. These judgments are based on a calibrated fuzzy scale derived from a survey with large number of respondents and applied in prioritisation of green technologies (Promentilla et al., 2018). Note that if an impact is less preferred than another, the reciprocal values are used.
2. The criteria set for the decision structure are then evaluated by pairwise comparison to obtain the relative importance of one criterion with respect to the others. The same fuzzy scales are used in this step.

3. The priority weights, w_i are calculated based on the nonlinear fuzzy preference programming model described by Promentilla et al. (2018). The model maximizes the degree of satisfaction λ with the given fuzzy triangular number $<l_{ij}, m_{ij}, u_{ij}>$:

$$\max \lambda \tag{6}$$

$$a_{ij} - l_{ij} \geq \lambda(m_{ij} - l_{ij}) \quad a_{ji} - l_{ji} \geq \lambda(m_{ji} - l_{ji}) \quad \forall(i,j) \,|\, i < j \tag{7}$$

$$u_{ij} - a_{ij} \geq \lambda(u_{ij} - m_{ij}) \quad u_{ji} - a_{ji} \geq \lambda(u_{ji} - m_{ji}) \quad \forall(i,j) \,|\, i < j \tag{8}$$

$$a_{ij} = w_i / w_j \quad a_{ji} = w_j / w_i \quad \forall(i,j) \,|\, i < j \tag{9}$$

$$\sum_i w_i = 1 \tag{10}$$

4. The final impact weights, W_i to be used for multi-objective optimization of oil palm value chains is given using the weighted sum of the priority weights of each impact i for each criterion k, w_{ik}. The criteria are also assigned with weights denoted by s_k using step 2:

$$W_i = \sum_k s_k w_{ik} \quad \forall i \tag{6}$$

4. Malaysian Oil Palm Value Chain Case Study

A case study based on the Malaysian palm oil industry is used to illustrate the decision framework. It is supposed that it is necessary to convert palm-based biomass materials such as palm oil mill effluent (POME), palm kernel shell (PKS) and empty fruit bunch (EFB) and to develop the value chain for the Peninsular Malaysia for the next 32 years.

To illustrate the generation of impact weights, supposed that an expert provides judgement based on future directions needed for the industry. The weights generated from FAHP are summarised in Table 1. The importance given to environmental impacts (i.e. climate change and water impacts) is higher than the economic benefits that can be generated from the value chain. Using these weights, the optimal value chain is presented in Figure 2. In this case, pathways to consider for the conversion of EFB lead to the production of energy products such as gasoline, jet fuel and diesel. On the other hand, POME is treated to produce usable water and undergoes anaerobic digestion to produce biogas. Pathways for PKS lead to generation of electricity used both internally and externally.

Table 1: Impact Weights Generated from FAHP

	Short-Term Benefits (0.038)	Long-Term Benefits (0.361)	Policy Development (0.361)	Social Acceptance (0.241)	Total
Economic Benefits	0.500	0.059	0.333	0.450	**0.269**
Climate Change Impact	0.250	0.471	0.333	0.300	**0.372**
Water Impact	0.250	0.471	0.333	0.250	**0.360**

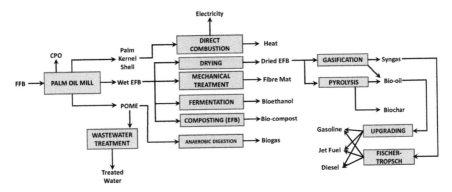

Figure 2: Optimal Value Web Pathways for Malaysian Palm Oil Industry

The resulting rate of production of palm oil per region, shares of energy distribution of palm-based biomass after conversion and the number of investments in units are shown in Figure 3. Three regions, namely Perak, Pahang and Johor contribute to the majority of the production having a total production of more than 3 MT of palm oil. Then, palm-based biomass materials are converted to different energy products, the majority of which is syngas. Biogas is also produced in the value chain to add value to palm oil mill effluent produced. The optimal solution also suggests investment in the beginning of the planning period and at the time period where most palm oil mills will retire. A summary of the results is shown in Table 2. The trade-offs between economic gains, climate change impact and water impact is balanced through expert judgment. Profit reduction of 8.93% is needed in order to achieve 31% less water impact and 11% less climate change impact if the expert judgment is to be incorporated as weights in the OPVC model. The contribution of FAHP in multi-objective planning of OPVC is that qualitative objectives are considered in the model. The decision framework can also provide scenarios for minimum climate change impact in which the highest attainable reduction up to 17% of the carbon footprint and 60% of the total water impact.

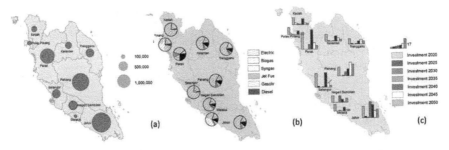

Figure 3: Results of the Malaysian case study: (a) palm oil production (t/y), (b) energy products from palm-based biomass and (c) conversion unit investment at each time period.

Table 2: Summary of scenarios for Malaysian oil palm value chain

Scenarios	Profit (billion MYR)	Climate Change Impact (Mt CO_2 equivalent)	Water Impact (million m^3 utilised H_2O)
Maximum Profit	414	426	12,923
Minimum Climate Change Impact	369	353	12,086
Minimum Water Impact	324	422	5,337
Expert-based Solution	377	375	8,932

5. Conclusions

A fuzzy analytic hierarchy process (FAHP) approach has been applied to multi-objective optimisation to generate an expert-based optimal plan of oil palm value chains. These weights, converted from verbal judgment by using FAHP, are used to generate an expert-based oil palm value chain design. A balance between economic gains, climate change impact and water pollution impact is obtained. Future work includes extending the case to incorporate biodiversity losses due to land use change.

6. Acknowledgement

The authors would like to thank the Newton Fund and the Engineering and Physical Sciences Research Council for financial support of this work through the BEFEW project (Grant No. EP/P018165/1) and the Science & Technology Facilities Council (STFC) ODA Institutional Award.

References

Abdulrazik, A., Elsholkami, A., Elkamel, A., & Simon, L., 2017, Multi-products productions from Malaysian oil palm empty fruit bunch (EFB): Analyzing economic potentials from the optimal biomass supply chain, Journal of Cleaner Production, 168, 131-148.

Corley, R. H. V., & Tinker, P. B., 2003, The origin and development of oil palm industry, in The Oil Palm, 4th ed, Blackwell Science Ltd.

Foong, S. Z. Y., Goh, C. K. M., Supramaniam, C. V., & Ng, D. K. S., 2019. Input–output optimisation model for sustainable oil palm plantation development, Sustainable Production and Consumption, 17, 31-46.

Jarvis, S., & Samsatli, S., 2018, Technologies and infrastructures underpinning future CO_2 value chains: A comprehensive review and comparative analysis, Renewable and Sustainable Energy Review, 85, 46-68.

Ooi, J., Promentilla, M. A. B., Tan, R. R., Ng, D. K. S., Chemmangattuvalappil, N., 2017, A fuzzy analytic hierarchy process approach for multi-objective molecular design problem. Computer Aided Chemical Engineering, 40, 967-972.

Promentilla, M. A. B., Janairo, J. I. B., Yu, D. E. C., Pausta, C. M. J., Beltran, A. B., Huelgas-Orbecido, A. P., Tapia, J. F. D., Aviso, K. B., Tan, R. R., 2018, A stochastic fuzzy multi-criteria decision-making model for optimal selection of clean technologies, Journal of Cleaner Production, 183, 1289-1299.

Samsatli, S., & Samsatli, N. J., 2018. A multi-objective MILP model for the design and operation of future integrated multi-vector energy networks capturing detailed spatio-temporal dependencies, Applied Energy, 220, 893-920.

Samsatli, S., Samsatli, N. J., & Shah, N., 2015. BVCM: a comprehensive and flexible toolkit for whole-system biomass value chain analysis and optimisation - mathematical formulation, Applied Energy, 147, 131-160.

Anton A. Kiss, Edwin Zondervan, Richard Lakerveld, Leyla Özkan (Eds.)
Proceedings of the 29th European Symposium on Computer Aided Process Engineering
June 16th to 19th, 2019, Eindhoven, The Netherlands. © 2019 Elsevier B.V. All rights reserved.
http://dx.doi.org/10.1016/B978-0-128-18634-3.50138-7

Numerical Simulation of Forced Convection in a Microchannel with Realistic Roughness of 3D Printed Surface

Seyed Alborz Manavi[a], Eugeny Y. Kenig[a,b,*]

[a]*Chair of Fluid Process Engineering, Faculty of Mechanical Engineering, Paderborn University, Paderborn 33098, Germany*

[b]*Gubkin Russian State University of Oil and Gas, Moscow, Russian Federation.*
eugeny.kenig@upb.de (E.Y. Kenig)

Abstract

This study aims at exploring the thermo-hydraulic performance of 3D printed micro heat exchangers. We performed CFD simulations of single-phase laminar fluid flow and heat transfer in a microchannel with rough surface and compared the results with those obtained in a smooth channel. The model was based on the Navier-Stokes and energy equation. These equations were implemented and solved in the STAR-CCM+ commercial software. The Reynolds number was varied in the range 100-500, while two values of Pr number, 0.71 and 6.0, were chosen. The height of the channel varied between 0.2 and 0.5 mm. The micro-geometry of the surface roughness representing a completely random configuration was reproduced by a 3D scanner. Our results demonstrate that decreasing channel height leads to rising heat transfer rate and pressure drop. At the height of 0.2 mm, a significant rise in pressure drop is evidenced, which indicates a critical height limit for designing such microchannels.

Keywords: 3D printing, Heat transfer, stochastic roughness, 3D scanner, microchannel

1. Introduction

The demand for enhancement of heat exchanger performance is ever increasing (Haarlemmer and Pigourier, 2016). Such enhancement is challenging when manufacturing constrains become a significant factor, especially for micro and mini heat exchangers. Additive manufacturing (3D printing), an innovative type of fabrication, offers enormous design freedom and great potential to outperform conventional methods of manufacturing. Consequently, this technology has been exploited by various industries, such as aerospace, automotive, medical and fluid process engineering, in particular regarding microfluidic devices (Femmer et al., 2016). Moreover, 3D printed objects are characterized by a certain surface roughness resulting from the fabrication process; such rough surface can be used as a passive method to increase the efficiency of heat exchangers. This beneficial combination of both variability and inherent roughness justifies a new study route toward improving heat exchangers performance.

It is worth noting that at the moment, 3D printed micro heat exchangers are still in an early development stage. This is the reason why just a limited number of publications on this topic can be found in the open literature. Few recent works are focused on the

Nomenclature

$Re = \dfrac{\rho\, V_m\, D_h}{\mu}$	Reynolds number	V_m (m/s)	Mean velocity	μ (Pa/s)	Dynamic viscosity
$Nu_{ave} = \dfrac{h_m D_h}{k}$	Average Nusselt number	D_h (m)	Hydraulic diameter	T_b (K)	Bulk temperature
$\dot{q}$ (W/m²)	Heat flux normal to the surface	ρ (Kg/m³)	Density	T_s (K)	Surface temperature
k (W/(m K))	Thermal conductivity	$h_m = \dfrac{\dot{q}_m}{T_s - T_b}$ (W/(m² K))			Mean heat transfer coefficient

design flexibility aspect of 3D printing allowing manufacturing of uniquely formed micro heat exchangers. For example, Arie et al. (2017) conducted an experimental and a numerical study which mainly aimed to compare the performance of a manifold microchannel with heat exchangers with conventional surfaces. Air-water manifold finned microchannels (with a manifold as a flow distributor positioned above the microchannels) were fabricated using one of the additive manufacturing methods, namely, direct metal laser sintering (DMLS). Thanks to the ability to build objects layer-by-layer, the authors could fabricate manifold and microchannel segments together as one united construction and eliminated the bonding process.

Ferster et al. (2017) performed an experimental study on the microchannel pin fin arrays fabricated by DMLS. Various geometries of pin fins, such as star-formed, triangular and dimpled sphere, with different spacing and number of pin fins, were built and their influence on the friction factor and heat transfer was analysed. One work, which considered the effect of the inherent surface roughness due to 3D printing on the performance of a heat exchanger has been recently published by Saltzman et al. (2018). They replicated a crossflow heat exchanger with 20×9.25×11.5 cm dimensions using laser-based powder bed fusion process. The additively manufactured heat exchanger was characterised by a lower weight and significantly rougher surfaces. The authors reported that the additively manufactured heat exchanger showed around 10% improvement in the overall heat transfer, whereas the pressure drop was doubled.

The necessity of surface roughness modelling in microchannels originates from its great potential to improve the micro heat exchanger efficiency, which is still an open problem. Moreover, experimental studies on such a small scale are characterized by measurement uncertainties which represent an interfering factor for the experiments beside surface roughness. Numerous studies contributed to the modelling of surface roughness in microchannels by setting different geometries, e.g. regular configurations, such as wavy sinusoidal one (Wang and Chen, 2002), triangular, square and irregular or random geometries (Guo et al., 2015). In the latter work, the authors used random functions like the Gauss function and the Fractal model to create random roughness.

In this study, we created the roughness geometry of a printed surface by a 3D scanner. This geometry is very close to the reality and thus it can be called realistic roughness. For this realistic roughness, we performed a fundamental numerical investigation of forced convection laminar flow in a microchannel. The results are presented for a variety of channel heights and Reynolds numbers, thus yielding valuable data on pressure drop and heat transfer characteristics in a 3D printed micro heat exchanger.

2. Physical model

The initially studied geometry was a 3D printed flat plate (Figure 1a). The scanning results yield the mean roughness depth equal to 85 μm. This geometry was then

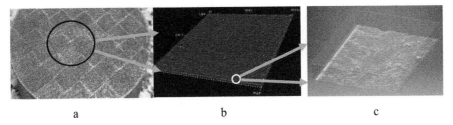

a   b   c

Figure 1. The steps of creating the geometry of stochastic roughness of 3D printed flat plate for CFD simulation: examined sample from 3D printing (a); scanning result of the selected area (b); prepared geometry for CFD study (c)

exported in CAD format (Figure 1b) which is readable by a corresponding software tool (Autodesk Inventor). The obtained surface geometry is represented by very small surfaces, which form the detailed roughness structure. To reduce computational effort, a small part of the surface was selected to perform the simulations (Figure 1c). The next step was to form the geometry of the CFD computational domain. This was done by adding side walls and an upper cover to the element. This configuration shown in Figure 1c was used for the CFD simulations.

3. CFD-based modelling

Three-dimensional fully developed steady-state laminar flow with constant physical properties in a microchannel with rough surface was studied. Finite volume approach implemented in STAR-CCM+ was applied in order to simulate the fluid flow and heat transfer in the duct. Periodic boundary condition was set at the inlet and outlet boundaries of the channel. In this way, the velocity profile is repeated after the channel length, so that after reaching convergence the whole periodic domain represents a hydraulically developed region. Thermally fully developed flow is characterized by a constant heat transfer coefficient. In STAR-CCM+, the temperature profile at the outlet is scaled and then used as the inlet profile, in such a way that the heat transfer coefficient remains constant for the whole domain. The bottom (rough) wall was maintained at a constant temperature, and the other walls were assumed to be adiabatic. No-slip boundary condition was assumed at all the walls. Figure 2 shows the geometry of the investigated microchannel element.

Figure 2. Periodic computational domain of microchannel and boundary conditions

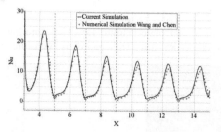

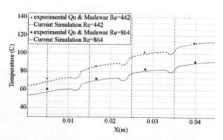

Figure 3. Local Nusselt number along the length of wavy channel

Figure 4. Wall temperature along the channel length obtained from our simulations and empirical data from Qu and Mudawar (2002)

A direct validation of the simulation results was not possible because of missing data on such geometry. Therefore, we selected and modelled two other configurations from the literature sufficiently close to the studied original geometry. The numerical simulation of fluid flow in a wavy duct reported by Wang and Chen (2002) at Re=300 and Pr=6.93 was replicated. In their work, the geometry of wavy wall was considered as a kind of roughness. Further model validation was carried out using the heat transfer experiment in a microchannel conducted by Qu and Mudawar (2002). The wall temperature was estimated along the channel length and compared with that obtained from Qu and Mudawar (2002) at Re = 442 and Re = 864. The validation results are shown in Figures 3 and 4. In both cases, a good agreement between the numerical and experimental data was achieved.

The primary mesh independency test was performed with respect to the heat transfer parameter (average Nusselt number). As can be seen from Table 1, the relative difference between the two finest grids are less than 1%. Additionally, a study of the velocity profile (Figure 5) along the channel height revealed that the grid setting with 3,322,691 cells is sufficient for the whole simulation studies, yielding a reasonable compromise between computational time and accuracy.

Table 1. Mesh independency results for Nu_{ave}

Number of cells	Nuave
1,502,520	5.051
3,322,691	5.040
7,877,453	5.037

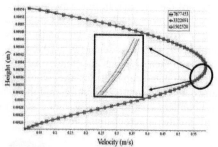

Figure 5. Velocity profile along the height of the channel

The effect of channel height on the pressure drop and average Nusselt number for various Re values between 100 to 500 and Pr = 6 are presented in Figures 6 and 7. As the channel height decreases, both Nusselt number and pressure drop increase. However, pressure drop change between 0.3 and 0.2 mm is much more intensive than the corresponding Nusselt number change, while this is true for all studied flow rates.

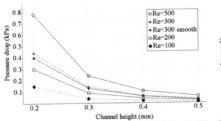

Figure 6. Pressure drop in rough channel versus channel height for Pr=6

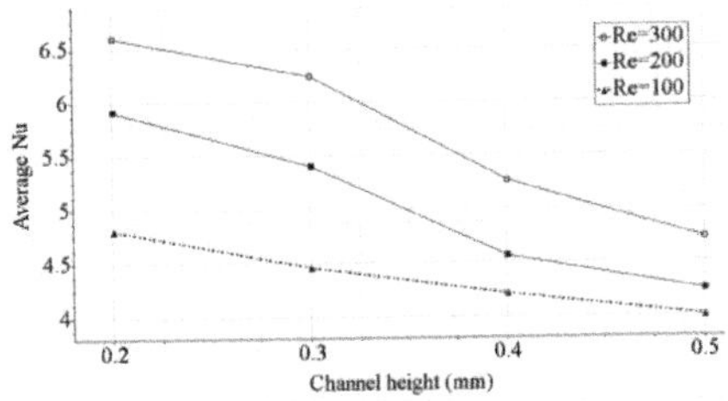

Figure 7. Average Nusselt number in rough channel versus channel height for Pr=6

Figure 7 demonstrates that the effect of the channel height on pressure drop is much more significant than the effect of surface roughness. For instance, for Re=300 and H=0.3mm, the roughness results in just 10% increase, whereas the channel height variation causes substantially larger changes.

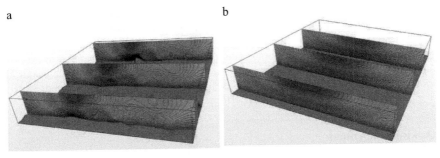

Figure 8. Isothermal line distribution in a rough (a) and a smooth (b) channel at Re=200 and H=0.3 mm

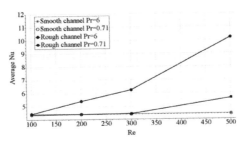

Figure 9. Nusselt number in a rough and a smooth channel as function of Reynolds number at H=0.3 mm

Figure 8 depicts the effect of stochastic surface roughness on the isothermal lines in a smooth and rough channel for Pr=6. They are shown in three different cross-sections normal to the flow direction. The isothermal lines in a smooth channel (Figure 8b) reveal regular structure throughout the whole channel. By contrast, in the channel with rough surface (Figure 8a), the stochastic geometry of the roughness perturbs the regular fluid behaviour leading to irregular configuration of isothermal lines. As the result, the interactions between hotter and colder layers become more intensive, which facilitates heat transfer. Another impact of the random roughness on the fluid flow can be seen in a shift of the cold fluid core position away from the top wall centreline visible in Figure 8a, unlike in the smooth channel, in which it is placed in the centreline of top wall with a symmetric configuration.

The influence of surface roughness on the average Nusselt number is illustrated in Figure 9 for two Prandtl numbers. As expected, for smooth channels, the average Nusselt number remains nearly constant for both Prandtl numbers. For a rough channel at Pr =6, the average Nusselt number increases with increasing Reynolds number. For the fluid with Prandtl number below one, the Nusselt number dependence on Reynolds number is less pronounced, especially for small Reynolds numbers. However, starting from a certain Reynolds number value, the effect of surface roughness on the heat transfer rate becomes significant.

4. Conclusions

The CFD-based study of fluid flow and heat transfer in a microchannel with realistic roughness of 3D printed surface was carried out. The 3D scanner was used to create the geometry of the roughness on microscale. The simulations of a fully developed laminar flow were performed for smooth and rough channels with a height varying between 0.2 and 0.5 mm. Random roughness results in an increase of both the average Nusselt number and pressure drop, while for the smallest studied channel height, the largest pressure drop and the highest average Nusselt number are found. This helps to estimate the critical channel height value, 0.2 mm, for the heat exchanger design. The use of 3D printing in manufacturing of micro heat exchangers offers design flexibility along with the possibility to reach a high thermal performance due to the surface roughness.

Acknowledgement

The authors gratefully acknowledge the technical support of the Direct Manufacturing Research Center (DMRC) at Paderborn University. Calculations were performed with resources provided by the Paderborn Center for Parallel Computing.

References

M. A. Arie, A.H. Shooshtari, V.V. Rao, S.V. Dessiatoun, M.M. Ohadi, 2017, Air-side heat transfer enhancement utilizing design optimization and an additive manufacturing technique. Journal of Heat Transfer. ASME, 139, 3, 031901-1.

T. Femmer, I. Flack, M. Wessling, 2016, Additive manufacturing in fluid process engineering, Chemie Ingenieur Technik, 88, 5, 535-55.

K.K. Ferster, K.L. Kirsch, K.A. Thole, 2017, Effects of geometry, spacing, and number of pin fins in additively manufactured microchannel pin fin arrays. Journal of Turbomachinery, ASME, 140, 011007-1.

L. Guo, H. Xu, L. Gong, 2015, Influence of wall roughness models on fluid flow and heat transfer in microchannels, Applied Thermal Engineering 84 ,399-408.

G.W. Haarlemmer, J. Pigourier, 2008, Towards a new generation heat exchanger models, Computer Aided Chemical Engineering, 25, 763-768.

W. Qu, I. Mudawar, 2002, Experimental and numerical study of pressure drop and heat transfer in a single-phase micro-channel heat sink, International Journal of Heat and Mass Transfer 45, 2549–2565.

D. Saltzman, M. Bichnevicius, S. Lynch, T.W. Simpson, E.W. Reutzel, C. Dickman, R. Martukanitz, 2018, Design and evaluation of an additively manufactured aircraft heat exchanger. Applied Thermal Engineering, 138, 254–263.

C.C. Wang, C.K. Chen, 2002, Forced convection in a wavy-wall channel, International Journal of Heat and Mass Transfer 45 ,2587–2595.

Anton A. Kiss, Edwin Zondervan, Richard Lakerveld, Leyla Özkan (Eds.)
Proceedings of the 29th European Symposium on Computer Aided Process Engineering
June 16th to 19th, 2019, Eindhoven, The Netherlands. © 2019 Elsevier B.V. All rights reserved.
http://dx.doi.org/10.1016/B978-0-128-18634-3.50139-9

Optimization of a large-scale biorefinery problem by decomposition

Varun Punnathanam[a] and Yogendra Shastri[a,*]

[a]*Indian Institute of Technology Bombay, India*
yshastri@che.iitb.ac.in

Abstract

The biorefinery system based on agricultural residue primarily consists of feedstock procurement and processing which need to be taken into consideration together in order to obtain a globally optimal design. This generally results in large-scale mixed integer linear programming (MILP) models that scale rapidly based on the number of technology and location options, resulting in highly complex and challenging optimization problems. This work considers a case study based on setting up a biorefinery system for the state of Maharashtra (India), and employs the Dantzig-Wolfe decomposition based approach to solve this problem. An approximation strategy is proposed to handle the binary variables of the problem. Our approach results in up to 92% reduction in computational time, and leads to a near linear increase in computational time as a function of the problem size. The proposed approach may be used to solve other large-scale optimization problems with a similar structure of various fields.

Keywords: Large-scale optimization, biorefinery, Dantzig-Wolfe decomposition

1. Introduction

A biorefinery is a plant which converts biomass into biofuels as well as other products. In the Indian context, biorefineries must largely rely on a variety of agricultural residues which can have varying compositions. Additionally, their availability is distributed and seasonal, due to which it may be required to collect them from large distances. The biorefinery problem primarily involves two aspects. Process synthesis is a large part of the problem, where the designer develops pathways to interconnect specific raw materials to products of interest. While there might be a myriad of possible pathways (Gong et al., 2016), the designer is required to identify a pathway which would optimize a specific objective, such as maximizing the profit generated by the industry. The selection of a process synthesis pathway is coupled with the design of an optimal supply chain network (Sun et al., 2018), which forms another significant part of the problem. As the raw materials can be procured from multiple sources, the selection of the raw material source as well as the quantity of raw material to be procured from individual sources can greatly impact the economics of the plant. In addition, there can be multiple potential locations for setting up one or more biorefineries. The biorefinery problem is generally formulated as a mixed integer linear programming (MILP) problem, and can potentially be very large in size, consisting of well over a hundred thousand variables and constraints.

In this work, we considered a biorefinery model described in literature (Vikash and Shastri, 2017) which incorporates a single fixed biorefinery and accounts for both feedstock procurement as well as processing. We have extended this model to consider the possibility of setting up multiple biorefineries, and to also optimize the locations of the biorefineries among several potential lo-

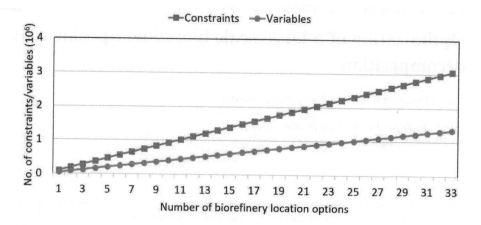

Figure 1: Increase in problem size with increase in potential number of biorefinery locations

cations. Figure 1 shows how the size of this MILP problem varies based on number of potential biorefinery locations. Depending on the specifics, we can expect the size of such a problem to increase rapidly with increase in model details. The full sized problem has more than 3 million constraints and 1.3 million variables including over 6500 binary variables, leading to enormous computational requirements. A popular method for solving large problems is to decompose them into smaller sub-problems which are easier to solve. These sub-problems are iteratively solved by employing certain strategies (Conforti et al., 2014) to ultimately obtain the optimal or near optimal solution to the original monolith problem. The constraint matrix for our biorefinery problem has a block diagonal structure except for a few constraints, which is a very favourable structure for employing Dantzig-Wolfe decomposition (DWD) (Dantzig and Wolfe, 1960).

We therefore propose a DWD based methodology to solve our large-scale biorefinery problem. The following section outlines the formulation of the optimization model. Section 3 presents the proposed solution methodology. The simulation results in terms of reduction in computational time requirement are discussed in Section 4. We conclude this report in Section 5 by mentioning some of the future directions for this work.

2. Problem formulation

The biorefinery problem from literature (Vikash and Shastri, 2017) integrated the biomass procurement and processing aspects into a single model, but considered the location of the biorefinery to be fixed. We expanded this model to consider multiple potential biorefinery locations, thereby drastically increasing the size of the model as shown in Figure 1. The revised model considers a second generation biorefinery which produces ethanol. The superstructure of the problem is conceptually shown in Figure 2 with the number of choices corresponding to each block mentioned in parenthesis.

A specific case study for the production of ethanol for the state of Maharashtra, India (Vikash and Shastri, 2017) is considered. The time horizon is taken to be one year, which is divided into 12 time periods. There are 14 varieties of biomass (N_B) which can be sourced from 33 biomass availability sites (N_H) corresponding to 33 district centroids within Maharashtra. There are potentially 33 locations (corresponding to the 33 district centroids) (N_L) where one or more biorefineries can be located. The biomass is transported via trucks, and can be stored at inventories located at the biorefinery facilities. Regarding the selections involving technological stages within each biore-

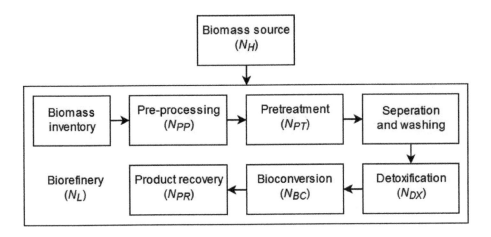

Figure 2: Biorefinery problem structure

finery, $N_{PP} = 1$, $N_{PT} = 8$, $N_{DX} = 4$, $N_{BC} = 4$ and $N_{PR} = 3$. All the necessary data for the problem is reported in literature (Vikash and Shastri, 2017). The objective of the optimization problem is to minimize the total annualized cost (TAC) while meeting a specific monthly demand of ethanol. The problem variables and constraints include:

- Binary variables corresponding to selection of biorefinery location(s), biomass type to be processed at each time period at each biorefinery and the various technological selections within each biorefinery.

- Continuous variables corresponding to the flow of biomass to biorefineries, the size of biomass storage facility at each biorefinery, the amount of biomass stored at each time period for each biorefinery and the flow of intermediate products within the biorefinery.

- Constraints corresponding to the overall biomass availability and demand for ethanol at each time period, economic cost calculations and limiting the selections of processing technologies within each biorefinery, and mass balance constraints within each biorefinery at each time period.

The biorefinery optimization problem can be concisely represented as follows:

$$\min \ \sum_{l}^{L} \left(C_{\text{Total CAPEX},l} + C_{\text{Variable OPEX},l} + C_{\text{Fixed OPEX},l} \right)$$

subject to [individual biorefinery specific constraints]

$$\sum_{l}^{L} f_{b,h,l,t} \leq F_{b,h,t} \qquad \qquad \forall b,h,t \in B,H,T$$

$$\sum_{l}^{L} e_{l,t} \geq D_{t} \qquad \qquad \forall t \in T$$

where, C, f, F, e and D are the annualized cost, flow of biomass, availability of biomass, ethanol production and demand for ethanol, respectively. B, H, T and L corresponds to the set of biomass types, biomass sources, time periods and potential biorefinery locations, respectively. The constraints mentioned as "*individual biorefinery specific constraints*" correspond to the distribution of biomass and intermediate products between processing stages, limiting the selections of processing technologies and maintaining the biomass inventory balance within a biorefinery. Thus, these are the process synthesis constraints focusing on process selection. We don't individually specify them for the sake of brevity. The problem in this form is referred to as the integrated problem.

3. Decomposition based solution approach

The Dantzig-Wolfe decomposition (DWD) (Dantzig and Wolfe, 1960) is a well known technique for solving problems in which the constraints have a block diagonal structure consisting of disjoint sets of variables linked by connecting or complicating constraints. In this section, we discuss the decomposition of the biorefinery problem such that DWD may be employed. Subsequently, we provide a detailed description on the proposed solution methodology for solving the biorefinery problem. In order to employ DWD, the biorefinery problem described in the previous section is decomposed in the following manner. Each individual biorefinery is modelled as a sub-problem, while the biomass supply and ethanol demand constraints connect the sub-problems and hence are part of the master problem. At iteration $i \in I$, the master problem is given as

$$\min_{\lambda} \sum_{l}^{L} \sum_{1}^{i} (\bar{C}^i_{\text{Total CAPEX},l} + \bar{C}^i_{\text{Variable OPEX},l} + \bar{C}^i_{\text{Fixed OPEX},l}) \lambda^i_l$$

$$\text{subject to} \sum_{l}^{L} \sum_{1}^{I} \bar{f}^i_{b,h,l,t} \lambda^i_l \leq F_{b,h,t} \qquad \forall b,h,t \in B,H,T$$

$$\sum_{l}^{L} \sum_{1}^{I} \bar{e}^i_{l,t} \lambda^i_l \geq D_t \qquad \forall t \in T$$

$$\sum_{1}^{i} \lambda^i_l = 1, \qquad \forall l \in L$$

$$\lambda^i_l \geq 0 \qquad \forall i \in I, \forall l \in L$$

where, $\bar{C}, \bar{f}$ and $\bar{e}$ denotes corresponding vertices obtained by solving sub-problems.

At iteration $i \in I$, sub-problem $l \in L$ has the following structure

$$\min_{\hat{X}_l} (C_{\text{Total CAPEX},l} + C_{\text{Variable OPEX},l} + C_{\text{Fixed OPEX},l}) -$$

$$\left(\sum_{b,h,t}^{B,H,T} \mu^i_{1,b,h,t} f_{b,h,l,t} + \sum_{t}^{T} \mu^i_{1,t} e_{l,t} \right) - \mu^{l,i}_2$$

$$\text{subject to} \quad [\textit{individual biorefinery specific constraints}]$$

$$\hat{X}_l \geq 0$$

where, $\hat{X}_l$ denotes all the variables specific to sub-problem l, μ^i_1 is the dual variables corresponding to the master constraints and $\mu^{l,i}_2$ is the dual variable corresponding the the lth convexity constraint in the master problem.

Figure 3 describes our approach for solving the decomposed problem. The first step is to define the master problem and sub-problem models, following which DWD is employed. Iterations corresponding to DWD terminates when (i) none of the sub-problem solutions correspond to a negative reduced cost, (ii) DWD exceeds the maximum number of iterations or (iii) change in objective function value over past few iterations is lower than a specified tolerance. In our implementation, we considered that the objective function value should change by at least 1% over 5 iterations. For the sake of brevity, we do not describe the implementation DWD as it is well documented in literature (Kalvelagen, 2003). For problems involving integer variables, the decomposition method

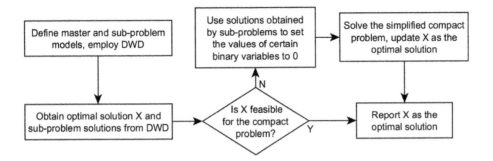

Figure 3: Flowsheet of the solution methodology

which we employ generates the lower bound for the problem, as the integrality of these variables are not guaranteed. Hence, if the solution obtained by DWD is feasible, this is reported as the final solution. On the other hand, if this is not feasible, we utilize the solutions obtained by the sub-problems over DWD iterations to simplify the integrated problem. This is done by filtering out certain selections (setting corresponding binary variable to 0) in the following manner. We identify the sub-problem solutions corresponding largest two λ for each sub-problem l. Subsequently, we filter out the processing technology selections (such as preprocessing, pretreatment, detoxification, bioconversion, fermentation strains and product recovery technologies) which do not appear in the solutions identified earlier. For instance, if the solutions corresponding to the largest and second largest λ for a particular biorefinery location selects pretreatment technologies Dilute Acid Hydrolysis and Lime Pretreatment, respectively, then all other pretreatment technologies are not considered in the simplified problem. The last step is to solve this simplified integrated problem using the standard CPLEX® solver in order to obtain the final optimal solution. Note that this method does not guarantee optimality, although we expect it to produce solutions reasonably close to optimality. In short, our approach is effectively to solve a decomposed problem in order to filter out options for various processing selections which seem to be sub-optimal, thus greatly reducing the complexity of the integrated problem. Subsequently, this simplified MILP problem is solved by standard procedures.

4. Results and discussion

This section presents the improvement in performance obtained by employing the decomposition based method as opposed to solving the integrated problem using the standard CPLEX® solver. The integrated and decomposed biorefinery problem models and the solution methodology were coded in GAMS® . The sub-problems and master problem at each iteration was solved using the standard CPLEX® solver. We do not describe the optimal solution in detail as the focus of our work is the solution methodology and the resulting reduction in computational time.

Figure 4 compares the performance of our approach with that of solving the integrated problem. Although solving the integrated problem requires lesser time for smallest three problem sizes ($N_L = 1$ to $N_L = 3$), the decomposition based approach is significantly faster for all the remaining cases ($N_L = 4$ to $N_L = 33$). For the $N_L = 18$ case, we observe a 92% reduction in computational time. Furthermore, this reduction in computational time is associated with no compromise in the optimal objective function value. It was observed that on employing the decomposition based approach, almost all of the computational time was utilized for solving the sub-problems, with the simplified integrated problem requiring comparatively negligible time. This is reflected in the fact that the computational time requirement for the decomposition based approach appears to be

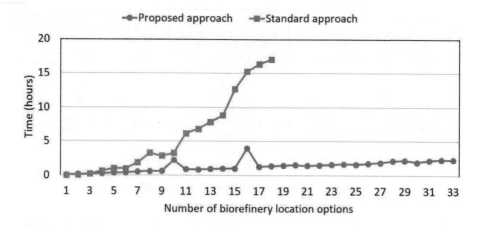

Figure 4: Comparison of computational time requirement of the proposed approach and solving the integrated problem

a linear function of the number of biorefinery options. In comparison, the time taken to solve the integrated problem seems to increase exponentially with increase in the number of biorefinery location options. For the largest problem size ($N_L = 33$), the optimal solution determined by implementing the decomposition based approach corresponded to setting up a single biorefinery located at the Beed district centroid. Ethanol was largely produced by using sugarcane bagasse and wheat based biomass at a price of INR 52.72 per litre.

5. Conclusion

We solve a large-scale biorefinery problem which considers both biomass procurement and process synthesis within each biorefinery. Although this results in a very large optimization problem, its inherent structure allowed us to employ DWD. We developed a DWD based approach and employed it to solve the biorefinery problem. As a result, we obtained up to 92% reduction in computational time while obtaining the same optimal objective function value. This allows us expand the biorefinery model such that it describes the real-world scenario more accurately. In addition, this approach may be tested on similarly structured problems in various fields.

References

M. Conforti, G. Cornuéjols, G. Zambelli, 2014. Integer programming. Vol. 271. Springer.

G. B. Dantzig, P. Wolfe, 1960. Decomposition principle for linear programs. Operations Research 8 (1), 101–111.
    URL http://dx.doi.org/10.1287/opre.8.1.101

J. Gong, D. J. Garcia, F. You, 2016. Unraveling optimal biomass processing routes from bioconversion product and process networks under uncertainty: an adaptive robust optimization approach. ACS Sustainable Chemistry & Engineering 4 (6), 3160–3173.

E. Kalvelagen, 2003. Dantzig-Wolfe Decomposition with GAMS. Amsterdam Optim. Model. Group LLC, Washington, DC, USA.

F. Sun, M. M. Aguayo, R. Ramachandran, S. C. Sarin, 2018. Biomass feedstock supply chain design – a taxonomic review and a decomposition-based methodology. International Journal of Production Research 0 (0), 1–34.
    URL https://doi.org/10.1080/00207543.2018.1475766

P. V. Vikash, Y. Shastri, 2017. Economic optimization of integrated lignocellulosic biorefinery. In: A. Espuña, M. Graells, L. Puigjaner (Eds.), 27th European Symposium on Computer Aided Process Engineering. Vol. 40 of Computer Aided Chemical Engineering. Elsevier, pp. 2503 – 2508.

Anton A. Kiss, Edwin Zondervan, Richard Lakerveld, Leyla Özkan (Eds.)
Proceedings of the 29th European Symposium on Computer Aided Process Engineering
June 16th to 19th, 2019, Eindhoven, The Netherlands. © 2019 Elsevier B.V. All rights reserved.
http://dx.doi.org/10.1016/B978-0-128-18634-3.50140-5

Planning of Supply Chains Threatened by Extreme Events: Novel Heuristic and Application to Industry Case Studies

Michael Ehrenstein[a], Chi-Hsiang Wang[b] and Gonzalo Guillén-Gosálbez[a,*]

[a]*Centre for Process Systems Engineering, Imperial College London, London SW7 2AZ, United Kingdom*
[b]*CSIRO Land and Water, Bayview Dr., Clayton, VIC 3168, Australia*
g.guillen05@imperial.ac.uk

Abstract

Chemical supply chains are a crucial component in the ongoing supply of large population centres. Unfortunately, episodes of extreme weather have, in recent years, revealed vulnerabilities in global supply networks to high-impact events. With a possible increase in both frequency and intensity of these events due to climate change, supply chains are at risk of disruption now more than ever, with potentially dire economic, societal, and environmental consequences. Acknowledging that the direct application of stochastic programming can quickly lead to very large CPU times, we propose an algorithm that combines the sample average approximation method with a selection heuristic for extreme event scenarios. Our method allows to analyse the tradeoff between economic performance and disruption risk, identifying supply chain configurations which are more resilient against extreme events. We demonstrate the effectiveness of this methodology in multiple case studies, showing how it identifies near optimal solutions in short CPU times.

Keywords: supply chains, optimization, stochastic programming, climate change, extreme events

1. Introduction

Supply chains today have evolved to become an integral and indispensable part of the global economy. What started out centuries ago as small scale, local trade networks, has evolved into an interconnected system spanning all inhabited continents. Along with unprecedented scale and reach, todays supply chains involve more stakeholders than ever: Owners and operators with direct financial stakes, customers depending on an ongoing supply of essential goods such as food and medicine, and local and national governments tasked to supply their populace with water, gas, and other utilities.

As the value and importance of supply chains has increased, so has the academic interest in making them more efficient, with the fields of chemical engineering and operations research at the forefront. Much work done on the optimisation of supply chains has been deterministic, meaning that full information on the state of current and future parameter values is presupposed. In recent years however, optimisation of supply chains under uncertainty has become an active and important field of research, illustrating the importance of reflecting the uncertainty of everyday real-world processes in an accurate manner. In this context, the main focus in the literate has been to hedge against what we call "operational uncertainties", e.g. fluctuations in price, demand, or raw material availability. Significantly less attention has been given to uncertain events of higher impact, but lower probability of occurrence. Extreme weather events, device failures, and black-outs (just to name a few) can all have potentially dire consequences for supply chains and the people that rely on them. This has been evidenced by periods of extreme weather affecting supply chains in recent years, like the 2011 Thailand floods, or the 2017 Atlantic hurricane season. And with recent findings projecting an increase in either frequency and/or intensity of such events due to climate change, the need for adequate methods to contribute to the resilience of such crucial systems is clear.

2. Problem statement

In this work, we will consider a multi-echelon supply chain similar to the one shown in Figure 1. We start with a number of potential and existing locations for production, storage, and sale of multiple products. Additionally, prices of materials and final products, costs of production, storage, and transport, as well as the cost of establishing new infrastructure are given. All production and storage locations may be disrupted by an extreme event with a certain probability of occurrence. The goal of this analysis is to determine the optimal supply chain configuration in terms of economic performance and risk, while considering said disruptions.

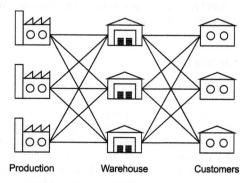

Figure 1: Example of a three-echelon supply chain (production, warehouse, customers), with transport connections linking adjacent echelons.

When applying a scenario-based, stochastic programming approach to such a task, the issue of problem size quickly becomes apparent. For example, a supply chain comprised of 10 disruptable units, along with 5 customer zones which can vary in demand between low, medium, and high, results in a set of $2^{10} \cdot 3^5 = 2.5 \cdot 10^5$ scenarios. While numerous methods exist to reduce the size of the problem to solve, these approaches often perform poorly when faced with disruption uncertainties, which are based on more heavy-tailed distributions than conventional operational uncertainties. The following section introduces a method to solve this problem efficiently.

3. Methodology

3.1. Two-stage stochastic programming

The method we propose to solve the issues mentioned above is based on two-stage stochastic programming (Birge and Louveaux, 1997), as well as the sample average approximation (SAA) method (Kleywegt et al., 2001). Two-stage stochastic programming, along with robust optimisation (Ben-Tal and Nemirovski, 2001), is one of the most common methods used to handle parameter uncertainty in mathematical programming, and usually relies on the partitioning of the underlying uncertainty into discrete realisations, or scenarios. Variables are partitioned into "first stage" and "second stage" variables. First stage variables are calculated before the realisation of any uncertainties and correspond to "here-and-now" decisions, such as initial capital investments. Second stage variables on the other hand are calculated after the uncertainties are revealed ("wait-and-see" decisions), and allow the model to take recourse, or corrective action. These second stage variables correspond to operational decisions, such as production rates and inventory levels.

3.2. Modeling disruptions

Applying stochastic programming, we can now introduce extreme event disruption into the supply chain model. These models typically contain constraints on the maximum available capacity for production or storage, of the form

$$prod_s \leq cap^{max} \tag{1}$$

where $prod_s$ is the current production level, and cap^{max} is the maximum production capacity. By introducing a disruption parameter φ_s, which can take a value between 0 and 1 for every scenario, we can vary the amount of capacity available for production, depending on the disruption scenario:

$$prod_s \leq \varphi_s \cdot cap^{max} \tag{2}$$

Assuming independence between disruption events, as well as binary disruption (disrupted, or not) with probability p, we can now construct a scenario set encompassing all units. For instance, let us consider a supply chain made up of two units, A and B. Four combinations of scenarios are possible here: 1. No disruption, 2. A disrupted, 3. B disrupted, 4. A & B disrupted. Assuming the disruption probability to be p and independent, the probability for each scenariowill be: 1. $(1-p)^2$, 2. $(1-p)p$, 3. $p(1-p)$, 4. p^2.

3.3. Sample average approximation

Our approach to improve the tractability of large supply chain problems is further based on the sample average approximation method, which is a Monte Carlo approach to reduce the problem size of large stochastic programs. When solving a conventional two-stage stochastic program, all first and second stage variables, as well as the full scenario space, are taken into account. The sample average approximation method on the other hand partitions the problem into two sub-problems, each of which is simpler to solve than the parent problem: First, the problem is solved using a random subset of N scenarios instead of the full scenario space. Next, the value of all first stage variables is fixed, and the problem is solved again using the full scenario space, ensuring feasibility of the solution in all scenarios. These two steps are now repeated K times, with a new independent sample of N scenarios chosen in each iteration. Finally, the best of the K candidate solutions is selected to approximate the true optimal solution. Figure 2 compares the SAA method to a two-stage stochastic programming model, in terms of scenarios and variables taken into account.

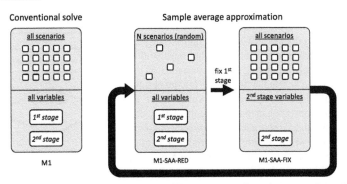

Figure 2: Illustration of the sample average approximation method (right), compared to a conventional two-stage stochastic programming solve.

3.4. Two-stage problem reduction

Based on these methods, we introduce the two-stage problem reduction (TSPR) algorithm, in which we follow the SAA, but apply a heuristic to formulate the sub-problems in a novel way. This heuristic capitalises on our knowledge of the structure of the disruption scenarios, as shown above. Specifically, instead of selecting N scenarios at random, we select scenarios with disruption of zero, one, and all units.

Exploiting our aprioristic knowledge of the scenario set allows the TSPR algorithm to approximate the true solution of the stochastic program after a single iteration, as opposed to K iterations in the SAA method. Furthermore, the TSPR method avoids the need to set parameter values (N and K), thereby simplifying implementation. Figure 3 illustrates this process.

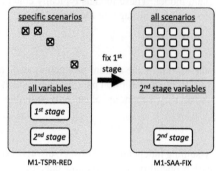

Figure 3: Illustration of the TSPR method. Compared to the sample average approximation, predetermined scenarios are selected for the first solve, and no iterations are performed.

3.5. Risk management and multiobjective optimisation

When assessing the risk posed by extreme event disruption to supply chains, it is of importance to analyse the results beyond the expected economic performance, and to obtain information on the variability of the objective function in the uncertain parameter space. This can be achieved by implementing risk metrics in the optimisation model, which allow for the assessment of the performance of the supply chain in different scenarios. We employ the downside risk (DR) and worst case (WC) metrics (Sabio et al., 2014), though in principle others like the conditional value-at-risk can be implemented. The DR is calculated by comparing the performance of the supply chain in each scenario to a predefined cut-off Ω. Each scenario that falls under the cut-off is penalised by the product of this shortfall and the respective probability of occurrence. The WC metric on the other hand is obtained simply by taking the performance of the worst scenario. Once a metric is implemented in the optimisation model, multiobjective optimisation, for instance by way of the epsilon-constraint method (Ehrgott, 2005), can be employed to investigate the trade-offs between economic performance and risk of the supply chain, yielding a set of Pareto-optimal solutions. Figure 4 illustrates the process of combining the TSPR method with multiobjective optimisation from start to finish.

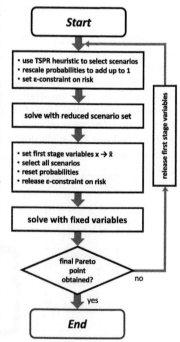

Figure 4: Combining the TSPR method with risk metrics and multiobjective optimisation.

Table 1: Comparing multiobjective optimisation of the petrochemical supply chain in terms of TSPR time reduction, difference in economic performance, and hypervolume measure.

Objectives	Time reduction	max E[profit] diff.	HV diff.
E[profit] vs. WC	93 %	0.0 %	3.2%
E[profit] vs. DR	99 %	0.0 %	0.0%

4. Case studies

4.1. Petrochemical supply chain

We demonstrate the capabilities of this methodology through its application to two case studies. The first is based on earlier work by Ruiz-Femenia et al. (Ruiz-Femenia et al., 2013), who investigated the trade-offs between environmental impact and economic performance in the design of a petrochemical supply chain in Europe.

In our case, the supply chain is made up of three eche-lons, with four potential locations for production plants, seven for warehouses, and four markets. The potential disruption of all plants and warehouses results in 2048 scenarios. The model seeks to optimise the supply chain's profit, and one of the risk metrics outlined above, while making decisions on production and storage capacities, transportation volumes, and inventory levels. We generated ten Pareto-optimal solutions using the epsilon-constraint method, both using the full scenario space, and the TSPR method. In order to adequately compare the two sets of solutions in each case, the hypervolume (HV) (Zitzler and Thiele, 1998) indicator was employed. This measure quantifies the area enclosed by the obtained solutions, and a reference point, as illustrated in Figure 5. The solutions obtained using the full scenario set are compared to the TSPR solutions in Table 1.

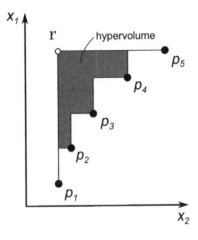

Figure 5: Illustration of the hypervolume (grey) enclosed by points p and the reference point r.

A significant reduction in solution time is evident, while at the same time the Pareto solutions of the TSPR run are close (WC) or near identical (DR) to their optimal counterparts.

4.2. Hydrogen supply chain

The TSPR method was further applied to the optimisation of a hydrogen supply chain for vehicle use in the UK, based on work by Almansoori and Shah (Almansoori and Shah, 2006). The model in our case has 9 regions, in each of which production and storage facilities can be established, along with a set customer demand. 512 disruption scenarios are considered, and the full-space solution is again compared to the TSPR solution for both the profit-WC and the profit-DR trade-off. A summary of the results can be found in Table 2, again showing that the TSPR method is able to achieve results close to the optimal case, while reducing the solution time significantly.

5. Conclusion

We addressed the problem of the design and risk management of optimal multi-echelon supply chains threatened by rare event disruptions, which to our knowledge had not been adequately

Table 2: Comparing multiobjective optimisation of the hydrogen supply chain in terms of TSPR time reduction, difference in economic performance, and hypervolume measure.

Objectives	Time reduction	max E[profit] diff.	HV diff.
E[profit] vs. WC	96 %	0.0 %	0.2%
E[profit] vs. DR	98 %	0.0 %	6.6%

addressed in the current literature. Combining the SAA algorithm with a selection heuristic, the TSPR methodology was developed to reduce the computational effort required to solve these types of problems. The effectiveness of the TSPR method was demonstrated through application to two supply chain case studies from the literature, achieving close to optimal results in significantly reduced time.

6. References

Almansoori, A., & Shah, N. (2006). Design and Operation of a Future Hydrogen Supply Chain. Chemical Engineering Research and Design, 84, 423-438.

Ben-Tal, A., & Nemirovski, A. (2001). Lectures on modern convex optimization: analysis, algorithms, and engineering applications (Vol. 2): Siam.

Birge, J. R., & Louveaux, F. (1997). Introduction to stochastic programming. In: Springer, New York. Ehrgott, M. (2005). Multicriteria Optimization: Springer-Verlag New York, Inc.

Kleywegt, A. J., Shapiro, A., & Homem-de-Mello, T. (2002). The Sample Average Approximation Method for Stochastic Discrete Optimization. SIAM Journal on Optimization, 12, 479-502.

Ruiz-Femenia, R., Guillén-Gosálbez, G., Jiménez, L., & Caballero, J. (2013). Multi-objective optimization of environmentally conscious chemical supply chains under demand uncertainty. Chemical Engineering Science, 95, 1-11.

Sabio, N., Pozo, C., Guillén-Gosálbez, G., Jiménez, L., Karuppiah, R., Vasudevan, V., Sawaya, N., & Farrell, J. T. (2014). Multiobjective optimization under uncertainty of the economic and life-cycle environmental performance of industrial processes. AIChE Journal, 60, 2098-2121.

Anton A. Kiss, Edwin Zondervan, Richard Lakerveld, Leyla Özkan (Eds.)
Proceedings of the 29th European Symposium on Computer Aided Process Engineering
June 16th to 19th, 2019, Eindhoven, The Netherlands. © 2019 Elsevier B.V. All rights reserved.
http://dx.doi.org/10.1016/B978-0-128-18634-3.50141-7

Turbulent flow modeling in continuous oscillatory flow baffled reactor using STAR CCM+

Nikola Kljajić, Branislav Todić, Danijela Slavnić, Nikola Nikačević*

Faculty of Technology and Metallurgy, University of Belgrade, Karnegijeva 4, Belgrade 11000, Serbia

nikacevic@tmf.bg.ac.rs

Abstract

A detailed transient tridimensional CFD model of the turbulent flow of liquid phase inside of 26 mm diameter continuous oscillatory baffled reactor (COBR) was developed using STAR CCM+ software. The model considered a large number of COBR cavities separated with single-orifice baffles. The CFD model was validated using residence time distribution experiments with several flowrates and frequencies. Different from previous studies, flow oscillations in our work were generated using a membrane pump, which enabled lower amounts of backflow. Simulations were used to analyse flow patterns and mixing for several values of inlet flowrate and oscillation frequencies.

Keywords: continuous oscillatory flow baffled reactors, process intensification, CFD modeling.

1. Introduction

Oscillatory flow baffled reactors are a successful example of process intensification in chemical engineering. They have been shown to provide improved performance in a number of process operations, including crystallization, polymerisation, adsorption, reaction etc. (Jolliffe et al., 2018). Typically, continuous oscillatory baffled reactors (COBRs) are made up of a number of equally spaced single-orifice baffles inside a tube. However, other designs (e.g. helical and double-helical ribbons) have been used as well. The main characteristic of COBRs is the enhancement of mixing by using flow oscillations, which periodically collide with baffles forming vortices. The intensity of mixing in COBRs is dependent on the oscillation amplitude and frequency, as well as reactor geometry. The application of these continuous reactors can lead to significant improvements in productivity, investment and operating cost savings, as well as better reaction control, for slow processes typically performed in batch systems. Initial studies with COBRs explained the mechanisms of oscillatory flow mixing by using a number of experimental approaches. Ni et al. (2002) presented the first 3-D CFD model which solved Navier–Stokes equations (i.e. without stream function) for oscillatory Reynolds numbers covering both symmetric and asymmetric flows. Due to computational complexity the model included only a few cavities (i.e. cells between baffles), and was validated with particle image velocimetry (PIV) experiments in oscillatory baffled column (OBC) with fixed baffles. Several other later CFD works also focused on a smaller number of cavities due to similar reasons (Hamzah et al., 2012).

In this study, the transient 3D CFD model of the turbulent flow of liquid inside of single-orifice baffled tube reactor was developed using K-Epsilon turbulence model and STAR CCM+ software. In order to provide a full picture of the flow inside the entire reactor, the model included a large number of cavities (total of 29). This enabled direct experimental validation using residence time distribution studies, conducted for several sets of input oscillation frequency and amplitude. Backflow created during generation of flow oscillations was minimized by feeding the fluid to the reactor using a membrane pump with a non-return valve. Furthermore, by using a membrane pump, there is no need for an oscillator in addition to the regular pump (net flow), used in many previous studies (i.e. more cost effective). Detailed analysis of velocity streamlines, vorticity, turbulent viscosity, and kinetic energy is used to provide insights into fluid flow and mixing flow inside of COBR with this design.

2. Methodology

2.1 Experimental setup and procedures

Experiments were performed in a 2 m long reactor with an internal diameter of 26 mm. Single-orifice baffles were placed along the reactor tube, equally spaced at 1.5 times the internal diameter of the tube. The primary stream was generated by the dosing membrane pump and carried fluid oscillatory movement. The control unit of this pump allows the volume and frequency of strokes to be adjusted. The process fluid was water at atmospheric pressure and temperature. The tracer used in experiments was a solution of methylene blue in the concentration of 2.0 g/l. The pulse-response method was used to examine the liquid flow pattern in the COBR. The samples were taken from the 29th cavity, placed 1.03 m downstream of the injecting point. The absorbance of samples was determined using a UV-VIS spectrophotometer. Details of the experimental setup and procedures can be found in Slavnic et al. (2017).

2.2 3D COBR model development

The 3D COBR model was defined using Simcenter STAR-CCM+ 12.04 software. The reactor geometry was drawn using SolidWorks 2011 CAD software and imported into STAR CCM+. Reactor dimensions corresponded to our experimental setup. Due to the reactor symmetry, only one horizontal half of the full volume was modelled, in order to speed up the computing time. The reactor geometry was split up into regions, which define boundaries and regions of interest. Surface and volume mesh was generated using Polyhedral and Prism Layer Meshers, respectively. To ensure higher precision, denser mesh settings were used in boundaries around the baffles. A higher computational speed was achieved by decreasing the density of meshes around tube walls.

The reactor model includes balance equations for momentum, mass and energy, as well as continuity equations. The balance equations used can be presented as:

$$\frac{\partial \rho}{\partial t} + \nabla \cdot \left[\rho \left(\bar{v} - v_g \right) \right] = 0 \tag{1}$$

$$\frac{\partial (\rho \bar{v})}{\partial t} + \nabla \cdot \left[\rho \bar{v} \left(\bar{v} - v_g \right) \right] = -\nabla \cdot \bar{p} I + \nabla \cdot (T + T_t) + f_b \tag{2}$$

where ρ is fluid density, t time, $\bar{v}$ and $\bar{p}$ are mean velocity and pressure, v_g referent velocity, I identity tensor, T viscous stress tensor, T_t Reynolds stress tensor and f_b is resultant of the body forces. Unsteady state turbulent flow of multi-component non-reacting liquid was modelled using the K-Epsilon turbulence model:

$$\frac{\partial(\rho k)}{\partial t} + \nabla \cdot \left(\rho k \overline{v} \right) = \nabla \cdot \left[\left(\mu + \frac{\mu_t}{\sigma_t} \right) \nabla k \right] + P_k - \rho \left(\varepsilon - \varepsilon_0 \right) + S_k \qquad (3)$$

$$\frac{\partial(\rho \varepsilon)}{\partial t} + \nabla \cdot \left(\rho \varepsilon \overline{v} \right) = \nabla \cdot \left[\left(\mu + \frac{\mu_t}{\sigma_\varepsilon} \right) \nabla \varepsilon \right] + \frac{1}{T_e} C_{\varepsilon 1} P_\varepsilon - C_{\varepsilon 2} f_2 \rho \left(\frac{\varepsilon}{T_e} - \frac{\varepsilon_0}{T_0} \right) + S_\varepsilon \qquad (4)$$

where μ is dynamic viscosity, μ_t is turbulent eddy viscosity, σ_t, σ_ε, $C_{\varepsilon 1}$, $C_{\varepsilon 2}$ model coefficients, P_k, P_ε terms which define generation of kinetic energy k and dissipation of turbulent energy ε, f_2 dampening function, S_k, S_ε source terms, T_e large-eddy time scale and T_0 specific time scale.

Inlet boundaries for base and tracer fluid were defined as oscillatory and impulse functions, respectively. The inlet of base fluid was defined using a data matrix generated in Matlab based on experimental measurements of the inlet flow. Schematic representation of base fluid oscillatory flow at the inlet is shown in Figure 1. The inlet of the tracer is defined as an impulse of flow with the volume of 2 ml in the 0.5 s interval, which replicates the syringe injection of tracer into the reactor.

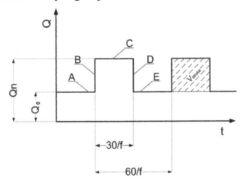

Figure 1 - Schematic representation of base fluid oscillatory flow at the reactor inlet (A, B, C, D and E represent specific moments during each oscillation). Notes: f – pump frequency; Q_0 – base flowrate; Q_n – total flowrate;

3. Results and discussion

3.1 Model validation

Reliable design, scale-up and control of COBRs are conditioned by fluid flow accurate representation. One of the most effective experimental approaches for defining non-ideal flow is still the investigation of residence time distribution (RTD) of fluid elements, realized through tracer experiments and population-based analysis. In order to validate our CFD model, comparison with experimental RTD under a range of conditions was performed. Three tracer experiments covered a range of net flow Reynolds numbers ($Re_n = 142$, 453 and 678), oscillatory Reynolds numbers ($Re_o = 670$, 1644 and 2458) and frequencies ($f = 0.5$, 1 and 2 s^{-1}).

By solving the material balance for the tracer component in STAR CCM+, and integrating (spatially) molar fractions at the outlet plane, we are able to calculate the residence time probability distribution (i.e. E-curve). Comparison of E-curves for two of the experiments is shown in Figure 2 and depicts a very good agreement between the CFD model and experiments. E-curve from the third experiment (not shown in Figure

2) also matched well with the CFD model. We also compared the resulting E-curve obtained by using the axial-dispersion (AD) model, based on the empirical correlation for Peclet number (Slavnic et al., 2017). Figure 2 shows that in the range of high Re_n values, CFD model considerably outperforms the AD model. Albeit slower to solve and with a significantly higher computational cost, an additional benefit of the CFD model is it provides a more detailed picture of the fluid flow inside of COBRs. This is valuable for further process intensification considerations of such reactors.

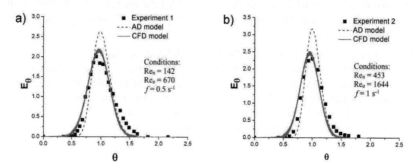

Figure 2 – Comparison of RTD for CFD model with the experimental and AD model results: a) Experiment 1; b) Experiment 2.

Recently, Kimuli et al. (2017) performed a similar investigation, where a CFD model (using STAR CCM+ software) with a large number of cavities was developed and validated using RTD experiments. However, they focused on lower values of Re_n (i.e. laminar flows with $Re_n = 8.4$ and 21.2) and smaller meso-scale reactors (5 mm internal diameter). Mazubert et al. (2016) also used commercial CFD software to simulate laminar liquid flow through meso-scale COBRs with multiple designs of baffles. Several previous studies, which focused on turbulent flow, performed simulations for a small number of cavities (i.e one to three) (Nogueira et al., 2013).

Our results show that the developed CFD model can be used to predict turbulent liquid flow in larger-scale COBRs and that such model can provide more reliable information compared to the more traditional models, such as the AD model.

One of the critical parameters which can affect the solutions of CFD models in various simulations is mesh refinement and its convergence. To that end, we conducted simulations with several mesh densities (i.e. lower and higher densities) in order to choose optimal mesh density, which both do not extensively affect the final results and does not slow down the simulations. Results with the optimized mesh density were within 2% of those obtained with a very fine mesh.

3.2 Analysis of turbulent flow in COBR

The mechanism of oscillatory flow mixing in COBRs was examined in the literature. However, previous studies focused on experiments were flow oscillations were generated by either a piston which periodically moves the entire fluid volume inside the reactor or mechanical periodic movements of baffles inside the reactor tube or movements of the entire reactor (i.e. column). These approaches result in a significant amount of backflow, and are in addition costly in terms of additional equipment and devices. In our experiments, input flow oscillations are generated by a dosing membrane pump which supplies the reactor with the fluid. In this type of design, fluids' forward flow rate is significantly higher than the backflow rate, due to the use of a non-return valve positioned after the pump. Thus, the mechanism of oscillatory flow mixing warrants a further evaluation for this case.

Simulation results were analysed in terms of velocity streamlines and intensity, vorticity, turbulent viscosity and kinetic energy for several key moments during each oscillation (marked A – E in Figure 1). Figure 3 shows the velocity streamlines for two sets of conditions. At higher inlet flowrates and oscillation frequency (Re_n = 678 and Re_o = 2458), velocity streamlines show that before the stoke of the oscillatory wave (period A), there is a recirculation of flow and mixing. Fluid energy is insufficient to be transported into the next or previous cavity, but is mixed inside of the current one. When the oscillatory component of flow is active (periods B, C and D), there is no considerable radial flow mixing and fluid energy is used for its transport through the reactor. At that time the flow core is formed by fluid moving through the baffle openings at higher velocities. However, a small fraction of fluid circumvents the baffles and moves along the tube walls at significantly lower velocities, due to loss of energy from the collision with the rings and wall friction (laminar flow). At the period after the stoke of the oscillatory flow wave (period E), inertial forces are decreased and there is intense (radial) fluid mixing. It is at this time turbulent eddies are formed, and their concentration is highest in the volume right behind the baffles. At lower flowrates and oscillation frequency (Re_n = 142 and Re_o = 670), the behaviour is quite different and fluid mixing is not pronounced in periods A-D. In this case, intense mixing only occurs in period E after the oscillatory flow wave impact.

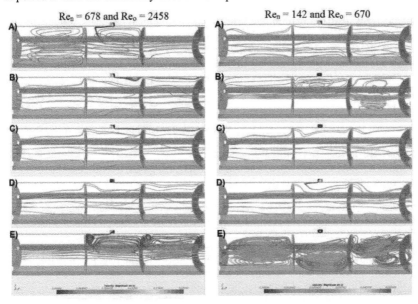

Figure 3 – Velocity streamlines at higher inlet flowrates and oscillation frequency (left figure) and lower flowrates and oscillation frequency (right figure) for characteristic time periods (periods A – E shown in Figure 2).

In both cases (high and low flowrates and oscillation peak velocities), observed vorticity before the oscillatory flow wave (period A) is minimal. This is due to the low backflow in our system. At the stroke start, during and right after the wave impact (B, C and D), vorticity increases in areas of fluid collision with the baffles. After the impact (period E), vortices spread within the same cavity, but decrease in intensity. The values of turbulent viscosity show the turbulent transport is dominant in both cases and the laminar layer only exists close to the walls. The laminar layer width for high and low inlet flowrates and oscillation frequency case is $0.5 - 2$ and $2 - 4$ mm, respectively.

4. Conclusions

3D CFD model of the oscillatory flow of liquid in turbulent regime inside of COBR was developed using STAR CCM+ software. The model included a large number of cavities and was validated by direct comparison to RTD experiments for several flowrates and oscillation frequencies. The developed CFD model was shown to outperform the classical AD model, based on literature correlation for Peclet number. The analysis of velocity streamlines, vorticity and turbulent viscosity, obtained with minimal backflow related to the generation of oscillations, revealed specific findings about fluid mixing inside of COBR with this particular design. Recirculation of fluid flow occurs when the oscillatory component of flow is not active, but its intensity can be affected by manipulating the magnitude and frequency of the flow. Turbulence is most intense in moments before and after the fluid wave collision. Higher frequencies and flowrates intensify the momentum transfer and cause for a higher fraction of reactor volume to be used in turbulent fluid mixing.

Acknowledgements

This work was realized within the framework of national projects funded by the Ministry of Education, Science and Technological Development of the Republic of Serbia [III 46001, III 46010 and 172022]. Branislav Todić would like to gratefully acknowledge the financial supprot of the Joint Japan-Serbia Center for the Promotion of Science and Technology and the ITO Foundation for this research.

References

A. A. Hamzah, N. Hasan, M. S. Takriff, S. K. Kamarudin, J. Abdullah, I. M. Tan, W. K. Sern, 2012, "Effect of oscillation amplitude on velocity distributions in an oscillatory baffled column (OBC)", Chem. Eng. Res. Des., 90, 1038-1044.

H. G. Jolliffe, D. I. Gerogiorgis, 2018, "Process modelling, design and technoeconomic evaluation for continuous paracetamol crystallisation" Comput-Aided Chem. Eng., 43, 1637-1642.

E. N. Kimuli, I. I. Onyemelukwe, B. Benyahia, C. D. Riellya, 2017, "Characterisation of axial dispersion in a meso-scale oscillatory baffled crystalliser using a numerical approach", Comput-Aided Chem. Eng., 40, 223-228.

A. Mazubert, D.F. Fletcher, M. Poux, J. Aubin, 2016, "Hydrodynamics and mixing in continuous oscillatory flow reactors—Part I: Effect of baffle geometry", Chem. Eng. Process., 108, 78-92.

X. Ni, H. Jian, A.W. Fitch, 2002, "Computational fluid dynamic modelling of flow patterns in an oscillatory baffled column", Chem. Eng. Sci., 57, 2849 – 2862.

X. Nogueira, B. J. Taylor, H. Gomez, I. Colominas, M. R. Mackley, 2013, "Experimental and computational modeling of oscillatory flow within a baffled tube containing periodic-tri-orifice baffle geometries", Comput. Chem. Eng., 49, 1-17.

D. Slavnic, L. Zivkovic, A. Bjelic, B. Bugarski and N. M. Nikacevic, 2017, "Residence time distribution and Peclet number correlation for continuous oscillatory flow reactors", J. Chem. Technol. Biotechnol., 92, 2178–2188.

Anton A. Kiss, Edwin Zondervan, Richard Lakerveld, Leyla Özkan (Eds.)
Proceedings of the 29th European Symposium on Computer Aided Process Engineering
June 16th to 19th, 2019, Eindhoven, The Netherlands. © 2019 Elsevier B.V. All rights reserved.
http://dx.doi.org/10.1016/B978-0-128-18634-3.50142-9

Overpotentials in Water Electrolysis: In-Silico Comparison of PEM-cell and GAP-cell performance

Luisa C. Brée[a], Tobias Schiekel[a] and Alexander Mitsos[a,*]

[a]*Aachener Verfahrenstechnik - Process Systems Engineering, RWTH Aachen University, Aachen, Germany*
amitsos@alum.mit.edu

Abstract

Many studies focus on the performance of electrochemical reactors and very often result in presenting a polarization curve.

Modeling and simulation can simplify the examination of overpotentials, which reduce process performance, and thus help finding an improved electrolyzer for an envisaged application. Moreover, they are useful for optimization of the design and operation at process level.

Herein, we develop a mechanistic, dynamic model for electrochemical water splitting and compare two established cell setups, the PEM-cell and the GAP-cell, in order to assess the performance and optimization potentials of these processes. We model ohmic overpotentials and mass transport limitations in order to show their impact on energy losses, especially towards higher cell potentials. Further, we consider the formation of gas bubbles which have been identified as major source of undesired overpotentials at high current densities. We model this decrease of the effective electrode area via geometrical considerations using experimental investigations of bubble dynamics, including the formation, growth, and detachment of single hydrogen bubbles during electrolysis carried out by Yang et al. (2015).

A parameter estimation results in a good match of the experimental data and the simulation results. For the GAP-cell, the contribution of different overpotentials to the whole electrolyzer performance is determined with high accuracy.

We use the model to show reachable current densities, cell efficiencies and dominant loss terms of the reactor setups and thus indicate optimization possibilities and potentials.

Keywords: water electrolysis, rigorous modeling and simulation, overpotential distribution, performance comparison

1. Introduction

Electrolyzers face increasing overpotentials towards high cell potentials reducing the energy efficiency of the reactor. At elevated cell potentials, the reactors even tend to reach a limiting current density with high energy losses due to mass transport limitations or electrode coverage by evolving product gases. Therefore, an optimal operating point balances high product formation and high energy losses. Additionally, different concepts of electrolyzer setups exist with specific dominating overpotentials, such that depending on the type of application, one or the other setup must be selected. Therefore, the most beneficial combination of setup and cell potential should be found for an envisaged application.

To simplify this search, research activities in the field of electrochemical cell modeling is extensive and numerous models exist for various applications, setups or even individual components. These models vary in their level of detail, including 0D, 1D, 2D or even 3D models, the number of assumptions taken into account, etc. For instance Wu (2016) presents a review on transport and performance modeling of PEM fuel cells.

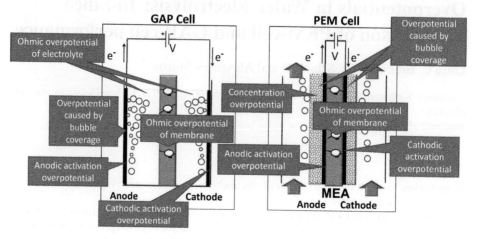

Figure 1: Scheme of both reactor setups with overpotentials taken into account in the model.

A classic application of electrolysis is water splitting. Here, the oxygen evolution reaction (OER) occurs at the anode and the hydrogen evolution reaction (HER) at the cathode. There are (among others) two established cell setups for water electrolysis: The older and more common is the alkaline GAP-cell, where an aqueous ionic solution as liquid electrolyte is present. The newer setup is the Proton Exchange Membrane (PEM) electrolysis. Here a solid polymer like Nafion is used as a membrane and electrolyte at the same time (see Fig. 1).

In order to assess the performance and optimization potentials of these processes, we develop dynamic models for water electrolysis in an electrochemical membrane reactor (ecMR) with both cell setups. Dynamic models allow the analysis of control-strategies or demand side management, though, for the herein presented results the dynamics are not needed. The models take into account all important overpotentials mostly via state-of-the art equations found in literature. We introduce a new model for simulating the overpotential due to bubble formation.

The models are validated with experimental data from literature and unknown parameters are determined. Simulations are then executed to characterize the behaviour of each setup. Knowing the influence of relevant loss terms, individual optimization approaches can be developed for each setup.

2. Modeling

We develop dynamic models for potentiostatic electrochemical water splitting in a PEM-cell and a GAP-cell for unpressurised reactors at room temperature based on mass balances, transport equations and electrochemical kinetics. This results in models considering the overpotentials shown in Figure 1. Additionally, we assume ideal gases, 100 % Faradaic efficiency, fully hydrated membranes, no cross-over of gases and a uniformly distributed current across the cell.

In a PEM-cell the reactants need to pass through the porous gas diffusion layers (GDL) to reach the electrode-membrane interface, the products need to be removed from this site of the electrochemical reaction. We describe the transport through the GDL via mass balances with diffusion by Fick's law. In a GAP-cell, the electrodes are immersed in an ionic solution. Here, we model mass transport through the electrolyte via mass balances taking into account diffusion and migration, as well as ionic equilibria with ph-calculation. Mass transport limitations causes the concentration of reactants to decrease and of products to increase leading to concentration overpotentials at the electrodes' surfaces.

We relate the molar consumption and production rates of the electrochemical reactions to the cell's current density by Faraday's law. The effect of changing concentrations on the concentration overpotential is then calculated via the Nernst equation (Newman and Thomas-Alyea, 2004).

The electrochemical reactions are induced by activation overpotentials. We calculate this activation loss via the Butler-Volmer equation (Newman and Thomas-Alyea, 2004) and use experimental results for nonlinear regression to estimate the reaction specific transfer coefficients α and exchange current densities j_0.

Ohmic overvoltages are caused by the resistance to the flow of electrons or ions by the electrolyte, the electrodes and their various interconnectors. According to Ohm's law, we correlate the ohmic overvoltage linearly proportional to the current by the conductivity factor.

In water electrolysis, a water flux through the membrane occurs, which is governed by: (i) electro-osmotic drag, (ii) diffusion driven by a concentration gradient and (iii) convection if a pressure gradient is present. In this study, no pressure gradient is considered.

The physical blocking of the electrodes in both setups by the gaseous reaction products is named as major source for undesired overpotentials according to Yang et al. (2015), though, no modeling approach could be found in literature. Therefore, we describe a first approach to model this effect:

Influence of electrode coverage by product gases   The gas bubbles are formed at the surface of the electrode where they grow until the uplift force exceeds the surface forces binding the bubbles to the electrodes. During the time span τ from formation till detachment, the gas bubbles reduce the effective surface of the electrode that can be used for electrochemical reactions.

$$\eta_{ohm_{el}} = \frac{R_{0_{el}} I_{total}}{A_{rel}} \tag{1}$$

$$
\begin{array}{ll}
\textbf{GAP} & \textbf{PEM} \\
A_{rel,GAP} = \frac{A_0 - A_{cov}}{A_0} & A_{rel,PEM} = \frac{V_0 - V_{gas}}{V_0} \\
A_{cov} = \frac{\pi d_{contact}^2}{4} number_{bub} & V_0 = x \cdot A_{PEM} \cdot \varepsilon \\
number_{bub} = \frac{V_{gas}}{\bar{V}_{bub}} &
\end{array}
\tag{2}
$$

$$V_{gas} = \dot{V}_{gas} \tau \tag{3}$$

$$\dot{V}_{gas} = \frac{\dot{n}_{gas} R_{ig} T}{p} \tag{4}$$

For modeling the overpotential due to bubble formation, we introduce a dimensionless variable A_{rel} into the ohmic relationship of the electrode's overpotential as shown in Eq. (1). A_{rel} describes the fraction of the total electrode surface, which can still be used for electrochemical reactions, and is calculated according to Eq. (2) comparing the original electrode surface A_0 to the covered electrode surface A_{cov} for the GAP-cell and for the PEM-cell via comparing the product gas volume in the catalyst layer V_{gas} and the inner reactive pore volume of the GDL $V_{0,GDL}$. This allows to introduce a linear relationship between the resistance and the (un)covered area with an infinite resistance when the whole surface is covered by bubbles. $R_{0_{el}}$ is the electrode's electric resistance when fully surrounded by water. This resistance is the product of the specific electric resistance of the electrode's material and a geometric factor. For determining A_{cov}, we calculate the number of bubbles $number_{bub}$ using the total volume of produced gas V_{gas} and the mean volume of a single bubble $\bar{V}_{bub} = 0.45e^{-12}$ m^3 which was calculated by averaging time dependent bubble radii measured by Yang et al. (2015). The mean diameter of the contact area $d_{contact} = 80\,\mu$m is taken from the same data and probably a parameter dependent on $\bar{V}_{bub}$.

Using the ideal gas law (4), we calculate the volume flows of the evolving gases $\dot{V}_{gas}$ from the electrochemical consumption and production rates giving the total volume of gas bubbles bound to the electrode via Eq. (3). The simplified assumption of spherical bubbles is justified as the contact angles between bubble and surface were small with values between 5° and 15° (Yang et al., 2015). V_0 for the PEM-cell is calculated using the GDL's porosity ε, its thickness x and the cross sectional area of the PEM-cell A_{PEM}.

3. Results

In Figure 2 we show the results of the parameter estimations comparing simulated and experimentally determined polarization curves for both reactor setups (upper row) as well as an analysis of the prevailing overpotentials (lower row). The estimated parameters are listed in Table 1. Note that τ for the PEM-cell is estimated as the value from literature holds for electrodes freely immersed in a liquid. The assumption of a constant membrane's proton conductivity is based on a well hydrated membrane due to the electro-osmotic drag. Especially for the GAP-cell it has to be noted, that the Butler-Volmer parameters correlate strongly and therefore, could not be identified.

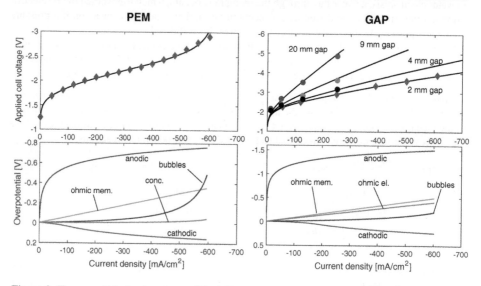

Figure 2: Top row: Polarization curves (black line: simulation results; Red diamonds: experimental data by Dedigama et al. (2014) for PEM-cell and by Phillips et al. (2017) for GAP-cell used for parameter estimation; Blue/green/purple circles: experimental data by Phillips et al. (2017) used for model validation). Bottom row: Overpotentials depending on current density for PEM-cell and GAP-cell with 2 *mm* gap. (shown: anodic activation; cathodic activation; ohmic overpot. of membrane; ohmic overpot. of electrolyte; concentration overpot.; overpot. caused by gas bubbles).

PEM-cell　　With parameter estimation, we achieve a good match of the experimental and simulated data for the PEM-cell, even for high applied cell voltages (Figure 2, upper row, left). Close to the onset potential, the cell behaviour depends almost completely on the anodic activation overpotential (see Figure 2, lower row, left). This is caused by a high activation energy of the water splitting reaction which is a consequence of a non-optimized platinum electrode used in the experiments. A catalyst optimized for the OER reaction could lower this loss term significantly.
The current density shows the characteristic exponential rise governed by the reaction kinetics which turns into a linear section governed by ohmic overpotentials. The ohmic overpotential exhibits a fairly high influence compared to standard PEM-cells. Simulations with the same model with a typical value for fully hydrated Nafion membranes of $9.4\,\frac{S}{m}$ results in a significantly lower ohmic overvoltage of $0.12\,V$ at $600\,\frac{mA}{cm^2}$.
The concentration overpotential is low, indicating a sufficient transport of reactants through the

Table 1: Estimated model parameters. α : transfer coefficient; j_0 : exchange current density; D_{H_2O} : diffusion coefficient; κ : proton conductivity; *an* : at anode; *cat* : at cathode; *mem* : in membrane; *el* : in liquid electrolyte

Symbol	Value PEM (*)	Value GAP(*)	Unit
α_{an}	$0.89(\pm 0.01)$	$0.92(\pm 2.2)$	–
α_{cat}	$0.15(\pm 0.02)$	$0.08(\pm 2.82)$	–
$j_{0,an}$	$7.16(\pm 1.61)$	$0.66(\pm 131)$	$A \cdot m^{-2}$
$j_{0,cat}$	$657(\pm 118)$	$1286(\pm 48780)$	$A \cdot m^{-2}$
τ	$0.036(\pm 0.001)$	–	s
$D_{H_2O,mem}$	$1.1 \cdot 10^{-10}(\pm 1.86 \cdot 10^{-10})$	$9.62 \cdot 10^{-11}(\pm 0.99)$	$m^2 \cdot s^{-1}$
κ_{mem}	$2.98(\pm 0.1)$	–	$S \cdot m^{-1}$

(*90% confidence interval)

GDL. Towards higher current densities the gradient of the current density curve increases going over to an asymptotic course due to increased gas production and an exponential rise of the over-voltage caused by gas bubbles.

To reach higher current densities with the PEM-cell, the removal of gases through the GDL has to be improved. While the study by Dedigama employs a GDL with a porosity of 0.4, porosities over 0.5 are available on the market. Another possibility is the employment of water vapour instead of liquid water. Here, bubble formation can be avoided but this has to be contrasted with a much lower water concentration.

The efficiencies calculated with the PEM-model for the experimental setup by Dedigama are fairly low. At a typical current density for industrial applications of $500 \frac{mA}{cm^2}$ the efficiency is only 46%. Simulating the same model with a membrane conductivity elevated to the literature value of $9.4 \frac{S}{m}$ causes a small improvement to 50%. At a lower current density of $200 \frac{mA}{cm^2}$ the cell efficiency reaches 61 %, which is significantly lower than typical values shown by state of the art PEM-electrolyzers located around 76% (Bertuccioli et al. (2014)) at the same current density. To reach desired efficiency values in the range of 80% or higher, the utilization of an optimized catalyst material is mandatory.

Alkaline GAP-cell   We validate the GAP-cell model with experimental investigations by Phillips et al. (2017) who varied the inter-electrode gap (the distance between anode and cathode) between 2 mm and 20 mm. We use the experimental results of the 2 mm cell for parameter estimation and achieve a good match of the simulated and experimentally determined polarization curve as shown in Figure 2 (upper row, right).

The ecMR investigated by Phillips shows a relatively high onset potential of 1.75 V due to the non optimized stainless steel electrodes used for the experiments. The current density rises exponentially. Around 2.5 V the curve reaches a linear section as the ohmic overpotential gains increasing influence on the ecMR's performance. The overvoltage caused by evolving gas bubbles is negligible at low and medium current densities and rises with a fast growing gradient at elevated current densities. However, at $600 \frac{mA}{cm^2}$ the overvoltage is still rather small with a value of 0.20 V.

Changing the inter-electrode gap-widths in the model, while keeping the estimated parameters constant we show that the simulations could be extrapolated to higher gap-widths (Figure 2, upper row, right, circles).

Comparison   The course of the anodic activation overpotentials of both reactor setups is similar, the absolute value, however, is about twice as high as for the GAP-cell. This indicates that the chosen stainless steel electrodes in the GAP-cell experiments have a significantly lower catalytic activity for the OER than the platinum electrode employed in the PEM-cell experiments. Even though different cathodes were also employed, this influence seems negligible, as the cathodic activation overpotentials reach similar values for PEM and GAP-cell. The ohmic overpotential of the membrane used in the GAP-cell experiments shows a higher value than the Nafion membrane in the PEM-cell. The maximum total ohmic overvoltage of the GAP-cell at $600 \frac{mA}{cm^2}$ of 0.90 V is much higher than the ohmic overvoltage of the PEM-cell due to the additional ohmic resistance caused by proton movement in the electrolyte, only present in the GAP-cell.

For comparison purposes, we refer to a third study by Siracusano et al. (2017) which introduces an optimized PEM-cell. Instead of the typical Nafion membrane Aquivion was used as membrane material, which offers a higher proton conductivity along with a lower thickness. The second and most important improvement was the implementation of an $Ir_{0.7}Ru_{0.3}O_x$ catalyst for the OER. In simulations with these adjustments, the limiting current density remains the same, though high current densities are reached much faster with a competitive energy efficiency of 76% at $200 \frac{mA}{cm^2}$.

4. Conclusion

In order to assess the performance and optimization potentials of different reactor setups for water electrolysis, we develop mechanistic, dynamic models for a PEM-cell and a GAP-cell. The models, based on mass balances, transport equations and electrochemical kinetics are mostly based on state-of-the art equations found in literature. We introduce a new model for simulating the influence of evolving gas bubbles on the reactor's performance.

The models are validated with chosen experiments from literature. We determine unknown parameters by estimation under consideration of reasonable upper and lower bounds. A good match of simulated and experimental data is achieved. We show that the GAP-cell model is able to be extrapolated to different gap widths.

We investigate the reactor setups with regard to reachable current densities, cell efficiency and dominant loss terms. For the chosen experimental setups we show that high anodic activation overpotentials due to poor catalytic activity of the anodic electrode for the OER limit the performance in both cases. Another major limitation for the PEM-cell is the formation of bubbles. A higher GDL porosity and the change from a liquid to a gaseous inlet stream could be possible solutions.

Acknowledgements The study was conducted under the project Sustainable Chemical Synthesis (SusChemSys), which is co-financed by the European Regional Development Fund (ERDF) and the state of North Rhine-Westphalia, Germany. The authors gratefully acknowledge the financial support of the Kopernikus-project SynErgie by the Federal Ministry of Education and Research (BMBF) and the project supervision by the project management organization Projektträger Jülich (PtJ). We are also grateful to Kristina Baitalow for valuable discussions.

References

Bertuccioli, L., Chan, A., Hart, D., Lehner, F., Madden, B., Standen, E., 2014. Study on development of water electrolysis in the eu. Final report in fuel cells and hydrogen joint undertaking.

Dedigama, I., Ayers, K., Shearing, P. R., Brett, D. J., 2014. An experimentally validated steady state polymer electrolyte membrane water electrolyser model. International Journal of Electrochemical Science 9 (5), 2662–2681.

Newman, J., Thomas-Alyea, K., 2004. Electrochemical systems, chapter 8: Models for electrode kinetics. John Wiley & Sons, 212–213.

Phillips, R., Edwards, A., Rome, B., Jones, D. R., Dunnill, C. W., 2017. Minimising the ohmic resistance of an alkaline electrolysis cell through effective cell design. International Journal of Hydrogen Energy 42 (38), 23986–23994.

Siracusano, S., Baglio, V., Van Dijk, N., Merlo, L., Aricò, A. S., 2017. Enhanced performance and durability of low catalyst loading pem water electrolyser based on a short-side chain perfluorosulfonic ionomer. Applied Energy 192, 477–489.

Wu, H.-W., 2016. A review of recent development: Transport and performance modeling of pem fuel cells. Applied Energy 165, 81–106.

Yang, X., Karnbach, F., Uhlemann, M., Odenbach, S., Eckert, K., 2015. Dynamics of single hydrogen bubbles at a platinum microelectrode. Langmuir 31 (29), 8184–8193.

Anton A. Kiss, Edwin Zondervan, Richard Lakerveld, Leyla Özkan (Eds.)
Proceedings of the 29th European Symposium on Computer Aided Process Engineering
June 16th to 19th, 2019, Eindhoven, The Netherlands. © 2019 Elsevier B.V. All rights reserved.
http://dx.doi.org/10.1016/B978-0-128-18634-3.50143-0

Study on the formation of chemical wave patterns for the *Belousov–Zhabotinsky* reaction system

Jiali Ai,[a] Wei Sun,[a] Chi Zhai[a]*

[a]*College of Chemical Engineering, Beijing University of Chemical Technology, North Third Ring Road 15, Chaoyang District, Beijing, 100029, China*

Abstract

The *Belousov–Zhabotinsky* (BZ) reaction system is famous because it can generate self-organized patterns, also known as "chemical waves". Pattern formation out of an initially homogeneous system is seemingly violating the 2nd-law of thermodynamics (order is produced out of disorder), while in fact, the BZ reaction is an open, far-from thermodynamic equilibrium system, where instability is the cause of morphogenesis and Hopf bifurcation of the reaction kinetics can generate self-oscillatory state trajectories. In this paper, the evolution of the BZ reaction in a two dimensional diffusion system is studied by the numerical computation methods, for the purpose of reconstructing the chemical wave patterns. The similarity of the chemical waves to many complex systems in biology, ecology and engineering makes current study potentially significant. With the study of the pattern formation, we hope provide some thoughts on complex system theory, thermodynamics of the self-oscillatory reaction system, and numerical computation methods on complex patterns, etc.

Keywords: far-from thermodynamic equilibrium, instabilities, reaction-diffusion system, Hopf bifurcation.

1. Introduction

As early as 1950s, Turing (1952) has studied the possibility of morphogenesis out of a diffusive-reactive system. While, Pattern formation out of an initially homogeneous system is seemingly violating the 2nd-law of thermodynamics (order is produced out of disorder), and is contradictory to the "equilibrium hypothesis" of the classic thermodynamics. Hence, instabilities may be the reason of morphogenesis, and since then, nonlinear dynamic theory has been introduced to study nonequilibrium systems. Prigogine (1978) expanded the domain of thermodynamics and developed the dissipative structure theory. By his theory, far from thermodynamic equilibrium may be the source of order (also means entropy decrease), and when the system is open and far from thermodynamic equilibrium, fluctuation could make the system unstable and self-organized patterns may form instead.

It is obvious that BZ reaction is a dissipative structure system because time-symmetric breaking bifurcation has taken place. In fact, various types of bifurcations may be the source of bio-complexity (Kitano, 2002). As for the BZ reaction kinetics, Hopf bifurcation causes the equilibrium point being unstable, changing stability via a pair of purely imaginary eigenvalues, and giving birth to a self-oscillator in the dynamic system, while the cooperative action of reaction and diffusion causes the (distributive) system to generate chemical-waves. As is shown in Fig. 1, when the 2-dimentional system is properly meshed, every "dot" on the picture can be viewed as a homogeneous subset, and they are identical because they all follow relation of BZ reaction kinetics. One can view the dots as agents who behave self-oscillatory state trajectories (or, change color periodically), and each dot exchanges information with its neighbor by following the Fick's law of diffusion, then, mass transfer by diffusion causes time-delay, hence as a whole, all dots exhibit chemical wave patterns.

Fig. 1. Pattern of the diffusive *Belousov–Zhabotinsky* reaction.

Traditionally, one can adopt numerical simulation method to solve a mathematical model, ie, a reaction-diffusion system, established on a chemical wave physical background in a specific reaction system on a computer. Since a set of partial differential equations are obtained for this BZ reaction system, often a finite elements method is adopted, which meshes the 2-dimentioanl reaction region into subsets, each is assumed to be homogeneous at very short time interval; while each subset correlates to its neighbors by diffusion law. Therefore, one can summarize that, for the formation of a complex pattern as shown in Fig. 1, identical agents are distributed in 2-dimentional reaction field, and by diffusion law, these agents transfer information to one another, which is coherent to the idea of "cooperative information consensus" (Olfati-Saber,et al, 2007) in computer science terminology. Hence, the formation of chemical wave is studied by a decomposed procedure: the property of agent first, then, information exchange between agents.

The algorithm of cellular automata (CA) is introduced in this study; this method is a parallel, temporally and spatially discrete one proposed by Von Neumann (1966). The basic idea of CA computation is that the agent should follow specific dynamics which is comparatively independent to the environment, and each agent will exchange information with its nearest neighbors by a few rules. Different from the traditional way of thinking, the CA adopts a bottom-up computing strategy, which uses simple unit changes and unit interaction to show the changes of complex systems, reflecting a systematic and integrated way of thinking. As to the development of the CA algorithm, Conway developed a program called a life game using a cellular automaton. After that, Wolfram gave a more systematic explanation of the cellular automata, classifying the cellular automata according to the dynamic behavior (Tyson, et al, 1980), and further expanding the original one-dimensional system to two-dimensional one(Wang et al, 2018).

Since CA computation provides a framework of studying the complex system, namely, decomposing the system into time-dependent independent agents and locally information exchange in a special scale. Hence, for the study of chemical waves, the following section is focused on the property of the BZ reaction kinetics, then, information exchange rules between agents, followed by the exhibition of CA simulation, at last, the conclusion remarks are provided.

2. The BZ reaction kinetics: a self-oscillator

Many models have been developed for BZ reaction kinetics, and the Oregonator is adopted here because it describes the self-oscillatory behavor properly, 5 species are identified and their reaction relations are provided as follows,

$$A + Y \rightarrow X + P \qquad r_1 = k_1 AY$$
$$X + Y \rightarrow 2P \qquad r_2 = k_2 XY$$
$$A + X \rightarrow 2X + 2Z \qquad r_3 = k_3 AX$$
$$2X \rightarrow A + P \qquad r_4 = k_4 X^2$$
$$B + Z \rightarrow 0.5 f X \qquad r_5 = k_5 BZ$$

Species identification with respect to the Field-Koros-Noyes (FKN) mechanism (Field, 1972) are X = HBrO2, Y = Br-, Z = Ce(IV), A = BrO3, B = Organic species, P = HOBr, and f is an adjustable stoichiometric factor. In fact, this is the reduction reaction of bromide iron, the overall reaction is A + B → P, while X, Y and Z are the intermediate species. The reactant species A and B are normally presented in much higher concentrations than the dynamic intermediate species X, Y and Z, and when A and B are viewed as constants, and a dynamic model is developed out of the Oregonator,

$$\begin{cases} X' = k_1 AY - k_2 XY + k_3 AX - 2k_4 X^2 \\ Y' = -k_1 AY - k_2 XY + 0.5 f k_5 BZ \\ Z' = 2k_3 AY - 0.5 f k_5 BZ \end{cases} \qquad (1)$$

From the viewpoint of dynamic system theory, nonlinearity of the intermediate terms (X, Y, Z) brings about a Hopf bifurcation where increasing one of the parameters beyond the critical point may cause a self-oscillatory structure to emerge. By properly normalizing of Eq. (1), bifurcation analysis can be implemented, and one can find that the working point ($f = 0.53$) is at the self-oscillatory region, as is shown in Fig.2.

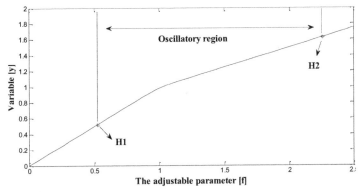

Fig. 2. Numerical continuation and bifurcation of the Oregonator with varying f.

3. Cellular automation and the results

A complete cellular automaton consists of four parts: cells, cellular space, neighbors, and local rules, where the cell is the self-oscillator, the neighbors and the local rules are the interaction ones and their properties nearest to the considered cell, and space related to the mash space and cell numbers.

To determine the local rules, the property of the oscillator needs to be re-investigated. Here, the Tyson model is used, which is the normalization of the Oregonator,

$$\begin{cases} \varepsilon a' = (qc - ac + a - a^2) \\ b' = a - b = g(a,b) \\ \delta c' = (-qc - ac + 2fb) \end{cases} \tag{2}$$

Since $\varepsilon \ll \delta \ll 1$, one can get that $-qc-ac+afb \approx 0$. Substitute this relation to the 1st-formula of Eq. (2), and the right hand side of this formula becomes $f(a, b)$. To determine the local rules, the nullclines is drawn on the (a, b) plane, as is shown in Fig.3.

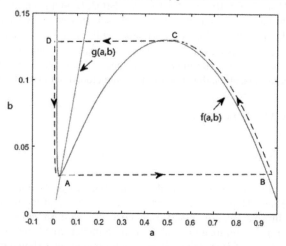

Fig. 3 The nullclines of the Tyson model.

The dashed line indicates the actual trajectory of the change of the state. At the intersection of the two zero lines is the only equilibrium point of the system, and is the equilibrium point of the local asymptotic stability. When the equilibrium is subjected to small disturbances, the medium can return fast; but once the disturbance exceeds a certain threshold, the change in the medium will pass through the excitation period, then, the drift period before it can finally return to the equilibrium state. In detail, the local rules are given in Fig. 4.

For the neighbors, the extended Moor type neighboring is selected. Since the diffusive character is decided by neighboring, one can select a weight *mask* to represent the effect of the distance on the cell. It can be seen from the simulation comparison that the *mask* has a good approximation to the diffusion coefficients, as is shown in Fig. 5.

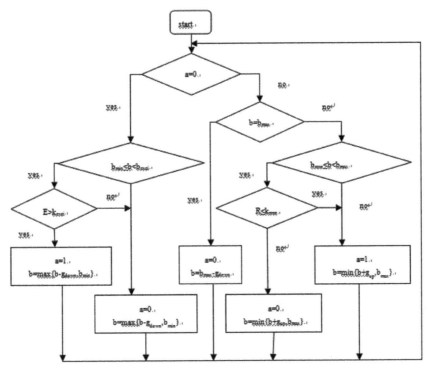

Fig 4. CA block diagram

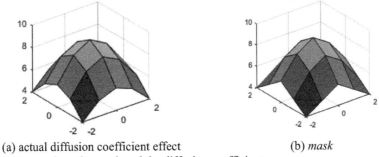

(a) actual diffusion coefficient effect   (b) *mask*

Fig 5. Comparison the musk and the diffusion coefficient.

With all the preceding work done, one can implement the CA computation. The result of the simulation on MATLAB is shown at Fig6.

4. Conclusions

By CA computation, the spiral wave is generated, as shown in Fig. 6, which simulates reasonable well the pattern of the diffusive BZ reaction shown in Fig. 1Therefore, the formation of complex system (such as the chemical waves) usually undergoes two scales of evolution: on time scale, the agents exhibit unique dynamic behavior, i.e., in the case of chemical waves, the reaction kinetics exhibits self-oscillatory state trajectories; on the spacial scale, an agent exchanges information with its neighbors by some kind of local rules, i.e., in current case, identical agents behave mass transfer with their neighbors by diffusion law. As a whole, chemical waves propagate in time and space. Through the deconstructing procedure, one can conclude that the formation of complex chemical wave patterns is caused by agents obeying typical local rules, and this analyzing structure may aid the exploration of other complex systems in biology, ecology and engineering.

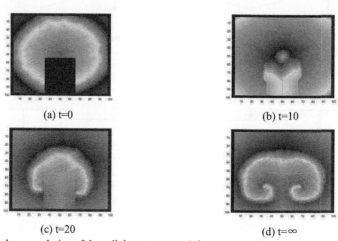

(a) t=0   (b) t=10

(c) t=20   (d) t=∞

Fig. 6 Spiral wave solution of the cellular automaton.(where t means time steps).

References

TuringA.M., 1952. The Chemical Basis of Morphogenesis, Biological Sciences, 237(641), 37-72.

Kitano H., 2002, Systems biology: a brief overview. Science, 295, 5560, 1662-1664.

Prigogine, I., 1978. Time, structure, and fluctuations. Science, 201(4358), 777-785.

Olfati-Saber, R., Fax, JA., Murray RM. Consensus and cooperation in networked multi-agent systems. Proceedings of the IEEE, 2007.

Von Neumann J. 1966, Theory of self-reproducing automta. University of Illinonis Press.

Field, R. J., Koros, E., Noyes, R. M., 1972. Oscillations in chemical systems. II.. Journal of the American Chemical Society, 94(25), 8649-8664.

Tyson J.J，Fife P.C. 1980, Target patterns In a realistic model of the Belousov-Zhabotlnskii reaction. Chem. Phys. 73, 2224-2237.

Anton A. Kiss, Edwin Zondervan, Richard Lakerveld, Leyla Özkan (Eds.)
Proceedings of the 29th European Symposium on Computer Aided Process Engineering
June 16th to 19th, 2019, Eindhoven, The Netherlands. © 2019 Elsevier B.V. All rights reserved.
http://dx.doi.org/10.1016/B978-0-128-18634-3.50144-2

Efficient design of intensified extractive distillation processes based on a hybrid optimization approach

Kai Fabian Kruber[a], Tamara Grueters[a], Mirko Skiborowski[a,*]

[a]*TU Dortmund University, Department of Biochemical and Chemical Engineering, Laboratory of Fluid Separations, Emil-Figge-Straße 70, 44227 Dortmund, Germany*

mirko.skiborowski@tu-dortmund.de

Abstract

Solvent-based separation processes, such as extractive distillation, show large potential for the separation of azeotropic mixtures. However, these processes are rather complex to design and optimize since the overall process performance depends strongly on the choice and amount of solvent and can only be evaluated for a process flowsheet with closed recycles. It is important to note that the potential for heat integration also depends strongly on the solvent choice. Consequently, a successive selection of a suitable solvent followed by process design and optimization and finally energy integration likely results in suboptimal choices. In order to allow for direct optimization of an extractive distillation process, including solvent selection and different means for energy integration, the current study proposes the use of a hybrid evolutionary-deterministic algorithm. The application is demonstrated for the separation of an azeotropic acetone-methanol mixture, considering six solvent candidates and up to four alternative means for energy integration. The results illustrate the existence of a multitude of suboptimal local solutions and demonstrate the capability of the proposed method to effectively overcome these limitations.

Keywords: hybrid optimization, evolutionary algorithm, solvent selection, energy integration

1. Introduction

The design of efficient separation processes is one of the key challenges for conceptual process design, as it accounts for almost 50 % of the overall process costs (Blahušiak et al., 2018). A considerable challenge, especially in the scope of a transition to bio-renewable feedstocks, is the separation of azeotropic mixtures (Skiborowski et al., 2013). Solvent-based separation processes, such as extractive distillation, are popular solutions for which process design is, however, a rather complex task. A key design decision is the choice of a suitable solvent that facilitates the desired separation and can be efficiently recovered. Since the choice of a suitable solvent is of major importance for the feasibility and performance of the separation process, a variety of computer-aided methods have been developed in order to support the solvent selection. Methods for computer-aided molecular design (CAMD), like the multi-level generate and test procedure by Harper and Gani (2000), screen solvents based on thermodynamic criteria, such as capacity and selectivity. The set of selected solvents can further be refined by a model-based evaluation of the process performance, for which shortcut methods and rigorous flowsheet optimization can be applied in a hierarchical fashion (Kossack et al., 2008, Kruber et al., 2018). Herein, the combination with a quantum mechanics-based property prediction allows for the screening of thousands of solvent candidates based on computationally efficient shortcut methods (Scheffczyk et al., 2016).

While similar methods have been proposed for several solvent-based separation processes, the investigation of energy integration is generally considered as a potential post-processing step, similar to the classical hierarchical approach to process design (Douglas, 1985). In the case of distillation-based separation processes, there are various options for energy integration, which need to be considered (Kiss et al., 2012). Especially for solvent-based processes, such as extractive or heteroazeotropic distillation, energy integration can have a considerable effect on the screening of potential solvents, as e.g. indicated in the recent study by Waltermann et al. (2018). Thus, simultaneous evaluation of energy integration and solvent selection should be performed in order to identify the optimal process design and best solvent. While this task can in principle be formulated as a mathematical programming problem, the solution to this problem is specifically complex. In order to enable an automated evaluation that overcomes suboptimal solutions, the current work proposes of the combination of hybrid evolutionary-deterministic optimization approach (Skiborowski et al., 2015a) with a tailored polylithic modeling and solution approach, considering rigorous MESH models (Waltermann et al., 2018). To the best of the author's knowledge, this is the first approach that enables an optimization-based design of an extractive distillation process with simultaneous consideration of solvent selection and energy and mass integration. The methodology is described in Section 2, while the case study for acetone-methanol separation and the obtained results are discussed in Section 3. Finally, Section 4 provides a brief conclusion and outlook on future work.

2. Methodology

In order to solve the highly complex process design problem, it is formulated as a mixed integer nonlinear programming problem (MINLP), which is solved by a two-level hybrid evolutionary-deterministic optimization approach. The concept of this approach, which also qualifies as a so-called memetic optimization algorithm, was introduced by Skiborowski et al. (2015a). The specific difference to other memetic algorithms, like the sophisticated method of Urselmann and Engell (2010), is the distinct feature that a full MINLP is solved by the gradient-based solver on the lower level. Thereby the search-space of the evolutionary algorithm (EA) is reduced significantly. The subsequent subsections provide a brief description of the hybrid optimization approach and describe the performed extension for additional means for energy integration.

2.1. Hybrid optimization approach

As indicated in Figure 1, the hybrid approach is a nested combination of an EA and a local deterministic optimization. The local deterministic optimization is performed in order to evaluate the fitness of the individuals in each generation of the EA. However, the genome of each individual is not representing all design degrees of freedom (DDoF) of the process optimization problem. Only discrete decisions that significantly affect the size and complexity of the design problem and initial values for setting up the superstructure model for the local deterministic optimization are optimized by the EA. In the initial optimization of an extractive distillation process presented by Skiborowski et al. (2015a), the EA handled the choice of solvent, as this determines the structure and parameterization of the thermodynamic models, as well as the maximum number of equilibrium trays per column and the feed tray. In the current study, the conventional process without energy integration (CONV) and additional four means for energy integration are considered, which are thermal coupling (TC), integration of both columns into a dividing wall column (DWC), direct heat integration (HI) and vapor recompression (VRC). As each of them requires modifications of the superstructure model, the type of energy integration is also introduced as DDoF optimized by the EA. This information extends the genome and is used for setting up the MINLP problem, which is to be solved by the local deterministic optimization.

2.2. Local deterministic optimization

The local optimization builds on a superstructure formulation, derived from the information of the genome that is to be evaluated in the EA. The superstructure is based on a rigorous MESH model with up to 190 equilibrium trays in total and a number of binary decisions w.r.t. the allocation for the feed, boil-up and recycle streams. The solution of this highly nonlinear MINLP is achieved via a polylithic modeling approach that integrates implicit functions for VLE and enthalpy computations (Skiborowski et al., 2015b) and the solution of a series of successive relaxed NLP problems with additional NCP-functions. The necessary extensions for the optimization of the energy-integrated process variants are further described in the articles of Waltermann et al. (2016, 2018). Each of the variants builds on the initialization of the basic process variant, while specific modifications of the superstructure model are automatically introduced in a sequence of refinement steps and embedded optimization problems.

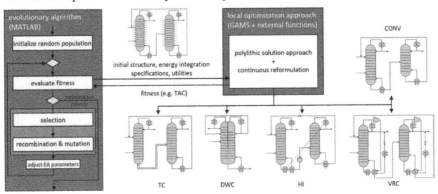

Figure 1: Scheme of hybrid optimization approach (based on Skiborowski et al. 2015)

3. Results

In order to illustrate the capabilities and the need for the developed optimization approach, the well-investigated separation of acetone and methanol is considered. Kossack et al. (2008) determined chlorobenzene, dimethyl sulfoxide (DMSO), ethanol, p-xylene, water and mesitylene as suitable solvent candidates based on an initial CAMD screening. Previous investigations showed that the hybrid optimization approach can reliably overcome local optima that might result in a sub-optimal solvent selection for the extractive distillation process (Skiborowski et al., 2015a), while the energy integration might again result in an alternative ranking of the different solvents (Waltermann et al., 2018). The objective of the current study is, therefore, to evaluate whether the extended hybrid optimization approach can reliably determine the optimal solvent choice for an extractive distillation process with the considered options for energy integration. The optimal process design is determined w.r.t. the total annualized costs (TAC).

The same thermodynamic properties, as well as feed and product specifications that were used by Kossack et al. (2008) and Skiborowski et al. (2015a) are used in the current study. Only the economic process model was updated w.r.t. more recent cost indices and utility prices, which nevertheless has a recognizable effect on the results. Considering the previous investigation of the energy integrated process variants by Waltermann et al. (2018), the HI and VRC variant are not considered for the solvent DMSO, due to the significant pressure increase required for heat integration. Since the necessary pressure shift can be evaluated based on simple flash calculations for known product compositions, the complex optimization of the energy integrated variants should generally be avoided to save unnecessary computational load. For the current study, a (μ, λ, κ)-selection with 50 individuals and 15 parents with a maximum age of 6 generations is used, while an initial population size of 150 individuals is considered, covering all combinations of solvents and means of energy integration. The algorithm terminates in case the TAC of the best individual does not improve by more than 10 €/y, which is less than 0,005% of the best solution, in 3 consecutive generations. The optimization problem was solved on a HP Z820 workstation with two Intel Xeon E5-2660 CPUs and an evaluation of up to 24 individuals in parallel by means of a multi-threading approach. Four independent runs, with a mean computation time of 5.5 h, confirmed the best solution with a maximum deviation of less than 1% in TAC.

Figure 2 compares the lowest TAC of all process configurations, solvents and considered

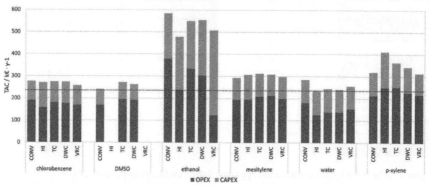

Figure 2: TAC of the best individuals of four independent runs considering OPEX and CAPEX

energy integration options. For each bar, the share of annual operating (OPEX) and capital expenditures (CAPEX) is illustrated. Interestingly, energy integration is only beneficial for ethanol and water. Depending on the product of the extractive distillation column, the potential decreases with increasing solvent boiling temperature. While ethanol results in the highest TAC, water becomes the favorable solvent in the HI variant and outperforms chlorobenzene and DMSO, which are superior in comparison to the basic sequence. Waltermann et al. (2018) obtained similar results in a local optimization study based on the embedded deterministic optimization approach. The results of the hybrid optimization approach further allow for an analysis of the sensitivity of the local optimization w.r.t. the initialization.

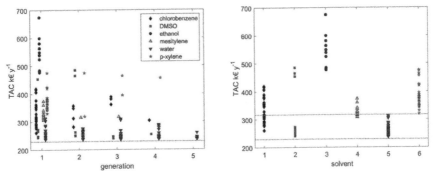

Figure 3: Evolution of the fitness over the generations (left) and variation for solvents (right)

Figure 3 summarizes the evolution of the fitness over the generations (left) and the distribution of the costs for all evaluations of each solvent (right) for a single run. The results indicate the capability of the hybrid optimization approach to quickly find a very good solution and confirm this in a few generations for which an increasing number of individuals focus on the preferred solvent and process variant. On the other side, the large variations in the TAC determined for the single solvents highlights the dependence of the results on the consideration of energy integration and the specifications of the initial superstructure, both of which are modified by the EA in the hybrid optimization approach. While the best individual for water outperforms all other solvents, a suboptimal solution may instead favor any of the remaining solvents (see dotted lines in Fig. 3 right), except ethanol, which can be discarded clearly.

Figure 4 further illustrates the distribution of the fitness of the evaluated individuals in the respective run in terms of OPEX and CAPEX (left) and a magnified illustration of the most effective water-based separation processes. Additional lines of constant TAC are introduced to highlight the existence of almost equivalent process designs with alternative DDoF. Thus, although a single objective optimization is performed, specific trade-offs of the different cost shares are automatically determined in the hybrid optimization approach. The illustration also highlights the concentration of solutions in close vicinity to the best performing process options (<5% higher TAC).

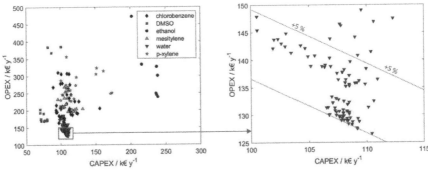

Figure 4: Cost distribution for all individuals (left) and for the best-performing processes utilizing water for a single run

4. Conclusion

The current work presents the purposeful extension of a previously introduced hybrid optimization approach and illustrates its capabilities for the optimal selection of solvents and the design of intensified separation processes. The investigated case study addresses the design of energy integrated extractive distillation columns and illustrates that superior solvent choices and process designs may easily be missed based on the limitation to a single locally optimal solution. The presented hybrid optimization approach effectively overcomes these limitations and increases the confidence in the determined optimization results. It furthermore provides information on possible trade-off solutions with similar TAC, but variations in CAPEX and OPEX, without the need for multi-objective process optimization. The fully algorithmic implementation should furthermore allow for an extension of the search space to an increased number of solvents and therefore enable integration with a CAMD approach that provides the necessary thermodynamic property predictions. However, as indicated for the case of DMSO, apparently infeasible or inferior process variants should be discarded directly to save unnecessary computational load. The transfer of the approach to other solvent-based separation processes requires the development of reliable deterministic optimization strategies, as well as the adaption of the EA and will be part of future work.

References

Blahušiak, M., Kiss, A.A., Babic, K., Kersten, S.R.A., Bargeman, G., Schuur, B., 2018, Insights into the selection and design of fluid separation processes, Sep. Purif. Technol., 194, 301-318

Douglas, J.M., 1985, A hierarchical decision procedure for process synthesis, AIChE J., 31(3), 353-362

Harper, P.M., Gani, R.: A multi-step and multi-level approach for computer aided molecular design, Comp. Chem. Eng., 2000, 24, 677–683.

Kiss, A.A., Flores Landaeta, S.J., Infante Ferreira, C.A., 2012. Towards energy efficient distillation technologies – Making the right choice. Energy 47 (1), 531–542.

Kossack, S., Kraemer, K. Gani, R., Marquardt, W., 2008, A systematic synthesis framework for extractive distillation processes, Chem. Eng. Res. Des., 86 (7), 781-792

Kruber, K., Scheffczyk, J., Leonhard, K., Bardow, A. and Skiborowski, M. 2018, A hierarchical approach for solvent selection based on successive model refinement, Comp. Aided Chem. Eng., 43, 325-330

Scheffczyk, J., Redepenning, C., Jens C.M., Winter B., Leonhard, K., Marquardt, W., Bardow, A., Massive automated solvent screening for minimum energy demand in hybrid extraction–distillation using COSMO-RS. Chem. Eng. Res. Des. 2016;115:433–42.

Skiborowski, M., Harwardt, A., Marquardt, W., 2013, Conceptual design of distillation-based hybrid separation processes, Annu. Rev. Chem. Biomol. Eng., 4, 45–68.

Skiborowski, M., Rautenberg, M., Marquardt, W., 2015a, A Hybrid Evolutionary-Deterministic Optimization Approach for Conceptual Design, Ind. Eng. Chem. Res., 54(41), 10054-10072.

Skiborowski, M., Harwardt, A., Marquardt, W., 2015b, Efficient optimization-based design for the separation of heterogeneous azeotropic mixtures. Comput. Chem. Eng., 72, 34–51.

Urselmann, M.; Engell, S., 2010, Optimization-based design of reactive distillation columns using a memetic algorithm. Comp. Aided Chem. Eng., 2010, 28,1243–1248.

Waltermann, T., Skiborowski, M., 2016, Efficient optimization-based design of energetically intensified distillation processes, Comp. Aided Chem. Eng., 38, 571-576.

Waltermann, T., Grueters, T., Skiborowski, M., 2018, Optimization of extractive distillation – integrated solvent selection and energy integration, Comp. Aided Chem. Eng., 44, 187-192.

Anton A. Kiss, Edwin Zondervan, Richard Lakerveld, Leyla Özkan (Eds.)
Proceedings of the 29th European Symposium on Computer Aided Process Engineering
June 16th to 19th, 2019, Eindhoven, The Netherlands. © 2019 Elsevier B.V. All rights reserved.
http://dx.doi.org/10.1016/B978-0-128-18634-3.50145-4

Flux Balance Analysis Incorporating a Coarse-grained Proteome Constraint for Predicting Overflow Metabolism in *Escherichia Coli*

Hong Zeng,[a] Aidong Yang [a,*]

[a]University of Oxford, Parks Road, Oxford OX1 3PJ, United Kingdom

aidong.yang@eng.ox.ac.uk

Abstract

Flux balance analysis (FBA) and its dynamic extension DFBA are typical constraint-based modelling tools in systems biology. They have been widely used for *in silico* analysis of intracellular metabolic flux distributions. The objective of this work is to use FBA and DFBA to predict quantitatively the extent of overflow metabolism in *E. coli* under a wide range of growth conditions. In light of the recently validated proteome allocation theory, we developed a coarse-grained constraint to represent the competition of the limited proteomic resource between energy biogenesis and biomass synthesis. Incorporating such constraint to FBA renders accurate predictions of the onset of overflow metabolism and the rates of acetate production at increased growth rates for various wild-type *E. coli* strains. On top of this, we further use DFBA to investigate how the production of a foreign protein affects the growth physiologies of recombinant *E. coli*. Simulation results show that the incorporation of proteomic burden and the tuning of cellular energy demand via strain-specific growth data are key to an accurate prediction. Although several limitations remain to overcome, this work provides a starting point of using FBA-based model as an efficient predictive tool to guide metabolic decisions to address issues such as reducing acetate production and enhancing protein productivity.

Keywords: *Escherichia coli*, overflow metabolism, resource allocation, recombinant protein production, genome-scale model

1. Introduction

Flux balance analysis (FBA) is a widely adopted modelling tool in metabolic engineering and systems biology for predicting intracellular metabolic fluxes (Orth et al., 2010). As a constraint-based modelling approach, the outcome of FBA depends on the constraints incorporated in the optimisation problem being solved. In addition to the built-in mass and energy balances, several constraints have been proposed to account for the previously proposed notion of constrained cellular resources (Molenaar et al., 2009) via quantifying the enzymatic cost of individual reactions (Nilsson et al., 2017). These constraints have been shown to improve efficiently the growth rate prediction by FBA. However, most of these models require extensive information of enzyme kinetics for thousands reactions involved in the metabolic network. In this work, we propose a coarse-grained constraint to represent the limit of cellular proteome resources and their allocation over (a small number of) energy pathways and the biomass synthesis flux, based on the recently-developed proteome allocation theory (PAT) for explaining the overflow metabolism in *E. coli* (Basan et al., 2015). We named this new constraint as the PAT constraint. Due to its coarse-grained nature, the PAT constraint introduces only a small number of parameters (independent of the scale of the metabolic model), which can be estimated using experimentally determined growth data. In particular, we have focused on the prediction of acetate production at high growth rates, a phenomenon commonly referred to as the overflow metabolism, which represents not only a waste of substrate carbon but also leads to low cell density and low product yield (Eiteman and Altman, 2006) due to acid toxicity. In this paper, we describe the modelling approach and the results of simulation experiments that have been carried out to obtain the predicted growth phenotype of various wild-type and recombinant *E. coli* under a wide span of growth conditions. Comparisons are made with the experimental data in terms of (i) the steady state acetate-growth rate profile and steady state biomass yield-growth rate profile for wild-type *E. coli* and (ii) the biomass accumulation, substrate consumption, acetate accumulation and protein production of batch cultures of recombinant *E. coli*. Future perspective in terms of using the modelling framework developed in this work to guide metabolic decisions for efficient microbial protein production processes is illustrated in the end of the result section.

2. Methodology

Following the philosophy of multi-scale modelling, we propose to construct a FBA model that combines (i) detailed stoichiometry and topology of the cellular metabolic network and (ii) a concise global regulation rule to govern an accurate flux prediction. More specifically, a genome-scale metabolic model was adopted, and a coarse-grained PAT constraint was constructed at pathway level (on the contrary to reaction level constraints adopted in previous studies) to depict the constrained proteome to be allocated between energy biogenesis and biomass synthesis. The energy pathways discussed here are fermentation (involving glycolysis, acetate pathways and oxidative phosphorylation) and respiration (comprising glycolysis, tricarboxylic acid cycle and oxidative phosphorylation). Biomass synthesis flux includes primarily catabolic reactions, anabolic reactions and ribosomal reactions for the synthesis and assembly of biomass building blocks

2.1. PAT Constraint

Based on the recently published proteome allocation theory (Basan et al., 2015), we proposed the following coarse-grained proteomic constraint:

$$w_f^* v_f + w_r^* v_r + b^* \lambda + \phi_{recP}^* \leq 1 \tag{1}$$

where v_f, v_r and λ are the fermentation, respiration and biomass synthesis flux, respectively; w_f^*, w_r^* and b^* are the proteomic cost parameters denoting the fractions of proteome required per unit fermentation, respiration and biomass synthesis flux, respectively; ϕ_{recP}^* represents the portion of proteome used for the synthesis of foreign proteins in recombinant strains, i.e. $\phi_{recP}^* = 0$ for wild-type strains. The equal sign of Eq. (1) is expected to hold in fast-growing conditions (e.g. overflow region) where the cell growth is limited predominantly by proteome resources; in other growth conditions this constraint is relaxed by the less-than sign. Eq. (1) is referred to as the PAT constraint.

2.2. Genome-scale modelling

The genome-scale metabolic model *i*AF1260 (Feist et al., 2007), integrated with the PAT constraint was used in FBA simulations to obtain the steady state growth rate and metabolic flux distribution for *E. coli* at different growth conditions. The generic optimization problem solved in FBA is formulated as:

Maximise growth rate λ, subject to

(i) $Sv = 0$

(ii) $v^L \leq v \leq v^U$ (2)

(iii) $w_f^* v_f + w_r^* v_r + b^* \lambda + \phi_{recP}^* \leq 1$

where S comprises the reaction stoichiometry defined by the *i*AF1260 model; v is a column vector containing intracellular metabolic fluxes with upper and lower bound set by v^L and v^U; the third constraint of Eq. (2) is the PAT constraint that depicts the global proteome allocation rule. The dynamic framework (DFBA) is achieved by coupling the standard FBA with a set of ordinary differential equations (ODEs) describing the dynamic extracellular environment:

$$\frac{dX}{dt} = \lambda X \tag{3}$$

$$\frac{dG}{dt} = -v_{glc}X \tag{4}$$

$$\frac{dA}{dt} = v_{ac}X \tag{5}$$

$$\frac{dP}{dt} = v_{recP}X \tag{6}$$

where X, G, A and P are the concentrations of biomass, glucose, acetate and recombinant protein in the bioreactor, respectively. The growth rate λ, glucose uptake flux v_{glc}, acetate production flux v_{ac} and protein synthesis flux v_{recP} are obtained from the solution of FBA. Dynamic simulation is carried out by exchanging information between FBA and ODEs at a number of time intervals: FBA is performed at the beginning of every time interval to give steady state flux distribution; the values of the fluxes of interest are then passed to the ODEs to update the outer environment state. This procedure is repeated until the entire time duration has been simulated.

3. Results

3.1. Predicting overflow metabolism for wild-type E. coli

Experimental data from the literature (Extended Data Figure 1, Basan et al., 2015) was used to estimate three PAT constraint parameters, namely w_f^*, w_r^* and b^*. FBA was then

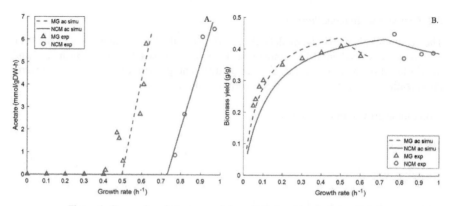

Figure 1: Comparison between model predictions and experimental data

performed to obtain the steady state acetate production rate for wild-type *E. coli* MG1655 and NCM3722 under aerobic-glucose conditions. The predicted acetate production rate is in good agreement with the experimental results (Figure 1A), which validates the suitability of using the concise pathway-level proteome allocation constraint as the global regulatory rule to guide the prediction of the overflow metabolism in a FBA model.

Furthermore, we calculated the simulated biomass yield on glucose (g biomass produced per g glucose consumed). Interestingly, we found that the accuracy of the biomass yield prediction is closely related to the cellular energy demand (i.e. overall ATP production rate at steady state). When FBA was performed with the default energy demand given in the *i*AF1260 model, considerable inconsistency was observed between the simulation results and the experimental data for both MG and NCM strains. Such deviation indicates that the carbon utilization in the model is not consistent with the real case. In FBA models, carbon balance is dictated by three aspects: (i) the assumed biomass content of the cell; (ii) the endogenous structure of the metabolic network and (iii) the energy demand for supporting cell maintenance and growth. In *i*AF1260, the first aspect is determined by experimentally measured dry cell composition of *E. coli*; the metabolic network is obtained by well-developed *E. coli*-specific biochemical characterization. Only the last aspect is constructed with assumptions and is reported with ±50% uncertainty. Therefore, we decided to modify the default energy demand using experimentally determined strain-specific growth data. Subsequently, the prediction of biomass yield (Figure 1B) became highly coincided with the experimental values without compromising the accuracy in the prediction of the onset and extent of the overflow metabolism.

3.2. The effect of recombinant protein production

Having validated the efficiency of using the PAT constraint to guide the prediction of overflow metabolism in wild-type E. coli, we further investigated the impact of recombinant protein production on the overall growth physiologies. According to the proteome allocation theory, the production of a foreign protein should occupy a certain fraction of the proteome. Therefore, we added a recombinant protein sector (ϕ^*_{recP} in Eq. (1)) to the wild-type PAT constraint. We also added the synthesis reaction of the recombinant protein (in this case green fluorescent protein, GFP) to the model. DFBA was performed to simulate the dynamic cell growth in a batch culture. During the analysis, we found that the introduction of ϕ^*_{recP} alone is not sufficient to render satisfied predicted results. Strong deviations were observed for both cell growth, glucose consumption, acetate accumulation and protein production when comparing with the experimental data. Based on the experience gained in the wild-type case, we considered that in this case it is likely that the energy demand again plays an important role. We thus co-estimated ϕ_{recP}^{*} and the maintenance energy (ATPM) simultaneously, and found that with $\phi_{recP}^{*} = 0.1333$ and ATPM = 32.6 mmol/gDW-h, the dynamic simulation results were in excellent agreement with the experimental data (Figure 2A). It is worth noting that the default ATPM of wild-type E. coli in iAF1260 is 8.39 mmol/gDW-h, which is significantly lower than the new ATPM determined for GFP-producing E. coli. The strong increase in maintenance energy for recombinant E. coli is consistent with previously proposed notion of "metabolic burden of recombinant protein production" (Wu et al., 2016). Our model suggests that the production of GFP provokes not only proteomic burdens to the allocation of cellular proteome resources, but also a significant increase in the overall energy demand, which is potentially used for plasmid maintenance, protein secretion and degradation of the misfolded protein. Building on the aforementioned findings on the impact of PAT constraint (with ϕ_{recP}^{*}) and energy demand on the growth predictions for GFP-producing E. coli, we further considered the potential of using the model to support the enhancement of protein productivity. According to the proteome allocation theory, the production of extra proteins, a desirable process from the engineering point of view, reduces the portion of proteome attainable to energy pathways and biomass synthesis, thus leads to more severe overflow phenomenon that gives rise to undesirable products such as acetate.

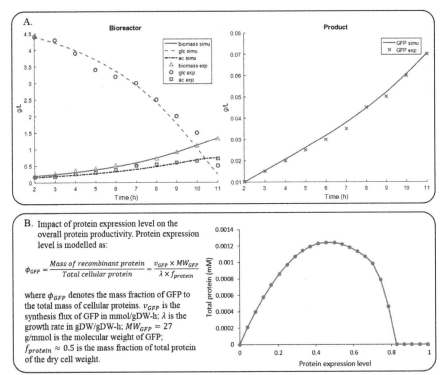

Figure 2: Modelling recombinant protein production and potential application

Investigating this trade-off, we performed further DFBA simulations with different protein production levels (while all the other conditions were kept identical between simulations), attempting to find an optimal expression level with highest GFP produced at the end of a batch culture (Figure 2B). Simulation results show the predicted existence of an optimal protein expression level ($\phi^*_{recP} \sim 0.5$), which offers a preliminary indication of the potential use of the proposed model for guiding metabolic engineering decisions. However, several limitations need to be resolved for the development of a fully predictive tool: (i) it is still unclear how the *in vivo* protein expression system is linked to the modelled proteomic burden ϕ^*_{recP}; (ii) a robust and reliable quantification of the protein expression level (currently quantified by mass fraction of the recombinant protein) remains unresolved; and (iii) how different protein expression levels affect the substrate uptake kinetics and the energy demand is still to be quantified.

4. Conclusions

This work shows that the incorporation of a coarse-grained proteome constraint into a genome-scale metabolic model can produce accurate prediction of the overflow metabolism in wild-type *E. coli* as well as predict key growth physiologies of a batch culture of recombinant *E. coli*. Although several limitations remain to overcome, the proposed modelling approach provides a basis of using FBA as an efficient predictive tool to guide metabolic engineering decisions to address issues such as reducing acetate production and enhancing the productivity of recombinant proteins.

References

Basan, M., Hui, S., Okano, H., Zhang, Z., Shen, Y., Williamson, J.R., Hwa, T., 2015. Overflow metabolism in Escherichia coli results from efficient proteome allocation. Nature 528, 99–104.

Eiteman, M.A., Altman, E., 2006. Overcoming acetate in Escherichia coli recombinant protein fermentations. Trends Biotechnol.

Feist, A.M., Henry, C.S., Reed, J.L., Krummenacker, M., Joyce, A.R., Karp, P.D., Broadbelt, L.J., Hatzimanikatis, V., Palsson, B.Ø., 2007. A genome-scale metabolic reconstruction for Escherichia coli K-12 MG1655 that accounts for 1260 ORFs and thermodynamic information. Mol. Syst. Biol. 3.

Molenaar, D., van Berlo, R., de Ridder, D., Teusink, B., 2009. Shifts in growth strategies reflect tradeoffs in cellular economics. Mol Syst Biol 5.

Nilsson, A., Nielsen, J., Palsson, B.O., 2017. Metabolic models of protein allocation call for the kinetome. Cell Syst. 5, 538–541.

Orth, J.D., Thiele, I., Palsson, B.Ø., 2010. What is flux balance analysis? Nat. Biotechnol. 28, 245–248.

Wu, G., Yan, Q., Jones, J.A., Tang, Y.J., Fong, S.S., Koffas, M.A.G., 2016. Metabolic Burden: Cornerstones in Synthetic Biology and Metabolic Engineering Applications. Trends Biotechnol. 34, 652–664.

Anton A. Kiss, Edwin Zondervan, Richard Lakerveld, Leyla Özkan (Eds.)
Proceedings of the 29th European Symposium on Computer Aided Process Engineering
June 16th to 19th, 2019, Eindhoven, The Netherlands. © 2019 Elsevier B.V. All rights reserved.
http://dx.doi.org/10.1016/B978-0-128-18634-3.50146-6

Adjoint system method in shape optimization of some typical fluid flow patterns

Alexis Courtais[a,*], François Lesage[a], Yannick Privat[b], Pascal Frey[c] and Abderrazak Latifi [a]

[a]*Laboratoire Réactions et Génie des Procédés, CNRS, Université de Lorraine, Nancy, France*
[b]*Institut de Recherche Mathématique Avancée, CNRS, Université de Strasbourg, Strasbourg, France*
[c]*Laboratoire Jacques-Louis Lions, CNRS, Sorbonne Universités, Paris, France*
alexis.courtais@univ-lorraine.fr

Abstract

In this paper a shape optimization approach based on the Hadamard geometric optimization method is developed. Four case studies representing typical fluid flow patterns in fluid dynamics, i.e. flow around an obstacle, flow in a 90 ° or 180 ° elbow pipe and flow in a dyadic tree, are considered. Low velocities are imposed at the inlet of each case study in order to operate in laminar flow regime. The objective is to determine the shape that minimizes the energy dissipated by viscous friction subjected to the Navier-Stokes equations and to iso-volumic constraint. The required gradients of the performance index and constraint with respect to the shape are computed by means of the adjoint system method. The momentum equations are implemented and solved using the OpenFOAM CFD software, and the solver "adjointShapeOptimizationFoam" is modified in order to compute the solution of the resulting optimization problems. The optimal shapes obtained in the four case studies are in very good agreement with the available literature works. Moreover, they allow a significant reduction of the dissipated energy ranging from 10.8 to 53.3 %.

Keywords: Shape optimization, Ajoint system, Energy dissipation, CFD, OpenFOAM

1. Introduction

Chemical industry is more than ever constrained to invest in research and innovation to remain competitive. This competitiveness necessarily requires the development of more flexible, intensified, efficient and compact processes. The shape of the units involved in these processes is very often critical to their efficiency and represents major scientific, technical and technological challenges. Shape optimization is a technology that is quite appropriate to meet these challenges. It consists of a set of techniques and methods allowing to find the best shape of an object that optimizes a cost function or a performance index while satisfying given constraints. Originally, shape optimization has been developed for aerodynamic industry and particularly for aircrafts. More recently, it has been used in chemical engineering to determine the optimal shape of a pipe (Henrot and Privat, 2010) or microchannels (Tonomura et al., 2010).

This paper presents the development of a shape optimization approach based on adjoint system method. The latter is used to derive the shape gradient needed in the optimal shape determination. OpenFOAM software is used as CFD solver for the flow model ,i.e. the Navier-Stokes equations, and adjoint system equations.

2. Case studies and modeling

The optimization approach developed in this paper is tested on four 2D case studies: flow around an obstacle, flow in a 90 ° or 180 ° elbow pipe and flow in a dyadic tree. Each initial domain, Ω_0, of the case studies is presented on Fig. 1. The boundary $\partial\Omega$ of the domain Ω is given by $\partial\Omega = \Gamma_{in} \cup \Gamma_{out} \cup \Gamma_{lat} \cup \Gamma$, where

- Γ_{in} is the inlet of the domain on which a quadratic velocity profile is imposed. Thus, the laminar flow is already developed at the inlet boundary (Eq (1c)).

- Γ_{out} is the outlet of the domain on which the normal component of the stress tensor is equal to zero (Eq (1e)).

- Γ_{lat} is the fixed edge of the domain on which a no-slip condition is applied (Eq (1d)).

- Γ is the free boundary of the domain, i.e. the unknown of the shape optimization problem. Moreover, it is the boundary that will evolve over the iterations of the optimization algorithm. A no-slip condition is applied on this boundary (Eq (1d)).

In each case, the velocity is set to a value leading to Reynolds numbers lower than 500, thus ensuring that the flow is laminar. The condition of zero absolute pressure is imposed at the outlet boundary. The system of Navier-Stokes equations describing the fluid flow is given as

$$
\begin{cases}
-\nu\Delta U + (U \cdot \nabla U) + \nabla p = 0 & \text{in } \Omega & \text{(1a)} \\
\nabla \cdot U = 0 & \text{in } \Omega & \text{(1b)} \\
U = U_{in} & \text{on } \Gamma_{in} & \text{(1c)} \\
U = 0 & \text{on } \Gamma_{lat} \cup \Gamma & \text{(1d)} \\
\sigma(U,p).n = 0 & \text{on } \Gamma_{out} & \text{(1e)}
\end{cases}
$$

In the above system, $\sigma(U,p)$ is the stress tensor, given by :

$$
\sigma(U,p) = 2\nu\varepsilon(U) - p\mathbf{I} \quad \text{with} \quad \varepsilon(U) = \frac{1}{2}(\nabla U + (\nabla U)^T). \tag{2}
$$

where ν is the fluid kinematic viscosity, I the identity matrix, U and p respectively the velocity and the absolute pressure of the fluid and $\varepsilon(U)$ the strain tensor.

3. Shape optimization formulation

3.1. Optimization problem

In this work, the objective is to determine the shape of the four aforementioned case studies that minimizes the energy dissipated by the fluid due to the work of viscous forces. Such a criterion is relevant in practice since the energy dissipated is directly related to pressure losses. The performance index is therefore defined as

$$
J(\Omega) = 2\nu \int_\Omega |\varepsilon(U)|^2 \, dx \tag{3}
$$

This optimization problem is subjected to Navier-Stokes equations (1) and to the volume constraint given by Eq. (4). It is solved using the adjoint system method.

$$
C(\Omega) = \mathcal{V}(\Omega) - \mathcal{V}(\Omega_0) = 0 \tag{4}
$$

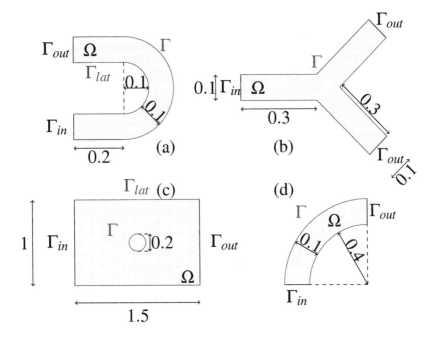

Figure 1: Initial shapes of the four case studies, (a) flow in a 180 ° elbow pipe, (b) flow in a diadyc tree, (c) flow around an obstacle, (d) flow in a 90 ° elbow pipe.

3.2. Adjoint system method

The shape optimization approach developed involves the differentiation with respect to the domain also called derivative in the sense of Hadamard (Allaire, 2007; Henrot and Pierre, 2005). It consists in moving all the meshpoints according to the following induction formula

$$\Omega_{i+1} = (\mathbf{X} + t\mathbf{V})(\Omega_i) \tag{5}$$

where $\mathbf{X}$ is the vector of meshpoints coordinates at iteration i, t the method's step and $\mathbf{V}$ is the vector field describing the mesh displacement. The objective of the method is to compute t and $\mathbf{V}$.

Let us introduce the lagrangian functional defined as

$$\mathscr{L}(\Omega) = J(\Omega) + \lambda C(\Omega) = 2\nu \int_{\Omega} |\varepsilon(\mathbf{U})|^2 \, dx + \lambda \left(\mathcal{V}(\Omega) - \mathcal{V}(\Omega_0) \right) \tag{6}$$

where λ is the Lagrange multiplier.

On the other hand, let $\mathbf{V} : \mathbf{R}^d \to \mathbf{R}^d$ be a regular vector field. The derivative of the Lagrangian $\mathscr{L}(\Omega)$ in the direction of $\mathbf{V}$ is defined by (Henrot and Privat, 2010)

$$\mathscr{L}'(\Omega)(\mathbf{V}) = < d\mathscr{L}(\Omega), \mathbf{V} > = \lim_{t \to 0} \frac{\mathscr{L}(\Omega_t) - \mathscr{L}(\Omega)}{t}, \qquad \text{with} \qquad \Omega_t = (\mathbf{X} + t\mathbf{V})(\Omega). \tag{7}$$

To implement the shape optimization algorithm, it is necessary to express the Lagrangian derivative in the following form

$$\mathscr{L}'(\Omega)(\mathbf{V}) = \int_{\partial\Omega} (G + \lambda)(\mathbf{V} \cdot \mathbf{n}) \tag{8}$$

where G is the shape gradient, i.e. a function defined on the boundary of the domain Ω depending on U but not on the vector field V. Under this form, it will be easy to determine a new mesh choice leading to a decrease of the Lagrangian. The adjoint method is based on the introduction of an adjoint state (U_a, p_a). Straightforward computations (see (Henrot and Privat, 2010) for more details) lead to the following shape derivative of the Lagrangian functional expressed as

$$\mathcal{L}'(\Omega)(V) = \int_{\partial\Omega} (2\nu(\varepsilon(U):\varepsilon(U_a) - \varepsilon(U):\varepsilon(U)) + \lambda)(V \cdot n) d\sigma \tag{9}$$

Thus, the shape gradient is given by

$$G = 2\nu(\varepsilon(U):\varepsilon(U_a) - \varepsilon(U):\varepsilon(U)) \tag{10}$$

where U_a is the velocity of the adjoint state (U_a, p_a) defined as the solution of the following equations

$$\begin{cases} -\nu\Delta U_a + (\nabla U)^T U_a - \nabla U_a U + \nabla p_a = 2\nu\Delta U & \text{dans } \Omega \tag{11a} \\ \nabla \cdot U_a = 0 & \text{dans } \Omega \tag{11b} \\ U_a = 0 & \text{sur } \Gamma_{in} \cup \Gamma_{lat} \cup \Gamma \tag{11c} \\ \sigma(U_a, p_a)n + (U \cdot n)U_a = 4\nu\varepsilon(U)n & \text{sur } \Gamma_{out} \tag{11d} \end{cases}$$

known as adjoint system equations. Finally, the mesh displacement V is computed by solving the following system

$$\begin{cases} -\Delta V + V = 0 & \text{dans } \Omega \tag{12a} \\ V = 0 & \text{sur } \Gamma_{in} \cup \Gamma_{out} \cup \Gamma_{Lat} \tag{12b} \\ \nabla V n = -(G + \lambda)n & \text{sur } \Gamma \tag{12c} \end{cases}$$

4. Implementation of the optimization algorithm

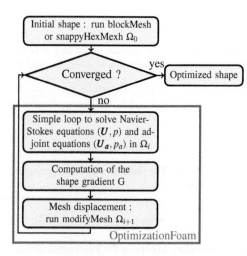

Figure 2: Shape optimization algorithm

The CFD equations are implemented using C++ language within OpenFOAM software (Weller et al., 1998). The latter is a free and open source software which allows to solve partial differential equations (Navier-Stokes and adjoint equations Eq. (1) and (11)) using finite volume method. OpenFOAM supplies a solver which solves the Navier-Stokes and an ajdoint system for topologic optimization. This solver is named "adjointShapeOptimizationFoam". The latter is modified and enriched in order to implement the optimization algorithm and determine the best shape in each of the four considered case studies. The algorithm is detailed in Fig.2. At each iteration, a test of the quality of the mesh is carried out through the aspect ratio. In 2D, the aspect ratio is defined as the ratio of its longer side to its shorter side. If the ratio is too large, i.e. higher than 5, the domain is remeshed.

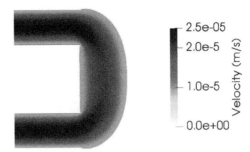

Figure 3: Initial shape of the 180 ° elbow   Figure 4: Optimized shape of the 180 ° elbow

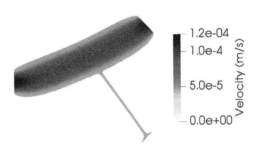

Figure 5: Initial shape of the dyadic tree   Figure 6: Optimal shape of the dyadic tree

Figure 7: Initial shape of the obstacle   Figure 8: Optimal shape of the obstacle

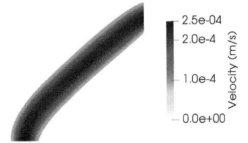

Figure 9: Initial shape of the 90 ° elbow   Figure 10: Optimal shape of the 90 ° elbow

5. Main results

Initial shapes and velocity distributions are presented in Figs. 3, 5, 7 and 9, and optimized shapes
are shown in Figs. 4, 6, 8 and 10. In each case, moving the free boundary allows a reduction

Table 1: Performances of the optimization apprch

Case	Iterations	Simulation time	Reduction of dissipated energy	Reduction of pressure losses
180 ° elbow	300	40 min	30.7 %	33.3 %
Dyadic tree	550	1 h 01	53.3 %	40.4 %
Obstacle	200	9 mn 14	10.8 %	15.4 %
90 ° elbow	80	2 mn 30	27 %	24 %

of the velocity distribution due to an increase in the width of the channel (for the elbows and the dyadic tree) or to a decrease of the width of the obstacle. Thus, the reduction of the velocity and the increase of the section lead to a reduction of the velocity gradient and, consequently, to a reduction of the performance index. All the optimal shapes obtained in this study are in very good agreement with the literature works (Tonomura et al., 2010; Dapogny et al., 2017).

The performances of the optimization approach for each case study are presented in Table 1. Depending on the case, a significant reduction of the dissipated energy is observed, between 10.8 and 53.3 %. Since the energy dissipated by the fluid and the pressure drops are related, a decrease of pressure losses is also observed in similar proportions, i.e. between 15.4 and 40.4 %. The dyadic tree case is the most costly in terms of computation time. Indeed, the geometry in that case undergoes huge changes, and therefore, one has to finely remesh many times. In this case, the flow seems to privilege one of the two branches. The small one cannot be remove because the outlet is a fixed boundary and the geometric algorithm cannot modify the topology of the domain.

From a numerical point of view, the case "flow around an obstacle" is the most difficult to implement. Indeed, the initial Lagrange multiplier must be properly chosen in order to avoid the removal of the obstacle which would result in wrong simulations due to invalid meshes. To overcome this problem, the initial Lagrange multiplier λ_0 is set to a value higher than the absolute value of shape gradient G.

6. Conclusion

In this work, a shape optimization approach has been developed and implemented within Open-FOAM software. Four case studies representing typical fluid flow patterns in fluid dynamics were considered. The objective was to determine the shape that minimizes the energy dissipated by viscous friction while meeting the volume constraint and satisfying the momentum equations. A significant reduction of pressure losses was observed in each case study which will result in important energy savings. The coming works will focus on shape optimization of a mass or heat exchangers and the mixing in a stirred tank.

References

G. Allaire, 2007. Conception optimale de structures . Vol. 58 of Mathématiques et Applications. Berlin: Springer.

C. Dapogny, P. Frey, F. Omnès, Y. Privat, 2017. Geometrical shape optimization in fluid mechanics using freefem++. Structural and Multidisciplinary Optimization, 1-28.

A. Henrot, M. Pierre, 2005. Variation et optimisation de formes. Vol. 48 of Mathématiques et Applications. Springer-Verlag, Berlin.

A. Henrot, Y. Privat, 2010. What is the optimal shape of a pipe? Archive for Rational Mechanics and Analysis, 196 (1), 281–302.

O. Tonomura, M. Kano, S. Hasebe, 2010. Shape optimization of microchannels using cfd and adjoint method. Computers and Chemical Engineering, 28, 37-42.

H. G. Weller, G. Tabor, H. Jasak, C. Fureby, 1998. A tensorial approach to computational continuum mechanics using object-oriented techniques. Computers in physics 12 (6), 620–631.

Anton A. Kiss, Edwin Zondervan, Richard Lakerveld, Leyla Özkan (Eds.)
Proceedings of the 29th European Symposium on Computer Aided Process Engineering
June 16th to 19th, 2019, Eindhoven, The Netherlands. © 2019 Elsevier B.V. All rights reserved.
http://dx.doi.org/10.1016/B978-0-128-18634-3.50147-8

Integrated white-box models for designing freezing processes of human induced pluripotent stem cells considering diversity within a container

Yusuke Hayashi,[a,*] Ikki Horiguchi,[b] Masahiro Kino-oka,[b] Masahiko Hirao,[a] Hirokazu Sugiyama[a]

[a] Department of Chemical System Engineering, The University of Tokyo, 7-3-1 Hongo, Bunkyo-ku, 113-8656, Tokyo, Japan

[b] Department of Biotechnology, Osaka University, 2-1, Yamadaoka, Suita, 565-0871, Osaka, Japan

y-hayashi@pse.t.u-tokyo.ac.jp

Abstract

This work presents a novel combination of white-box models that describes heat transfer, mass transfer, and intracellular ice formation during freezing of human induced pluripotent stem (hiPS) cells. The models can be applied to the design of freezing processes for hiPS cells considering the diversity in cell quality within a container. In the case study, two design variables were defined, i.e., the cooling rate of a programmed freezer as an element of {1.0, 1.2, ..., 3.8, 4.0 K/min} and the diameter of a vial as an element of {5, 50, 150 mm}. The objective functions were defined as the maxima of cell volume change and intracellular ice crystal volume as the proxy for the cell survival rate. The Pareto optimal solutions were obtained as 5 mm as the vial diameter with all considered cooling rates; given a threshold of the ice crystal volume, the feasible range of the cooling rate was strongly influenced by the diameter of the vial.

Keywords: Regenerative medicine, Cells, Cryopreservation, Numerical simulation, Multiobjective process design

1. Introduction

Regenerative medicine is the future technology that aims to heal or restore human tissues and organs damaged by age, disease, or trauma, back to the original condition (Mao and Mooney, 2015). Human induced pluripotent stem (hiPS) cells are considered as one of the promising sources of regenerative medicine products because of various advantages compared to the conventional sources. Towards industrialization of hiPS cells, freezing processes are essential in order to transport, distribute, and preserve the cells. However, hiPS cells are known to be sensitive to damages caused by freezing (Hunt, 2011), which could lead to undesired deviation of cell quality in the process. Several authors tackled the design of the freezing process by experiments using a programmed freezer (Li et al., 2018) or cryoprotective agents (Xu et al., 2014). However, it is yet to design reasonably the freezing process based on the fundamental understanding of physicochemical mechanisms.

In this work, we present a set of white-box models that describes heat transfer, mass transfer, and intracellular ice formation during freezing of hiPS cells. The novelty of this work is that the three models are integrated in such a way that the diversity in cell quality inside a container can be evaluated, which would enable precise design of freezing processes.

2. Freezing process of hiPS cells

2.1. Manufacturing process of hiPS cells

Figure 1 shows the manufacturing process of hiPS cells. First, somatic cells are derived from a donor. Second, the somatic cells are converted to hiPS cells by introducing specific genes to the cells. Third, the number of hiPS cells is increased by cultivation. Finally, hiPS cells are differentiated to the target cells. It is estimated that a hiPS-based liver would require 10^{10} units of the cells, suggesting the importance of homogeneous cell quality. The freezing process is required to transport hiPS cells to the next process with protecting the cells from degeneration. In the freezing process, hiPS cells filled in a container named as vial with a cryoprotective agent are cooled in a programmed freezer as shown in Figure 2.

2.2. Damages to hiPS cells during freezing

As cooling progresses, extracellular water including a cryoprotective agent begins to freeze. At this point of time, the intracellular water is not yet frozen but remains in the supercooled state. Osmotic pressure difference between the inside and the outside of the cells occurs because the osmotic pressure of supercooled water is higher than that of frozen water. The pressure difference causes the dehydration of hiPS cells, decrease of the cell volume, and ultimately a damage to the cells (Mazur et al., 1972). Along with the further progress of cooling, intracellular water is eventually frozen, and ice crystals grow in the cell. The volume of intracellular ice crystals affects the degree of the additional damage to the cells (Mazur et al., 1972).

2.3. Formulation of the optimization problem

The optimization problem was defined as shown in Eq. (1):

$$\min \begin{cases} \Delta V_{cell}^{max}(B, d_v) \\ V_{ice}^{max}(B, d_v) \end{cases} \quad s.t. \quad \begin{array}{ll} B & \in \{1.0, 1.2, \ldots, 3.8, 4.0\} \\ d_v & \in \{5, 50, 150\} \end{array} \quad (1)$$

where ΔV_{cell}^{max} [m^3] is the maximum cell volume change inside a vial, V_{ice}^{max} [m^3] is the maximum intracellular ice crystal volume inside a vial, B [K min^{-1}] is the cooling rate of a programmed freezer, and d_v [mm] is the diameter of a vial. The final objective of the

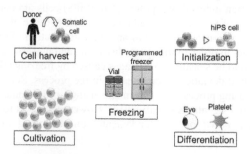

Figure 1 Manufacturing process of hiPS cells

Integrated white-box models for designing freezing processes of human
induced pluripotent stem cells considering diversity within a container

879

design is to determine the decision variables that could maximize the survival rate of cells after the entire freezing process. Based on the analysis presented in section 2.2, we considered the cell volume change due to the osmotic pressure difference and the formation of intercellular ice crystal as the key factors for the cell survival (Mazur et al., 1972).

3. Construction of the white-box models

3.1. Heat transfer model

Considering that the primary mode of heat transfer in a vial is conduction rather than convection, we adopted the following equations to calculate the temperature inside a vial (Hu and Argyropoulos, 1996):

$$\frac{\partial T}{\partial t} = \alpha_w \left(\frac{\partial^2 T}{\partial r^2} + \frac{1}{r} \frac{\partial T}{\partial r} \right) \tag{2}$$

$$\frac{\partial T}{\partial t} = \alpha_{ice} \left(\frac{\partial^2 T}{\partial r^2} + \frac{1}{r} \frac{\partial T}{\partial r} \right) \tag{3}$$

$$\frac{\partial T}{\partial t} = \alpha_v \left(\frac{\partial^2 T}{\partial r^2} + \frac{1}{r} \frac{\partial T}{\partial r} \right) \tag{4}$$

where T [K] is the temperature, t [s] is the time, α [m^2 s^{-1}] is the thermal diffusion coefficient, r [m] is the radial distance from the center of a vial, and the subscripts of w, ice, and v represent water, ice, and vial, respectively. According to Hu and Argyropoulos (1996), the position of the solid-liquid interface from the center of a vial δ [m] can be calculated as follows:

$$\frac{\rho_{ice} \Delta H_f}{M_{ice}} \frac{d\delta}{dt} = k_{ice} \left(\frac{\partial T}{\partial r} \right)_{r=\delta} - k_w \left(\frac{\partial T}{\partial r} \right)_{r=\delta+d\delta} \tag{5}$$

where ρ [kg m^{-3}] is the density, ΔH_f [J mol^{-1}] is the molar heat of fusion of ice, M [kg mol^{-1}] is the molar mass, and k [J s^{-1} m^{-1} K^{-1}] is the thermal conductivity.

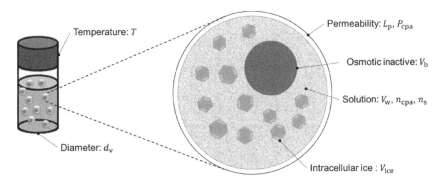

Figure 2 Schematic representation of the freezing process (adapted from Fadda et al., 2010)

3.2. Mass transfer model

Transmembrane mass transport by the osmotic pressure difference was modelled using the following equations (Xu et al., 2014):

$$\frac{dV_{\text{cell}}}{dt} = -\frac{L_p A_{\text{cell}} RT}{v_w}\left[\frac{\Delta H_f}{R}\left(\frac{1}{T_0}-\frac{1}{T}\right)-\ln\left\{\frac{V_w}{V_w+v_w\left(\mu_s n_s + n_{\text{cpa}}\right)}\right\}\right] \tag{6}$$

$$\frac{dn_{\text{cpa}}}{dt} = \frac{\left(C_{\text{ex}}+C_{\text{in}}\right)\left(1-\sigma\right)}{2}\frac{dV_{\text{cell}}}{dt} + A_{\text{cell}} P_{\text{cpa}}\left(C_{\text{ex}}-C_{\text{in}}\right) \tag{7}$$

where V [m³] is the volume, L_p [m s⁻¹ Pa⁻¹] is the water permeability, A [m²] is the surface area, R [J mol⁻¹ K⁻¹] is the gas constant, v [m³ mol⁻¹] is the partial molar volume, μ [–] is the dissociation constant, n [mol] is the molar amount, C [mol m⁻³] is the cryoprotective agent concentration, σ [–] is the reflection coefficient, P_{cpa} [m s⁻¹] is the cryoprotective agent permeability. The subscripts of cell, 0, s, cpa, in, and ex represent cell, reference, salt, cryoprotective agent, intracellular, and extracellular, respectively. According to Xu et al. (2014), the cell membrane permeability coefficients of L_p and P_{cpa} are temperature-dependent and can be calculated using the following equations:

$$L_p = L_{p0}\exp\left[-\frac{E_w}{R}\left(\frac{1}{T}-\frac{1}{T_0}\right)\right] \tag{8}$$

$$P_{\text{cpa}} = P_{\text{cpa0}}\exp\left[-\frac{E_{\text{cpa}}}{R}\left(\frac{1}{T}-\frac{1}{T_0}\right)\right] \tag{9}$$

where E [J mol⁻¹] is activation energy.

3.3. Crystal growth model

Nucleation of ice in a cell occurs by two different mechanisms: homogeneous nucleation (HOM) and heterogeneous nucleation (HET). HET is further categorized into two types: surface-catalysed nucleation (SCN) that occurs at cell membrane and volume-catalysed nucleation (VCN) that occurs inside a cell. The nucleation rate of ice in a cell was modelled using the following equations (Zhao et al., 2014):

$$J_{\text{ice}} = \begin{cases} 0 & \left(T_m < T\right) \\ I^{\text{HOM}}V_w + I^{\text{SCN}}A_{\text{cell}} + I^{\text{VCN}}V_w & \left(T \leq T_m\right) \end{cases} \tag{10}$$

where J [s⁻¹] is the nucleation rate, I [s⁻¹ m⁻³ or s⁻¹ m⁻²] is the nucleation rate per unit, and the subscript of m represents melting point.

In order to estimate ice crystal growth under non-isothermal conditions, the radius of intracellular ice crystals was modelled using the following equations (Fadda et al., 2010; Karlsson et al., 1994):

$$r_{\text{ice},i} = \begin{cases} 0 & \left(0 \leq N_{\text{ice}} < 1\right) \\ \sqrt{\int_{t_i}^{t} \gamma_{\text{ice}}^2 D_{\text{av}}\, dt} & \left(1 \leq N_{\text{ice}}\right) \end{cases} \tag{11}$$

where r_{ice} [m] is the radius of an ice crystal, N_{ice} [–] is the number of intracellular ice crystals, γ_{ice} [–] is the non-dimensional ice crystal growth parameter, τ [s] is the starting time of ice crystal formation, and D_{av} [m² s⁻¹] is the average water diffusion coefficient. According to Fadda et al. (2010), the total volume of intracellular ice crystals V_{ice} can be calculated using the following equation.

$$V_{ice}(r) = \sum_{i=1}^{N_{ice}} \frac{4}{3} \pi r_{ice,i}^3 \tag{12}$$

4. Results and discussion

Figure 3 shows the relationship between the design variables, i.e., cooling rate B and the diameter d_v, and the objective functions, i.e., the maximum intracellular ice crystal volume V_{ice}^{max} and the maximum cell volume change ΔV_{cell}^{max}. The calculation results at $d_v = 5$ mm are the most favourable, and thus all values of B at $d_v = 5$ mm are the Pareto optimal solutions to the problem defined in Eq. (1). The graph shows that the change of ΔV_{cell}^{max} due to the difference in B and d_v is less significant than that of V_{ice}^{max}, and thus in practice, ΔV_{cell}^{max} could be ignored. Focusing on the results of V_{ice}^{max}, the values of B and d_v should be as small as possible. In case a threshold of V_{ice}^{max} is given, e.g., 8 µm³, the volume of a human mitochondrion, Figure 3 indicates that the largest possible B would differ depending on d_v, i.e., dimensionality. In the literature, the ideal cell volume changes and ice crystal growth have been simulated for a type of mouse cells during the freezing process (Karlsson et al., 1994) by considering mass transfer and crystal growth. With a focus on hiPS cells, this study integrated heat transfer (see Eqs. (2-5)) in addition, so that the dependence of the cell quality on the intra-container dimensionality can be quantified, which is the novelty of this work.

A solver adopted solving partial differential equations was the Crank-Nicolson method and the algorithm was implemented in Python 3.6. The total CPU time that the results shown in Figure 3 was obtained was about 8 hours, using Intel(R) Core(TM) i5-6500 CPU@3.2 GHz with 8 GB RAM memory.

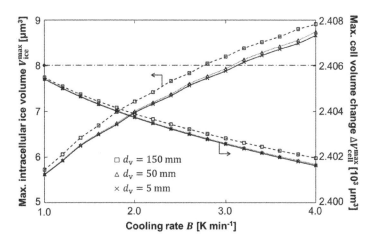

Figure 3   Relationship between cooling rate and volume change or ice crystal volume

5. Conclusions and outlook

We presented the white-box models that are applicable to dynamic and simultaneous simulation of heat transfer, mass transfer, and intracellular ice formation. The three models are integrated in such a way that the diversity in cell quality inside a container can be evaluated, which would enable precise design of freezing processes. We applied the models to calculate the change of the cell volume and the formation of the intracellular ice crystal that are considered to affect the survival rate of the hiPS cells. The Pareto optimal solutions were obtained as 5 mm as the vial diameter with all considered cooling rates; given a threshold of the ice crystal volume, the feasible range of the cooling rate was influenced by the diameter of the vial. The result implies the significance of the intra-container dimensionality in considering cell quality, which was made possible by the proposed models for the first time. In future, we will conduct dynamic optimization of the process parameters by quantifying the temperature distribution inside the freezer, and by evaluating the productivity of the entire process.

Acknowledgement

This study was supported by the Japan Agency for Medical Research and Development (AMED) in the project "Development of cell manufacturing and processing system for industrialization of regenerative medicine" (No. P14006).

References

S. Fadda, A. Cincotti, G. Cao, 2010, The effect of cell size distribution during the cooling stage of cryopreservation without CPA, AIChE J., 56, 2173–2185

H. Hu, S. A. Argyropoulos, 1996, Mathematical modelling of solidification and melting: a review, Model. Simul. Mater. Sci. Eng., 4, 371–396

C. J. Hunt, 2011, Cryopreservation of Human Stem Cells for Clinical Application: A Review, Transfus. Med. Hemother., 38, 107–123

J. O. M. Karlsson, E. G. Cravalho, M. Toner, 1994, A model of diffusion - limited ice growth inside biological cells during freezing, J. Appl. Phys., 75, 4442–4455

R. Li, G. Yu, S. Azarin, A. Hubel, 2018, Freezing Responses in DMSO-Based Cryopreservation of Human iPS Cells: Aggregates vs. Single Cells, Tissue Eng. Part C Methods, 24, 289–299

A. S. Mao, D. J. Mooney, 2015, Regenerative medicine: Current therapies and future directions, Proc. Natl. Acad. Sci., 112, 14452–14459

P. Mazur, S. P. Leibo, E. H. Y. Chu, 1972, A two-factor hypothesis of freezing injury: Evidence from Chinese hamster tissue-culture cells, Exp. Cell Res., 71, 345–355

Y. Xu, L. Zhang, J. Xu, Y. Wei, X. Xu, 2014, Membrane permeability of the human pluripotent stem cells to Me2SO, glycerol and 1,2-propanediol, Arch. Biochem. Biophys., 550–551, 67–76

G. Zhao, H. Takamatsu, X. He, 2014, The effect of solution nonideality on modeling transmembrane water transport and diffusion-limited intracellular ice formation during cryopreservation, J. Appl. Phys., 115, 1–13

Anton A. Kiss, Edwin Zondervan, Richard Lakerveld, Leyla Özkan (Eds.)
Proceedings of the 29th European Symposium on Computer Aided Process Engineering
June 16th to 19th, 2019, Eindhoven, The Netherlands. © 2019 Elsevier B.V. All rights reserved.
http://dx.doi.org/10.1016/B978-0-128-18634-3.50148-X

Improving the prediction of multi-component tablet properties from pure component parameters

Hikaru G. Jolliffe[a*], Foteini Papathanasiou[b], Elke Prasad[a], Gavin Halbert[a], John Robertson[a], Cameron J. Brown[a], Alastair J. Florence[a].

a EPSRC Centre for Innovative Manufacturing in Continuous Manufacturing and Crystallisation, University of Strathclyde, Technology and Innovation Centre, 99 George Street, Glasgow G1 1RD, United Kingdom.

b Strathclyde Institute of Pharmacy & Biomedical Sciences, University of Strathclyde, 161 Cathedral St, Glasgow G4 0RE, United Kingdom.

hikaru.jolliffe@strath.ac.uk

Abstract

Direct compaction tabletting, a widely used secondary downstream processing operation, has recently received significant research attention. Experimental data can be used to fit model parameters for the prediction of single-component tablet thickness and hardness with good agreement, and this has been done for two components (Avicel® PH-101 and Pharmatose® 50M). These pure component parameters have then been used to predict multicomponent tablet properties, with the use of novel modified parameter averaging calculations improving predictions. Furthermore, a relation has been developed to estimate the required gap between tablet press punch faces for multicomponent tablets based on the gaps required for pure components; a quick and efficient way to estimate the necessary equipment settings to generate the desired compaction forces is a useful tool.

Keywords: direct compaction, tablet prediction, optimisation.

1. Introduction

Continuous Pharmaceutical Manufacturing (CPM) is a promising alternative to the current paradigm of batch production, and mathematical modelling and simulation is a useful tool within the methodology of CPM (Lee et al., 2015). The final step in many production process is final product formulation. In the case of solid dosage forms such as tablets the critical quality attributes include tablet tensile strength and thickness; appropriate dissolution rates are also crucial (Velasco et al., 1999). Currently, time-consuming design-of-experiment (DOE) approaches are commonly used to determine the necessary conditions to achieve the required tablet properties, and the need for cost-effective R&D methodologies brings process modelling and simulation to the forefront of initial stages of process option evaluation (Diab and Gerogiorgis, 2018).

In the present work, we predict the properties of multicomponent tablets using parameters determined from pure component compaction data; a model by Gavi and Reynolds (2014) has been used to fit the parameters for tablet compaction. The use of pure component parameters in the prediction of multicomponent tablet properties entails the use of some form of mixing or averaging rule, and the appropriateness of currently implemented rules are analysed, with novel modifications made where necessary.

2. Compaction experiments

Experiments (Papathanasiou, 2018) were performed for varying tablet weights (200, 250 or 300 mg) and components (microcrystalline cellulose: Avicel® PH-101; α-lactose monohydrate: Pharmatose® 50M). Tablet thickness and hardness were recorded for a range of compaction forces. Tablet masses were also measured after ejection (due to material flowability, there was always some variation from target tablet mass, approximately ± 2 %). For each compaction force, experiments were performed 10 times (*i.e.* 10 tablets were produced). In addition to the above experiments being done for pure components, a similar set of experiments were done for binary tablets of lactose and cellulose, to allow the assessment of binary tablet predictions.

The pure component experiments showed the expected trends, such as hardness increasing with increasing compaction force, and thickness decreasing with increasing compaction force (routine data not shown due to space constraints – available in the work of Papathanasiou, 2018). Cellulose achieves significantly higher hardness values (up to 450 N for 250 mg tablets) than lactose (up to approximately 50 N), which is unsurprising as Avicel® PH was introduced with direct compaction in mind. The hardness values achieved with the mixtures fall between those of pure cellulose and pure lactose, as one might expect.

3. Compaction model

The compaction model used here is one developed by Gavi and Reynolds (2014), and is also included in the FormulatedProducts module of the gPROMS software package (henceforth called gFormulate), produced by Process Systems Enterprise (PSE, 2018). The model has several key equations. The first computes the tablet relative density ρ^* (Equation 1). Here, ρ_0^* is the relative density at zero compaction pressure (taken to be the tapped density of the powder), P is compaction pressure (MPa) and K is the compressibility constant (a dimensionless fitting parameter). Tablet ρ^* values can be calculated from the compressed tablet densities and the true density of the material (ρ^{crys}, determined experimentally with a gas pycnometer). Equation 1 is used first in the calculations – the model is sequential. With relative density calculated, tablet thickness h is then calculated for known ρ^{crys}, mass M, and diameter d (Equation 2; assumes flat-faced cylinders) (Fell and Newton, 1970).

Another key equation is that governing tensile strength, σ (Equation 3). Here, σ_0 is the tensile strength at zero porosity (i.e. a fitting parameter corresponding to the theoretical maximum possible compaction, units of MPa), k_b is the bonding capacity (also a dimensionless fitting parameter), and ε is tablet porosity (Equation 4). The three key parameters, then, are the compressibility constant (K), the tensile strength at zero porosity (σ_0) and bonding capacity (k_b). Experimentally, tensile strength can be calculated from hardness via Equation 5, where F is the compaction force in kN.

$$\rho^* = \rho_0^* P^{1/K} \tag{1}$$

$$h = \frac{M}{\rho^* \rho^{crys}} \frac{4}{\pi d^2} \tag{2}$$

$$\sigma = \sigma_0 e^{-k_b \varepsilon} \tag{3}$$

$$\varepsilon = 1 - \rho^* \tag{4}$$

$$\sigma = \frac{2}{\pi} \frac{F}{hd} \tag{5}$$

4. Pure component parameter estimation

Comprehensive experimental data allows for parameters to be fitted for use in empirical and data-driven models. In this work, the parameters being fitted are compressibility constant (K), tensile strength at zero porosity (σ_0) and bonding capacity (k_b).

The pure component experimental data were imported into gFormulate, where a digital flowsheet of the process was created. The control variables are compaction pressure P and tablet weight M, while the key measured variables are tablet thickness h and hardness H (the diametrical load which causes tablet failure). With three fitted parameters and four variables (two control, two measured), the problem was straightforward, and computationally undemanding; the parameters themselves (for cellulose/Avicel® PH-101 and lactose/Pharmatose® 50M) are given in Table 1.

5. Multi-component tablet property prediction

Pure component parameters that reliably predict single-component tablets have been determined. The subsequent use of these for multi-component tablet property prediction has been investigated, which entails the use of some form of averaging or mixing rule for the model parameters K, σ_0 and k_b. Doing this by pre-compaction component volume fractions is one option (Equation 6) (Gavi and Reynolds, 2014). Results for mixtures of lactose-cellulose indicate that while predictions for hardness are good at lower compaction forces, there is a trend of over-prediction which becomes more evident at higher compaction forces (Fig. 1). However, this trend is not present for pure components, *i.e.* pure lactose and pure cellulose tablets are predicted reasonably well, with no significant hardness over-prediction at higher compaction forces (Fig. 1B). This implies the potential for prediction improvement from using alternative parameter averaging/mixing rules.

The volume fractions of the components after compaction (as opposed to prior) can be estimated by assuming they compact at similar rates as when they are a pure component (*i.e.* a 25 % volume reduction for pure material *i* when subjected to a given force implies a 25 % reduction for component *i* when a mixture is subjected to the same force), and can be computed via Equation 7 (Reynolds et al., 2017).

Table 1. Optimal pure component parameter values for Avicel® PH-101 and Pharmatose® 50M.

Component	Tensile strength at zero porosity		Bonding capacity		Compressibility constant	
	σ_0 (MPa)	99% CI	k_b (-)	99% CI	K (-)	99% CI
Avicel® PH-101	12.0067	±1.9080	7.5847	±0.6362	4.2008	±0.1372
Pharmatose® 50M	1.6789	±0.3212	11.6020	±0.8704	9.0901	±0.2130

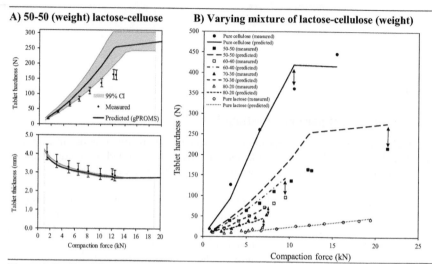

Figure 1. Predicted (Gavi and Reynolds, 2014) vs measured 250 mg tablet hardness and thickness for varying mixtures of lactose-cellulose. For each substance, the predicted curves use the same respective set of parameters. The parameters can be found in Table 1. Arrows in B are a visual aid, to indicate which predicted curve corresponds with which experimental data set.

$$p_{mix} = \sum_{i \in C} \varphi_i p_i \;, \qquad p = \{K, \sigma_0, k_b\} \tag{6}$$

$$\varphi'_i = \frac{\left. m_i \middle/ (1 - \varepsilon_i) \rho_i^{crys} \right.}{\sum_{i \in C} \left. m_i \middle/ (1 - \varepsilon_i) \rho_i^{crys} \right.} \tag{7}$$

$$\sigma_{Tab} = \prod_{i \in C} \sigma_i^{\varphi'_i} \tag{8}$$

The Reynolds et al. (2017) model then use Equation 8 to compute the tensile strength of multicomponent tablets. In essence, tensile strengths for each component are calculated on a pure basis, then averaged using Equation 8. However, this approach relies on the components being of similar particle size (Reynolds et al., 2017). For applications where the particle sizes are different, such as in this work (Avicel® PH-101 has an average particle size of 50 μm, Pharmatose® 50M has an average size of 360 μm), an alternative approach is required.

The approach used in this work is to use Equation 6 to average the compressibility constant K as before, then use Equation 7 to compute component volume fractions in the compact (φ'_i), and then use these volume fractions to average the post-compaction tensile strength (σ_0) and bonding capacity (k_b) parameters (Equation 9) for use with Equation 3.

$$\sigma_{0mix} = \sum_{i \in C} \varphi'_i \sigma_{0i} \;, \qquad k_{bmix} = \sum_{i \in C} \varphi'_i k_{bi} \tag{9}$$

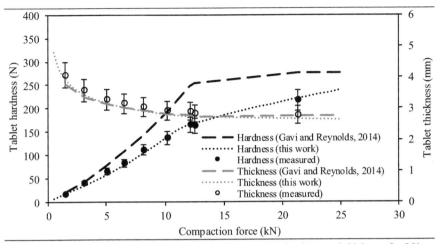

Figure 2. Predicted vs measured (experimental) 250 mg tablet hardness and thickness for 250mg lactose-cellulose tablets (50-50 by weight), illustrating prediction improvements from using post-compaction volume fractions to weight the pure component parameters.

This approach results in improved predictions (Fig. 2). Compared with the previous method (Fig. 1, Fig. 2 dashed lines) the improvements are evident, especially for tablet hardness. While predictions using the previous method agreed with measured data at lower compaction forces, the method outlined in here produces predictions which match the experimental data across the entire range of compaction forces.

The main variable in the compaction model used here is, as with many compaction models, the pressure applied (or the force in some cases) (Equation 1). However, in tablet presses there frequently is not a setting or dial for pressure, but a way to set the distance to which the punch faces compact the material (punch gap, PG); knowing what pressure or force is required might not be immediately useful to a user in the lab. We have taken the compaction force and PG data, and have been able to determine a relation between them, adjusted for tablet weight. An example of this for cellulose is given in Fig. 3A. This variable, which we have called the gap-mass factor γ, has units of mm/g. When plotted against compaction pressure as in Fig. 3A, a power law relation (Equation 10) can be determined for the curved portion corresponding to lower compaction pressures; the horizontal portion, corresponding to the limit of zero porosity, is less useful as there is no improvement in tablet properties at these compaction pressures. This fitting of the curved portion will result in two parameters a and b for a given pure component, and we have then used a mass fraction (m_i)-based mixing rule (Equation 11) to estimate what PG might be required for a binary tablet of given weight M. The predicted PG values are in good agreement with the experimentally required values for binary tablets, with the difference being of a similar order of magnitude as tablet thickness (Fig. 3B). Such a relation is envisaged to be useful to users wishing to apply a certain compaction force.

$$\gamma_i = a_i P^{b_i} \tag{10}$$

$$PG = M \sum_{i \in C} m_i \gamma_i \tag{11}$$

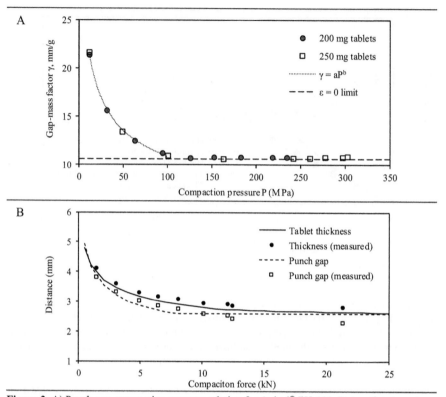

Figure 3. A) Punch gap-compaction pressure relation for Avicel® PH-101. Data points have been normalized by dividing punch gap values (mm) by tablet weights (g). B) Prediction from pure component data of required punch gap values of multicomponent tablets (Equations 10–11).

6. Conclusions

Pure component parameters can be fitted with good statistical results. The use of these pure parameters for the prediction of multicomponent tablet properties is possible, and predictions have been improved by a novel use of model equations. In addition, a relation between tablet press punch gap values and applied compaction pressures has been developed, which predicts necessary punch gaps with good accuracy.

References

Diab, S & Gerogiorgis, DI, 2018. *Ind. Eng. Chem. Res.* 57, 9489–9499.
Fell, JT, Newton, JM, 1970. *J. Pharm. Sci.* 59, 688–691.
Gavi, E, Reynolds, GK, 2014. *Comput. Chem. Eng.* 71, 130–140.
Lee, SL, O'Connnor, TF, Yang, X, Cruz, CN, Chatterjee, S, Madurawee, RD, Moore, CMV, Yu, LX, Woodcock, J, 2015. *J Pharm Innov.* 10, 191–199.
Papathanasiou, F, 2018. (Masters Thesis). University of Strathclyde.
Reynolds, GK, Cambell, JI, Roberts RJ, 2017. *Int J Pharm.* 531, 215–224.
PSE, 2018. gPROMS Formulated Products. www.psenterprise.com (accessed 10.30.18).
Velasco, MV, Ford, JL, Rowe, P, Rajabi-Siahboomi, AR, 1999. *J. Control. Release* 57, 75–85.

Anton A. Kiss, Edwin Zondervan, Richard Lakerveld, Leyla Özkan (Eds.)
Proceedings of the 29th European Symposium on Computer Aided Process Engineering
June 16th to 19th, 2019, Eindhoven, The Netherlands. © 2019 Elsevier B.V. All rights reserved.
http://dx.doi.org/10.1016/B978-0-128-18634-3.50149-1

Total Organic Carbon Prediction with Artificial Intelligence Techniques

Eda Goz[a*], Mehmet Yuceer[b], Erdal Karadurmus[c]

[a]Ankara University, Faculty of Enginering, Dept. of Chemical Engineering, Ankara 06100, Turkey
[b]Inonu University, Faculty of Enginering, Dept. of Chemical Engineering, Malatya 44280, Turkey
[c]Hitit University, Faculty of Enginering, Dept. of Chemical Engineering, Çorum 9200, Turkey
esemizer@eng.ankara.edu.tr

Abstract

This study used the Extreme Learning Machine (ELM), Kernel Extreme Learning Machine (KELM) and Artificial Neural Network (ANN) models with a feed-forward neural network structure and partial least squares (PLSR) methods to estimate total organic carbon. In order to develop models, on-line data measured at five-minute time intervals were collected through one year (2007-2008) from the online-monitoring stations which were built near the River Yeşilırmak in Amasya in North-Eastern Turkey. These stations were the first practice in Turkey. Twelve parameters as luminescent dissolved oxygen (LDO), pH, conductivity, nitrate nitrogen (NO_3-N), ammonium nitrogen (NH_4-N), total organic carbon (TOC), chloride, orthophosphate, temperature, turbidity, suspended solid and flow rate were measured at the on-line monitoring stations. To predict the total organic carbon, four input variables, pH, conductivity, dissolved oxygen and temperature were selected. Moreover, the data were also collected at the central office in Ankara via a General Packet Radio Service (GPRS) channel. The validity of models was tested by using statistical methods in MATLAB including correlation coefficients (R), mean absolute percentage error (MAPE%) and root mean square error (RMSE). The best result was obtained in the presence of KELM with a radial basis function (RBF) kernel. R_{test}=0.984, $MAPE_{test}$=3.01, $RMSE_{test}$=0.9676. Additionally, R_{train}=0.995, $MAPE_{train}$=1.58 and $RMSE_{train}$=0.532. Among the other two algorithms ANN provided better results than ELM and PLSR.

Keywords: Artificial Neural Network, Extreme Learning Machine, On-line monitoring, River water quality

1. Introduction

Rivers play a vital role not only as sources of drinking water but also basic elements in sustainable development especially in industrial and agricultural activities. Additionally, rivers and streams also serve as the lifelines of the population staying in the basins. Increased anthropogenic and other effects cause substantial increase in river pollution. Water quality in rivers has also been changed by environmental factors, but the main reason for water contamination is known to be caused by human activities. Especially in agricultural activities such as usage of chemical fertilizers, animal feeding and mining, combustion of fossil fuels affect the quality of all natural water bodies the most. Destruction of wetlands, point or diffuse pollution sources, large amounts of industrial waste discharge and the exponential increase of population growth have also affected water quality within environmental factors. In the last decades, monitoring of water quality from several rivers by regular measurements has received increasing demand. In this context, a real-time monitoring station, as the first practice in Turkey, was built near the River Yeşilırmak in Turkey. The system involved two in-situ on-line analysis stations in River Yeşilırmak and a central monitoring office at Ankara University. Pollutant parameters of luminescent dissolved oxygen (LDO), pH, conductivity, nitrate nitrogen (NO_3-N), ammonium nitrogen (NH_4-N), TOC, o-phosphate, chloride, temperature, turbidity, suspended solid and flow rate were measured at five-minute intervals at the on-line monitoring stations. The data were collected at the central office in Ankara via General Packet Radio Service (GPRS). In these parameters, measurement of total organic carbon was the most expensive -about eight-fold of the total amount of LDO, conductivity, pH and temperature- parameter, therefore, various models for prediction of TOC was proposed in this study. Various types of river water quality models such as parametric, statistical and deterministic models were proposed in the literature. The use of water quality models is inevitable in explaining some problems like nonlinearity, subjectivity and cause-effect relationships between water quality variables and water status. However, deterministic modelling approaches for water quality parameters need a lot of information on various hydrological processes and several different units of input data to arrive the results, while these methods have been seen to be very effortful and time-consuming. Artificial intelligence methods have some advantages over semi empirical or deterministic models due to the fact that they contain a set of input data without assumption, and they are also able to map the nonlinear relationships that are characteristics of aquatic ecosystems. For these reasons ANNs, which are artificial intelligence methods, have widespread use in hydrological processes and modelling river water quality. Moreover, ANNs are used to forecast of water quality parameters, as well as determining the uncertainty of contaminant source and nonlinearity of water quality data. Csabragi et al. (2017) applied a neural network structure on dissolved oxygen levels in the River Danube. Within this context, four models were used. In order to estimate dissolved oxygen, multivariate linear regression, multilayer perceptron neural network, radial basis function network and general regression neural network models were developed. Another dissolved oxygen prediction study was carried out by Olyaie et al. (2017). In their study, they used two types of ANN structures, namely multi linear perceptron and radial basis functions. Moreover, linear genetic programming and support vector machine (SVM) were also proposed to estimate dissolved oxygen levels in the River Delaware. An extreme learning machine technique was used to predict dissolved oxygen concentration with and without water quality parameters by Heddam and Kisi (2017). Their study compared a standard extreme learning machine with a sigmoid activation function (S-ELM), an extreme learning machine with a radial basis function (R-ELM), an on-line sequential ELM (OS-ELM), and an optimally pruned extreme learning algorithm (OP-ELM). Temperature, specific conductance, turbidity and pH were used as the input variables. In the study without water quality parameters, year, month, day and month numbers were used as predictors. Using extreme learning machines for river water quality parameters is quite limited in literature.

We compared three data-driven approaches to predict TOC concentration from data collected from real-time monitoring stations. Extreme learning machine (ELM), kernel extreme learning machine (KELM) and artificial neural network (ANN) modelling methods were used to predict TOC. TOC is one of the most important pollution parameters in the topic of river water quality and measurement of this parameter is more expensive than measuring other parameters. This state is important to reduce the costs of building stations. According to the results of our statistical analysis, KELM was better than the artificial neural network and ELM.

2. Data collection and modelling studies

A real-time central river monitoring system was built to monitor river pollution. The system involved two in-situ on-line monitoring stations. One of the stations was positioned in the Aynalı Cave region after the sewage system and Tersakan stream, while the other one was stationed at the Administration of Hydraulic Works' Durucasu station which had a 26.876 km distance from the first station and after the yeast factory. Furthermore, a central monitoring office was designated at Ankara University. The data were collected in a database at the station. The data were transferred from the stations to the central office in Ankara through a GPRS transmission channel as shown in Figure 1 and continuously monitored and displayed in different formats.

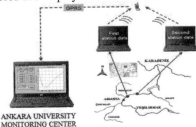

Figure 1. The locations of the on-line measurement stations and the data collection process

The study area has various pollution sources such as industrial, domestic, municipal and agricultural run-off. Real-time data were measured at five-minute time intervals for the parameters of luminescent dissolved oxygen (LDO), pH, conductivity, nitrate nitrogen (NO_3-N), ammonium nitrogen (NH_4-N), TOC, o-phosphate, chloride, temperature, turbidity, suspended solid and flow rate.

2.1 Modelling Studies

2.1.1 Artificial Neural Network

An artificial neural network is a type of artificial intelligence technique, and it was inspired by the learning algorithm of the human brain. An ANN is composed of a large number of processing elements with their connections, and it has three distinctive layers, namely input, hidden and output layers as shown in Figure 2.

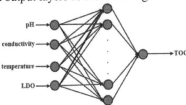

Figure 2. Artificial neural network structure

These layers are called the basic elements of architecture and known as nodes/neurons. Connection of nodes is achieved with synapses, and each node has a weight factor. In an artificial neural network design, signals are passed through the neurons, and simultaneously, the weights and transfer functions are modified, and this process is repeated until a broad output is reached. The numbers of neurons numbers in each layer is determined depending on the structure of the problem.

In this study, we used data for the one-year period of 2007-2008. Especially outlier detection, which was coded in MATLAB, was carried out to sort out the data that deviated from the normal value. The 70% and 30% of the remaining data were used for training and testing respectively. At the stage of artificial neural network modelling, a feed-forward neural network architecture was designed. Feed-forward neural networks have been shown to be an effective neural design for forecasting water quality parameters. The numbers of neurons in the input layer, hidden layer and output layer determined as 4, 25 and 1 respectively. In the training network, number of iterations, degree of training, number of neurons were determined by using a trial and error approach as in training of most network architectures. The transfer function was selected as tangent-sigmoid, and in the training of the network, a Bayesian Regularization Backpropagation (*'trainbr'*) algorithm was used. *trainbr* is a network training function that updates the weight and bias values based on the Levenberg-Marquardt optimization. It minimizes a combination of squared errors and weights, and then, determines the correct combination to produce a network which generalizes well. This process is known as Bayesian regularization.

2.1.2 Extreme Learning Machine

Extreme Learning Machine has become a new method developed in recent years (Huang et al. 2006). In the proposed method, learning algorithms, hidden node weights and biases randomly assigned and need not to be tuned, as well as output weights, are calculated by a simple inverse operation. Due to these properties and less human intervention, ELM provides an extremely fast learning speed and better generalization capability in comparison to traditional learning algorithms. However, ELM is not capable of managing large amounts of data with a high number of dimensions. The number of nodes of the ELM that was required was higher than those of traditional algorithms. So, in this study, we used five different activation functions and numbers of neurons in the ELM. These activations functions were triangular radial basis (*'tribas'*), radial basis (*'radbas'*), hard limited (*'hardlim'*), sigmoidal (*'sigmoid'*) and sinusoidal (*'sine'*) functions. In the KELM, the RBF kernel and linear kernel functions were used as activation functions in the presence of different numbers of neurons. The schematic representation of the extreme learning machine is given in Figure 3.

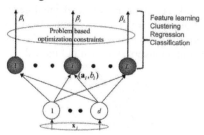

Figure 3. ELM architecture

The algorithm of ELM is given in the following steps (Ding et al. 2014)

Input: a training set $(x_i, t_i) \in R^n x R^m \, (i = 1, 2, \ldots \ldots N)$, activation function and number of neurons in the hidden layer (N); Output: the output weights, β (the output weights between the hidden and output layers which is calculated with Moore Penrose inversion as given in the last step)

Step 1: Randomly assign the parameters of the hidden layer

Step 2: Calculate the output matrix of the hidden layer

Step 3: Calculate the output weight β=H† T

According to these steps, we may say that ELM includes two phases: in the first phase, the hidden layer is initialized by ELM so that the input data can be mapped into a feature space. In the second phase, solution of β (linear parameters) is calculated by Moore Penrose inversion.

2.1.3 Kernel Extreme Learning Machine

In the kernel-based extreme learning approach, kernel functions are used as activation functions in the hidden nodes. In KELM, feature mapping is unknown, and the kernel matrix of ELM based on Mercer's condition can be defined. There are many types of Kernel functions that can be used. The most commonly used one of these are gaussian kernel, linear kernel, hyperbolic tangent kernel, radial basis function and polynomial kernel functions. In this study, RBF kernel and Linear Kernel functions were used.

2.1.4 Partial Least Square Regression (PLSR)

Partial least square regression is a generalization form of multiple linear regression. In this method, collinear, correlated, noisy and numerous X-variables can be analyzed according to this several response variables Y can also be simultaneously modelled.

3. Results and Discussion

In this study, three different artificial intelligence techniques were used to determine total organic carbon in the River Yeşilırmak. For this purpose, we used five different activation functions and numbers of neurons in ELM. These activation functions were triangular radial basis, radial basis, hard limit, sigmoidal and sinusoidal functions. The best result in ELM was obtained in the presence of the tribas activation function, and the number of neurons in the hidden layer was 350. In KELM, RBF kernel and linear kernel functions were used as activation functions in the presence of different numbers of neurons. In this study, 150 neurons were used, and a radial basis function was selected. The artificial neural network test was carried out with 4, 25 and 1 neurons in the input, hidden and output layers respectively.

The kernel-based extreme learning machine provided the best result. A kernel-based extreme learning machine is a powerful learning algorithm in comparison to an extreme learning machine and an artificial neural network. In fact, the ELM technique has many advantages, but ELM is not capable of managing data with high numbers of dimensions. In this case, ELM needs more nodes than traditional learning algorithms. In KELM, kernel functions were used instead of activation functions as shown in Table 1. Moreover, for KELM, it was not needed to choose the number of hidden neurons, and feature mapping was not needed to be known. KELM had the same generalization, but it was more stable than ELM. The performances of the models were tested by the results of statistical analysis as correlation coefficient (R), root mean square error (RMSE) and mean absolute percentage error (MAPE%). The results of the statistical analyses are given in Table 1.

Table 1. Statistical performance indices of the modelling techniques

Modelling techniques	Activation Function	Number of Neurons	Training			Test		
			RMSE	MAPE (%)	R	RMSE	MAPE (%)	R
Kernel ELM	RBF Kernel	150	0.532	1.58	0.995	0.968	3.01	0.984
ELM	Triangular Basis	350	1.374	6.40	0.967	1.764	8.22	0.947
ANN	Tangent Sigmoid	25	1.430	6.09	0.966	1.430	6.48	0.965
PLSR	--	--	3.638	20.23	0.750	3.647	20.31	0.740

4. Conclusion

In this study, three different artificial intelligence techniques were used to predict the total organic carbon concentration in the River Yeşilırmak in Turkey. Actually, the River Yeşilırmak is the most important water resource considering its agricultural potential and other human activities. 12 river water quality parameters were monitored in two on-line measurement stations, but among these monitoring total organic carbon raised the cost considerably. For this reason, prediction of total organic carbon from the other parameters that are cheaper than directly measuring TOC significantly reduced the cost of building stations. The results showed that the kernel-based extreme learning machine is a good tool to predict TOC concentration. This may be explained by the reduction of the cost of measuring stations with the developed algorithm. The extreme learning machine worse than Kernel ELM due to data size, and this method required a higher number of neurons than the traditional ANN algorithm as shown in Table 1. Although the generalization ability of a kernel ELM is the same as ELM, a kernel ELM has good stability. Additionally, PLSR algorithm has the worst scenario. In the next time, other ELM and different kernel ELM structures will be used to predict river water quality parameters.

Acknowledgment

This study was supported by TUBITAK (Project Number: 105G002).

References

A. Csabragi, S. Molnar, P. Tanos, J. Kovacs, 2017, Application of Artificial Neural Networks to the Forecasting of Dissolved Oxygen Content in Hungarian Section of the River Danube, Ecological Engineering, 100, 63-72

E. Olyaie, H.Z. Abyaneh, A.D. Mehr, 2017, A Comparative Analysis among Computational Intelligence Techniques for Dissolved Oxygen Prediction in Delaware River, Geoscience Frontiers 8, 3, 517-527

G.B. Huang, Q.Y. Zhu and C.K. Siew, 2006, Extreme Learning Machine: Theory and Applications, Neurocomputing 70, 1-3, 489-501

S. Ding, X. Xu, R. Nie, 2014, Extreme Learning Machine and applications, Neurocomputing and Applications, 25, 3-4, 549-556

S. Heddam, O. Kisi, 2017, Extreme Learning Machines: A New Approach for Modeling Dissolved Oxygen (DO) Concentration with and without Water Quality Variables as Predictors, Environmental Science and Pollution Research, 24, 20, 16702-16724

Anton A. Kiss, Edwin Zondervan, Richard Lakerveld, Leyla Özkan (Eds.)
Proceedings of the 29th European Symposium on Computer Aided Process Engineering
June 16th to 19th, 2019, Eindhoven, The Netherlands. © 2019 Elsevier B.V. All rights reserved.
http://dx.doi.org/10.1016/B978-0-128-18634-3.50150-8

On the Design and Implementation of a Process Modelling Language for Uncertainty

Pedro I. O. Filho[a] and Eric S. Fraga[a,*]

[a]Centre for Process Systems Engineering, Department of Chemical Engineering, University College London, WC1E 7JE, London, United Kingdom
e.fraga@ucl.ac.uk

Abstract

A modelling framework focusing on the treatment of uncertainty is proposed. The framework is based on Julia, given that it is an open-source, modern, computationally efficient language (scripted but with just-in-time compilation) providing support for the design of domain specific languages via abstract types, multiple dispatch, operator overloading and full Unicode support. The framework provides a concise and natural syntax, allowing for a traditional mathematical notation. For instance, users can write $t = 700 \pm (3\delta)$ (uncertainty range), $X \sim \mathcal{N}\left(\mu, \sigma^2\right)$ (probability distribution) or $F_0 = V^3 + [21.3, 21.7]$ (interval arithmetic) without having to compromise between speed and code readability. A case study on the scale-up of an Aerosol-Assisted Chemical Vapour Deposition (AACVD) process is presented to exemplify the use of the framework.

Keywords: Modelling language, uncertainty, process modelling.

1. Introduction

The formulation of engineering processes has different stages. Importantly, uncertain parameters can be found from the synthesis and design through to the process operation. The ubiquity of uncertainty can be explained by its many sources, such as conceptual modelling errors (wrong or incomplete assumptions, simplifications, wrong equations); unknown consequences that depend on future events; imprecise decision-maker preferences; etc. Therefore, treating uncertainty is a key element in process modelling. Even though process simulation systems (e.g. Aspen, Hysys, gPROMS) and/or modelling systems (e.g. GAMS, AIMMS, AMPL) have made it easier for practitioners to apply process systems engineering methodologies to industrial applications, the treatment of uncertainty is not always straightforward. There is, therefore, a necessity of further research on the development of tools aimed at the modelling of uncertainty.

This paper proposes a framework characterised by methods and operators which allow users to easily write down models with intrinsic parameter uncertainty or distributed quantities and evaluate these models. Such a framework has the final goal of becoming a computational modelling language for incorporating uncertainty in mathematical modelling and also supporting communication with currently available modelling and simulation systems. The next sections present the background in uncertainty modelling; introduce the framework, and present examples to show the ease with which models can be developed. This includes a case study on the scale-up of an Aerosol-Assisted Chem-

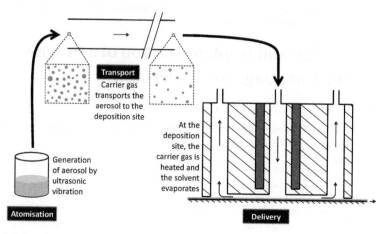

Figure 1: Schematics of the AACVD process, including the atomisation of the solution containing the reactants, the aerosol transport, the chemical deposition and the film formation.

ical Vapour Deposition (AACVD) process. Such a process, schematically represented in Figure 1, can be summarised as a deposition method employed to produce high-quality, high-performance, solid materials. The process is often applied in the semiconductor industry to produce thin films, such as Transparent Conducting Oxides, used from personal digital devices through to solar panels.

2. Uncertainty in Computational Models

Uncertainty is ubiquitous in process design, given that there is always imperfect or unknown information where it is impossible to exactly describe all the parameters. Some of them may have a single exact value, which cannot always be known with precision, for example, transfer coefficients. Other parameters are themselves inherently distributed due to variability or heterogeneity, for example, the sizes of droplets generated by ultrasonic vibration. Both cases can be mathematically represented using the same approach, namely, probability theory. The strengths of this approach are exemplified by how straight forward it becomes to quantify and understand how likely different outcomes are and to visualise potential scenarios. There are a number of quantities which help decision makers to understand the impacts of uncertain variables, such as the mean, variance, skewness, upper and lower quantile values, confidence intervals, etc. Such information can also be represented graphically, using probability density functions or cumulative distribution functions. Once the uncertain parameters are modelled, all the pertinent information should be automatically provided by a computational tool focused on uncertainty representation.

The modelling of uncertainty is essential in process design and optimisation, evidenced by Grossmann et al. (2016), who also shared some challenges in the field. In particular, they showed how important it is to develop tailored solution strategies, which can be facilitated when there is a framework that allows easy prototyping, especially with specific tools dedicated to representing uncertainty. Additionally, when dealing with uncertainty, running simulations helps to rationalise and explain the results from models. That can be done, for example, incorporating Monte Carlo experiments and the associated statistical

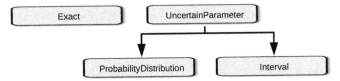

Figure 2: Current type hierarchy of the Uncertainty.jl framework.

methods into the stochastic models. A modelling language focused on the treatment of uncertainty would, therefore, be helpful to facilitate writing, running, maintaining and sharing computational models.

3. Uncertainty.jl

This paper introduces the Uncertainty.jl framework, a high-level interface to represent uncertainty in process modelling, built to address some of the challenges previously mentioned. The framework is user-friendly and straight forward to be employed, aiming therefore at users who are not experts in computer programming. It was written in Julia[1] for a number of reasons. Firstly, Julia is a high-level, high-performance, dynamic language, which allows both large-scale computation and flexible prototyping without having to simultaneously use two or more languages; for example, many engineers use MATLAB (high-level, but slow) and C (fast, but low-level) at the same time. On the other hand, Julia is a high-level language and yet has been shown to at least approach the performance of C (Bezanson et al., 2017). Finally, the users of Uncertainty.jl can also join the large and active community of Julia and have access to a vast and growing number of packages focused on scientific computing, which they can employ and, when necessary, extend.

Chen and Grossmann (2017) outlined the current trend of allowing modellers direct access to model objects, which are easily created using Uncertainty.jl within Julia. This facilitates code sharing and the generation of models that are more readable and easier to validate. However, the main advantage is the use of Julia's multiple dispatch feature, allowing the overloading of generic functions using different type signatures (Zappa Nardelli et al., 2018). This gives a greater expressive power, since additional code can be written in a concise and clear style. Function calls will be dispatched to the relevant method, according to the type signature.

Another advantage of using multiple dispatch is how straight forward it becomes to extend any of the Julia packages already available. For example, Algorithm 1 shows how Uncertainty.jl extended the ODEProblem function, from the package DifferentialEquations.jl (Rackauckas and Nie, 2017). It now became possible to input uncertain parameters, which can be intervals or probability distributions, before solving the differential equations. Uncertainty.jl currently has the object hierarchy shown in Figure 2, which takes advantage of Julia's multiple dispatch. This allows, for example, that the appropriate ODEProblem method will be called according to the types of the input variables as follows: if the uncertain variables are all of the Interval type, Latin hypercube sampling will be used to generate samples. If there is a mix of intervals and probability distributions, a random

---

[1] https://julialang.org/

```
1   Size = 500
2   Range = [0, 20]
3   X = ProbabilityDistribution(Size, Range)
4   k = 7
5   X ~ X²(k)
```

```
X ⌄ ProbabilityDistribution
    > x → Float64[500]
      minimum → 0.00
      maximum → 20.0
    > P → Float64[500]
      mean → 7
      percentile25 → 4.25…
      median → 6.35…
      percentile75 → 9.04…
```

Figure 3: Definition of a random variable with 500 entries ranging from 0 to 20 and following a chi-squared distribution with 7 degrees of freedom. The output of line 5 is shown on the grey section, at the right-hand side. Screenshot from Atom editor.

sampling will be performed. The differential equations are then solved using the generated samples from the uncertain variables, according to their distributions. The output will itself be a distribution built from the solutions of the ODEs. The relevant statistics are also automatically provided. The framework also includes methods to perform sensitivity and uncertainty analysis for the whole model or its parts.

```
1   δ = 20
2   x = 700 ± 3δ
3   y = x + [20, 50]
y ⌄ Interval
      min → 660
      max → 810
```

Figure 4: Example of consecutive operations using interval arithmetic. The final output is in grey, at the bottom. Screenshot from Atom editor.

Uncertainty.jl allows users to take advantage of the full expressiveness of the Julia programming language while writing their models, supporting all of the basic Julia arithmetic operators, Boolean operators, and comparison operators, which are similar to C. However, Uncertainty.jl also defined and/or extended some operators to perform specific tasks. For example, the $\sim$ operator was defined for declaring a random variable following a specific probability distribution, as exemplified in Figure 3. Uncertainty.jl also supports interval arithmetic, allowing the user to perform operations such as the ones shown in Figure 4. Additionally, the operator $\pm$ was also defined, acting on real numbers to produce an interval, which can then be used in any further interval arithmetic operations. Finally, independent model evaluations, including the solution of differential equations, are intrinsically compatible with parallel computing, easily done in Julia.

4. Case Study: Aerosol-Assisted Chemical Vapour Deposition

In the context of the AACVD process, the first step is to atomise a solution containing the reactants, generating the aerosol that will be transported to the reaction chamber. As seen in Figure 1, the aerosol is characterised by droplets of different sizes, which should be accounted for by the models, since the droplet sizes impact the loss of aerosol during transport and the solvent evaporation in the reactor. Details about the modelling and experimental validation of the aerosol transport system, accounting for the distributed nature of the droplet sizes, were previously presented by Filho et al. (2017). Subsequently, the uncertainty and sensitivity analysis of the overall AACVD system, including the aerosol generation, transport and delivery to the reaction chamber was performed by Filho et al. (2018). Finally, when the aerosol reaches the reaction chamber, the solvent evaporates and chemical reactions take place, resulting in the film formation. Equation 1 represents

---

Algorithm 1 Overloading the function ODEProblem from the DifferentialEquations.jl package. The function generateSamples identifies which parameters are exact and creates samples for the uncertain parameters.

Input: set of differential equations **f**; initial condition $\mathbf{u_0}$; time interval $\mathbf{t_{span}}$; set of exact and uncertain parameters **allParameters**.
Output: inferred probability distribution and its properties using the solutions of the ODEs system.

```
1       function ODEProblem(f, u₀, t_span, allParameters)
2           samples := generateSamples(allParameters);
3           sol := {};
4           for each exactParameters ∈ samples do
5               prob := ODEProblem(f, y₀, t_span, exactParameters);
6               sol := sol ∪ {solve(prob)};
7           end for
8           distribution := inferDistribution(sol);
9       return distribution;
```

---

general chemical reactions, where the film is formed mainly by the component D:

$$A_{(g)} \xrightarrow[k_1]{\text{gas}} B_{(g)} + C_{(g)}, \qquad B_{(s)} \xrightarrow[k_2]{\text{surface}} C_{(s)} + D_{(s)}, \qquad A_{(s)} \xrightarrow[k_3]{\text{surface}} 2C_{(s)} + D_{(s)} \qquad (1)$$

Although these equations are general, Vallerio et al. (2016) used them specifically for the production of high-grade polysilicon, using monosilane as the reactant. Performing mass balances, the dynamic model equations for the CVD reactor is shown in Equation 2:

$$\frac{dC_i^g}{dt} = \frac{\dot{F}_{in}}{V} \cdot C_i^{in} - \frac{\dot{F}_{out}}{V} \cdot C_i^g - h_{m,i} \cdot \frac{A}{V} \cdot \left(C_i^g - C_i^s\right) - k_j \cdot C_i^g \qquad (2)$$

where $C_i^g \left[\text{mol/m}^3\right]$ and $C_i^{in} \left[\text{mol/m}^3\right]$ are, respectively, the gas phase concentration and the inlet feed concentration of component i; $C_i^s \left[\text{mol/m}^3\right]$ is the volumetric concentration of component i on the surface of the glass, whose thickness grows with time, $t \left[s\right]$; $\dot{F}_{in} \left[\text{m}^3/\text{s}\right]$ and $\dot{F}_{out} \left[\text{m}^3/\text{s}\right]$ are, respectively, the inlet and outlet volumetric flow rates; $k_j \left[\text{units vary}\right]$ is the kinetic constant of reaction j, in the gas phase or on the surface; $h_{m,i} \left[\text{m/s}\right]$ is the gas to solid phase mass transfer coefficient of component i; $V \left[\text{m}^3\right]$ is the volume in which the gas phase reactions take place; and $A \left[\text{m}^2\right]$ is the glass surface area in contact with the gas.

```
1   (k₁, μ, σ²) = (ProbabilityDistribution(), 25, 4)
2   (k₂, Range₂) = (ProbabilityDistribution(), [150, 250])
3   (k₃, Range₃) = (ProbabilityDistribution(), [0.03, 0.05])
4
5   k = [k₁ ~ 𝒩(μ,σ²), k₂ ~ 𝒰(Range₂), k₃ ~ 𝒰(Range₃)]
6   h = [Interval(100, 300), Interval(4, 20), Interval(20, 50)]
```

Figure 5: Defining the uncertain parameters, namely the three reaction kinetic constants and the three mass transfer coefficients, before solving the system of ODEs.

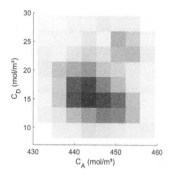

Figure 6: Plot showing the likelihood regions of the concentrations of components A and D, given the uncertainties in the model parameters. The darker the region, the more likely it is to represent reality.

The reaction rate constants and the mass transfer coefficients are usually quantified experimentally or using correlations from the literature. Such coefficients are known for their uncertainties and can be represented using probability distributions. Figure 5 shows how straight forward it is to define uncertain variables using Uncertainty.jl. Once k and h are defined, they can join any additional exact parameters to be the input for the ODEProblem function, which will return a distribution. Figure 6 shows a plot exemplifying how the information from the output can be visualised. Using similar visualisation tools and the statistics returned by Uncertainty.jl, users can understand what the most likely values of the variables are and make educated decisions.

5. Conclusions and Future Work

This paper introduced Uncertainty.jl, a user-friendly environment for the modelling of uncertainty. The examples provided, the case study on AACVD and the obtained solutions demonstrated the viability of this prototype language. Much more is required, especially in terms of incorporating existing methods for handling uncertainty. Future work will address, for example, the representation of model uncertainty. It will also facilitate and encourage the use of Machine Learning in the context of process modelling, from additional Monte Carlo algorithms through to defining and learning models using inference algorithms and probabilistic programming. Finally, Uncertainty.jl aims at supporting optimisation algorithms and the communication with the most established modelling platforms, such as GAMS, AMPL and gPROMS.

Acknowledgements: The authors acknowledge the support provided by Conselho Nacional de Desenvolvimento Científico e Tecnológico (CNPq) and EPSRC (EP/L017709/1).

References

J. Bezanson, A. Edelman, S. Karpinski, V. B. Shah, 2017. Julia: a fresh approach to numerical computing. SIAM Review 59 (1), 65–98.

Q. Chen, I. Grossmann, 2017. Recent developments and challenges in optimization-based process synthesis. Annual Review of Chemical and Biomolecular Engineering 8, 249–283.

I. E. Grossmann, R. M. Apap, B. A. Calfa, P. García-Herreros, Q. Zhang, 2016. Recent advances in mathematical programming techniques for the optimization of process systems under uncertainty. Computers & Chemical Engineering 91, 3–14.

P. I. O. Filho, P. Angeli, E. S. Fraga, 2018. Modelling under uncertainty for process design and scale-up of an industrial AACVD. Computer Aided Chemical Engineering 44 (1), 253–258.

P. I. O. Filho, D. B. Potter, M. J. Powell, C. J. Carmalt, P. Angeli, E. S. Fraga, 2017. Probability density functions for droplet sizing in aerosol transport modelling. Computer Aided Chemical Engineering 40 (1), 2245–2250.

C. Rackauckas, Q. Nie, 2017. DifferentialEquations.jl – a performant and feature-rich ecosystem for solving differential equations in Julia. Journal of Open Research Software 5 (1), 1–10.

M. Vallerio, D. Telen, L. Cabianca, F. Manenti, J. Van Impe, F. Logist, 2016. Robust multi-objective dynamic optimization of chemical processes using the sigma point method. Chem. Eng. Science 140, 201–216.

F. Zappa Nardelli, J. Belyakova, A. Pelenitsyn, B. Chung, J. Bezanson, J. Vitek, 2018. Julia subtyping: a rational reconstruction. Proceedings of the ACM on Programming Languages 2 (1), 1–27.

Anton A. Kiss, Edwin Zondervan, Richard Lakerveld, Leyla Özkan (Eds.)
Proceedings of the 29th European Symposium on Computer Aided Process Engineering
June 16th to 19th, 2019, Eindhoven, The Netherlands. © 2019 Elsevier B.V. All rights reserved.
http://dx.doi.org/10.1016/B978-0-128-18634-3.50151-X

Simulation of Food Waste Pyrolysis for the Production of Biochar: A Qatar Case Study

Samar Elkhalifa,[a] Ahmed AlNouss,[a,b] Tareq Al-Ansari,[a] Hamish R Mackey,[a]
Prakash Parthasarathy,[a] Gordon Mckay[a,*]

[a]*Division of Sustainable Development, College of Science and Engineering, Hamad Bin*

Khalifa University, Qatar Foundation, Doha, Qatar

[b]*Department of Chemical Engineering, College of Engineering, Qatar University,*

Doha, Qatar

gmckay@hbku.edu.qa

Abstract

One-third of the edible parts of food produced for human consumption is lost or wasted globally, amounting to 1.3 billion tonnes per year. Food waste contains many constituents, which makes it a promising source for fuels and chemicals production. Moreover, the State of Qatar, which is situated in a hyper arid region is characterized by a disproportionate distribution of resources. It is rich in natural energy resources, but suffers from water scarcity and its natural environment does not encourage food production. Qatar's economy continues to expand rapidly and faces a number of environmental challenges which include the management and disposal of wastes that are generated by industrial and domestic activities. As such, the pyrolysis of biomass waste and food waste specifically is a viable option to transform waste, which would have otherwise been disposed into the natural environment, into value-added products which can be utilized to enhance resource efficiency, especially water. In this work, the pyrolysis of different food waste has been simulated using Aspen Plus software to produce value-added biochar products. The pyrolysis of food waste in steady-state mode has been studied using a yield reactor, in the 300−600 °C temperature range, by feeding five types of food waste with different ultimate and proximate properties. In addition, the optimum feedstock is identified in which the objective is to optimize food waste blends for maximizing solids to syngas ratio. The optimization results indicated an increase in the yield of the solid biochar product from 36.56% to 41.81%, while both the ash and carbon content decreased slightly. These findings open the doors to the transformation of food waste into value-added biochar via pyrolysis. Furthermore, the produced chars can be utilized in carbon sequestration when applied as soil amendment and as precursors for higher value-added products such as adsorbents.

Keywords: Food Waste, Pyrolysis, Biochar, Simulation, Optimization

1. Introduction

With the predicted increase in population to 9.8 billion by 2050 according to UNO, the world is inevitably facing multiple dilemmas. Human and industrial activities are responsible for the creation of most types of waste. Urban and industrial wastes need to be managed sustainably if we are to avoid serious, lasting effects such as global warming. Furthermore, food waste is generated in abundance globally with estimated losses of 1.3

billion tonnes per year (Gustavsson et al., 2011) and hence it constitutes an attractive source for the recovery of energy and the production of value-added products (e.g. fuels and chemicals).

Pyrolysis is a promising thermochemical conversion method (Panwar et al., 2012; White et al., 2011) that transforms biomass into value-added products. In this process, biomass is heated to temperatures greater than 400 °C, under the partial presence of/or the complete absence of oxygen (Laird et al., 2009). The main products of the process are bio-oil, bio-gas, and biochar. There is a wide range of applications of the highly porous material and their composites that are produced by pyrolysis, which include their use as supercondensers, catalytic support materials, and adsorbents (Gordienko et al., 2017).

Many soils suffer from water deficiency and low soil fertility (Basso et al., 2013; Koide et al., 2015). Therefore, it is essential to improve soil fertility in order to achieve food security. Biochar, a product of the thermochemical conversion of biomass, can be implemented into soils as an enhancer that improves the fertility and quality of agricultural soils while enhancing the sustainability of biomass and crop production (Zhang et al., 2016).

The use of Aspen Plus in simulating the pyrolysis of waste streams, particularly municipal green waste, was previously demonstrated (Kabir et al., 2015). In their pyrolysis study, they investigated the production of bio-fuel from Australian municipal green waste (MGW) and then validated the simulation results against experimental results. The objective of this paper is to simulate the pyrolysis of different food wastes that are available in the State of Qatar using Aspen Plus software with the aim of producing a value-added biochar product. The pyrolysis of food waste in steady-state mode has been studied using a yield reactor, in the 300–600 °C temperature range, by feeding five types of food waste with different ultimate and proximate properties. The food waste includes banana peel, mango endocarp, orange peel, tea waste and cooked rice.

2. Methodology

2.1. Data: Proximate and Ultimate Analysis

The problem formulated in this study is based on experimental data obtained from the literature for food items that are available in the state of Qatar. Table 1 summarizes the proximate and ultimate analyses of the different food wastes considered here.

Table 1: Proximate and ultimate analyses of biomass (food waste) feedstocks

	Banana peel	Mango endocarp	Orange peel	Tea waste	Cooked rice
Moisture (wt. %)[*c]	10.36[*a]	4.760[*a]	9.910[*a]	12.00[*a]	64.44[*b]
Proximate analysis (wt. %)[*c]					
Volatile matter	78.90	63.81	55.86	64.17	62.50
Fixed carbon	10.82	33.19	41.14	30.09	37.05
Ash	10.28	3.000	3.000	5.740	0.4500
Ultimate analysis (wt. %)[*c]					
C	35.65	40.06	41.13	45.81	43.28
H	6.190	5.530	5.630	5.120	8.040
N	1.940	0.2900	0.5800	2.450	1.530
O	45.94	51.12	49.66	40.88	46.44
S	0.0000	0.0000	0.0000	0.0000	0.2600
Cl	0.0000	0.0000	0.0000	0.0000	0.0000
Ash	10.28	3.000	3.000	5.740	0.4500
LHV (MJ/kg) (dry basis)	17.33	11.64	12.08	12.66	17.33

	Banana peel	Mango endocarp	Orange peel	Tea waste	Cooked rice
Reference	(Kabenge et al., 2018)	(Lam et al., 2016)	(Lam et al., 2016)	(Yadav et al., 2016)	(Liu et al., 2016)

*a Air-dried basis, *b As received basis, *c Total dry-basis

2.2. Modelling and Simulation

2.2.1. Model Development

The base model developed in this work and used in the generation of the carbon-rich biochar solid is based on the pyrolysis of different feedstocks. Moreover, the simulation software is composed of several unit operation blocks which are models of specific process operations (e.g. reactors). The blocks were placed on a flowsheet through the specification of material and energy streams. The pyrolysis of food waste in this study is modelled based on the assumptions of steady state, kinetic-free equilibrium model, isobaric process, neglected pressure drops, and neglected tar formation. Moreover, the RYield reactor type was used to convert the feed material into its constituent elements (i.e. pyrolysis part of the modelling) through using the calculator block formulation from (AlNouss et al., 2018), while the nonstoichiometric Gibbs free energy equilibrium-based splitter model was used for solid yield separation.

2.2.2. Simulation of the Results

A computational model has been developed in this study to simulate this process using Aspen Plus software. Aspen Plus is a process-oriented software that facilitates calculation of physical, chemical and biological parameters (Puig-Arnavat et al., 2010). It can handle solid, liquid and vapour phases in the process. The process simulator does not have a built-in pyrolysis model; however it contains a number of built-in unit block models which enable the realistic specification of processes (Kabir et al., 2015). A pyrolysis process diagram is presented in Figure 1. An Aspen Plus model was developed based on this pyrolysis process flow diagram. The function of each block is summarized in Table 2.

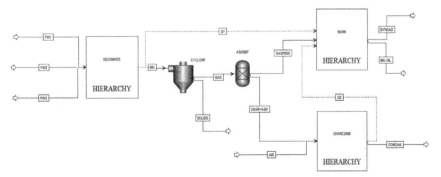

Figure 2: Aspen plus flowsheet of the food waste pyrolysis

Table 2: Summary of the functions of each block in the developed Aspen flowsheet

Block ID	Aspen name	Description
DECOMP	RYield	Converts the non-conventional attributes into conventional components
CYCLONE	Cyclone	Simulates the separation of bio-char using cyclone

Block ID	Aspen name	Description
ASHSEP	Sep	Separates gases from ash and small part of carbon by specifying split fraction
CHARCOMB	Stoic	Simulates combustion of carbon and ash to provide heat
BURN	RGibbs	Simulates the separation of syngas and bio-oil using flash separator and further syngas pyrolysis through Gibbs reactor restricting chemical equilibrium

2.2.3. Process Optimization

After the development of the pyrolysis model, the five food waste feedstocks were optimized to determine the optimum blended stream. The objective of the optimization problem is to maximize the solids to syngas ratio. The optimization equations are as below:

$$\text{Maximize} \quad \frac{Solid}{Syngas} \qquad \qquad \text{Eq. (1)}$$

$$\text{Subject to} \quad \sum_{i=1}^{n} x_i = 1 \forall i \in BiomassSources \qquad \text{Eq. (2)}$$

Where, Solid is the molar flowrate of the generated biochar, Syngas is the molar flowrate of the generated H_2-rich synthesis gas, and x is the blending fraction of each biomass feedstock.

3. Results and Discussion

The developed model has been tested against data provide in Table 1 in order to find the optimum blended feedstock. The results before and after the optimization are presented in Table 3 and Table 4 respectively.

Table 3: Results for Biomass Feedstock Blending without optimization at original moisture content

Total Biomass Input (kg/h)	5000 (1000 each biomass)		
LHV (MJ/kg) Input (dry basis)	12.94		
	Solids	**SYN**	**Oil**
Output (kg/h)	1828	3172	0.3700
N_2	0.0000	52.38	0.0000
O_2	0.0000	1871	0.0000
H_2O	0.0000	1015	0.0000
S	0.0000	0.9400	0.0000
H_2	0.0000	232.5	0.0000
C	1628	0.0000	0.3700
ASH	199.8	0.0000	0.0000
% Yield (kg/kg input)	36.56	63.43	0.0100
Energy Requirement (T=500 °C)	DECOMP	CHARCOMB	BURN
Heat Flow (kJ/h)	31.08	2.900	-28.40

It could be noticed that the use of Cyclone has driven almost all the carbon and ash to the solid biochar flow. In addition, the reported composition of syngas is before utilizing it for further pyrolysis through Gibbs free energy.

Furthermore, a restriction on the modelling terms of the maximum amount of any of the feeds used has been identified. The results are highlighted in Table 4. The model results demonstrated almost an equal amount of the 4 feed waste streams (2 through 5) as optimum blend. This reflect the amounts of carbon and ash per pure feed stream that these streams contain. Where, Banana peel contains around 41% (carbon+ ash), Mango endocarp (41%), Orange peel (40%), Tea Waste (45%) and cooked rice (16%). From this analysis it is clear that cooked rice has the lowest Carbon and Ash content and the highest moisture content and it is not of an interest.

Table 4: Results for Biomass Feedstock Blending with optimization at original moisture content

Total Biomass Input (kg/h)	3984.90				
Biomass Blends	FW1	FW2	FW3	FW4	FW5
	24.70%	25.10%	25.10%	25.10%	0.0000%
LHV (MJ/kg) Input (dry basis)	12.48				
	Solids	**SYN**	**Oil**		
Output (kg/h)	1666	2318	0.4400		
N_2	0.0000	46.66	0.0000		
O_2	0.0000	1699	0.0000		
H_2O	0.0000	369.3	0.0000		
S	0.0000	0.0200	0.0000		
H_2	0.0000	203.1	0.0000		
C	1469	0.0000	0.4400		
ASH	196.7	0.0000	0.0000		
% Yield (kg/kg input)	41.81	58.18	0.0100		
Energy Requirement (T=500 °C)	DECOMP	CHARCOMB	BURN		
Heat Flow (kJ/h)	26.12	2.310	-24.79		

According to the results, prior to optimization, a percentage by weight of biochar obtained is 36.56 % w/w. The results of the optimization then improve to reach a yield of 41.81 % w/w biochar when a total food waste input of 3984.90 kg/h and a contribution of ~25 % w/w of each food waste except cooked rice is implemented. With respect to the ash and carbon contents of the produced biochars through the simulation, it can be observed that there is a slight reduction in their quantities (see Table 3 and Table 4).

With drying all the food waste streams to a maximum of 9.000 % moisture content and still restricting the flow of each food waste to 1000, the results showed equal distribution for all the feedstock. The drying energy requirement for the different food wastes were estimated at 0.1500, 0.0000, 0.0400, 0.0700 and 7.170 kJ/h, respectively. When releasing the restriction on the flow of each food waste to high number (~10^5), the optimization yields a feed of only Tea waste. This can be explained since it contains the highest Carbon and Ash content and with the releasing of the feed constraint, it has dominated the result.

4. Conclusion

In this work, the pyrolysis of different food waste feedstocks is simulated using Aspen Plus software in order to obtain biochar products at optimum conditions. While producing the value-added products, the objective is to optimize the food waste blends for maximizing solids to syngas ratio. The base model developed in this work used in the generation of the carbon rich biochar solid is based on the pyrolysis of different feedstocks with different ultimate and proximate properties and that are available in the State of Qatar. The results of the optimization indicated an increase in the yield of the solid biochar product from 36.56 % w/w (1000 kg/h of each of the food wastes as initial input) to 41.81 % w/w (food waste input of 3984 kg/h and ~25 % w/w of each food waste except cooked rice), while both the ash and carbon content decreased slightly. These findings are promising because they open doors to the transformation of the abundant amounts of food waste that are available globally into value-added biochar via pyrolysis.

Furthermore, the produced chars can be utilized in carbon sequestration when applied as soil amendment and as precursors for higher value-added products such as adsorbents.

Acknowledgment

The authors would like to express their gratitude to Hamad Bin Khalifa University and Qatar Foundation for the provision of support during this project. The authors thank the Supreme Committee for Legacy and Development in Qatar for the further support of this research and development programme.

References

A. AlNouss, G. McKay, and T. Al-Ansari, 2018, Optimum Utilization of Biomass for the Production of Power and Fuels using Gasification, Computer Aided Chemical Engineering, 43, 1481-86.

A.S. Basso, F.E. Miguez, D.A. Laird, R. Horton, and M. Westgate, 2013, Assessing potential of biochar for increasing water-holding capacity of sandy soils, GCB Bioenergy, 5, 2, 132-43.

M. Gordienko, D. Belous, A. Tyrtyshnikov, I. Mitrofanov, N. Menshutina, and E. Lebedev, 2017, Prediction of structure changes of organic-silica aerogels during pyrolysis, Computer Aided Chemical Engineering, 40, 181-86.

J. Gustavsson, C. Cederberg, U. Sonesson, R.v. Otterdijk, and A. Meybeck, 2011, Global food losses and food waste: extent, causes and prevention, Food and Agriculture Organization of the United Nations (FAO).

I. Kabenge, G. Omulo, N. Banadda, J. Seay, A. Zziwa, and N. Kiggundu, 2018, Characterization of Banana Peels Wastes as Potential Slow Pyrolysis Feedstock, Journal of Sustainable Development, 11, 2, 14–24

M. Kabir, A. Chowdhury, and M. Rasul, 2015, Pyrolysis of Municipal Green Waste: A Modelling, Simulation and Experimental Analysis, Energies, 8, 8, 7522.

R.T. Koide, B.T. Nguyen, R.H. Skinner, C.J. Dell, M.S. Peoples, P.R. Adler, and P.J. Drohan, 2015, Biochar amendment of soil improves resilience to climate change, GCB Bioenergy, 7, 5, 1084-91.

D.A. Laird, R.C. Brown, J.E. Amonette, and J. Lehmann, 2009, Review of the pyrolysis platform for coproducing bio-oil and biochar, Biofuels, Bioproducts and Biorefining, 3, 5, 547-62.

S. S. Lam, R. K. Liew, X. Y. Lim, F. N. Ani, and A. Jusoh, 2016, Fruit Waste as Feedstock for Recovery by Pyrolysis Technique, International Biodeterioration and Biodegradation, 113, 325–333

H. Liu, J. E, X. Ma, and C. Xie, 2016, Influence of Microwave Drying on the Combustion Characteristics of Food Waste, Drying Technology, 34, 12, 1397–1405.

N.L. Panwar, R. Kothari, and V.V. Tyagi, 2012, Thermo chemical conversion of biomass – Eco friendly energy routes, Renewable and Sustainable Energy Reviews, 16, 4, 1801-16.

M. Puig-Arnavat, J.C. Bruno, and A. Coronas, 2010, Review and analysis of biomass gasification models, Renewable and Sustainable Energy Reviews, 14, 9, 2841-51.

J.E. White, W.J. Catallo, and B.L. Legendre, 2011, Biomass pyrolysis kinetics: A comparative critical review with relevant agricultural residue case studies, Journal of Analytical and Applied Pyrolysis, 91, 1, 1-33.

D. Yadav, L. Barbora, L. Rangan, and P. Mahantaa, 2016, Tea Waste and Food Waste as a Potential Feedstock for Biogas Production, Environmental Progress & Sustainable Energy, 35, 5, 1247–1253

C. Zhang, L. Zhou, P. Chhabra, S.S. Garud, K. Aditya, A. Romagnoli, G. Comodi, F. Dal Magro, A. Meneghetti, and M. Kraft, 2016, A novel methodology for the design of waste heat recovery network in eco-industrial park using techno-economic analysis and multi-objective optimization, Applied Energy, 184, 88-102.

Anton A. Kiss, Edwin Zondervan, Richard Lakerveld, Leyla Özkan (Eds.)
Proceedings of the 29th European Symposium on Computer Aided Process Engineering
June 16th to 19th, 2019, Eindhoven, The Netherlands. © 2019 Elsevier B.V. All rights reserved.
http://dx.doi.org/10.1016/B978-0-128-18634-3.50152-1

The robust pooling problem

Johannes Wiebe[a,*], Inês Cecílio[b] and Ruth Misener[a]

[a]*Department of Computing, Imperial College London, 180 Queen's Gate, SW7 2AZ London, UK*
[b]*Schlumberger Cambridge Research, Cambridge, UK*
j.wiebe17@imperial.ac.uk

Abstract

The pooling problem is a widely studied case study in global optimization. To date, it has largely been treated deterministically, neglecting the influence of parametric uncertainty. This work introduces a robust optimization formulation of the standard pooling problem with uncertain component concentrations. The quality constraints in which these uncertain parameters occur are non-linear and non-convex in the decision variables — something which has rarely been explored in the context of robust optimization. The resulting reformulation is a global optimization problem with the complexity determined by the selected uncertainty set. We compare the computational performance of three commonly used uncertainty sets on 14 pooling problem instances and demonstrate how accounting for uncertainty changes the optimal solution.

Keywords: robust optimization, global optimization, pooling problem

1. Introduction

The widely studied pooling problem has applications in oil and gas refining, water systems, supply chains, and more (Misener et al., 2011). It consists of optimizing material flow through a network of sources, pools, and terminals. Due to bilinear mixing terms at the pools it is non-linear and non-convex and is known to be NP-hard (Alfaki and Haugland, 2013). The pooling problem has frequently been used as a case study in global deterministic optimization (e.g. Floudas and Visweswaran, 1990; Meyer and Floudas, 2004; Quesada and Grossmann, 1995; Tawarmalani and Sahinidis, 2004; Wicaksono and Karimi, 2008; Gounaris et al., 2009; Misener and Floudas, 2010; Alfaki and Haugland, 2013; Baltean-Lugojan and Misener, 2018). Parameters of the pooling problem can be subject to uncertainty. In particular, the concentrations of components and pollutants entering the system can be subject to measurement errors and/or fluctuations over time. These concentrations will have a large effect on product quality at the terminals, which is often subject to constraints. Violating these constraints can have a negative impact on profit, health and safety, or the environment.

Nonetheless, to the best of our knowledge, only Li et al. (2011, 2012b) and Li et al. (2012a) have considered uncertainty in the pooling problem to date. Li et al. (2011) consider component concentration uncertainties for the extended pooling problem and pooling network synthesis. They utilize a two-stage stochastic programming approach: the first stage determines the number of sources, pools, and product terminals developed and the connections between them. The second stage assumes the uncertainty has been realized and optimizes the pooling network production. Li et al. (2012b) propose a decomposition strategy for solving the stochastic program. Li et al. (2012a) apply robust optimization to demand uncertainty in the standard pooling problem. An advantage of the robust approach is that the increase in problem complexity is moderate and no decomposition is required (Grossmann et al., 2016).

This work applies robust optimization to uncertain component concentrations in the quality constraints of the standard pooling problem. The process systems engineering community has recently been increasingly interested in applying robust optimization to chemical processes (e.g. Gounaris et al., 2013; Zhang et al., 2015; Janak and Floudas, 2005; Vujanic et al., 2016; Li and Ierapetritou, 2008; Ning and You, 2017; Shang and You, 2018). Most of these applications have been limited to linear models. The work by Li et al. (2012a) on the pooling problem is an early exception to this, even though the uncertain demand constraints considered are still linear. In fact, robust optimization in general is largely focused on problems which are convex in the decision variables and concave in the uncertain parameters (Ben-Tal et al., 2015). While concavity in the uncertain parameters is necessary for robust optimization reformulation, the restriction on convexity is largely due to a focus in the robust optimization literature on applications which are solvable in polynomial time. "Robust optimization" problems which are non-convex in the decision variables and non-concave in the uncertain parameters can generally only be addressed with semi-infinite programming.

In this work, we are interested in constraints which are non-convex in the decision variables but concave in the uncertain parameter, as is the case for the quality constraints in the standard pooling problem. Robust optimization reformulation can be applied to these constraints, but the result is a global optimization problem. In Section 2, a robust formulation for the standard pooling problem is derived. Section 3 demonstrates the computational complexity of the resulting problem for box, ellipsoidal, and polyhedral uncertainty sets and how the optimal flows in the network change when varying degrees of uncertainty are considered.

2. A robust pooling formulation

We consider the q-formulation of the standard pooling problem (Haverly, 1978) in which the uncertain component concentrations only occur in the quality constraints. This formulation is favorable for robust optimization because the uncertain parameters do not occur in any equality constraints. The robust counterpart of the uncertain quality constraint is

$$\sum_{\substack{l:(l,j)\in T_Y \\ i:(i,l)\in T_X}} \tilde{C}_{i,k}\cdot q_{i,l}\cdot y_{l,j} + \sum_{i:(i,j)\in T_Z} \tilde{C}_{i,k}\cdot z_{i,j} \begin{cases} \geq P^L_{j,k}\left(\sum_{l:(l,j)\in T_Y} y_{l,j} + \sum_{i:(i,j)\in T_Z} z_{i,j}\right) \\ \leq P^U_{j,k}\left(\sum_{l:(l,j)\in T_Y} y_{l,j} + \sum_{i:(i,j)\in T_Z} z_{i,j}\right) \end{cases}, \forall j,k, \tilde{C}_{i,k}\in\mathcal{U}_p,$$

(1)

where $\tilde{C}_{i,k}$ is the uncertain concentrations of component k in source i, $P^L_{j,k}$ and $P^U_{j,k}$ are their lower and upper limits at pool j respectively, and $\mathcal{U}_p$ is the uncertainty set. The decision variables are $q_{i,l}$, the fraction of flow to pool l from source i, $y_{l,j}$, the flow from pool l to terminal j, and $z_{i,j}$, the direct flow from source i to terminal j. The sets T_X, T_Y, T_Z describe the connections between sources, pools and terminals. By introducing the indicator function

$$\mathbb{1}(s\in S) = \begin{cases} 1 & s\in S \\ 0 & s\notin S \end{cases}$$

and rearranging, we can bring eqn. 1 into standard form

$$\sum_i \tilde{C}_{i,k}a_{i,j} \begin{cases} \leq b^U_{j,k} \\ \geq b^L_{j,k} \end{cases}, \quad \forall j,k, \tilde{C}_{i,k}\in\mathcal{U}_p,$$

where

$$a_{i,j} = \sum_{l:(l,j)\in T_Y} \left[\mathbb{1}\left((i,l)\in T_X\right) y_{l,j} q_{i,l} \right] + \mathbb{1}\left((i,j)\in T_Z\right) z_{i,j}, \text{ and} \tag{2}$$

$$b_{j,k}^{U/L} = P_{j,k}^{U/L} \left(\sum_{l:(l,j)\in T_Y} y_{l,j} + \sum_{i:(i,j)\in T_Z} z_{i,j} \right). \tag{3}$$

We define the uncertainty set $\mathcal{U}_p$ as

$$\mathcal{U}_p = \left\{ \tilde{C}_{i,k} = C_{i,k} + \hat{C}_{i,k}\xi_{i,k} \mid \|\xi_k\|_p \leq r \right\},$$

where $\xi_k = (\dots, \xi_{i,k}, \dots)^T$, $C_{i,k}$ is the nominal value of $\tilde{C}_{i,k}$, and $\hat{C}_{i,k}$ its maximum deviation. For $p = 1$ this corresponds to a polyhedral, for $p = 2$ to an ellipsoidal, and for $p = \infty$ to a box uncertainty set. For each set, standard robust optimization reformulation techniques can be used to obtain the deterministic equivalent of the robust counterpart:

$$\sum_i C_{i,k} a_{i,j} + r[\cdots] \leq b_{j,k}^u \qquad\qquad \forall j,k \tag{4a}$$

$$-\mu_{i,j} \leq a_{i,j} \leq \mu_{i,j} \qquad\qquad \forall i,j \tag{4b}$$

$$\left(\lambda_{j,k}^u \geq \hat{C}_{i,k}\mu_{i,j} \right) \qquad\qquad \forall i,j,k \tag{4c}$$

where $[\cdots]$ is $\sum_i \hat{C}_{i,k}\mu_{i,j}$ for $p = \infty$, $\sqrt{\sum_i \hat{C}_{i,k}^2 \mu_{i,j}^2}$ for $p = 2$, and $\lambda_{j,k}^u$ for $p = 1$ and constraint 4c is only needed for $p = 1$. Substituting eqn. 2 for $a_{i,j}$ and simplifying gives

$$r[\cdots] \leq b_{j,k}^u - \sum_{\substack{l:(l,j)\in T_Y \\ i:(i,l)\in T_X}} C_{i,k} \cdot q_{i,l} \cdot y_{l,j} - \sum_{i:(i,j)\in T_Z} C_{i,k} \cdot z_{i,j} \qquad \forall j,k \tag{5a}$$

$$-\mu_{i,j} \leq \sum_{l:(l,j)\in T_Y} q_{i,l} y_{l,j} + z_{i,j} \leq \mu_{i,j} \qquad\qquad \forall (i,j)\in T_Z \tag{5b}$$

$$-\mu_{i,j} \leq \sum_{l:(l,j)\in T_Y} q_{i,l} y_{l,j} \leq \mu_{i,j} \qquad\qquad \forall (i,j)\notin T_Z \tag{5c}$$

$$\left(\lambda_{j,k}^u \geq \hat{C}_{i,k}\mu_{i,j} \right) \qquad\qquad \forall i,j,k \tag{5d}$$

where $[\cdots]$ is defined in the same way as above.

While the box and ellipsoidal uncertainty set both add $\mathcal{O}(|i| \cdot |j|)$ constraints, the polyhedral set adds $\mathcal{O}(|i| \cdot |j| \cdot |k|)$ constraints. An advantage of the polyhedral set, however, is that the problem remains bilinear, while the ellipsoidal set introduces a square root, which can be problematic numerically. Squaring each side of eqn. 5a avoids this, but the squared constraint is only equivalent if the nominal quality constraints (eqn. 1 with $\tilde{C}_{i,k}$ replaced by $C_{i,k}$) are added, increasing the total number of constraints once again.

3. Results

The robust formulation outlined above was applied to 14 instances from the literature (Adhya et al., 1999; Foulds et al., 1992; Ben-Tal et al., 1994; Haverly, 1978; Audet et al., 2004). The model was implemented in GAMS 25.1.2 and solved using ANTIGONE 1.1 (Misener and Floudas, 2014) on an i7-6700 CPU with 8×3.4GHz and 16GB RAM. Each instance was solved for 30 values of r using the box, ellipsoidal, and polyhedral uncertainty set with a time limit of 1 hr, a tolerance of 10^{-6}, and $\hat{C}_{i,k} = C_{i,k}$.

Fig. 1 shows the performance of each uncertainty set as a function of its size r for four representative instances. As expected, the fraction of the nominal objective value achieved decreases as

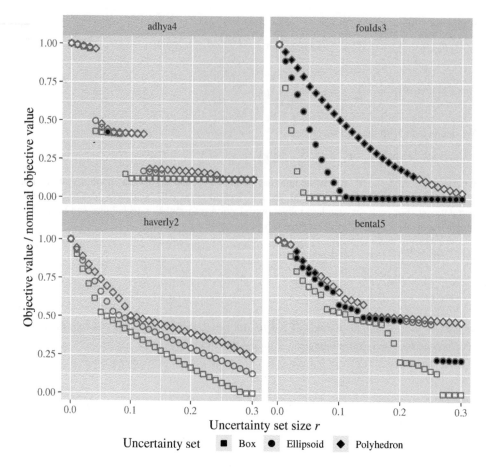

Figure 1: Objective value (relative to nominal case) for different uncertainty set types and sizes for four literature instances. Points filled black were not solved to global optimality within 1 hr.

the uncertainty set size r is increased. Since the polyhedral set is always smallest and the box set always largest, they consistently achieve the best and worst objective value respectively. For points filled in black the model could not be solved to optimality within 1 hr. Table 1 shows the fraction of instances solved for each uncertainty set. While the box uncertainty set could be solved for all instances, the polyhedral and especially the ellipsoidal cannot, due to the increased number of constraints for these formulations. The consistency between solutions which have and have not been solved globally indicates however, that in a lot of cases the global optimum (or a solution close to it) may have already been found though it has not been certified. For those instances which could be solved to optimality, Table 1 shows the median time taken across instances. While the box and polyhedral uncertainty set have very similar median times, the ellipsoidal set shows a moderate increase. The solution times for the box and polyhedral set are generally very close to the nominal case. As in linear robust optimization, the ellipsoidal set increases the complexity of the nominal problem, while the box and polyhedral set largely retain it.

Fig. 2 shows the obtained solutions for three different values of r for instance Adhya1 (Adhya et al., 1999) using a polyhedral set. The width of the arrows between nodes indicates the fraction of flow from/to each pool. Edges from a source to a pool are also labeled with this fraction, while edges from a pool to a terminal are labeled with the absolute flow. In the nominal case ($r = 0$),

Uncertainty set	% instances solved	median time [s]
Box	100	0.14
Ellipsoid	66	1.42
Polyhedron	83	0.15

Table 1: Percentage of instances solved to global optimality within 1 hr time limit for different uncertainty set types.

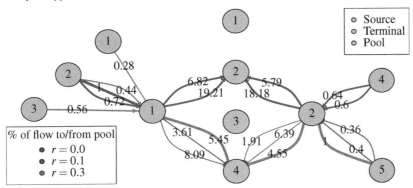

Figure 2: Active source, pools, and terminals for three different uncertainy set sizes r using instance Adhya1 with the polyhedral uncertainty set. The width of the arrows shows the percentage of flow to/from each pool.

both product 2 and 4 are produced. As r is increased, hedging against more uncertainty, the total amount of products 2 and 4 produced remains constant, but the fraction coming from pool 1 increases drastically. The utilization of sources largely remains the same, with the exception of source 1. Once r is increased past 0.14, the quality of product 2 cannot be guaranteed anymore for all possible realizations of the uncertainty. This leads to a jump in the expected profit from 446.2 to 65.9. Similar jumps can be seen in Fig. 1 for instances Adhya4 and Bental5. In this regime, both sources 1 and 4 are replaced by source 3. All of this shows that optimal solution is clearly very dependent on how much uncertainty one wants to hedge against. In practice, the size of the uncertainty set therefore has to be determined based on the risk aversion of the decision maker.

4. Conclusion

Applying robust optimization to the non-convex pooling problem leads to a global optimization problem with increased complexity compared to the nominal case. The tractability of the resulting reformulation with global optimization solvers is highly dependent on the selected uncertainty set. While simple box uncertainty sets hardly increase computational time, more advanced ellipsoidal and polyhedral sets are more difficult to solve. The relevance of optimization under uncertainty is supported by the significant changes in the solution observed when different degrees of uncertainty are taken into account.

5. Acknowledgements

This work was funded by the Engineering & Physical Sciences Research Council (EPSRC) Center for Doctoral Training in High Performance Embedded and Distributed Systems (EP/L016796/1), an EPSRC/Schlumberger CASE studentship to J.W. (EP/R511961/1, voucher 17000145), and an EPSRC Research Fellowship to R.M. (EP/P016871/1).

References

N. Adhya, M. Tawarmalani, N. V. Sahinidis, 1999. A Lagrangian Approach to the Pooling Problem. Industrial & Engineering Chemistry Research 38 (5), 1956–1972.

M. Alfaki, D. Haugland, 2013. Strong formulations for the pooling problem. Journal of Global Optimization 56 (3), 897–916.

C. Audet, J. Brimberg, P. Hansen, S. L. Digabel, N. Mladenović, 2004. Pooling Problem: Alternate Formulations and Solution Methods. Management Science 50 (6), 761–776.

R. Baltean-Lugojan, R. Misener, 2018. Piecewise parametric structure in the pooling problem: from sparse strongly-polynomial solutions to NP-hardness. Journal of Global Optimization 71 (4), 655–690.

A. Ben-Tal, D. den Hertog, J.-P. Vial, 2015. Deriving robust counterparts of nonlinear uncertain inequalities. Mathematical Programming 149 (1-2), 265–299.

A. Ben-Tal, G. Eiger, V. Gershovitz, 1994. Global minimization by reducing the duality gap. Mathematical Programming 63 (1-3), 193–212.

C. Floudas, V. Visweswaran, 1990. A global optimization algorithm (GOP) for certain classes of nonconvex NLPsI. Theory. Computers & Chemical Engineering 14 (12), 1397–1417.

L. R. Foulds, D. Haugland, K. Jörnsten, 1992. A bilinear approach to the pooling problem.

C. E. Gounaris, R. Misener, C. A. Floudas, 2009. Computational Comparison of PiecewiseLinear Relaxations for Pooling Problems. Industrial & Engineering Chemistry Research 48 (12), 5742–5766.

C. E. Gounaris, W. Wiesemann, C. A. Floudas, 2013. The Robust Capacitated Vehicle Routing Problem Under Demand Uncertainty. Operations Research 61 (3), 677–693.

I. E. Grossmann, R. M. Apap, B. A. Calfa, P. García-Herreros, Q. Zhang, 2016. Recent advances in mathematical programming techniques for the optimization of process systems under uncertainty. Computers and Chemical Engineering 91, 3–14.

C. A. Haverly, 1978. Studies of the behavior of recursion for the pooling problem. ACM SIGMAP Bulletin (25), 19–28.

S. L. Janak, C. A. Floudas, 2005. Advances in robust optimization approaches for scheduling under uncertainty. Computer Aided Chemical Engineering 20 (C), 1051–1056.

J. Li, R. Misener, C. A. Floudas, 2012a. Scheduling of crude oil operations under demand uncertainty: A robust optimization framework coupled with global optimization. AIChE Journal 58 (8), 2373–2396.

X. Li, E. Rmagan, A. Tomasgard, P. I. Barton, 2011. Stochastic pooling problem for natural gas production network design and operation under uncertainty. AIChE Journal 57 (8), 2120–2135.

X. Li, A. Tomasgard, P. I. Barton, 2012b. Decomposition strategy for the stochastic pooling problem. Journal of Global Optimization 54 (4), 765–790.

Z. Li, M. G. Ierapetritou, 2008. Robust Optimization for Process Scheduling Under Uncertainty. Industrial & Engineering Chemistry Research 47 (12), 4148–4157.

C. A. Meyer, C. A. Floudas, 2004. Trilinear Monomials with Mixed Sign Domains: Facets of the Convex and Concave Envelopes. Journal of Global Optimization 29 (2), 125–155.

R. Misener, C. A. Floudas, 2010. Global Optimization of Large-Scale Generalized Pooling Problems: Quadratically Constrained MINLP Models. Industrial & Engineering Chemistry Research 49 (11), 5424–5438.

R. Misener, C. A. Floudas, 2014. ANTIGONE: Algorithms for coNTinuous / Integer Global Optimization of Nonlinear Equations. Journal of Global Optimization 59 (2-3), 503–526.

R. Misener, J. P. Thompson, C. A. Floudas, 2011. APOGEE: Global optimization of standard, generalized, and extended pooling problems via linear and logarithmic partitioning schemes. Computers & Chemical Engineering 35 (5), 876–892.

C. Ning, F. You, 2017. A data-driven multistage adaptive robust optimization framework for planning and scheduling under uncertainty. AIChE Journal 63 (10), 4343–4369.

I. Quesada, I. Grossmann, 1995. Global optimization of bilinear process networks with multicomponent flows. Computers & Chemical Engineering 19 (12), 1219–1242.

C. Shang, F. You, 2018. Distributionally robust optimization for planning and scheduling under uncertainty. Computers and Chemical Engineering 110, 53–68.

M. Tawarmalani, N. V. Sahinidis, 2004. Global optimization of mixed-integer nonlinear programs: A theoretical and computational study. Mathematical Programming 99 (3), 563–591.

R. Vujanic, P. Goulart, M. Morari, 2016. Robust Optimization of Schedules Affected by Uncertain Events. Journal of Optimization Theory and Applications 171 (3), 1033–1054.

D. S. Wicaksono, I. A. Karimi, 2008. Piecewise MILP under- and overestimators for global optimization of bilinear programs. AIChE Journal 54 (4), 991–1008.

Q. Zhang, I. E. Grossmann, C. F. Heuberger, A. Sundaramoorthy, J. M. Pinto, 2015. Air separation with cryogenic energy storage: Optimal scheduling considering electric energy and reserve markets. AIChE Journal 61 (5), 1547–1558.

Anton A. Kiss, Edwin Zondervan, Richard Lakerveld, Leyla Özkan (Eds.)
Proceedings of the 29th European Symposium on Computer Aided Process Engineering
June 16th to 19th, 2019, Eindhoven, The Netherlands. © 2019 Elsevier B.V. All rights reserved.
http://dx.doi.org/10.1016/B978-0-128-18634-3.50153-3

A model identification approach for the evaluation of plant efficiency

Keivan Rahimi-Adli[a,b,*], Patrick D. Schiermoch[a], Benedikt Beisheim[a,b], Simon Wenzel[b] and Sebastian Engell[b]

[a]*INEOS Manufacturing Deutschland GmbH, Alte Str. 201, 50769 Köln, Germany*
[b]*Process Dynamics and Operations Group, Department of Biochemical and Chemical Engineering, TU Dortmund University, Emil-Figge-Str. 70, 44227 Dortmund, Germany*
keivan.rahimi-adli@ineos.com

Abstract

Regulations and the public expectations on improving efficiency, reducing the carbon footprint and lowering the environmental impact drive the process industry towards improved operation and the development of new technologies. The efficiency of an existing production plant depends on a variety of factors like capacity utilisation, raw material quality, ambient temperature or operational performance. Identifying the influence of these factors on the performance of the plant helps to take suitable measures to drive it towards a more efficient operation. One approach to assess the resource efficiency potential of a plant is the comparison of the actual performance with the best possible operation under the given circumstances. This work presents a surrogate modelling approach for the identification of the best possible operation based on historical data. The surrogate model is compared to a more detailed rigorous model and advantages and possible shortcomings of the surrogate approach are discussed based on real production data at INEOS in Köln.

Keywords: Surrogate models, plant efficiency, energy management systems, model detail level, model identification

1. Introduction

The process industry is constantly developing methods for the evaluation of their resource consumption and the identification of possible improvement potentials. In cases where there are no structural changes of the process planned, on the one end this can be achieved by implementing Advanced Process Control (APC) solutions, which is time consuming and expensive. On the other end, there are well-trained operators who are often able to realize a significant fraction of the APC saving potential, if information on the magnitude of the performance gaps is accessible and the experience about how to improve the operational efficiency can be used. The international standard ISO50001:2011 demands the use of energy performance indicators (EnPI) which have to be compared with an energy baseline. The idea of the Best Demonstrated Practice (BDP), as shown

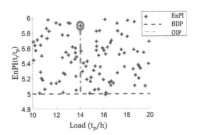

Figure 1: Illustrative example of the BDP concept

in Fig. 1, is similar and provides the operators with a performance reference model which represents the most resource efficient and stable production at a specific instance of non-influenceable circumstances, as e.g. plant load. By comparing the real-time EnPI, which is defined as the specific steam consumption at a particular point in time in this example, with its BDP, the operational improvement potentials (OIP) can be identified (NAMUR WG 4.17, 2017).

2. BDP Model

The level of detail of the BDP models can vary from rigorous models to simple input-output models. The accuracy and the extrapolation capability of rigorous models are advantageous. However, the time and effort needed to develop these models is usually high. On the other end of the scale are input-output models based on linear regression which cannot always represent the complexities of the chemical processes properly.

An alternative to these two types of models are surrogate models (see e.g. Cozad et al. (2014)). In this modelling approach the process data is used to fit a model to the observations. The development of such models requires considerably less effort compared to the development of rigorous models and they are able to capture the plant behaviour better than linear regression models. Furthermore, the evaluation of the surrogate models is easier which makes them attractive for large scale optimisation (Søndergaard, 2003). On the downside, the validity of the surrogate models is limited to the range of the data that is used for their fitting and the results of the model for extrapolated data must be used with care.

2.1. Surrogate modelling procedure

This section briefly discusses the approach to surrogate modelling of the BDP curves that has been developed and implemented at INEOS in Köln. A detailed description of the procedure can be found in Beisheim et al. (2018). As depicted in Fig. 2, the method consists of five general steps. The first step is the acquisition of measurement data. The goal of this step is to collect representative and reliable measurements of the performance of the plant, where aspects as e.g. removal of gross errors, stationarity, selection of suitable sampling times and removal of abnormal operation windows have to be considered.

The second step is the preprocessing of the data. The goal of this step is to remove outliers, classify the data and to standardise. For the latter mean centring and unit variance scaling is used. Data standardisation is useful for the clustering of the data, which is explained in the next step.

The third step of the method is data clustering. The goal of this step is to reduce the large amount of the measurement data into a much smaller number of a few representatives of different operating regimes, which are then used for model fitting. In this work, the kmeans++ algorithm (Arthur and Vassilvitskii, 2007) is applied, which is an extension of the kmeans algorithm (MacQueen et al., 1967). The distance metric used for clustering is the Euclidean distance of the data from the cluster centres and therefore it is sensitive to the magnitude of the data and is prone to the assignment of a higher influence on a variable with a higher magnitude. As the important factor to consider in this work is the effect of the variation of the noninfluenceable factors on the resource efficiency, the data is pre-processed by the subtraction of the mean of each variable and dividing the values by the

Figure 2: Steps of the BDP modelling procedure

standard deviation. The kmeans++ algorithm requires the number of the clusters as an input. The clustering algorithm assigns a centre to each cluster that represents the average of the points in that cluster. As the goal of the BDP model is to calculate the most efficient operational domain, the cluster centres are not used as representative values. Instead, a percentile analysis for each cluster is performed:

$$\mathbf{r}_j = \frac{1}{|\mathscr{R}_j|} \sum_{\mathbf{x} \in \mathscr{R}_j} \mathbf{x} \tag{1}$$

$$\mathbf{x} \in \mathscr{R}_j \quad \forall \quad P_{j,n} \leq \text{EnPI}(\mathbf{x}) \leq P_{j,m} \tag{2}$$

$$\mathscr{R}_j \subseteq \mathscr{X} \tag{3}$$

$$\text{EnPI}_{\mathscr{R}_j} = \frac{1}{|\mathscr{R}_j|} \sum_{\mathbf{x} \in \mathscr{R}_j} \text{EnPI}(\mathbf{x}), \tag{4}$$

where $\mathscr{R}_j$ denotes the set of points which are assigned to the cluster j, $|\mathscr{R}_j|$ is its cardinality and $\mathbf{r}_j$ is the cluster centre. $P_{j,n}$, $P_{j,m}$ are the lower and and upper percentile bounds for cluster j. These bounds are used to select achievable good operation points as representatives, $\text{EnPI}_{\mathscr{R}_j}$, for each cluster. The chosen percentiles are tuning factors and can be modified for each case.

The surrogate model development is an adapted ALAMO approach (Cozad et al., 2014). It generates simple and accurate models from simulated or experimental data. In order to overcome the drawbacks of linear regression models, ALAMO selects a combination of transformed inputs using simple basis functions that fit the responses with an acceptable accuracy. The set of basis functions are defined by the user and ALAMO selects the most suitable ones and their respective parameters as a result of an optimisation. The details of the implemented adapted version of the ALAMO approach can be found in Beisheim et al. (2018). The model is fitted by solving an optimisation problem formulated as:

$$\min_{\beta, y} \quad \sum_{i=1}^{N} e_i \tag{5}$$

$$\text{s.t.} \quad e_i \geq z_i - \sum_{j \in \mathscr{B}} \beta_j X_{ij} \quad i = 1, \dots, N \tag{6}$$

$$e_i \geq \sum_{j \in \mathscr{B}} \beta_j X_{ij} - z_i \quad i = 1, \dots, N \tag{7}$$

$$\sum_{j \in \mathscr{B}} y_j = B \tag{8}$$

$$-U_j(1 - y_j) \leq \sum_{i=1}^{N} X_{ij} \left(z_i - \sum_{j \in \mathscr{B}} \beta_j X_{ij} \right) \leq U_j(1 - y_j) \qquad j \in \mathscr{B} \tag{9}$$

$$\beta^l y_j \leq \beta_j \leq \beta^u y_j \qquad j \in \mathscr{B} \tag{10}$$

$$y_j = \{0, 1\} \qquad j \in \mathscr{B}, \tag{11}$$

where z_i are the values of the responses, X is the matrix of the transformed inputs and β is the coefficient vector of X. $\mathscr{B}$ is the set of the basis functions and B is the number of the maximum allowed terms of the model. The binary variables y_j are equal to 1 if their respective basis function is selected. β^u, and β^l are the upper and lower bounds for the coefficient vector. N is the number of the samples and the indices i and j correspond to the samples and the basis functions respectively. The optimisation is done repeatedly for increasing values of B and the suitable level of complexity is decided based on the modified corrected Akaike Information Criterion (AIC_c). Eq. 9 is an additional constraint, which as described in Beisheim et al. (2018) uses the relaxed bounds U_j to convert the problem formulation into an MILP.

2.2. Application to production data at INEOS in Köln

In this section, the surrogate BDP modelling approach introduced in Sec. 2.1 is applied to two sections of the ethylene oxide production plant at INEOS in Köln and the results are compared to the results of a rigorous model. All of the plots and information in this section are presented in the scaled space due to the confidentiality of the data.

2.2.1. Surrogate approach

The algorithm described in Sec. 2.1 is used with $[1, x^{\pm[1,2,3]}, \exp(x)]$ as basis functions. The first example is a section of the plant which processes the products from the ethylene oxide reactor. The upper and lower percentile limits, $P_{j,n}$ and $P_{j,m}$ are defined as 5 and 10 respectively. As a result of discussions with plant personnel, the production load ($\dot{m}_p$) is defined as the only non-influenceable factor and is used to calculate the resource efficiency of the specific steam consumption (EnPI$_{s,1}$). The number of the clusters is defined as 16. The algorithm results in a model with two basis functions:

$$\text{EnPI}_{s,1} = -3.1902\,\dot{m}_p^2 + 1.4843\exp(\dot{m}_p) \qquad (12)$$

Fig. 3 depicts the results of the model fitting. Each data cloud (shown by coloured points) represents a cluster and the circles and the + signs represent the cluster centres and the percentile centres that are used for model fitting. As mentioned in Sec. 2, extrapolation of the model should be avoided. Therefore, the range of validity of the model is defined as the range between the minimum and maximum of the percentile centre values, and the data outside of this range are shown with dark diamonds.

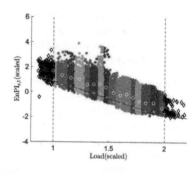

Figure 3: Surrogate BDP model of the product processing section of the ethylene oxide plant

The second investigated section is the ethylene oxide reactor. Both the main and the side reactions are exothermic and the produced heat is used for steam generation. The heat of reaction of the side reaction is significantly higher than the heat produced by the main reaction. Therefore, the reduction of the catalyst selectivity increases the steam production. Considering this fact, the load of the reactor ($\dot{m}_{p,r}$) and the catalyst selectivity (S) which is available as a measurement, are used as non-influenceable factors for modelling the resource efficiency of the steam production (EnPI$_{s,2}$). As the number of non-influenceable factors in this case is higher than the previous one, the number of the clusters is increased to 30. The other modification in this case is the choice of the percentile limits. Considering that this case is about the modelling of the production of steam, so higher values are preferable, the BDP is defined as the highest possible

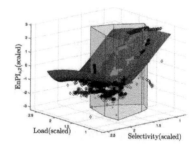

Figure 4: Surrogate BDP model of the steam production of the ethylene oxide reactor

amount of steam production. Therefore the lower and upper percentile limits are defined as 90 and 95 respectively. The algorithm identifies a model, shown in Fig. 4, using three basis functions as:

$$\text{EnPI}_{s,2} = -0.0669\,\dot{m}_{p,r}^3 - 5.7478\,S + 3.0651\exp(S). \qquad (13)$$

A conservative method for the definition of the domain of validity of regression models in higher dimensions is the "Convex Hull" of the input variables (Brooks et al., 1988). This method is used here to calculate the validity bounds of the model. The importance of the validity range is more obvious in this example compared to the previous model. It can be seen that outside of the convex hull, the model diverges from the data and should not be trusted.

2.2.2. Rigorous approach

In this section, a more detailed model of the ethylene oxide reactor is developed that is based on physico-chemical principles and measurement data. This model is then used to make a comparison between the detailed model and the proposed surrogate modelling approach and to identify the advantages and shortcomings of each. The model is based on the energy balance around the reactor as follows:

$$\frac{\partial Q}{\partial t} = \bar{C}_{p,in} \dot{n}_{in} T_{in} - \bar{C}_{p,out} \dot{n}_{out} T_{out} - \dot{Q}_{cool} + \sum_i (-\Delta H_{R,i} r_i) - \dot{Q}_{loss}, \tag{14}$$

where the left hand side of the equation is set to zero due to the assumed stationarity of the process. The first two terms on the right hand side of the equation represent the amount of the heat entering and leaving the reactor with the material streams. $\bar{C}_{p,j}, \dot{n}_j, T_j$ denote average specific heat capacity of the gas mixture, mole flow and temperature at position j. $\sum_i (\Delta H_{R,i} r_i)$ represents the produced heat of reaction, $\dot{Q}_{cool}$ is the heat transferred from the reactor to the cooling fluid inside the jacket and $\dot{Q}_{loss}$ is the amount of heat that is transferred to the environment.

$\bar{C}_p$ is calculated as the weighted average of the values $C_{p,j}$ of the different components using the volumetric percentage values available in the plant, where the dependencies of the values of $C_{p,j}$ of the components on the temperature are determined based on the Shomate equation (Linstrom and Mallard, 2018). The molar flow $\dot{n}_{in}$ is not measured, but can be calculated based on the volumetric flow rate and the ideal gas law. The situation for $\dot{n}_{out}$ is more complex, as there is no direct flow measurements at the output of the reactor. However, using the composition measurements and the change of the volumetric percentage of an inert gas present in the mixture, this flow can be estimated.

The values of $\Delta H_{R,i}$ for each reaction are known and $\sum_i (-\Delta H_{R,i} r_i)$ is calculated using this information together with the selectivity measurement and the estimation of the ethylene conversion based on its volumetric percentage at the inlet and outlet flows. $\dot{Q}_{cool}$ is assumed to be equal to the amount of the heat required for the production of steam.

Considering the above mentioned assumptions, the value of $\dot{Q}_{loss}$ can be calculated from eq. 14. $\dot{Q}_{loss}$ can also be described as:

$$\dot{Q}_{loss} = k(T_{cf} - T_{amb}), \tag{15}$$

where T_{cf} and T_{amb} are equal to the cooling fluid and ambient temperature, and k is the heat transfer coefficient. Assuming that k remains constant for an unchanged setup (physical structure, cooling fluid etc.), its value can be estimated based on eq.15.

Eq. 14 is rearranged and $\dot{Q}_{cool}$, and thus the amount of steam produced is calculated based on the energy balance. Fig. 5 depicts the real steam production together with the values that are calculated based on the surrogate BDP model and the detailed model at two different time windows. The x-axis and the y-axis represents the time and the resource efficiency of steam production EnPI$_{s,2}$. From Fig. 5a it can be seen that the surrogate model predicts a higher steam production rate compared to the real data and the detailed model. As the result of a deeper investigation it became clear that the conversion of ethylene in the reactor is lower in this period, which is not considered by the surrogate model and thereby deviates from reality. It is expected that the addition of conversion as a new non-influenceable factor to the surrogate model improves the accuracy of its prediction. Results from a second interesting time window are presented in Fig. 5b. Here it can be seen that the amount of produced steam predicted by the detailed model is significantly higher after a period of time. The reason is, that the heat exchanger that is used for steam production has a limit for the heat removal. Therefore, as a result of the decrease of the catalyst selectivity and the increase of the amount of heat produced by the reaction, the heat removal system is not able to convert all of the heat into steam, and this heat is lost in an extra heat exchanger against a large stream of cooling

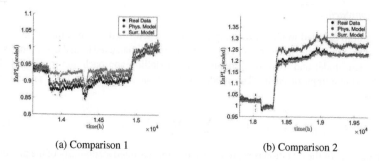

(a) Comparison 1   (b) Comparison 2

Figure 5: Comparison of the physical and the surrogate BDP models against production data

water. This limitation is identified with the help of the rigorous model, which is not possible with a surrogate BDP model.

3. Conclusions

In this work a surrogate and a more detailed modelling approach were used to calculate the BDP of production plants. It was observed that the surrogate modelling approach has a good performance in fitting the BDP data and requires a considerably lower modelling effort compared to more rigorous models. The proposed surrogate modelling approach is flexible and does not require a large effort. The time spent for the development of the surrogate model of the reactor was approximately 20 % of time that was needed for the development of the rigorous model. However, the range of trustworthiness of surrogate models is limited to the range of the observed data. Therefore, the performance of the models cannot be trusted beyond the data used for fitting them. Also, as discussed above for the situation depicted in Fig. 5b, deviations of the observed BDP from the possible best performance cannot be detected using a surrogate model and improvements of the plant that realize the potential cannot be deduced.

Acknowledgment

The project leading to this publication has received funding from the European Union's Horizon 2020 research and innovation programme under grant agreement No 723575 (CoPro) in the framework of the SPIRE PPP.

References

D. Arthur, S. Vassilvitskii, 2007. k-means++: The advantages of careful seeding. In: Proceedings of the eighteenth annual ACM-SIAM symposium on Discrete algorithms. Society for Industrial and Applied Mathematics, pp. 1027–1035.

B. Beisheim, K. Rahimi-Adli, S. Krämer, S. Engell, 2018. Energy performance analysis of continuous processes using surrogate models. Submitted to Energy, Manuscript No. EGY-D-18-07030.

D. G. Brooks, S. S. Carroll, W. A. Verdini, 1988. Characterizing the domain of a regression model. The American Statistician 42 (3), 187–190.

A. Cozad, N. V. Sahinidis, D. C. Miller, 2014. Learning surrogate models for simulation-based optimization. AIChE Journal 60 (6), 2211–2227.

P. Linstrom, W. Mallard, 2018. Nist chemistry webbook, nist standard reference database number 69, national institute of standards and technology data.

J. MacQueen, et al., 1967. Some methods for classification and analysis of multivariate observations. In: Proceedings of the fifth Berkeley symposium on mathematical statistics and probability. Vol. 1. Oakland, CA, USA, pp. 281–297.

NAMUR WG 4.17, 2017. Resource efficiency indicators for monitoring and improving resource efficiency in processing plants. NAMUR Recommendation 162, NAMUR, NAMUR, Leverkusen, Germany.

J. Søndergaard, 2003. Optimization using surrogate models-by the space mapping technique. Ph.D. thesis, Technical University of Denmark.

Anton A. Kiss, Edwin Zondervan, Richard Lakerveld, Leyla Özkan (Eds.)
Proceedings of the 29th European Symposium on Computer Aided Process Engineering
June 16th to 19th, 2019, Eindhoven, The Netherlands. © 2019 Elsevier B.V. All rights reserved.
http://dx.doi.org/10.1016/B978-0-128-18634-3.50154-5

Reinforcement Learning for Batch-to-Batch Bioprocess Optimisation

P. Petsagkourakis[a], I. Orson Sandoval[b], E. Bradford[c], D. Zhang[a,d] * and E.A. del Rio-Chanona[d,*]

[a]*School of Chemical Engineering and Analytical Science,The University of Manchester, M13 9PL, UK*
[b]*Instituto de Ciencias Nucleares, Universidad Nacional Autónoma de México, A.P. 70-543, C.P. 04510 Ciudad de México, Mexico*
[c]*Department of Engineering Cybernetics, Norwegian University of Science and Technology, Trondheim, Norway*
[d]*Centre for Process Systems Engineering (CPSE), Department of Chemical Engineering, Imperial College London, UK*
dongda.zhang@manchester.ac.uk, a.del-rio-chanona@imperial.ac.uk

Abstract

Bioprocesses have received great attention from the scientific community as an alternative to fossil-based products by microorganisms-synthesised counterparts. However, bioprocesses are generally operated at unsteady-state conditions and are stochastic from a macro-scale perspective, making their optimisation a challenging task. Furthermore, as biological systems are highly complex, plant-model mismatch is usually present. To address the aforementioned challenges, in this work, we propose a reinforcement learning based online optimisation strategy. We first use reinforcement learning to learn an optimal policy given a preliminary process model. This means that we compute diverse trajectories and feed them into a recurrent neural network, resulting in a policy network which takes the states as input and gives the next optimal control action as output. Through this procedure, we are able to capture the previously believed behaviour of the biosystem. Subsequently, we adopted this network as an initial policy for the "real" system (the plant) and apply a batch-to-batch reinforcement learning strategy to update the network's accuracy. This is computed by using a more complex process model (representing the real plant) embedded with adequate stochasticity to account for the perturbations in a real dynamic bioprocess. We demonstrate the effectiveness and advantages of the proposed approach in a case study by computing the optimal policy in a realistic number of batch runs.

Keywords: Reinforcement Learning, Batch Process, Recurrent Neural Networks, Bioprocesses

1. Introduction

There has been a global interest in using sustainable bio-production systems to produce a broad range of chemicals and substitute fossil derived synthetic routes (Harun et al., 2018). Bioprocesses exploit microorganisms to synthesise platform chemicals and high-value products by using different means of resources (Jing et al., 2018). Compared to a traditional chemical process, a biochemical process is highly complex due to the intricate relationships between metabolic reaction networks and culture fluid dynamics (del Rio-

Chanona et al., 2018). As a result, it is difficult to construct accurate dynamic models to simulate general large-scale biosystems, and plant-model mismatch is inevitable. Furthermore, bioprocess dynamics are often stochastic due to the underlying metabolic pathways which are sensitive to even mild changes in operating conditions (Zhang and Vassiliadis, 2015; Thierie, 2004). Therefore, developing control and optimisation strategies for bioprocesses remains an open challenge. Given these critical limitations in physical models, in this work we propose a data-driven approach to address this challenge.

We must seek a strategy that can handle both the system's stochasticity and plant-model mismatch. It is here that we have opted to use *reinforcement learning* and more specifically, *policy gradients*, the rationale behind this is next explained. Reinforcement learning (RL) addresses the problem of solving nonlinear and stochastic optimal control problems (Bertsekas, 2000). Two main branches have been established on how to solve dynamic optimisation problems via RL. The first one is based on *dynamic programming* (DP), hence termed approximate dynamic programming (ADP). DP relies on the Hamilton-Jacobi-Bellman equation (HJBE), the solution of which becomes intractable for small size problems with nonlinear dynamics and continuous state and control actions. Hence, past research has relied on using ADP techniques to find (approximate) solutions to this type of problem (Sutton and Barto, 2018). The second branch, is to use *policy gradients* which directly obtain a policy by maximising a desired performance index. This approach is well suited for problems where both the state and control space are continuous. We have therefore adopted this approach for this work. Policy gradient methods are further explained in Section 2.2.

Finally, to address plant-model mismatch, we have applied a data-driven approach. Although there are knowledge-based modelling strategies such as iterative learning (Moore et al., 2006), here we propose a fully data-driven method that can learn from the true dynamics of the system while incorporating previous knowledge.

2. Preliminaries

In this section we introduce important concepts for the proposed work.

2.1. Recurrent Neural Network

Recurrent neural networks, (RNNs) (Rumelhart et al., 1986), are tailored to address sequential data. RNNs produce an output at each time step and have recursive connections between hidden units. This allows them to have a "memory" of previous data and hence be well suited to model time-series. Thus, it could be said that RNNs are essentially simulating a dynamic system for a given set of parameters. In this work, RNNs are applied to parameterise the stochastic policy.

2.2. Policy Gradient Methods

A particular family of RL methods that do not require an explicit estimate of the value of state-action pairs are called *policy gradient methods*. These methods rely on a parametrised policy function $\pi_\theta(\cdot)$ that returns an action a given a state of the system s and a set of intrinsic parameters θ. In the case of stochastic policies, the policy function returns the defining parameters of a probability distribution over possible actions, from which the actions are sampled:

$$a \sim \pi_\theta(a|s) = \pi(a|s,\theta) = p(a_t = a|s_t = s, \theta_t = \theta). \tag{1}$$

In this work, an RNN is used as the parametrised policy, which takes states and past controls as inputs and returns a mean and a variance from which a control is drawn. In this setting, the exploitation-exploration trade-off is represented explicitly as the variance of the underlying distribution of the policy. Deterministic policies may be approached as a limiting case where variance fades upon convergence. Let a sequence of H states and actions be called an *episode* τ. An episode τ is a secuence of states and actions generated by following the current policy, $\tau \sim p(\tau|\theta)$. The reward function $(R(\cdot))$ may be estimated over K episode samples:

$$\hat{R}(\theta) = \mathbb{E}_\theta[R(\tau)] = \int_\tau p(\tau|\theta)R(\tau)\mathrm{d}\tau \approx \frac{1}{K}\sum_{k=1}^{K} R(\tau^{(k)}). \tag{2}$$

The objective of policy gradient methods is to maximise a reward function $\hat{R}(\theta)$ by using gradient ascent techniques over a continuously differentiable policy. The evolution of the intrinsic parameters at each optimisation step m is given by

$$\theta_{m+1} = \theta_m + \alpha_m \nabla_\theta R|_{\theta=\theta_m}. \tag{3}$$

Differentiable policies guarantee smooth changes over sufficiently small variations of the parameters.

2.3. REINFORCE Algorithm

The REINFORCE (Williams, 1992) algorithm approximates the gradient of the policy to maximise the expected reward with respect to the parameters θ without the need of a dynamic model of the process. For this, it is necessary to take advantage of the gradient of a logarithm and a decomposition of the likelihood of an H step episode τ under a policy π_θ (Sutton and Barto, 2018; Peters and Schaal, 2008),

$$p(\tau|\theta) = p(s_0)\prod_{h=0}^{H} p(s_{h+1}|s_h, a_h) \cdot \pi_\theta(a_h|s_h), \tag{4}$$

to express approximate the desired gradient as

$$\nabla_\theta \hat{R}(\theta) = \int_\tau R(\tau)p(\tau|\theta)\nabla_\theta \log p(\tau|\theta)\mathrm{d}\tau \approx \frac{1}{K}\sum_{k=1}^{K} R(\tau^{(k)})\nabla_\theta \log p(\tau^{(k)}|\theta) \tag{5}$$

$$\approx \frac{1}{K}\sum_{k=1}^{K} R(\tau^{(k)})\sum_{h=1}^{H} \nabla_\theta \log \pi_\theta\left(a_h^{(k)}|s_h^{(k)}\right).$$

The variance of this estimation can be reduced with the aid of an action-independent baseline b without introducing bias. A simple but effective baseline is the expectation of reward under the current policy, approximated by the mean over the sampled paths:

$$b = \hat{R}(\theta) \approx \frac{1}{K}\sum_{k=1}^{K} R(\tau^{(k)}), \tag{6}$$

$$\nabla_\theta \hat{R}(\theta) \approx \frac{1}{K} \sum_{k=1}^{K} \left(R(\tau^{(k)}) - b \right) \sum_{h=1}^{H} \nabla_\theta \log \pi_\theta \left(a_h^{(k)} | s_h^{(k)} \right). \tag{7}$$

This selection increases the log likelihood of an action by comparing it to the expected reward of the current policy.

3. Reinforcement Learning for Bioprocess Optimisation under Uncertainty

In this work, during Stage 1, we assume a preliminary model has been constructed to approximate the real system's dynamics. This approximate model can be used to generate a large size of episodes (different control actions subject to probability) for each training epoch (an epoch corresponds to a specific set of RNN parameter values) to *initially* design a control policy network that produces the model identified optimal policy. Hence the control policy is an RNN which takes states (including time to termination) and past controls as inputs and returns a mean and a variance from which a control action is drawn.

During Stage 2 (real plant optimal control), the policy network is directly updated using the real system (the plant) in a *batch-to-batch* framework. Accuracy of the control policy (*i.e.* the RNN) is therefore consolidated during an online implementation. The stochastic control policy is a RNN that represents a conditional probability distribution π_θ. The RNN predicts the mean and standard deviation of the next action through a deterministic map using the measurements (the previous states s_i, a sequences of previous actions (a_i) with $i \in \{-N, \ldots, -1\}$) and the time that is left for the end of the batch process. This proposed stochastic control policy is trained using the REINFORCE algorithm (see Section 2). This algorithm aims to maximise a given reward (*e.g.* concentration of target product at the final time), with the mean value of this reward being employed as a baseline during the update of RNN parameter values (see Eq. 6 & 7). The use of a baseline has been proven to be advantageous as long as it is independent of the control actions (Sutton and Barto, 2018).

Initially (Stage 1), the policy network is trained *off-line* using an available approximate model. The algorithm runs for several epochs and episodes until convergence. The network is then adopted to generate initial optimal policies for the real system (the plant, simulated by a model complex process model which is not available for RNN construction)(Stage 2). Methods used in the REINFORCE algorithm usually require a large number of episodes and epochs, therefore a good initial solution is paramount so that Stage 2 (which is assumed to be done in the actual plant) can be completed with few batch-to-batch runs. In order to keep the problem realistic, only a small number of batches is utilised in Stage 2 to refine the policy network.

4. Computational Case Studies

The proposed methodology is applied to a fed-batch bioreactor, where the objective is to maximise the concentration of target product (y_2) at the end of the batch time, using light and an inflow rate (u_1 and u_2) as control variables. The plant (real photo-production system) is simulated using the following equations:

$$\frac{dy_1}{dt} = -(u_1 + 0.5\, u_1^2)y_1 + 0.5\frac{u_2 y_2}{(y_1 + y_2)} \qquad \frac{dy_2}{dt} = u_1\, y_1 - 0.7 u_2\, y_1 \tag{8}$$

where u_1, u_2 and y_1, y_2 are the control variables and the outlet concentrations of the reactant and product, respectively. The batch operation time course is normalised to 1.

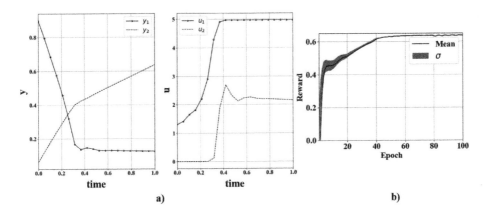

Figure 1: (a) The time trajectories produced by the trained policies. (b) The reward computed for the approximate model.

Additionally, a random disturbance is assumed, which is given by a Gaussian distribution with mean value 0 and standard deviation 0.02. It is assumed that only the following approximate model (simplified from the complex model) is known, and the preliminary training is performed based on this model to construct the control policy network, whilst the real system model is unknown due to the complexity of the process mechanisms.

$$\frac{dy_1}{dt} = -(u_1 + 0.5\, u_1^2)y_1 + u_2 \qquad\qquad \frac{dy_2}{dt} = u_1\, y_1 - u_2\, y_1 \qquad (9)$$

Initially, 100 epochs and 800 episodes are generated from the simplified model to search the optimal control policy that maximises the reward for Eq. 9. Control variables are constrained to be in $[0,5]$. The control policy RNN is designed to contain 3 hidden layers, each of which comprising 15 neurons embedded by a hyperbolic tangent activation function. Adam (Kingma and Ba, 2014) is employed to compute the network parameter values. It should be mentioned that the reward computed after convergence is almost the same in comparison to the result given by the optimal control problem (OCP) at Stage 1. The maximum rewards for RL and OCP are 0.637 and 0.640, respectively. The reward for its epoch is depicted in Figure 2b) and the process trajectories after the final update of the policy network are shown in Figure 2a). This policy is then used to initialise the REINFORCE algorithm for the plant's RL (Stage 2), where 25 episodes are used (*i.e.* 25 real plant batches). The solution after only 4 epochs is 0.575 whilst the stochastic-free optimal solution identified using the *unknown* (complex) model of the plant is 0.583. The reward of this epoch is depicted in Figure 1b) and the process trajectories after the last epoch are depicted in Figure 1a).

5. Conclusions

In this work we show that by adapting reinforcement learning techniques to uncertain and complex bioprocesses we are able to obtain a near optimal policy for a stochastic system where the true dynamics are unknown. Furthermore, we obtain this result in a realistic scenario where only a modest number of batch runs is used. We emphasise that

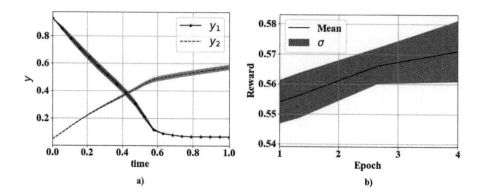

Figure 2: (a) The time trajectories produced by the real plant. (b) The reward computed by the updated training using the plant ("real" system) for each epoch.

we assume no process structure and embed both stochasticity and plant-model mismatch into the considered system, the optimisation of which is generally known to be intractable. Future work will focus on more complex case studies and exploring other RL methods, such as bias reduction and sample efficiency strategies.

References

D. P. Bertsekas, 2000. Dynamic Programming and Optimal Control, 2nd Edition. Athena Scientific.

E. A. del Rio-Chanona, J. L. Wagner, H. Ali, D. Zhang, K. Hellgardt, 2018. Deep learning based surrogate modelling and optimization for microalgal biofuel production and photobioreactor design. AIChE Journal, in press.

I. Harun, E. A. Del Rio-Chanona, J. L. Wagner, K. J. Lauersen, D. Zhang, K. Hellgardt, aug 2018. Photocatalytic Production of Bisabolene from Green Microalgae Mutant: Process Analysis and Kinetic Modeling. Industrial & Engineering Chemistry Research 57 (31), 10336–10344.

K. Jing, Y. Tang, C. Yao, E. A. del Rio-Chanona, X. Ling, D. Zhang, feb 2018. Overproduction of L-tryptophan via simultaneous feed of glucose and anthranilic acid from recombinant Escherichia coli W3110: Kinetic modeling and process scale-up. Biotechnology and Bioengineering 115 (2), 371–381.

D. P. Kingma, J. Ba, 2014. Adam: A Method for Stochastic Optimization. ArXiv:1412.6980.

K. L. Moore, Y. Chen, H. Ahn, Dec 2006. Iterative learning control: A tutorial and big picture view. In: Proceedings of the 45th IEEE Conference on Decision and Control. pp. 2352–2357.

J. Peters, S. Schaal, 2008. Reinforcement learning of motor skills with policy gradients. Neural networks 21 (4), 682–697.

D. E. Rumelhart, G. E. Hinton, R. J. Williams, 1986. Learning representations by back-propagating errors. Nature 323, 533.

R. Sutton, A. Barto, 2018. Reinforcement Learning: An Introduction, second edition Edition. MIT Press.

J. Thierie, feb 2004. Modeling threshold phenomena, metabolic pathways switches and signals in chemostat-cultivated cells: the Crabtree effect in Saccharomyces cerevisiae. Journal of theoretical biology 226 (4), 483–501.

R. J. Williams, 1992. Simple statistical gradient-following algorithms for connectionist reinforcement learning. Machine learning 8 (3-4), 229–256.

D. Zhang, V. S. Vassiliadis, nov 2015. Chlamydomonas reinhardtii Metabolic Pathway Analysis for Biohydrogen Production under Non-Steady-State Operation. Industrial & Engineering Chemistry Research 54 (43), 10593–10605.

Anton A. Kiss, Edwin Zondervan, Richard Lakerveld, Leyla Özkan (Eds.)
Proceedings of the 29th European Symposium on Computer Aided Process Engineering
June 16th to 19th, 2019, Eindhoven, The Netherlands. © 2019 Elsevier B.V. All rights reserved.
http://dx.doi.org/10.1016/B978-0-128-18634-3.50155-7

A primal bounding approach for multistage stochastic programs of resource-constrained planning and scheduling with stochastic task success

Zuo Zeng, Selen Cremaschi*

Department of Chemical Engineering, Auburn University, Auburn, AL 36849, USA
selen-cremaschi@auburn.edu

Abstract

Resource-constrained planning and scheduling problems under stochastic task success, which are common in chemical industries, lend themselves well to being modelled using multistage stochastic programming (MSSP) because most projects involve a series of tasks that needs to be completed in stages and that may or may not be successful. However, these MSSP models rapidly grow and quickly become computationally intractable for real world problems. This paper presents three alternative ways to estimate objective function values in a general primal bounding framework for MSSP models of resource-constrained planning and scheduling with stochastic task success. The framework extends the concept of expected value solution. We apply the proposed framework with alternative objective function estimation approach to instances with varying project sizes (i.e., 3-, 4-, 5-, and 6- projects) with up to 4096 scenarios. The framework yields primal bounds within 1.01% of the true solutions for all tested cases with a reduction in solution times up to four orders of magnitude.

Keywords: multistage stochastic programming, primal bound, endogenous uncertainty, resource constrained planning, probabilistic task success

1. Introduction

This paper considers resource-constrained planning and scheduling problem with project selection and execution under uncertainties, where the development of projects will be extended or terminated depending on the results of success or failure of associated tasks (Honkomp, 1998). Each project requires a variety of the shared limited resources for completing the required tasks associated with it. If a project fails, it is abandoned, the resources that were originally assigned to that project become available and the return associated with that project is not realized. In these planning problems, the decisions are which projects to pursue and the best way to assign the resources to the chosen projects to maximize the returns. The uncertainties associated with the tasks are resolved once these tasks are in execution or are completed, which makes them endogenous. One approach for modeling and solving these problems is multistage stochastic programming.

Multistage stochastic programming (MSSP) is a scenario-based approach that considers recourse actions in multiple stages after observing uncertainties. Uncertainties are represented by scenarios, which usually are obtained as the Cartesian product of all possible outcomes of uncertain parameters. In explicit formulation, the decision variables are defined independently for each scenario, and non-anticipativity constraints (NAC) are added to prevent the current stage decisions from anticipating future realizations of uncertain parameters. Size of a MSSP model, especially with endogenous uncertain parameters, grows rapidly with the number of uncertain parameters and their outcomes leading to both space and time complexities. In general, the solution approaches for these problems rely on heuristic or approximation approaches, and it has been shown that moderate-size problems can be solved to optimality. Example approaches are rolling-horizon heuristic approach (Colvin and Maravelias, 2009), sample average approximation (SAA) algorithm (Solak et al., 2010), decision-rules based approximation (Vayonos et al. 2011), improved Lagrangean decomposition framework (Gupta and Grossmann, 2014), sequential scenario decomposition approach (Apap and Grossmann, 2017), branch and bound algorithm (Brianna and Cremaschi, 2017), a generalized knapsack decomposition algorithm (Brianna and Cremaschi, 2015; Zeng et al., 2018), and absolute expected value solution (AEEV) framework (Zeng and Cremaschi, 2019).

In this paper, we investigate three approaches to estimate the expected objective function value to be used in the AEEV framework for generating tight primal bounds and implementable solutions for large-scale planning and scheduling problems under stochastic task success and. We present this approach using clinical-trial planning problem (Colvin and Maravelias, 2008), which is summarized in §2. AEEV framework and the proposed approaches to estimate the expected objective function value are presented in §3. The problem instances and the solutions obtained by three alternatives are given, compared and discussed in §4. Finally, we present concluding remarks in §5.

2. Clinical Trial Planning Problem

Under limited resources, the goal of clinical-trial planning is to maximize the expected net present value (ENPV) by determining which clinical trials of drugs to start and when to start them (Colvin and Maravelias, 2008). The endogenous uncertainty is in the outcomes of clinical trials. If a drug fails a clinical trial in a phase, it is abandoned. The observation of a clinical trial outcome depends on whether and when it has been started. There are three clinical trials, $J = \{PI, PII, PIII\}$, that must be completed for a drug under limited resources before the drug can generate revenue, rev_i^{max}. Drug $i \in I$ has known required resources ρ_{ijr}, cost C_{ij}, and fixed duration τ_{ij} associated with clinical trial j. There is a random variable, Ω_i, associated with each uncertain parameter for drug i, and its support is {PI-F, PII-F, PIII-F, and PIII-P}. Here, PI-F, PII-F, PIII-F correspond to drug i failing in clinical trials PI, PII, and PIII, and PIII-P indicates that drug i has successfully passed all clinical trials (Colvin and Maravelias, 2008). The scenario set, S, is constructed as the Cartesian product of uncertain parameter outcomes. The planning horizon is discretized $t = 1, 2, 3 \dots T$ (period t starts at time $t - 1$ and ends at time t).

A slightly modified MSSP formulation (Colvin and Maravelias, 2008) for this problem is given in Eqns. (1) – (8). The MSSP model uses a binary variable $X_{i,j,p,s}$ which is equal to 1 if clinical trial (i, j) is started at time t in scenario s. Two continuous variables, $Y_{i,j,p,s}$ and $Z_{i,j,p,s}$, are bounded between 0 and 1, where $Y_{i,j,p,s}$ turns 1 if drug i completes clinical trial j by the beginning of time period t in scenario s, and $Z_{i,j,p,s}$ becomes 1 if drug i completes clinical trial $j - 1$ by time period p and has not started clinical trial j. Losses are represented by two penalty terms: γ_i^p (loss of market) and γ_i^L (loss of patent life).

$$max\ ENPV = \sum_s p_s(Rev_s + FRev_s - Cst_s) \tag{1}$$

$$Cst_s = \sum_{i,j,t} cd_t C_{i,j} X_{i,j,t,s} \quad \forall s \tag{2}$$

$$Rev_s = \sum_i success_{i,s} \left\{ \sum_t \{rev_i^{max} X_{i,PII,t,s} - \gamma_i^D (Z_{i,PII,t,s} + Z_{i,PIII,t,s}) - \gamma_i^L (t \right. $$
$$\left. + \tau_{i,PIII}) X_{i,PIII,t,s} \} \right\} \quad \forall s \tag{3}$$

$$FRev_s = \sum_i success_{i,s} \left\{ \sum_j rev_{i,j}^{open} f_{i,j} Z_{i,j,|T|,s} \right\}$$
$$+ \sum_i success_{i,s} \left\{ \sum_{j \in \{PI,PII\}} \sum_{t > |T| - \tau_{i,j}} rev_{i,j,t}^{run} f_{i,j+1} X_{i,j,t,s} \right\} \quad \forall s \tag{4}$$

$$f(X_{i,j,t,s}, Y_{i,j,t,s}, Z_{i,j,t,s}) \le 0 \quad \forall i,j,t,s \tag{5}$$

$$h(X_{i,j,t,s}, Y_{i,j,t,s}, Z_{i,j,t,s}) = 0 \quad \forall i,j,t,s \tag{6}$$

$$X_{i,1,1,s} = X_{i,1,1,1} \quad \forall i,s \tag{7}$$

$$-\sum_{t' \le t} Z_{i^s,s^{s'},j^s,s^{s'},t',s} \le Y_{i,j,t,s} - Y_{i,j,t,s'} \le \sum_{t' \le t} Z_{i^s,s^{s'},j^s,s^{s'},t',s} \quad \forall i,j, (s,s') \in \Psi, t > 1 \tag{8}$$

The objective function is represented by Eqns. (1) – (4), including the probability of scenario s (p_s), the costs Cst_s, current revenue Rev_s, and future revenue $FRev_s$. Current and future revenue depends on the outcome of uncertain parameter, $success_{i,s} \in \{0,1\}$, which is equal to 1 for drug i successfully passing all clinical trials in s, 0 otherwise. The total cost is discounted using the time discounting factor cd_t (Eq. (2)). The parameter $f_{i,j}$ (Eq. (4)) represents the fraction of the revenue that would be realized by completing all remaining trials at the end of the planning horizon. Inequalities, Eq. (5), and equalities, Eq. (6), are scenario specific constraints, which include resource and clinical trial sequencing constraints. Constraints (7) and (8) are NACs. The model grows rapidly due to the increases in number of candidate drugs, scenario size, which results in exponential growth in size of NACs (Eqns. (7) and (8)). It is important to note that for this type of planning problems that has uncertain task outcomes, the uncertain parameters are only incorporated in the objective function (Eqns. (3) and (4) in clinical trial planning model) because the outcomes of clinical trials only impact the ENPV in objective function.

3. Absolute Expected Value Solution (AEEV) framework

The framework generates and solves a series of deterministic sub-problems (DSPs) based on the observation of uncertainties and yields a feasible solution for the original MSSP model. Future unknown information is assumed to be at its expected value, and here-and-now decisions are made based on the current available information and expected values of future events. The uncertainties are observed after here-and-now decisions are made, and recourse actions are determined for each observed uncertain outcome. The AEEV framework repeats this process of making decisions with current and expected future information, observing uncertainties, and taking recourse actions until the end of the planning horizon. Details of the framework can be found in Zeng and Cremaschi (2019).

In resource-constrained planning and scheduling under stochastic task success, there are no recourse actions. The AEEV framework starts by making decision 1 by solving DSP$_{1,1}$, where indices (1,1) are the indices of sub-problems and time. In DSP$_{1,1}$, which is generated at the beginning of the planning horizon (Figure 1), all uncertain parameters take their expected values. After decision 1 is implemented, uncertainties associated with decision 1 are observed (observation 1). Based on observation 1, new sub-problems are generated and solved to determine decisions, and associated uncertainties are observed. This process continues until the end of the planning horizon.

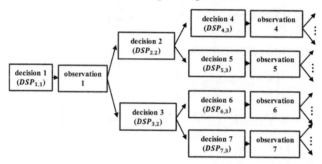

Figure 1. Traditional decision-making process under uncertainty for resource-constrained planning and scheduling under stochastic task success and the AEEV framework

Scenario tree observed for MSSP under endogenous uncertainty depends on decisions made, unlike the scenario tree for MSSP under exogenous uncertainty, which is fixed. AEEV framework works efficiently especially with endogenous uncertainties, where only partial scenarios and uncertainties can be observed in the planning horizon. The framework has a scenario-free structure and only generates and solves the necessary deterministic problems based on the realized outcomes, where the non-anticipativity is implicitly enforced. The objective function value obtained by AEEV framework is a valid primal bound for MSSP models with complete recourse.

3.1. The formulation of deterministic sub-problems (DSPs)

We use clinical trial planning model to illustrate the DSP formulation (Eqns. (9) – (15)) in AEEV framework. In DSPs, the scenario index and NACs are removed from the MSSP model, and the uncertain parameter values are set to their expected values ($E[success_i]$ in Eqns. (11) and (12)). The realizations of clinical trial outcomes until the current time period are incorporated in set F_n, where n is the sub-problem index. For failure outcomes, the values of the decision variables associated with subsequent trials are set to zero in F_n. Because the MSSP model contains uncertain parameters only in its objective function, scenario-specific constraints in DSPs are identical to the ones in the MSSP model.

$$max\ ENPV = Rev + FRev - Cst \tag{9}$$

$$Cst = \sum_{i,j,t} cd_t C_{i,j} X_{i,j,t} \tag{10}$$

$$Rev = \sum_i E[success_i] \left\{ \sum_t \left\{ rev_i^{max} X_{i,PII,t} - \gamma_i^D (Z_{i,PII,t} + Z_{i,PIII,t}) - \gamma_i^L (t + \tau_{i,PIII}) X_{i,PIII,t} \right\} \right\} \tag{11}$$

$$FRev = \sum_i E[success_i] \left\{ \sum_j rev_{i,j}^{open} f_{i,j} Z_{i,j,|T|} \right\}$$

$$+ \sum_i E[success_i] \left\{ \sum_{j \in \{PI,PII\}} \sum_{t > |T| - \tau_{i,j}} rev_{i,j,t}^{run} f_{i,j+1} X_{i,j,t} \right\} \tag{12}$$

$$f(X_{i,j,t}, Y_{i,j,t}, Z_{i,j,t}) \le 0 \qquad \forall i,j,t \tag{13}$$

$$h(X_{i,j,t}, Y_{i,j,t}, Z_{i,j,t}) = 0 \qquad \forall i,j,t \tag{14}$$

$$X_{i,j,t} \in F_n \qquad \forall i,j,t \tag{15}$$

3.2. Three alternative ways to estimate objective function values in DSPs

In the MSSP model, $success_{i,s}$ is an uncertain parameter indicating if drug i passed all clinical trials in scenario s. The expected value of this parameter in MSSP model is $\sum_s^{s \in S} p_s success_{i,s}$, where p_s is the probability of scenario s. There is no scenario index in DSPs, and the uncertain parameter is replaced with an approximate expected value ($E[success_i]$, Eqns. (11) and (12)). Here, we propose three alternative ways to estimate this approximate expected value:

    (1) A1: take $E[success_i] = \sum_s^{s \in S} p_s \cdot success_{i,s}$ at the initial time period, and it is fixed throughout the planning horizon.

    (2) A2: take $E[success_i] = \sum_s^{s \in S} p_s \cdot success_{i,s}$ at the initial time period, and update $E[success_i]$ based on the realized outcomes of clinical trial for the drug.

    (3) A3: update $E[success_i] = \sum_s^{s \in DSP} p_s \cdot success_{i,s}$, where $E[success_i]$ is calculated based on the scenario groups that belong to the sub-problem DSP.

The values of $E[success_i]$ in $DSP_{1,1}$ are equal to each other for all three approaches.

4. Case Study

We applied the AEEV framework to generate primal bounds for the clinical-trial planning problem with 3-, 4-, 5-, and 6-products, and three clinical trials with different planning horizon lengths. The complete parameters of the instances can be found in Brianna and Cremaschi (2017). We also solved the corresponding MSSP models to compare the objective function values obtained using A1, A2, and A3 by the AEEV framework. The models and algorithms were implemented in Pyomo and solved using CPLEX 12.6.3 to 0.1% optimality gap on a standard node of Auburn University Hopper Cluster. The MSSP and AEEV framework solution results are presented in Tables 1 and 2, respectively.

Table 1. Partial parameters of the clinical trial planning instances and the MSSP solution

Instance	Trials	Time Periods	Scenarios	ENPV	Soln. Time (CPUs)
3-prod	3	12	64	1193	12
4-prod	3	6	256	1700	20
5-prod	3	6	1,024	2087	1776
6-prod	3	6	4,096	2460	104,541

Table 2. The relative gap and solution times of AEEV framework using three alternative expected value estimation approaches (A1, A2, and A3)

Instance	Relative Gap from MSSP solution			Solution Time (CPU s)		
	A1	A2	A3	A1	A2	A3
3-prod	0.75%	0.08%	0.76%	6	6	6
4-prod	0.00%	0.00%	0.00%	4	5	4
5-prod	0.43%	1.01%	0.58%	8	7	6
6-prod	0.65%	0.81%	0.82%	55	54	52

Table 1 reveals the exponential growth in scenario size with the number of drugs and the corresponding growth in MSSP solution times. As can be seen from Table 2, the AEEV framework yields the optimum solution for 4-product instance and the largest relative gap is 1.01% for 5-product instance obtained by A2. The solution times seems to grow super-linearly but not exponentially. A1 performs better among all except for 3-prod case with relative large 0.75% gap. Considering the fast solution time, we would recommend taking the best feasible solution from all three approaches, which we can summarize relative gaps as 0.08%, 0.00%, 0.43%, 0.65% for 3-, 4-, 5-, and 6-product instances.

5. Conclusion

This paper contributes three alternative objective function estimation approaches for AEEV framework to obtain primal bounds for MSSP of resource constrained planning and scheduling problems with stochastic task success. In such problems, the uncertain parameters are only incorporated in objective function, and scenario specific constraints can be readily transferred to deterministic models. Using all three approaches, the AEEV framework obtains the best feasible bounds within 0.65% of the true optimal for all instances of the clinical trial planning problem. The AEEV framework and the proposed objective function estimation approaches can be used to obtain feasible solutions and tight primal bounds for MSSPs under endogenous uncertainties where the model has complete recourse, and the AEEV framework do not suffer from space and time complexities. It should be noted that the AEEV framework may yield infeasible solutions if the MSSP model does not have complete recourse.

6. Acknowledgements

This work was financially supported RAPID Manufacturing Institute, the U.S.A and was completed in part with resources provided by the Auburn University Hopper Cluster.

References

Apap, R. M., & Grossmann, I. E. (2017). Models and computational strategies for multistage stochastic programming under endogenous and exogenous uncertainties. Comput. Chem. Eng, 103, 233-274.

Honkomp, S. J. (1998). PhD Dissertation, Purdue University

Christian, B., & Cremaschi, S. (2017). Variants to a knapsack decomposition heuristic for solving R&D pipeline management problems. Comput. Chem. Eng, 96, 18-32.

Christian, B., & Cremaschi, S. (2015). Heuristic solution approaches to the pharmaceutical R&D pipeline management problem. Comput. Chem. Eng, 74, 34-47.

Colvin, M., & Maravelias, C. T. (2008). A stochastic programming approach for clinical trial planning in new drug development. Comput. Chem. Eng, 32(11), 2626-2642.

Colvin, M., & Maravelias, C. T. (2009). Scheduling of testing tasks and resource planning in new product development using stochastic programming. Comput. Chem. Eng, 33(5), 964-976.

Gupta, V., & Grossmann, I. E. (2014). A new decomposition algorithm for multistage stochastic programs with endogenous uncertainties. Comput. Chem. Eng, 62, 62-79.

Solak, S., Clarke, J. P. B., Johnson, E. L., & Barnes, E. R. (2010). Optimization of R&D project portfolios under endogenous uncertainty. Eur. J. Oper Res, 207(1), 420-433.

Vayanos, Phebe, Daniel Kuhn, and Berç Rustem. (2011). Decision rules for information discovery in multi-stage stochastic programming Decision and Control and European Control Conference (CDC-ECC), 2011 50th IEEE Conference on. IEEE

Zeng, Z., Christian, B., & Cremaschi, S. (2018). A generalized knapsack-problem based decomposition heuristic for solving multistage stochastic programs with endogenous and/or exogenous uncertainties. Ind. Eng. Chem. Res., 2018, 57 (28), pp 9185–9199.

Zeng, Z., & Cremaschi, S. (2019). A general primal bounding framework for large-scale multistage stochastic programs under endogenous uncertainties. Chemical Engineering Research and Design, 141, 464-480.

Anton A. Kiss, Edwin Zondervan, Richard Lakerveld, Leyla Özkan (Eds.)
Proceedings of the 29th European Symposium on Computer Aided Process Engineering
June 16th to 19th, 2019, Eindhoven, The Netherlands. © 2019 Elsevier B.V. All rights reserved.
http://dx.doi.org/10.1016/B978-0-128-18634-3.50156-9

Rigorous Bayesian Inference VS New Approximate Strategies for Estimation of the Probability Distribution of the Parameters of DAE Models

Francesco Rossi,[a,*] Linas Mockus,[a] Gintaras Reklaitis[a]

aPurdue University, Forney Hall of Chemical Engineering, 480 Stadium Mall Drive, West Lafayette, IN 47907-2100, United States

frossi@purdue.edu

Abstract

This manuscript assesses the accuracy and computational efficiency offered by three different strategies for the estimation of probability distributions, applied to DAE systems. Specifically, two approximate PDF estimation techniques, named ODMCMC and PDFE&U, are compared to Bayesian Markov-chain Monte Carlo (BMCMC), using a simulation-based approach. The results of our analysis show that ODMCMC and PDFE&U offer a good trade-off between accuracy and computational efficiency, thus are excellent choices for time-critical PDF estimation tasks.

Keywords: Uncertainty quantification, Bayesian inference, optimization, drug delivery.

1. Introduction

The application of statistical techniques to the quantification of model uncertainty is a new paradigm, which has recently emerged due to the growing interest of industry and of the PSE community in stochastic optimization, robust design, real-time quality control and quantitative risk assessment. As an example, strategies for uncertainty quantification have been applied in areas such as robust process and product design (Mockus et al., 2011), drug delivery (Laínez et al., 2011) and stochastic dynamic optimization (Rossi et al., 2016).

Typically, model uncertainty quantification comes down to the estimation of the joint probability distribution (PDF) of some key uncertain parameters of the model, which often consists of a system of differential-algebraic equations (DAEs). To solve this type of PDF estimation problem, we usually rely on Bayesian inference methods such as Bayesian Markov-chain Monte Carlo (Green and Worden, 2015), which are well-established but also extremely computationally demanding. Therefore, it is important to investigate and develop new approximate PDF estimation strategies, which offer a good trade-off between accuracy and computational efficiency, and to validate them against state-of-the-art Bayesian inference approaches.

To that end, this contribution considers two approximate PDF estimation strategies plus a conventional one, and compares them to identify the most suitable method for solving PDF estimation problems, in which the underlying model is a DAE system. The approximate PDF estimation methods, analysed in this manuscript, include: (I) a novel Bayesian Markov-chain Monte Carlo algorithm, where sampling is performed by optimization (ODMCMC); and (II) a likelihood-free approach, recently proposed by

Rossi et al. (2018), which relies on a combination of parameter estimation, projection techniques and maximum likelihood estimation (PDFE&U). On the other hand, the conventional Bayesian inference strategy, included in this analysis, is standard Bayesian Markov-chain Monte Carlo (BMCMC). Note that we do not include Variational Inference (Beal, 2003) in our study because Yao et al. (2018) recently showed that this type of technique performs satisfactorily only for 28 % of all the problems they considered (over 200).

The comparison of approximate and conventional PDF estimation algorithms is performed by analysing both their computational efficiency and their outputs, i.e. their PDFs, using well-known statistical indicators (expectation, variance and quantiles) and the concept of confidence/credible region. The DAE model, selected for this study, is a pharmacokinetic (PB/PK) model for the administration of Gabapentin.

The rest of the paper is organized as follows: first, we introduce the rationale of PDFE&U and ODMCMC, with particular emphasis on the latter; then, we report the most significant results of our analysis on the accuracy and computational performance of PDFE&U, ODMCMC and BMCMC; finally, we discuss the most relevant consequences of these analyses.

2. Fundamental features of ODMCMC and PDFE&U

ODMCMC and PDFE&U are approximate strategies for estimation of the probability distribution of the uncertain parameters of a nonlinear system, using experimental data and (optionally) an existing PDF of the parameters (a so-called prior). These algorithms are designed for maximum computational efficiency, thus can easily handle DAE models, unlike conventional Bayesian inference frameworks. This section describes their features, novelties and implementation rationale.

ODMCMC is a novel type of Markov-chain Monte Carlo algorithm, in which sampling is performed by optimization. Specifically, this method does not make use of conventional random strategies to sample the posterior PDF (e.g. Metropolis-Hastings, Gibbs and No-U-Turn samplers), which only accept about 30 % of all the samples analysed. On the other hand, it selects optimal posterior samples by iterative solution of small-scale, multi-objective optimization problems, which measure the degree of optimality of every single sample based on two indices, namely, its linear and angular distances from all the other samples and its posterior probability density. This innovative sampling approach can efficiently identify samples, which uniformly span only those regions of the uncertainty space that are associated with high values of posterior probability density. Therefore, it allows us to approximate the posterior PDF with fewer samples and, consequently, to save computational resources. In addition, unlike conventional random samplers, it allows reliable and efficient approximation of complex, multi-modal posterior PDFs.

The rationale of ODMCMC is summarized in Figure 1. The algorithm is comprised of two phases, called Phase I and Phase II, of which the second is executed in an iterative fashion until convergence is reached. Phase I involves first computation of all the modes of the posterior PDF via multi-start optimization methods (step A), and then division of the uncertainty space into a user-supplied number of regions (step B), selected such that every one of them encompasses an appropriate interval of values of posterior probability density (further details cannot be reported due to space limitations).

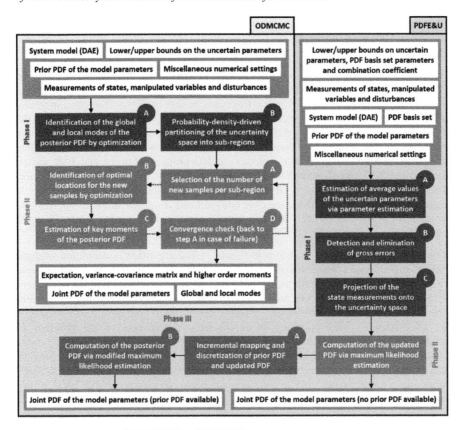

Figure 1: Architecture of ODMCMC and PDFE&U.

Phase II involves iterative execution of steps A, B and C in series, until the variation in the first, second and third order moments of the posterior PDF over two consecutive iterations is smaller than some predefined error tolerance (step D). In step A, we compute the number of samples that must be added to every region of the uncertainty space in the current iteration, using an estimate of the algorithm convergence rate calculated by error extrapolation. Step B involves solution of several multi-objective optimization problems (one problem per region) via goal programming, which allow identification of the optimal locations of the new samples. All of these optimization problems are independent of each other, thus can be solved in parallel to improve the overall computational efficiency of the algorithm. Finally, in step C, we estimate the first, second and third order moments of the posterior PDF, using the samples selected up to the current iteration. These calculations rely on simple formulas, derived by discretization of well-known integral expressions, utilized to compute the moments of continuous probability distributions.

Before moving on, two final remarks are in order. First, note that ODMCMC technically requires identification of all the modes of the posterior PDF (Phase I – step A) via multi-start optimization. However, this requirement can be relaxed without affecting the accuracy of the algorithm, but at the cost of longer computation time. Second, note that the bottleneck for computational efficiency in ODMCMC is represented by step A of Phase I and step B of Phase II, which are both parallelizable. Therefore, ODMCMC exhibits very good scalability features, unlike many conventional Bayesian inference strategies.

After introducing ODMCMC, we offer a brief description of the principal features of PDFE&U (the reader is invited to refer to Rossi et al. (2018) for further details). This is an innovative likelihood-free algorithm that relies neither on Bayes theorem nor on any sampling techniques to approximate the posterior PDF. In particular, it first projects the available experimental data (specifically the state measurements) onto the uncertainty space, by solving several small-scale, dynamic optimization problems. Then, it utilizes maximum likelihood estimation to convert the data projections into a new PDF, called the updated PDF. Finally, it combines updated and prior PDFs to compute a posterior. This sampling-free, two-stage strategy for estimating the posterior PDF offers a significant computational advantage over conventional Bayesian inference approaches. In addition, it allows PDFE&U to easily handle correlated/non-Gaussian measurement errors, features which make it difficult to apply standard Bayesian inference.

The rationale of PDFE&U is shown in Figure 1. The algorithm is composed of three phases, called Phase I, Phase II and Phase III, each of which involves one or more steps. However, due to space limitations, we only discuss step C of Phase I, which is the core of PDFE&U. In this step, we project every state measurement onto the uncertainty space by solving several small-scale, dynamic optimization problems, thus obtaining a set of "samples". This operation is conceptually the inverse of the problem of propagation of a probability distribution through a DAE system. It is the most computationally demanding task of PDFE&U but can be fully parallelized because all the dynamic optimization problems, previously mentioned, are independent of each other. As a consequence, the overall computational efficiency of PDFE&U is not negatively impacted.

Before moving on to our case study, it is important to comment on the implementation of both ODMCMC and PDFE&U. Both rely on the sequential approach, but the first has been implemented in a MATLAB® script while the second has been coded in C++, utilizing the BzzMath library as numerical engine (Buzzi-Ferraris and Manenti, 2012). In addition, the implementation of PDFE&U exploits parallel computing while that of ODMCMC currently allows only serial execution. All of this information will be useful for purposes of computational performance analysis (see the next section).

3. General assessment of ODMCMC, PDFE&U and BMCMC

The computational performance and accuracy offered by PDFE&U, ODMCMC and by a well-established implementation of BMCMC, i.e. Stan (Carpenter et al., 2017), have been analysed using a PB/PK model, which simulates the response of a patient to the administration of Gabapentin. Specifically, this case study involves estimation of the joint probability distribution of the 10 uncertain parameters of this PB/PK model, comprised of 34 nonlinear DAEs. The data set, used in this PDF estimation problem, includes about 150 data points, and consists of measurements of drug concentration in plasma and urine.

The results of the aforementioned PDF estimation problem are summarized in Figure 2 and Figure 3. Specifically, Figure 2 reports the most important statistical properties of the 10 uncertain model parameters, computed by PDFE&U, ODMCMC and Stan

(BMCMC + Random Effects). On the other hand, Figure 3 shows the 95 % credible regions of drug concentration in a patient's blood stream, predicted by both PDFE&U and ODMCMC.

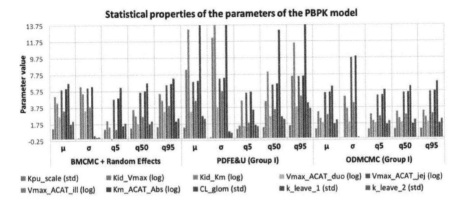

Figure 2: Statistical analysis of the PDFs computed by PDFE&U, ODMCMC and Stan (some quantities are reported in log-scale to improve the chart readability; μ, σ and qX stand for expectations, standard deviations and X % quantiles).

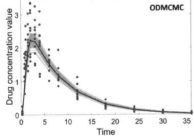 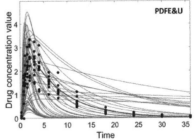

Figure 3: Predicted enclosures of the profiles of drug concentration in a patient's blood stream at 95% confidence level (the black/blue dots are the experimental data; the black/blue curves represent the profiles of drug concentration in the blood stream of the average patient).

Both Figure 2 and Figure 3 confirm that PDFE&U tends to overestimate variance but provides decent estimates of the central tendency measures and of the qualitative properties of the PDF (specifically variance ratios), at a very attractive computational cost (Table 1).

Table 1: Computational performance of PDFE&U, ODMCMC and Stan.

Case study	Model size	Number of uncertain parameters	Time elapsed for solving a single PDF estimation problem [h]		
			PDFE&U	ODMCMC	Stan
Administration of Gabapentin	34 DAEs	10	$0.3 - 0.6$[a]	≈ 40[b]	≈ 120[a]

[a] Simulations performed with custom C++ codes; [b] Simulation performed with MATLAB® R2018a

On the other hand, ODMCMC proves to be more accurate than PDFE&U (Figure 2) in terms of both variance and central tendency measure estimates, but also demonstrates to be slightly less computationally efficient (since ODMCMC has been implemented in a MATLAB® script, its computational time, shown in Table 1, must be divided by at least a factor of 20). In addition, it tends to underestimate variance, as shown in Figure 3.

4. Conclusions

The results of the case study, discussed in the previous section, suggest that both ODMCMC and PDFE&U provide a favourable trade-off between accuracy and computational efficiency, by comparison to Bayesian Markov-chain Monte Carlo methods. This allows us to conclude that ODMCMC and PDFE&U are more suitable for time-critical applications, where the PDF estimation task must be completed as soon as possible (e.g., in stochastic dynamic optimization, robust data reconciliation and robust soft-sensor systems). Conversely, Bayesian Markov-chain Monte Carlo is more accurate and reliable, and is more suitable for offline, detailed PDF estimation studies.

In the near future, we are planning to improve and augment both ODMCMC and PDFE&U, with the aim of reducing the gap in accuracy between these two strategies and BMCMC without negatively affecting their computational efficiency.

References

M.J. Beal, 2003, Variational algorithms for approximate Bayesian inference, London: University of London, UK.

G. Buzzi-Ferraris, F. Manenti, 2012, BzzMath: library overview and recent advances in numerical methods, Computer Aided Chemical Engineering, 30, 1312-1316.

B. Carpenter, A. Gelman, M.D. Hoffman, D. Lee, B. Goodrich, M. Betancourt, M. Brubaker, J. Guo, P. Li, A. Riddell, 2017, Stan: A probabilistic programming language, Journal of Statistical Software, 76, 1-32.

P.L. Green, K. Worden, 2015, Bayesian and Markov chain Monte Carlo methods for identifying nonlinear systems in the presence of uncertainty, Philosophical Transactions A, 373, 20140405.

J.M. Laínez, G. Blau, L. Mockus, S. Orçun, G.V. Reklaitis, 2011, Pharmacokinetic based design of individualized dosage regimens using a Bayesian approach, Industrial and Engineering Chemistry Research, 50, 5114-5130.

L. Mockus, J.M. Laínez, G. Reklaitis, L. Kirsch, 2011, A bayesian approach to pharmaceutical product quality risk quantification, Informatica, 22, 537-558.

F. Rossi, L. Mockus, F. Manenti, G. Reklaitis, 2018, Assessment of accuracy and computational efficiency of different strategies for estimation of probability distributions applied to ODE/DAE systems, Computer Aided Chemical Engineering, 44, 1543-1548.

F. Rossi, G. Reklaitis, F. Manenti, G. Buzzi-Ferraris, 2016, Multi-scenario robust online optimization and control of fed-batch systems via dynamic model-based scenario selection, AIChE Journal, 62, 3264-3284.

Y. Yao, A. Vehtari, D. Simpson, A. Gelman, 2018, Yes, but did it work?: evaluating variational inference, arXiv preprint arXiv: 1802.02538.

Anton A. Kiss, Edwin Zondervan, Richard Lakerveld, Leyla Özkan (Eds.)
Proceedings of the 29th European Symposium on Computer Aided Process Engineering
June 16th to 19th, 2019, Eindhoven, The Netherlands. © 2019 Elsevier B.V. All rights reserved.
http://dx.doi.org/10.1016/B978-0-128-18634-3.50157-0

Deterministic Global Process Optimization: Flash Calculations via Artificial Neural Networks

Artur M. Schweidtmann[a], Dominik Bongartz[a], Wolfgang R. Huster[a] and Alexander Mitsos[a*]

[a]*Process Systems Engineering (AVT.SVT), RWTH Aachen University, Aachen 52074, Germany*
amitsos@alum.mit.edu

Abstract

We recently demonstrated the potential of deterministic global optimization in a reduced-space formulation for flowsheet optimization. However, the consideration of implicit unit operations such as flash calculations is still challenging and the solution of complex flowsheets incorporating such operations can be intractable. We show that the solution of flash equations can be integrated in global optimization via artificial neural networks (ANNs). Thus, flash calculations are no longer performed within the flowsheet optimization. Instead, flash equations are solved offline and then learned using ANNs. ANNs have been used successfully in the literature to learn flash equilibria but have not yet been included in deterministic global optimization for this task. We embed the ANNs in a hybrid model and use deterministic global optimization to solve it. In addition, we utilize deterministic global optimization to calculate a guaranteed worst-case accuracy of ANNs compared to a rigorous model. We demonstrate the proposed approach on an illustrative five-component vapor-liquid equilibrium flash using our in-house solver MAiNGO.

Keywords: Reduced-space, McCormick relaxations, Guaranteed accuracy, Flowsheet

1. Introduction

The optimization of process flowsheets is still a major challenge after many years of important advances in process systems engineering. Flowsheet optimization problems typically result in nonlinear programs (NLPs) that exhibit nonconvexities and multiple local optima. In contrast to local and stochastic global solution methods, deterministic global optimization methods are guaranteed to identify global optima, making them a desirable solution method.

In the previous literature, deterministic global optimization of flowsheet problems has mostly been performed using general-purpose global solvers and an equation-oriented modeling approach (also known as full-space). However, when complex processes are considered, this leads to large-scale optimization problems. In addition, the equation-oriented modeling approach necessitates bounds on all modeling variables which can be difficult to determine. An alternative to this is a hybrid between the equation-oriented and a sequential modular approach where the branch-and-bound solver operates only in a subset of the model variables (also known as a reduced-space approach) (Byrne and Bogle (2000); Balendra and Bogle (2009)). Similar reduced-space approaches have long been used for simulation and local optimization (e.g., Tolsma et al. (2002); Poth et al. (2003)). We recently demonstrated the potential of reduced-space for deterministic global flowsheet optimization (Bongartz and Mitsos (2017)) and hybrid flowsheet problems with artificial neural networks (ANNs) embedded (Schweidtmann and Mitsos (2018); Rall et al. (2019)). Therein and herein, we use our in-house solver MAiNGO (Bongartz et al. (2018)) which in turn relies on propagation of McCormick relaxations (McCormick (1976)) through external functions (Mitsos et al.

(2009); Chachuat et al. (2015))

However, a particular challenge of realistic flowsheet optimization problems lies in the consideration of accurate thermodynamic calculations and complex unit operations because these often include implicit functions and complex calculations. In the reduced-space formulation, these can lead to additional variables, equality constraints, and weak McCormick relaxations (Stuber et al. (2015); Schweidtmann et al. (2019); Bongartz and Mitsos (2019)). A possible solution to this is to substitute complex model parts by surrogate models. This can essentially reduce the number of optimization variables and equality constraints that the B&B algorithm branches on because the surrogate models are called as external functions (Schweidtmann and Mitsos (2018)). In some cases, the McCormick relaxations of surrogate models are even tighter than the ones of the substituted model (Schweidtmann et al. (2019)).

Machine learning surrogate models have been used extensively in the previous process systems engineering literature (Lee et al. (2018)), e.g., for embedding them in hybrid process models (e.g., Caballero and Grossmann (2008); Mistry et al. (2018); Rall et al. (2019)) or black-box optimization of simulations (e.g., Wilson and Sahinidis (2017); Boukouvala et al. (2017)). In addition, multiple works have addressed the learning of single species thermodynamic properties (e.g., Chouai et al. (2002); Laugier and Richon (2003)) and vapor-liquid equilibrium compositions (e.g., Sharma et al. (1999); Sözen et al. (2004); Şencan et al. (2006); Nentwich and Engell (2016); Keßler et al. (2017)) demonstrating that ANNs are capable of learning those properties accurately. In our previous organic Rankine cycle case study, we have showed that substituting an implicit Helmholtz thermodynamic model for ethanol by ANNs leads to favorable solution times for the optimization because of a reduction in the number of optimization variables and equality constraints as well as tighter relaxations (Schweidtmann et al. (2019)). However, many chemical engineering applications include flash calculations which do not lend themselves as naturally to a reduced-space formulation and may require a number of variables and constraints to remain in the optimization problem (Bongartz and Mitsos (2019)). ANNs for thermodynamic equilibrium equations have not yet been included in deterministic global optimization. Further, the previous literature does not provide guarantees on the accuracy of trained ANNs but mostly indicates their performance on a finite test set.

We propose to learn thermodynamic equilibrium via ANNs in order to include them subsequently in deterministic global optimization problems. The method learns the solution of flash calculations retrieved from a nonsmooth model that describes not only the two-phase region, but also single-phase output streams (Sahlodin et al. (2016); Watson et al. (2017)). Furthermore, we compute a guarantee on the worst-case performance of ANNs compared to an analytical model using deterministic global optimization. The method is illustrated on a five-species nonideal mixture.

2. Flash calculations & illustrative case study

Many chemical flowsheets include flash separations that are assumed to be in equilibrium. Herein, we consider a vapor-liquid equilibrium (VLE) flash: Given an inlet stream flow rate (F) and its molar fractions ($\mathbf{z}$), the flash calculation determines the outgoing flow rates of the liquid stream (L) and vapor stream (V) with their corresponding molar fractions $\mathbf{x}$ and $\mathbf{y}$, respectively. The flash has two degrees of freedom that are either specified by design or are optimization variables. In this work, we use temperature (T) and pressure (p) as the degrees of freedom because intensive properties are advantageous for data-driven modeling (see Section 4).

The flash model consists of balance equations for overall molar flow rates Eqn. (1), component flow rates Eqn. (2), the isofugacity equation Eqn. (3), and the closure relation Eqn. (4) (c.f., Watson et al. (2017)):

$$F - L - V = 0 \tag{1}$$

$$F \cdot z_i - L \cdot x_i - V \cdot y_i = 0 \qquad\qquad i = 1,..,N \tag{2}$$

$$f_i^V(p,T,\mathbf{y}) - f_i^L(p,T,\mathbf{x}) = 0 \qquad\qquad i = 1,..,N \tag{3}$$

$$\text{mid}\left(V/F, \quad \sum_{i=1}^{N}(x_i - y_i), \quad V/F - 1\right) = 0 \qquad (4)$$

where N is the number of components and f_i^V, f_i^L are the fugacities of component i in the vapor and liquid phase, respectively. Note that herein we use the nonsmooth closure relation proposed by Watson et al. (2017) which is based on the commonly used closure relation $\sum_{i=1}^{N}(x_i - y_i) = 0$ and which can model both two-phase and single-phase outlet streams. We use the flash model Eqns. (1) - (4) to generate data for training the ANNs (Section 3) and as a reference model for comparison to the data-driven approach (Sections 4 & 5). Note that we use the isofugacity equation Eqn. 3 and thus cannot guarantee stable states because we want to avoid a bilevel problem which arises when the Gibbs free energy is minimized as an embedded optimization problem. However, the proposed approach can in principle be applied to these as well.

For illustration, we consider a five-species mixture of hydrogen (H_2), carbon dioxide (CO_2), carbon monoxide (CO), methanol (MeOH), and water (H_2O). We assume ideal gas/liquid phases, use Henry's law for the supercritical species H_2, CO_2, and CO being dissolved in liquid methanol and water, and use model parameters and the solvent mixing rule from AspenPlus. The case study is described in more detail in Bongartz and Mitsos (2019) where rigorous, not hybrid, flash models with the common closure relation were optimized.

3. Training of the artificial neural networks

In order to generate the training data set, we create a Latin hypercube of 20,000 points on $z_i \in [0,1], T \in [300,512]$ K, $p \in [1, 66.5]$ bar with $\sum_{i=1}^{N} z_i = 1$. Then, we simulate the fully specified flash model Eqns. (1) - (4) in MAiNGO. Herein, we use an inlet stream flow rate of 1 kmol/s without loss of generality. As we use the nonsmooth closure relation Eqn. 4, data on the complete box-constrained input domain is feasible.

For training, the input vector of the ANNs is set to $(z_{H_2}, z_{CO_2}, z_{CO}, z_{MeOH}, T, p)^T$ and the output vector is set to $(x_{H_2}, x_{CO_2}, x_{CO}, x_{MeOH}, \beta)^T$ with $\beta = V/F$. The training is conducted in MATLAB using Bayesian regularization backpropagation because we observed that regularization leads to tighter relaxations and favorable performance in subsequent optimization studies. However, the comparison of training algorithms is not within the scope of this work. All outputs are learned using individual ANNs with two hidden layers with ten nodes each. Furthermore, the hyperbolic tangent activation function is used in the hidden and output layers as we know from physical understanding that our outputs are bounded.

4. Optimization of hybrid flash model

In this section, the learned ANNs are embedded in an hybrid optimization problem that is solved using our deterministic global solver MAiNGO. In particular, the ANNs are used to compute $x_{H_2}, x_{CO_2}, x_{CO}, x_{MeOH}, \beta$ and the remaining mole fractions and flows are obtained by solving overall and component molar balances. This gives a hybrid flash model where the equilibrium is learned via ANNs and the balances are given by mechanistic equations. This allows for applying the hybrid model to any given input flow rate. All problems were solved on an Intel(R) Core(TM) i7-4790 CPU with 3.60 GHz, 16 GB RAM, and Windows 7 64 bit operating system.

For the illustrative case study, we consider an inlet stream of $F = 1$ kmol/s with the composition $\mathbf{z} = (0.644, 0.195, 0.025, 0.072, 0.064)^T$. The objective of the problem is to identify $T \in [300, 512]$ K and $p \in [1, 66.5]$ bar that maximize the amount of methanol recovered in the liquid phase, i.e., $\min -L \cdot x_{MeOH}/(F \cdot z_{MeOH})$, subject to the purity constraint $x_{CO_2} \leq 0.01$. As shown in Table 1, the solution point of the hybrid ANN model is close to the one of the rigorous model. The optimal point of the illustrative problem is at the lower temperature boundary, intermediate pressure, and results in a two-phase outlet stream. The solution time of the hybrid

Table 1: Problem size and solution statistics of the illustrative flash case study (relative optimality tolerance 10^{-3}). In the table we use the following abbreviations: Var.: number of optimization variables, Eq.: number of equality constraints, Ineq.: number of inequality constraints, CPU: computational time, Iter.: number of iterations, T: temperature, p: pressure, Obj.: objective value.

Formulation	Problem size			Performance		Solution point		
	Var.	Eq.	Ineq.	CPU [s]	Iter.	T [K]	p [bar]	Obj. [%]
Rigorous flash	6	4	1	3.74	2,195	300	16.7	93.2
Hybrid flash	2	0	1	0.59	347	300	16.5	93.7

model gives a considerable speedup as it takes less than 16% of the solution time of the rigorous model. One reason for the speedup is the smaller problem size of the hybrid model, i.e., the B&B algorithm has to branch only on the two degrees of freedom and requires less iterations. In contrast, the optimization problem including the rigorous flash model has four additional optimization variables and equality constraints because the model is not explicit in the degrees of freedom (c.f. *ideal flash formulation* in Bongartz and Mitsos (2019)).

5. Guaranteed accuracy of the artificial neural networks

When ANNs and other surrogate models are used in decision-making processes, trust in the accuracy of their predictions is a major concern. Typically, ANNs are trained on a large set of training data and subsequently validated on an independent test set. However, even in cases where accurate fits are obtained on both the training and test set, there is no guarantee that the model gives reasonably good predictions on the whole input or even out of the sampled training domain because of the universal approximator theorem (e.g., Hornik et al. (1989)). This means that an ANN of sufficient size can in principle represent any continuous function - also unphysical functions between training and test points. Previous works addressed this problem, e.g., Wilson and Sahinidis (2017) use an adaptive sampling technique where they iteratively select new training points by maximization of the error between the surrogate model and the underlying simulation used for data generation using a stochastic black-box solver. However, the stochastic solution approach does not provide a guaranteed worst-case accuracy.

In this section, we propose a method that computes a guaranteed accuracy of ANNs for cases where an algebraic formulation of the underlying model used for data generation is available. In particular, we maximize a norm of an error between the underlying model for data generation and our surrogate model on a compact input domain using deterministic global optimization. Any upper bound of this maximization problem provides a guarantee on the worst-case performance of the surrogate model.

For illustration, we maximize the squared distance of the component molar liquid streams of the rigorous flash model and the previously trained ANN. This problem is reformulated to an equivalent minimization problem as the optimization literature usually formulates minimization problems:

$$\min \quad -||(\mathbf{L}_{\text{ANN}} - \mathbf{L}_{\text{Rig flash}})||_2^2 \tag{5}$$

subject to the rigorous flash model Eqns. (1) - (4) and the hybrid flash model where $\mathbf{L}_{\text{Rig flash}} = L_{\text{Rig flash}} \cdot \mathbf{x}_{\text{Rig flash}}$ is the liquid molar flow rate vector from model Eqns. (1) - (4) and $\mathbf{L}_{\text{ANN}}$ is the vector of corresponding predictions computed by the hybrid flash model. Herein, we compare component molar flow rates and not mole fractions because they are a relevant measure for the error for both the two-phase and the single-phase case. Given inlet mole fractions of $\mathbf{z} = (0.644, 0.195, 0.025, 0.072, 0.064)^{\text{T}}$ and a total inlet stream of $F = 1$ kmol/s, the optimization problem Eqn. (5) is solved for the degrees of freedom $T \in [300, 512]$ K and $p \in [1, 66.5]$ bar.

The solution point with the largest squared distance that has been found in the B&B algorithm is $2.05 \cdot 10^{-4}$ kmol^2/s^2 at $T^* = 315$ K, $p^* = 1.1$ bar with $\mathbf{L}^*_{\text{Rig flash}} = (1.2 \cdot 10^{-7}, 1.2 \cdot 10^{-6}, 6.4 \cdot 10^{-9}, 1.3 \cdot 10^{-3}, 5.0 \cdot 10^{-3})^{\text{T}}$ and $\mathbf{L}^*_{\text{ANN}} = (1.3 \cdot 10^{-6}, 1.6 \cdot 10^{-5}, 1.8 \cdot 10^{-7}, 5.0 \cdot 10^{-3}, 1.9 \cdot 10^{-2})^{\text{T}}$ in kmol/s. This solution is near the phase boundary, i.e., $\beta = 0.994$, indicating that inaccuracies of the ANNs are higher near the phase boundary. Also, the solution point is near the box constraints of the training data indicating that it is sensible to extend the training set outside the actually used input domain. However, the result also shows the worst-case absolute inaccuracies are relatively small. The lower bound of the problem gives a guaranteed worst-case performance of $1.41 \cdot 10^{-3}$ kmol^2/s^2. Herein, an absolute optimality gap of $1.21 \cdot 10^{-3}$ kmol^2/s^2 remains after the maximum solution time of 43,200 CPU seconds showing that the guaranteed accuracy optimization problem is much harder to solve than the optimization of the hybrid flash model in Section 4.

6. Conclusion

We propose a hybrid modeling approach that learns thermodynamic equilibria of multicomponent mixtures via ANNs for subsequent deterministic global process optimization. The ANNs learn liquid equilibrium mole fractions and the vapor-to-feed ratio from a set of data covering both two-phase and single-phase regions. Then, we combine the ANNs with rigorous balance equations to form a hybrid flash model. An illustrative five-component flash case study shows that the hybrid flash model can be optimized in less than 16% of the CPU time necessary to optimize a rigorous flash model. Finally, deterministic global optimization is used to compute a guaranteed worst-case accuracy of the ANNs compared to a rigorous flash simulation.

The considerable speedup of the optimization does, however, come at the cost of offline data generation and training of the ANNs (on the order of minutes to hours). Thus, the hybrid modeling of a single flash calculation does not seem practical unless the optimization problem needs to be solved very quickly. However, it is expected that the substitution of several flash calculations in larger flowsheet problems will give much larger speedups due to the exponential worst-case runtime of B&B algorithms. Furthermore, this work presents a first step towards the learning and subsequent deterministic global optimization of complete separation columns. This is a promising future work because the reduced-space optimization of rigorous column models requires tear variables and flash calculation on every stage whereas an ANN could learn the column as a whole.

The computation of a guaranteed worst-case performance of ANNs is also a relevant contribution because it can be used as a rigorous tool to identify regions in the input domain with large errors, choose new training points accordingly, or select a suitable network architecture/complexity. In addition, the method allows us to use ANNs as a model reduction technique with guaranteed accuracy in the future.

Acknowledgments: The authors gratefully acknowledge the financial support of the Kopernikus project SynErgie by the German Federal Ministry of Education and Research (BMBF) and the project supervision by the project management organization Projektträger Jülich (PtJ). The authors gratefully acknowledge funding by the BMBF within the Kopernikus Project P2X: Flexible use of renewable resources exploration, validation and implementation of 'Power-to-X' concepts. We thank Tim Kerkenhoff and Nils Graß for their help on the data generation and implementation.

References

S. Balendra, I. D. L. Bogle, 2009. Modular global optimisation in chemical engineering. Journal of Global Optimization 45 (1), 169–185.

D. Bongartz, A. Mitsos, 2017. Deterministic global optimization of process flowsheets in a reduced space using McCormick relaxations. Journal of Global Optimization 20 (9), 419.

D. Bongartz, A. Mitsos, 2019. Deterministic global flowsheet optimization: between equation-oriented and sequential-modular methods. AIChE Journal 65 (3), 1022–1034.

D. Bongartz, J. Najman, S. Sass, A. Mitsos, 2018. MAiNGO – McCormick-based Algorithm for mixed-integer Nonlinear Global Optimization. Tech. rep., Process Systems Engineering (AVT.SVT), RWTH Aachen University. URL http://permalink.avt.rwth-aachen.de/?id=729717

F. Boukouvala, M. F. Hasan, C. A. Floudas, 2017. Global optimization of general constrained grey-box models: new method and its application to constrained PDEs for pressure swing adsorption. Journal of Global Optimization 67 (1-2), 3–42.

R. Byrne, I. Bogle, 2000. Global optimization of modular process flowsheets. Industrial & engineering chemistry research 39 (11), 4296–4301.

J. A. Caballero, I. E. Grossmann, 2008. An algorithm for the use of surrogate models in modular flowsheet optimization. AIChE journal 54 (10), 2633–2650.

B. Chachuat, B. Houska, R. Paulen, N. Peri'c, J. Rajyaguru, M. E. Villanueva, 2015. Set-theoretic approaches in analysis, estimation and control of nonlinear systems. IFAC-PapersOnLine 48 (8), 981–995. URL http://omega-icl.bitbucket.org/mcpp/

A. Chouai, S. Laugier, D. Richon, 2002. Modeling of thermodynamic properties using neural networks. Fluid Phase Equilibria 199 (1-2), 53–62.

K. Hornik, M. Stinchcombe, H. White, 1989. Multilayer feedforward networks are universal approximators. Neural Networks 2 (5), 359–366.

T. Keßler, N. Mertens, C. Kunde, C. Nentwich, D. Michaels, S. Engell, A. Kienle, 2017. Efficient global optimization of a novel hydroformylation process. In: Computer Aided Chemical Engineering. Vol. 40. Elsevier, pp. 2113–2118.

S. Laugier, D. Richon, 2003. Use of artificial neural networks for calculating derived thermodynamic quantities from volumetric property data. Fluid Phase Equilibria 210 (2), 247–255.

J. H. Lee, J. Shin, M. J. Realff, 2018. Machine learning: Overview of the recent progresses and implications for the process systems engineering field. Computers & Chemical Engineering 114, 111–121.

G. P. McCormick, 1976. Computability of global solutions to factorable nonconvex programs: Part i convex underestimating problems. Mathematical Programming 10 (1), 147–175.

M. Mistry, D. Letsios, R. Misener, G. Krennrich, R. M. Lee, 2018. Optimization with gradient-boosted trees and risk control. arXiv preprint arXiv:1803.00952.

A. Mitsos, B. Chachuat, P. I. Barton, 2009. McCormick-based relaxations of algorithms. SIAM Journal on Optimization 20 (2), 573–601.

C. Nentwich, S. Engell, 2016. Application of surrogate models for the optimization and design of chemical processes. In: 2016 International Joint Conference on Neural Networks (IJCNN). IEEE.

N. Poth, D. Brusis, J. Stichlmair, 2003. Rigorous optimization of reactive distillation in gams with the use of external functions. In: Computer Aided Chemical Engineering. Vol. 14. Elsevier, pp. 869–874.

D. Rall, D. Menne, A. M. Schweidtmann, J. Kamp, L. von Kolzenberg, A. Mitsos, M. Wessling, 2019. Rational design of ion separation membranes. Journal of Membrane Science 569, 209 – 219.

A. M. Sahlodin, H. A. Watson, P. I. Barton, 2016. Nonsmooth model for dynamic simulation of phase changes. AIChE Journal 62 (9), 3334–3351.

A. M. Schweidtmann, W. R. Huster, J. Lüthje, A. Mitsos, 2019. Deterministic global process optimization: Accurate (single-species) properties via artificial neural networks. Computers & Chemical Engineering 121, 67 – 74.

A. M. Schweidtmann, A. Mitsos, 2018. Deterministic global optimization with artificial neural networks embedded. In Press: Journal of Optimization Theory and Applications.

A. Şencan, K. A. Yakut, S. A. Kalogirou, 2006. Thermodynamic analysis of absorption systems using artificial neural network. Renewable Energy 31 (1), 29–43.

R. Sharma, D. Singhal, R. Ghosh, A. Dwivedi, 1999. Potential applications of artificial neural networks to thermodynamics: vapor–liquid equilibrium predictions. Computers & Chemical Engineering 23 (3), 385–390.

A. Sözen, M. Özalp, E. Arcaklioğlu, 2004. Investigation of thermodynamic properties of refrigerant/absorbent couples using artificial neural networks. Chemical Engineering and Processing: Process Intensification 43 (10), 1253–1264.

M. D. Stuber, J. K. Scott, P. I. Barton, 2015. Convex and concave relaxations of implicit functions. Optimization Methods and Software 30 (3), 424–460.

J. E. Tolsma, J. A. Clabaugh, P. I. Barton, 2002. Symbolic incorporation of external procedures into process modeling environments. Industrial & engineering chemistry research 41 (16), 3867–3876.

H. A. Watson, M. Vikse, T. Gundersen, P. I. Barton, 2017. Reliable flash calculations: Part 1. nonsmooth inside-out algorithms. Industrial & Engineering Chemistry Research 56 (4), 960–973.

Z. T. Wilson, N. V. Sahinidis, 2017. The ALAMO approach to machine learning. Computers & Chemical Engineering 106, 785–795.

Anton A. Kiss, Edwin Zondervan, Richard Lakerveld, Leyla Özkan (Eds.)
Proceedings of the 29th European Symposium on Computer Aided Process Engineering
June 16th to 19th, 2019, Eindhoven, The Netherlands. © 2019 Elsevier B.V. All rights reserved.
http://dx.doi.org/10.1016/B978-0-128-18634-3.50158-2

An Efficient MILP-Based Decomposition Strategy for Solving Large-Scale Scheduling Problems in the Offshore Oil and Gas Industry

Natalia P. Basán,[a] Mariana E. Cóccola,[a] Alejandro García del Valle,[b] Carlos A. Méndez[a,*]

[a]INTEC (UNL –CONICET), Güemes 3450, Santa Fe, 3000, Argentina

[b]University of A Coruña, C/ Mendizábal s/n, Ferrol, 15403, Spain

cmendez@intec.unl.edu.ar

Abstract

This paper presents a MILP-based decomposition algorithm for solving large-scale scheduling problems with assembly operations in flexible flow shop environments. First, a rigorous mixed-integer linear (MILP) formulation based on the general precedence notion is developed for the problem under study. Then, the MILP model is embedded within a decomposition algorithm in order to accelerate the resolution of large-size industrial problems. Finally, the proposed solution approach is tested on several examples derived from a real-world case study arising in a company that builds vessels for the offshore oil and gas industry.

Keywords: flexible flow shop, scheduling problem, assembly operations, MILP model, decomposition strategy.

1. Introduction

The flexible flow shop scheduling problem (FFSP) is a generalization of the classical flow shop problem (FSP), wherein all products follow the same flow processing line but all of them may not visit all processing stages. When some stage on the line performs an assembly operation, the problem is known as FFSP-A. Generally, the objective is to minimize the completion time of all products (makespan). This type of scheduling problem appears in many industrial applications such as automotive industry, paint companies, and shipbuilding industry, between others.

The FFSP-A is strongly NP-hard (Pinedo, 2016). Consequently, real-world industrial problems lead to intractable model sizes when rigorous mathematical formulations are used. To overcome this drawback, this works presents a decomposition algorithm that allows finding high quality solutions with low computational effort even for large-size instances. The decomposition approach first obtains a good schedule (constructive stage), by using an insertion method, and then improves it (improvement stage) by executing partial rescheduling actions. All decisions in the iterative procedure are taken by solving a MILP model featuring a reduced search space. Specifically, the mathematical formulation used in this paper was developed applying the general precedence notion, but other alternative approaches can be considered too. The applicability and efficiency of the solution strategy is tested by solving a challenging real-world problem dealing with the construction of a ship for the development of marine resources, specifically for the offshore oil and gas industry.

2. Mathematical formulation

The FFSP-A problem consists of a set of products $i \in I$ $(i = 1, 2, \ldots, |I|)$ processed through several consecutive operation stages $s \in S$ $(s = 1, 2, \ldots, |S|)$ with parallel identical units $k \in K_s$ working in parallel at each stage s. The subset S_i identifies all stages processing product i, while the parts $i' \in I$ that integrates a product i are defined by the subset SA_i. The subset $S^a \subseteq S$ contains all stages performing assembly operations. The final products obtained on the line are identified by subset I^f $(I^f \subset I)$. Either the non-intermediate storage (NIS) policy or the unlimited intermediate storage (UIS) policy between stages can be adopted. When a NIS strategy is used, each processing unit becomes intermediate storage if its processing has finished and the next step is not available yet.

The problem constraints can be mathematically modelled using any of the continuous-time formulations that have been published in the literature for the short-term scheduling of multistage batch plants (Méndez, Henning and Cerdá, 2001). Particularly, the MILP model developed in this work and presented follow is based on the general precedence notion. It is worth to remark that some changes have been incorporated to the original proposal in order to consider the assembly operations. As shown Eq. (1), the main goal is to minimize the total time required to obtain the final products.

$$minimize \; MK \tag{1}$$

$$\sum_{k \in K_s} Y_{ik} = 1 \qquad\qquad \forall \, i \in I, s \in S_i \tag{2}$$

$$Tf_{is} \geq Ts_{is} + tp_{is} \qquad\qquad \forall \, i \in I, s \in S_i \tag{3}$$

$$Ts_{is} = Tf_{i(s-1)} \qquad\qquad \forall \, i \in I, s \in S_i, (s-1) \in S_i, s > 1 \tag{4a}$$

$$Ts_{is} \geq Tf_{i(s-1)} \qquad\qquad \forall \, i \in I, s \in S_i, (s-1) \in S_i, s > 1 \tag{4b}$$

$$Ts_{is} \geq Tf_{i'(s-1)} \qquad\qquad \forall \, i \in I, i' \in SA_i, s \in S^a, s \in S_i, (s-1) \in S_{i'} \tag{5}$$

$$Ts_{i's} \geq Tf_{is} - M(1 - W_{ii's}) - M(2 - Y_{ik} - Y_{i'k})$$
$$\forall \, i \in I, i' \in I, s \in S_i, s \in S_{i'}, k \in K_s, i < i' \tag{6}$$

$$Ts_{is} \geq Tf_{i's} - MW_{ii's} - M(2 - Y_{ik} - Y_{i'k})$$
$$\forall \, i \in I, i' \in I, s \in S_i, s \in S_{i'}, k \in K_s, i < i' \tag{7}$$

$$MK \geq Tf_{is} \qquad\qquad \forall i \in I, s \in S_i: s = |S| \tag{8}$$

Eq. (2) defines the allocation constraint. Binary variable Y_{ik} takes 1 as value when product i is processed in unit k; otherwise, it is set to zero. Eq. (3) computes the ending time Tf_{is} of product i at stage s as its starting time Ts_{is} plus the associated processing time pt_{is}. The storage police between two consecutive stages is represented by Eq. (4a) for NIS or Eq. (4b) for UIS. Constraint (5) determines that the assembly of a product i in stage $s \in S^a$, with $s \in S_i$, must begin after its associated sub-assemblies $i' \in SA_i$ have completed their processing in the previous stage. Eqs. (6) and (7) define the sequencing constraints on a same unit k. Binary variable $W_{ii's}$ is the general precedence variable in stage s. Finally, Eq. (8) states a lower bound for the variable MK to be minimized.

3. The MILP-based decomposition algorithm

The computational efficiency of the full space approach presented in the above section or any other rigorous formulation is rapidly deteriorated when increasing the problem size. For industrial applications, the solvers report solutions with a high GAP after several CPU hours. This weakness can be overcome by solving the mathematical model several times but considering a reduced search space at each iteration. Even though this solution strategy does not guarantee the optimality of the solution found, it allows reporting practical solutions with reasonable computational time.

The decomposition method presented here is based on the strategy of first obtaining an initial solution (*constructive stage*), to then gradually enhance it by applying several rescheduling iterations (*improvement stage*). Both algorithmic stages have as core the general precedence MILP model presented previously. At this point, it is worth mentioning that other alternative mathematical formulations (Méndez et al., 2006) may also be easily adapted to the proposed decomposition strategy.

The general structure of the algorithm is given in Figure 1. Note that a feasible initial scheduling solution is obtained from inserting order by order in the constructive stage. Then, an iterative enhancement-based technique is used to improve the current solution. The assignment and sequencing decisions are left free only for the product that is being rescheduled in each improvement iteration, which significantly reduces the optimization search space. When no improvements are obtained for the objective function, the current solution is reported as the best solution for the problem under study.

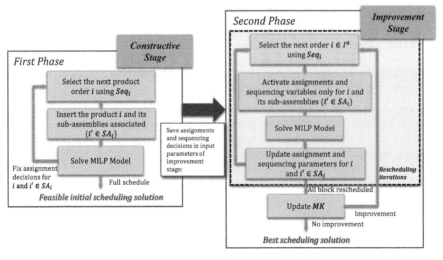

Figure 1: Overview of the iterative MILP-based algorithm.

3.1. First phase: Constructive step

The first phase of decomposition algorithm aims at generating an initial full schedule with low computational effort. The constructive method is based on the insertion technique presented by Kopanos et al. (2010) for solving large-scale pharmaceutical scheduling problems. These authors propose to insert (schedule) the products one-by-one in an iterative mode. As the FFSP-A problem includes assembly operations, it is needed that a product $i \in I^f$ and its sub-assemblies $i' \in SA_i$ will be inserted and scheduled at each iteration. Every time the MILP model (1)-(8) is solved, the binary variables Y_{ik} and $W_{ii's}$ for the new products scheduled are fixed at their optimal values.

One key point to consider in the constructive stage is to define the order in which the products will be inserted. The insertion criterion should be determined according to the problem features (Roslöf et al., 2001, 2002), for example, it can follow the lexicographic order or is based on a specific sequence. The aim should always be to find a good initial scheduling solution in a short computational time.

The constructive stage procedure ends when all products have been scheduled. Next, the initial solution is sent to the next algorithmic phase (improvement stage) using the parameters sY_{ik} and $sW_{ii's}$, which indicate the assignment and sequencing decisions taken by the constructive stage.

3.2. Second phase: Improvement step

Taking as starting point the assignments sY_{ik} and sequencing decisions $sW_{ii's}$ obtained as initial solution in the constructive step, this second phase applies the strategy of rescheduling each product $i \in I$ in a sequential way to try to improve the current solution. In other words, reassignment and reordering decisions are iteratively taken for each product i and its sub-assemblies $i' \in SA_i$. The improvement stage is executed sequentially until no improvement can be achieved to the makespan.

A boolean parameter $active_i$ is used for determining the subset of products i that can be rescheduled at each iteration. Thus, the MILP formulation (1)-(8) will active only the binary variables Y_{ik} and $W_{ii's}$ for products i with $active_i = true$. For other products, only timing decisions can be made. Reassignment to other units is not allowed for products with parameter $active_i$ set to false. Furthermore, their relative position in the processing sequence remains unchanged. This decomposition strategy allows reducing the number of binary variables of the mathematical formulation with regards to the full space approach, reducing drastically the CPU time needed to solve the model. Note that solving the full space approach is equivalent to set $active_i = true \ \forall \ i \in I$.

Every time a rescheduling action is executed, the current solution is updated. Once the rescheduling step was applied for all products, the procedure checks the makespan achieved. If the solution found is better than the best solution obtained until that moment, the algorithm updates the makespan and goes to execute the improvement step for all products again. Otherwise, the algorithm ends and reports the current solution as the best solution found for the problem under study.

4. Computational results

The MILP-decomposition algorithm is applied for the solution of a complex case study arising in a shipbuilding company, which constructs ships for the development of marine resources, specifically for the offshore oil and gas industry. This real-world FFSP-A problem involves 7 processing stages, each one with K_s processing units working in parallel, as is shown in Figure 2. A ship is built using dozens of blocks of specific size. A block is the largest construction unit of a ship. In turn, each block is assembled from one or more sub-blocks, which are composed of steel plates according to the design drawing for the ship. Both blocks and sub-blocks are considered intermediate products in the ship, which contains other components such as pipes, supports, and electronic equipment. From Figure 2, it follows that stage s_1-s_2 process sub-blocks, which are then assembled in stage s_3 to form the block. The last processing stages on the line (s_4-s_6) perform operations on the blocks, which are finally transported and positioned in a dry dock (*stage s_7*) for assembling the ship. Note that this manufacturing process includes two assembly stages: in the first one, each block is constructed by one or more sub-blocks while in the second one the mounting of these blocks is carried out to build the ship.

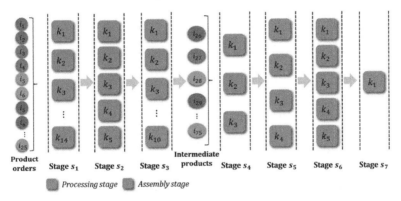

Figure 2: FFSP-A process – case study.

From the original case study, 10 problem instances were derived in order to test the computational performance of the decomposition algorithm when facing different problem sizes. Alternative storage policies, UIS and NIS, were considered for each problem size. Moreover, it is assumed that the blocks are formed by two sub-blocks. All experimental studies were implemented in GAMS 24.9.2 with CPLEX 12.6.3.0 as MIP solver and run on a PC with four-core Intel Xeon X5650 Processor (2.6 GHz). Besides, the termination criterion imposed for the solution of all problem instances has been either 0 % optimality gap or 3600 sec of CPU time.

Table 1 presents a comparison of both the results reported by MILP model and those reached by the decomposition algorithm. The expression $N \times M$ refers to a ship constructed with N blocks and M sub-blocks. The smallest problem addressed involves 10 sub-blocks and 5 blocks, while the biggest one deals with a ship built with 50 sub-blocks and 25 blocks. From Table 1, it follows that when the amount of blocks exceeds the number of 5, the full space approach does not find the optimal solution within the time limit specified, reporting a high integrality GAP for all examples. Instead, near-optimal solutions, sometimes the optimal one, are found by the solution strategy for all problem instances in few seconds of CPU time. For the more complex instance, P.10, the algorithm finds a solution of 270.5 days after 56.6 seconds, reaching an improvement of 16.5% with regards to the solution reported by the MILP model after 3600 seconds of CPU time.

Table 1: Comparison between exact MILP formulation and MILP-based algorithm statistic.

Problem	Size $N \times M$	Storage policy	MILP Model			MILP-based strategy			Enhanced solution (%)
			MILP solution	GAP (%)	CPU Time (s)	Initial solution	Best solution	Total CPU (s)	
P.01	5×10	UIS	126.3	0	2.3	144.0	126.3	2.3	0
P.02	5×10	NIS	126.3	0	2.2	144.4	126.3	2.1	0
P.03	10×20	UIS	160.1	12.7	3600	176.3	162.9	11.1	-1.7
P.04	10×20	NIS	161.4	13.4	3600	177.9	167.8	6.8	-3.8
P.05	15×30	UIS	207.0	25.9	3600	239.1	205.8	16.3	0.6
P.06	15×30	NIS	210.6	27.2	3600	241.9	206.5	24.1	1.9
P.07	20×40	UIS	231.1	27.8	3600	248.8	221.0	37.6	4.4
P.08	20×40	NIS	240.2	30.6	3600	255.4	228.6	41.2	4.8
P.09	25×50	UIS	287.8	37.3	3600	301.1	262.8	49.8	8.7
P.10	25×50	NIS	323.8	44.3	3600	298.3	270.5	56.6	16.5

5. Conclusions

A MILP-based iterative solution algorithm for solving industrial-scale FFSP-A problems has been presented in this work. The procedure was based on a MILP scheduling formulation rely on the general precedence notion. The performance of the proposed methodology has been deeply evaluated by solving several instances derived from a real-world case of study. Computational results showed that high-quality solutions can be efficiently found by the algorithm in short computational time, outperforming the rigorous optimization approach.

References

Kopanos G. M., Méndez C. A., Puigjaner L., 2010, MIP-based decomposition strategies for large-scale scheduling problems in multiproduct multistage batch plants: A benchmark scheduling problem of the pharmaceutical industry, European Journal of Operational Research, 207(2), 644–655.

Méndez C. A., Cerdá J., Grossmann I.E., Harjunkoski I., Fahl, M., 2006, State-of-the-art review of optimization methods for short-term scheduling of batch processes, Computers and Chemical Engineering, 30(6–7), 913–946.

Méndez C. A., Henning G. P., Cerdá J., 2001, An MILP continuous-time approach to short-term scheduling of resource-constrained multistage flowshop batch facilities, Computers & Chemical Engineering, 25(4–6), 701–711.

Pinedo M. L., 2016, Scheduling: Theory, Algorithms, and Systems. Fifth Edit, Scheduling: Theory, Algorithms, and Systems. Fifth Edit. New York: Springer.

Roslöf J., Harjunkoski I., Bjorkqvist J., Karlsson S., Westerlund T., , 2001, An MILP-based reordering algorithm for complex industrial scheduling and rescheduling, Computers & Chemical Engineering, 25(4–6), 821–828.

Roslöf J., Harjunkoski I., Westerlund T., Isaksson J., 2002, Solving a large-scale industrial scheduling problem using MILP combined with a heuristic procedure, European Journal of Operational Research, 138(1), 29–42.

Anton A. Kiss, Edwin Zondervan, Richard Lakerveld, Leyla Özkan (Eds.)
Proceedings of the 29th European Symposium on Computer Aided Process Engineering
June 16th to 19th, 2019, Eindhoven, The Netherlands. © 2019 Elsevier B.V. All rights reserved.
http://dx.doi.org/10.1016/B978-0-128-18634-3.50159-4

Computer-aided Design of Solvent Blends for the Cooling and Anti-solvent Crystallisation of Ibuprofen

Oliver L. Watson[a], Amparo Galindo[a], George Jackson[a], Claire S. Adjiman[a,*]

[a]*Department of Chemical Engineering, Centre for Process Systems Engineering, Imperial College London, South Kensington Campus, London SW7 2AZ, U.K.*

c.adjiman@imperial.ac.uk

Abstract

We present a general computer-aided mixture/blend design (CAM^{b}D) formulation for the design of optimal solvent mixtures for the crystallisation of pharmaceutical products. The proposed methodology enables the simultaneous identification of the optimal process temperature, solvent and anti-solvent molecules, and solvent mixture composition. The SAFT-γ Mie equation of state is used for the first time in the design of crystallisation solvents; based on an equilibrium model, the formulation considers both the crystal yield and solvent consumption. This design formulation is implemented in gPROMS and successfully applied to the crystallisation of ibuprofen, showing that this more general approach to crystallisation design can be used effectively to optimise the desired metrics.

Keywords: Crystallisation, CAM^{b}D, SAFT, solvent mixture design.

1. Introduction

The majority of pharmaceutical products are delivered to patients in solid form, such as tablets or aerosols. During their manufacture, crystallisation is particularly important in determining the properties of the crystalline form of the drug, which can impact downstream processing and ultimately the *in vivo* efficacy of the pharmaceutical product (Variankaval et al., 2008). Solvent-based crystallisation is commonly employed; as such, the effect of solvent choice is wide-reaching. Thermodynamically, the impact of this decision will manifest itself as changes to the solubility of the Active Pharmaceutical Ingredient (API), and thus as differences in two key performance indicators: the yield of API; and the mass of solvent required to complete the crystallisation. Currently, the selection of solvents for the crystallisation of newly discovered drug molecules is often performed via time-consuming and expensive experiments (Brown et al., 2018). Due to the material constraints inherent in early drug development, alongside the short timeframes required to maximise active patent life, the full range of solvent mixtures and process conditions cannot be completely explored.

With the aim of guiding experiments towards optimal candidate molecules, the application of Computer Aided Molecular Design (CAMD) in solvent selection and design has been explored (Achenie et al., 2003; Gani, 2004) over the last decades, thus facilitating faster development of crystallisation processes (Karunanithi et al., 2006). Karunanithi et al. (2005) proposed a decomposition-based approach, whereby smaller, successive subproblems are posed and solved to avoid being overwhelmed by the number of potential solutions. Most existing methodologies follow a similar approach; a specific crystallisation technique is utilised, process operating conditions are fixed, and the problem is then focused on the selection of a single solvent. More integrated problems, in which cooling and anti-solvent effects are treated simultaneously and solvent mixtures are considered, have not yet received attention. This is likely due to the complexity of formulating and solving a mixed-integer optimisation problem to represent these design choices; such problems result in challenging non-convex feasible regions for the continuous variables, in addition to the combinatorial solution space. More recently, the use of Generalised Disjunctive Programming (GDP) within the CAM^{b}D framework has been proposed to design optimal solvent mixtures that maximise solubility (Jonuzaj et al., 2016; Jonuzaj and Adjiman, 2017); optimal mixtures were shown to outperform pure compounds.

In view of the potential limitations highlighted in the current CAMD framework for solvent selection, a more comprehensive CAM^{b}D formulation for the design of crystallisation solvent systems is proposed here. This is developed via a general methodology, whereby the identities of solvent and anti-solvent molecules are optimised, in conjunction with their compositions and the process operating conditions, to maximise the crystal yield. This design formulation is implemented in gPROMS and successfully applied to the design of the solvent-based crystallisation of ibuprofen.

2. Crystallisation design

2.1. Problem definition

The CAM^{b}D problem is based on a generic formulation for the design of a crystallisation solvent system, whereby optimal solvent and anti-solvent molecules (s_1 and s_2 respectively), their compositions and the process temperatures are identified to maximise the performance objective, taken here to be the API crystal yield. Hence, the design considers both the initial state, where all the API is dissolved in the solvent blend, and the final state, where the system has reached an equilibrium between the crystalline API product and the remaining API dissolved in the final solvent mixture. By using solvent blends in both the initial and final states, the anti-solvent can serve a dual purpose. The enhanced solubility often exhibited by solvent mixtures (Granberg and Rasmuson, 2000) can first be exploited in the initial state, followed by a large reduction in API solubility in the final state after further addition of anti-solvent. Moreover, the proposed formulation enables simultaneous cooling and anti-solvent crystallisation, allowing the design to incorporate the benefits of both techniques simultaneously.

2.2. Model formulation

The formulation is based on an equilibrium model, where the SAFT-γ Mie equation of state (EoS) (Papaioannou et al., 2014) is used to calculate the activity coefficients required to determine the solubility of the API molecule in the solvent mixture in the initial and final states; Hutacharoen et al. (2017) have shown recently that this thermodynamic platform can provide high quality predictions of solubility. Furthermore, because anti-solvent crystallisation is dependent on both solvent and anti-solvent remaining in a single liquid phase, a miscibility function is included in the formulation to ensure the solubility of the binary solvent pair at the initial and final stages. Whilst this only guarantees the phase stability of the binary solvent mixture, calculation of the stability of the ternary mixture would lead to a more challenging problem. The addition of the API is assumed not to significantly affect the calculated phase stability – this is then validated after a solution to the design problem is found.

In addition, whilst the selected solvent and anti-solvent must remain in the liquid phase throughout the crystallisation process, how this requirement is implemented into the formulation can affect the optimisation outcome. It is often chosen to design a cooling crystallisation by fixing the initial and final temperatures, and thus to exclude any solvents with melting or boiling temperatures which lie within those operating limits (Karunanithi et al., 2006). Whilst this is likely chosen to reduce the complexity of the problem – operating temperature is no longer a manipulated variable of the CAM^{b}D problem, and consequently solvent candidates only need to be screened once – this method may also limit the results by screening out powerful yet volatile solvents or anti-solvents. With the approach proposed here, the optimal process temperature and solvent molecules are selected simultaneously, highlighting potentially interesting solvent mixtures regardless of volatility. A liquid range constraint is thus included for all solvent molecules.

The key model equations are provided in Table 1, where the crystal yield, Y_{API}, is defined as the difference in the number of moles of API dissolved in the liquid phase, n_{API}^L, between the initial state (subscript 0) and final state, relative to the number of moles dissolved in the initial state before crystallisation. The solubility of the API of equilibrium, x_{API}^*, is related to the activity coefficient of the API at equilibrium, γ_{API}^*, the enthalpy of melting of the API, ΔH_{API}^m, the melting temperature of the API, T_{API}^m, and the operating temperature of the system, T; R is the ideal gas constant. When determining the phase stability of the binary solvent mixture, the partial derivative of the chemical potential of the anti-solvent in the binary mixture, $\mu_{S_2}^{S_1,S_2}$, is calculated with respect to the mole fraction of the anti-solvent in the binary mixture, $x_{S_2}^{S_1,S_2}$, at fixed temperature and pressure, and must be non-negative for the solvents to be miscible.

Table 1: Key model equations.

Description	Equation
Objective function: Maximise crystal yield	$\max Y_{API} = \dfrac{n_{API,0}^L - n_{API}^L}{n_{API,0}^L}$
Solid-liquid equilibrium model	$\ln x_{API,0}^* + \ln \gamma_{API,0}^* = \dfrac{\Delta H_{API}^m}{R}\left(\dfrac{1}{T_{API}^m} - \dfrac{1}{T_0}\right),$ $\ln x_{API}^* + \ln \gamma_{API}^* = \dfrac{\Delta H_{API}^m}{R}\left(\dfrac{1}{T_{API}^m} - \dfrac{1}{T}\right)$
Miscibility constraint	$\left(\dfrac{\partial \mu_{S_2,0}^{S_1,S_2}}{\partial x_{S_2,0}^{S_1,S_2}}\right)_{T_0,P} \geq 0, \quad \left(\dfrac{\partial \mu_{S_2}^{S_1,S_2}}{\partial x_{S_2}^{S_1,S_2}}\right)_{T,P} \geq 0$

3. Case study: maximising the crystal yield of ibuprofen

3.1. Problem description

Ibuprofen is a widely-used pharmaceutical compound known for its anti-inflammatory properties. The objective of the design problem examined here is to identify an optimal solvent mixture and corresponding process conditions required to maximise the crystal yield of the API, ibuprofen. In addition to this, it is important to investigate how the choice of solvent and temperatures affects the overall solvent consumption for the crystallisation, whereby a lower consumption is preferable. Solvents are selected from a list of eight candidate molecules, compiled from low-toxicity solvents with parameters available in the SAFT-γ Mie framework (Dufal et al., 2014). To understand the effects of the process temperature on the design problem, six design scenarios are run; in each, the upper temperature limit is different, ranging from 290 K to 330 K, whilst the lower temperature limit is always fixed at 290 K and the solvent consumption was not constrained. These specifications are summarised in Table 2.

3.2. Results and discussion

The formulation is implemented in gPROMS version 5.1.1.55066, using gSAFT to perform calculations using the SAFT-γ Mie EoS. The results of the design problems pertaining to the integrated cooling and anti-solvent method are summarised in Figure 1, and the comparison between cooling, anti-solvent, and the integrated approach are given in Table 3. For all problem solutions, the stability of the ternary system is confirmed using gSAFT within gPROMS.

As can be seen in Figure 1, the combination of cooling and anti-solvent crystallisation, utilising solvent mixtures, leads to a high crystal yield, which is fractionally increased by relaxing the upper temperature limit. Furthermore, the solvent consumption improves simultaneously with the objective function as the upper temperature limit is increased, leading to increasingly environmentally benign design. This is largely due to an increase in the ratio of solvent to anti-solvent in the initial solvent mixture, meaning a smaller mass of anti-solvent is required to drive forward the crystallisation to the final state. Interestingly, the optimal process temperature of the initial state is not always equal to the upper temperature limit. When the maximum temperature is fixed at 320 K, the optimal initial temperature found is 319.15 K, as a solvent liquid range constraint becomes active near the boiling point of acetone. Additional optimisations confirm that this result remained optimal up to an upper temperature limit of 323 K. Maximising the temperature range, $T_{max}-T_{min}$, is thus not always optimal and this emphasises the importance of employing a general formulation.

In addition to the combined cooling and anti-solvent crystallisation approach, problems involving only cooling or anti-solvent crystallisation are solved, as summarised in Table 3. Although the solvent consumption decreases when using cooling crystallisation, a much lower crystal yield is obtained. Anti-solvent crystallisation allows one to achieve a similar result to the integrated approach, but the crystal yield is marginally lower and the solvent consumption is higher. Here, Y_{API} is the crystal yield of the ibuprofen, and χ_s is the solvent consumption of the crystallisation, defined as the total mass of solvent mixture used in the final state, normalised by the mass of crystalline API produced.

Table 2: Problem specifications.

Description	Model inputs
Components in the mixture	API, s_1, s_2
Candidate molecules	water, acetone, ethanol, 1-propanol, 1-butanol, 1-pentanol, n-pentane, n-heptane 28 potential binary solvent pairs
Temperature limits	$T_{min}/K = 290,$ $T_{max}/K = \{290, 300, 310, 320, 325, 330\}$

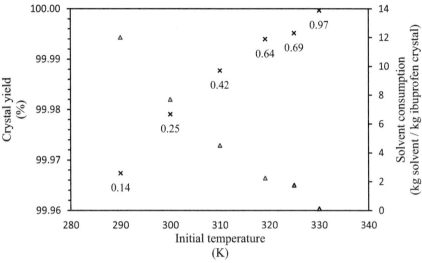

Figure 1: Optimised crystal yield of ibuprofen for different initial operating temperatures. The final temperature for all crystallisations was 290 K, whilst the upper temperature limit is changed per design, which in turn affects the initial operating temperature. The × symbol indicates the percentage crystal yield (left axis), whilst the △ symbol refers to the solvent use, normalised by the mass of API crystal produced (right axis). For points below 320 K, the solvent mixture is formed with acetone and water, whereas above this temperature the mixtures comprise of ethanol and water. The data points are labelled with the mole fraction of anti-solvent in the initial binary solvent mixture.

Table 3: Comparison of the integrated methodology to standalone methods.

Case	Solvent selection	T_0 /K	T /K	$x_{s,0}^{s_1,s_2}$	$x_s^{s_1,s_2}$	Y_{API} %	χ_s /(g/g)
Integrated	s_1: Acetone s_2: Water	310	290	s_1: 0.5809 s_2: 0.4191	s_1: 0.0253 s_2: 0.9747	99.99	4.329
Anti-solvent	s_1: Acetone s_2: Water	310	310	s_1: 0.5814 s_2: 0.4186	s_1: 0.0264 s_2: 0.9736	99.97	4.506
Cooling	s_1: Acetone s_2: Water	310	290	s_1: 0.4249 s_2: 0.5751	s_1: 0.4249 s_2: 0.5751	95.28	0.705

4. Conclusions

A general formulation for the design of optimal solvent blends for the crystallisation of pharmaceuticals is presented, based on a (CAM^{b}D) framework. With this general approach the optimal solvent and anti-solvent molecules, their compositions and the process temperatures required to maximise the crystal yield of a given API can be identified simultaneously. The general formulation is successfully applied to the crystallisation of ibuprofen, where the optimal solvent mixture is determined for several operating temperatures. The simultaneous design of the solvent mixture and operating temperature lead to improved results compared to those achieved when the temperature range is fixed. Better results are also found for the integrated cooling and anti-solvent crystallisation technique compared to standalone methods. A ranked list of potential solvent mixtures can be generated using the proposed methodology, with the overall aim to guide experiments rapidly towards high performance crystallisation systems.

Acknowledgements: The authors gratefully acknowledge financial support from the EPSRC DTP grant (Grant Ref: EP/R513052/1), and the EPSRC and the Future Continuous Manufacturing and Advanced Crystallisation Research Hub (Grant Ref: EP/P006965/1) for funding this work. The Molecular Systems Engineering Group also appreciated support from the EPSRC (grants GR/T17595, GR/N35991, EP/E016340 and EP/J014958), the Joint Research Equipment Initiative (JREI) (GR/M94426), and the Royal Society-Wolfson Foundation refurbishment scheme.

References

L. E. K. Achenie, R. Gani, V. Venkatasubramanian, 2003, Computer aided molecular design: theory and practice, Elsevier, Amsterdam, The Netherlands.

C. J. Brown, T. McGlone, S. Yerdele, V. Srirambhatla, F. Mabbott, Gurung R, M. L. Briuglia, B. Ahmed, H. Polyzois, J. McGinty, F. Perciballi, 2018, Enabling precision manufacturing of active pharmaceutical ingredients: workflow for seeded cooling continuous crystallisations, Molecular Systems Design & Engineering, 3, 518-549.

S. Dufal, V. Papaioannou, M. Sadeqzadeh, T. Pogiatzis, A. Chremos, C. S. Adjiman, G. Jackson, A. Galindo, 2014, Prediction of thermodynamic properties and phase behavior of fluids and mixtures with the SAFT-γ Mie group-contribution equation of state, Journal of Chemical & Engineering Data, 59, 10, 3272-3288.

R. Gani, 2004, Chemical product design: challenges and opportunities, Computers & Chemical Engineering, 28, 12, 2441-2457.

R. A. Granberg, Å. C. Rasmuson, 2000, Solubility of paracetamol in binary and ternary mixtures of water acetone toluene, Journal of Chemical & Engineering Data, 45, 3, 478-483.

P. Hutacharoen, S. Dufal, V. Papaioannou, R. M. Shanker, C. S. Adjiman, G. Jackson, A. Galindo, 2017, Predicting the solvation of organic compounds in aqueous environments: from alkanes and alcohols to pharmaceuticals, Industrial & Engineering Chemistry Research, 56, 38, 10856-10876.

S. Jonuzaj, P. T. Akula, P. Kleniati, C. S. Adjiman, 2016, The formulation of optimal mixtures with generalized disjunctive programming: A solvent design case study, AIChE Journal, 62, 5, 1616-1633.

S. Jonuzaj, C. S. Adjiman, 2017, Designing optimal mixtures using generalized disjunctive programming: Hull relaxations, Chemical Engineering Science, 159, 106-130.

A. T. Karunanithi, L. E. K. Achenie, R. Gani, 2005, A new decomposition-based computer-aided molecular/mixture design methodology for the design of optimal solvents and solvent mixtures, Industrial & Engineering Chemistry Research, 44, 4785–4797.

A. T. Karunanithi, L. E. Achenie, R. Gani, 2006, A computer-aided molecular design framework for crystallization solvent design, Chemical Engineering Science, 61, 4, 1247-1260.

V. Papaioannou, T. Lafitte, C. Avendaño, C. S. Adjiman, G. Jackson, E. A. Müller, A. Galindo, 2014, Group contribution methodology based on the statistical associating fluid theory for heteronuclear molecules formed from Mie segments, The Journal of Chemical Physics, 140, 5, 054107.

N. Variankaval, A. S. Cote, M. F. Doherty, 2008, From form to function: Crystallization of active pharmaceutical ingredients, AIChE Journal 54, 7, 1682-1688.

Anton A. Kiss, Edwin Zondervan, Richard Lakerveld, Leyla Özkan (Eds.)
Proceedings of the 29th European Symposium on Computer Aided Process Engineering
June 16th to 19th, 2019, Eindhoven, The Netherlands. © 2019 Elsevier B.V. All rights reserved.
http://dx.doi.org/10.1016/B978-0-128-18634-3.50160-0

Process model validation and analysis for intensification of an industrial scale process

Renata Chinda[a,§], Rotjana Ponsatorn[b,§], Amata Anantpinijwatna[b], Fernando P. Pessoa[c], John M. Woodley[d] and Seyed Soheil Mansouri[d,*]

[a]Department of Chemical Engineering, Federal University of Rio de Janeiro, Av. Athos da Silveira Ramos, 149, CT, Sala E-207, 21941-909, Rio de Janeiro - RJ, Brazil
[b]Department of Chemical Engineering, Faculty of Engineering, King Mongku's Institute of Technology Ladkrabang, Chalongkrung Rd., Ladkrabang, Bangkok, TH-10520
[c]SENAI CIMATEC,Av. Orlando Gomes, 1845, Salvador - Ba, Brazil
[d]Department of Chemical and Biochemical Engineering, Technical University of Denmark, Building 229, Søltofts Plads, DK-2800 Kgs. Lyngby, Denmark
§ Authors contributed equally to this work.
*seso@kt.dtu.dk

Abstract

Adopting reliable process models is one of the main requisites for wide spread use of process models in industry for design, control, operation and troubleshooting purposes. Validating a model against operational conditions is a plausible way to guarantee assurance and reproducibility of model outputs. Economic and sustainability analysis together with process intensification (PI) can provide feasible solutions for industrial hot-spot identification and removal. In this work, an industrial scale urea plant was modelled and simulated in a commercial process simulator. More than thirty different industrial process parameters were statistically analysed and used to perform the model validation. Economic and sustainability analyses were performed and the main hot-spots were identified. Process intensification at phenomena-level was employed to obtain more sustainable intensified process flowsheets. The results show that economic and environmental factors can be improved to reliable extent since the process model is closely replicating the reality in the base case and it fits well with industrial data.

Keywords: industrial data validation, process intensification, sustainable solutions.

1. Introduction

Modelling and simulation plays an important role in the development of chemical engineering systems. For laboratory, pilot or even industrial scale, computer aided solutions are one of the most cost effective tools available and, sometimes, the only option for engineering judgments. In order to guarantee the accuracy of these judgments it is necessary that the computational models correspond very well to the industrial data. Then, they can also be a good tool for real improvements trough analysis like economic, sustainability, Life Cycle Assessment (LCA) and even reaching Process Intensification in order to achieve a more sustainable process.

This paper is on demonstrating the importance of validating simulations against real industrial data to make development of more advanced modelling approaches and even intensified solutions for existing chemical process possible.

2. Process description and modelling

The base case studied in this paper is the production of urea through CO_2 stripping. This process is divided into five blocks: Synthesis, Evaporation, Desabsorption and Hydrolysis, Recirculation and Prilling, as it can be seen in Fig.1.

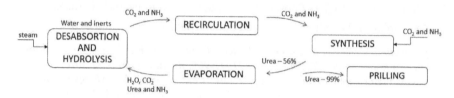

Figure 1: Simplified block diagram for the urea production process.

The principal section of this process is the Synthesis where reactions between NH_3 and CO_2 to produce ammonium carbamate and urea take place. The product of this section goes to Evaporation section to concentrate the urea and then it is sent to the Prilling. The remaining unconverted reactants are processed and recovered in the Hydrolysis and Desorption sections and, before they are sent again to Synthesis section, pressure and temperature need to be adjusted in the Recirculation step. The main equipment in each section are: Synthesis – pool condenser, reactor, stripper and scruuber; Evaporation – Pre-evaporator, 1st and 2st evaporator; Desabsorption and Hydrolysis – adsorber, dessorber I and II; Recirculation – rectifying column and condenser; Prilling – prilling tower. The reactions occurring at this process and considered in this paper are the well know ammonia and carbon dioxide producing ammonium and this one dehydrating in urea and, finally, the biuret formation, which presents a lack in literature of the area and it occurs from the condensation of two urea molecules resulting in biuret and ammonia. This process was modelled assuming steady state conditions, SR-POLAR for thermodynamic representation, production of biuret in the Pool Condenser, Reactor, Stripper and in all the Evaporators. Kinetics models were taken from Chinda et al. (2017).

3. Process validation

The experimental data used for validating the simulation was provided by an industrial urea plant in Brazil. A statistical analysis based on dispersion was performed with the plant capacity in order to exclude data that may have been taken in transient process conditions. For this, it was considered that coefficient of variation to be less than 1.5% would reflect stability in operation of the industrial plant. Statistical concepts such as arithmetic mean and standard deviation sample to calculate the variation coefficient were employed. Using this criteria it was found that the set of points at steady state available for validating the simulation was in range capacity from 86.45% to 98.21%. Validation of the simulation was performed by calculating the difference between industrial and simulated data and dividing it per industrial data.

A total of 37 different process parameters were evaluated following this criteria, among them stream temperature, steam generation, mass fraction composition for CO_2, NH_3, urea, H_2O and biuret, CO_2 conversion in the reactor and stripper efficiency. For all evaluated mass fractions, the deviation between the value predicted by the simulation and the real value obtained from industrial data were less than 5%, while for steam generation and streams temperature the deviation was less than 8%. Fig. 2(a) shows the comparison between mass fraction for each component in the outlet of the reactor and the stripper. While in Fig 2(b) it is possible to see no deviation tendency for the 10 points evaluated in the steam generated in the Pool Condenser and in the outlet temperature of the Stripper liquid phase corresponding to the production capacity of the urea plant.

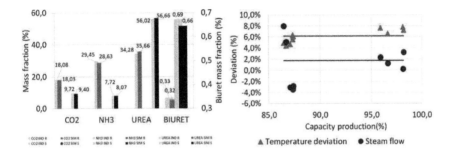

Figure 2 (a): Comparison between mass fraction composition in the outlet of the reactor and the liquid outlet of stripper. **(b)** Deviation analysis of the simulation data for the steam generation in the Pool Condenser and outlet temperature of the Stripper.

4. Process performance analysis & Hot-spots identification

Economic analysis was performed using ICAS-ECON. Sustainability analysis was carried out using the framework by Carvalho et al. (2008), Mansouri et al. (2013), and Tallis (2002); and for LCA analysis UK Government GHG conversion factors and IPCC emission factors were used.

4.1   Economic, life cycle assessment and sustainability analysis

The economic and life cycle assessment as a part of the performed analysis provide evidence that the main drivers for operating costs in urea production process are, heating (56.06 %), cooling (9.43 %) and electricity (34.51%). The analysis also showed that the rectifying column, the pre-evaporator, the 1st evaporator and the CO_2 compressor have the large utility cost, around 89.52% collectively. Furthermore, CO_2 compressor also has the largest carbon footprint because of its high-energy consumption, around 40.95 Wh.

The sustainability analysis performed in this study is a set of calculated closed- and open- paths. The method calculates and ranks as a set of mass and energy indicators, from the data obtained from steady-state simulation validated with industrial data. The main sustainability indicators are given in Table 1; and their corresponding paths are given in Fig. 2.

Table 1: Base case more expressive economic and sustainability indicators.

Path	Compound	MVA (10^3\$ /year)	TA (10^3\$ /year)	EWC (10^3\$ /year)	AF (10^3\$ /year)	MJ energy/kg product	kg product/kg raw material	Total kg CO_2 Equivalent
OP150	H_2O	-11	-177.204	166.427	-			
CP284	H_2O	-	-	47.220	0.030	2.18	0.75	0.20
CP1	NH_3	-	-	36.148	0.295			

Note: MVA – mass value added, TVA – total value added, EWC – energy to waste cost, CO2 equivalent, carbon footprint, OP – open path, CP – closed path.

It can be seen in the Table 1, that water in the OP150 water is losing its value as it exits the process through this path. On the other hand, on the CP284 it is possible to see a high flow of water being recycled resulting in high loads of energy and waste/use of utilities for raw material recovery. The same also applies to ammonia in CP1 and water in the CP284. Fig. 3 shows a task-based flowsheet with the main closed- and open-paths.

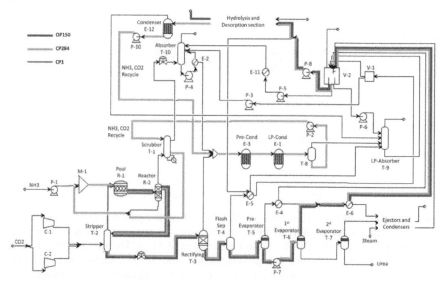

Figure 3: Base-case design for Synthesis, Evaporation and Recirculation sections for the production of urea, including process bottlenecks, closed- and open- paths.

4.2   *Process hot-spots identification*

The hot-spots identified based on the results of the economic, LCA and sustainability analysis are present in Table 2 and indicates the necessity of reducing the utility consumption. Utility is highly demanded in Evaporation and Recirculation sections. Thus, the Process Intensification was focused just in these sections.

Table 2: Urea Process hot-spots.

Hot-Spots	Design targets	Improvement solution
Limiting equilibrium	Un-reacted raw materials	-Reduction in number of unit operations
High energy consumption and/or demand	products recovery	- Improvement in sustainability and LCA factors

5. Process Intensification

Process Intensification was performed using a multi-stage framework according to (Babi et al, 2015) and (Garg et al, 2018). The base case was translated in a task-based flowsheet in order to identify Phenomena Building Blocks (PBB's), and generate Simultaneous Phenomena Building Blocks (SPB's). The total number of SPB's calculated were 16278, for 11 PBB's. Since, not all of them are feasible, following connectivity rules, it was found possible only 70 SPB's. The identified feasible SPB's are combined to form basic structures and then they were translated into unit-operations, as reactive distillation as it can be seen in Fig. 4.

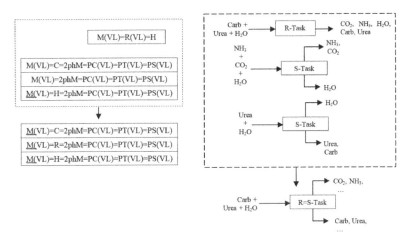

Figure 4: Basic structures combined into intensified unit operations: reactive distillation.

Finally, two intensified flowsheet alternatives are generated, as shown in Fig. 5 for Evaporation and Recirculation sections. Alternative 1 is the combined basic structure translated into Pervaporation membrane, while in Alternative 2 it is translated to Vapour permeation membrane.

The two process alternatives offer superior performance in terms of all indicators to the base case process, given that the best process alternative is the pervaporation membrane option (alternative 1). The energy consumption per one unit of urea is significantly reduced (53.48%) as well as utility cost (42.27%). The hot utilities (steam/hot water) and cold utilities (cooling water) usage were reduced to 68.63% and 29.15%, respectively. In addition, the carbon footprint, HTPI and GWP were reduced to 41.63%, 1.51% and 1.39%, respectively.

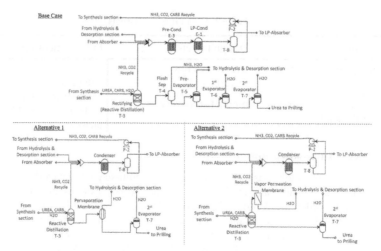

Figure 5: Base case and intensified flowsheet analysis.

5. Conclusions

Modelling and simulation of a urea plant was performed and validated with industrial data. Hot-spots were identified through economic and sustainability analyses. For Evaporation and Recirculation sections two feasible intensified alternatives were proposed using membranes. The pervaporation membrane unit for the separation of H_2O/Urea shows itself as the most sustainable one. The validation step with industrial data was an essential factor to perform a reliable and realistic study in order to suggest improvements to the process.

Acknowledgments

R.C. would like to acknowledge CAPES (Coordenação de Aperfeiçoamento de Pessoal de Nível Superior – Finance Code 001) and R.P. would like to acknowledge KMITL (King Mongkut's Institute of Technology Ladkrabang) for the research grants.

References

Babi, D.; Holtbruegge J.; Lutze P.; Gorak, A.; Woodley, J.; Gani, R.. Sustainable Process Synthesis-Intensification. Comput. Chem. Eng. 2015, 81, 218-244.

Carvalho, A.; Gani, R.; Matos, H. Design of sustainable chemical processes: Systematic retrofit analysis generation and evaluation of alternatives. Process Saf. Environ. Prot. 2008, 86, 328–346.

Chinda, R., Yamamoto, C., Lima, D., & Pessoa, F. (2017/July). Modeling and Simulating the Synthesis Section of an Industrial Urea Palnt: Analyzing the Biuret Formation. UreaKnowHow.com.

Garg, N.; Kontogeorgis G.; Woodley, J,: Gani, R. A Multi-stage and multi-level Computer Aided Framework for Sustainable Process Intensification. Proceedings of the 28th European Symposium on Computer Aided Process Engineering. Graz, Austria.

Mansouri, S.S.; Ismail, M.I.; Babi, D.K.; Simasatitkul, L.; Huusom, J.K.; Gani, R. Systematic sustainable process design and analysis of biodiesel processes. Processes 2013, 1 (2), 167-202

Tallis, B., Sustainable Development Progress Metrics, IChemE Sustainable Development Working Group, IChemE, Rugby, UK, 2002.

Anton A. Kiss, Edwin Zondervan, Richard Lakerveld, Leyla Özkan (Eds.)
Proceedings of the 29th European Symposium on Computer Aided Process Engineering
June 16th to 19th, 2019, Eindhoven, The Netherlands. © 2019 Elsevier B.V. All rights reserved.
http://dx.doi.org/10.1016/B978-0-128-18634-3.50161-2

BIOPRO-Sim: A benchmark simulation model for bio-manufacturing processes

Giorgio Colombo[a], Isuru A. Udugama[b], Krist V. Gernaey[b], Seyed Soheil Mansouri[b,*]

[a]*Department of Chemistry, Materials and Chemical Engineering "G.Natta", Politecnico di Milano, Piazza Leonardo da Vinci 32, 20133 Milano, Italy*
[b]*Process and Systems Engineering Centre, Department of Chemical and Biochemical Engineering, Technical University of Denmark, Building 229, 2800 Lyngby, Denmark*

*seso@kt.dtu.dk

Abstract

In this work, an end to end bio-pharmaceutical production process of the API lovastatin is developed through a systematic process synthesis and design approach, and then simulated. The developed simulation is intended to be used as benchmark process model as it captures the generic process dynamics of a bio-pharmaceutical process, and as such it is well-suited to use as a test problem to evaluate different processing scenarios in continuous fermentation processes. The synthesis and design of the simulation is realised through a methodology based on two complimentary steps, that can be applied individually or in conjunction, and is adopted to synthesize the upstream and downstream processing pathway. As such, the process model can be operated either as a whole, or as an individual upstream or downstream process. The open loop response of the whole benchmark simulation is presented here.

Keywords: upstream design, process development, benchmark process model, process modelling and simulation.

1. Introduction

Pharmaceutical manufacturing is a highly regulated field, where the regulations together with economics dictate that the process for production of an active pharmaceutical ingredient (API), which is generally synthesized in lab scale for clinical trials, must be quickly scaled up to full scale manufacturing once approval of the drug is granted. As a result, industry in general focuses on batch synthesis processes while downstream purification typically runs in a semi continuous manner, despite the inherent cost of inventory (Plumb, 2005). Due to this limited time for process development as well as the changing of operating regimes, there is a need for accurate benchmark process models. This work focuses on the field of fermentation as previous work in the domain of API continuous manufacturing through traditional organic synthesis has been carried out by Benyahia et al., whose work has then been exploited for control and other purposes (Ramin, Mansouri, Udugama, Benyahia, and Gernaey 2018), Mansouri, Udugama, Huusom, Gernaey, & Benyahia, 2018). In this work we will discuss the synthesis of an end to end benchmark process model for bio-pharmaceutical manufacturing with an emphasis on illustrating how process systems engineering principles were used develop the benchmark, in particular the downstream unit operation selection and layout. The dynamic behavior of both upstream and downstream unit operations is illustrated with relevant step test and disturbances in the following sections. The intended uses for this benchmark include but are not limited to process control and proc optimization, while the benchmark is also designed so the process can be operated as an end to end model or as a separate downstream process model. The benchmark model is developed in Matlab Simulink environment and can be obtained by contacting the corresponding author; while a full manuscript detailing the modeling of each unit operation will be published in the near future.

2. Upstream design

The upstream process is designed through a three step hierarchical methodology as described below. The feed to the upstream is a liquid mixture with dissolved solid compounds which are lactose, adenine and cells, responsible for the production of the API lovastatin.

Level 1 (kinetic model selection)
The first step requires the selection of a kinetic model to describe the underlying physical and chemical phenomena occurring during the chemical reaction. Macro-kinetic unstructured models are preferred to micro-kinetic models since they are able to represent the system as a whole thus being suitable for the purpose of reactor modeling.

Level 2 (batch to continuous)
A subsequent step in the methodology would require the shifting of batch reactor model/operations to continuous reactor operations as the kinetic models are generally developed using batch operations.

Level 3 (choice of upstream design and simulation)
In this stage the upstream process is modelled and its operating parameters are optimized. One major issue common to many pharmaceutical processes is the dilution of the desired product in the reacting mixture, thus an efficient solution for the upstream design has to be chosen to achieve a tradeoff between the product final titer and productivity, in order to facilitate the downstream recovery and purification operations.

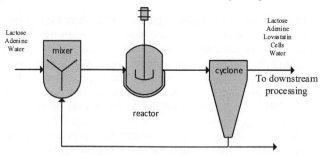

Figure 1: Upstream recirculation process design

These issue are remedied by selecting an upstream process with cell recirculation, embedding a mixer, a continuous reactor and a cyclone for biomass recirculation. The upstream process model has been solved by means of steady state component and total material balance equations to test the effect of a couple of design parameters which are the recirculation factor, defined as the ratio between the recycle flowrate and the outflow from the reactor, and the cell recycle factor characterized as the ratio between biomass concentration in the recycle stream and reactor outlet stream. Figure 2 illustrates the effect of recycling on overall upstream productivity (subplots A and C) and reactor productivity (Subplot B), and is based on the implementation of the upstream process design illustrated in Figure 1 in the Matlab Simulink environment. The highest upstream productivity has been achieved with the largest recycle ratio whereas the opposite is true for the reactor productivity, as indicated by the arrow which points out the direction of increasing recirculation factor. Despite a trade-off between maximum and minimum recycle ratio, a higher recirculation factor is suggested to accomplish a higher final titer of the desired product directed downstream (Subplot D), where the recirculation factor is increasing in the direction of the arrow. It is important to note that the productivity of the overall upstream system (Subplots A and C), benefits from an increase in the amount of cells recycled, namely an increase in the β parameter. The evidence presented by this analysis thus far supports the idea that the upstream design benefits from a high volumetric flow recirculation rate and a large cell recycle.

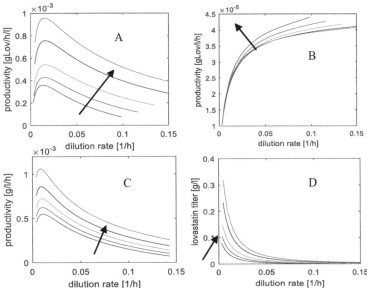

Figure 2: Figure showing overall upstream productivity (Subplot A), reactor productivity (Subplot B), and final titer (Subplot D) upon increasing of the recirculation factor. Subplot C shows changes in the overall upstream productivity with increasing cell recirculation factor β.

3. Downstream process synthesis

The methodology currently adopted in the downstream process synthesis employs physicochemical properties and their relation to separation techniques to develop separation processing pathways. All separation techniques achieve their separation task by exploiting physicochemical property differences between the separating components. The methodology has been extended, along with the inclusion of new physicochemical properties, including the most frequently used separation technologies in the bio-pharmaceutical field, which are centrifugation, electrophoresis, size exclusion and reversed phase chromatography, nanofiltration and reverse osmosis. The application of the methodology to the Lovastatin case study results in the processing route depicted in figure 3.

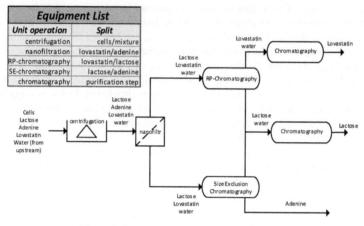

Figure 3: Downstream process synthesis result

4. Process simulation

In this section the upstream (Figure 1) and downstream process (figure 4) are connected and simulated as a continuous process by means of unit operation models either retrieved in the literature or derived from first principles.

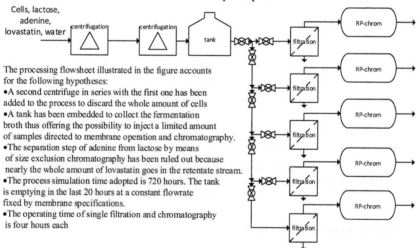

The processing flowsheet illustrated in the figure accounts for the following hypotheses:
• A second centrifuge in series with the first one has been added to the process to discard the whole amount of cells
• A tank has been embedded to collect the fermentation broth thus offering the possibility to inject a limited amount of samples directed to membrane operation and chromatography.
• The separation step of adenine from lactose by means of size exclusion chromatography has been ruled out because nearly the whole amount of lovastatin goes in the retentate stream.
• The process simulation time adopted is 720 hours. The tank is emptying in the last 20 hours at a constant flowrate fixed by membrane specifications.
• The operating time of single filtration and chromatography is four hours each

Figure 4: Overview of the downstream benchmark process

Figure 5 highlights the behavior of the four components of interest in the cyclone outlet flow, which is directed downstream for final recovery and purification and is obtained by the benchmark process model (overall process illustrated in figure 1 and 2) developed in the Matlab Simulink environment. The increase of lovastatin (subplot A) and cells concentration (subplot B) comes along with a decreasing concentration of lactose (dashed line, right plot) and adenine (dotted line, right plot).

Subplot C of Figure 6 shows the separation of lovastatin from lactose and adenine. Subplots A and C of Figure 6 instead show how sample dilution in the processing mixture decreases as an effect of membrane filtration which contributes to achieving a final product which is more concentrated.

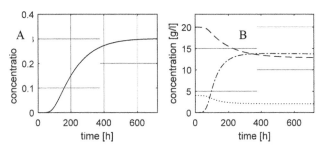

Figure 5: Cyclone concentration of lovastatin (subplot A), cells, lactose and adenine (subplot B)

Please note that no energy integration has been included in the model in view of the fact that reactor temperature is not an issue for the present reaction as reported in the literature (Bizukojc & Ledakowicz, 2007). Besides, the downstream separation technologies employed in the process are isothermal.

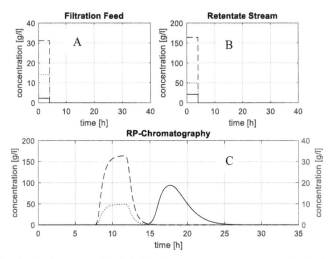

Figure 6: Filtration feed concentration (subplot A), retentate stream concentration (subplot B) and the final chromatogram (Subplot C)

5. Conclusion

It has been successfully demonstrated that such a benchmark simulation has the ability to reproduce component behavior in a fermentation process, therefore representing an alternative to experimental evaluations, which could be time consuming and expensive. Furthermore the benchmark process allows evaluating different scenarios as its flexibility lies in the wide range of operational parameters that can be changed. We do believe the process represents a valid playground to test different control strategies, which would be a future work to be carried out on the presented process flowsheet.

Acknowledgments

This work partially recived financial support from Innovation Fund Denmark through the BIOPRO2 strategic research centre (Grant number 4105-00020B). The project also received funding from the Carlsberg Foundation of Denmark (Grant Number CF17-0403)

References

Benyahia, B., Lakerveld, R., & Barton, P. I. (2012). A Plant-Wide Dynamic Model of a Continuous Pharmaceutical Process. *Industrial & Engineering Chemistry Research, 51*(47), 15393–15412. https://doi.org/10.1021/ie3006319

Bizukojc, M., & Ledakowicz, S. (2007). A macrokinetic modelling of the biosynthesis of lovastatin by Aspergillus terreus. *Journal of Biotechnology, 130*(4), 422–435. https://doi.org/10.1016/j.jbiotec.2007.05.007

Mansouri, S. S., Udugama, I. A., Huusom, J. K., Gernaey, K. V., & Benyahia, B. (2018). A shortcut approach for decision-making and operational analysis of an integrated end-to-end continuous pharmaceutical process (pp. 2107–2112). https://doi.org/10.1016/B978-0-444-64241-7.50346-3

Plumb, K. (2005). Continuous processing in the pharmaceutical industry: Changing the mind set. *Chemical Engineering Research and Design, 83*(6 A), 730–738. https://doi.org/10.1205/cherd.04359

Ramin, P., Mansouri, S. S., Udugama, I. A., Benyahia, B., & Gernaey, K. V. (2018). Modelling continuous pharmaceutical and bio-based processes at plant-wide level: A roadmap towards efficient decision-making. *Chimica Oggi/Chemistry Today, 36*(2), 26–30.

Anton A. Kiss, Edwin Zondervan, Richard Lakerveld, Leyla Özkan (Eds.)
Proceedings of the 29th European Symposium on Computer Aided Process Engineering
June 16th to 19th, 2019, Eindhoven, The Netherlands. © 2019 Elsevier B.V. All rights reserved.
http://dx.doi.org/10.1016/B978-0-128-18634-3.50162-4

Development of the Texas A&M Superfund Research Program Computational Platform for Data Integration, Visualization, and Analysis

Rajib Mukherjee[a,b], Melis Onel[a,b], Burcu Beykal[a,b], Adam T. Szafran[c], Fabio Stossi[c], Michael A. Mancini[c], Lan Zhou[d], Fred A. Wright[e], Efstratios N. Pistikopoulos[a,b,*]

[a] *Artie McFerrin Department of Chemical Engineering, Texas A&M University, College Station, TX*
[b]*Texas A&M Energy Institute, Texas A&M University, College Station, TX*
[c]*Molecular and Cellular Biology, Baylor College of Medicine, Houston, TX*
[d]*Department of Statistics, Texas A&M University, College Station, TX*
[e]*Bioinformatics Research Center, Center for Human Health and the Environment, Department of Biological Sciences, North Carolina State University, Raleigh, NC.*
*stratos@tamu.edu

Abstract

The National Institute of Environmental Health Sciences (NIEHS) Superfund Research Program (SRP) aims to support university-based multidisciplinary research on human health and environmental issues related to hazardous substances and pollutants. The Texas A&M Superfund Research Program comprehensively evaluates the complexities of hazardous chemical mixtures and their potential adverse health impacts due to exposure through a number of multi-disciplinary projects and cores. One of the essential components of the Texas A&M Superfund Research Center is the Data Science Core, which serves as the basis for translating the data produced by the multi-disciplinary research projects into useful knowledge for the community via data collection, quality control, analysis, and model generation. In this work, we demonstrate the Texas A&M Superfund Research Program computational platform, which houses and integrates large-scale, diverse datasets generated across the Center, provides basic visualization service to facilitate interpretation, monitors data quality, and finally implements a variety of state-of-the-art statistical analysis for model/tool development. The platform is aimed to facilitate effective integration and collaboration across the Center and acts as an enabler for the dissemination of comprehensive ad-hoc tools and models developed to address the environmental and health effects of chemical mixture exposure during environmental emergency-related contamination events.

Keywords: Data analytics, data integration, statistical analysis, collaborative networks.

1. Introduction

The risk of chemical contamination and exposure to hazardous chemicals are elevated during and after natural catastrophic events (*i.e.,* hurricanes) due to the increased mobility of many chemical toxicants. In such situations, the rapid and precise examination of potential sources and pathways of chemical contamination becomes essential: (i) for identifying their adverse health impacts and (ii) for delivering solutions to mitigate such adverse effects. To this end, Texas A&M Superfund Research Program (TAMU Superfund Research Center, 2018) aims to build both experimental and computational models, methods and tools through exposomics research and data analysis. The program extensively studies the health, economic and social impacts of hazardous complex chemical mixtures after environmental emergencies with Galveston Bay/Houston Ship Channel area being selected as a case study.

TAMU SRP is a cross-disciplinary program and has a tightly integrated structure which governs four main research projects (two environmental and two biomedical research projects). The two environmental projects, namely Project 1 and 2, focus on understanding dynamic exposure pathways under the conditions of environmental emergencies and designing novel broad-acting sorption materials for reducing bioavailability of contaminants. Project 3 and 4, being the two biomedical projects, are studying *in vitro* and *in vivo* hazard, kinetics and inter-individual variability of responses to chemical mixtures and developing *in vitro* multiplex single-cell assays to detect endocrine disruption potential of mixtures. Each of these projects utilizes various experimental methodologies for detecting, assessing, evaluating and characterizing the effects of complex chemical contaminants including Gas Chromatography-Mass Spectrometry (GC-MS), Ion Mobility-Mass Spectrometry (IM-MS), Inductively Coupled Plasma Mass Spectrometry (ICP-MS), Ultraviolet-Visible Spectroscopy (UV-Vis), high-throughput imaging and image analysis. Hence, these four projects generate large quantities of highly diverse datasets, where their maintenance and analysis require a systematic approach through the development of a computational platform.

In addition to the four main research projects, there are three research supporting cores within the TAMU SRP, one of which is the Data Science Core. The Data Science Core serves as the basis for translating the data produced by the four research projects into useful knowledge for the community via data collection, quality control, analysis, visualization and model generation. This Core functions as a hub that collects, processes and integrates the aforementioned diverse datasets over a computational platform to draw specific conclusions via supervised (*i.e.,* regression, classification) and unsupervised (*i.e.,* clustering) analysis. These techniques are widely used in process systems engineering (PSE) including process monitoring (Onel et al., 2018b) and grey-box optimization (Beykal et al., 2018). In this work, we present the TAMU SRP computational platform which aims to promote collaboration across the Center and facilitate dissemination of methods/data across all projects of the program as well as to the wider community. The computational platform is developed as an online tool that specifically uses a relational database for data storage as well as statistical and machine learning techniques to create decision support models, housing both novel computational methodologies and state-of-the-art data analytics techniques. It establishes an accessible front-end interface for the application of the high-performance models and tools developed during collaborations with individual research projects (Onel et al., 2018a). The details of the computational platform are provided in the following sections where its integration and connection with one of the biomedical projects is demonstrated as a motivating example.

2. Computational Platform

The online computational platform is developed in Python environment, whereas the backend functionalities utilize either R or Python environments. The relational database for storing and sharing data across the Center is based on SQLite. A flow diagram of the platform is shown in Figure 1. The computational platform is developed and implemented in two stages. The first stage entails the dissemination of datasets and methodologies across the Center for supplying a convenient environment for collaboration among all projects. The second stage enables access to the extracted knowledge, models, and tools with the scientific community, government and commercial stakeholders. In this work we will only present the developments of the first stage.

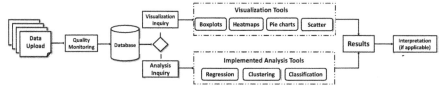

Figure 1. Online computational platform flowchart.

The computational platform first requires a data upload by the user, which is further passed to an initial quality monitoring module. The quality monitoring module checks the dataset for any missing data and/or outliers. Missing data is handled two-fold: (i) Deletion of rows or columns that include missing data, (ii) imputation by k-nearest neighbor (k-NN) methodology (Ramaswamy et al., 2000). This pre-processed data is stored under the relational database for future reference. A summary of this first module is provided as a feedback to the user. Second, the user specifies a type of inquiry, namely visualization and analysis. Currently, four visualization techniques are implemented within the platform including, boxplots, heatmaps, pie charts and scatter plots. Guidelines for selecting the relevant visualization technique is provided online. The generated plots or maps are then displayed on the interface which can be downloaded by the user. Specifically, further interpretation of boxplots, containing the summary of statistics (*i.e.*, median, interquartile range etc.) is provided along with the visuals. Next, the datasets can be analyzed via unsupervised or supervised techniques depending on the purpose of the study. For untargeted analysis, clustering with hierarchical, k-means, and deep learning techniques are utilized. For targeted analysis, where the output of certain experiments is known and used for training models, supervised learning approaches are chosen. Specifically, for the datasets with discrete type of output (or label), classification techniques are used. Current classification techniques include Support Vector Machines (SVM), Random Forest (RF) Algorithm, and logistic regression. Whereas if the output of the dataset is continuous, regression techniques are employed. Here, in addition to SVM and RF Algorithm, interpolation (*i.e.*, Kriging, radial basis functions) and multivariate regression techniques (*i.e.*, linear, quadratic) are employed. The analysis selection is guided by the collaboration between the Data Science Core personnel and individual research projects. Once the data analysis methodology is established for a specific type of data, custom tools are generated and implemented within the platform. This automates the workflow across the Center, minimizes repetitive efforts, thus increasing the overall efficiency.

It is important to note that the large (*i.e.,* exposomics and imaging) datasets generated by the two biomedical research projects under TAMU SRP are in high dimensional space. This necessitates the use of dimensionality reduction techniques along with the aforementioned data analysis methodologies. To this end, numerous dimensionality reduction methodologies are implemented in the computational platform. These include

Principal Component Analysis, Chi-squared test, built-in feature ranking algorithms of RF and in-house developed SVM-based feature selection algorithms (Onel et al., 2018b).

3. Motivating Example

Here, we present a motivating example from TAMU SRP Project 4 to showcase the use of the developed computational platform. This project focuses on understanding the hazardous effects of environmental contaminants and mixtures that may interfere with proper function of the human endocrine system, causing several adverse health effects (*i.e.,* reproductive, developmental, metabolic etc.) due to modulations in hormone nuclear receptors' action. Hence, Project 4 personnel develop single-cell high throughput microscopy experiments with associated image analysis and informatics, thus producing high dimensional imaging data to fingerprint the endocrine disruptor potential of chemicals and environmental mixtures, whereas Data Science Core personnel use the generated data to build predictive models that classifies and quantifies the endocrine disruptor potential. Below, the development of data-driven models that predict potential activity of chemicals on a prototypical target, the estrogen receptor (ER), and their use through the computational platform are described in detail.

In order to establish a framework, 45 known chemical compounds (agonists, antagonists and inactive for the ER) used by the United States Environmental Protection Agency (US EPA) are utilized to determine the effectors of ER action (Judson et al., 2015). The GFP-ERα:PRL-HeLa cell line, and its derivatives, is an engineered model that allows multi-parametric simultaneous measurements of many important features, including, ligand binding, DNA binding, chromatin remodeling and transcriptional output, required for the activation of Estrogen Receptors (ER) (Szafran et al., 2017). This high throughput microscopy assay is used to test the responses to the EPA 45 reference compounds as well as to the control agonist 17β-estradiol (E2) and antagonist 4-hydroxytamoxifen (4OHT). The effect of these test chemicals can broadly be classified three-fold: (i) agonist (which elicits a positive response of the ER signaling pathway – akin to E2), (ii) antagonist (mimicking a response like 4OHT), or (iii) inactive. By treating the cells with a six-point dose-response of these compounds, high throughput imaging data is generated and analyzed. This yields a data matrix of 180 (4 measurements for each 45 compounds) by 70 descriptors (features). Each descriptor considers various aspects of the ER pathway (*i.e.,* Is the ER level changing? Does ER bind to DNA? How much chromatin remodeling happens? etc.). This dataset is later passed to the Data Science Core for further analysis and for modeling the ER disrupting potential of the tested compounds. The details on model generation and step-by-step use of the developed model within the computational platform are provided below.

Step 1 – Data Quality Monitoring: As an initial step, the quality of the received experimental data is inspected by identifying any potential missing data. In this case study, there are no missing data. The complete dataset is analyzed to detect any potential outliers via hierarchical clustering algorithm with complete linkage methodology and Euclidean distance metric. Identification and removal of outliers is essential in order to ensure accurate model development. The results reveal "Reserpine" as an outlier, which has been removed from further analysis (Figure 2).

Step 2 – Normalization: The goal is to classify the compounds based on agonist/antagonist activity. To achieve this, inactive compounds must be separated prior to normalization and model building. This is done by using a threshold for the cell population with a visible nuclear spot, signifying ER-DNA binding. Less than 10% of the cell population, that has a visible nuclear spot, are considered to be inactive and removed from further analysis. Then, the dataset is normalized in order to attain a consistent range per feature. Specifically, the order of magnitude of intensity related measurements significantly differ from measurements derived from nucleus shape. Therefore, normalization is performed by using Equation 1.

$$sample_{normalized} = \frac{sample - median(media)}{median(E2) - median(media)} \qquad (1)$$

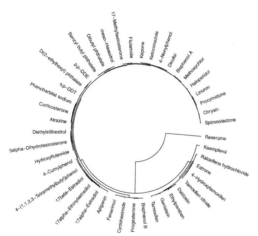

Figure 2. Outlier identification via hierarchical clustering. Reserpine is identified as outlier.

Step 3 – Predictive Modeling & Dimensionality Reduction: Once the data is pre-processed, cleaned from outliers and normalized, various classification algorithms are applied to build predictive models. In this study, RF algorithm is employed for the classification of agonist/antagonist activity and for identifying important descriptors through the built-in feature ranking property (Breiman, 2001). Tuning is performed and optimal number of trees is identified as 500. Final model is then built with the optimal number of trees by using 5-fold cross-validation. The top 10 informative features achieved during modeling are also reported in Table 1. The model accuracy before dimensionality reduction is achieved as 90%, whereas the end-model, the reduced model that use the top 10 informative features, has 92% accuracy.

Step 4 – Automation of Analysis: This end-model is then converted into an executable tool and implemented to the Python based environment of the computational platform.

4. Future directions

Development of the computational platform is an ongoing process. As new data are generated, corresponding tools and models are tailored, updated and incorporated in the platform. Current limitation of the platform is that the analysis only covers the Center projects and datasets. However, access to historical data provided by government agencies is crucial for comparative analysis in TAMU SRP (*e.g.,* ToxCast and Tox21 initiatives). Therefore, additional features will be provided for access to the relevant public data repositories through integration. Finally, one of the main goals of the Data Science Core is to serve as a basis to facilitate TAMU SRP data analysis and understanding. Therefore, training for the use of generated models and tools within the computational platform will be provided in collaboration with the Research Translation and Training Cores.

Table 1. Top 10 informative features for agonist/antagonist classification.

Rank	Measurement	Rank	Measurement
1	Nucleoplasm GFP Pixel Intensity Variance	6	Ratio of Nuclear Spot to Nucleoplasm GFP Intensity
2	Nuclear GFP Pixel Intensity Variance	7	Nuclear Spot GFP Pixel Intensity Variance
3	Nucleoplasm 90th Percentile GFP Pixel Intensity	8	Cytoplasm 75th Percentile GFP Pixel Intensity
4	Nuclear 90th Percentile GFP Pixel Intensity	9	Nuclear Spot 75th Percentile GFP Pixel Intensity
5	Nuclear Spot 90th Percentile GFP Pixel Intensity	10	Cytoplasm 90th Percentile GFP Pixel Intensity

5. Conclusions

In this study, development of a computational platform for the Texas A&M Superfund Research Center is presented. This platform provides on-demand, intuitive access to the custom-made data analysis tools and models developed for the environmental and biomedical projects within the Center. These analysis techniques are applicable to PSE problems. The ultimate goal is to establish an online data analytics services for rapid decision-making during environmental emergencies. This research is funded by U.S. National Institute of Health grant P42 ES027704 and Texas A&M Energy Institute.

References

A.T. Szafran, F. Stossi, M.G. Mancini, C.L. Walker, M.A. Mancini, 2017, Characterizing properties of non-estrogenic substituted bisphenol analogs using high throughput microscopy and image analysis, PloS one, 12(7), e0180141.

B. Beykal, F. Boukouvala, C.A. Floudas, N. Sorek, H. Zalavadia, E. Gildin, 2018, Global Optimization of Grey-Box Computational Systems Using Surrogate Functions and Application to Highly Constrained Oil-Field Operations, Computers & Chemical Engineering, 114, 99-110.

L. Breiman, 2001, Random Forests, Machine Learning, 45, 1, 5-32.

M. Onel, B. Beykal, M. Wang, F.A. Grimm, L. Zhou, F.A. Wright, T.D. Phillips, I. Rusyn, E.N. Pistikopoulos, 2018a, Optimal Chemical Grouping and Sorbent Material Design by Data Analysis, Modeling and Dimensionality Reduction Techniques, Computer Aided Chemical Engineering, 43, 421-426.

M. Onel, C.A. Kieslich, Y.A. Guzman, C.A. Floudas, E.N. Pistikopoulos, 2018b, Big Data Approach to Batch Process Monitoring: Simultaneous Fault Detection and Diagnosis Using Nonlinear Support Vector Machine-based Feature Selection, Computers & Chemical Engineering, 115, 46-63.

R.S. Judson, F.M. Magpantay, V. Chickarmane, C. Haskell, N. Tania, J. Taylor, M. Xia, R. Huang, D.M. Rotroff, D.L. Filer, K.A. Houck, M.T. Martin, N, Sipes, A.M. Richard, K. Mansouri, R.W. Setzer, T.B. Knudsen, K.M. Crofton, R.S. Thomas, 2015, Integrated Model of Chemical Perturbations of a Biological Pathway Using 18 *In Vitro* High-Throughput Screening Assays for the Estrogen Receptor, Toxicological Sciences 148(1), 137-154.

TAMU Superfund Research Center (2018). https://superfund.tamu.edu/ (accessed 9 November 2018).

Anton A. Kiss, Edwin Zondervan, Richard Lakerveld, Leyla Özkan (Eds.)
Proceedings of the 29th European Symposium on Computer Aided Process Engineering
June 16th to 19th, 2019, Eindhoven, The Netherlands. © 2019 Elsevier B.V. All rights reserved.
http://dx.doi.org/10.1016/B978-0-128-18634-3.50163-6

Modelling Paraffin Wax Deposition Using Aspen HYSYS and MATLAB

Ana M. Sousa[a*], Henrique A. Matos[a], Maria J. Pereira[a]

aCERENA, Instituto Superior Técnico, Universidade de Lisboa, Av. Rovisco Pais 1, 1049-001 Lisboa, Portugal

ana.margarida.sousa@tecnico.ulisboa.pt

Abstract

Wax deposition problems are an increasingly important research topic in the oil industry, as wells and pipelines become longer and heavier crude oils are explored. Much has been published within pipelines domain but information about such challenge in wells is much scarcer. Wax deposition is due to the cooling process, which occurs when oil flows from the high-pressure reservoir to the surface. Heat loss, with temperature reduction, induces wax crystallization and the subsequent well plugging. This leads to the decrease of well flowrates, and eventually causes the total blockage.

One of the goals of this work was to determine wax deposition by applying Aspen HYSYS, as a modelling tool and developing a numerical model in Matlab to face some limitations encountered in Aspen HYSYS.

One major accomplishment of the conceived Matlab model was being able to accurately consider internal pipe insulation, the effect of pipe-in-pipe, as well as the underlying geological conditions. Also, two comprehensive engineering solutions, including heating and insulation, were assessed for one oil well with proven wax deposition problems.

In conclusion, Aspen HYSYS is highly recommended for most applications since, beyond showing reliable results, is very versatile, user-friendly and has a vast database of worldwide oils' common properties. However, Aspen HYSYS does not accurately allow esteeming wax precipitation curve, nor the Wax Appearance Temperature, given the oil properties. This is quite a hindrance for wax deposition simulations and leads to the need for experimental data.

Keywords: Wax deposition, Paraffinic oil crudes, Flow Assurance.

1. Introduction

Among the naturally occurring hydrocarbons that compose crude oils are the alkanes, or paraffin hydrocarbons, with the chemical formula C_nH_{2n+2}. Groups of normal paraffins, with 16 or more carbon atoms, form crystalline solid substances (designated wax), when the fluid temperature decreases below the wax appearance temperature (WAT). As cooling proceeds, the dissolved paraffins align together and bind a solid crystalline wax structure. Such wax deposits reduce the net internal diameter and consequently affect the crude oil production (Averbuch, 2006).
Developing improved computational models can help to predict upcoming operational problems, by allowing to take preventive measures so that the losses caused by the well shutting down can be avoided (Coutinho et al., 2004).
This article will focus on the prediction of the wax precipitation from crude oils.

2. Methodology

Modelling wax deposition is a complex endeavour because it involves several disciplines, such as: chemistry, thermodynamics and fluid mechanics. In this case, Aspen HYSYS and Matlab were applied to perform the simulations. The modelling approach encompassed the following steps:

i. Experimental data was collected, so that a broad database of wax deposition measurements was synthesized. Then, using Aspen HYSYS, the experimental conditions were simulated;

ii. The results were compared with the gathered experimental data. A critical evaluation was performed, validating Aspen HYSYS models;

iii. Once observing Aspen HYSYS software limitations for the analysis purpose, a Matlab model was considered to overcome them;

iv. Matlab model was applied to a real case of a well. Finally, the model was used to assess a wide range of possible engineering strategies for avoiding or controlling wax deposition.

3. Aspen HYSYS simulation

3.1. Fluid characterization

Aspen HYSYS was used to simulate 8 published experimental data sets, presented in Rosvold's work (2008). The pipeline system, tested in this experiment, was composed by a horizontal pipe, with 5.31 m of length and an inner diameter of 51.70 mm. The temperature around this pipeline was kept constant and equals to 10 °C. In these experiments, a condensate from the North Sea was used and its wax appearance temperature was 45 °C. The characteristics of each experiment and the wax precipitation curve are referred in the Table 1.

Table 1 – Rosvold's experiments data (Rosvold, 2008)

Lab. tests	Flow rate (m^2/h)	Inlet temp. (°C)	Wax precipitation curve
A	5	20	
B	10	20	
C	15	20	
D	21	20	
E	25	20	
F	21	15	
G	21	30	
H	21	40	

To evaluate the wax deposition behaviour in time, as function of the flow rate and the oil inlet temperature, the graphs shown below were drawn considering the experimental data (Rosvold, 2008).

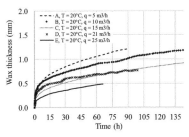
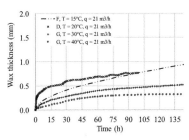

Figure 1 – Temporal evolution of wax deposition thickness for different flow rates and inlet temperatures.

For the same oil inlet temperature, the higher the flow rates are, the lower the wax deposition thickness will be. Maintaining the flow rate constant, the general tendency is to have fewer wax deposits as the temperature is higher.

3.2. Process flowsheet diagram

For this case, the steady-state model was performed in Aspen HYSYS, using the process flowsheet presented in Figure 2.

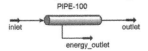

Figure 2 – Process flowsheet to simulate the wax deposition inside a pipe, using Aspen HYSYS

HYSYS contains a tool called pipe segment model, in which two of the following variables are required: inlet pressure, outlet pressure, or flow rate. Once two of these parameters are specified, the third will be computed. Furthermore, geometrical inputs need to be included, such as: length, elevation change, pipe diameter and material.

To calculate pressure and temperature, HYSYS uses an iterative routine to estimate these parameters. Once the inner pressure loop has converged, the outlet temperature is calculated, using the Eq. (1):

$$Q = U \times A \times \Delta T \tag{1}$$

Where, Q is the amount of heat transferred (W), U is the overall heat transfer coefficient $(W/(m^2 \cdot K))$, A is the outer heat transfer (m^2) and ΔT is the log mean temperature difference (K).

The wax equilibrium calculations were performed using the AEA model, given by the Eq. (2):

$$\ln K_i = \frac{\Delta h_i^f}{RT}\left(1 - \frac{T}{T_i^f}\right) + \frac{\Delta C_p}{R}\left[1 - \frac{T_i^f}{T} + \ln\frac{T_i^f}{T}\right] + \int_0^P \frac{V_i^L - V_i}{RT}\,\partial P \tag{2}$$

Where, K_i is the equilibrium constant, which is the ratio of concentrations of a particular component in the solid and liquid phase, Δh_i^f is the enthalpy of melting, R is the gas constant, T is the temperature, T_i^f is the melting temperature, ΔC_p is the heat capacity difference between solid and liquid, V_i^L is the molar volume, and P is the pressure.

Peng and Robinson Equation of State has been selected for its accuracy and the simplicity (Luo et al., 2014).

3.3. Analyses and Simulation Results

These eight experiments were simulated in Aspen HYSYS to understand the software ability to forecast the wax deposition in real scenarios. The results obtained were synthetized in the Figure 3.

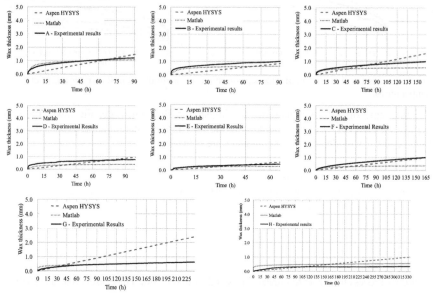

Figure 3 – Aspen HYSYS and MATLAB simulation results and the Rosvold's experimental data

The maximum deviation between the experimental data and the simulated results happened in the experiment G. In this case, the relation between the wax deposition thickness and the inner radius obtained in laboratory experiments was 2.5%, while for the simulated results this relation was 9.3%.

A sensibility test was performed to understand the influence of the overall heat transfer coefficient (OHTC) on the wax deposition thickness. As it was expected for higher OHTC, the estimated wax deposition will be higher. Using the OHTC automatically determined by the software, the results from the simulations and the experimental differed no more than 6 mm.

Doing this sensibility test, it was possible to perceive that Aspen HYSYS has some limitations, namely, the impossibility to include the effect of internal pipe insulation, since only an external one is allowed.

The influence of pressure on the paraffin deposition is negligence when modelling this system, because the fluid pressure was not substantial. Nevertheless, this parameter can be relevant in other cases (Coutinho et al., 2004).

4. MATLAB simulation

4.1. Description and Methodology

MATLAB model most significant accomplishments are the ability to accurately consider internal pipe insulation, the effect of pipe-in-pipe (tubing plus casing), as well as the heat transfer for different geological layers around the well. These are some of the aspects that HYSYS does not allow simulating, yet. The procedure developed in MATLAB to determine the wax deposition inside the well is presented in Figure 4.

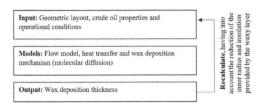

Figure 4 – Methodology to determine the wax deposition

Molecular diffusion, given by Eq. (3), was the chosen mechanism to model wax deposition, due to its most wide acceptance in the bibliography (Huang et al., 2015).

$$\frac{dm_i}{dt} = -\rho \times D_i \times A \times \frac{dw_i}{dT}\frac{dT}{dr} \tag{3}$$

Where, m_i is the mass, D_i is the effective diffusion coefficient, A is the deposition area, w_i is the weight fraction, r is the radial distance and i is the component i.

In order to consider the effect of insulation provided by the wax deposit layer, Eq. (4) was used for computing the overall heat transfer coefficient, U_{in} (W/(m².°C)):

$$\frac{1}{U_{in}} = \frac{r_{in}}{r_{deposit}}\frac{1}{h_{in}} + \frac{r_{in}}{k_{deposit}}ln\left(\frac{r_{in}}{r_{deposit}}\right) + \frac{r_{in}}{k_{pipe}}ln\left(\frac{r_{out}}{r_{in}}\right) + \frac{r_{in}}{r_{out}}\frac{1}{h_{out}} \tag{4}$$

In this equation, h_{in} is the inside convective heat transfer coefficient (W/(m².°C)), k_{pipe} is the thermal conductivity of the steel pipe, $k_{deposit}$ is thermal conductivity of waxes deposit (W/(m.°C)), h_{out} is the outside convective heat transfer coefficient (W/(m².°C)), $r_{deposit}$ is the distance between the centre and the deposit (m), r_{in} and r_{out} are the inner and outer pipe radius, respectively (m).

4.2. Fluid characteristics

This model considers fluid properties provided by Aspen HYSYS, which were determined by the pseudo-compounds estimated through the TBP curves (Cuadros et al., 2009). Viscosity laboratorial tests were also used to further tune the fluid model.

4.3. Analysis and Simulation results

Firstly, the results from MATLAB model were validated trough the comparison with Rosvold's experimental data. Estimated thicknesses are quite similar to those obtained experimentally, as presented in the Figure 3. There is, however, a slight tendency (of 0.6 mm, in maximum) to underestimate the thickness at the beginning and to overestimate (by no more than 0.3 mm, in maximum) as time progresses. The same MATLAB model was used to simulate one productive well. Also, two comprehensive engineering solutions, including heating and insulation, were assessed for one oil well with proven wax deposition problems. The geometric characteristics of the oil well and the simulated profiles are shown in the Figure 5.

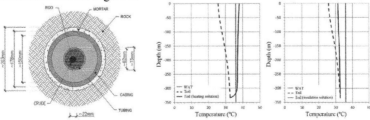

Figure 5 – Well cross section characteristics and MATLAB simulation results for two scenarios

Assessing both scenarios, it is possible to conclude that the only one capable of maintaining crude oil temperature above the WAT is the heating solution. However, this technique can eventually damage the geologic formation (Newberry and Barker, 2013).

5. Conclusions

In conclusion, Aspen HYSYS is highly recommended for most applications since, beyond showing reliable results, is very versatile, user-friendly and has a vast database of worldwide oils' common properties. However, Aspen HYSYS does not allow esteeming wax precipitation curve, nor the wax appearance temperature, given the oil properties. This is quite a hindrance for wax deposition simulations and leads to the need for experimental data. The proposed methodology combines accurate and highly reliable Aspen HYSYS modelling with versatile Matlab programming to provide a novel approach for wax deposition estimation in wells. Allowing the consideration of internal pipe insulation, pipe-in-pipe and the different geological layers around the well effects into the numerical simulations is regarded as a major advantage for this proposal.

On the drawbacks side, both the Aspen HYSYS and the conceived Matlab model do not account for the effect of pressure on the wax precipitation curve nor the inside well pumping system effect onto the wax deposition dynamics. Thus, those are the model current restrictions. While conceived models' reliability and truthfulness has been observed against experimental data where the aforementioned restrictions do not play a major role, further developments on such matters are required for increasing the model applicability towards cases where pumping systems are used and significant pressure in the well lower length is observed. Such developments are ongoing.

6. Acknowledgements

Authors would like to acknowledge Partex Oil&Gas and FCT support through the project UID/ECI/04028/2013 and the PhD grant number SFRH/BD/131005/2017.

References

Averbuch, D., 2006. Recent developments in the risk management of offshore production systems. Comput. Aided Chem. Eng. 21, 39–44. https://doi.org/10.1016/S1570-7946(06)80024-6

Coutinho, J.A.P., Pauly, J., Daridon, J., 2004. Chapter 10 : Modelling Phase Equilibria in Systems with Organic Solid Solutions. Comput. Aided Prop. Estim. Process Prod. Des. 229–249. https://doi.org/10.1016/S1570-7946(04)80012-9

Cuadros, J.F., Maciel Filho, R., Maciel, M.R.W., Benedito Batistella, C., Medina, L.C., 2009. Evaluation and Application of the Extended TBP Curves in Processing and Refining of Heavy Oil Fractions. Comput. Aided Chem. Eng. 26, 195–200. https://doi.org/10.1016/S1570-7946(09)70033-1

Huang, Z., Zheng, S., Fogler, H.S., 2015. Wax deposition: experimental characterizations, theoretical modeling, and field practices.

Luo, X., Mistry, K., Okezue, C., Wang, M., Cooper, R., Oko, E., Field, J., 2014. Process Simulation and Analysis for CO2 Transport Pipeline Design and Operation – Case Study for the Humber Region in the UK, Computer Aided Chemical Engineering. Elsevier. https://doi.org/10.1016/B978-0-444-63455-9.50107-0

Newberry, M.E., Barker, K.M., 2013. Formation Damage Prevention Through the Control of Paraffin and Asphaltene Deposition. SPE. https://doi.org/10.2118/13796-MS

Rosvold, K., 2008. Wax deposition models. Master Thesis. NTNU.

Anton A. Kiss, Edwin Zondervan, Richard Lakerveld, Leyla Özkan (Eds.)
Proceedings of the 29th European Symposium on Computer Aided Process Engineering
June 16th to 19th, 2019, Eindhoven, The Netherlands. © 2019 Elsevier B.V. All rights reserved.
http://dx.doi.org/10.1016/B978-0-128-18634-3.50164-8

Optimal distributed load allocation and resource utilisation in evaporation plants

Maria P. Marcos[a,b,*], Jose L. Pitarch[a], Christian Jasch[c] and Cesar de Prada[a,b]

[a]*Systems Engineering and Automatic Control Department, EII, Universidad de Valladolid. C/ Real de Burgos S/N, Valladolid, 47011, Spain.*
[b]*Sustainable Processes Institute (IPS), Universidad de Valladolid.*
[c]*Lenzing AG. Werkstraße 2, Lenzing, 4860, Austria*
* maria.marcos@autom.uva.es

Abstract

This work aims to optimise the operation of an evaporation network with shared resources in real time. The goal is minimising the resource utilisation (live steam and cooling water) while satisfying a set of operational constrains. Hence, problems of optimal load allocation of feeds to plants and cooling-water distribution among them arise. The work bases on plants surrogate models, experimentally obtained, and analyses different formulation alternatives of the optimisation from the practical point of view: centralised vs distributed approaches. In particular for the distributed approach, we propose a problem decomposition which allows us to solve the problem in two iterative ways: 1) as two independent optimisations or 2) via price-coordination schemes.

Keywords: decomposition methods, RTO, evaporation network, resource efficiency

1. Description of the case study

Manufacture of viscose fibers in Lenzing AG bases on a continuous spinning process where cellulose pulp transforms into very thin threads. This process performs in an acid bath ("spinbath" from now on) which is progressively degraded. Consequently, it must be continuously recovered. Therefore, a side evaporation process is performed in parallel to remove part of water. For this task, an evaporation network of 15 plants is available to serve in 5 different types of spinbath, where a single plant is formed by several equipment. See Pitarch et al. (2017b) for a deeper description.

Plants efficiency depends on several factors: the evaporation flow removed from the spinbath (plant load) EC, the spinbath temperature T and circulating flow F_s, the fouling state in the heat exchangers and the performance of the cooling system (see Figure 1a). In particular, the more cooling water (shared resource) is provided to the surface condenser, the less live steam consumption (utility) is needed to achieve the evaporation setpoint.

Denote the *specific steam consumption* (SSC) by the live steam usage per unit of evaporated water (Pitarch et al., 2017a). Then, the *absolute steam consumption* (ASC) in each plant is computed by $ASC = SSC \cdot EC$.

This research is funded by the European Union's Horizon 2020 research and innovation programme under grant agreement No. 723575. The first author also acknowledges the European Social Fund and the "Consejería de Educación de la Junta de Castilla y León".

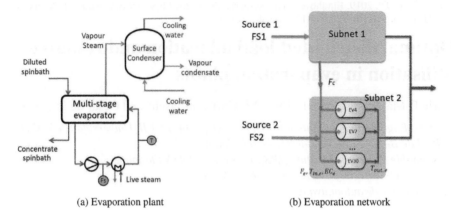

(a) Evaporation plant   (b) Evaporation network

Figure 1: Systems simplified schemes.

Plant surrogate models were developed to estimate the *SSC* in Kalliski et al. (2019), which, after straightforward manipulations, is found to depend on *EC* and on the cooling capacity of the surface condenser C_{pow}, as shown in (1). The cooling system performance is also modelled experimentally: the outlet cooling-water temperature of the condensers T_{out} is estimated by a polynomial function up to degree 3 on the cooling-water flow F_{w} and affine in its inlet temperature T_{in}, as proposed in (Marcos et al., 2018):

$$SSC = \beta_2 \cdot EC + \beta_1 \cdot C_{\text{pow}} + \beta_0; \qquad C_{\text{pow}} = 4.18 \cdot F_{\text{w}}(T_{\text{out}} - T_{\text{in}})/3600 \qquad (1)$$

$$T_{\text{out}} = \alpha_0 + \alpha_1 F_{\text{w}} + \alpha_2 F_{\text{w}}^2 + \alpha_3 F_{\text{w}}^3 + T_{\text{in}} \qquad (2)$$

Here, $\theta = \{\beta_0, \beta_1, \beta_2, \alpha_0, \alpha_1, \alpha_2, \alpha_3\}$ are experimental regression parameters.

According to the physical layout of the evaporation network, the plants can be grouped in two subnets, each one directly supplied by an independent water source. The water distribution among plants is done in parallel and, additionally, the exceeding water in Subnet 1 (F_{c}) can go to Subnet 2 but not backwards (see Figure 1b). Further details on the evaporation network can be found in Palacín et al. (2018); Marcos et al. (2018).

2. Problem formulation

The objective is to allocate feeds to plants and distribute the cooling-water in the network at minimum cost. This cost is a trade-off between the usage of resources: live steam and cooling water, times their respective "prices" (P_s and P_w). Three sets of decision variables are defined: $X_{e,p} \in \{0,1\}$ to link product p to plant e, $EC_{e,p} \in \mathbb{R}$ defining the evaporation flow of p to be achieved in plant e, and $F_{\text{w } e} \in \mathbb{R}$ defining the water sent to plant e. Further, an additional variable $F_{\text{c}} \in \mathbb{R}$ indicates the flow of water sent from Subnet 1 (SN1) to Subnet 2 (SN2). Hence, for a given set of $e \in \mathcal{E}$ evaporation plants that have to process $p \in \mathcal{P}$ spinbaths, the centralised formulation of the optimisation problem is:

$$\min_{X_{e,p}, EC_{e,p}, F_{\text{w } e}, F_{\text{c}}} J = \sum_{e}^{\mathcal{E}} \left(\sum_{p}^{\mathcal{P}} ASC_{e,p} \cdot P_s + F_{\text{w } e} \cdot P_w \right) \qquad (3a)$$

$$\text{s.t.:} \quad \sum_{p}^{\mathcal{P}} X_{e,p} \leq 1 \quad \forall e \in \mathcal{E}; \qquad X_{e,p} = 0 \quad (e,p) \in \mathcal{N} \qquad (3b)$$

$$\sum_{e}^{\mathscr{E}} EC_{e,p} \geq SP_p \quad \forall p \in \mathscr{P} \tag{3c}$$

$$\sum_{e}^{\mathscr{E}_{SN1}} F_{w\ ee} + F_c \leq F_{S1}; \quad \sum_{e}^{\mathscr{E}_{SN2}} F_{w\ e} - F_c \leq F_{S2}; \quad F_c \geq 0 \tag{3d}$$

$$\underline{EC}_{e,p} \cdot X_{e,p} \leq EC_{e,p} \leq \overline{EC}_{e,p} \cdot X_{e,p} \quad \forall e \in \mathscr{E}, \ \forall p \in \mathscr{P} \tag{3e}$$

$$\sum_{p}^{\mathscr{P}} X_{e,p} \cdot \underline{F}_{w\ e} \leq F_{w\ e} \leq \overline{F}_{w\ e} \cdot \sum_{p}^{\mathscr{P}} X_{e,p} \quad \forall e \in \mathscr{E} \tag{3f}$$

$$T_{\text{out}\ e} \leq T_{\text{max}} + (1 - \sum_{p}^{\mathscr{P}} X_{e,p}) \cdot M \quad \forall e \in \mathscr{E} \tag{3g}$$

Where the sets $\mathscr{E}_{SN1}$ and $\mathscr{E}_{SN2}$ ($\mathscr{E} = \mathscr{E}_{SN1} \cup \mathscr{E}_{SN2}$) include the plants belonging to SN1 and SN2 respectively, the set $\mathscr{N}$ represents connections between some plants and spinbaths that are forbidden due to the factory layout, and M is a big enough number.

The problem constraints are: (3b) each plant can only serve in one spinbath loop at a time; (3c) total evaporation demands per spinbath (SP_p) have to be fulfilled; (3d) total water consumption in each subnet has to be lower than the available at the sources (F_s), considering that exceeding water can go from SN1 to SN2 but not backwards; (3e)-(3f) evaporation and water flows are bounded and; (3g) outlet water temperatures have to be lower than a limit (T_{max}), stated by the environmental regulation.

The presence of discrete and continuous variables as well as the nonlinear dependency of (3a) and (2) on them, makes (3) become an MINLP problem.

3. Problem decomposition

In order to avoid the issues that commonly arise with MINLP (slow convergence, high computational demands, etc.), we propose a suitable decomposition of (3) in two local optimisation subproblems, according to the physical layout of the evaporation network. In fact, the overall equipment can be grouped in two sets or networks: 1) the spinbath allocation one, composed by the evaporation plants and the spinbath loops themselves, and 2) the water distribution from the sources to the respective plant surface condensers. Hence, a first local problem can handle the plants load allocation whereas a second one optimises the water distribution. By this decomposition, only the magnitudes EC and C_{pow} are shared between problems 1) and 2).

1. Load-allocation problem:

$$\min_{X_{e,p}, EC_{e,p}} J_1 = \sum_{e}^{\mathscr{E}} \sum_{p}^{\mathscr{P}} SSC_{e,p} \cdot EC_{e,p} \cdot P_s \quad \text{s.t.:} \quad (3b), (3c), (3e) \tag{4}$$

In this way, (4) is a mixed integer quadratic programming (MIQP) problem, provided that C_{pow} in (1) is assumed known.

2. Cooling-water distribution problem:

$$\min_{F_{w\ e}, F_c} J_2 = \sum_{e}^{\mathscr{E}} \left(SSC_e \cdot \sum_{p}^{\mathscr{P}} EC_{e,p} \cdot P_s + F_{w\ e} \cdot P_w \right) \quad \text{s.t.:} \quad (3d), (3f), (3g) \tag{5}$$

Thus, assuming that the load allocation ($EC_{e,p}$) is known, (5) is an non linear programming (NLP) problem.

Now, we can solve the original problem in two iterative ways: sequentially as two fully independent optimisations, or in a price-coordination fashion. See next section.

4. Implementation

The above formulated optimisation problems (3), (4) and (5) are coded in Pyomo (Hart et al., 2017). The centralised version (3) uses Bonmin as MINLP solver (Bonami et al., 2008), whereas Gurobi Optimization (2018) is used to solve the MIQP (4) and Ipopt (Wächter and Biegler, 2006) to solve the NLP (5). In order to implement the decomposition approach in an iterative fashion, we propose the following.

4.1. Sequential approach

Take $C_{\text{pow } e}$ as known (computed by (1)-(2) and from given flows $F_{\text{w } e}$) and solve (4). Then, from the obtained solution, take the values of $EC_{e,p}$ and solve (5), getting a new set of values $F_{\text{w } e}$ to compute the $C_{\text{pow } e}$ and so on. The procedure is formalised in:

Algorithm 1 Sequential optimisation

1: Compute the $C_{\text{pow } e}$ from current (measured) $F_{\text{w } e}, T_{\text{out } e}, T_{\text{in}}$ and set $\varepsilon = 1$
2: **while** $\varepsilon > 0.001$ **do**
3:      Solve (4) and save the computed allocation $EC_{e,p}$
4:      Solve (5) using the $EC_{e,p}$ from Step 3 and get a water distribution $F_{\text{w } e}, T_{\text{out } e}$
5:      Compute $\varepsilon = \sum_e^{\mathscr{E}} \left\| C_{\text{pow } e} - 4.18 F_{\text{w } e} \cdot (T_{\text{out } e} - T_{\text{in}})/3600 \right\|_2^2$
6:      Update $C_{\text{pow } e} = 4.18 F_{\text{w } e} \cdot (T_{\text{out } e} - T_{\text{in}})/3600$ with values from Step 4

4.2. Distributed approach

In a distributed fashion, we need to decouple problems (4) and (5) to allow a "true" parallel implementation. Thus, we make use of the well-known Lagrangean or price-driven decomposition approaches (Cheng et al., 2007).

Indeed, now $C_{\text{pow } e}$ will be also *local* decision variables in (4) and EC_e will be so in (5) as well[1]. Then, we have to add a *coordination* layer to progressively force both sets of magnitudes to be equal in both local optimisations (shared constraints). As usual in Lagrangean decomposition, these constraints will be added as a penalty in the respective objective functions:

$$J_1 = \sum_e^{\mathscr{E}} \left(\sum_p^{\mathscr{P}} SSC_{e,p} \cdot EC_{e,p} \cdot P_s + \frac{1}{2} \left(p_{11e}(C_{\text{pow } e} - \mathbf{C}^*_{\text{pow } e})^2 + p_{12e}(\sum_p^{\mathscr{P}} EC_{e,p} - \mathbf{EC}^*_e)^2) \right) \right) \quad (6)$$

$$J_2 = \sum_e^{\mathscr{E}} \left(SSC_e \cdot EC_e \cdot P_s + F_{\text{w } e} \cdot P_w + \frac{1}{2} \left(p_{21e}(C_{\text{pow } e} - \mathbf{C}^*_{\text{pow } e})^2 + p_{22e}(EC_e - \mathbf{EC}^*_e)^2) \right) \right) \quad (7)$$

---
[1]Note that variables EC_e equivalently replace $\sum_p^{\mathscr{P}} EC_{e,p}$ in (5) to reduce the problem size.

Where $p_{ije} \in \mathbb{R}^+$ are the *shadow prices* for "resource" utilisation and $\mathbf{R}^* := \{\mathbf{C}^*_{\text{pow } e}, \mathbf{EC}^*_e\}$ are the reference values, computed somehow from the local solutions of both optimisations in in the previous iteration. In this way, both problems will be managed by a co-ordinator which, in each iteration k, will receive the values got for the shared variables $R_e := \{C_{\text{pow } e}, EC_e\}$, and it will update the prices as well as the reference values for the next iteration $k+1$ according to the following rules:

$$p_{ije}^{[k+1]} = p_{ije}^{[k]} + (R_{ije}^{[k]} - \mathbf{R}^{*[k]})^2 \cdot \mu^{[k]}; \quad R_{ije} \in R, \ \mathbf{R}^* \in R \tag{8}$$

$$\mu^{[k+1]} = \mu^{[k]} \cdot \lambda; \quad \lambda > 1 \tag{9}$$

$$\mathbf{C}_{\text{pow } e}^{*[k+1]} = C_{\text{pow } e}^{[k]}(2); \quad \mathbf{EC}_e^{*[k+1]} = EC_e^{[k]}(1) \tag{10}$$

Where notation $R_e^{[k]}(i)$ denotes the values of variables R_e, solution of subproblem i at iteration k. Progressive hedging (Rockafellar and Wets, 1991) is used in (9) to update the factor μ in each iteration, via the user-defined parameter λ. The procedure to solve the distributed optimisation is summarized below.

Algorithm 2 Distributed optimisation

1: Set $\mathbf{R}^*$ to the current values measured from the plants and $p_{ije} = \varepsilon = 0.1$
2: **while** $\varepsilon > 0.001$ **do**
3:     Solve subproblems (4) and (5), and get new values for R_{ije}
4:     Compute $\varepsilon = \left\| R_{ije} - \mathbf{R}^* \right\|_2^2$
5:     Update prices p_{ije} and references $\mathbf{R}^*$ with (8)-(10)

Of course, due to the non-convex nature of the problem, global optimality is not guaranteed in either of the implementations, centralised or distributed.

5. Results and discussion

For the sake of comparison/analysis, we have solved the problem from a particular network situation following the three presented ways. Table 1 shows a brief summary.

Table 1: Optimised cost and computational effort for the 3 approaches.

	Total CPU Time (s)	Optimal cost (€/h)	Iterations
Centralised	29.64	962.82	-
Sequential	0.89	964.81	3
Distributed	1.73	964.33	6

We can conclude that the three approaches are able to reach nearly the same (local) optimal solution[2]. However, as expected, the centralised problem elapses more time to reach the solution. This is not a major issue in this application (the execution period for real-time optimisation is about 30 min.) but, it will be so if the problem grows by considering fouling predictions over time or by including more parts of the factory (the water network is larger and also serves to other processes, and there is a heat-recovery network which also interacts with the evaporation one).

---

[2]Values $p_{ije}^{[0]} = 0.1$, $\mu^{[0]} = 1$ and $\lambda = 1000$ were set for the distributed approach.

6. Conclusions

In this work we addressed a medium-scale real-time optimisation problem ($\sim$200 variables, it depends on the approach) on resource efficiency in an industrial evaporation network with shared resources. The proposed approaches will support the operators to take better decisions in real time, thus, improving the operation of the overall network: product-plant allocation and water distribution to the cooling systems.

The plant models are incorporated in three different optimisation schemes, analysing the convenience of the decomposition approaches vs the centralised one. In this case study, the three approaches solve the problem in acceptable CPU time for real-time purposes, although the iterative sequential approach has arisen as the most efficient one. The key is the proposed decomposition for the original centralised problem, which allows us to formulate two effortless independent problems (MIQP and NLP), solved efficiently by modern optimisation algorithms.

Apparently, the price-coordination approach does not have any advantage here: the optimal cost is slightly higher than the one reached by the centralised and it elapses double time than the sequential. This is because the centralised problem is not so large-scale, many constraints are affine in the decision variables, and the advantages of parallel computation cannot be exploited with just two local optimisation subproblems. Nevertheless, this approach will clearly beat the other two if the problem is extended to consider uncertainty in an explicitly way via, for instance, two-stage stochastic optimisation.

References

P. Bonami, L. T. Biegler, A. R. Conn, G. Cornuéjols, I. E. Grossmann, C. D. Laird, J. Lee, A. Lodi, F. Margot, N. Sawaya, A. Wächter", 2008. An algorithmic framework for convex mixed integer nonlinear programs. Discrete Optimization 5 (2), 186–204.

R. Cheng, J. Forbes, W. Yip, 2007. Price-driven coordination method for solving plant-wide mpc problems. Journal of Process Control 17 (5), 429 – 438.

L. L. C. Gurobi Optimization, 2018. Gurobi optimizer reference manual. http://www.gurobi.com.

W. E. Hart, C. D. Laird, J.-P. Watson, D. L. Woodruff, G. A. Hackebeil, B. L. Nicholson, J. D. Siirola, 2017. Pyomo–optimization modeling in python, 2nd Edition. Vol. 67. Springer Science & Business Media.

M. Kalliski, J. L. Pitarch, C. Jasch, C. de Prada, 2019. Apoyo a la toma de decisión en una red de evaporadores industriales. Revista Iberoamericana de Automática e Informática industrial 16 (1), 26–35.

M. P. Marcos, J. L. Pitarch, C. de Prada, C. Jasch, Oct 2018. Modelling and real-time optimisation of an industrial cooling-water network. In: 2018 22nd International Conference on System Theory, Control and Computing (ICSTCC). pp. 591–596.

C. G. Palacín, J. L. Pitarch, C. Jasch, C. A. Méndez, C. de Prada, 2018. Robust integrated production-maintenance scheduling for an evaporation network. Computers & Chemical Eng. 110, 140 – 151.

J. L. Pitarch, C. G. Palacín, C. de Prada, B. Voglauer, G. Seyfriedsberger, 2017a. Optimisation of the resource efficiency in an industrial evaporation system. Journal of Process Control 56, 1–12.

J. L. Pitarch, C. G. Palacín, A. Merino, C. de Prada, 2017b. Optimal operation of an evaporation process. In: H. G. Bock, H. X. Phu, R. Rannacher, J. P. Schlöder (Eds.), Modeling, Simulation and Optimization of Complex Processes HPSC 2015. Springer International Publishing, Cham, pp. 189–203.

R. T. Rockafellar, R. J.-B. Wets, 1991. Scenarios and policy aggregation in optimization under uncertainty. Mathematics of operations research 16 (1), 119–147.

A. Wächter, L. T. Biegler, Mar 2006. On the implementation of an interior-point filter line-search algorithm for large-scale nonlinear programming. Mathematical Programming 106 (1), 25–57.

Anton A. Kiss, Edwin Zondervan, Richard Lakerveld, Leyla Özkan (Eds.)
Proceedings of the 29th European Symposium on Computer Aided Process Engineering
June 16th to 19th, 2019, Eindhoven, The Netherlands. © 2019 Elsevier B.V. All rights reserved.
http://dx.doi.org/10.1016/B978-0-128-18634-3.50165-X

Modelling and optimal operation of a natural gas fired natural draft heater

Richard Yentumi[a,b], Bogdan Dorneanu[b], Harvey Arellano-Garcia*[b,c]

[a]Department of Engineering & Maintenance, Ghana National Gas Company, Accra, Ghana

[b]Department of Chemical & Process Engineering, University of Surrey, Guildford, United Kingdom

[c]LS Prozess- und Anlagentechnik, Brandenburgische Technische Universität Cottbus-Senftenberg, Cottbus, Germany

h.arellano-garcia@surrey.ac.uk

Abstract

Current industrial trends promote reduction of material and energy consumption of fossil fuel burning, and energy-intensive process equipment. It is estimated that approximately 75% of the energy consumption in hydrocarbon processing facilities is used by such equipment as fired heater, hence even small improvements in the energy conservation may lead to significant savings [1, 2]. In this work, a mathematical modelling and optimisation study is undertaken using gPROMS® ProcessBuilder® to determine the optimal operating conditions of an existing API 560 Type-E vertical-cylindrical type natural draft fired heater, in operation at the Atuabo Gas Processing Plant (GPP), in the Western Region of Ghana. It is demonstrated that the optimisation results in significant reduction of fuel gas consumption and operational costs.

Keywords: fired heater, tubular heater, mathematical modelling, optimisation, gPROMS.

1. Introduction

Fired heaters, also commonly called furnaces, are a primary source of thermal energy for process heating operations in petroleum refining and chemical plants. They have been studied extensively, both experimentally and theoretically, and previous work [1-3] draws attention to the need of conserve energy, improve energy efficiency and reduce carbon emissions. Notably, most fired heaters models from literature are lumped parameter models with steady-state assumptions, mainly due to the complex thermodynamic mechanisms making the problem computationally expensive to solve [1-3]. For instance, longitudinal and radial variations or temperature gradients of the hot flue gases along the vertical height of the fired heater are normally ignored. The novel approach adopted for this work involves the distributed parameter system modelling of the temperature profiles in the tubular coils and the heat transfer fluid (HTF). The resulting 'white-box' model may serve as basis for conducting simulation studies to aid decision-making and to identify the best operating conditions within the specified constraints that minimise the operational costs. The model is applied to a 15.8 MW fired heater (H600) in operation at the GPP. The total heat input is supplied by the combustion reaction of fuel gas and combustion air occurring in 8 sets of floor mounted, upwards firing, gas only pre-mix main burners. A fuel gas-fired pilot is also supplied to each set of main burners. Aside the need to improve efficiency, significant deviations from the desired HTF supply temperature have on many occasions hampered smooth operation. Currently, there is no validated model of H600 to aid monitoring of thermal efficiency, to identify areas for process improvements and to aid trouble-shooting of process deviations. Furthermore, the current temperature control scheme has been ineffective at rejecting disturbances such as changes in fuel gas pressure.

2. Mathematical model

The mathematical model is applied for each section of H600 (Fig.1), namely convection (CS), shield (SS) and radiant section (RS). A 1D tube coil running through the RS, SS and CS is considered. The axial variation is related to the tube wall and the HTF temperatures, while the flue gas temperature along the sectionalised vertical height of the heater is lumped. The tubes in the SS are assumed isolated from the RS. All tube coils are uniformly heated. The combustion process is assumed to be steady-flow and the CO_2, N_2 and other non-hydrocarbon components of the fuel are ignored in combustion reaction calculations. Key geometrical characteristics of H600 are summarised in Table1.

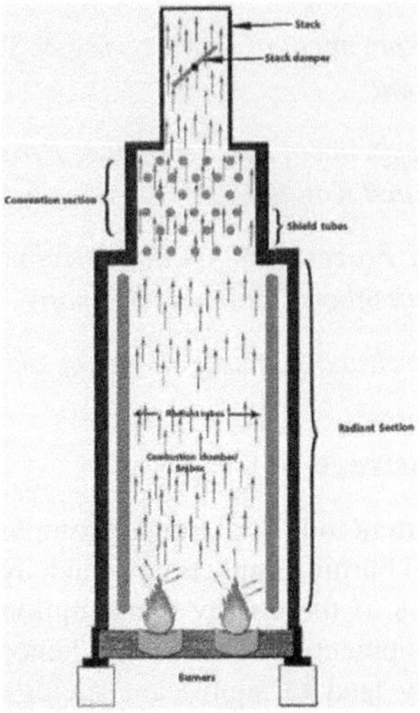

Fig.1: The distinct sections in a box-type style fired heater

Table1: Geometry of the fired heater

Parameter	Radiant section	Shield section	Convection section
Number of tubes	88	24	72
Overall length [m]	138.69	21.8	62.94
Outside tube diameter [mm]	114.3	114.3	114.3
Effective tube length [m]	12.192	6.245	6.245
Cold plane surface area [m²]	217.8	33.27	-
Total heating area (bare) [m²]	398.46	53.86	-
Total heating area [m²]	-	-	1946
Orientation of tubes	Vertical	Horizontal	Horizontal
Tube material of construction	ASTM A106 Gr.B	ASTM A106 Gr.B	ASTM A106 Gr.B

2.1. Radiant section/firebox
On a rate basis, the conservation of energy in the fired heater is given by:
$$Q_F + Q_{air} = Q_R + Q_{WL} + Q_G \tag{1}$$
Where Q_F=the total rate of heat released by the combustion of the fuel gas [W]; Q_{air}=the rate of heat flow into the burners in the combustion of air [W]; Q_R=the heat duty of the RS [W]; Q_{WL}=total rate of heat loss through the fired heater walls [W]; Q_G=rate of heat flow out of the RS in the flue gases [W].
$$Q_F = N_B \cdot \left(min \left(\eta_{MB} \cdot \left(\frac{\dot{m}_{F-MB} \cdot LHV_F}{N_B} \right), Q_{MaxHR-MB} \right) + min \left(\eta_{PB} \cdot \left(\frac{\dot{m}_{F-PB} \cdot LHV_F}{N_B} \right), Q_{MaxHR-PB} \right) \right) \tag{2}$$

With N_B=number of burner in use; η_{MB}, η_{PB}=efficiency of the main/pilot burners; LHV_F=lower heating value of the fuel gas [J/kg]; $Q_{MaxHR-MB}$, $Q_{MaxHR-PB}$=design maximum rate of heat released per main/pilot burner [W]; $\dot{m}_{F-MB}$, $\dot{m}_{F-PB}$=total mass flowrate of fuel gas supplied to main/pilot burners [kg/s]. Based on the ratios of the maximum heat released per pilot burner to the main burner, $\dot{m}_{F-PB}$ is assumed to be 0.0133% of $\dot{m}_{F-MB}$.

$$Q_{air} = \dot{m}_{act-air} \cdot c_{air} \cdot \left(T_{air} - T_{ref}\right) \tag{3}$$

Where $\dot{m}_{act-air}$=actual mass flowrate of air supplied to burners [kg/s]; c_{air}=mass specific heat capacity of air [J/kgK]; T_{ref}=reference temperature [K]; T_{air}=temperature of air [K].

$$Q_R = F \cdot \sigma \cdot \alpha \cdot A_{cp,r} \cdot \left(T_{Gr}^4 - T_{w,avg,r}^4\right) + h_{Gr} \cdot A_{Sr} \cdot \left(T_{Gr} - T_{w,avg,r}\right) \tag{4}$$

With F=overall heat exchange factor to allow for both geometry and non-blackbody emissivities of cold and hot bodies; σ=the Stefan-Boltzmann constant [W/m²K⁴]; $A_{cp,r}$=area of cold plane replacing a bank of RS tubes [m²]; $A_{S,r}$=total outside area of the RS tubes [m²]; h_{Gr}=convection heat transfer coefficient flue gas-outside of the tube wall [W/m²K]; T_{Gr}=temperature of flue gases leaving RS [K]; $T_{w,avg,r}$=average temperature of the wall in the RS, calculated as the mean between the temperature at the entrance and the temperature at the exit of the section [K].

$$Q_{WL} = f_{WL} \cdot Q_{in} \tag{5}$$

With f_{WL}=factor of fired heater wall losses; Q_{in}=total rate of heat into the fired heater [W]. The overall enthalpy of the flue gases is expressed as the sum of the product of the molar flow rates and the specific heat capacities of each component gas. Thus:

$$Q_G = \sum n_i \cdot \Delta H_{m,i} \tag{6}$$

With n_i=molar flowrate of component i released by the combustion reaction [kmole/s]; $\Delta H_{m,i}$=the molar enthalpy change of component i [J/kmole].

The rate of change and axial variation of the thermal energy per unit length of tube wall and the HTF are given as:

$$\frac{\partial H_{wr}(t,z)}{\partial t} = F \cdot \sigma \cdot \pi \cdot D_o \cdot \left(T_{Gre}^4 - T_{wr}^4(t,z)\right) + h_{Gr} \cdot \pi \cdot D_o \cdot \left(T_{Gre} - T_{wr}(t,z)\right) - h_{Lr} \cdot \pi \cdot D_i \cdot \left(T_{wr}(t,z) - T_{Lr}(z,t)\right) \tag{7}$$

$$\frac{\partial H_{Lr}(t,z)}{\partial t} = -u_{Lr} \cdot \frac{\pi \cdot D_i^2}{4} \cdot H_{Lr}(t,z) + h_{Lr} \cdot \pi \cdot D_i \cdot \left(T_{wr}(t,z) - T_{Lr}(z,t)\right) \tag{8}$$

Where H_{Lr}=the enthalpy of the wall in the RS; D_o, D_i=the outer/inner tube diameter [m]; T_{Gre}=the effective radiating gas temperature [K]; T_{wr}=temperature of the wall in the RS [K]; h_{Lr}=convection heat transfer coefficient wall-HTF [W/m²K]; T_{Lr}=temperature of the HTF in the RS [K].

A general balance equation for the combustion of gaseous hydrocarbon fuels with dry excess air is published by [2] in the form:

$$C_A H_B + \varepsilon \left(A + \tfrac{B}{4}\right)(O_2 + 3.762 N_2) \rightarrow A \cdot CO_2 + \tfrac{B}{2} H_2O + (\varepsilon - 1)\left(A + \tfrac{B}{4}\right)O_2 + \varepsilon \left(A + \tfrac{B}{4}\right) 3.762 N_2 \tag{9}$$

Where ε = excess air.

While the conservation of mass for the flue gases is expressed as: $\dot{m}_F + \dot{m}_{Air} = \sum \dot{m}_i$ (10).

The composition of the fuel gas is assumed as: 65.59% C1; 17.8032% C2; 12.2454C3; 0.8817% i-C4; 1.5703 n-C4; 0.1766% i-C5; 0.1303 n-C5; 0.0515% C6+; 0.0231% N₂ and 1.4976% CO₂.

With $\dot{m}_F$=total mass flowrate of fuel gas [kg/s]; $\dot{m}Air$=total mass flowrate of air [kg/s]; i=CO₂; H₂O; O2; N2. The temperature control valve is modelled as in [8].

For the SS and CS, the heat transfer equations are written as:

$$Q_{Section} = Q_{Section,in} - Q_{Section,out} \tag{11}$$

The rates of heat for the flue gases in and out of the sections are calculated using a third-degree polynomial function for the specific heat in the form: $\bar{C}_p = \alpha + \beta T + \gamma T^2 + \delta T^3$.

For the wall and the HTF, equations like (7) and (8) are used and adapted to the geometries and operating conditions of the CS and SS, respectively.

For each section of the fired heater, the general form of the initial and boundary conditions for the temperature of the wall, Tw and the fluid, T_F are expressed as:

$$T_{L,Section}(0,z) = T_{Lout,Section-1}; \qquad T_{w,Section}(0,z) = T_{wout,Section-1}; \qquad T_{L,Section}(t,0) =$$
$$T_{Lout,Section-1}, \forall t; T_{w,Section}(t,0) = T_{wout,Section-1}, \qquad \forall t \qquad (12)$$

The Berman equation [1] is used to determine the convection heat transfer coefficient, h_{Gs} in the CS: $h_{Gs}=1.1(h_{Cs}+h_{Rs})$. The radiant heat transfer coefficient is not considered for the finned tube bank of the CS.

$$h_{Cs} = \left(1.273 T_{f,s}^{0.28} \cdot G_{max,s}^{0.6}\right)/D_0^{0.4} \qquad (13)$$

With $\quad G_{max,s} = \dot{m}_G/A_{min,s}$ = flue gas max flux [m/s]; $A_{min,s}$=the minimum cross-section flow area [m²]; $T_{f,s}$=the film temperature [K].

The film temperature, $T_{f,s}$ and the radiant heat transfer coefficient, h_{Rs} are calculated from:

$$T_{f,s} = 0.5\left(T_{w,avg} + T_{Gr}\right) \qquad (14)$$
$$h_{Rs} = 0.2565 T_{Gr} - 2.84 \qquad (15)$$

For each section of the heater, the convection heat transfer coefficients for the inside tube wall and the HTF, varying with the axial position, are calculated from the relation:

$$h_L(z) = Nu(z) \cdot k_L(z)/D_i \qquad (16)$$

While, within the application ranges, the local Nusselt number is calculated from the Gnielinski correlation [5] and the local Darcy friction factor using Petukhov's correlation [6]. The heat transfer coefficient for the RS, h_{Gr} is specified as 11.36 W/m²K as reported by [7]. The thermophysical properties (density, specific heat capacity, thermal conductivity, and kinematic viscosity) of the tube coil material and the HTF, all of which vary with temperature are expressed in polynomial regression forms obtained using curve fitting techniques of the manufacturer's thermal data. The heat capacity relation of ASTM A106 Grade B as a function of temperature could not be obtained from literature and Type 304 stainless steel was used instead [4]. The different sections, RS, SS, CS of H600 are connected by mass an energy flows at their boundaries (see Figure 2).

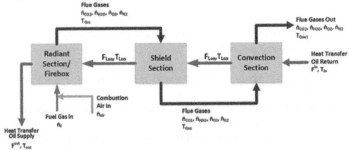

Figure 2: Connectivity between the distinct zones of the fired heater

The parameters for H600, mostly consisting of geometrical quantities are specified in Table 2.

3. Optimisation

Energy consumption in the fired heater is to be optimised to identify the best process operating conditions within the specified constraint that minimise fired heater operational costs. The objective function is formulated as an economic model describing the sum of two key daily operating costs: the fuel gas burned, and the electrical power consumed in pumping the HTF:

$$\min \; f = (86400 \cdot c_F \cdot \dot{m}_F \cdot LHV_F) + \left(c_E \cdot \frac{F_L^{in} \cdot \rho \cdot g \cdot H_P}{3.6 \cdot 10^6 \cdot \eta_P \cdot \eta_M}\right) \cdot t_r \qquad (17)$$

Subject to
$$25 \leq VT \leq 75$$
$$1.0 \leq \varepsilon \leq 1.5$$
$$130 \leq F_L^{in} \leq 340$$
$$523.15 \leq T_{out} \leq 548.15$$

With VT=valve travel [%]; F_L^{in}=total return volumetric flowrate of HTF to fired heater [m³/h]; T_{out}=HTF supply temperature [K]; η_P=pump efficiency=0.75; η_M=motor efficiency=0.85; c_F=fuel cost=$6.161 \cdot 10^{-9}$ [$/J]; c_E=cost of electric power=0.32 [$/kWh]; g=acceleration due to gravity [m/s²]; H_P=pump head=51 [m]; t_r=pump runtime per day [h]; ρ=average density of the fluid=735.16 [kg/m³]. The lower heating value of the flue gas, LHV_F was considered equal to 46,890 kJ/kg.

Table 2: Parameters for the sections of the heater.

Parameter	Radiant section	Shield section	Convection section
σ, [W/m²K⁴]	$5.7604 \cdot 10^{-8}$	$5.7604 \cdot 10^{-8}$	-
D_i, [m]	0.1023	0.1023	0.1023
D_o, [m]	0.1143	0.1143	-
Equivalent cold plane area, [m²]	217.88	33.27	-
Overall exchange factor, F	0.590	0.559	-
Reference temperature, T_{ref} [K]	298.15	298.15	298.15
$Q_{MaxHR-MB}$, [W]	1,472,682	-	-
$Q_{MaxHR-PB}$, [W]	29,307	-	-
Mass per unit length of radiant tube coil, [kg/m]	16.07	16.07	20.5

4. Results and discussion

A plot of HTF temperature versus the axial position and time in the CS, SS, and RS, are illustrated in Figures 3-5, respectively. An overall temperature profile for the HTF is shown in Figure 6.

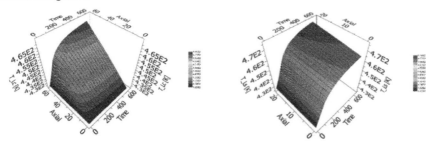

Figure 3: HTF temperature in the CS   Figure 4: HTF temperature in the

Table 3 shows a summary of the simulation results compared with measured data from the plant. A base case scenario is considered where the daily operating cost is 1,599.81 $/day, based on a flow of fuel gas of 0.632 kg/s, a HTF return volumetric flow rate of 139.5 m3/h, and a total operating number of burners of 8. The optimisation using the model in gPROMS® resulted in an operating cost of $776.18 $/day, which equals to

283,305.70 $/year. Overall, this translates into savings of about $360,625 $/year compared with the base case scenario. In percentage terms, savings of about 51.48% could be achieved.

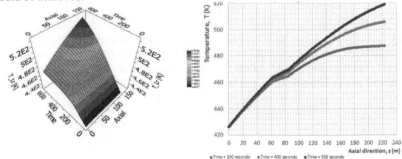

Figure 5: HTF temperature in the RS   Figure 6: HTF temperature in H600

Table 3: Simulation results at 380 seconds.

Parameter	Predicted	Measured	%Error
Valve travel, VT [%]	50	37.45	-33.51
HTF Supply temperature, T_{out} [K]	505.58	523.95	3.51
Flue gas temperature, T_{Gr} [K]	647.19	758.7	14.7
Average radiant tube wall temperature, [K]	511.84	544.47	5.99
Flue gas temperature at exit of CS, [K]	546.13	520.50	-4.92

For a simulation time of 786 seconds, the optimum supply temperature is identified at 548.4 K. These results demonstrate how a model-based process systems approach can be deployed to achieve optimal operation of the fired heater. However, a more comprehensive study, with a validated model must be carried out before optimal operating conditions can be clearly identified.

5. Conclusions

The simulation results of the heater model indicate that the distributed parameter dynamic model proposed in this work closely approximates the actual process behaviour under varied operating conditions. Potential for significant annual savings have been identified. Furthermore, a parameter estimation and model validation should be performed to ensure good agreement between the model predictions and the actual behaviour of H600.

References

[1]. H.L. Berman, Fired Heaters, Chemical Engineering, 1978; [2]. J. Baukal, E. Charles, John Zink, 2013, Hamworthy Combustion Handbook – Fundamentals, Vol.1, 2nd Edition, Taylor & Francis Group LLC; [3]. G. Ashbutosh, 1997, Optimise fired heater operations to save money, Hydrocarbon Processing; [4]. J.J. Valencia, P.N. Quested, 2008, Thermophysical properties, ASM Handbook, Vol. 15; [5]. V. Gnielinski, 1976, Int. Chem.Eng. 16, 359; [6]. P. Frank, D.P Dewitt, T.L. Bergman, A.S. Lavine, 2007, Introduction to Heat transfer, 5th Edition, John Wiley & Sons; [7]. R.K. Shah, E.C. Subbarao, R.A. Mashelkar, 1988, Heat transfer equipment design-Advanced Study Institute Book, Hemisphere Publishing Corporation; [8]. ISA Standard 75.01.01-2007 (IEC60534-2-1 Mod), 2007, Flow Equations for Sizing Control Valves

Anton A. Kiss, Edwin Zondervan, Richard Lakerveld, Leyla Özkan (Eds.)
Proceedings of the 29th European Symposium on Computer Aided Process Engineering
June 16th to 19th, 2019, Eindhoven, The Netherlands. © 2019 Elsevier B.V. All rights reserved.
http://dx.doi.org/10.1016/B978-0-128-18634-3.50166-1

Molecular Modelling of Co-processing Biomass Pyrolysis Oil with Vacuum Gasoil in an Oil Refinery Fluid Catalytic Cracking Unit

Mohamed Al Jamri, Robin Smith, Jie Li[*]

Centre for Process Integration, School of Chemical Engineering and Analytical Science, The University of Manchester, Manchester M13 9PL, UK

Jie.li-2@manchester.ac.uk

Abstract

Integration of biomass resources in petroleum refining for sustainable production of transportation fuels has gained increased attention in the last few decades (IEA, 2013). One potential integration option is to mix biomass-based pyrolysis oil (BPO) with petroleum gas oil (VGO) and then co-process the blend in oil refinery fluidised catalytic cracking (FCC) units (Naik *et al.*, 2017). It is important to establish the prediction model of product yield and quality with such coprocessing in FCC units. In this work, a novel molecular-level modelling approach is proposed for kinetic modelling of co-processing BPO with VGO in an oil refinery FCC unit. Molecular-level characterisation of BPO and VGO blends using Molecular Type and Homologous Series matrix is first conducted. Then, a novel reaction network is synthesized and a reaction model is developed for the proposed reaction network which considers not only the complex intermolecular interactions between various types of molecular attributes in the feed, but also the interactions between individual molecules and catalyst surface. A hybrid optimisation strategy combining genetic algorithm with deterministic optimisation algorithm is developed to obtain the optimal parameters in the reaction model. The results demonstrate an overall good agreement between measured and predicted yields using the developed kinetic model for VGO: BPO blending ratio of 90:10, C/O ratio between 5 and 8, and reaction temperature of 525°C. PONA composition, oxygen compounds compositions and oxygen content in each product fraction such as gasoline, diesel and gas oil can also be predicted. The effect of different blending ratios of BPO and VGO on oxygenates compositions is demonstrated.

Keywords: Catalytic cracking, Fast pyrolysis oil, biomass, refinery, MTHS matrix.

1. Introduction

Integration of renewable biofuels into transportation sector is gaining increased attention. Several integration options (pyrolysis oil upgrading, fermentation, and gasification/F-T synthesis) have been proposed and investigated for biofuels production (Huber *et al.*, 2006; Petrus and Noordermeer, 2006; Vispute *et al.*, 2010; Serrano-Ruiz and Dumesic, 2011). Among these options, co-processing biomass pyrolysis oil (BPO) with heavy petroleum fractions such as vacuum gasoil (VGO) in the refinery fluid catalytic cracking (FCC) unit arises as a promising option. This is mainly due to the efficiency of pyrolysis processes in phase transformation (up to 70% liquid yield), as well as the low capital investment required as a result of using refinery's economy of scale (Wang *et al.*, 2016).

To evaluate and optimise this co-processing option, it is important to develop mathematical models for product yields and properties prediction in the FCC unit with such co-processing of BPO and VGO. Although several approaches have been proposed for modelling of conventional FCC units (Feng et al., 1993; Xu et al., 2005; Gomez-Prado, 2009), only limited efforts have been reported for modelling of co-processing BPO with VGO in FCC units (Naik et al., 2017). Conventional modelling approaches cannot be directly applied for modelling of co-processing option due to their inability to accurately characterise oxygenated molecules in the feedstock. Molecular-level characterisation and molecular-level reaction models can be used to overcome the limitations of the previously mentioned approaches. Such techniques are based on detailed description of the sizes and types of the various molecules present in process streams. A detailed molecular-level reaction network that takes into account the various interactions between the molecules themselves and the catalyst (if any) surface is employed to describe the chemical and physical changes that occur inside process units.

In this work, a novel molecular-level modelling approach is proposed for the modelling of co-processing BPO with VGO in an FCC unit. The proposed approach comprises molecular-level characterisation of blended feedstock using Molecular Type and Homologous Series (MTHS) matrix method, as well as molecular-level reaction network for catalytic cracking of hydrocarbons and oxygenated species found in blended feedstock. The proposed reaction network is tuned using a hybrid optimisation strategy combining Genetic Algorithm (GA) and Successive Quadratic Programming (SQP) to guarantee obtaining a reproducible solution in the vicinity of global optimum using a robust search method. The proposed approached is applied for the modelling of a pilot-scale FCC riser used for co-processing catalytic-pyrolysis-derived bio oil with VGO at a blending ratio of 10 wt.%. The results demonstrate an overall good agreement between measured and predicted yields using the developed kinetic model for VGO: BPO blending ratio of 90:10, C/O ratio between 5 and 8, and reaction temperature of 525°C. PONA composition, oxygen compounds compositions and oxygen content in each product fraction such as gasoline, diesel and gas oil can also be predicted. The effect of different blending ratios of BPO and VGO on oxygenates compositions is demonstrated.

2. Methodology

2.1 Process Stream Characterisation

The developed characterisation approach in this work provides detailed molecular-level information compatible with reaction models, efficiently and at low cost. In particular, the proposed method is based on Molecular Type and Homologous Series (MTHS) matrix which uses a 2-D matrix to capture the size and the type of the various molecules present in the stream, simultaneously (see Figure 1). The characterisation methodology used in this work is similar to the methodology presented in a previous work (Al Jamri et al., 2018). The only difference is that in this work VGO and BPO are characterised independent from each other using two matrices. The two matrices are then blended according to the required blending ratio used in the feed stream to the process. In addition, the degrees of freedom (DOF) in the characterisation problem is reduced via introducing Volume Average Boiling Point (VABP) concept. This allowed to reduce the number of DOF from 3 to 2 for each hydrocarbon homologous series, which resulted in total reduction of DOF from 21 to 17 in the characterisation problem of VGO.

Molecular Modelling of Co-processing Biomass Pyrolysis Oil with
Vacuum Gasoil in an Oil Refinery Fluid Catalytic Cracking Unit

993

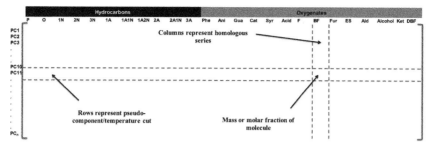

Figure 1 Proposed MTHS Representation Matrix for Characterisation of Mixed Stream

2.2 Reaction Network Modelling Methodology

Modelling of conventional catalytic cracking reaction network is a complex task. The complexity of this problem increases significantly when BPO oxygenated molecules are considered. This is mainly due to the limited information available in literature on bio oil molecules catalytic cracking pathways and kinetics compared to conventional hydrocarbon molecules usually found in petroleum streams. In addition, the already known kinetic behaviour of conventional petroleum fractions maybe affected when BPO is co-processed with VGO in a refinery FCC unit. Therefore, molecular-level reaction network is devised to quantify the effects of introducing oxygenated molecules on the kinetic behaviour of catalytic cracking reactions. The reaction network is synthesised by considering two different categories of molecules: hydrocarbons and oxygenates. Reaction pathways and kinetics for hydrocarbon molecules are deduced from previous work of Gómez-Prado (2009). Model compound studies for catalytic conversion of bio oil oxygenated molecules (Adjaye and Bakhshi, 1995a) are used for the synthesis of bio oil molecules catalytic cracking reaction network. The kinetic expressions and kinetic parameters values used to populate the kinetic network are taken from previous work (Adjaye and Bakhshi, 1995b).

The developed reaction network comprises 328 reaction terms, 299 of which are used for the description of hydrocarbons catalytic cracking reactions. The remining 29 reactions are used for the representation of catalytic conversion of bio oil oxygenated molecules. The main feature of the proposed reaction network is its ability in predicting the composition of various hydrocarbons (PONA) and oxygenates (Phenolics, aldehydes and ketones, acids and esters, and alcohols) in each liquid product fraction, which can be used to satisfy industrial requirements in monitoring and controlling product quality. In addition, the proposed methodology avoids the need for kinetic parameters re-fitting when feedstock composition and/or blending ratio changes as a result of using molecular-level reaction network.

Kinetic parameters tuning problem is formulated as a non-linear optimisation problem. The objective function considers the absolute difference between measured ($Y_{L,OP}^{msd}$) and model-predicted ($Y_{L,OP}^{PRE}$) products' yields of each lump (L) and operating condition (OP) (see Eq. 1). Different weights (W_L) are used to give similar sizes for each difference between the different product yields.

$$Obj = \sum_{L,OP} W_L \sqrt{\left(Y_{L,OP}^{msd} - Y_{L,OP}^{PRE}\right)^2} \qquad \text{Eq. 1}$$

Kinetic parameters regression problem is solved using hybrid optimisation framework. Both stochastic and deterministic optimisation algorithm are employed in a unified framework (Figure 2). Initially, stochastic search methods (GA) is used to increase the chance of obtaining a solution in the vicinity of global optimum. The solution obtained from GA is fed to the deterministic algorithm (SQP) to improve the quality of the solution. This increases the chance of obtaining a reproducible solution in the vicinity of global optimum. The results obtained using this hybrid optimisation framework show good agreement between predicted and measured products' yields.

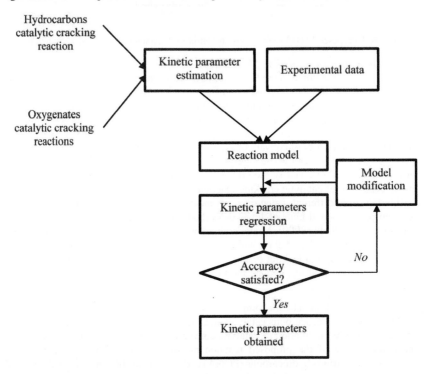

Figure 2 Kinetic Parameters Tuning Problem Solution Algorithm

3. Results and Discussion

The proposed characterisation approach has been tested in the characterisation of a blend of 90:10 VGO:BPO. This blend is used as a feedstock for pilot-plant scale FCC riser (Wang *et al.*, 2016). In this work, BPO stream is characterised independently from VGO. The two characterisation matrices obtained are combined together according to the specified blending ratio and fed to the reaction model. This way, blending ratio in the reaction model can be varied without the need to re-characterise the blended stream. Figure 3A shows the values of relative error when measured bulk properties of VGO are compared to model-predicted values. A maximum error of 5% was found in the prediction of molecular weight (MW) and aniline point (AP). Figure 3B shows a comparison between measured and predicted boiling curve of BPO.

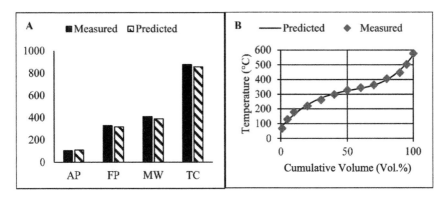

Figure 3 VGO and BPO characterisation results

The compositional matrix obtained is fed to the reaction model, and kinetic parameters tuning is carried out using the proposed hybrid optimisation framework. The results obtained are shown in Figure 4. The value of index of correlation (R^2) for this fitting is found to be 0.933, which indicates good correlation with measured data.

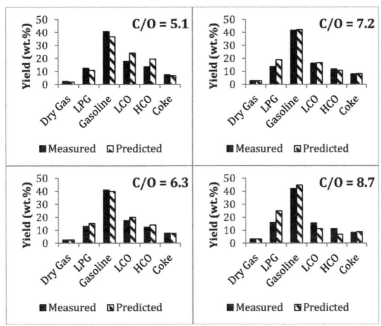

Figure 4 Comparison between Measured and Predicted Yields at different C/O ratio

The novelty of the proposed modelling approach lies in the ability of the developed modelling framework in predicting PONA and oxygenates yields at different blending ratios. Figure 5 shows oxygenates yields in heavy gasoline fractions as a function of blending ratio.

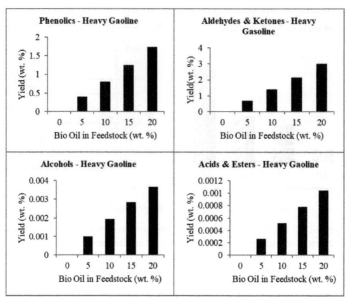

Figure 5 Oxygenates Yields in Heavy Gasoline Fraction at different Blending Ratio

4. Conclusions

A novel approach for molecular-level modelling of co-processing BPO with VGO in an FCC unit is proposed. The methodology comprises a novel characterisation framework in which bulk properties are converted to molecular information using optimisation-based modelling approach. A novel molecular-level reaction network comprising 328 reactions is proposed and used for the modelling of pilot-plant scale FCC riser. The results obtained showed good accuracy when compared to experimentally measured data. The model exhibits ability in predicting the various molecular attributes (hydrocarbons and oxygenates) at different blending ratios.

References

Adjaye, J. D. and Bakhshi, N. N. (1995a), *Biomass and Bioenergy*, 8(4), pp. 265–277.
Adjaye, J. D. and Bakhshi, N. N. (1995b), *Fuel Processing Technology*, 45(3), pp. 185–202.
Feng, W., Vynckier, E. and Froment, G. F. (1993), *Industrial & Engineering Chemistry Research*, 32(12), pp. 2997–3005.
Gomez-Prado, J. (2009). University of Manchester.
Huber, G. W., Iborra, S. and Corma, A. (2006), *Chemical Reviews*, 106(9), pp. 4044–4098.
IEA (2013) *World Energy Outlook 2013*.
Al Jamri, M., Smith, R. and Li, J. (2018) *28th European Symposium on Computer Aided Process Engineering*. Elsevier (Computer Aided Chemical Engineering), pp. 1439–1444.
Naik, D. V *et al.* (2017), *Chemical Engineering Science*, 170, pp. 790–798.
Petrus, L. and Noordermeer, M. A. (2006), *Green Chem.* The Royal Society of Chemistry, 8(10), pp. 861–867.
Serrano-Ruiz, J. C. and Dumesic, J. A. (2011), *Energy Environ. Sci.* The Royal Society of Chemistry, 4(1), pp. 83–99.
Vispute, T. P. *et al.* (2010), *Science*. American Association for the Advancement of Science, 330(6008), pp. 1222–1227.
Wang, C., Li, M. and Fang, Y. (2016), *Industrial & Engineering Chemistry Research*, 55(12), pp. 3525–3534.
Xu, C. *et al.* (2005), *Fuel*, 84(6), pp. 669–674.

Anton A. Kiss, Edwin Zondervan, Richard Lakerveld, Leyla Özkan (Eds.)
Proceedings of the 29th European Symposium on Computer Aided Process Engineering
June 16th to 19th, 2019, Eindhoven, The Netherlands. © 2019 Elsevier B.V. All rights reserved.
http://dx.doi.org/10.1016/B978-0-128-18634-3.50167-3

A Chance-Constrained Nonlinear Programming Approach for Equipment Design Under Uncertainty

Javier Tovar-Facio,[a] Yankai Cao,[b] José M. Ponce-Ortega,[a*] Victor M. Zavala,[b]

[a]*Departmen of Chemical Engineering, Universidad Michoacana de San Nicolás de Hidalgo, Francisco J. Mugica S/N, Morelia 58030, Mexico*

[b]*Department of Chemical and Biological Engineering, University of Wisconsin-Madison, 1414 Engineering Dr, Madison 53706, USA*

jmponce@umich.mx

Abstract

In this work there are shown different strategies to cope uncertainty in large-scale chance-constrained nonlinear programs. We present the design of a flare system as a case study. The design of this system is influenced by several uncertain factors, such as the volume and composition of the waste flow stream to be combusted and the ambient conditions. These systems are currently designed based on typical historical values for waste fuel gases and ambient conditions. Consequently, an improperly designed flare can be susceptible to extreme events previously not experienced. Particularly, we use moment matching (MM) when the algebraic form of the moments and the quantile function of the chance constrained (CC) distribution is known, and for more general settings when the distribution cannot be predicted we use the scenario approach (AS), the popular conditional value at risk (CVaR) and the recently proposed sigmoid value at risk (SigVaR). We demonstrate that the SigVaR approximation offers the best results and this approach overcome the conservative results of the AS and CVaR.

Keywords: Uncertainty, design, sigmoid conditional value at risk, flares.

1. Introduction

We study the chance-constrained nonlinear program:

$$\min_{d \in D} \varphi(d) \tag{1a}$$

Subject to

$$\mathbb{P}\left(f(d, \Xi) \le \bar{f} \right) \ge 1 - \alpha \tag{1b}$$

We review exact approaches to handle chance constrained problems (CC-P). We consider the special case in which the algebraic form of the quantile function is known or approximately known, and we propose to use moment matching to compute its parameters. However, there are some cases where the nonlinear chance constrained problems are particularly difficult to solve because nonlinear propagation makes it hard to obtain the distribution of output variables (this case will be analysed in a future work).

To handle more general settings, we consider the use of three different approximations. The first one is the scenario approximation, in this approach we approximate the chance constrain ensuring that the constrain is satisfied for each scenario or with probability of 1, and this implies that the constraint is satisfied for any probability different to one. This is extremely conservative; nevertheless, it let us express the chance constrain using the standard scenario-based stochastic programming formulation. The second approximation is the conditional value at risk, this approximation enables expressing our problem as a common nonlinear optimization problem, but CVaR can be slightly conservative. Moreover, the CVaR approximation does not offer a mechanism to enforce convergence to a solution of CC. The third approximation is the sigmoid value at risk approximation (Cao and Zavala, 2018), which provides a mechanism to determine exact solutions for CC-P.

2. Flare systems

Gas flares are used as safety (relief) devices that are used all over the world to manage abnormal situations in infrastructure systems (natural gas and oil processing plants and pipelines), manufacturing facilities (chemical plants, offshore rigs), and power generation facilities. Abnormal situations include equipment failures, off-specification products, and excess materials in start-up/shutdown procedures. In particular, flares prevent over pressurization of equipment and use combustion to convert flammable, toxic or corrosive vapors to less-dangerous compounds (Sorrels et al., 2017). A proper design of flare systems is vitally important due to it is influenced by several uncertain factors, such as the amount and composition of the waste fuel gases to be combusted and the ambient conditions like wind velocity. An improperly designed flare can be susceptible to extreme events previously not experienced or have as a result an oversized and expensive equipment. Here, it is proposed to use stochastic programming formulations to systematically capture uncertain conditions in the design procedure.

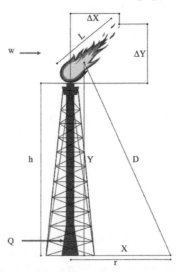

Figure 1. Flare system generic diagram.

3. Physical model

It was formulated a mathematical model for sizing a flare system (see Figure 1). The design goals are to minimize the equipment cost while controlling the thermal radiation level at ground level. It was based on the American Petroleum Institute standard 521 as follows:

The heat released by combustion H (BTU/h) is a function of the random input waste flow Q (lb/h) and the heat of combustion h_c (BTU/lb):

$$H = h_c Q \tag{1}$$

The flame length L (ft) can be calculated as a function of the released heat using an approximation of the form:

$$\log L = a_1 \log H - a_2 \tag{2}$$

The wind speed w (ft/s) is an important environmental factor that affects the tilting of the flame and the distance from the center of the flame. The following correlations capture the flame distortion as a result of the wind speed and the exit velocity:

$$\log \Delta X = \log(a_5 L) + a_6 \left(\log w - \log U\right) \tag{3}$$

$$\log \Delta Y = \log(a_7 L) - a_8 \left(\log w - \log U\right) \tag{4}$$

The flare stack diameter t (ft) is sized on a velocity basis. This is done by relating this to the Mach number M and the waste flow as:

$$M^2 = \left(\frac{a_3}{t^2}\right) Q^2 \tag{5}$$

The flare tip exit velocity U (ft/s) is function of the flow and the diameter:

$$U = a_4 \frac{Q}{t^2} \tag{6}$$

Here, ΔX and ΔY (ft) are the horizontal and vertical distortions. The distortions are used to compute the horizontal X, vertical Y, and total distance D (ft) to a given ground-level safe point (r,0) as:

$$X = r - \left(\frac{1}{2}\right) \Delta X \tag{7}$$

$$Y = h + \left(\frac{1}{2}\right)\Delta Y \tag{8}$$

$$D^2 = X^2 + Y^2 \tag{9}$$

Here, h (ft) is the flare height. The flame radiation K (BTU/h ft^2) is a function of the heat released and the total distance:

$$K = a_9 \left(\frac{H}{D^2}\right) \tag{10}$$

A primary safety goal in the flare stack design problem is to control the risk that the radiation exceeds a certain threshold value $\bar{k}$ (BTU/h ft^2) at the ground-level reference point (r,0). This is modelled using the CC:

$$\mathbb{P}\left(K \leq \bar{k}\right) \geq 1 - \alpha \tag{11}$$

The objective function is the cost (USD), which is a function of height and diameter:

$$\varphi(t, h) = \left(a_{10} + a_{11} t + a_{12} h\right)^2 \tag{12}$$

The height and the diameter play a key role in controlling the radiation at the reference point (i.e., a higher and wider flare reduces the radiation intensity). As a result, there is an inherent trade-off between capital cost and safety that must be carefully handled.

4. Case study

The design was considered of a flare stack that combusts a waste fuel gas flow, Q (see Figure 1). The goal is to design a flare system that minimizes cost and satisfies CC on the thermal radiation using the AS, CVaR, SigVaR, and MM approaches. In this work, the case is presented in which the input flow to the flare stack follows a log-normal distribution (with mean a = 10,000 lb/h and standard deviation b = 3,000 lb/h to exemplify a distribution with isolated events). All formulations were solved using 1000 random samples for the inlet flow (see Figure 2). The flare design must satisfy a CC on the radiation with a maximum threshold ($\bar{k}$) of 2,000 BTU/h ft^2 and with a probability $1 - \alpha = 0.95$. The optimization formulation is an NLP with 9,005 variables that was implemented using the open-source modelling language JuMP (Bezanson et al., 2017) and solved with Ipopt (Wächter and Biegler, 2006).

5. Results

Table 1 presents the optimal cost, diameter, and height for the flare system under the used approaches. The results show that the design of the AS approximation is the most conservative. The design is 64% more expensive than the MM design. This is since the

AS approach does not allow for explicit control of the probability of constraint satisfaction. The CVaR approximation reduces this highly conservatism, but it considerably overdesigns the flare stack. The optimal height obtained with CVaR is 67.70% larger and 20% more expensive than those obtained with MM; therefore, CVaR approximation reduces the extreme conservatism of the AS, but it still overdesigned. Table 1 also presents that the optimal solution of SigVaR ad MM are very close. The SigVaR design is only 1% more expensive than the MM approach, and that let to highlight the fact that the SigVaR solution is rightly conservative.

Table 1. Optimal Values for Design Variables

	AS	CVaR	SigVaR	MM
Cost (USD)	233,179	172,329	143,609	142,128
Diameter (ft)	1.70	1.70	1.70	1.70
Height (ft)	179.87	105.08	65.16	63.00

Figure 2 shows the empirical PDFs for the input flow and for the radiation at the optimal solution of the CVaR, SigVaR, and MM approaches. First, it is observed that, for the MM approach, the distribution of the radiation is indeed log-normal. This indicates that the structure of the flare model preserves the log-normal shape of the input flow. It is also observed that the histograms of SigVaR and MM are quite similar, with SigVaR being slightly more conservative. In particular, the tail of the SigVaR distribution is very similar to that of MM (the tail reaches values of 6,000 BTU/h ft^2 for SigVaR, compared to 6,100 BTU/h ft^2 with MM). The histogram of CVaR further validates the observation that this approach is very conservative (the tail reaches values of 4,000 BTU/h ft^2)

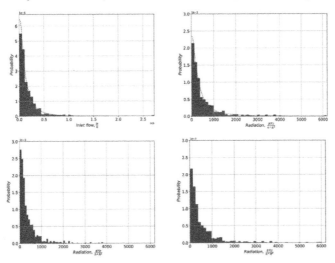

Figure 2. (Top-left) Inlet flow PDF, (top-right) radiation PDF using MM, (bottom-left) radiation PDF using CVaR, and (bottom-right) radiation PDF using SigVaR.

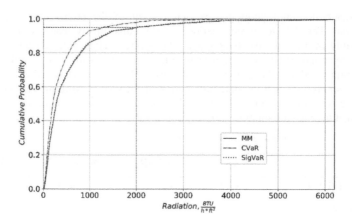

Figure 3. Radiation CDFs using MM, CVaR and SigVaR.

Figure 3 compares the optimal radiation CDFs obtained with CVaR, SigVaR, and MM. It can be seen again that CVaR is very conservative, achieving probability levels for the chance constraint of 98–99% (when 95% is only required). Also, the CDFs for SigVaR and MM overlap for the log-normal case, reinforcing that SigVaR provides good quality approximations and that the distribution of the radiation is indeed log-normal and thus MM is a good approach to solve the problem.

6. Conclusions

An application of moment matching techniques was presented to reformulate chance constraints when the shape of the underlying density function is known. It was also demonstrated the use of conservative approximations, that can be applied to more general setting in which the shape of the density function in unknown. A flare system design study showed that a sigmoid approximation overcomes the conservativeness of the popular conditional value-at-risk and scenario approaches, and it can be an excellent alternative when moment matching is not applicable. The proposed approaches enable the solution of large-scale NLPs with chance constraints.

References

J. Sorrels, J. Coburn, K. Bradley, and D. Randall, 2017, Air Pollution Control Cost Manual, United States Environmental Protection Agency: Washington, DC.

American Petroleum Institute (API), 1997. Recommended Practice 521, Guide for Pressure Relieving and Depressuring Systems.

Y. Cao and V. Zavala, 2018, A sigmoidal approximation for chance-constrained nonlinear programs. Under review (see the following URL: http://zavalab.engr.wisc.edu/publications/journalpubs/sigvar.pdf?attredirects=0).

J. Bezanson, A. Edelman, S. Karpinski, V. Shah, 2017, Julia: A fresh approach to numerical computing. SIAM Rev, 59, 65 – 98.

A. Wächter and L. Biegler, 2006, On the implementation of a primal-dual interior point filter line search algorithm for large-scale nonlinear programming, Math. Program., 106, 25 – 57.

Anton A. Kiss, Edwin Zondervan, Richard Lakerveld, Leyla Özkan (Eds.)
Proceedings of the 29th European Symposium on Computer Aided Process Engineering
June 16th to 19th, 2019, Eindhoven, The Netherlands. © 2019 Elsevier B.V. All rights reserved.
http://dx.doi.org/10.1016/B978-0-128-18634-3.50168-5

Sustainable Strategic Planning for a National Natural Gas Energy System Accounting for Unconventional Sources

Esbeydi Villicaña-García,[a] J. Betzabe González-Campos,[a] José María Ponce-Ortega[a,*]

[a]Chemical Engineering Department, Universidad Michoacana de San Nicolás de Hidalgo, Av. Francisco J. Múgica S/N, Ciudad Universitaria, Edificio V1, Morelia, Michoacán, 58060, México

jmponce@umich.mx

Abstract

This work presents an optimization model for the strategic planning to satisfy the national demands of natural gas considering unconventional extraction such as shale gas and offshore extraction and conventional ways to produce associated and non-associated natural gas using enhanced gas recovery systems, as well as importation. The model incorporates a multi-objective optimization strategy to obtain trade-offs between economic, environmental and health issues.

A case study from Mexico is presented to show the applicability of the proposed approach to satisfy the increasing national demand of natural gas through different extraction ways. Furthermore, in the presented study, economic, environmental and health factors were evaluated to select the best option. The economic factors consider costs associated with the production and treatment of natural gas, the used fresh water and the costs that involve the transportation of natural gas from its point of extraction to final markets. Regarding to the environmental impact, the fresh water consumption and CO_2 emissions are considered. The occupational health of the involved processes in the production of natural gas is also evaluated, this because workers are continuously exposed to hazardous substances that can cause long-term damage. Results show that it is possible to decrease imports to satisfy the national demands for natural gas only with their own resources, and taking care for the economic, environmental and health issues.

Keywords: Strategic planning, Natural gas, Fresh water, CO_2 emissions, Occupational health.

1. Introduction

Several works have analysed the strategic planning of shale gas to satisfy diverse demands; in this sense, Gao and You (2015) proposed a model for designing a shale gas supply chain accounting for the involved water supply, as well as the economic and environmental impacts.

It should be noticed that a large part of the oil reserves is below the sea. In Mexico, more than 80% of total oil production is provided from the sea. This zone is in the states of Campeche, Yucatán and Quintana Roo, and includes approximately 189,056 square kilometres (PEMEX, 2017). However, this method is very challenging, since it does not only must deal with extracting oil to the surface by drilling in the sea, without having visibility, but also avoiding the sea contamination with hydrocarbons.

Once the oil is not extracted from the well, means that this is exhausted. However, there are several improved recovery techniques that stimulate the subsoil, these are known as Enhanced Oil/Gas recovery (EOR/EGR), causing the release of oil that is currently contained in the deposit. Li et al. (2018) investigated the natural gas production from fracture-filled methane hydrate reservoirs by the CO_2 replacement method.

Moreover, occupational health deals with all aspects of health and safety in the workplace and it has a strong focus on primary prevention of hazards. The health of the workers has several determinants, including risk factors at the workplace leading to cancers, accidents, musculoskeletal diseases, respiratory diseases, hearing loss, circulatory diseases, stress related disorders and communicable diseases and others (WHO, 2018).

However, it is important to note that the reported approaches for the strategic planning for satisfying the national demands of natural gas have not considered simultaneously conventional and unconventional resources with economic, environmental (associated to emissions and used water) and health implications for the proper analysis. These are important points that must be studied for the correct planning to satisfy the national demands of natural gas for any country, because these are intrinsically related. Therefore, this paper presents a general mathematical model to obtain energy independence from a country to take advantage of its own reserves of fossil fuels through using unconventional extraction methods such as shale gas, offshore extraction, and considering conventional ways to obtain natural gas that the country already has. In addition, in this paper the nexus between environment and health damages together with the economic implications is involved; also, the model considers reducing the consumption of fresh water and generation of CO_2 emissions, considering the configuration that represents the least damage for the workers that dangerous substances present in the extraction and production processes.

2. Problem Statement

Throughout the years, the conventional extraction of fossil fuels has been decreasing but the energy needs have increased; this way, different unconventional forms for the extraction of natural gas have been explored. However, these new ways of extraction have considered the costs and environmental damage mainly associated to emissions of CO_2, but the chronic diseases caused in workers and the implications in the use of fresh water have not been properly addressed since the planning stage.
The objective is to satisfy the national demands of natural gas for a given country.

3. Optimization Model

The proposed mathematical programming model is general, it is based on the superstructure presented in Figure 1, and it involves different forms of unconventional extraction such as shale gas, offshore extraction, and conventional forms; for example, the extraction of associated reservoirs using improved recovery techniques, the conventional extraction of non-associated deposits and even the importation of natural gas. Fresh water and seawater are used for producing natural gas through different extraction methods. According to the type of extraction, the produced natural gas is separated, and it can be treated to eliminate dangerous substances to health. The natural gas obtained by each extraction method is distributed to the different markets. The model includes costs for producing natural gas, fresh water, treatment and transportation. In addition, the sale of oil obtained in offshore extraction and associated conventional extraction is considered.

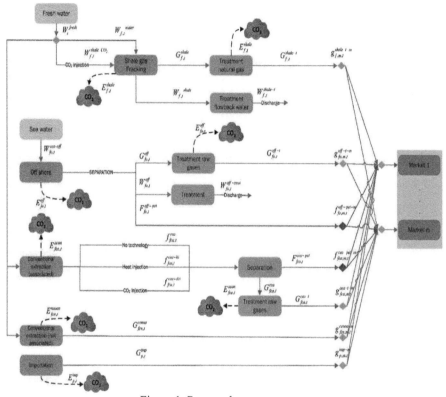

Figure 1. Proposed superstructure

3.1. Profit

The profit is obtained by the sum of the sale of oil and natural gas, minus all the involved expenses:

$$Profit = Sale^{PET} + Sale^{NG} - Cost^{shale-prod} - Cost^{fresh-shale} - Cost^{treatment-shale} - Cost^{off-prod}$$

$$-Cost^{seawater} - Cost^{treatment-off} - Cost^{cea-prod} - Cost^{fresh-acon} - Cost^{treatment-cea} - Cost^{cenoa-prod} \quad (1)$$

$$-Cost^{fresh-nacon} - Cost^{imp} - Cost^{pet} - Cost^{transp-pet} - Cost^{transp-ng}$$

3.2. Total fresh water

The total used fresh water is the sum of each flow needed of water in shale, conventional associated and non-associated production:

$$TFW = \sum_{f} \sum_{t} W_{f,t}^{shale} + \sum_{fca} \sum_{t} w_{fca,t}^{fresh-acon} + \sum_{fcn} \sum_{t} w_{fcn,t}^{fresh-nacon} \tag{2}$$

3.3. Total emissions

The total emissions are the sum of the generated emissions in each process as it follows:

$$TE = \sum_{f} \sum_{t} E_{f,t}^{shale} + \sum_{wo} \sum_{t} E_{wo,t}^{off} + \sum_{wca} \sum_{t} E_{wca,t}^{acon} + \sum_{wcn} \sum_{t} E_{wcn,t}^{nacon} + \sum_{p} \sum_{t} E_{p,t}^{imp} \tag{3}$$

3.4. Occupational health

Occupational health has been evaluated in each of the options to produce natural gas that are considered in the superstructure. Equation 4 relates natural gas flows for each case multiplied by a factor that shows the relationship of damage between each of the options with respect to the most damaging. It is worth mentioning that shale gas is the one that generates the most health damage for workers who are exposed continuously to the substances present in the process.

$$HD = I^{shale} \cdot \sum_{f,t} G_{f,t}^{shale-t} + I^{off} \cdot \sum_{fo,t} G_{fo,t}^{off-t} + I^{cea} \cdot \sum_{fca,t} G_{fca,t}^{cea-t} + I^{cenoa} \cdot \sum_{fcn,t} G_{fcn,t}^{cenoa} + I^{imp} \cdot \sum_{p,t} G_{p,t}^{imp} \tag{4}$$

3.5. Objective functions

The formulation of the mathematical programming model is a multi-objective problem, where the objectives are to maximize the profit, minimize the consumption of fresh water, the total emissions and the health damage, subject to relationships (1-4).

$$ObjectiveFunction = MaxProfit; MinTFW; MinTE; MinHD \tag{5}$$

The model is a mixed integer linear programming model, and this was coded in the software GAMS.

4. Case Study

The consumption of natural gas in any country is of special interest to ensure independence on foreign countries to meet fuel needs. In this context, Mexico was selected as a case study, since this country has natural gas reserves by 31,904.7 billion cubic feet, of which 70.3% is associated natural gas and the rest is not associated. The associated natural gas is the one that is in presence with oil and other compounds in the reservoir and non-associated is because there is only natural gas in the reservoir. In addition, it is important to note that Mexico is in 6th place worldwide with a reserve of unproven but technically recoverable resources of shale gas with 545,000 billion cubic feet (EIA, 2018).

5. Results

The results for optimizing each objective separately are shown in Table 1. It should be noticed that by maximizing the PROFIT, there is a profit of 1.58×10^{10} \$/y, which is 186% higher than the case of minimizing the TFW (fresh water consumption), 2.1% greater than minimizing TE (total emissions) and 2,119% higher with respect to minimizing HD (damage to health).

Table 1. Results for optimizing different objectives separately

	Max PROFIT	Min TFW	Min TE	Min HD
PROFIT ($/y)	1.58×10^{10}	5.51×10^{9}	7.11×10^{8}	7.12×10^{8}
HEALTH DAMAGE	1,509,500	105,820	0.137	0.137
(MMmetric ton CO_2e/y)	22.774	1.091	0.690	0.690
Importation	0	0.273	0.273	0.272
Offshore	1.977	0.818	0	0
Shale	19.389	0	0	0
Associated	0.844	0	0	0
Non-associated	0.564	0	0.417	0.418
TOTAL FRESH WATER	36.576	0	14.333	14.333
(MMm^3/ y)				
Importation	0	0	0	0
Offshore	0	0	0	0
Shale	2.729	0	0	0
Associated	14.464	0	0	0
Non-associated	19.386	0	14.333	14.333
Natural gas produced	1,901,853	1,901,847	1,901,853	1,901,843
(MMcfy)				
Importation	0	1,773,910	1,770,660	1,770,650
Offshore	309,142	127,937	0	0
Shale	1,252,970	0	0	0
Associated	162,304	0	0	0
Non-associated	177,437	0	131,193	131,193

On the other hand, health damage provides different scenarios, where this value helps to determine the harmful level of an option; where the higher the value, the greater the damage. In this case, the HD values are quite different. Minimizing TE and HD, there is less damage (0.137), in addition, when TFW is minimized, there is a decrease of 92.9% compared with the case when PROFIT is maximized, which represents the scenario with the greatest damage to health.

The total demand of natural gas in the country is 1,901,888.77 MMcfy; by maximizing PROFIT, 65.9% is satisfied through the production of shale gas, 16.2% with offshore production, 9.3% by associated conventional extraction and 8.5% by non-associated conventional extraction. It is important to highlight that in this scenario, importation is not used and despite having the greatest health damage, emissions and water consumption, it would be no dependence on another country to satisfy the demand for natural gas. When TFW is minimized, 93.3% is satisfied through importation and the rest through offshore production. In the cases when TE and HD are minimized, the results are very similar, 93.1% is imported natural gas and the rest is from the conventional production of non-associated natural gas.

The fresh water required to maximize PROFIT is used to produce shale gas, associated and non-associated natural gas. When TFW is minimized there is no water consumption since everything was satisfied through importation and offshore extraction. On the other hand, for the minimum TE and HD, there is only fresh water consumption due to the production of non-associated natural gas.

The greatest amount of total emissions (millions of tons of CO_2 equivalent per year) occurs when the PROFIT is maximized (22,774), where 85.1% is generated due to shale gas. In the case of minimum TFW (1.091), there is a decrease of 95.2% with respect to the maximum PROFIT scenario; for the minimum TE and HD, the decrease in emissions is 96.9%.

6. Conclusions

This paper has presented a mathematical programming model for the strategic planning to satisfy the national demands of natural gas. The proposed model incorporates non-conventional options, particularly shale gas, which can be used to decrease the imports. Furthermore, in the proposed model, in addition to economic objectives, the minimization for the fresh water consumption, CO_2 emissions and the health damage to the involved workers were considered.

Throughout the presented analysis for the case of satisfying the national demands of natural gas in Mexico, there was determined that is possible to satisfy these demands with a greater profit, less damage, fresh water consumption and emissions of CO_2. Also, occupational health was evaluated showing that when the profit increases, the higher the damage, but the less the damage, the more the dependence with another country because the needed imports. However, it can be noted that the dependence of Mexico (maximizing profit) with another country is reduced because the demand of natural gas can be satisfied with the national production, only by substituting importation with shale gas production and using the conventional reservoirs that already exist.

Finally, the proposed model is general, and it can be applied to different cases with different conditions.

7. References

EIA, 2018, Energy Information Administration. www.eia.gov. [Accessed March 2018].

J. Gao, F. You, 2015, Shale gas supply chain design and operations toward better economic and life cycle environmental performance: MINLP model and global optimization algorithm, ACS Sustainable Chemistry and Engineering 3(7), 1282-1291. DOI:10.1021/acssuschemeng.5b00122.

B. Li, T. Xu, G. Zhang, W. Guo, H. Liu, Q. Wang, L. Qu, Y. Sun, 2018, An experimental study on gas production from fracture-filled hydrate by CO2, and CO2/N2 replacement. Energy Conversion and Management, 165: 738-747. DOI:10.1016/j.enconman.2018.03.095.

PEMEX, 2017, Mexican oil. www.pemex.com/saladeprensa/boletines_nacionales/Paginas/2017-043-nacional.aspx, www.pemex.com/ayuda/preguntas_frecuentes/Paginas/reservas_hidrocarburos.aspx. [Accessed May 2017].

WHO, 2018, World Health Organization. www.who.int/topics/occupational_health/en. [Accessed August 2018].

Anton A. Kiss, Edwin Zondervan, Richard Lakerveld, Leyla Özkan (Eds.)
Proceedings of the 29th European Symposium on Computer Aided Process Engineering
June 16th to 19th, 2019, Eindhoven, The Netherlands. © 2019 Elsevier B.V. All rights reserved.
http://dx.doi.org/10.1016/B978-0-128-18634-3.50169-7

Modelling Full Cycles of Carbonation-Calcination for Calcium Looping Process Simulation

Miguel Abreu Torres,[a] Paula Teixeira,[a] Rui M. Filipe,[b,c] Luis Domingues,[d] Carla I. C. Pinheiro,[a] Henrique A. Matos[c*]

[a]Centro de Química Estrutural, DEQ, Instituto Superior Técnico/Universidade de Lisboa, Av. Rovisco Pais 1, Lisboa 1049-001, Portugal

[b]Instituto Superior de Engenharia de Lisboa/Instituto Politécnico de Lisboa, R. Conselheiro Emídio Navarro 1, Lisboa 1959-007, Portugal

[c]CERENA, DEQ, Instituto Superior Técnico/Universidade de Lisboa, Av. Rovisco Pais 1, Lisboa 1049-001, Portugal

[d]Process Systems Enterprise, 5th Floor East, Hammersmith Grove 26-28, London W6 7HA

henrimatos@tecnico.ulisboa.pt

Abstract

This work is part of a study to develop a multi-scale model of a Ca-looping (CaL) post-combustion process for CO_2 capture that relies on the carbonation reaction of CaO (s) and on the calcination of the resulting $CaCO_3$ (s) to generate a stream of highly concentrated CO_2 (g).

The literature lacks models that combine the modelling of both reactions with a cyclic structure that accounts for sorbent deactivation and allows for a realistic estimation in the case of incomplete reactions or different reaction media. Therefore, in this work two sub-models are combined to form this novel modelling approach for the simulation of complete carbonation-calcination cycles of the CaL process: The overlapping grain model for the carbonation reaction, and a proposed modified version (mRThPSD) of the rate equation theory for the pore size distribution (PSD) of calcined $CaCO_3$ (RThPSD) for the calcination.

The cyclic structure accounting for sorbent deactivation present in the proposed model was justified using data from fixed bed reactor experiments which highlights the relationship between loss of superficial area of CaO sorbents and loss of reactivity.

The model was implemented in gPROMS ModelBuilder® software and was validated with data from fixed bed reactor experiments for different CaL sorbents. One full CaL cycle was simulated successfully for dolomite, with the model estimating both reactions profiles and changes to the calcinated particle PSD with errors below 3%.

Keywords: Calcium-looping, CO_2 capture, modelling, carbonation, calcination.

1. Introduction

Calcium-looping (CaL) is a post-combustion technique for carbon capture and storage, where the carbonation of CaO (s) is used to capture CO_2 (g) and form $CaCO_3$ (s), the calcination of which yields a stream of highly concentrated CO_2 (g). CaL is a very promising candidate for industrial post-combustion CO_2 capture due to the fact that widely available and low-cost natural limestone can be used as a sorbent.

Several carbonation and calcination reaction models can be found in literature, but one complete model that includes both reactions and a cyclic structure accounting for sorbent deactivation during reaction cycling does not exist. An existing model by Zhou et al. (2013) attempts a similar concept by combining the Overlapping Grain Model (OGM) by Liu and Dennis (2012) with an empirical equation that correlates sorbent deactivation with the cycle number. However, the lack of a detailed calcination model restricts it to the experimental conversion loss profile that originated the correlation, and respective temperatures and atmosphere compositions.

This work is part of a study aiming to techno-economically evaluate the implementation of a CaL CO_2 capture process in a Portuguese cement producer's industrial plant based on a multi-scale model of a CaL reactor. Hence there is an urgent need for a model of carbonation and calcination reaction cycles to be used for different reaction temperatures and reaction media, and thus different extents of reaction. By modeling the changes of the sorbent particle's porous structure during calcination using a modified version of the model originally proposed by Li et al. (2016), it is possible to estimate the changes on the sorbent particle's surface area during this reaction, which can be experimentally correlated to the loss of carbonation conversion. By estimating the post-calcination sorbent surface area, one can simulate the loss of carbonation conversion along multiple carbonation-calcination cycles for different extents of both reactions, as well as different temperatures and CO_2 partial pressures.

The objective of this work is to model the complete cycle: the carbonation reaction, the calcination reaction and the subsequent changes on the sorbent porous structure. The model was then implemented and validated in the gPROMS ModelBuilder® software. In this work, data from fixed bed reactor experiments are used to validate both sub-models. Experimental data are used to justify the relationship between the loss of superficial area of CaO sorbents and the loss of carbonation conversion, which allows to extend the simulation to multiple reaction cycles.

2. Model Development

To simulate a complete CaL cycle, two different models were combined as sub-models: the OGM by Liu and Dennis (2012) for the carbonation reaction, and a proposed modified version (mRThPSD) of the rate equation theory for the pore size distribution (PSD) of calcined $CaCO_3$ (RThPSD) by Li et al. (2016) for the calcination reaction.

2.1. Carbonation – Overlapping Grain Model - OGM

The OGM grain model considers that each CaO particle is composed of solid and randomly distributed spherical grains with different sizes. The formation of $CaCO_3$ during carbonation reaction is assumed to happen at the grain surface, causing the grain's volume to expand concentrically, increasing its radius, and shrinking the radius of the CaO core.

The known two main reaction regimes of carbonation are considered: a kinetic controlled profile for small reaction times and a diffusional regime for longer reaction times. By modelling the particle as an aggregate of dynamic grains with shells of $CaCO_3$ and allowing for particle porosity, two mechanisms can control the rate of reaction. The particle porosity allows the inclusion of the diffusion of CO_2 in the porous network, and the layer of $CaCO_3$ around the grain adds an additional resistance to the transport of CO_2 between the pore and the front of reaction. In addition to the intrinsic reaction rate, these mechanisms contribute to more accurate carbonation simulations.

However, the OGM cannot estimate the maximum conversion for a given cycle and uses the deactivated fraction V_d as an input parameter, calculated as the difference between the theoretical maximum conversion and the experimentally observed conversion, that scales down the conversion estimated by the OGM to achieve the desired maximum conversion. The theoretical maximum conversion X_{Max} is a function of porosity of the initial CaO particle ε_0 and of the volumetric expansion coefficient between product and reactant α and can be calculated using Eq. (1).

$$X_{Max} = \frac{\varepsilon_0}{(1-\varepsilon_0)(\alpha-1)} \tag{1}$$

The OGM allows for CaO particles with non-reacting impurities by considering their molar volume in the calculation of α, as defined by Liu and Dennis (2012), thus this value varies between particles – e.g. 2.18 for pure CaO and 1.82 for dolomite. Due to this theorical maximum conversion, there is an experimental limitation that should be accounted for when attempting to fit the OGM to data from carbonation experiments.

Figure 1 displays a plot of X_{Max}, with values larger than 1 computed as 1; and shows that X_{Max} is increasingly sensitive to the value of ε_0 as α decreases. Generically, the porous characteristics of a sample of sorbent particles are not homogeneous, so it might occur that the porosity considered to be characteristic of a given sorbent sample of particles results in lower values of X_{Max} than the experimentally observed maximum conversion, which is of course impossible. As such, when fitting the model to the experimental results, and especially for the samples rich in CaO (e.g. commercial $CaCO_3$), one should verify that this is not the case. If this condition is not verified, the variability of the sorbent sample porosity should be known and used to increase the value of ε_0 in the OGM to ensure that X_{Max} will at least equal the experimental maximum conversion, and only then should the parameter estimation be performed. With the maximum possible ε_0 being 1, the difference in sensitivity means samples less pure in CaO (e.g. dolomite) have more possible ε_0 values for which $X_{Max} > 1$, and thus it is less likely that the condition is not verified. Nonetheless, it can still happen, since ultimately it is the variability of sample's porosity that is more indicative of the likeliness of the condition not being verified – more likely for batches with high variability and less likely if otherwise.

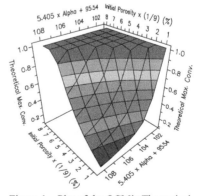

Figure 1 – Plot of the OGM's Theoretical Maximum Conversion (Eq. 1) for Initial Porosity between 0% and 60% and Alpha between 1.01 and 2.20.

2.2. Calcination – A rate equation theory for the PSD of calcined CaCO₃ - RThPSD

The RThPSD models the calcination reaction based on a shrinking core model, where a $CaCO_3$ core leads to a shell of CaO. It also models the dynamics of the porous structure using a rate equation based on balances to the number of vacancies of various sizes. The original RThPSD considers that two phenomena can change the porous structure during the calcination reaction: the release of CO_2 from the reaction, which creates vacancies by leaving the lattice; and the sintering process, which occurs naturally in CaO due to the high temperatures necessary for calcination.

The model, as presented by Li et al. (2016), has its shortcomings addressed by the modified version, mRThPSD, developed in this work, with the lack of initial conditions for the vacancy distribution being one those drawbacks. Without these, the parameter values that result from model validation will not accurately represent the decomposition and sintering processes. The original model assumes that the particle is initially a solid with no porosity and that the porous structure present in the final PSD is formed solely from the release of CO_2 and from the sintering of those vacancies, which is not true, since the unreacted $CaCO_3$ is already porous, as seen in the work of Dennis and Pacciani (2009). The final PSD is thus inextricably linked to the PSD of the unreacted $CaCO_3$. The mRThPSD model addresses this problem by deriving initial conditions from the PSD of the initial unreacted $CaCO_3$, through the assumption that the measured total pore volume for a given pore diameter is equal to the total volume of vacancies of that respective size, assuming these vacancies to be spherical. It is also assumed that these vacancies are homogenously distributed throughout the particle. The initial conditions are calculated with Eq. (2), where $N_{i,k,Initial}$ is the initial number of vacancies of size i in the kth layer, V_{Pore_i} is the porous volume for pore diameter i of the unreacted $CaCO_3$ in m^3g^{-1}, Vol_{R_0} is the particle volume in m^3 and k_{Layers} is the number of layers. The remaining variables and respective units are found in the original paper by Li et al. (2016).

$$N_{i,k,Initial} = \frac{V_{Pore_i} M_{CaO} Vol_{R_0}}{V_{CaO}^M v_1 q^{i-1} k_{layers}}, \forall \, \kappa \in [1, k_{layers}] \tag{2}$$

Furthermore, in the original model, the area of the solid surface around the vacancies is calculated as the surface area of a sphere of the same diameter. However, sorbents for CaL are typically analyzed using N_2 adsorption-desorption experiments together with the BJH model, where the cylindrical pores assumption, among others, leads to Eq. (3).

Since for a sphere of volume V and radius r, the superficial area S is $3V/r$, assuming the vacancies as spherical when calculating their solid surface area generates values 1.5 larger than using Eq. (3). Since, as reported by Dennis and Pacciani (2009), the total pore surface area plays an important role in the carbonation reactivity of the sorbent, overestimating this property will skew future simulations towards unconservative conversion values. To address this, the mRThPSD assumes that the total surface area of pores of a given size is equal to the superficial area of a cylinder with the same total volume as the vacancies of the same size, calculated by Eq. (3) (SI units).

$$V_{Pore_i} = D_{Avg}.S_i / 4 \tag{3}$$

Also, on the proposed mRThPSD the vacancy balance was modified to make the effects of $CaCO_3$ decomposition and CaO sintering simultaneous. Also, an error was corrected in the vacancy balance where the total volume of vacancies would decrease, which does not occur during calcination, as stated in the work by Li et al. (2016), as no pore straightening mechanism is present.

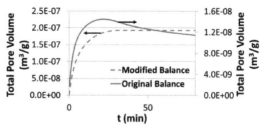

Figure 2 – Total Pore Volume along time using the Original and the Modified Vacancy Balance in the RThPSD model;

Figure 2 highlights this error by showing the evolution of the total pore volume along the time during simulation with the original balance versus with the modified balance. The decrease in pore volume in the original balance is very apparent in Figure 2, caused by the artificial volume consumption brought on by this error being larger than the vacancy generation. As for the modified balance, it is possible to see that the volume created is conserved, as expected.

3. Results

Experimental data from fixed bed reactor experiments were used to validate both models. The OGM was validated for three different sorbents: commercial $CaCO_3$, dolomite, and waste marble powder, a residue from the Portuguese marble industry, shown to have economic potential as a CaL sorbent (Pinheiro et al., 2016). As for the mRThPSD, it is currently only validated for dolomite due to the extensive experimental work required, and its validation with other sorbents is underway. The OGM was able to replicate both reaction regimes for all sorbents with an excellent accuracy, as shown on Figure 3 and by an average error of approximately 2%, for all sorbents. The reaction regimes are highlighted for the dolomite series as line segments i and ii (Figure 3). As for the validation of the mRThPSD, in terms of the estimation of the post-calcination particle's total pore volume, Figure 4 shows a quite satisfactory fitting, considering the complexity of the system. Despite observing that part of the volume allocated to the peak of the mRThPSD post-calcination curve should be located in higher pore diameters, there is an excellent agreement between the estimated and the experimental total pore volume, with a deviation of approximately 3%. As for the calcination conversion profile the proposed

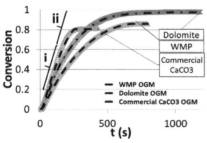

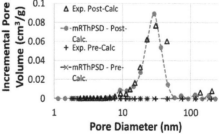

Figure 3 – Validation of the OGM for different sorbents (700 °C, 0.15 bar CO_2). Reaction domains for Dolomite: i – Kinetic Regime, ii – Diffusional Regime;

Figure 4 – Validation of the mRThPSD for Dolomite (800 °C, 0% CO_2);

mRThPSD can estimate it precisely, with an average deviation of approximately 1.2% to the experimental results. The fact that the solid's porous structure influences the reaction rate, highlights the necessity of an adequate fitting to the evolution of the particle's PSD, as seen in Figure 4. However, the inclusion of Eq. (3) limits the effect of an imperfect fit to the superficial area, whereas the overestimation of this

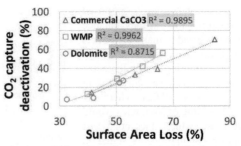

Figure 5 – Sorbent Deactivation (%) Vs. Surface Area Loss (%) for cycles 2, 5, 10 and 20 (from left to right);

property in the original model would result in lower diffusivity values and thus lower reactions rates, hindering the fitting to the conversion profile. As for the cyclic structure of the model, it was implemented using the relationship between the loss of superficial area and sorbent deactivation, shown on Figure 5. This was used to redefine the OGM's deactivated fraction V_d, thus connecting the sub-models. The mRThPSD estimates the total loss of area during calcination, which determines the extent of the following carbonation. Figure 5 shows the importance of using the mRThPSD to model these mechanisms to estimate sorbent deactivation in the case of incomplete reactions, different temperatures and CO_2 partial pressures.

4. Conclusions

A new model that combines carbonation and calcination was implemented in gPROMS ModelBuilder®. Both sub-models were successfully validated using data from fixed bed reactor experiments, for three different sorbents, commercial $CaCO_3$, dolomite, and waste marble powder, a Portuguese marble industry residue, recently shown to have economic potential as an industrial sorbent for CaL. The predicted values have errors below 3% for both sub-models, when compared to experimental results. Only dolomite was used for the validation of mRThPSD and further experimental work with other sorbents is underway. The proposed model contains a cyclic structure accounting for sorbent deactivation, based on the relationship between loss of superficial area of CaO sorbents and loss of reactivity. While only one cycle was simulated in this work, experimental work is underway to validate the cyclic structure for more reaction cycles.

References

J. S. Dennis, R. Pacciani, 2009, The rate and extent of uptake of CO_2 by a synthetic, CaO-containing sorbent, Chemical Engineering Science, 64, 9, 2147–2157.

Z. S. Li, P. T. Liang, N. S. Cai, 2016, A rate equation theory for the pore size distribution of calcined $CaCO_3$ in calcium looping, Faraday Discussions, 192, 197-216.

W. Liu, J. S. Dennis, S. Sultan, S. A. T. Redfern, S.A. Scott, 2012, An investigation of the kinetics of CO2 uptake by a synthetic calcium based sorbent, Chemical Engineering Science , 69, 1, 644-658.

C. I. C. Pinheiro, A. Fernandes, C.Freitas, E. T. Santos, M. F. Ribeiro, 2016, Waste marble powders as promising inexpensive natural CaO-based sorbents for post-combustion CO_2 capture, Industrial & Engineering Chemistry Research, 55, 29, 7860–7872.

Z. Zhou, P. Xu, M. Xie, Z. Cheng, W. Yuan, 2013, Modeling of the carbonation kinetics of a syntethic CaO-based sorbent, Chemical Engineering Science, 95, 283-290.

Anton A. Kiss, Edwin Zondervan, Richard Lakerveld, Leyla Özkan (Eds.)
Proceedings of the 29th European Symposium on Computer Aided Process Engineering
June 16th to 19th, 2019, Eindhoven, The Netherlands. © 2019 Elsevier B.V. All rights reserved.
http://dx.doi.org/10.1016/B978-0-128-18634-3.50170-3

Determination of the optimal distribution of active centers in a multifunctional catalyst pellet using global searching combined with reduced-order modeling approach

Katarzyna Bizon[a,*], Gaetano Continillo[b]

[a]*Cracow University of Technology, ul. Warszawska 24, 31-155 Kraków, Poland*

[b]*Università degli Studi del Sannio, Piazza Roma 21, 82100 Benevento, Italy*

kbizon@chemia.pk.edu.pl

Abstract

The problem of optimal distribution of two types of catalytic active sites for yield maximization is solved for a spherical porous catalyst pellet. The case where two consecutive chemical reactions with one reversible step following arbitrary kinetics occur under isothermal conditions is investigated numerically using the global searching technique. The constraints given by mass balances of the reactants within the pellet accounting both for internal and external mass transfer resistances are reduced by means of Proper Orthogonal Decomposition combined with Galërkin projection method. The applied computational procedure gives significant savings in calculation time as compared to classical discretization approach based on finite differences. Results demonstrate that particle microstructuring via optimal catalyst distribution within the pellet may constitute a powerful means of multistep process intensification.

Keywords: multifunctional catalyst pellet, numerical optimization, reduced order modeling, proper orthogonal decomposition

1. Introduction

Multifunctional catalyst pellets are a relatively new concept, therefore many issues concerning their performance, design, and feasibility of technological implementation as well as economic aspects remain open. Multifunctionality extended down to the particle level may consist both in the integration of sorptive mass storage and catalytic sites as well as coupling of two or more catalytic active sites in a single particle of the catalyst (Grünewald and Agar, 2004; Lugo and Wilhite, 2016). Due to the reduction of mass transfer resistances both applications may result in the enhancement of process performance, as compared to the processes carried out in reactors that integrate different functionalities solely on the apparatus level.

According to Grünewald and Agar (2004), the enhancement of yield through particle microstructuring depends on many factors including the reaction rate constant and composition of the gaseous phase. The authors demonstrated superiority of some selected non-uniform over the uniform distribution of active sites. However, the analysis was limited to a discrete set of a priori selected particle structures. Moreover, while the optimization of the distribution of a single active component within catalyst particles was examined thoroughly in the past decades (Morbidelli et al., 2001), there are no reports dealing with optimization of the distribution of multiple active components.

In this work, the optimal distribution of two active centers in terms of the yield is determined for a single isothermal catalyst pellet by means of a global searching technique. In order to increase the efficiency of the numerical algorithm, differential equations describing concentration profiles of the reactants within catalyst pellet are reduced using Galërkin projection onto empirical modes determined via Proper Orthogonal Decomposition.

2. Mathematical model and algorithms

2.1. Model of a single isothermal catalyst pellet

Let us consider as a test case a general multistep chemical reaction:

$$A \underset{k_{-1}}{\overset{k_1}{\rightleftarrows}} B \overset{k_2}{\longrightarrow} C \tag{1}$$

developing in an isothermal spherical catalyst pellet. Under the assumption that all chemical reactions are first order, the steady-state mass balances in a catalyst written in terms of dimensionless variables are (Bizon, 2017):

$$\frac{d^2\beta_A}{d\zeta^2} + \frac{2}{\zeta}\frac{d\beta_A}{d\zeta} - f_1\Phi_1^2\frac{k_1\beta_A - k_{-1}\beta_B}{k_1 + k_{-1}} \tag{2a}$$

$$\frac{d^2\beta_B}{d\zeta^2} + \frac{2}{\zeta}\frac{d\beta_B}{d\zeta} + f_1\Phi_1^2\frac{k_1\beta_A - k_{-1}\beta_B}{k_1 + k_{-1}} - f_2\Phi_2^2\beta_B \tag{2b}$$

where $\zeta = r/R_p \in [0,1]$ is the dimensionless radial coordinate with R_p being the dimensional particle radius, $\beta_i = C_i/C_{ref}$ is the dimensionless concentration, whereas f_1 and $f_2 = 1 - f_1$ denote the volume fractions of two types of catalytic active sites which are function of the radial coordinate ζ. If the pore diffusion occur with the same effective diffusion coefficient D_{eff} for all reactants, then Thiele moduli Φ_1 and Φ_2 can be defined, respectively, as (Roberts and Lamb, 1996):

$$\Phi_1 = R_p\sqrt{\frac{k_1 + k_{-1}}{D_{eff}}}; \quad \Phi_2 = R_p\sqrt{\frac{k_2}{D_{eff}}} \tag{3}$$

The boundary conditions associated with Eq. (2) are:

$$\frac{d\beta_A}{d\zeta}\bigg|_{\zeta=0} = 0; \quad \frac{d\beta_A}{d\zeta}\bigg|_{\zeta=1} = \text{Bi}\left(\beta_{bulk,A} - \beta_A(1)\right) \tag{4a}$$

$$\frac{d\beta_B}{d\zeta}\bigg|_{\zeta=0} = 0; \quad \frac{d\beta_B}{d\zeta}\bigg|_{\zeta=1} = \text{Bi}\left(\beta_{bulk,B} - \beta_B(1)\right) \tag{4b}$$

where the mass Biot number is defined as $Bi = k_m R_p / D_{eff}$.

2.2. Formulation of the optimization problem

Several indices may quantify the performance of a single catalyst pellet when multiple chemical reactions occur, including effectiveness factor, selectivity or yield. Let us assume that C (Eq. (1)) is the desired product. Following Morbidelli et al. (2001), the yield of product C with respect to reactant A can be defined as the ratio between the actual production rate of C and the consumption rate of A in absence of internal and external transport resistances. Hence, for the yield, the objective function is given by:

$$Y_{CA} = \frac{3 \int_0^1 f_2 k_2 \beta_B \zeta^2 d\zeta}{k_1 - k_{-1}} \tag{5}$$

The optimization problem consists therefore in finding the distribution $f_2(\zeta)$, which maximizes the yield given by Eq. (5) under the constraint given by Eq. (2) and Eq. (4), and the constraints related to the volume fractions of each functionality and to the constant total amount of each catalyst:

$$0 \le f_2(\zeta) \le 1 \quad \text{and} \quad 3 \int_0^1 f_2(\zeta) \zeta^2 d\zeta = \upsilon \quad \text{where} \quad 0 \le \upsilon \le 1 \tag{6}$$

Since the cost function has local minima, the global search algorithm with a scatter-search mechanism for generating start points (Urgay et al., 2007) was applied to solve the optimization problem. The problem was solved directly using the Galërkin projection combined with Proper Orthogonal Decomposition (POD) to transform the boundary value problem given by Eq. (2) into a set of algebraic equations, along with the trapezoidal rule to evaluate the integrals given by Equations (5) and (6). Thus, the adjustable parameters of the problem are the values of the distribution f_2 at the discrete nodes ζ_i, $i = 1,...,N$ with $N = 51$.

2.3. Model reduction

Let us consider a steady-state boundary value problem:

$$L(y(x)) + F(y(x)) = 0, \quad x \in [a, b] \tag{7a}$$
$$B_a(y(a)) = A, \quad B_b(y(B)) = B \tag{7b}$$

where L is a linear operator containing spatial derivatives, F is a non-linear function of y whereas B_a, and B_b are boundary operators. The approximation of the spatial derivatives by finite differences leads to the transformation of Eq. (7) into the following system of N algebraic equations, where N is the number of discretization nodes:

$$\mathbf{Ay} + \mathbf{G(y)} = 0 \tag{8}$$

where $\mathbf{y}$ is a state variable vector, $\mathbf{A}$ is a coefficient matrix whereas $\mathbf{G(y)}$ is a vector accounting for the system nonlinearities and non-homogenous boundary conditions. By employing a POD basis (Bizon, 2017) the state variable vector can be represented in a truncated form as:

$$\mathbf{y} \approx \mathbf{\Phi}_K \mathbf{c}_K \tag{9}$$

where $\mathbf{c}_K$ are modal coefficients, and $\mathbf{\Phi}_K$ are K leading POD modes, $K \leq N$ determined by solving the eigenvalue problem:

$$\mathbf{C\Phi} = \mathbf{\Lambda\Phi} \quad \text{where} \quad \mathbf{C} = \frac{1}{M}\mathbf{YY}^T \tag{10}$$

with the autocorrelation matrix $\mathbf{C}$ calculated from M solutions of the system given by Eq. (8) for various values of the selected model parameters. Introduction of the truncated state variable (9) into the system (8) and its projection onto the basis yield the following reduced order model consisting of K algebraic equations:

$$\mathbf{\Phi}_K^T \mathbf{A} \mathbf{\Phi}_K \mathbf{c}_K + \mathbf{\Phi}_K^T \mathbf{G}(\mathbf{\Phi}_K \mathbf{c}_K) = 0 \tag{11}$$

3. Results and discussion

Table 1 reports the values of the model parameters employed in the numerical simulations. The values of dimensionless concentration of reactant A and intermediate product B in the bulk gas were set respectively to $\beta_{bulk,A} = 1$ and $\beta_{bulk,B} = 0$. In terms of the entire tubular reactor, such boundary conditions can be interpreted by assuming that the considered particle is located in the vicinity of the reactor inlet.

Table 1. Main model parameters used in the numerical simulations

Parameter	Value	Unit	Parameter	Value	Unit
D_{eff}	10^{-6}	m²/s	k_2	10	1/s
k_1	10	1/s	k_m	0.01	m/s
k_{-1}	5	1/s	R_p	10^{-3}	m

The POD basis functions used for order reduction of the constraint (2) were determined from the solutions of the mass balance equations determined with three arrangements of catalyst 1 and catalyst 2. Figure 2a shows the employed distributions of the volume fraction along the particle radius for the catalyst 2, $f_2(\zeta)$.

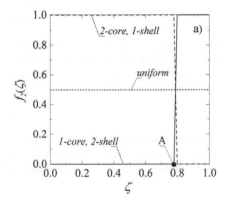
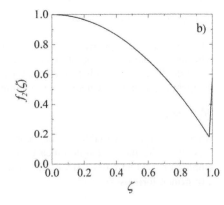

Figure 1. Distributions of the catalyst f_2 used for the determination of the POD basis (a) and optimal distribution of the catalyst f_2 determined via optimization method.

In each case the total volume fraction of each type of active centers was set to $\upsilon = 0.5$, therefore for both core-shell arrangements the point A (Fig. 2a) corresponds to $\zeta = 0.7937$. Since three leading POD modes resulted to contain more than 99% of the so-called cumulative correlation energy (Bizon, 2017), $2 \cdot N = 102$ algebraic equations obtained from the discretization of the Eq. (2) using finite differences were reduced using the Galërkin projection to $2 \cdot K = 6$ equations.

Figure 2b shows the optimal distribution $f_2(\zeta)$ obtained from the optimization procedure coupled with POD-Galërkin. It needs to be mentioned that the computations were also performed using non-reduced mass balance equations. The results obtained, that is both the optimal profile of the volume fraction and the corresponding value of the cost function Y_{CA} were almost identical to those achieved when applying POD-Galërkin. However, the computational time was about 20 times greater.

The determined optimal distribution $f_2(\zeta)$ provides a substantial yield Y_{CA} enhancement with respect to the values of Y_{CA} that may be obtained with a uniform and core-shell distribution of the catalyst (Table 2).

Table 2. Comparison of the selectivity of A towards C, Y_{CA}, achieved using the uniform, core-shell and optimal distribution of active centers within the catalyst pellet

Catalyst arrangement	Uniform	1-core 2-shell	2-core 1-shell	Optimal
Y_{CA}	0.1808	0.1148	0.1263	0.3093

The analysis of Figure 2 demonstrates that the type of catalyst arrangement within the particle strongly influences the concentration profiles of reactant A (Fig. 2a) and intermediate product B (Fig. 2b) within the particle and, as a consequence, the average process rate and the desired product concentration.

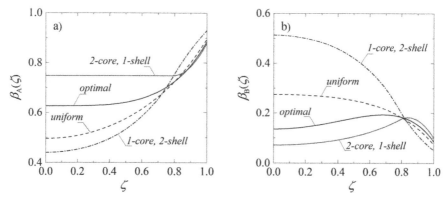

Figure 2. Concentration of reactant A (a) and intermediate product B (b) within particle calculated for different arrangement of the active centers.

Keeping in mind the spherical shape of the particle, it can be observed that in fact the optimal distribution of f_2 (Fig. 2a) provides the highest conversion of the intermediate product B (Fig. 2b) towards the desired product C. Although for the *1-core* and *2-shell* arrangement the average concentration of B is the highest, it should be remembered that in this case the second chemical reaction takes place only in the outer shell of the pellet.

4. Conclusions

Comparison of the catalyst performance indices that may be achieved when using a uniform or a core-shell arrangement of active sites, with the performance achieved for the optimal catalyst distribution within the pellet, confirms that particle microstructuring is a powerful tool for multistep process intensification. The methodology discussed can be easily adapted to more complex chemical kinetics and non-isothermal processes or even to multiscale optimization of the catalyst distribution both at particle and at reactor scale. In such case, computational expenses resulting from additional constraints in the form of a larger number of mass and/or energy equations can still be kept at a reasonable level, thanks to model order reduction based on POD-Galërkin. Moreover, the computed optimal distributions of active centers are non-uniform and can be non-smooth or even discontinuous functions, which is of great importance in view of the catalyst preparation.

Acknowledgements

The research was financed by the Polish National Science Centre, project number 2017/26/D/ST8/00509.

References

K. Bizon, 2017, Assessment of a POD method for dynamical analysis of a catalyst pellet with simultaneous chemical reaction, adsorption and diffusion: Uniform temperature cases, Computers & Chemical Engineering, 97, 259-270.

M. Grünewald, D.V. Agar, 2004, Enhanced catalyst performance using integrated structured functionalites, Chemical Engineering Science, 59, 5519-5526.

E.L. Lugo, B.A. Wilhite, 2016, A theoretical comparison of multifunctional catalyst for sorption-enhanced reforming processes, Chemical Engineering Science, 150, 1-5.

M. Morbidelli, A. Gavriilidis, A. Varma, 2001, Catalyst design. Optimal distribution of catalyst, pellets, reactors, and membranes, Cambridge University Press, UK.

G.W. Roberts, H.H. Lamb, 1996, The effect of reversibility on the selectivity of parallel reactions in a porous catalyst, 51, 441-448.

Z. Urgay, L. Lasdon, J. Plummer, F. Glover, J. Kelly, R. Marti, 2007, Scatter search and local NLP solvers: A multistart framework for global optimisation, INFORMS Journal of Computing, 19, 328-340.

Anton A. Kiss, Edwin Zondervan, Richard Lakerveld, Leyla Özkan (Eds.)
Proceedings of the 29th European Symposium on Computer Aided Process Engineering
June 16th to 19th, 2019, Eindhoven, The Netherlands. © 2019 Elsevier B.V. All rights reserved.
http://dx.doi.org/10.1016/B978-0-128-18634-3.50171-5

Sequential and Simultaneous Optimization Strategies for Increased Production of Monoclonal Antibodies

Chrysoula D. Kappatou[a], Oktay Altunok[a], Adel Mhamdi[a], Athanasios Mantalaris[b], Alexander Mitsos[a*]

[a] *RWTH Aachen University, Aachener Verfahrenstechnik – Process Systems Engineering, Forckenbeckstraße 51, 52074 Aachen, Germany*

[b] *Dept. of Chemical Engineering, Centre for Process Systems Engineering (CPSE), Imperial College London SW7 2AZ, London, U.K*

amitsos@alum.mit.edu

Abstract

Monoclonal antibodies (mAbs) represent a significant class of biopharmaceutics with a wide range of diagnostic and therapeutic applications. Typically, mAbs are produced by cultivated mammalian cells, to meet the high quality product specifications. For new products and cell lines, an adaptation of cultivation conditions is required. This is usually performed experimentally. Model-based approaches can be a powerful tool to reduce experimental efforts and accelerate process development. We present optimizations using the process model in Kappatou et al. (2018), which is based on Quiroga et al. (2016). In particular, we perform fed-batch optimizations following a sequential and a simultaneous approach. In the sequential approach, we first find optimal initial conditions for the batch process using different objectives, and then we optimize the feeding for constant initial conditions. In the simultaneous approach, we directly optimize for initial conditions and appropriate feed rates. The optimizations lead to significant improvements compared to the base case presented in Quiroga et al. (2016). The results indicate that the sequential approach is sometimes able to outperform the simultaneous one by overcoming limitations of the local optimization used. This may be due to the flexibility of the sequential approach to use different objectives for the two steps (batch and fed-batch). Therefore, the results further highlight the importance of utilizing good initialization procedures in local optimization.

Keywords: monoclonal antibodies, bioprocess intensification, model-based optimization

1. Introduction

Within the biopharmaceutical industry, monoclonal antibodies (mAbs) are important products. Their increasing demand, together with the advent of biosimilar products and the necessity for incorporation of quality by design (QbD) principles, constitute current challenges (Shukla et al., 2017 & Collins, 2018). Therefore, a shift towards methods that can provide better mechanistic process understanding, and thus facilitate process intensification and control, is needed. To this end, model-based approaches outweigh considerable advantages.

Although recent advances in modelling have paved the way for model-based optimization strategies, there is so far only a limited amount of publications reporting on optimization of mAb production using mathematical models. In batch processes, optimization of the initial nutrient composition is a key feature. In fed-batch, optimal feeding compositions and rates are explored. Nevertheless, the great majority of existing studies considers only feeding of glucose and/or glutamate, which might not be the only growth limiting nutrients (Pörtner and Schäfer, 1996). In an industrial scale, fed-batch optimizations are often performed empirically, based on a long history of data usually obtained from batch experiments. Optimizing the fed-batch culture for both initial concentrations and feeding strategies is advantageous, as it reduces experimental costs (fewer experiments) and product time to market.

We focus on dynamic optimization of mAb producing processes in fed-batch mode of operation. We optimize using a reformulated version of the metabolic model proposed by Quiroga et al. (2016) that we presented in Kappatou et al. (2018). These models enable multiple component feeding. To describe cell's metabolism, metabolic shifts are also incorporated. More information about the modelling part can be found in Quiroga et al. (2016, 2018) and about the undertaken reformulations in Kappatou et al. (2018).

The remainder of the article is organized as follows: In Section 2 we present fed-batch optimizations following the two different methodologies, namely the sequential and the simultaneous approach. Section 3 discusses the formulation of the optimization problems. The optimization results are presented in Section 4. Section 5 summarizes this work and provides conclusions and future directions.

2. Fed-batch process optimization

We consider two different approaches for optimization of initial concentrations and feeding profiles of nutrients, as shown in Fig. 1. The ultimate goal in both cases is to maximize the final antibody concentration (mg/L), which corresponds to the high-value pharmaceutical product.

In the sequential approach, we first find optimal initial concentrations for the batch process (batch optimization), and then we optimize the feeding using the previously derived optimal initial concentrations (fed-batch optimization). Different objectives can be used in these steps. For the batch optimization, we consider to maximize final product concentration (mAb) and/or to maximize viable cell density (Xv), as these turned out to be the most promising objectives for our case study. The subsequent fed-batch optimization maximizes the final product concentration. In the simultaneous approach, we directly optimize for both initial concentrations and appropriate feed rates with the objective to maximize the final antibody concentration. Note that the terminology

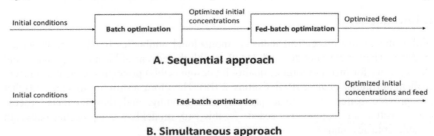

Figure 1- Solution approaches considered in the case studies

sequential and simultaneous should not be confused with that typically used in dynamic optimization theory to describe the indirect numerical solution methods single-shooting and orthogonal collocation, respectively.

3. Problem formulation

We investigate optimization problems with embedded process dynamics, using the reformulated metabolic model in Kappatou et al. (2018). The model consists of 31 differential, 81 algebraic equations and 41 parameters. The key components for the different optimization problems are summarized in Table 1. A brief description of the constraints and the control variables included into the optimization formulations is given.

Table 1- Optimization problem formulations

Optimization approach	Sequential		Simultaneous
Operation mode	Batch	Fed-batch	Fed-batch
Objective	max mAb or Xv	max mAb	max mAb
Constraints			
Viability	Viab ≤ 60 %		
Residual nutrients	$[NUT(t_f)] \leq 0.1\,[NUT]_0$		
Glutamate depletion	$t_{cr,GLU} \leq 92.5$ h	n/a	$t_{cr,GLU} \leq 92.5$ h
Volume limitation	n/a		$V \leq 1.1\,V_0$
Control variables			
Final time	$t_{batch} \leq t_f \leq 2\,t_{batch}$		
Feeding rate	n/a	$0 \leq F_{in} \leq F_{in,max}$	
Initial nutrients	$[NUT]_{min} \leq [NUT]_0 \leq [NUT]_{max}$	n/a	$[NUT]_{min} \leq [NUT]_0 \leq [NUT]_{max}$

3.1. Control variables

In this study, six growth limiting nutrients (NUT) are considered, namely glucose (GLC), glutamate (GLU), arginine (ARG), asparagine (ASP), isoleucine (ILE) and leucine (LEU). Optimal initial concentrations for these nutrients are sought. As concentration ranges of the nutrients, we consider the bounds reported by Pörtner et al. (2014). Fed-batch optimization aims at deriving optimal feeding strategies (feeding -composition, -time and -rates). Note that the feeding composition is already optimized in a previous study (Quiroga et al., 2018), and thus is not examined here. The final time of the culture is also an optimization degree of freedom, and is allowed to vary between 144 h (batch time) and 288 h. From our current experience, the upper bound in the culture time is sufficiently large (Kappatou et al., 2018).

3.2. Constraints

Cell viability refers to the percentage of viable cells into the culture. In the considered optimization problems, it represents an indirect quality measure, and thus should be kept above a critical value. This way quality reducing effects are avoided. In this study, we impose a lower value for viability at 60 %. To reduce unnecessary residual nutrients, we impose an additional constraint on the residual concentrations to be lower than 10% of their initial concentrations. This is because, although on the one side nutrient exhaustion induces cell starvation, on the other side, excessive supply can cause inhibition of cell growth and increased production of inhibitory by-products (Bibila and Robinson, 1995). One of the essential nutrients is glutamate. The cells can only survive for a limited duration, after glutamate depletion (Meister et al., 1980). Therefore, an additional constraint on the culture duration after exhaustion of glutamate (92.5 h) is incorporated to the model. This value corresponds to the value, at which culture was terminated after glutamate depletion at the real batch experiments used for model validation. Finally, in the fed-batch optimizations we impose an additional constraint that the volume is at most increased by 10% to account for dilution effects (Kiparissides et al., 2015).

4. Results and discussion

The optimization studies are performed using gPROMS v.5.0.1 (Process Systems Enterprise, 1997-2018) using a piecewise constant discretization of the controls. The simulation times vary from a few seconds for the batch cases to a few hours for the fed-batch cases with no significant differences with respect to the different approaches.

We show the optimal initial concentrations for all cases in Table 2 and the key indicators for the optimizations of the batch processes in Table 3. The max (mAb) case achieves a higher antibody concentration than maximizing the viable cell concentration, max (Xv). However, the max (Xv) case aiming at (and achieving) a higher viable cell concentration, does not reach the bound on the viability constraint and yields a lower accumulation of toxic lactate. All these are desired characteristics, and indicate the potential of utilizing these optimal concentrations for subsequent fed-batch optimization studies.

We give the optimization results for the fed-batch processes in Table 4. A comparison of the results between the simultaneous and the sequential approach reveals that the simultaneous max (mAb) performs slightly better than the sequential max (mAb, mAb) within identical process duration. This is expected due to the higher degree of freedom in the simultaneous approach. However, the latter is outperformed by the sequential max (Xv, mAb) approach that achieves 7 % higher product concentration with 12 % longer process duration. This approach yields a final mAb improvement of 244 % and an expansion of the culture spam around 1.5 days compared to the unoptimized batch case presented in Quiroga et al. (2016).

Table 2- Optimal initial nutrients concentrations in mM

Objectives	Approach	ARG	ASP	GLC	GLU	ILE	LEU
max(mAb)	Sequential batch	3.82	1.38	28.51	2.99	3.13	4.27
max (Xv)	Sequential batch	3.71	1.28	24.80	2.22	2.86	4.27
max (mAb)	Simultaneous fed-batch	4.27	1.43	35.31	3.03	3.33	4.27

Table 3- Batch optimization results

Objectives	mAb (mg/L)	Xv (cells/L)	Culture Duration (h)	LAC (mM)	Viability (%)
max (mAb)	487	3.87E9	166	10.9	60
max (Xv)	393	4.44E9	157	8.8	73

Table 4- Fed-batch optimization results

Optimization Approach	mAb (mg/L)	Culture Duration (h)	LAC (mM)	Viability (%)
Sequential max (mAb, mAb)	582	166	11.5	60
Sequential max (Xv, mAb)	635	186	10.5	60
Simultaneous max (mAb)	592	166	11.7	60

An illustrative representation of the optimization results for the different approaches is shown in Fig. 2. The sequential max (mAb, mAb) and the simultaneous max (mAb) case perform quite similarly. The feeding is introduced early in order to extend the exponential growth phase of the culture. The culture grows faster, but also the release of lactate is faster (results not shown here). In contrast, in the sequential max (Xv, mAb) approach the feeding is added a later time period, which initially slows down the growth, but leads to extended process duration and a higher final product concentration.

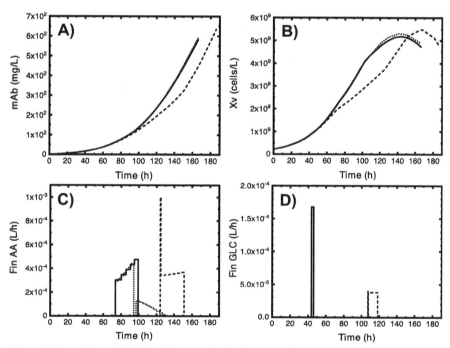

Figure 2- Key trajectories for the different optimization approaches
(A) Optimized mAb production [mg/L], (B) Viable cell concentration [cells/L], (C) Optimal feeding profiles of amino acids [L/h], (D) Optimal feeding profiles of glucose [L/ h]
—— Sequential max (mAb, mAb) ······· Sequential max (Xv, mAb) ------ Simultaneous max (mAb)

If the dynamic optimization problem was solved globally, the simultaneous approach would give the best results in terms of maximizing process objective. The better performance of the sequential approach in case that different objectives are used in the two stages can be explained by the limitations of local optimization. More precisely, by solving the optimization problems locally, we end up with suboptimal solutions, the performance of which (as shown) can be strongly affected by good initial guesses.

5. Conclusions

This work applies dynamic optimization studies to a predictive mathematical model developed by Quiroga et al. (2016) and numerically improved by Kappatou et al. (2018). The main scope of the study is to develop computationally efficient and biologically meaningful optimization strategies for mAb process intensification. In practice, being able to optimize a fed-batch culture for both initial concentrations and feeding strategies at the same time provides a real commercial advantage due to its general cost- and time to market- reducing effect. Following a sequential and a simultaneous approach for fed-batch optimization, we exploit different suboptimal solutions to our problem. The higher flexibility of the sequential approach, in terms of being able to utilize different objectives for the two step batch and fed-batch optimization, seems to offer certain advantages. In order to overcome such limitations of local solutions, future research focus should be shifted towards global dynamic optimization techniques.

6. Acknowledgements

This work has received funding from the European Union's Horizon 2020 research and innovation programme under the Marie Skłodowska-Curie grant agreement no.675251.

References

T. A. Bibila, D. K. Robinson, 1995, In pursuit of the optimal fed-batch process for monoclonal antibody production, Biotechnology progress, 11(1), 1-13.

P. C. Collins, 2018, Chemical engineering and the culmination of quality by design in pharmaceuticals, AIChE Journal, 64(5), 1502-1510.

C. D. Kappatou, A. Mhamdi, A. Quiroga-Campano, A. Mantalaris, A. Mitsos, 2018, Model-Based Dynamic Optimization of Monoclonal Antibodies Production in Semibatch Operation—Use of Reformulation Techniques, Industrial & Engineering Chemistry, 57(30), 9915-9924.

A. Kiparissides, E. N. Pistikopoulos, A. Mantalaris, 2015, On the model-based optimization of secreting mammalian cell (GSNS0) cultures, Biotechnology & bioengineering, 112(3), 536-548.

A. Meister, 1980, Catalytic mechanism of glutamine synthetase; overview of glutamine metabolism, In Glutamine: metabolism, enzymology, and regulation, 1-40.

R. Pörtner (ed.), 2014, Animal Cell Biotechnology, Humana Press, DOI: 10.1007/978-1-62703-733-4.

R. Pörtner, T. Schäfer, 1996, Modelling hybridoma cell growth and metabolism—a comparison of selected models and data, Journal of biotechnology, 49(1-3), 119-135.

A. L. Quiroga-Campano, N. Panoskaltsis, A. Mantalaris, 2018, Energy-based culture medium design for biomanufacturing optimization: A case study in monoclonal antibody production by GS-NS0 cells, Metabolic Engineering, 47, 21-30.

A. L. Quiroga-Campano, M. Papathanasiou, E. N. Pistikopolous, A. Mantalaris, 2016, A predictive model for energy metabolism and ATP balance in mammalian cells: towards the energy-based optimization of mAb production, Computer Aided Chemical Engineering, Elsevier, 38, 1581-1586.

A. A. Shukla, L.S. Wolfe, S. S. Mostafa, C. Norman, 2017, Evolving trends in mAb production processes, Bioengineering & translational medicine, 2(1), 58-69.

Process Systems Enterprise, gPROMS, 1997-2018, www.psenterprise.com/gproms.

Anton A. Kiss, Edwin Zondervan, Richard Lakerveld, Leyla Özkan (Eds.)
Proceedings of the 29th European Symposium on Computer Aided Process Engineering
June 16th to 19th, 2019, Eindhoven, The Netherlands. © 2019 Elsevier B.V. All rights reserved.
http://dx.doi.org/10.1016/B978-0-128-18634-3.50172-7

Operating regime model based multi-objective sensor placement for data reconciliation

Gyula Dorgo[a], Mate Haragovics[b] and Janos Abonyi[a*]

[a]*MTA-PE Lendület Complex Systems Monitoring Research Group, Egyetem str. 10, Veszprém, H-8200, HUNGARY*
[b]*MOL Danube Refinery, Olajmunkás str. 2., Százhalombatta, H-2443, HUNGARY*
janos@abonyilab.com

Abstract

Although the number of sensors in chemical production plants is increasing thanks to the IoT revolution, it is still a crucial problem what to measure and how to place the sensors as such the resulted sensor network be robust and cost-effectively provide the required information. This problem is especially relevant in flexible multi-purpose, multi-product production plants when there are significant differences among the operating regions. The present work aims the development of a sensor placement methodology that utilizes the advantages of local linear models. Realizing the often conflicting nature of the key objectives of sensor placement, the problem is formulated as a multi-objective optimization task taking into consideration the cost, estimation accuracy, observability and fault detection performance of the designed networks and simultaneously seeking for the optimal solutions under multiple operating regimes. The effectiveness of the Non-dominated Sorting Genetic Algorithm-II (NSGA-II)-based solution of the defined problem is demonstrated through benchmark examples.

Keywords: sensor placement, multi-objective optimization, data reconciliation

1. Introduction

Data reconciliation is a widely applied technique to increase the accuracy of the measured variables and calculate the unmeasured variables using the known uncertainty of the applied sensors and the structure and the balance equations as technological constraints. Data reconciliation-based optimal sensor placement can be considered as an optimization problem (Bagajewicz (1997)). As several objectives can be defined to measure the goodness of a sensor placement in a given technology, the visualization of the Pareto optimal solutions can facilitate the work of the decision makers (Bagajewicz and Cabrera (2003)). The problem is much more complex when the process is flexible and its structure changes in time. Xie et al. (2018) incorporated multiple operation modes to data reconciliation. However, in this work the optimal and robust placement of the sensors is not studied although the solution of this crucial problem significantly determines the applicability of data reconciliation in complex multi-mode technologies. To handle this problem we define a multi-objective optimization task that ensures the observability of the system, and generates the Pareto front of the best solutions in terms of estimation accuracy, fault detection performance and cost of the designed sensor networks in all of the operating modes of the technology. Formerly, Brown et al. (2005) incorporated multiple objectives to process measurement system design.

The core concept of our methodology and the main contributions of the present paper is twofold: first, we describe how a multi-objective optimisation problem can be formulated taking into consideration the general aspects of observability, detectability, estimation accuracy and cost-effectiveness and highlight the conflicting nature of these objectives. Second, as many of the modern production technologies can be operated in multiple modes, the optimal sensor placement solution is sought globally for multiple operating modes. The main steps of the methodology are represented by the blue arrows in Figure 1. The boxes above and below the arrows show the required input and the obtained output information, respectively. Therefore, first the structure of the technology is analysed in order investigate the observability, estimation accuracy of the variables and the cost of the tested sensor network. Then data reconciliation is applied to reconcile and estimate the variables and determine the reconciliation accuracy. In the following, the detectability of faults is tested based on Type I and II errors using simulated gross errors on the measurement values. Finally, the optimisation algorithm evaluates the given performance measures and creates the next candidate sensor placement.

The roadmap of the present paper is as follows. Section 2 describes the proposed multi-objective and multi-operating mode sensor placement problem. Firstly, the reconciliation and estimation of measured and unmeasured variables are discussed, together with the fault detection basics. This will be followed by the presentation of the performance measures used in the objective function of the multi-objective optimisation problem. The applicability and effectiveness of the proposed solution is described in Section 3.

To stimulate further research, the resultant MATLAB codes of the optimisation algorithms are publicly available on the website of the authors (www.abonyilab.com).

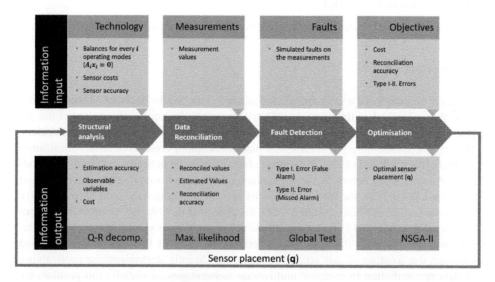

Figure 1: The workflow of the proposed optimisation-based sensor placement methodology. The optimisable variable is the **q** binary vector indicating whether the kth variable is measured ($q_k = 1$) or not ($q_k = 0$).

2. The multiobjective multi-mode sensor placement problem

The balance equations of chemical technologies can be compactly represented as the functions of the variables ($\mathbf{x}$) and the inputs ($\mathbf{u}$), $\dot{x} = f(\mathbf{x}, \mathbf{u})$, which is represented by a nonlinear algebraic equation system $\mathbf{0} = f(\mathbf{x}, \mathbf{u})$ in the case of steady state operations. Generally, the variables ($\mathbf{x}$) can be classified into three major groups: variables, whose values are exactly known ($\mathbf{w} = [w_1...w_{N_w}]^T$), measured variables ($\mathbf{y} = [y_1...y_{N_y}]^T$) and unmeasured variables ($\mathbf{z} = [z_1...z_{N_z}]^T$). $[\mathbf{w}\,\mathbf{y}\,\mathbf{z}]^T = \mathbf{Px}$ where $\mathbf{P}$ is a permutation matrix, which reorders the elements of vector $\mathbf{x}$ according to this classification system. The general $\mathbf{Ax} = \mathbf{0}$ form of the linearised balance equations can be written as $\mathbf{Ax} = \mathbf{AP}^T\mathbf{Px} = \mathbf{AP}^T[\mathbf{w}\,\mathbf{y}\,\mathbf{z}]^T = \mathbf{0}$ where $\mathbf{AP}^T = [\mathbf{A_w}\quad \mathbf{A_y}\quad \mathbf{A_z}]$ and the matrices $\mathbf{A_w}$, $\mathbf{A_y}$ and $\mathbf{A_z}$ are the columns of the original $\mathbf{A}$ matrix assigned to the variables $\mathbf{w}$, $\mathbf{y}$ and $\mathbf{z}$, respectively. Hence, the $\mathbf{Ax} = \mathbf{0}$ form of the balance equations can be expressed as $\mathbf{A_w}\mathbf{w} + \mathbf{A_y}\mathbf{y} + \mathbf{A_z}\mathbf{z} = \mathbf{0}$. The aim of data reconciliation is to minimize the difference between the measured and the reconciled values taking into consideration the variance of the measurements and the constraints formed by the balance equations of the system. This can be expressed by the following constrained objective function:

$$\min_{\hat{\mathbf{y}}}(\mathbf{y} - \hat{\mathbf{y}})^T\mathbf{V}^{-1}(\mathbf{y} - \hat{\mathbf{y}}) \tag{1}$$

subject to $\mathbf{A_y}\hat{\mathbf{y}} + \mathbf{A_z}\hat{\mathbf{z}} = \mathbf{b}$ (2)

where the vectors $\hat{\mathbf{y}}$ and $\hat{\mathbf{z}}$ are the vectors of estimates (reconciled values) for the measured and the unmeasured variables, respectively. If $rank(\mathbf{A_z}) = r$ and N_u is the number of unmeasured variables then we know that at least $N_u - r$ variables are unobservable and the vector of unmeasured variables can be divided into observable and unobservable variables $\mathbf{z} = [\mathbf{z_r}\quad \mathbf{z}_{N_u - r}]^T$. Since observability is a key aspect of industrial process control, in the following we investigate the observability of $\mathbf{z_r}$.

Most industrial processes can be operated under multiple operating modes and this can be indicated by the modified incidence matrix of the technology. Therefore, the general $\mathbf{Ax} = \mathbf{0}$ equation can be replaced by the $\mathbf{A}_i\mathbf{x}_i = \mathbf{0}$ equation, where $i = 1...N_m$ indicates the operating mode. However, in order to keep the representation simple, we only indicate the operating modes in situations where it needs to be highlighted. An example for different operating modes can be the optional deletion of Stream 3 in certain operating modes in Figure 2 (marked with red). Since the element $\mathbf{A_w}\mathbf{w}$ is known, it is useful to replace it by $-\mathbf{b}$ and reformulate the equation as $\mathbf{A_y}\mathbf{y} + \mathbf{A_z}\mathbf{z} = \mathbf{b}$.

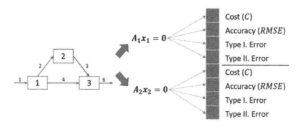

Figure 2: Definition of the operating modes and their objective functions

The core concept of optimal sensor placement design is to determine which process variables to measure in order to maintain an optimal trade-off between the cost (both in terms of capital and operational costs) and accuracy of measurements. However, primarily the cost and accuracy of measurements is mentioned, these goals call for further practical aspects: the control goals of the optimized industrial facility and the robustness of the control network. According to Bagajewicz (1997), the robustness of a network incorporates three properties: availability, error detectability, and resilience. Based on this, the following objectives are defined:

Cost of the network: For all the measured variables there is a measuring instrument with an associated cost c_k. Assuming a binary vector variable $\mathbf{q}$ with the following definition: $q_k = 1$ if x_k is measured, $q_k = 0$ if x_k otherwise. The cost of the sensor network can be expressed as $C(q) = \sum_k c_k q_k$.

Observability: The observability of the variables of the analysed or planned technology is a crucial industrial factor. Therefore, the placement of sensors aims to maximize the number of observable sensors through both measurements and the estimation of unmeasured variables, $N_{obs} = N_y + N_r$.

Reconciliation error: Assigning the reconciled and estimated observable variables as $\hat{\mathbf{o}} = \begin{bmatrix} \hat{\mathbf{y}} & \hat{\mathbf{z}}_\mathbf{r} \end{bmatrix}$ and $\mathbf{o}$ as the nominal value of these variables, the reconciliation error can be calculated. In the following this error term is marked as *RMSE*.

Gross error detection: In most of the cases during data reconciliation, only normally distributed random errors are assumed to be present on the measured data. However, due to different faults in the analysed process, gross errors can be present as well. In order to determine the presence of gross errors, one of the first test proposed by Ripps (1965) and Almasy and Sztano (1975), the global test was applied. However, the test does not indicate the place of the gross error, it provides a good preliminary analysis before the application of more advanced techniques. Therefore, the results of the hypothesis tests are applied as a performance measure to describe the detectability of the network using the *Type I* error (false alarm) and *Type II* error (missed alarm).

Our aim is to design sensor networks that simultaneously meet multiple requirements, so we intend to design sensor networks that optimal from the view of all m properties in every N_m operating modes $\mathbf{Z}(\mathbf{q}) = \begin{bmatrix} Z_{1,1}(\mathbf{q}), \dots Z_{1,m}(\mathbf{q}) \dots Z_{N_m,1}(\mathbf{q}), \dots Z_{N_m,m}(\mathbf{q}) \end{bmatrix}$. In practice, we look for four properties to be optimal: $Z_{i,1}(\mathbf{q}) = min_q\, C(q)$, $Z_{i,2}(\mathbf{q}) = min_q\, RMSE$, $Z_{i,3}(\mathbf{q}) = min_q\, Type\ I$, $Z_{i,4}(\mathbf{q}) = min_q\, Type\ II$.

The huge search space is further complicated by the often competing objectives of the design process. A genetic algorithm is a promising method for the generation of multipurpose senor configurations. Multi-objective optimization algorithms generate a set of optimal solutions. The Pareto fronts of these solutions simultaneously consider several design aspects. Since when solving the problem multiple operating modes and objectives must be taken into consideration at the same time; the problem has been implemented in a well-established genetic algorithm-based multi-objective optimization environment, the Non-dominated Sorting Genetic Algorithm-II (NSGA-II) Deb et al. (2000). The search space is conveniently described by the binary $\mathbf{q}$ vector. The observability is tested by feasibility constraints.

3. Application example

The applicability of the proposed optimisation-based sensor placement methodology is demonstrated on two benchmark data reconciliation tasks, the mass flow network originally published by Rosenberg et al. (1987) and the steady state steam-metering example of the methanol synthesis unit of a large chemical technology Serth and Heenan (1986) as presented in part (a) and (b) of Figure 3. The multiple operating modes are defined by deletion of the streams marked by red in (a) and (b) of Figure 3 (Stream 9 in part (a) and Stream 2 and 14 in part (b)). The networks in part (c) and (d) show an exemplary optimal sensor placement solution for the networks presented in part (a) and (b), respectively.

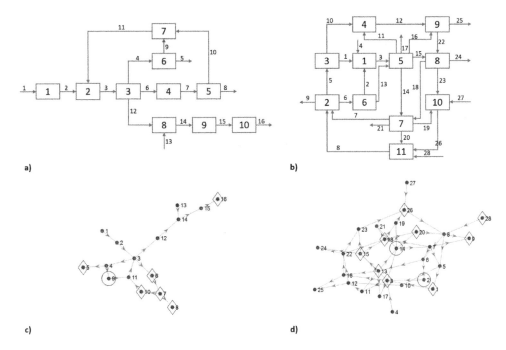

Figure 3: Network representation of the analysed technologies and an exemplary solution of their optimal sensor placement. The mass flow network of Rosenberg et al. (1987) and its solution (a, c) and the steam-metering system for methanol synthesis of Serth and Heenan (1986) and its solution (b, d). In the exemplary solution of networks (c, d) the streams are represented by the nodes, the nodes marked by red and green stars show the measured and estimated variables, respectively, while the nodes framed with a diamond shape are the nonredundant measurements. The circles show the streams that are neglected in certain operating modes (same as the red streams in part (a, b)).

As can be seen in the bottom part of Figure 3, every streams are observable in the network, although some of them are estimated instead of sensory measurements. The redundant measurements increase the accuracy of data reconciliation and increase the detectability of the network. Figure 4 shows the normalized values of the cost function of the obtained Pareto optimal solutions on a parallel coordinates-based visualisation for the problem published by Rosenberg et al. (1987).

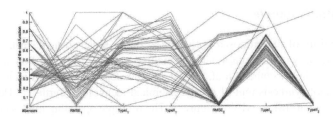

Figure 4: Parallel coordinate representation of the conflicting objectives

4. Conclusions

According to our knowledge, this paper is the first (and yet only introductory) work that defines the problem of multi-mode sensor placement as a multi-pbjective optimization problem. The cost, accuracy, Type I and II errors of the gross error detection performance were defined as cost functions to evaluate each configurations of the technology, while the constrains were defined to ensure the observability of the system. To handle these conflicting objectives and the complexity of the search space, the NSGA-II evolutionary optimization algorithm has been utilized. The efficiency of the proposed approach is examined through two modified benchmark problems with multiple operating modes. The results prove the applicability of the proposed algorithm and motivate our work for the improvement of the algorithm for dynamic sensor placement with different sensor types.

Acknowledgments This research has been supported by the National Research, Development and Innovation Office (NKFIH) OTKA-116674 project. Gyula Dorgo was supported by the ÚNKP-18-3 New National Excellence Program of the Ministry of Human Capacities.

References

G. Almasy, T. Sztano, 1975. Checking and correction of measurements on the basis of linear system model. Problems of Control and Information Theory 4.

M. Bagajewicz, E. Cabrera, 2003. Pareto optimal solutions visualization techniques for multiobjective design and upgrade of instrumentation networks. Industrial & Engineering Chemistry Research 42 (21), 5195–5203.

M. J. Bagajewicz, 1997. Design and retrofit of sensor networks in process plants. AIChE Journal 43 (9), 2300–2306.

D. Brown, F. Maréchal, G. Heyen, J. Paris, 2005. Application of multi-objective optimisation to process measurement system design. In: European Symposium on Computer-Aided Process Engineering-15. Computer-aided chemical engineering.

K. Deb, S. Agrawal, A. Pratap, T. Meyarivan, 2000. A fast elitist non-dominated sorting genetic algorithm for multi-objective optimization: Nsga-ii. In: M. Schoenauer, K. Deb, G. Rudolph, X. Yao, E. Lutton, J. J. Merelo, H.-P. Schwefel (Eds.), Parallel Problem Solving from Nature PPSN VI. Springer Berlin Heidelberg, Berlin, Heidelberg, pp. 849–858.

D. L. Ripps, 1965. Adjustment of experimental data. Chemical Engineering Progress Symposium Series 61, 8–13.

J. Rosenberg, R. S. H. Mah, C. Iordache, 1987. Evaluation of schemes for detecting and identifying gross errors in process data. Industrial & Engineering Chemistry Research 26 (3), 555–564.

R. W. Serth, W. A. Heenan, 1986. Gross error detection and data reconciliation in steam-metering systems. AIChE Journal 32 (5), 733–742.

S. Xie, C. Yang, X. Yuan, X. Wang, Y. Xie, 2018. Layered online data reconciliation strategy with multiple modes for industrial processes. Control Engineering Practice 77, 63 – 72.

Anton A. Kiss, Edwin Zondervan, Richard Lakerveld, Leyla Özkan (Eds.)
Proceedings of the 29th European Symposium on Computer Aided Process Engineering
June 16th to 19th, 2019, Eindhoven, The Netherlands. © 2019 Elsevier B.V. All rights reserved.
http://dx.doi.org/10.1016/B978-0-128-18634-3.50173-9

Fouling Modelling in Crude Oil Heat Exchanger Networks using Data Reconciliation and Estimation of Unmeasured Process Variables

José Loyola-Fuentes[a,*], Megan Jobson[a] and Robin Smith[a]

[a]Centre for Process Integration, School of Chemical Engineering and Analytical Science, The University of Manchester, M13 9PL, UK
jose.loyolafuentes@manchester.ac.uk

Abstract

In crude oil refineries, fouling has a significant impact on operating and maintenance costs. The growth of fouling layers on the surface of heat exchangers in a crude oil heat exchanger network (HEN) also increases both energy use and CO_2 emissions. Fouling models facilitate process design and integration while systematically accounting for the impact of fouling. The most common models use a series of parameters that are specific to the type of crude oil, as well as the operating conditions of the pre-heat train. These models are of great importance as they can indicate the set of operating conditions (stream velocities and temperatures) at which the occurrence of fouling might be avoided. A key challenge is to define an accurate method for determining fouling models for each side of a heat exchanger within a network. To achieve this goal, plant-measured data are used to monitor the thermal performance of a pre-heat train, and to obtain specific insights related to the impact of fouling. The main concern related to these data and their interpretation is the effect of measurement error and the limited number of measurements available in the process. This work presents a new methodology for calculating fouling model parameters for both sides of shell-and-tube heat exchangers using simulated plant-data along with data reconciliation and gross error detection. A heat exchanger network model coupled with fouling dynamics is used for simulating a crude oil pre-heat train and for the prediction of fouling behaviour. The effect of full and partial instrumentation in the estimation of reconciled measurements is accounted for in a case study, where the prediction of fouling deposition is assessed.

Keywords: Crude Oil Distillation, Heat Integration, Optimisation, Process Simulation

1. Introduction

The reduction of energy demand is a global concern. A considerable amount of research efforts has been centred in developing new technologies to continuously decrease the energy use, specifically in crude oil refining processes. In general, crude oil is initially pre-heated to approximately 380°C before entering the crude distillation unit (CDU). A heat exchanger network (commonly known as the pre-heat train) is used for this pre-heating, recovering around 60-70% of the heat needed in the CDU (Panchal and Huangfu, 2000). Unfortunately, fouling deposition in the Pre-heat Train decreases the thermal and hydraulic performance of the network. In order to avoid the growth of fouling layers on the surface of heat exchangers, fouling models can be used for model-based predictions and design of mitigation strategies.

Fouling models can be grouped according to their physical basis. In particular, the concept of the so-called fouling threshold (Ebert and Panchal, 1995) provides a useful theoretical basis for establishing a relationship between the fouling phenomena and the pre-heat train operating conditions. Fouling threshold models are crude oil-dependent; the set of parameters in each model captures the characteristics of a particular crude oil or a crude oil blend. These parameters can be determined using experimental or field data by fitting these data to an appropriate fouling model. Both methods have their own advantages and disadvantages; however, the use of field data contributes to a more realistic representation of the process, when such data is appropriately processed.

Data Reconciliation is a widely used method for processing measured data. This method reduces the impact of measurement error in a data-set. In general, measurement error is defined as the sum of random and gross (or systematic) errors (Narasimhan and Jordache, 2000). To account for these two contributions, gross error detection should be included in the data reconciliation method; this simultaneous strategy is able to estimate the presence and value(s) of miscalibration(s) within the set of data. An equally important challenge is the presence of unmeasured process variables. When a set of process variables is unmeasured, the number of degrees of freedom and available linearly independent equations limit the estimation of this unmeasured variables (Romagnoli and Sánchez, 1999). Therefore, the selection of unmeasured variables should be (in principle) such that the available information is sufficient for the estimation of all unmeasured variables.

This work proposes a methodology to determine fouling threshold models for a crude oil pre-heat train subject to fouling in both the shell and tube sides. Data reconciliation and gross error detection techniques are integrated with an optimisation-based parameter fitting to calculate fouling model parameters associated with different mechanisms within the network. The effects of different gross error and unmeasured process variables is analysed in a case study, in which the set of missing measurements is classified according to whether each missing process variable in the set can be estimated or not.

2. Modelling and Formulation

This work uses a matrix-based HEN simulation strategy along with data reconciliation and gross error detection, together with a hybrid optimisation approach to calculate specific fouling models for a crude oil pre-heat train. The effect of missing process measurements are accounted for by exploiting the matrix formulation of the HEN and by classifying such missing measurements according to the concepts of observability and redundancy defined by Narasimhan and Jordache (2000), as described in Section 2.2.

2.1. HEN and Fouling Modelling and Simulation

The model used in this work calculates the internal flow rates and temperatures of the HEN using inlet information from the crude oil and the CDU side-products streams. The simulation strategy was proposed by de Oliveira Filho et al. (2007) and later modified by Ochoa-Estopier et al. (2015) to include the simulation of unit operations such as desalters and flash units. The proposed approach integrates the dynamic effects of fouling using an explicit Euler integration, as it was previously shown in Loyola-Fuentes et al. (2017). The HEN is simulated in order to obtain a set of simulation-based data. Random and gross errors are systematically added to these simulated data in order to replicate the variability of an existing process. Following the reconciliation of these measured data, the HEN and fouling models are used for prediction of fouling depostion.

2.2. Data Reconciliation and Gross Error Detection

The data reconciliation algorithm minimises the value of the measurement error, which is defined as the difference between the measurements (y_m) and the reconciled process variables (y_r). These reconciled variables are estimated via nonlinear constrained optimisation, where each measured value is weighted by the corresponding accuracy of the measurement (usually approximated by the variance of such measurement) in matrix ψ. The whole set of constraints considers the presence of unmeasured process variables in the vector y_u. The set of equality constraints $f(y_r, y_u)$ represents mass and energy conservation equations, and the set of inequality constraints $g(y_r, y_u)$ represents specific lower and upper bounds for each measurement. The effect and presence of gross error is accounted for by including the gross error magnitude (measurement bias is assumed in this work) g_ξ in the measurement error vector. The simultaneous optimisation problem is solved by the combinatorial strategy proposed by Romagnoli and Sánchez (1999), which is updated in this work to take into account nonlinear systems. The data reconciliation and gross error detection problem is defined in Eq. (1).

$$
\begin{aligned}
\min_{y_r, y_u} \quad & (y_m - y_r - g_\xi)^T \psi^{-1} (y_m - y_r - g_\xi) \\
\text{subject to} \quad & f(y_r, y_u) = 0 \\
& g(y_r, y_u) \leq 0
\end{aligned}
\tag{1}
$$

The minimisation problem in Eq. (1) is solved via Sequential Quadratic Programming (SQP). The values of reconciled and unmeasured process variables are estimated simultaneously. The effect of missing measurements is analysed based on the concepts of observability and redundancy (Narasimhan and Jordache, 2000).

- Observability: An unmeasured variable is observable if it can be estimated using measurements and process constraints.

- Redundancy: A measured variable is redundant if it is observable even when its measurement is missing.

2.3. Fouling Model Parameter Estimation

A hybrid optimisation approach is implemented for determining fouling parameters. The value of fouling resistance is calculated using the overall heat transfer coefficient in clean and fouled conditions. The parameter estimation is formulated as a nonlinear constrained optimisation problem and solved using Genetic Algorithm. The solution of this problem is then fine-tuned using a deterministic nonlinear programming technique; in this work, the interior point method is implemented.

The objective function shown in Eq. (2) represents the minimisation of the root mean squared error between measured and fitted fouling resistances, defined by R_f^{msr} and R_f^{fit} respectively. The optimisation variables correspond to the specific fouling parameters (vector b) of a fouling model that is previously selected according to operating conditions. Each data-set and the total amount of data-sets are represented by the counter k and number n respectively.

$$\min_{b} \quad \sqrt{\frac{\sum_{k=1}^{n} \left(R_{f,k}^{msr} - R_{f,k}^{fit}(b) \right)}{n}} \tag{2}$$

$$\text{subject to} \quad b^L \leq b \leq b^U$$

3. Case Study

This new methodology is tested in a HEN case study, comprising of eight process-to-process heat exchangers, one desalter unit, three cold utilities and one hot utility. The pre-heat train is depicted in Figure 1. Fouling is assumed in the shell-side and the tube-side of all process-to-process heat exchangers. Deposition of waxes is considered in both sides of the heat exchangers at the cold end of the pre-heat train (exchangers E1 to E4) as well as in the shell-side of the heat exchangers at the hot end (exchangers E5 to E8). The fouling rate for this mechanism, α_1, is set to be 5.50×10^{-4} m^{2}K kW^{-1}h^{-1}. Chemical reaction fouling based on the model proposed by Polley et al. (2007) is assumed to occur in the tube-side of exchangers at the hot end of the pre-heat train. The fouling models are shown in Eq. (3) and Eq. (4) respectively, where Re, Pr, R_g and T_W are the relevant Reynolds number, Prandtl number, the ideal gas constant and the tube-wall temperature. The parameters of the chemical reaction model α_2, E_A and γ are given in Table 1. The simulation time is one year and the operational data are generated using the simulation strategy described in Section 2.1. Random and gross errors are systematically added in order to replicate the variability of a real operating process.

The cold stream outlet flow rate of exchanger E3 and the hot side outlet temperature of exchanger E7 are chosen as unmeasured variables. These variables are to be estimated using the available measurements, in order to check the observability of such missing data. Random errors are added to each measurement across the whole time-span. A constant single gross error of magnitude of 4°C is added to the furnace inlet temperature. After reconciliation and identification of gross errors, the fouling parameters for the shell and tube-sides of all heat exchangers are back-calculated via the parameter estimation method explained in Section 2.3.

$$\frac{dR_f}{dt} = \alpha_1 \tag{3}$$

$$\frac{dR_f}{dt} = \alpha_2 Re^{-0.8} Pr^{-0.33} exp\left(\frac{-E_A}{R_g T_W}\right) - \gamma Re^{0.8} \tag{4}$$

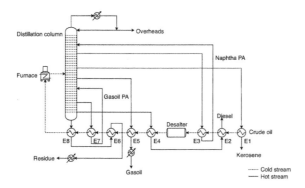

Figure 1: Crude Oil Pre-Heat Train Process Flow Diagram

Table 1: Fouling model parameters for chemical reaction mechanism (Polley et al., 2007)

Parameter	Units	Value
α_2	$m^2K\ kW^{-1}h^{-1}$	1.00×10^6
E_A	$kJ\ mol^{-1}$	48.00
γ	$m^2K\ kW^{-1}h^{-1}$	1.50×10^{-9}

The results from the estimation of missing measurements are compared with a fully-instrumented scenario. The missing flow rate estimation results give a constant value of 194 kg s^{-1}, as no mass losses are considered. This value is in accordance with the full instrumentation scenario. The comparison for the missing temperature measurement is shown in Figure 2. The agreement between these two scenarios indicates that both of these unmeasured variables are observable, as their magnitudes are accurately estimated.

The average value of the estimated gross error is 3.98°C, which is in good agreement with the initially simulated value of 4°C. The performance of the data reconciliation can be assessed by analysing the values of the fitted fouling parameters for all heat exchangers. These values are shown in Table 2. The agreement of each parameter with respect to their corresponding base-value (see Table 1) shows how well these parameters can be used for the prediction of fouling behaviour in the network.

Table 2: Fitted fouling model parameters for all heat exchangers

	α_1 $(m^2K\ kW^{-1}h^{-1})$	E_A $(kJ\ mol^{-1})$	γ $(m^2K\ kW^{-1}h^{-1})$	α_2 $(m^2K\ kW^{-1}h^{-1})$
E1	5.42×10^{-4}	–	–	–
E2	5.42×10^{-4}	–	–	–
E3	5.42×10^{-4}	–	–	–
E4	5.42×10^{-4}	–	–	–
E5	9.36×10^{-4}	44.18	1.11×10^{-7}	3.85×10^5
E6	9.70×10^{-4}	51.54	9.89×10^{-8}	2.66×10^6
E7	8.43×10^{-4}	44.10	6.65×10^{-8}	4.16×10^5
E8	8.66×10^{-4}	48.28	5.05×10^{-8}	1.11×10^6

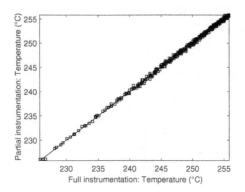

Figure 2: Comparison between full and partial instrumentation scenarios for the missing temperature measurement

4. Conclusions

This work proposes a new method for regressing fouling models for shell and tube-sides of a crude oil pre-heat train using data reconciliation and gross error detection. The Data Reconciliation method accounts for the effect of two different types of measurement errors and the presence of missing measurement(s). These missing measurements are classified according to their observability in order to identify their potential for accurate estimation. The proposed methodology is tested in a case study, where significant agreements were found when full and partial instrumentation scenarios were compared. Further study is needed for multiple combinations of missing measurements presenting different degrees of observability. For achieving this goal, a topological analysis of the network, together with a set of measured values are needed. The degree of observability for this case can be evaluated using matrix-based techniques such as Q-R decomposition.

References

L. O. de Oliveira Filho, E. M. Queiroz, A. L. Costa, 2007. A matrix approach for steady-state simulation of heat exchanger networks. Applied Thermal Engineering 27 (14), 2385–2393.

W. Ebert, C. B. Panchal, 1995. Analysis of Exxon crude oil-slip-stream coking data. In: Fouling Mitigation of Industrial Heat-Exchange Equipment. Begell House, pp. 451–460.

J. Loyola-Fuentes, R. Smith, M. Jobson, 2017. Fouling modelling in crude oil preheat systems. In: A. Espuña, M. Graells, L. Puigjaner (Eds.), Computer Aided Chemical Engineering. Vol. 40. Elsevier, pp. 409–414.

S. Narasimhan, C. Jordache, 2000. Data Reconciliation & Gross Error Detection: An Intelligent Use of Process Data. Gulf Publishing Co., Houston, Texas, USA.

L. M. Ochoa-Estopier, M. Jobson, L. Chen, C. A. Rodríguez-Forero, R. Smith, 2015. Optimization of heat-integrated crude oil distillation systems. Part II: Heat exchanger network retrofit model. Industrial & Engineering Chemistry Research 54 (18), 5001–5017.

C. Panchal, E.-P. Huangfu, 2000. Effects of mitigating fouling on the energy efficiency of crude-oil distillation. Heat Transfer Engineering 21 (3), 3–9.

G. T. Polley, D. I. Wilson, S. J. Pugh, E. Petitjean, 2007. Extraction of crude oil fouling model parameters from plant exchanger monitoring. Heat Transfer Engineering 28 (3), 185–192.

J. A. Romagnoli, M. C. Sánchez, 1999. Data Processing and Reconciliation for Chemical Process Operations. Academic Press, Inc., Orlando, Florida, USA.

Anton A. Kiss, Edwin Zondervan, Richard Lakerveld, Leyla Özkan (Eds.)
Proceedings of the 29th European Symposium on Computer Aided Process Engineering
June 16th to 19th, 2019, Eindhoven, The Netherlands. © 2019 Elsevier B.V. All rights reserved.
http://dx.doi.org/10.1016/B978-0-128-18634-3.50174-0

Reduced model-based global optimisation of large-scale steady state nonlinear systems

Min Tao[a], Jie Li[a] and Constantinos Theodoropoulos[a*]

[a]*School of Chemical Engineering and Analytical Science, The University of Manchester, M13 9PL, UK*
k.theodoropoulos@manchester.ac.uk

Abstract

Many engineering systems can be accurately simulated using partial differential equations (PDEs), resulting in large-scale distributed parameter systems. Deterministic global optimisation algorithms (GOP) can compute global optimal solutions offering theoretical guarantees on the global optimality. However, distributed parameter systems pose computational challenges for these optimisation methods. Model reduction techniques can produce low-order systems that are computationally amenable. In this work, a combined principal component analysis (PCA) and artificial neural networks (ANNs)-based model reduction methodology is employed for the global optimisation of large-scale distributed steady state systems. Still, the optimisation problem is hard to solve due to the high nonlinearity of activation functions in the reduced ANN structure. A novel piece-wise linear approximation reformulation is introduced to reduce the complexity of the original problem and to provide a good globally approximate solution. The performance of the proposed PCA-ANN-GOP framework is demonstrated through an illustrative example: a tubular reactor where an exothermic reaction takes place.

Keywords: Model reduction, Distributed parameter systems, Artificial neural networks, Global optimisation

1. Introduction

PDE-constrained black/grey box modelling and optimisation methodologies have wide applicability in industrial engineering areas where many finite approximation-based generic commercial simulators or input-output data from real complex systems are available (Boukouvala et al., 2017). However, many simulators solely provide input-output results of simulation process and can not perform optimisation tasks. Hence, the optimisation of real complex systems is problematic. Even if the high dimensional complex model codes are available, the cost of computing derivatives is often unacceptable. One of the most effective techniques to reduce computational costs for input/output systems is the use of *equation-free* methods (Theodoropoulos, 2011). Recently, equation-free based reduced SQP algorithms have been exploited for large-scale local optimisation with black-box steady-state simulators (Bonis and Theodoropoulos, 2012). With a small set of input-output data from the simulator, matrix-free reduced Jacobian and Hessian matrix techniques can be employed. The aim of this work is to construct deterministic global optimisation methods for large-scale input/output simulators. Such deterministic global optimisation methods are usually computationally intensive due to the repeated utilisation of branch-and-bound algorithms. Hence, in terms of computational cost, detailed models of large-scale problems are very hard or even impossible to deal with.

In this work, a data-driven methodology is employed first to create a good approximate surrogate model for large-scale steady-state systems. Principal component analysis (PCA) in combination with artificial neural networks (ANNs) is used to produce a reduced order model. The reduced model (ANN-constrained model) is then utilized by the global general-purpose optimisation solver BARON (Tawarmalani and Sahinidis, 2005). Furthermore, we present a novel piece-wise linear approximation reformulation for the nonlinear constraints in order to accelerate the computation of the global optimum for the reduced system.

2. Model Reduction

The focus of this work is on optimisation of spatially distributed processes, described by a set of steady-state dissipative PDEs with accompanying boundary and initial conditions:

$$\frac{\partial X}{\partial t} = D\{\frac{\partial X}{\partial y}, \frac{\partial^2 X}{\partial y^2}, ..., \frac{\partial^n X}{\partial y^n}\} + R(X, P_m) \tag{1}$$

where D is a dissipative spatial differential operator, $R(X, P_m)$ is a nonlinear function, P_m are the parameter variables and X the set of state variables. If we consider the steady state analysis of these equations, we assume that $X(t, y) \to X(y)$, and we can set $\frac{\partial X}{\partial t} = 0$, giving the equations:

$$0 = D\{\frac{\partial X}{\partial y}, \frac{\partial^2 X}{\partial y^2}, ..., \frac{\partial^n X}{\partial y^n}\} + R(X, P_m) \tag{2}$$

Due to the large number of variables in the corresponding discretised problems, the full model is usually too big for global optimisation (Houska and Chachuat, 2017). This barrier can be overcome by employing model reduction methodologies such as artificial neural networks and principal component analysis. Principal component analysis (PCA) is a powerful methodology for data compression. Common linear PCA is a transformation of the original data space spanned by the principal components (PCs). *PCs* are the basis vectors for the new space and are ranked by the magnitude of variance of the original data projected onto the corresponding PCs. PCs can be computed by matrix decomposition as in (Jackson, 2005):

$$Y = TP^T + E \tag{3}$$

where $Y \in R^{N \times m}$ is the high dimensional sample data from the large-scale steady state simulator given by Eq.(2), N and m, the number of sample data and data dimension, respectively. $T \in R^{N \times a}$, is the score matrix for the *PCs* and a $(a \leq m)$, the number of *PCs*. $P \in R^{m \times a}$ is the loading matrix and $E \in R^{N \times m}$ the residual matrix.

In order to compute a representation for the outputs produced by the the black-box simulator, the Latin hyper-cube (LHC) sampling method is applied to collect snapshots. LHC sample method can maximize the sample information content for a limited number of samples. After snapshots collecting and PCA reduction steps applied, the high dimensional input-output data is transformed into lower dimensional PC scores. Subsequently a reduced order model is built through the use of the reduced data obtained. Here, we adopt artificial neural networks (ANNs) because standard feed-forward artificial neural network (ANN) with one hidden layer can be an universal approximator for any smooth function (Hornik et al., 1989). The structure of the feed-forward ANN is relatively simple and easy to be constructed. In this work, the training process for ANN is performed in MATLAB R2017a with Neural Networks toolbox. The activation function is chosen to be the hyperbolic tangent function. The neural network is trained with the Levenberg-Marquardt back-propagation algorithm, which can reduce the mean square error quickly. The input is the low-dimensional input parameter matrix from the black-box simulators. The output is the reduced principal component scores of the output data from black-box simulators. At this point, data-driven PCA-ANN based surrogate model has been built that can be employed for global optimisation.

3. Model reduced global optimisation

The general nonlinear optimisation problem with embedded neural networks (reduced model) is considered. The general problem can be formulated as follows:

$$\min_{x \in R^c, y \in R^d} \quad f(x,y)$$
$$s.t. \quad h(x,y) = 0,$$
$$g(x,y) \le 0 \tag{4}$$

where the objective function $f(x,y) : R^c \times R^d \to R$, $x \in R^c$ is an input vector of the black-box simulator, $y \in R^d$ is an output vector of the black-box simulator, $h(x,y)$: $R^c \times R^d \to R$ is ANN constraint derived from the reduced model, and $g(x,y)$: $R^c \times R^d \to R$ represents other constraints.

In the current work, $g(x,y)$ are the bound constraints for the state variables. The intrinsic nonlinearity of the optimisation problem lies on $h(x,y)$ due to the activation function of the ANN structure. The feed-forward ANN uses the hyperbolic tangent function $tanh(\cdot)$. The general global optimisation software BARON is employed to solve the above problem. General global solvers in GAMS such ANTIGONE and BARON can not identify $tanh(\cdot)$, so its explicit algebraic form $(tanh(x) = \frac{e^x-1}{e^x+1})$ is utilized. The basic formulation is transformed into $tanh(x) = \frac{-2}{e^x+1} + 1$ in order to produce a tighter under-estimator for the global solver.

However, the computational cost of global solvers increases exponentially when reducing the high non-convexity of the activation function. We propose a novel piece-wise linear approximation (PWA) reformulation for the activation function. With an accurate PWA model, a good approximation to the true global solution can be obtained. It should be, however, noted that a PWA reformulation transforms the high non-convex NLP problem into a set of MILP problems. The global solvers for both NLP and MILP problems are based on the branch and bound framework. The biggest difference is that they turn the continuous variables into auxiliary binary variables on the branch step. The advantage of the PWA reformulation lies on the use proven MILP software such as CPLEX. Here, we present an iterative way to collect piece-wise points for PWA models. $tanh(x)$ is an odd function of central symmetry, which is concave on $[0,+\infty]$ and convex on $[-\infty,0)$. So it is easy to compute the grid points for piece-wise approximation of $tanh(x)$ on $[-\infty,0)$ when the grid points on $[0,+\infty]$ are available. On the range of $[0,+\infty]$, $tanh(x)$ experiences a short-time' increase and then tends to be "static" (very slow growth to its limit value). In the current work, we start from only two intervals and three grid points (original point and two static points) in this range. The linear model in a static interval can approximate the activation function accurately. For the 'initial short-time' increasing interval, we reduce the error between the multiple linear models and the nonlinear $tanh(x)$ by iteratively narrowing the interval sizes.

The iteration procedure is performed by adding more partitioning points where the largest error is calculated. In addition, a sub-interval is acceptable if the biggest error or the number of intervals satisfies a set requirement. This iteration process efficiently produces a set of collecting points, which contribute to a tight piece-wise linear representation of the highly nonlinear activation function. Assume that there are N linear models, $N+1$ generated grid points $x_1, x_2, ..., x_{N+1} \in R$ and approximate function $f = tanh(x_i)$ in the ith interval. By introducing auxiliary variables h_i and λ_i, we can generalize the formulation of a piece-wise linear approximation as follows (Floudas, 1995):

$$
\begin{aligned}
f(x) &= \sum_{i=1}^{N+1} \lambda_i f(x_i) \\
x &= \sum_{i=1}^{N+1} \lambda_i x_i \\
\sum_{i=1}^{N+1} \lambda_i &= 1 \\
\lambda_1 &\leq h_1 \\
\lambda_i &\leq h_i + h_{i-1}, \forall i \in \{2, 3, ..., N\} \\
\lambda_{N+1} &\leq h_N \\
\lambda_i &\geq 0, \forall i \in \{1, 2, ..., N+1\} \\
\sum_{i=1}^{N} h_i &= 1 \\
h_i &\in \{0, 1\}^N
\end{aligned}
\tag{5}
$$

In the next section, this algorithm is employed to a system of steady-state PDEs after collecting a "good" set of snapshots in order to illustrate its computational capabilities.

4. Application

We first apply our methodology to an example with known global optima for illustration purposes. Then we apply our PCA-ANN-GOP framework to a large-scale steady state nonlinear PDE-based system.

4.1. Illustrative example

In this illustrative example, a two-dimensional multimodal function is chosen, obtained by translating and scaling Gaussian distributions:

$$
g_{peaks} = 3(1-x)^2 exp(-x^2 - (y+1)^2) - 10(\frac{x}{5} - x^3 - y^5) exp(-x^2 - y^2) \\
- \frac{1}{3} exp(-(x+1)^2 - y^2)
\tag{6}
$$

where variables $x, y \in [-3, 3]$. Multiple local solutions exist in this defined domain. The known unique global optimum lies on the point $(0.228, -1.626)$ where the function value is -6.551. We just use it to show the performance of our reduced global optimisation methodology.

Table 1: Comparative results of ANN-constrained model and PWA models

Model	Solver	Optimal value	CPU time (s)	Rel.gap
ANN-constrained model	BARON	-6.555	30294.26	0.002
PWA model1 (31 grid points)	CPLEX	-6.542	1004.71	0.002
PWA model2 (59 grid points)	CPLEX	-6.540	4190.16	0.002

After sampling and ANN learning , we obtain an ANN-constrained reduced model with 52 neurons. we do the global optimisation with reduced model and PWA models. ANN-constrained model is the surrogate model after ANN step. PWA model1 is the piece-wise approximation model for hyperbolic activation function with 31 grid points while PWA model2 is the piece-wise approximation model with 59 grid points. The number of grid points depends on the chosen error during the above iteration process. The NLP with ANN-constrained model is solved by the general global solver BARON 17.4.1/GAMS 24.8.5, and MILP with PWA model is dealt with CPLEX 12.7.1/GAMS 24.8.5 on a Desktop (Intel Core(TM) CPU 3.3 GHz, 8 GB memory, 64-bit operating system) running Windows 7. The results are given in Table 1. From Table 1, we can see that we obtain almost the same optimal solution, very close to the true global optimizer of the original problem. In addition, our proposed PWA formulation can reduce the computation time greatly with high accuracy.

4.2. Case study

The effectiveness of our PCA-ANN-GOP is illustrated using a chemical engineering application; a tubular reactor, where an exothermic reaction takes place. The mathematical formulation of the tubular reactor optimisation is given below:

$$\max_{T_{wi}} C_{exit}$$

$$s.t. 0 = \frac{1}{Pe_1}\frac{\partial^2 C}{\partial y^2} - \frac{\partial C}{\partial y} + Da(1-C)exp(T/(1+T/\gamma))$$

$$0 = \frac{1}{LePe_2}\frac{\partial^2 T}{\partial y^2} - \frac{1}{Le}\frac{\partial T}{\partial y} - \frac{\beta}{Le}T + BDa(1-C)exp(T/(1+T/\gamma)) + \frac{\beta}{Le}T_w \qquad (7)$$

$$0 \leq Twi \leq 5$$

Here C and T are the dimensionless concentration and temperature respectively, while C_{exit} is dimensionless output concentration .The system parameters are $Pe1 = 5, Pe2 = 5, Le = 1, Da = 0.1, \beta = 1.5, \gamma = 10, B = 12$; T_w is the adiabatic wall temperature of the cooling problem with three cooling zones, expressed as following:

$$T_w(y) = \sum_{i=1}^{N}(H(y-y_{i-1})-H(y)-y_i)T_{wi} \qquad (8)$$

The resulting discretised 500 algebraic equations comprise our house-made simulator . After model reduction step (PCA and ANN steps), a small size ANN-constrained optimisation problem (3 input, 12 output, 20 neurons ANN) is generated, which is easy to be solved. In order to compare the computation efficiency of ANN-constrained model and PWA models, we compute the results with different numbers of neurons. All these computation cases converge to almost the same

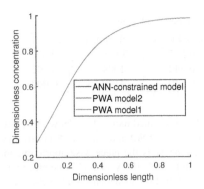

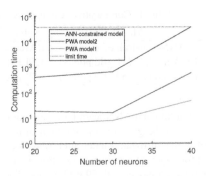

Figure 1: Solution profiles at optimum for concentration

Figure 2: Computation time (sec) under different number of neurons

solution, whose objective values are extremely close to 0.999. Figure 1 gives the optimal solution profiles for concentration distribution under 30-neuron ANN structures. The three concentration distribution curves for different approximate models almost overlap. Hence, our PWA models show high computation accuracy. Figure 2 illustrates the comparison of the computation cost for the different models. The limit time (max time for computations to stop)is set to be 36000 seconds. As it can be seen, computation time increases rapidly as with increasing number of neurons. The computation cost reaches the limit time for the ANN-constrained model with only 40 neurons while the computation times are much smaller for both PWA models. This verifies the high computation efficiency of our PWA models.

5. Conclusion

We propose a reduced model-based global optimisation framework for large-scale steady state nonlinear systems. Data-driven PCA and ANN techniques are employed to produce a small or middle size surrogate model for the original system. To further reduce computation complexity, novel PWA models are utilized to replace the reduced ANN-constrained model. Illustrative examples are presented to verify the efficiency of our framework. Computation results reveal that our PCA-ANN-GOP framework can capture the global optimum with acceptable computational cost, especially when PWA approximations are used.

References

I. Bonis, C. Theodoropoulos, 2012. Model reduction-based optimization using large-scale steady-state simulators. Chemical engineering science 69 (1), 69–80.

F. Boukouvala, M. F. Hasan, C. A. Floudas, 2017. Global optimization of general constrained grey-box models: new method and its application to constrained pdes for pressure swing adsorption. Journal of Global Optimization 67 (1-2), 3–42.

C. A. Floudas, 1995. Nonlinear and mixed-integer optimization: fundamentals and applications. Oxford University Press.

K. Hornik, M. Stinchcombe, H. White, 1989. Multilayer feedforward networks are universal approximators. Neural networks 2 (5), 359–366.

B. Houska, B. Chachuat, 2017. Global optimization in hilbert space. Mathematical Programming, 1–29.

J. E. Jackson, 2005. A user's guide to principal components. Vol. 587. John Wiley & Sons.

M. Tawarmalani, N. V. Sahinidis, 2005. A polyhedral branch-and-cut approach to global optimization. Mathematical Programming 103 (2), 225–249.

C. Theodoropoulos, 2011. Optimisation and linear control of large scale nonlinear systems: a review and a suite of model reduction-based techniques. In: Coping with Complexity: Model Reduction and Data Analysis. Springer, pp. 37–61.

Anton A. Kiss, Edwin Zondervan, Richard Lakerveld, Leyla Özkan (Eds.)
Proceedings of the 29th European Symposium on Computer Aided Process Engineering
June 16th to 19th, 2019, Eindhoven, The Netherlands. © 2019 Elsevier B.V. All rights reserved.
http://dx.doi.org/10.1016/B978-0-128-18634-3.50175-2

Advanced Model Design Based on Intelligent System Characterization And Problem Definition

Edrisi Munoz [a*], Elisabet Capon-Garcia [b] , Luis Puigjaner[c]

[a]*Centro de Investigacion en Matemáticas A.C., Jalisco S/N, Mineral y Valenciana 36240, Guanajuato, Mexico11*

[b]*ABB Switzerland Ltd., Segelhofstrasse 1K, 5405 Baden-Dättwil, Switzerland*

[c] *Chemical Engineering Department, EEBE, Universitat Politècnica de Catalunya, Av. Eduard Maristany, 10-14, 08019 Barcelona, Spain*

emunoz@cimat.com

Abstract

Enterprises comprise highly complex systems that need to be coordinated in order to maintain their productivity and competitiveness. During last years, companies have developed information systems to support end users to exploit data and models, with the final objective of improving the decision-making task. Main decisions concern key process characteristics, which are essential for the viability to achieve enterprise wide optimization (EWO) and industry 4.0 approaches. This work focuses on the automated creation of a semantically enriched problem statement of production processes based on system characterization and problem definition. First, features related to the system are defined and the characterized by making use of knowledge models. As a result the system is semantically defined and conceptual enriched. Next, the second step of the approach consists on an automated problem definition process. This process comprises eight main phases to obtain a systematic problem definition. Finally, this work presents a case study base on scheduling problem in order to show the performance of the tool. The case study comprises a system that has been treated with mathematical models for solving a multistage scheduling problem.

Keywords: Artificial Intelligence; Problem Modelling; Intelligent Systems

1. Introduction

Enterprises comprise highly complex systems that need to be correctly managed and coordinated in order to maintain their productivity and competitiveness. During last years, due to accessibility to technological advances, companies have been focused on developing information systems to support end users to exploit data and models, with the final objective of improving the decision-making task in an automated and semi-automated processes environment. Nevertheless, decision-making modeling lies in to human factor (human capacity and expertise). Thus, tools that support fast and reliable problem solve activities related to production process are crucial elements in those information systems.

What is more, nowadays industry is deep into in the fourth industrial revolution, so-called Industry 4.0, where computers and process devices aim for autonomous process by interacting together. In this context, sensors and actuators should be connected remotely to computer systems, equipped with sophisticated algorithms that can understand, learn and decide with small intervention from human operators. The success on improving decision-making broadly depends on how analytical models and data are integrated. On the one hand, the correct modelling task, when a problem or certain reality is found, increases the success of the decision. On the other hand, the responsiveness and accuracy to get information quality and data complement how good the decision can be. Thus, a key task in the improvement of decision- making depends on having an appropriate and enhanced characterization of the system. This work focuses on the main decisions concerning key process characteristics, which are essential for the viability and competitiveness of the enterprise.

This work presents a methodology for an automated problem definition resulting in a semantically enriched problem statement. This problem statement comprises system characterization and problem definition process, which are based on formal knowledge models namely ontologies. First, features related to the system are defined and then characterizing by making use of knowledge models. System features comprises to general tactical and strategic process issues. Besides, knowledge models enable identifying and matching every process with their functions, objectives and relations regarding different levels of process abstraction within the enterprise structure. As a result of this first step system features are extracted and presented in a taxonomical structure manner conceptually enriched. Next, an automated problem definition comprising nine main phases, namely: a) automated process system definition, b) Problematic situation recognition; c) Solution goal statement; d) General system relations; e) Definition of variables; f) system assumptions; g) parameters and engineering metrics (time & space scales); h) definition of problem statement and solution objectives; and i) search for similar problematic or solutions.

Finally, this work presents a case study base on scheduling problem in order to show the performance of the approach. Scheduling problems are critical in the decision-making of process operations.. The case study comprises a system that has been treated with mathematical models for solving a multistage scheduling problem.

2. Proposal description

Decision Support Systems (DSS) are information technology solutions that can be used to support complex decision-making and problem solving. DSS are defined as aid computer systems at the management company level that combine data and sophisticated analytic models for support decision-making (Simon and Murray, 2007). Classic DSS design is comprised of components for (i) sophisticated database management capabilities with access to internal and external data, information, and knowledge; (ii) modeling functions accessed by a model management system, (iii) simple user interface designs that enable interactive queries, reporting, and graphing functions, and (iv) optimization by mathematic algorithms and or intuition/knowledge.

This work is based on formal knowledge technologies, which allow working in a semantical environment where machines can understand domain and human knowledge. Besides, the development of models and solution strategies to tackle the decision-making from a broad perspective has been the result of integration and collaboration from areas, such as, Process Systems Engineering (PSE), Information Technologies and Communications (ITC), and Operations Research (OR).

Thus, the proposed approach can be generally stated as follows. Given a formal domain knowledge model, the following information must be captured in order to obtain semantically system features: i) Production system characterization comprising Physical, Procedural and Recipe (Site & General) models; ii) Products to be produced according to the processing order activity in the industry recipes defining the production requirements and production path for the products in the Physical, Process and Recipe (Master & Control) models, and; iii) Resource availability and plant status provided by the process management and production information management activities, as shown in Figure 1, Part I-A and Part I-AA.

The main goal consists on create an enriched problem statement. Thus the following nine steps have been automated comprising: definition of the process system from tactical, strategic and operational views (see Figure 1, Part II - a); an algorithm for monitoring key process features (isolated or integrated) for detecting abnormal or problem situations (see Figure 1, Part II - b); an option for choosing among economical, time or other aim solution perspective (see Figure 1, Part II - c); important relations among problem and direct features in the system are stated (see Figure 1, Part II - d); decision variables, assumptions of the process and the engineering metrics are suggested by the proposal and chosen by the user (see Figure 1, Part II - c, d and e); finally a sematic enriched problem statement is obtained (see Figure 1, Part II – h and i)

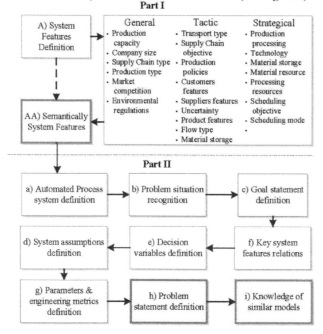

Figure 1. Intelligent system characterization and problem definition procedure diagram.

3. Methodology

This work develops a software platform in Jython, which is integrated to the knowledge models described previously by using OWLAPI as an improved modeling and communication tool in the process domain. Then the proposed framework consists on two main processes, Enterprise Structure Definition and Problem Definition (Figure 1).

On the one hand, enterprise structure definition comprises conception of a real system, considering general, tactic and strategic features (Figure 1, part I). Then, a semantic enriched taxonomical model of the features is obtained. Likewise, this work tackles the conciliation, standardization and management of data and information existing in the process system. On the other hand, the different phases of the proposed framework (Figure 1, part II) define the phases to obtain the systematic problem definition.

4. Case Study

The case study comprises a system that has been treated with mathematical models for solving a multistage scheduling problem. Specifically, the scheduling problem presented in the paper by Capon-Garcia et al. 2011 and detailed in Muñoz et al. 2018, is considered, where acrylic fibers are produced along 14 stages in a batch production plant, structured in 8 recipe unit procedures and 6 recipe operations. As primary information, production process was defined in a master recipe involving 27 different resources, which are basically material and energy resources. Two alternative production processes are assessed in this work, namely acrylic fiber A uses acetone as solvent in the polymerization and acrylic fiber B uses benzene

Thus, system features definition requirements have been defined and fulfill, comprising information as shown in Table 1, based on Enterprise Ontology Project from Munoz et al. 2012.

Table 1. General, tactic and strategic features for system characterization.

General Feature	Value	Tactic features	Value	Strategic features	Value
Production capacity	Medium	Transport type	Land	Production processing	Sequencial
Company size	medium	Supply chain objective	Economic	Technology	Multi task
Supply chain type	Good availability	Production policies	Defined	Material storage	Limited
Production Type	Multi Stage	Customer features	-	Material resource	Not perishable
Market competition type	Low	Suppliers features	-	Processing resources	Limited
Environmental regulations	Defined	Process flow type	Forward	Scheduling objective	Timing
Demand feature	High volume	Material storage type	Limited	Scheduling mode	On-line

Next, in order to obtain a problem definition Part II from Figure 1 is explained and detailed.

a) *Automated Process system definition.* From previous system's instantiation within EOP knowledge model, a semantically enriched machine-readable system structure is obtained. The model comprises 934 instances concerning 295 classes, 257 Object properties, 33 data properties. As example of class instantiation made, the *RawMaterial* class has *Input1_1 (Acrylonitrile), Input1_2 (MethylMetaacrilate), Input1_3 (VinilChloride), Input1_4 (solvent-Acetone)* as instances.

b) *Problem situation recognition.* In this phase, indicators derived from an automated SWOT are defined. Each indicator is mapped into a semantic concept (class) from the EOP knowledge model. Then, upper and lower boundaries of control are set. One of the main advantages of the system is the fact that problem recognition is coming from the knowledge model. As a result data and information, usually hidden for a human, can be easily manage by the system. Table 2 shows the different indicators and their corresponding upper and lower boundaries values.

Table 2. Indicators and control boundaries of the problem recognition.

SWOT	Indicator	Related feature	Metric	UBV	LBV
O	Energy comsumption	Electric comsuptiom	kWh	30000	50000
		Water comsumption	m^3/ton	6000	10000
		Natural gas comsumption	m^3/ton	39000	45000
W	Time delivered failure	Tardiness finish orders	u/month	15	45
W	Demand unacomplishment	Orders out of schedule	u/month	5	15
		Outsourcing orders	u/month	10	20
T	Changes in product order	Product demand changes	u/month	30	50
T	Cleaning overtimes	Cleaning task with overtime	u/month	0	5
T	New product order	Order pleced out of the shcedule	u/month	0	40

c) *Goal statement.* Once that a problem has been identified an optimization goal can be obtained by specifying the minimization or maximization of the indicator chose in the previous phase. *Time Delivered Failure* indicator has been defined as a problem by the system, due to a violation in the upper boundary. Besides, the goal is stated as a minimization problem.

d) *Key system features relations.* Based on the EOP knowledge model, the proposed framework is capable of finding the closer relations among the indicator (EOP class) chose in (b) and other process systems' concepts, potentially to be converted into decisions variables. Table 3 shows some examples of properties involved in the query in this phase.

Table 3. Domain and range of "Resource" class and subclasses.

Processing time	
hasID	ResourceID
hasUpperBound/hasLowerBound	float
hasResourceCost	ResourceCost
hasEnvironmentalPerformanceIndex	EnvironmentalPerformanceIndex

e) *Decision variables definition.* In his phase, a decision about which and which not concepts (EOP classes) are defined as decision variables provided in (d) must be done.

Table 4. Main classes and derived classes potentially become decision variables.

ProcessingTime	TimeInterval	ProcessingActivity
Information	Information	ProcessAction
Parameter	Parameter	ProcessStage
ProcessInformation	ProcessInformation	ProcessOperation
ProcesParameter	ProcessParameter	Thing
Thing	ClaeningTime	
TimeInterval	WaitingTime	
	ProcesssingTime	
	Thing	

f) *System assumptions definition.* From the system structure defined in (a), the most important and used assumptions based on the appropriate physical laws governing the process can be chosen to form part of the current problem definition. For this case study the process conditions are fixed according to the recipe definition.

g) *Parameters & engineering metrics definition*. In the same manner, parameters coming from the EOP's classes' data properties are chosen and defined. Then, engineering metrics are also specified automatically.

h) *Problem statement definition*. As the main goal of this approach, the proposed framework is capable of creating a problem statement in the form of natural language, which can be used to verify and validate the problem in an easy human readable way. The following paragraph has been obtained as a resulting problem statement from the current case study: "A problem regarding *tardiness finish orders* has been detected, resulting from violating upper bound of control, an optimization problem statement is proposed as follow: Taking into account variables *StartingTime*, *BatchSequencing*; parameters *ChangeOverTime*, *BatchProcessingTime*; Minimize *FinishTime*"

i) *Knowledge of similar models*. Finally, the framework executed a query that classifies similar optimization problems in order to suggest possible solutions to those similar problems, based on Capon-Garcia et al. (2017).

5. Conclusions

This work develops a semi-automatic process for semantically enriched problem statement based on formal knowledge models. Thus, features related to the system are easily defined and characterized, resulting in a virtualization of the system that comprises strategic, tactical and operational features. Next an automated problem definition process improves how information and data are considered lying in the potential of knowledge models and semantics technologies. In addition, knowledge models provide additional reasoning capabilities to support decision support system for the Wide Optimization and Industry 4.0 approaches. For illustrating purposes, a case study was presented using a scheduling of a multiproduct batch plant, where the systematic approach presented was used resulting in a semantic problem statement and presented in natural language.

Acknowledgements

Financial support received from the Spanish "Ministerio de Economía, Industria y Competitividad" and the European Regional Development Fund, both funding the research Project AIMS (ref. DPI2017-87435-R), and from the "Generalitat de Catalunya" (AGAUR 2017-SGR-1092-CEPEiMA)" is thankfully acknowledged

References

Grossmann I. E. Advances in mathematical programming models for enterprise-wide optimization. Computers and Chemical Engineering, 47, 2012.

Harjunkoski, I., Maravelias, C.T., Bongers, P., Castro, P.M., Engell, S., Grossmann, I.E., Hooker, J., Méndez, C., Sand, G., Wassick, J., 2014. Scope for industrial applications of production scheduling models and solution methods. Comput. Chem. Eng. 62, 161-193.

Maravelias, C.T., Sung, C., 2009. Integration of production planning and scheduling: Overview, challenges and opportunities. Comput. Chem. Eng. 33, 1919-1930.

Muñoz, E., Capón-García, E., Espuña, A., Puigjaner, L., 2012. Ontological framework for enterprise-wide integrated decision-making at operational level. Comput. Chem. Eng. 42, 217–234.

Edrisi Muñoz, Elisabet Capón-Garcia, and Luis Puigjaner Supervised Life-Cycle Assessment Using Automated Process Inventory Based on Process Recipes. ACS Sustainable Chemistry & Engineering 2018 6 (9), 11246-11254.

Elisabet Capón-García, Edrisi Muñoz, José Miguel Laínez-Aguirre, Konrad Hungerbühler, Knowledge-Driven Multi-Label Classification of Process Scheduling Problems,Computer Aided Chemical Engineering, Elsevier 2017, 40, 2353-2358.

Anton A. Kiss, Edwin Zondervan, Richard Lakerveld, Leyla Özkan (Eds.)
Proceedings of the 29th European Symposium on Computer Aided Process Engineering
June 16th to 19th, 2019, Eindhoven, The Netherlands. © 2019 Elsevier B.V. All rights reserved.
http://dx.doi.org/10.1016/B978-0-128-18634-3.50176-4

Probabilistic Design Space

Linas Mockus,[a]* Gintaras Reklaitis,[a] Ken Morris,[b] David LeBlond,[c]

[a]*Purdue University, 480 W. Stadium Ave., West Lafayette, IN 47907-2100, USA*

[b]*Long Island University, 75 Dekalb Ave., Brooklyn, NY 11201-8423, USA*

[c]*CMC Statistics, 3091 Midlane Drive, Wadsworth, IL 60083, USA*

lmockus@purdue.edu

Abstract

In this work we develop a Bayesian framework for building surrogate stochastic models of complex multi-step processes for which tractable mechanistic models are difficult to construct. The probabilistic process envelope defined by the design space provides an extra level of assurance of product quality over and above that provided by traditional process control. While the application we report is specific to drug products manufactured using traditional batch processing, the proposed framework is applicable in general to batch and continuous manufacturing of products that must meet a set of critical product quality specifications.
Keywords: stochastic process model; surrogate process model; batch process; continuous process; Bayesian statistics.

1. Introduction

The ICH guideline on pharmaceutical development (ICH, Q8(R2)) introduced the concept of design space, a construct that defines the operating region within which the resulting product can be assured to be at the required quality level. Recognizing the inherently stochastic nature of the design space, (Peterson, 2008) demonstrated the use of Bayesian statistics to facilitate its construction. More recently, (Bano, et al., 2018) proposed an approach based on partial least square regression to establishing a probabilistic design space, under the assumption that product quality is linearly related to process inputs. The key distinctions of the approach proposed in our work is, first, that the stochastic model utilizes historical process performance. Second, it is parametric with regards to product quality attributes as opposed to process performance and therefore aleatoric uncertainties (unknown unknowns) can be implicitly captured. In addition, the proposed framework is independent of linearity assumptions.

To find the design space of a process, quantification of the "assurance of quality" for the product under development or being manufactured is required. In this study, the experimental data for multiple pharmaceutical products manufactured by different manufacturers is used to determine the variation between and within product lots. Uncertainty quantification is obtained by employing multi-level hierarchical models at different levels of fidelity combined with Bayesian inference. This allows prediction of the TRUE between- and within-lot variability. In addition, several ways to predict the TRUE measurement uncertainty are identified.

2. Probabilistic design space

We identify the design space by constructing a process envelope which ensures that the manufactured product is of required quality. The ICH Q8(R2) Guideline (ICH, 2009) defines "Design Space" as: "The multidimensional combination and interaction of input variables (e.g. material attributes) and process parameters that have been demonstrated to provide assurance of quality." From a Bayesian perspective, one could define the ICH Q8 design space as:

$$DS = \left\{ x \in X \mid \Pr\left(Y \in A \mid x, data\right) \geq R \right\},$$

where x is a vector of process input variables, X is the experimental region, Y is a vector of product attributes defining quality (assay, % dissolved at Q time, tablet hardness, etc.), A is the acceptance region for the product, R is a reliability value which defines the desired level of "assurance" of quality, and DS is the design space. Q is the time point at which the dissolution performance specified in the corresponding pharmacopeial monograph must be satisfied.

The above probability measure is based upon the posterior predictive distribution for Y given the process inputs. The specifications are typically established based on human clinical trials to ensure absence of adverse events and efficacy of the product.

In this work we propose to define the design space in terms of the parameter space associated with the process responses, namely, the product quality attributes. Specifically, these consist of the product grand mean of these attributes as well as the intra and inter lot variability of these attributes. This allows the quality of a product to be determined by measuring the probability of meeting specifications established during pivotal clinical trials. The product quality is deemed sufficient if the probability is equal to, or greater than, an assigned threshold.

For a complex multi-step batch process, it is difficult and often infeasible to derive a rigorous and explicit model, therefore we propose to use a surrogate model expressed in terms of the product quality attributes, specifically, the attribute means and intra/inter lot variabilities. It should be noted that the traditional concept of lot may be extended to continuous processing by defining the lot in terms of an appropriate time interval of production during which product attributes and external intervention (human operator actions, raw material supply, etc.) are constant within some tolerance. Over that time period the process is said to be in the state of control.

In addition, the proposed stochastic model utilizes historical process performance which is incorporated as prior information via a Bayesian framework. It is parametric with regards to product quality attributes as opposed to process performance and therefore aleatoric uncertainty (unknown unknowns) is implicitly considered.

The proposed methodology is easily generalizable to batch and continuous processing industries (i.e., conformance to grade requirements in oil refinery). Significant change in between/within lot variability indicates that measures have to be taken to ensure adequate process control (i.e., quality of incoming materials).

By making the simplifying assumptions of normality, the surrogate process model may be expressed as follows:

$$
\begin{aligned}
Y_{ij} &= \mu_j + \eta_{ij} \\
\mu_j &\sim N\left(\mu, \sigma_B^2\right), \\
\eta_{ij} &\sim N\left(0, \sigma_W^2\right) \\
\theta &= \left(\mu, \sigma_B, \sigma_W\right)
\end{aligned}
\tag{1}
$$

where Y_{ij} is the true value of product attribute (for assays this is expressed as % of label content, while for dissolution this is expressed as % dissolved), μ_j is the true mean for lot j, and η_{ij} is a deviation of the true value of unit i from lot j from the true lot j mean. σ_B and σ_W are corresponding inter-lot and intra-lot variabilities. μ is the attribute mean. The prior $P(\theta)$ for $\theta=(\mu,\sigma_B,\sigma_W)$ encapsulates expert knowledge and could be derived from historical data.. Without loss of generality and to simplify further development, we assume that $P(\theta)\sim 1$.

It should be noted that the simplifying normality assumptions may be relaxed by treating the intra and inter lot variations to be distributed according to a more robust Student t distribution or even more general distributions such as the four parameter Johnson SU (Johnson, 1949) or the skew-normal or skew-t distributions which can model the presence of skewness and/or kurtosis (Dagne, 2013; Sahu, et al., 2003; Azzalini & Capitanio, 2003). However, in this work we will focus on the simplest normal form since under that assumption the design space may be expressed in terms of an analytical expression. In more complicated cases the design space boundaries have to be estimated using numerical simulation.

The design space boundaries based on the normality assumption may be expressed as:

$$DS_b = pnorm\left(ub, \mu, \sqrt{\sigma_B^2 + \sigma_W^2}\right) - pnorm\left(lb, \mu, \sqrt{\sigma_B^2 + \sigma_W^2}\right), \qquad (2)$$

where pnorm is the quantile function for the normal distribution, ub is the upper bound of product attribute, lb is lover bound of product attribute (for assays the typically lower/upper bounds are 90/110%, for dissolution the lower/upper bounds are % dissolved at Q time.

In the multidimensional case (i.e. assay, % dissolved, and tablet hardness are bounded) the design space boundaries may be derived analytically using multivariate normal distribution. For purposes of the present discussion, we assume that inter and intra lot variabilities are independent.

3. Case study

We have experimentally tested 18 different immediate release drug products manufactured by different generic manufacturers and determined their product quality attribute means and inter/intra lot variabilities from the experimental data (Morris, 2018). We also assume that the reliability measure is R=0.95. The choice of R is based on acceptable quality level (typically 5%). This choice is very important: higher values may be chosen for narrow therapeutic range products as is the case with some oncology therapies.

The 50% highest probability density region of the estimated joint distribution for mean, intra and inter lot variability of dissolution attribute (% dissolved at Q time) are depicted in Figure 1. To simplify the presentation, we combine the inter and intra lot variabilities by using:

$$\sigma^2 = \sigma_B^2 + \sigma_W^2, \qquad (3)$$

where σ is a lumped standard deviation.

The joint probability distribution estimates for mean μ, standard deviations σ_B and σ_W were obtained using Markov Chain Monte Carlo procedure (Morris, 2018) using a hierarchical model by also considering analytical variability.

We observe that for some products those regions are close to the design space boundary (black line). The number beside the product name indicates the probability of the tablet being within design space. Each oval corresponds to a different product and manufacturer combination. The names of the drug products that are below desired quality level are shown next to their corresponding oval. The probability of a given product being within the design space is shown to the right of product name. For example, Product P12 manufactured by M11 has probability of 34% being within design space.

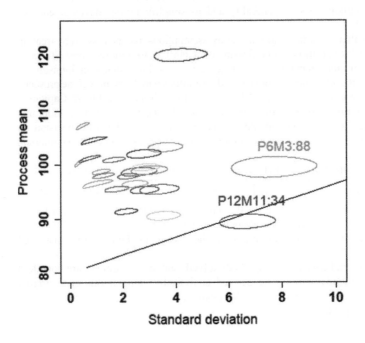

Figure 1. Probabilistic design space for dissolution. Ovals represent various products. The probability of a given product being within the design space is shown to the right of product name. The units of process mean and standard deviation are % dissolved.

The corresponding landscape for the product assay is depicted Figure 2. Since the assay is bounded from both sides of the design space, the boundary has a parabolic shape. Note that there are a number of products that fall outside of the design space boundary. One reason for this being that manufacturers overshoot to ensure that the content of active pharmaceutical ingredient (API) is not too low. Another artefact is that the assay is defined as the average content over several tablets, as specified by US Pharmacopeia. Averaging effectively masks intra-lot variability. While the average active content is below the upper bound the active content in individual tablets fluctuate. The proposed framework allows detecting "unobserved" behaviour.

It is of interest to note that the four large ovals lying outside of the design space on the top right corner of the Figure 2 represent the same product P11 manufactured by different manufacturers M1, M5, M2, and M10. It is very possible that overage is explicitly specified in the corresponding batch record.

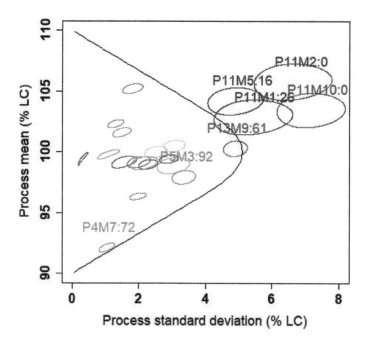

Figure 2. Probabilistic design space for assay. Ovals represent various products. The probability of a given product being within the design space is shown to the right of product name. The units of process mean and standard deviation are % of label claim.

The distributions of the probability that the product is within assay specifications for well performing (within design space) and poorly performing (outside design space) processes are depicted in Figure 3. A well performing process (solid line) is characterized by probability mass concentrated around one which is indicated by a sharp peak close to one. A poorly performing process (dashed line) is characterized by a diffuse probability mass that is indicated by a low and very wide hump in the distribution profile.

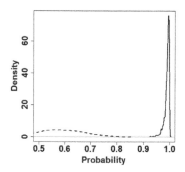

Figure 3. The probability distributions of probability that product is within assay specifications.

4. Conclusion

In this work we develop a Bayesian framework for building surrogate stochastic models of complex multi-step processes for which tractable mechanistic models are not available. The proposed framework may be a valuable tool to detect the "unobserved" process shifts and serve as an additional measure to ensure product quality.

The proposed framework can be easily extended to batch and continuous processing manufacturing of products that must meet a set of critical product quality specifications (i.e., conformance to grade requirements in oil refinery).

In addition, we expect that this work could potentially support FDA's risk based approach and quality metrics initiative - the proposed framework explicitly identifies the sites that may require attention - as well as continuous process verification as delineated in (FDA, 2011).

References

Azzalini, A. & Capitanio, A., 2003. Distributions generated by perturbation of symmetry with emphasis on a multivariate skew t distribution. *J. Roy. Statist. Soc., series B,* Volume 65, p. 367–389.

Bano, G., Facco, P., Bezzo, F. & Barolo, M., 2018. Probabilistic design space determination in pharmaceutical product development: a Bayesian/latent variable approach.. *AIChE J,* 64(7), p. 2438–2449.

Dagne, G. A., 2013. Bayesian Inference for Skew-Normal Mixture Models With Left-Censoring. *J Biopharm Stat.,* 23(5), p. 1023–1041.

FDA, 2011. *Guidance for Industry – Process Validation: General Principles and Practices,* s.l.: s.n.

ICH, 2009. *ICH Harmonised Tripartite Guideline Pharmaceutical Development Q8(R2),* s.l.: s.n.

Johnson, N. L., 1949. Systems of Frequency Curves Generated by Methods of Translation. *Biometrika,* 36(1/2), p. 149–176.

Morris, K., 2018. *Annual Report,* New York, NY: Lachman Institute for Pharmaceutical Analysis.

Morris, K., 2018. *Building towards Statistically-Based Pharmaceutical Quality Standards,* New York, NY: Lachman Institute for Pharmaceutical Analysis.

Peterson, J., 2008. A Bayesian Approach to the ICH Q8 Definition of Design Space. *Journal of Biopharmaceutical Statistics,* Volume 18, pp. 959–975.

Sahu, S., Dey, D. & Branco, M., 2003. A new class of multivariate skew distributions with applications to Bayesian regression models. *The Canadian Journal of Statistics,* 31(2), p. 129–150.

Anton A. Kiss, Edwin Zondervan, Richard Lakerveld, Leyla Özkan (Eds.)
Proceedings of the 29th European Symposium on Computer Aided Process Engineering
June 16th to 19th, 2019, Eindhoven, The Netherlands. © 2019 Elsevier B.V. All rights reserved.
http://dx.doi.org/10.1016/B978-0-128-18634-3.50177-6

Modeling Impacts of Tracking on Greenhouse Gas Emissions from Photovoltaic Power

Ian Miller,[a,b] Emre Gençer,[a,*] Francis M. O'Sullivan[a]

[a] MIT Energy Initiative, Massachusetts Institute of Technology, 77 Massachusetts Avenue, Cambridge MA 02139, US

[b] Department of Chemical Engineering, Massachusetts Institute of Technology, 77 Massachusetts Avenue, Cambridge MA 02139, US

emregencer@mit.edu

Abstract

A life cycle assessment (LCA) of photovoltaic (PV) power is conducted. The PV LCA is used to estimate the emissions impact of a common PV practice that has not been comprehensively analyzed by LCA: solar tracking. Relative to stationary mounting, solar tracking is found to decrease the greenhouse gas emissions of power from multi-crystalline silicon PV in most regions analyzed (by 0 to ~12%, or 0 to ~4 gCO$_2$e/kWh), and to increase the emissions of power from cadmium telluride PV in most regions analyzed (by 0 to ~12%, or 0 to ~4 gCO$_2$e/kWh). This dependence on cell type is explained by the interaction of tracker production emissions, module production emissions, and tracking energy gain. For both PV cell types, if the ratio of module production emissions to tracker production emissions increases in future, independent of absolute emission values, tracking will more commonly decrease PV carbon intensity. Conversely, if the ratio decreases, tracking will more commonly increase PV carbon intensity. Equations are presented to explain this relationship between module production emissions and tracker production emissions. These equations apply to emissions of all pollutants, not only greenhouse gases.

Keywords: photovoltaic (PV) power, life cycle assessment (LCA), greenhouse gas (GHG) emission, solar tracking

1. Introduction

Since 2008, solar tracking has grown from rare to common in photovoltaic (PV) power production. In the US from 2008 to 2014, 19 % of new utility-scale projects with cadmium telluride (CdTe) modules employed tracking (16 of 86 projects); in 2015 and 2016, the number was 56 % (44 of 79 projects), including locations outside the exceptionally sunny US southwest, such as Colorado and Tennessee (EIA 2016). For all PV module types, tracking was used on 53 % of cumulative and 70 % of new capacity at utility-scale sites in 2016 in the US (EIA 2016). The impact of solar tracking on emissions from PV generation has not been comprehensively analyzed by life cycle assessment (LCA). This study fills that gap. It provides a general methodology for estimating the emissions impact of adding performance enhancing equipment to PV, and applies this methodology to model the impact of solar tracking on emissions of greenhouse gases (GHGs). This paper refers to life cycle GHG emissions from AC electricity generation as "carbon intensity", and the units of grams-CO$_2$-equivalent/kilowatthour as "g$_C$/kWh".

Several LCAs analyzed the impact of solar tracking on carbon intensity, but with limited geographic scope and tracking set-ups that do not (and do not claim to) represent industry practice. Desideri et al. (2013) analyzed 1-axis tracking systems with 30° tilt in southern europe. In contrast, the industry norm for PV tracking is horizontal 1-axis tracking; in the US in 2016, 97 % of utility-scale tracking PV projects used horizontal 1-axis tracking (Bolinger et al. 2017). Two PV LCAs did analyze industry-representative tracking. Leccisi et al. (2016) found that horizontal 1-axis tracking reduced carbon intensity by 11 % and 1 % for mc-Si and CdTe PV, respectively, given installation in the US southwest. Sinha et al. (2013) estimated that tracking reduced the carbon intensity of CdTe PV by 3 % in the US southwest. This paper aims to build on these studies by calculating and explaining tracking's impact on PV carbon intensity over a range of locations.

2. Methodology

We developed a solar life cycle assessment tool (SoLCAT) following ISO 14040 standards for LCA (ISO 14040 2006) and IEA PV LCA guidelines. To estimate GHG emissions from PV power, SoLCAT integrates four elements: published PV life cycle inventories (LCIs), background emission factors from Ecoinvent, known physical correlations, and capacity factors from PVWatts, a software tool from the US National Renewable Energy Laboratory.

The goal of our LCA is to estimate the impact of solar tracking on the carbon intensity of PV power. The system is electricity production by PV. The functional unit is a kilowatthour of AC electricity supplied to the grid. In addition to electricity, the other system output analyzed is GHG emissions. These two system outputs combine into our central metric: GHGs emitted per AC electricity generated (g_C/kWh), or carbon intensity. PV electricity production can be elaborated as shown in Figure 1.

Figure 2 gives an overview of SoLCAT's operation and utilization of data sources. Our primary sources for PV LCIs are the IEA Report "Life Cycle Inventories & Life Cycle Assessments of PV Systems" (Frischknecht et al. 2015) and the ESU Report "Life Cycle Inventories of Photovoltaics" (Jungbluth et al. 2012). Sinha et al. (2013) provides an LCI of a horizontal 1-axis tracking system. For emission factors of background processes, our primary source is the Ecoinvent V3 database. In the absence of data, our model does not account for emissions from PV EOL processes.

SoLCAT converts amounts (a) to GHG emissions (e_{total}) using three general equations:

$$e_{total} = \sum_i e_{stage\ i} \tag{1}$$

$$e_{stage\ i} = \sum_j e_{input\ j\ to\ stage\ i} - \sum_k^{stages\ before\ i} e_{stage\ k} \tag{2}$$

$$e_{input\ j\ to\ stage\ i} = a_{input\ j\ to\ stage\ i}\ EF_j \tag{3}$$

where e is emissions (g_C), a is amount (e.g., kg-iron), and EF is emission factor (e.g., g_C/kg-iron). Amounts ($a_{input\ j\ to\ stage\ i}$) provided by the PV LCIs or determined by parameters input to SoLCAT. Emission factors (EF_j) are provided by Ecoinvent or SoLCAT inputs. Miller et al. (2018) describes how SoLCAT input variables impact amounts and emission factors.

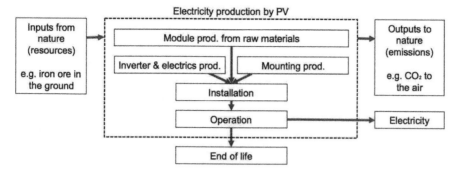

Figure 1. Life cycle stages of PV electricity production.

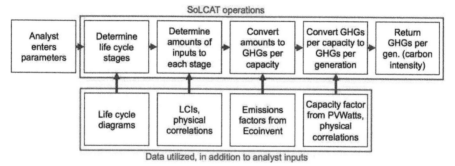

Figure 2. Flowchart of SoLCAT operations and utilization of data sources.

SoLCAT's last operation utilizes capacity factor estimates from PVWatts (Dobos 2014). As detailed in Miller et. al (2018), our model adjusts capacity factors from PVWatts to account for shading, snow, degradation, and tracker energy consumption, to calculate a lifetime average capacity factor (F). Carbon intensity is then calculated as:

$$I = e_{total} / (Fc_g t_{hr})$$ (4)

where I is carbon intensity (g$_C$/kWh), e_{total} is life cycle GHG emissions (g$_C$), c_g is rated power capacity, and t_{hr} is PV system lifetime (h).

Analysis of solar tracking's impact on carbon intensity requires calculation of tracking energy gain (TEG). TEG is the percent increase in PV power output that results from tracking the sun, relative to a fixed-position system, and can be estimated as

$$TEG = (\bar{P}_{AC,track} - \bar{P}_{AC,fixed}) / \bar{P}_{AC,fixed} \times 100\,\%$$ (5)

where $P_{AC,track}$ is the AC power output of a PV system with tracking, and $P_{AC,fixed}$ is the output of a PV system with fixed orientation and otherwise identical features (location, modules, etc.). The fixed base case orientation is assumed here to be irradiance-maximizing, with equator-facing azimuth and near-latitude tilt. The tracking system is horizontal 1-axis tracking with ± 45 ° rotation limits.

3. Results and discussion

Using SoLCAT, base case results are calculated and shown in Figure 3:

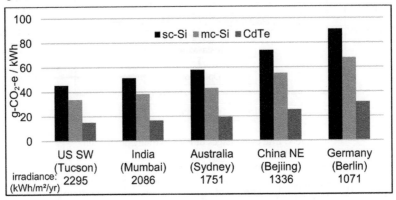

Figure 3. Carbon intensities of PV power installed in different locations circa 2015. Installation type is large-scale, open-ground, fixed-tilt. Lifetime is 30 years. Rated efficiencies are 17, 16, and 15.6 % for sc-Si, mc-Si, and CdTe. Degradation is 0.7 %/yr. GHG emissions of upstream electricity are 660 & 510 gc/kWh for module and BOS production, assuming 2015 China & world averages.

We find that in the US southwest, for mc-Si PV, horizontal 1-axis tracking reduces carbon intensity by 12 % relative to the fixed-tilt base case (from 34 to 30 g_C/kWh), consistent with previous results (Leccisi, Raugei, and Fthenakis 2016). Tracking produces this reduction despite requiring ~50 % more structural metal and ~30 % more copper cable per module, compared to fixed mounting (Sinha et al. 2013). Emissions from producing tracker materials are offset by increased generation from tracking, such that overall emissions per generation decreases.

Analogous calculations are conducted for PV systems in 4 other locations and presented in Figure 4, which underlines several related findings. (1) location influences the emissions impact of tracking, via TEG; (2) tracking decreases the carbon intensity of mc-Si PV in most locations; (3) consistent with Sinha et al. (2013), tracking reduces the carbon intensity of CdTe PV in the US southwest by ~3 %; and (4) the US southwest is exceptional: for most locations analyzed, tracking increases the carbon intensity of CdTe PV power.

The dependence on location is driven by latitude and cloud cover. The greater the latitude, the greater the module incline that maximizes incident irradiance, and the more irradiance is lost by "reclining" to horizontal for 1-axis tracking. Greater latitude also means more atmosphere for sunlight to travel through. This increases light scattering, as does greater cloud cover. The greater the fraction of ambient light that is scattered (i.e., diffuse), the less energy there is to be gained from tracking the sun's non-diffuse direct beam irradiance. Lower tracking energy gain (TEG) means less extra electricity over which to amortize extra emissions from tracker-production. For both module types, this explains why, as TEG decreases left to right in Figure 4, tracking's emissions impact increases.

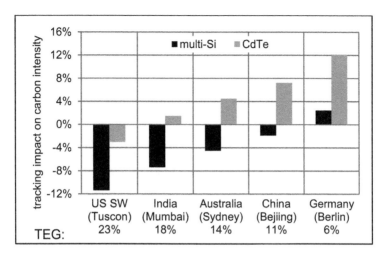

Figure 4. Relative impact of horizontal 1-axis tracking on PV carbon intensity in different locations, for mc-Si PV and CdTe PV.

The varying impact by module type can be explained with the following equations. Let:

$T \equiv$ factor by which tracking increases electricity generation.

$e_{f,i} \equiv$ emissions of fixed PV system (g_C). $i =$ mc-Si or CdTe

$e_t \equiv$ emissions from adding tracking (g_C)

$E_f \equiv$ generation from fixed PV system (kWh)

$E_t \equiv$ generation from tracking PV system (kWh)

$I_f \equiv$ emissions per generation (carbon intensity) of fixed PV system (g_C/kWh)

$I_t \equiv$ emissions per generation (carbon intensity) of tracking PV system (g_C/kWh)

$M \equiv$ factor by which tracking changes carbon intensity

$$M = I_t / I_f$$
$$= [(e_{f,i} + e_t) / E_t] / [e_{f,i} / E_f] = [(e_{f,i} + e_t) / (TE_f)] / [e_{f,i} / E_f]$$
$$M = (e_{f,i} + e_t) / (Te_{f,i}) \tag{6}$$

Consider Eq. (6) when $e_{f,i} \gg e_t$, i.e., when emissions from module production are much larger than emissions from tracker production:

$$M_{f\,large} = 1/T \tag{7}$$

$M_{f\,large}$ will always be less than 1, because T always exceeds 1. In other words, for a module type with large production emissions, adding tracking always reduces carbon intensity. This explains why adding tracking reduces the carbon intensity of mc-Si PV in most locations (blue bars in Figure 4). Multi-Si module production is significantly more carbon intensive than CdTe module production, as seen in Figure 3 and previously reported (Frischknecht et al. 2015). $e_{f,multi-Si}$ is approximately 11 x e_t whereas $e_{f,CdTe}$ is approximately 5 x e_t. Eq. (6) thus also explains why adding tracking increases CdTe PV's carbon intensity in most locations (red bars in Figure 4):

$$M_{CdTe} \approx (e_{f,CdTe} + e_{f,CdTe} / 5) / (Te_{f,CdTe}) = 1.2 / T \tag{8}$$

For M_{CdTe} to be less than 1, T must exceed 1.2. In other words, CdTe PV requires TEG above 20 % for tracking to reduce its carbon intensity, a TEG only possible in exceptionally sunny regions like the US southwest.

4. Conclusion

A modeling tool (SoLCAT) is presented. SoLCAT estimates GHG emissions from solar PV generation under a broad range of conditions, partly by combining life cycle inventories and PV performance models. Using this tool, we find that solar tracking decreases the GHG emissions of power from multi-crystalline silicon PV in most regions analyzed (by 0 to ~12 %, or 0 to ~4 gCO_2e/kWh), and increases the emissions of power from cadmium telluride PV in most regions analyzed (by 0 to ~12 %, or 0 to ~4 gCO_2e/kWh). For any PV cell type and any emitted pollutant, if the ratio of module production emissions to tracker production emissions increases in future, independent of absolute emission values, tracking will more commonly decrease PV emissions intensity.

References

Bolinger, Mark, Joachim Seel, and Kristina Hamachi LaCommare. 2017. "Utility-Scale Solar 2016."

Desideri, U., F. Zepparelli, V. Morettini, and E. Garroni. 2013. "Comparative Analysis of Concentrating Solar Power and Photovoltaic Technologies: Technical and Environmental Evaluations." *Applied Energy* 102:765–84. https://doi.org/10.1016/j.apenergy.2012.08.033.

Dobos, Aron P. 2014. "PVWatts Version 5 Manual (NREL/TP-6A20-62641)." *National Renewable Energy Laboratory (NREL)*.

EIA. 2016. "Form EIA-860 : Annual Electric Generator Report."

Frischknecht, R, R Itten, P Sinha, M de Wild-Scholten, J Zhang, and Vasilis Fthenakis. 2015. "Life Cycle Inventories and Life Cycle Assessment of Photovoltaic Systems; Report IEA-PVPS T12-04:2015." Paris, France.

ISO 14040. 2006. "The International Standards Organisation. Environmental Management — Life Cycle Assessment — Principles and Framework." *ISO 14040*. https://doi.org/10.1136/bmj.332.7550.1107.

Jungbluth, Niels, Matthias Stucki, Karin Flury, Rolf Frischknecht, and Sybille Büsser. 2012. "Life Cycle Inventories of Photovoltaics." Ulster, CH.

Leccisi, Enrica, Marco Raugei, and Vasilis Fthenakis. 2016. "The Energy and Environmental Performance of Ground-Mounted Photovoltaic Systems - A Timely Update." *Energies* 9 (8). https://doi.org/10.3390/en9080622.

Miller, Ian, Emre Gençer, Hilary S Vogelbaum, Patrick R Brown, Sarah Torkamani, and O'Su. 2018. "Parametric Modeling of Life Cycle Greenhouse Gas Emissions from Photovol-Taic Power." *[Under Review]*.

Sinha, P, M Schneider, S Dailey, C Jepson, and M De Wild-Scholten. 2013. "Eco-Efficiency of CdTe Photovoltaics with Tracking Systems." In *39th IEEE Photovoltaic Specialists Conference (PVSC)*. Tampa, FL, US.

Anton A. Kiss, Edwin Zondervan, Richard Lakerveld, Leyla Özkan (Eds.)
Proceedings of the 29th European Symposium on Computer Aided Process Engineering
June 16th to 19th, 2019, Eindhoven, The Netherlands. © 2019 Elsevier B.V. All rights reserved.
http://dx.doi.org/10.1016/B978-0-128-18634-3.50178-8

Recent Advances in Graph-Based Abstractions for Modeling and Simulating Complex Systems

Jordan Jalving[a,b] and Victor Zavala[a,*]

[a]*Department of Chemical and Biological Engineering, University of Wisconsin-Madison, 1415 Engineering Dr, Madison, WI 53706, USA*
[b]*Decision and Infrastructure Sciences Division, Argonne National Laboratory, 9700 South Cass Ave, Lemont, IL 60439, USA*
victor.zavala@wisc.edu

Abstract

Current graph-based approaches for modeling, simulation and optimization of complex cyber-physical systems have motivated the development of new graph-based abstractions. We propose an algebraic graph to represent physical connectivity in complex optimization models and a computing graph to capture computational aspects of cyber/control architectures. The algebraic graph facilitates the analysis and decomposition of optimization problems and the computing graph enables the simulation of optimization and control algorithms in virtual distributed environments. The proposed abstractions are implemented in a `Julia` software package called `Plasmo.jl`.

Keywords: cyber-physical, structured modeling, complex systems, decomposition

1. Introduction

Modeling and simulating cyber-physical systems is becoming increasingly important, but capturing interdependencies between cyber and physical systems in a coherent manner is technically challenging. Physical systems (such as chemical processes) can be driven by control systems, which in turn are cyber systems comprised of computing devices (e.g. sensors, controllers, actuators) that execute tasks (e.g., data processing, control action computation) and that exchange information (e.g., measurements and control actions) through a communication network. Physical systems are expressed mathematically in the form of *algebraic models* while cyber systems are expressed in the form of *algorithms* which are often executed under heterogeneous computing architectures that exhibit complex communication protocols.

This work discusses newly proposed *graph-based* abstractions that facilitate modeling and simulation of cyber-physical systems. Graph-based modeling approaches have appeared in various engineering applications. Preisig (2007) used graph-theoretic approaches to perform on-line mass and energy balancing in large-scale plants given incomplete sensor data. Couenne et al. (2007) presented bond-graph modeling for chemical engineering applications and highlighted the advantages of model encapsulation and re-use. Elve and Preisig (2018) recently applied graph-based concepts to develop a process simulator with automatic code generation capabilities.

In this work we analyze the concept of an *algebraic model graph* that facilitates the implementation and solution of physical systems and the concept of a *computing graph* that facilitates simulation of cyber systems. The graph abstractions exploit *physical and communication topology* to facilitate model construction, data management, and analysis. Both abstractions are implemented in the Julia package Plasmo.jl (https: //github.com/zavalab/Plasmo.jl).

2. Algebraic Graphs

Here we present a **model graph** abstraction to represent complex optimization models found in physical applications. A model graph $\mathcal{MG}(\mathcal{N}, \mathcal{E})$ is a *hypergraph* wherein each node $n \in \mathcal{N}(\mathcal{MG})$ has an associated component optimization model of the form:

$$\min_{x_n \in \mathcal{X}_n} \quad f_n(x_n). \tag{1}$$

where x_n are decision variables, $\mathcal{X}_n := \{x \,|\, c_n(x) \geq 0\}$ is the feasible set with associated constraint vector mapping $c_n(\cdot)$, and the mapping $f_n(\cdot)$ is a scalar objective function.

Coupling is captured between component models using *link constraints*. In particular, we consider linear linking constraints of the form:

$$\sum_{n \in \mathcal{N}(e)} \Pi_{e,n} x_n = 0 \quad e \in \mathcal{E}(\mathcal{MG}). \tag{2}$$

where $e \in \mathcal{E}(\mathcal{MG})$ are the hyperedges of the model graph and $n \in \mathcal{N}(e)$ is the set of nodes that support hyperedge e. The matrix $\Pi_{e,n}$ corresponds to the coefficients of the linking constraints between edge e and node n.

We can represent hierarchical optimization structures using subgraphs as shown in Figure 1. A model graph can contain an arbitrary number of subgraphs by defining $\mathcal{SG}(\mathcal{MG}_0)$ (with elements $\mathcal{SG}$) as the set of subgraphs defined on the parent model graph $\mathcal{MG}_0$. This allows us to express the model graph in the form of Equation 3.

$$\min_{x_{\mathcal{MG}_0}} \sum_{n \in \mathcal{N}(\mathcal{MG}_0)} f_n(x_n) \qquad \text{(Graph objective function)} \tag{3a}$$

$$\text{s.t.} \quad x_n \in \mathcal{X}_n, \quad n \in \mathcal{N}(\mathcal{MG}_0) \qquad \text{(Local node constraints)} \tag{3b}$$

$$\Pi_{\mathcal{MG}_0} x_{\mathcal{MG}_0} = 0 \qquad \text{(Graph link constraints)} \tag{3c}$$

$$\Pi_{\mathcal{SG}} x_{\mathcal{SG}} = 0 \quad \mathcal{SG} \in \mathcal{SG}(\mathcal{MG}_0) \qquad \text{(Subgraph link constraints)} \tag{3d}$$

Graph models provide structural information which facilitates decomposition and model management. For example, Formulation (3) has a partially separable structure because eliminating the linking constraints (3c and 3d) results in a fully separable problem. These problems can be solved using Schur decomposition schemes such as done in Chiang et al. (2014). It is also possible to aggregate the nodes in a model graph and into a traditional optimization form which can be solved with an off-the-shelf solver such as Ipopt (Wächter and Biegler (2006)). The graph structure also allows one to produce decompositions using graph analysis techniques such as partitioning and community detection (Tang et al. (2017)).

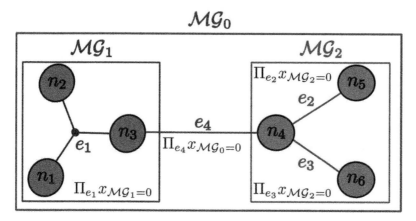

Figure 1: A model graph with two subgraphs. $\mathcal{MG}_1$ contains three nodes (n_1, n_2, n_3) and one linking constraint (e_1). $\mathcal{MG}_2$ contains three nodes (n_4, n_5, n_6) and two linking constraints $(e_2$ and $e_3)$. $\mathcal{MG}_0$ is the top layer of the graph containing all six nodes and connects the two subgraphs with a single linking constraint between nodes n_3 and n_4 (e_4).

3. Computing Graphs

Simulating a cyber system requires capturing real-time computing aspects such as as latency, failures, and asychronicity. To approach these challenges, we introduce the **computing graph** which is a directed multi-graph that we denote as $\mathcal{CG}(\mathcal{N}, \mathcal{E})$ and that contains a set of nodes $\mathcal{N}(\mathcal{CG})$ which execute tasks and edges $\mathcal{E}(\mathcal{CG})$ which communicate attributes to other nodes.

In a computing graph, A node $n \in \mathcal{N}(\mathcal{CG})$ contains a set of *attributes* $\mathcal{A}_n$ and tasks $\mathcal{T}_n$ and an edge $e \in \mathcal{E}(\mathcal{CG})$ contains a pair of attributes $\mathcal{A}_e$ which it communicates between supporting nodes $\mathcal{N}(e)$. The attributes $\mathcal{A}_n$ represent data and tasks $\mathcal{T}_n$ are computations that operate with and/or change attributes. Tasks require execution time $\Delta\theta_t$ and edges involve communication delay $\Delta\theta_e$. Under the proposed abstraction, computing and communication can be synchronous (a task is not executed until all attributes are received) or asynchronous (a task is executed with current values). This enables capturing a wide range of behaviors seen in cyber-system applications.

A simple computing graph is depicted in Figure 2. Each node contains a single task which operates on its attributes x, y, and z as input and updates one of their values. The nodes communicate attribute values with each other using six edges. For example, attribute y is communicated to both nodes n_2 and n_3 which updates the value of y on these respective nodes. The superscript $+$ means that attributes are updated after a given time which captures computing and communication delays.

The computing graph differs from the model graph abstraction in that it contains a dynamic component (a task) while a node in a model graph contains a static component (a model). Moreover, edges in a computing graph connect attributes while edges connect algebraic variables in a model graph. We highlight that the *solution* of a model graph is a computing task and we can thus use model graphs in individual nodes of the computing graph. This greatly facilitates simulating the behavior of cyber-physical systems.

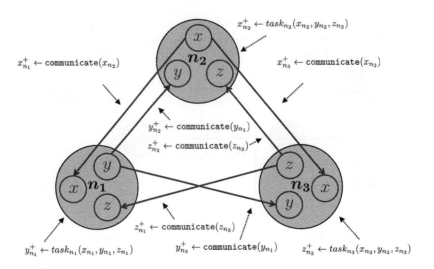

Figure 2: Depiction of a computing graph with three nodes and six edges. Node n_1 computes $task_{n_1}$ using the data attributes (x, y, and z) and updates the value of attribute y. Similarly, node n_2 computes $task_{n_2}$ and updates attribute x, and node n_3 computes $task_{n_3}$ and updates attribute z. Attribute values are communicated between nodes using edges.

4. Case Study: Evaluating Control Architectures

This case study demonstrates how a model graph can be used to formulate and solve an optimal control problem for a dynamic physical system and how solving the model graph can be embedded in a computing graph to evaluate various distributed control architectures subject to real-time latency (i.e., computation and communication times). We consider a reactor-separator system (see Figure 3) from Stewart et al. (2010) which is a standard for evaluating distributed model predictive control.

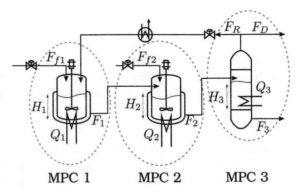

Figure 3: Reactor separator process. The control can be decomposed into 3 MPC controllers.

We first create a model graph using `Plasmo.jl` for the process in Figure 3 using three nodes. Two nodes contain optimization models to track reactor setpoints, and the other node contains a model to track the separator setpoints. The three nodes are linked together using algebraic *link constraints* which represent the flows that couple the systems together.

The process is simulated using the computing graph for three different control architec-

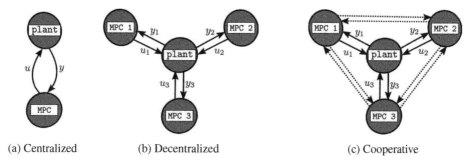

(a) Centralized   (b) Decentralized   (c) Cooperative

Figure 4: Simulated control architecture topologies. (Left): Centralized control. (Middle): Decentralized Control. (Right): Cooperative Control

tures. We simulate a *centralized* model predictive control (MPC) architecture wherein a central MPC controller calculates all inputs for the process. To do so, we solve the entire model graph as a single MPC node in the computing graph (Figure 4a) and use another computing node to simulate and advance the state of the plant.

We also decompose the process into three MPC controllers and simulate a *decentralized* control architecture wherein controllers do not communicate (Figure 4b) and a *cooperative* architecture (Figure 4c) such that controllers share state and intended control trajectories. For these cases, the nodes in the computing graph (MPC1,MPC2, and MPC3) compute tasks which solve and update the individual model nodes we defined in the model graph. We highlight that the computing graph captures the *asynchronous* behavior of the decentralized and cooperative schemes. Because we account for real computation times, the controllers inject their inputs when they finish their computation as opposed to all at the same time.

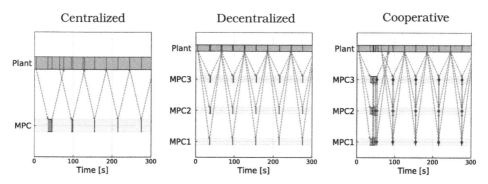

Figure 5: Communication pattern for each simulated MPC architecture

Figure 5 presents communication and computation patterns for each MPC algorithm. The centralized MPC pattern shows the communication delays between the plant and the controller (grey arrows), the time required to compute the control action (the purple bar), and highlights how the plant state advances continuously while computation and communication tasks execute. Despite the delays enforced for the controller, centralized MPC is able to drive the state to the setpoint (as shown in Figure 6). Decentralized MPC does

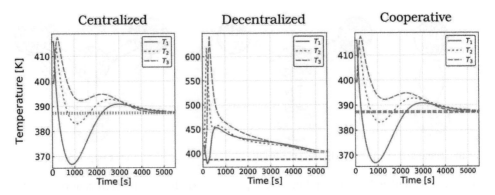

Figure 6: Temperature evolution for each simulated MPC architecture

not require communication between controllers which decreases computing times, but we observe that the setpoint cannot be reached. Finally, cooperative MPC shows a more complex communication pattern but we observe that this mimics the performance of centralized MPC.

5. Conclusions

We have presented graph-based abstractions that facilitate modeling complex cyber-physical systems. We showed how a model graph abstraction facilitates modeling complex physical systems and how a computing graph enables simulating computational behaviors. We provided a case study using the package `Plasmo.jl` that demonstrates how these abstractions can be used to evaluate distributed computing architectures.

6. Acknowledgements

This material is based on work supported by the U.S. Department of Energy (DOE), Office of Science, under Contract No. DE-AC02-06CH11357. This work was also partially supported by the U.S. Department of Energy grant DE-SC0014114.

References

N. Chiang, C. G. Petra, V. M. Zavala, 2014. Structured Nonconvex Optimization of Large-Scale Energy Systems Using PIPS-NLP. 2014 Power Systems Computation Conference, 1–7.

F. Couenne, C. Jallut, L. Lefevre, Y. Le Gorrec, B. Maschke, 2007. Basis for bond-graph modeling in chemical engineering. Computer Aided Chemical Engineering 24, 69–74.

A. T. Elve, H. A. Preisig, 2018. From Process Graph to Process Simulation with Proper Model Documentation. Computer Aided Chemical Engineering 43, 235–240.

H. A. Preisig, 2007. A Graph-Theory-Base Approach to the Analysis of Large-Scale Plants. Computer Aided Chemical Engineering 24, 81–86.

B. T. Stewart, A. N. Venkat, J. B. Rawlings, S. J. Wright, G. Pannocchia, 2010. Cooperative distributed model predictive control. Systems and Control Letters 59 (8), 460–469.

W. Tang, A. Allman, D. B. Pourkargar, P. Daoutidis, 2017. Optimal decomposition for distributed optimization in nonlinear model predictive control through community detection. Computers & Chemical Engineering 111, 43–54.

A. Wächter, L. T. Biegler, 2006. On the implementation of an interior-point filter line-search algorithm for large-scale nonlinear programming. Mathematical Programming 106 (1), 25–57.

Anton A. Kiss, Edwin Zondervan, Richard Lakerveld, Leyla Özkan (Eds.)
Proceedings of the 29th European Symposium on Computer Aided Process Engineering
June 16th to 19th, 2019, Eindhoven, The Netherlands. © 2019 Elsevier B.V. All rights reserved.
http://dx.doi.org/10.1016/B978-0-128-18634-3.50179-X

Spatio-Temporal Control of Nutrient Pollution from Organic Waste

Yicheng Hu[a], Gerardo Ruiz-Mercado[b] and Victor Zavala[a*]

[a]*Department of Chemical and Biological Engineering, University of Wisconsin-Madison, 1415 Engineering Drive, Madison 53706, USA*
[b]*National Risk Management Research Laboratory, U.S. Environmental Protection Agency, 26 W. Martin Luther King Drive, Cincinnati 45268, USA*
victor.zavala@wisc.edu

Abstract

Better management of anthropogenic organic waste and other primary sources of nutrient pollution such as agricultural, municipal, and industrial waste, will reduce the human impact on the environment. Harmful algal blooms (HABs) are a major environmental impact from organic waste and nutrient pollution. HABs can pose severe threats to human health due to the release of dangerous toxins in fresh or marine water that can negatively affect public health, increase treatment costs for drinking water, and cause enormous economic loss in industries that depend on clean water. In this study, the effect of decisions made in the organic waste supply chain (SC) on reducing the potential for HABs is investigated by integrating three types of models: a SC optimization model, a nutrient transport model, and an algae growth model. This contribution presents a comprehensive spatio-temporal management strategy for short-term HAB reduction by adjusting components in the SC, including technologies, logistics, nutrient management plans (NMPs) or environmental costs, and seasonal waste storage planning. In addition, it is presented a case study of the Upper Yahara Watershed in the State of Wisconsin to illustrate the practicability of this modeling framework.

Keywords: supply chain, nutrient pollution, spatial-temporal control, harmful algal blooms

1. Introduction

The role of nutrient pollution (specifically nitrogen and phosphorous) is central to the underlying causes of HABs. Sources of nutrient pollution are classified as either non-point source or point source. Non-point sources include agricultural land, stormwater etc., and the point sources include permitted facilities, e.g. wastewater treatment plants (WWTPs). Complex point and non-point nutrient management strategies will be required to achieve a more comprehensive and permanent solution to controlling the nutrient pollutions. The increasing rate of HAB development is a complicated problem faced by human populations around the world. Algal species involved in a HAB can generate significant levels of toxins threatening public health. According to Heisler et al. (2008), HABs have economic impacts in the form of remediation costs for water treatment and reduction in property value of the impacted areas . Graham et al. (2009) estimated that 30% of lakes from 36 states in the US have reported toxic cyanobacterial bloom issues . The US Environmental Protection Agency (US EPA) reported the tourism losses of one billion dollars annually and commercial fishing losses on the order of tens of millions of dollars annually [1].

By designing an appropriate transportation network for organic matter and incorporating technology placement for treatment and processing, the nutrients in organic waste can be more efficiently recycled for agricultural use in the growth of crops, feeding of grazing animals, and ultimately for human benefit. However, from Zandi Atashbar et al. (2018), current sustainable SC design studies typically incorporate metrics such as global warming potential and eutrophication potential which measure the chronic environmental impacts. Yet, the effects of seasonal variations in nutrient loading must be considered. Therefore, an extended modeling framework is needed to better describe the explicit environmental consequences caused by decisions made in the organic waste SC design.

In this work, we apply, adapt, and combine multiple types of modeling tools, including a SC design model, a nutrient transport model, and an algae growth model to create an optimization framework that analyzes the effect of nutrient controlling strategies in SCs on HABs. We present a case study in the Upper Yahara Watershed in the State of Wisconsin.

2. Modeling Framework

In this section, we introduce a modeling framework to connect the decision-making and control strategies in the SC with the environmental consequence of HABs. The modeling structure is shown in Figure 1.

Algae growth shows seasonal dependence, and this is because its growth is affected by water temperature, sunlight, nutrient concentration, and other factors. Steady-state modeling will not adequately capture the impact of seasonality, nor will models with large time steps (e.g. annual based decision making). For example, nutrient leaching in cold months will raise the probability of HABs in the spring. Therefore, management and prevention actions must be taken in advance, but there is still ambiguity about the optimal lead time for actions to be effective. The models for algae growth, nutrient transport, and SC, all have an explicit time dependence.

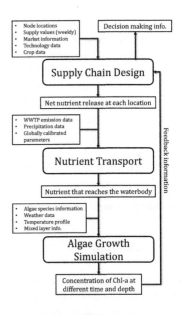

Figure 1: Modeling structure

2.1. Supply Chain Model

We extend the supply chain framework from Sampat et al. (2017) and Hu et al. (2018). The SC model is a constrained dynamic optimization model, which takes the input of node locations (e.g., dairy farms), the weekly supply amount of organic waste, market information including demand amount and price for each product, technology data (yield factors, investment and operational costs), and crop data, such as the crop type, yield, growing season, and nutrient uptake rate.

---

[1] https://www.epa.gov/nutrientpollution/effects-economy

The SC structure is shown in Figure 2. The farms can send organic waste to transportation sites to process it, storage systems to store it temporarily, or directly apply it to agriculture lands. The value-added products from technologies can be purchased by external customers. The main decision variables in the model are transportation flows, inventory levels, installation of technologies and storage systems, and amount of commercial fertilizers applied. The SC model can also output the amount of applied organic waste, which can be fed into the nutrient transport model to support runoff calculation.

The constraints in the optimization model include: the flow conservation at each node (product balance), the product conversion at technology sites, capacity constraints for demand, inventory, and processed waste, the nutrient requirement for each crop at each node and time period, and the economic metrics. The objective function is to minimize the overall costs plus the excess nutrients in the system, where the weight can be interpreted as unit environmental costs or the strictness of environmental policies regarding nutrient management plan at each node.

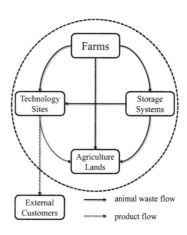

2.2. Nutrient Transport Model

A nutrient transport model tracks the nutrient transport process from point and non-point sources to surface water. To reduce the computational burden,

Figure 2: Supply chain structure

increase the compatibility of the framework, and generate results at preliminary development stages, instead of using advanced and data-intensive simulation tools such as SWAT (Neitsch et al. (2011)), we select a watershed-level model called NEWS2 (Nutrient Export from WaterSheds 2) proposed by Mayorga et al. (2010). The NEWS2 model is a more general model that takes input data of WWTP emission data, precipitation data at a watershed level, globally calibrated parameters, and the net nutrient release information from the organic waste SC management model.

The model calculates the phosphorus and nitrogen that reach the water body considering both the contributions from point and non-point sources. The point source part is calculated using the population data and nominal nutrient release per person. The contribution from non-point sources is calculated using some global parameters, precipitation data (which is used for surface runoff calculation), and the net nutrient release accounting for fertilizer, animal waste application, fixation and deposition, and crop need.

We note that in the application of the NEWS2 model, two main assumptions are made. First, the NEWS2 model is originally used for annual nutrient transport. We assume a biweekly nutrient transport amount can be assessed using the same approach with finer input data, and with a transport delay included. Second, we assume the model can be fit into the use of small watershed. The modeling framework is equipped with more powerful functions under these functions, which might lead to lower accuracy. We will continue to extend the scope in the nutrient transport modeling and simulation.

2.3. Algae Growth Model

An algae growth model is used to relate the nutrient concentration in a water body with the HAB level and the corresponding consequences. The algae growth model used in this framework is the PROTECH (Phytoplankton RespOnses To Environmental CHange) model, which is proposed by Reynolds et al. (2001), and takes the input of nutrient concentration data, algae species information, weather data, lake profile (e.g. temperature). The model uses the concentration of chlorophyll-a (chl-a) as a measurement of the abundance of algae.

The PROTECH model calculates the daily concentration of chl-a by considering the growth rate, the rate of decrease due to animal grazing, settling out (algae movement), and dilution. For each term, the rate is mainly related to temperature, nutrient level, and sunlight intensity. The model can output the concentration of chl-a at different times and at different depths of the lake.

3. Case Study

We apply this modeling framework to a case study considering the region of Upper Yahara Watershed within Dane County in the State of Wisconsin. This region has suffered from nutrient pollution for years. The NBI (nutrient balance index, defined as the ratio of nutrient applied to land over the amount of nutrient that is removed by crops) was 1.95 and 1.35 in the year of 2012 and 2013 respectively (Larson et al. (2016)) . For the year 2017, the NBI index was 1.46 based on our estimation. The Lake Mendota has been categorized as eutrophic since the 1980s.

In the case study, we use the crop and weather data of the year 2017. The time period of interest is from April 1st to October 31st, where the HABs are more likely to happen. The data of nutrient recovery technologies are from previous studies (Sharara et al. (2018); Sampat et al. (2018)). The decision-making procedure in this case study is illustrated in Figure 3, and the control techniques in the SC are the strictness of NMPs, the availability of nutrient recovery technologies, and the seasonal storage planning. Although the SC framework has the capability of placing facilities, the facility sites in this case study are predetermined using real data. After solving the SC optimization problem, it can provide a spatio-temporal strategy containing different transportation flows and inventory levels in different times, which is able to control the net nutrient release in the system while balancing the economic objective. Based on this procedure, we start from the worst scenario (no technologies or NMPs, and poor storage planning), and compare the effectiveness of each technique individually. Finally, we study the overall influence of adopting three techniques simultaneously. We obtain economic information from the SC model. From the difference of scenarios, we

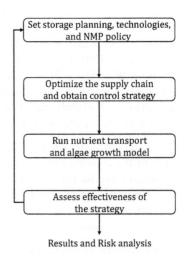

Figure 3: Decision-making scheme

can estimate the preventive cost for reducing HABs risk.

4. Results and Discussion

First, we compare the predicted TSI (trophic state index, proposed by Carlson (1977)) of the scenario closest to reality with observed data. A lake is defined as eutrophic when TSI is between 50-70. The predicted TSI is between 55 and 65; while the observed TSI fluctuates between 50 and 60, which indicates the practicability of the framework.

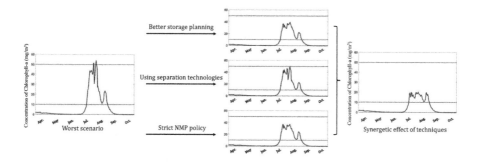

Figure 4: Model prediction

In Figure 4, we show the predicted concentration of chl-a under different control strategies. We observe that, in the worst scenario, the concentration exceeds the warning line of a high risk of acute health effect for humans suggested by the World Health Organization World Health Organization (2003) (50 mg chl-a/m^3), while the control techniques can reduce the HAB level under the warning line. From the comparison between the three control techniques, we find the incorporation of separation technologies is the less effective strategy, which may have attributed to the fact that the derived products are not valuable, and the economic driving force is not large enough. On the other hand, direct environmental policy changes (better storage planning or strict NMP policy) are more effective at controlling the nutrient runoff and thus the HAB level. Additionally, we observe that, by combining the three techniques, the HAB level can be reduced substantially, which means the strategies have an overall synergistic effect. However, even for the best scenario, the concentration of chl-a still exceeds the middle warning line (moderate risk of having acute health problems, 10 mg chl-a/m^3). This indicates that long-term effort (perennial SC optimization and nutrient management) is necessary to further eliminate the HABs risk.

From the economic results of the SC optimization problem, we can obtain the overall cost in the system (operational cost of technology, transportation cost, and fertilizer cost). For the worst scenario, the overall cost is 1.18 million USD while for the best scenario, the overall cost is increased by 32.2 % and reaches 1.56 million USD. This indicates the cost corresponding to the prevention of HABs in the same year can reach 0.38 million USD. We note that this estimation is conservative because the cost of implementing strict policies, the increased holding cost in inventory management, and the investment cost of technologies are not included.

5. Conclusions

In this work, we formulate a dynamic modeling framework by combining a SC optimization model, a nutrient transport model, and an algae growth model. The management elements in the SC network can be regarded as controlling techniques, and the output from the algae growth model can provide feedback information for the SC design. We provide a case study of Upper Yahara Watershed to illustrate the practicability of the model. We find by designing appropriate SCs, the nutrient loading in runoff can be decreased and the risk of HABs will be lower, but a corresponding cost of prevention will be incurred. In future work, we will conduct more scenario analyses and study the influence of logistics and the cost distribution at different times. We will extend our framework so that a perennial influence can be forecast.

6. Acknowledgements

We acknowledge support from the U.S. Department of Agriculture (grant 2017-67003-26055), from the National Science Foundation (grant CBET-1604374), and from the U.S. EPA (contract number EP-18-C-000016).

Disclaimer: The views expressed in this article are those of the authors and do not necessarily reflect the views or policies of the U.S. Environmental Protection Agency. Mention of trade names, products, or services does not convey, and should not be interpreted as conveying, official U.S. EPA approval, endorsement, or recommendation.

References

R. E. Carlson, 1977. A trophic state index for lakes. Limnology and oceanography 22 (2), 361–369.

J. Graham, K. A. Loftin, N. Kamman, 2009. Monitoring recreational freshwaters. Lakelines 29, 18–24.

J. Heisler, P. M. Glibert, J. M. Burkholder, D. M. Anderson, W. Cochlan, W. C. Dennison, Q. Dortch, C. J. Gobler, C. A. Heil, E. Humphries, et al., 2008. Eutrophication and harmful algal blooms: a scientific consensus. Harmful algae 8 (1), 3–13.

Y. Hu, M. Scarborough, H. Aguirre-Villegas, R. A. Larson, D. R. Noguera, V. M. Zavala, 2018. A supply chain framework for the analysis of the recovery of biogas and fatty acids from organic waste. ACS Sustainable Chemistry & Engineering 6 (5), 6211–6222.

R. Larson, M. Sharara, L. Good, T. Porter, V. Zavala, A. Sampat, A. Smith, 2016. Evaluation of manure storage capital projects in the yahara river watershed. Technical Report for Dane County, WI.

E. Mayorga, S. P. Seitzinger, J. A. Harrison, E. Dumont, A. H. Beusen, A. Bouwman, B. M. Fekete, C. Kroeze, G. Van Drecht, 2010. Global nutrient export from watersheds 2 (news 2): model development and implementation. Environmental Modelling & Software 25 (7), 837–853.

S. L. Neitsch, J. G. Arnold, J. R. Kiniry, J. R. Williams, 2011. Soil and water assessment tool theoretical documentation version 2009. Tech. rep., Texas Water Resources Institute.

C. Reynolds, A. Irish, J. Elliott, 2001. The ecological basis for simulating phytoplankton responses to environmental change (protech). Ecological modelling 140 (3), 271–291.

A. M. Sampat, E. Martin, M. Martin, V. M. Zavala, 2017. Optimization formulations for multi-product supply chain networks. Computers & Chemical Engineering 104, 296–310.

A. M. Sampat, E. Martín-Hernández, M. Martín, V. M. Zavala, 2018. Technologies and logistics for phosphorus recovery from livestock waste. Clean Technologies and Environmental Policy, 1–17.

M. A. Sharara, T. Runge, R. Larson, J. G. Primm, 2018. Techno-economic optimization of community-based manure processing. Agricultural Systems 161, 117–123.

World Health Organization, 2003. Guidelines for safe recreational water environments: Coastal and fresh waters. Vol. 1. World Health Organization.

N. Zandi Atashbar, N. Labadie, C. Prins, 2018. Modelling and optimisation of biomass supply chains: a review. International Journal of Production Research 56 (10), 3482–3506.

Anton A. Kiss, Edwin Zondervan, Richard Lakerveld, Leyla Özkan (Eds.)
Proceedings of the 29th European Symposium on Computer Aided Process Engineering
June 16th to 19th, 2019, Eindhoven, The Netherlands. © 2019 Elsevier B.V. All rights reserved.
http://dx.doi.org/10.1016/B978-0-128-18634-3.50180-6

Optimal design and planning multi resource-based energy integration in process industries

Shabnam Morakabatchiankar[a], Fernando D. Mele[b], Moisés Graells[a], Antonio Espuña[a]

[a]Chemical Engineering Department, Universitat Politècnica de Catalunya, EEBE. Av. Eduard Maristany, 10-14, Edifici I, Planta 6, 08019 Barcelona, Spain
[b]Departamento de Ingeniería de Procesos, FACET, Universidad Nacional de Tucumán (UNT),Avenida Independencia 1800, S. M. de Tucumán T4002BLR, Argentina
shabnam.morakabatchiankar@upc.edu

Abstract

Recently, process industries have experienced a significant pressure to shift from centralized energy supplying systems to the in-situ exploitation of renewable resources. Special attention has been paid to multi resource-based energy systems, a particular case of distributed generation where processing nodes include energy generation and can operate either grid-connected or isolated. This work proposes a general model to determine the optimal retrofitting of a supply chain integrating renewable energy sources under uncertain conditions and to analyze the effect of different planning horizons in the solution. The proposed mixed integer linear programming (MILP) formulation allows determining the best combination of available technologies that satisfies the internal energy demand of a given set of scenarios while addressing total expected cost and expected environmental impact minimization. The potential of the approach is illustrated through a case study from the sugar cane industry proposed by Mele et al. (2011).

Keywords: Multi resource-based energy, Optimization under uncertainty, renewable energies, closed-loop energy integration

1 Introduction

Growing energy demand about 60% over the last 30 years and increased industrial electricity and gas prices more than double in comparison with 20 years ago ((Zukunft, 2014) force industries to plan their eventual transition to a new energy system that will be largely based on Renewable Energy Sources (RES). This is one of the greatest challenges of our time. Over the latest years, process integration involving different renewable resources for their more efficient use, managing and controlling their uncertain availability, has been considered. Therefore, several alternative approaches are available to satisfy process energy demand and exploit the availability of renewable sources. In this line, a number of studies have been focused on single renewable sources such as first and second generation bioethanol production processes, which were integrated to use the excess of energy when processing lignocellulosic biomass for ethanol dehydration (Čuček et al. 2011; Mele et al. 2011), and cogeneration exploitation (Morakabatchiankar, Hjaila, Mele, Graells, & Espuña, 2018). Different energy sources have also been integrated with biomass types (Martín & Grossmann, 2017; Prasad et al. 2017; Vidal & Martín, 2015). Recently, Martín et al. (2018) proposed an integrated renewable energy resource network to produce biofuels and generate power combining two supply chains that traditionally are developed as independent entities. However, the satisfaction of large scale demands of multiple resources, such the one that should be faced at regional or country level, requires the integration of resources at a larger scale and needs more flexibility in terms of resources configuration. Hence, this work is focused on the development of a general optimization model for the retrofitting of sustainable process systems integrated with multi-energy generation system. The model is applicable to different ranges and scales while considering energy demand uncertainty to optimize the decisions of country-size SCs in the presence of conflicting objectives at different time spans.

2   Problem statement

According to the objective previously outlined, the proposed model determines a generic multi resource-based integration supply chain network as illustrated in Fig. 1. It is aimed to propose configurations associated with structural decisions that can be considered more sustainable. These decisions include the type, number, location and capacity of the energy generation units and production process plants (including the technologies selected in each of them); their capacity expansion policy and the transportation links between the energy-material SCs entities. The operational decisions are the energy generation level, the production rate at the plants in each time period, the flows of materials and energy between plants, warehouses and product markets, and the sales of final products and excess energy. Then, the SC configurations obtained by means of stochastic mathematical programming at different planning horizons can be compared. Additionally, this generic model determines the power to be installed at each internal or external resource and also the capacity of the required storage systems.

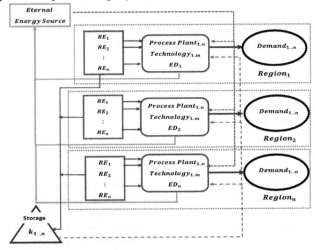

Fig 1. Multi resource-based Energy Integration SC

3   Multi-Objective stochastic Model

In this work, a scenario-based stochastic MILP formulation, considering a given distribution probability along the whole time horizon, based on the models introduced by Mele et al., (2011) (production process part) and Alabert et al., (2016) (multi resource energy integrated part) is proposed. Sizing is constrained to accomplish all scenarios, and operation variables are calculated according to each scenario. The number of necessary scenarios will be set in accordance with the characteristics of the case study to deal with. The model equations are classified as i) production process mass balances and capacity constraints; ii) energy generation mass/energy balances and capacity constraints; iii) energy storage management iv) External resources management; and v) objective function. The result of the model provides a set of Pareto solutions to be used by the decision maker in order to take the optimum tactical/strategical decision.

3.1 Energy generation

The balance representing the need to meet the (uncertain) energy demand during a certain period is shown in equation 1:

$$\sum_{ei} EnIJ_{ei,g,t,sc} + \sum_{ex} EnXJ_{ex,g,t,sc} + \sum_{k} EnKJ_{k,g,t,sc} = ED_{g,t,sc} \qquad \forall g,t,sc \qquad (1)$$

where $EnIJ_{ei,g,t,sc}$ is the energy flux between source ei and region g at time period t for scenario sc; $EnXJ_{ex,g,t,sc}$ is the energy flux between the external source x and region g at time period t for scenario sc; $EnKJ_{k,g,t,sc}$ is the energy flux between storage k and region g and $ED_{g,t,sc}$ is total energy demand in region g at time period t.

For the management of the own energy sources, the energy balances in equations (2) and (6) consider that all the generated energy has to be consumed or sold. The variable $EnEx_{ei,t,sc}$ represents the eventual excess of energy, and SL represents the slot length.

$$EnIG_{ei,g,t,sc} = PwIG_{ei,g,t,sc} \times SL \qquad \forall ei,g,t,sc \qquad (2)$$

$$PwI_{ei} \le PwIMax_{ei} \qquad \forall ei,g \qquad (3)$$

$$TotalEnIG_{t,sc} \ge TotalED_{g,t,sc} \qquad \forall g,t,sc \qquad (4)$$

$$\sum_{g} EnIJ_{ei,g,t,sc} + \sum_{ex}\sum_{g} EnIX_{ei,g,ex,t,sc} + \sum_{k}\sum_{g} EnIK_{ei,k,g,t,sc} + EnEx_{ei,t,sc} = \sum_{g} EnIG_{ei,g,t,sc} \qquad \forall ei,t,sc \qquad (5)$$

$$PwEx_{ei,t,sc} = EnEx_{ei,t,sc} / SL \qquad \forall ei,t,sc \qquad (6)$$

Equations (7-9) allow the management of external energy sources; they are similar to (4-5), but adding the possibility to sell energy. In these equations, $EnXP_{ex,t,sc}$ denotes energy purchase, whereas $EnXS_{ex,t,sc}$ represents the energy sales. Energy to be sold can only come from stand-alone generation, and it is considered that extra energy can be accumulated in storage elements.

$$PwX_{ex} \le PwXMax_{ex} \qquad \forall ex \qquad (7)$$

$$EnXP_{ex,t,sc} = \sum_{g} EnXJ_{ex,g,t,sc} + \sum_{k} EnXK_{ex,k,t,sc} \qquad \forall ex,t,sc \qquad (8)$$

$$EnXS_{ex,t,sc} = \sum_{ei}\sum_{g} EnIX_{ei,g,ex,t,sc} \qquad \forall ex,t,sc \qquad (9)$$

Storage units are modelled through equations (10) to (12), which introduce the charge and discharge limits.

$$EnK_{k} \le EnKMax_{k} \qquad \forall k \qquad (10)$$

$$EnKCh_{k,t,sc} = \left[\sum_{ei} \sum_{g} EnIK_{ei,g,k,t,sc} + \sum_{ex} EnXK_{ex,k,t,sc} \right] \times EfCh_k \qquad \forall k,t,sc \qquad (11)$$

$$EnKDh_{k,t,sc} = \sum_{g} EnKJ_{k,g,t,sc} \times 1/EfDh_k \qquad \forall k,t,sc \qquad (12)$$

3.2 Costs equations

The objective function considers the installation and operational costs of the facilities along with the planning horizon (eq. (13) and (14)), also considering the environmental impact costs for installation and operation Eq. (15) and (16).

$$CIns = \sum_{ei} \sum_{g} \Pr PwI_{ei} \times PwI_{ei,g} + \sum_{k} \Pr EnK_k \times EnK_k \qquad (13)$$

$$COP_{t,sc} = HL/PL(\sum_{ei} \sum_{g} \Pr EnI_{ei} \times EnIG_{ei,g,t,sc}) + \qquad \forall t,sc \qquad (14)$$

$$\sum_{ex} (\Pr EnP_{ex} \times EnXP_{ex,t,sc} - \Pr EnS_{ex} \times EnXS_{ex,t,sc}) +$$

$$\sum_{ex} (\Pr EnCh_k \times EnKCh_{k,t,sc} + \Pr EnDh_k \times EnKDh_{k,t,sc})$$

$$GHGIns = \sum_{ei} \sum_{g} GHGPwI_{ei} \times PwI_{ei,g} + \sum_{k} GHGEnK_k \times EnK_k \qquad (15)$$

$$GHCOP = \begin{array}{l} (HL/PL) \sum_{ei} \sum_{g} GHGEnI_{ei} \times EnIG_{ei,g,t,sc} \\ + \sum_{ex} GHGEnX_{ex} \times EnXP_{ex,t,sc} \\ + \sum_{k} GHGEnCh_k \times EnKCh_{k,t,sc} \\ + GHGEnDh_k \times EnKDh_{k,t,sc} \end{array} \qquad \forall t,sc \qquad (16)$$

3.3 Objective functions

The whole SC system must attain two targets: an economic objective, represented by the NPV, and an environmental objective quantified by the global warming potential (GWP). Different NPV values are obtained for each scenario under study, so an expected value ($E[NPV]$) of the resulting NPV distribution can be computed by considering the estimated probability for each scenario:

$$E[NPV] = \sum_{sc} Prob_{sc} \times NPV_{sc} \qquad (17)$$

The resulting objective functions are finally expressed as follows:

$$Min\{-E[NPV]; E[GWP]\} \qquad \text{S.t. constraints 1-17 and the constraints} \qquad (18)$$
proposed by Alabert et al., 2016; Mele et al., 2011

The solution of this problem consists of a set of Pareto optimal SC configurations, which can be by applying the ε-constraint method.

4   Case Study

The first example introduced by Mele et al. (2011), which addresses the optimal retrofit of an existing sugar cane industry established in Argentina, is revisited herein: 5 different technologies are available to manufacture 2 main products: ethanol and sugars. Nominal capacity of the sugar mill and the distillery plants are 350 and 300 thousand tons per year. The time horizon is divided into a set of time periods, and the specific geographic area is divided into a set of regions where the facilities of the SC can be located. Each region has an associated supply capacity (sugar cane crop) at every time interval. Waste (bagasse) is supposed to be sent to cogeneration units to produce electricity as added-value product. Energy demand uncertainty is represented by 3 scenarios. Following Illukpitiya et al. (2013) assumptions, the estimated total electricity requirement for internal use in the processing plants is 0.0441 kWh per kg of cane. It is also assumed that the nominal capacity of the power plant is 8.33 MW and the power generation is available on a continuous basis for at least 7800 h annually. The electricity market price and the operational cost of electricity generation are 0.15USD/kWh and 0.08USD/kWh respectively.

5 Results

Figure 2 shows the Pareto curve obtained using the stochastic approach under several CO_2 emission levels and depicts a compromise between Expected Net Present Value and Expected Global Warming Potential. Each solution represents a specific design configuration of whole energy/material supply chain system. The results show that by increasing planning horizon length NPV value increases so it is also interesting to point out that, for the same cogeneration capacities of renewable resources, NPV increases up to 50% in longer planning horizons but tends to be constant for horizons longer than 10 years (Fig. 3). It is observed that the solutions allow operating at most for satisfying energy demand so that it involves more resources for generating renewable energies. As it is also shown in Fig. 4, a significant part of the expected electricity demand should be supplied by wind turbines.

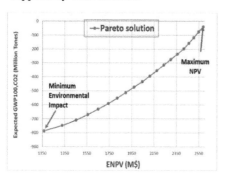

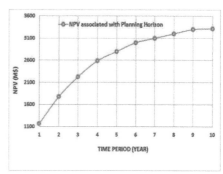

Fig. 2 Pareto set of solutions EGWP100 vs ENPV

Fig. 3 NPV variation in Planning Horizons

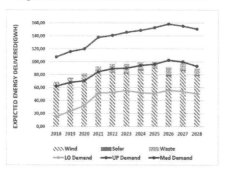

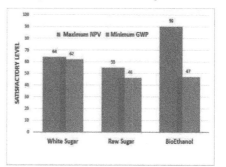

Fig. 4 Energy generation per Resource

Fig. 5 Satisfaction level of Products Demand

The results show the maximum satisfaction level of products demand with a maximum expected NPV and minimum expected GWP conditions (Fig. 5).

6 Conclusions

A MILP formulation to address the retrofitting problem of a multi-resource based energy integrated SC under uncertainty has been presented. The model produces a set of feasible energy/material networks addressing the optimization of conflictive objectives. The capabilities of the model are highlighted through its application to a case study. The proposed stochastic approach maximizes the expected profit while satisfying a minimum environmental impact for each scenario. The interaction between the objectives has been shown. This way of generating feasible configurations will help the decision-maker to determine the best design according to the selected objectives. In this particular case, the results show that 100% of internal energy demand and 94% of biofuel demand can be met by an entirely renewables-based process network, which majorly generates energy by cogeneration unit and wind power.

References

Alabert, A., Somoza, A., De La Hoz, J., & Graells, M. (2016). A general MILP model for the sizing of islanded/grid-connected microgrids. *2016 IEEE International Energy Conference, ENERGYCON 2016*. http://doi.org/10.1109/ENERGYCON.2016.7514112

Čuček, L., Martín, M., Grossmann, I. E., & Kravanja, Z. (2011). Energy, water and process technologies integration for the simultaneous production of ethanol and food from the entire corn plant. *Computers and Chemical Engineering*, *35*(8), 1547–1557. http://doi.org/10.1016/j.compchemeng.2011.02.007

Illukpitiya, P., Yanagida, J. F., Ogoshi, R., & Uehara, G. (2013). Sugar-ethanol-electricity co-generation in Hawai'i: An application of linear programming (LP) for optimizing strategies. *Biomass and Bioenergy*, *48*, 203–212. http://doi.org/10.1016/j.biombioe.2012.11.003

Martín, M., & Grossmann, I. E. (2017). Optimal integration of a self sustained algae based facility with solar and/or wind energy. *Journal of Cleaner Production*, *145*, 336–347. http://doi.org/10.1016/j.jclepro.2017.01.051

Martín, M., & Grossmann, I. E. (2018). Optimal integration of renewable based processes for fuels and power production: Spain case study. *Applied Energy*, *213*(November 2017), 595–610. http://doi.org/10.1016/j.apenergy.2017.10.121

Mele, F. D., Kostin, A. M., Guillén-Gosálbez, G., & Jiménez, L. (2011). Multiobjective Model for More Sustainable Fuel Supply Chains. A Case Study of the Sugar Cane Industry in Argentina. *Industrial & Engineering Chemistry Research*, *50*(9), 4939–4958. http://doi.org/10.1021/ie101400g

Morakabatchiankar, S., Hjaila, K., Mele, F. D., Graells, M., & Espuña, A. (2018). Economic and environmental benefits of waste-based energy closed-loop integration in process industries under uncertainty. In *Computer Aided Chemical Engineering* (Vol. 43, pp. 501–506). Elsevier.

Prasad, A. A., Taylor, R. A., & Kay, M. (2017). Assessment of solar and wind resource synergy in Australia. *Applied Energy*, *190*, 354–367. http://doi.org/10.1016/j.apenergy.2016.12.135

Vidal, M., & Martín, M. (2015). Optimal coupling of a biomass based polygeneration system with a concentrated solar power facility for the constant production of electricity over a year. *Computers and Chemical Engineering*, *72*, 273–283. http://doi.org/10.1016/j.compchemeng.2013.11.006

Zukunft, F. (2014). Process News, (4). Retrieved from https://www.industry.siemens.com/topics/global/en/magazines/process-news/archive/Documents/en/process-news-2014-1_en.pdf

Anton A. Kiss, Edwin Zondervan, Richard Lakerveld, Leyla Özkan (Eds.)
Proceedings of the 29th European Symposium on Computer Aided Process Engineering
June 16th to 19th, 2019, Eindhoven, The Netherlands. © 2019 Elsevier B.V. All rights reserved.
http://dx.doi.org/10.1016/B978-0-128-18634-3.50181-8

Heat-integrated water allocation network design: a novel hyperstructure and sequential solution strategy for industrial applications

Maziar Kermani[a,*], Ivan Kantor[a], Adriano Ensinas[b] and François Maréchal[a]

[a]*École Polytechnique Fédéral de Lausanne (EPFL) Valais Wallis, , IPESE group, Rue de l'Industrie 17,1951 Sion, Switzerland*
[b]*Universidade Federal de Lavras. Departamento de Engenharia (DEG/UFLA), 3037 Lavras, MG-Brazil*
maziar.kermani@epfl.ch

Abstract

Daily industrial operations consume large quantities of energy and water but are often considered marginal to their processes. Energy is used to heat or cool water; water is frequently used in production or utility systems as steam or cooling water. This emphasizes the interconnectivity of water and energy, stipulating their simultaneous consideration to address resource use in industrial processes which requires systematic methodologies. Two main complications have been observed within methodologies proposed in literature. As discussed in this work, these difficulties affect the overall mathematical formulation in mixed-integer nonlinear programming models; thus, resulting in a complex formulation. These difficulties have been addressed in this work by proposing a novel hyperstructure and a sequential solution strategy for the design of heat-integrated water allocation networks. Emphasis is placed on generating a set of promising solutions by addressing different performance indicators which is achieved via implementation of integer cut constraints to support decision-making for potential configurations. Applying the proposed methodology on several test cases from literature illustrated that the methodology is not only able to reach minimum total cost of the system, but also generates a set of alternative solutions exhibiting various performances with respect to other indicators.

Keywords: mathematical programming, superstructure optimization, heat-integrated mass allocation network, non-linear programming, non-isothermal mixing.

1. Introduction

Savulescu and Smith (1998) published the first work on heat-integrated water allocation network (HIWAN)s. They emphasized the importance of simultaneous consideration of heat and water and provided a graphical approach. Since then, many authors have proposed methodologies to better capture the trade-offs among the two resources which can be categorized into either conceptual or mathematical. The latter is based on developing mathematical models, incorporating all potential alternatives, and optimizing the system with respect to a well-chosen objective function. Several comprehensive reviews have been published on the subject (Ahmetović et al., 2015; Kermani et al., 2018). Two main complications have been observed within the mathematical methodologies proposed in literature, namely, the choice of the thermal state of a water stream (being hot or cold) and its thermal matches. The formulation of the latter requires the knowledge of the thermal state of the water stream *a priori*. Both complexities have been addressed in the literature via considering binary variables. This results in a mixed-integer nonlinear programming (MINLP) model. Comprehensively addressing the two requires a complex formulation which may fail to provide promising solutions in a reasonable time-horizon. This has prompted researchers to propose several solution strategies to facilitate the solving process (Kermani et al., 2018). This work proposes a novel sequential solution strategy and a novel nonlinear programming (NLP) hyperstructure, addressing the aforementioned difficulties in a systematic manner.

2. Problem definition

Given are two sets of water unit operations (source, sink) with their specific operating temperatures. Maximum allowed inlet (outlet) contamination levels are defined for each sink (source). Mass load removal rates are also defined in case a water unit operation is a mass-transfer unit. Furthermore, non-water process and utility (steam, cooling water) streams are also present. Freshwater sources and wastewater sinks at different temperature and contamination levels are also provided. The objective is to design the total heat-integrated water allocation network exhibiting the lowest total annualized cost. This cost consists of operating costs (consumption of freshwater, wastewater treatment, and thermal utilities) and investment costs (heat exchanger network (HEN) cost, equipment cost, etc.).

3. Methodology

The overall HIWAN problem is generally formulated as an MINLP. In this work the problem is reformulated into three subproblems, namely: targeting, heat load distribution (HLD), and design. The focus of this work is on formulation of the design stage together with the overall solution strategy.

Problem P1 - Targeting: Problem **P1** is formulated as mixed-integer linear programming (MILP) model (Kermani et al., 2017). This problem considers water network constraints, heat network constraints (Maréchal and Kalitventzeff, 1998), and connections between the two. The linearized formulation of non-isothermal mixing (NIM) allows for modeling sets of potential water thermal streams for each water unit operation (assignment of binary variables to each water thermal stream). This formulation solves the first difficulty in design of HIWANs, i.e., the thermal state of water streams. In addition, the solution of problem **P1** provides utility targets and a feasible water allocation network. The problem is solved by minimizing the total annualized cost of the system.

Problem P2 - HLD: Problem **P2** is the well-known HLD model (Papoulias and Grossmann, 1983; Marechal et al., 1989; Cerda and Westerburg, 1983) formulated as MILP with the objective of minimizing the number of thermal matches in each pinch interval, i.e., minimizing the number of heat exchangers. HLD solves the second difficulty in the design of HIWANs, i.e., the potential thermal matches. Furthermore, the solution of problem **P2** provides the heat loads of each thermal match which is used as a good initialization point for the subsequent design stage.

Problem P3 - Design: Knowing the set of thermal streams from problem **P1** and the potential thermal matches from problem **P2**, problem **P3** is formulated as an NLP hyperstructure. It is adapted from HEN hyperstructure of Floudas and Ciric (1989) for thermal streams. More specifically, in the classical approach by Floudas and Ciric (1989), no interconnection is allowed among different superstructures of thermal streams; however, considering the fact that these thermal streams are water streams, these connections bring potential mixing and splitting opportunities which can further reduce the HEN cost. Several structural changes are implemented in the HEN hyperstructure to consider the new possibilities (Figure 1) including removing the final mixer (initial splitter) from a superstructure if the stream is associated to a source (sink) unit. It should be highlighted that the non-water thermal streams keep the original formulation. Problem **P3** minimizes the HEN cost subject to mass, contamination, and energy balance constraints.

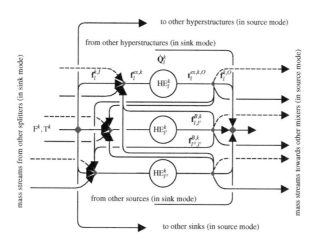

Figure 1: Schematic of the proposed hyperstructure (dashed arrows indicate flows among hyperstructures of the same source (sink) similar to the definition of $\mathbf{f}_{l,l'}^{B,k}$ and $\mathbf{f}_{l'',l'}^{B,k}$)

3.1. solution strategy

Problems **P1**, **P2**, and **P3** are solved in sequence. The original HEN model of Floudas and Ciric (1989) can be solved before problem **P3** to provide an initialization point. The solution of this model is also considered a feasible solution to the overall HIWAN problem. Several drawbacks can be observed in this sequential solution strategy, namely that it fails to: address the trade-off between operating and investment costs, guarantee the global optimality due to non-convexity of the problem, and guarantee a solution with overall minimum HEN cost (Floudas and Ciric, 1989). To address these drawbacks, an iterative sequential solution strategy is proposed, more specifically, by applying integer cut constraints on problems **P1** and **P2** and solving the overall problem for different values of heat recovery approach temperature (HRAT). This approach can be regarded as iteratively optimizing the overall MINLP model within different regions of the global search space (as imposed by the formulations of problems **P1** and **P2** at each iteration).

4. Results and discussion

Two test cases from the literature were selected to validate the proposed approach. The maximum allowed number of integer cuts was limited to 50. The value of HRAT was varied between 1–10°C. These values are passed to problem **P3** as heat exchanger minimum approach temperature (ΔT_{min}). Test case I is a threshold problem and hence the value of HRAT does not affect the utility consumptions. This, however, becomes a decisive factor for test case II where both hot and cold utilities are required. Several key performance indicator (KPI)s are considered:

- Resource indicators: freshwater ($\dot{m}_{fw}$) and thermal utility consumptions ($\dot{Q}_u^H$, $\dot{Q}_u^C$);
- Network indicators: number of thermal streams (N_s^{th}), number of heat exchangers (N_{HE}), total area of heat exchangers (A_{HEN}^{total}), number of mixing points (N_{mixer}), number of non-isothermal mixing points (N_{mixer}^{NIM}), number of mass streams (N_s^m), and total heat load of all heat exchangers (Q_{HEN}^{total});
- Economic indicators: HEN cost (C^{HEN}) and total annualized cost (TAC) (C^{TAC}).

4.1. Test case I: single-contaminant problem

Test case I is a single-contaminant problem proposed by Bagajewicz et al. (2002) that consists of eight water unit operations. The solution with minimum operating cost exhibits 125.94 kg/s of freshwater consumption and 5,289.6 kW of hot utility consumption. Out of 26,010 possible solutions, 5,260 solutions exist to problem **P2**. The objective value of problem **P2** varies between 6–15. From this set of solutions, 565 solutions converged for problem **P3**, among which, HEN cost varies between 272.1–529.3 kUSD/yr for 554 solutions. The minimum HEN cost reported by the literature is 257.2 kUSD/yr (Ibrić et al., 2014), however, the freshwater and utility consumptions were reported to be 126.71 kg/s and 5,322.1 kW, respectively. Several filters were applied to further reduce the number of solutions to aid in visualization based on their corresponding maximum values reported in literature: $N_s^m \leq 32$, $N_{mixer} \leq 21$, $N_{mixer}^{NIM} \leq 17$.

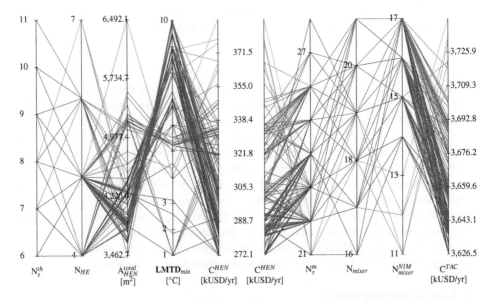

Figure 2: Visualization of selected KPIs for test case I (155 solutions)

Figure 2 presents the remaining 155 solutions. Considering total annualized cost as the main objective in this case study, the proposed set of solutions encompass the design with the lowest cost of 3,626.5 kUSD/yr. Comparing this with the minimum reported in the literature (3,628 kUSD/yr), one can observe that the proposed sequential solution strategy can reach the minimum while also proposing a set of alternatives which show varying performance for the defined objective and other KPIs. The advantage of such an approach is providing many potential solutions which may yield more desirable solutions in non-objective KPIs which would not be discovered by conventional approaches. For instance, among all solutions with the lowest HEN cost, the solution with the lowest number of mixers and mass streams exhibits a simpler network design while its HEN cost is penalized by less than 0.1%.

4.2. Test case II: multi-contaminant problem

Test case II is a pinch, multi-contaminant problem proposed by Dong et al. (2008) with the minimum freshwater consumption of 70 kg/s. The value of HRAT affects the thermal utility consumptions. Jagannath and Almansoori (2016) proposed a solution in which they constrained the number of heat exchangers and mass exchanges to four and seven, respectively, and reached 74.3 kg/s of freshwater consumption, 8,760 kW of hot utility and 2,520 kW of cold utility ($\Delta T_{min} = 20°C$). Although they reported the lowest HEN cost (117.2 kSUD/yr), their solution exhibits the highest total cost and the highest thermal utility consumption among the reported values in the literature. Out of 26,010 possible solutions, 982 solutions exist to problem **P2**. The objective value of problem **P2** varies between six and nine thermal matches. Among these solutions, 299 converged for problem **P3** with minimum and maximum HEN costs of 146.3 kUSD/yr and 353.8 kUSD/yr, respectively. Figure 3 illustrates the KPIs of these 299 solutions.

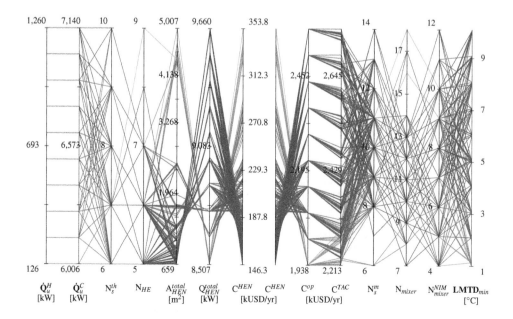

Figure 3: Visualization of selected KPIs for test case II (299 solutions)

5. Conclusions

Two main complexities are observed within literature methodologies for HIWANs. The first difficulty is selecting the thermal state of water streams, leading to the second difficulty of selecting thermal matches with undefined thermal states. Accounting for these complexities results in a complex MINLP formulation which is difficult to solve optimally with current solutions strategies; therefore, this work proposes a novel hyperstructure and solution strategy to treat this complex problem. An initial MILP model provides minimum utility consumptions with a list of potential thermal streams for achieving them. In the second step, thermal matches are identified by solving the HLD model minimizing the number of thermal matches. A novel NLP hyperstructure was developed in the last step for a complete design of the network combining the water allocation the HEN hyperstructures. Results indicate that the approach reaches optimal designs efficiently, and additionally generates a set of near-optimal solutions; thus, providing a practical approach to selecting the final implementation and contrasts the single-solution approach in literature. This approach allows experts to provide additional insights into the performance of all solutions with respect to additional indicators before selecting the solution for implementation. Finally, all possible interconnections are incorporated; therefore, providing a comprehensive approach that allows any type of heating and cooling for any water stream, bringing novel improvements to the state of the art.

Acknowledgements: This research project is financially supported by the Swiss Innovation Agency Innosuisse and is part of the Swiss Competence Center for Energy Research SCCER EIP.

References

E. Ahmetović, N. Ibrić, Z. Kravanja, I. E. Grossmann, Nov. 2015. Water and energy integration: A comprehensive literature review of non-isothermal water network synthesis. Computers & Chemical Engineering 82, 144–171.

M. Bagajewicz, H. Rodera, M. Savelski, Jan. 2002. Energy efficient water utilization systems in process plants. Computers & Chemical Engineering 26 (1), 59–79.

J. Cerda, A. W. Westerburg, Jan. 1983. Synthesizing heat exchanger networks having restricted stream/stream matches using transportation problem formulations. Chemical Engineering Science 38 (10), 1723–1740.

H.-G. Dong, C.-Y. Lin, C.-T. Chang, 2008. Simultaneous optimization approach for integrated water-allocation and heat-exchange networks. Chemical Engineering Science - CHEM ENG SCI 63 (14), 3664–3678.

C. A. Floudas, A. R. Ciric, Oct. 1989. Strategies for overcoming uncertainties in heat exchanger network synthesis. Computers & Chemical Engineering 13 (10), 1133–1152.

N. Ibrić, E. Ahmetović, Z. Kravanja, Aug. 2014. Two-step mathematical programming synthesis of pinched and threshold heat-integrated water networks. Journal of Cleaner Production 77, 116–139.

A. Jagannath, A. Almansoori, Jul. 2016. Sequential synthesis of heat integrated water networks: A new approach and its application to small and medium sized examples. Computers & Chemical Engineering 90, 44–61.

M. Kermani, I. D. Kantor, F. Maréchal, May 2018. Synthesis of Heat-Integrated Water Allocation Networks: A Meta-Analysis of Solution Strategies and Network Features. Energies 11 (5), 1158.

M. Kermani, Z. Périn-Levasseur, M. Benali, L. Savulescu, F. Maréchal, 2017. A novel MILP approach for simultaneous optimization of water and energy: Application to a Canadian softwood Kraft pulping mill. Computers & Chemical Engineering.

F. Maréchal, B. Kalitventzeff, Mar. 1998. Process integration: Selection of the optimal utility system. Computers & Chemical Engineering 22, Supplement 1, S149–S156.

F. Marechal, I. Boursier, B. Kalitventzeff, Apr. 1989. Synep1 : A methodology for energy integration and optimal heat exchanger network synthesis. Computers & Chemical Engineering 13 (4–5), 603–610.

S. A. Papoulias, I. E. Grossmann, 1983. A structural optimization approach in process synthesis—II: Heat recovery networks. Computers & Chemical Engineering 7 (6), 707–721.

L. E. Savulescu, R. Smith, 1998. Simultaneous energy and water minimisation. In: 1998 AIChE Annual Meeting. Miami Beach, Florida, pp. 13–22, unpublished work.

Anton A. Kiss, Edwin Zondervan, Richard Lakerveld, Leyla Özkan (Eds.)
Proceedings of the 29th European Symposium on Computer Aided Process Engineering
June 16th to 19th, 2019, Eindhoven, The Netherlands. © 2019 Elsevier B.V. All rights reserved.
http://dx.doi.org/10.1016/B978-0-128-18634-3.50182-X

Describing CO_2-Absorbent Properties in AspenPlus®

Jasper A. Ros[a], Derk W. F. Brilman[a], Ida M. Bernhardsen[b] and Hanna Knuutila[b,*]

[a]*Sustainable Process Technology, University of Twente, Drienerlolaan 5, 7522NB Enschede, The Netherlands*
[b]*Department of Chemical Engineering, Norwegian University of Science and Technology, Høgskoleringen 1, Trondheim, N-7491, Norway*
hanna.knuutila@ntnu.no

Abstract

For the modelling of novel solvent systems for CO_2-capture in AspenPlus®, data fitting of physical-chemical properties is needed. In this work the challenges and results are presented for fitting such experimental data for aqueous solutions of 2-(diethylamino)ethanol (DEEA) and 3-(methylamino)propylamine (MAPA). Without CO_2 present, the default regression tool of AspenPlus® gave good data fits for the binary systems H_2O-MAPA and H_2O-DEEA. In the presence of CO_2, regression of parameters was not successful and an additional Particle Swarm Optimization (PSO) algorithm was needed to determine the many molecule-ion parameters for the ELECNRTL model. With this, for DEEA a good fit to experimental data has been obtained, whereas for MAPA, due to the high number of ionic species, the results were still not satisfactory. To resolve this, independent measurement of equilibrium constants for the ionic equilibria is recommended.

Keywords: CO_2 capture, novel solvents, thermodynamic modelling, regression

1. Introduction

Post-combustion CO_2 capture from coal and natural gas fired power plants is widely recognized as one of the most effective techniques to reduce CO_2 emissions. The conventional technology is chemical absorption using aqueous amine solutions, in which amines react with CO_2 and the solvent circulates between the absorption and desorption column. The benchmark solvent is monoethanolamine (MEA), which is a primary amine solvent. However, the energy requirements in the regeneration step of this process are significant, leading to a continuous search for novel solvent systems that require less energy for regeneration (Bernhardsen and Knuutila, 2017). Interesting solvents have higher CO_2 capacities often combined with a lower heat of absorption. Tertiary amines are potentially good candidates, having lower heat of absorption and higher CO_2 capacity compared to primary and secondary amines. Unfortunately, their kinetic absorption rates are much lower compared to primary and secondary amines, which means that larger absorption columns are needed. A promoter (primary/secondary amine) could increase the kinetic absorption rates, while keeping a relatively low heat of absorption and high capacity (Arshad et al., 2013). A blended amine solution consisting of the tertiary amine 2-(diethylamino)ethanol (DEEA) and the primary/secondary amine 3-(methylamino)propylamine (MAPA) is described by Pinto et al. (2014b) as a potential replacement for the conventional MEA solvent. A mixture of these solvents shows high CO_2 capacities, high kinetic absorption rates and relatively low heat of absorption in experiments. This work focused on the thermodynamic modeling of the DEEA+MAPA mixture in the AspenPlus® flowsheet program in order to determine the industrial viability of these novel solvents.

2. Chemistry

The molecular structures of DEEA and MAPA are shown in Figure 1 below. DEEA acts as a free base in the hydration reaction with CO_2 to form bicarbonate and MAPA reacts with the CO_2 to form primary and secondary MAPA carbamate and MAPA di-carbamate, as shown in Equation 1. Additional reactions that are present in both reaction schemes but not shown below are the dissociation reactions of water and bicarbonate (Monteiro et al., 2013).

$$2\,H_2O + CO_2 \rightleftharpoons H_3O^+ + HCO_3^- \tag{1a}$$

$$DEEA + H_3O^+ \rightleftharpoons DEEAH^+ + H_2O \tag{1b}$$

$$MAPAH^+ + H_2O \rightleftharpoons MAPA + H_3O^+ \tag{1c}$$

$$MAPAH^{2+} + H_2O \rightleftharpoons MAPAH^+ + H_3O^+ \tag{1d}$$

$$MAPA + H_2O + CO_2 \rightleftharpoons MAPACOO^-_{(p)} + H_3O^+ \tag{1e}$$

$$MAPA + H_2O + CO_2 \rightleftharpoons MAPACOO^-_{(s)} + H_3O^+ \tag{1f}$$

$$MAPAH^+COO^-_{(p)} + H_2O \rightleftharpoons MAPACOO^-_{(p)} + H_3O^+ \tag{1g}$$

$$MAPAH^+COO^-_{(s)} + H_2O \rightleftharpoons MAPACOO^-_{(s)} + H_3O^+ \tag{1h}$$

$$2\,HCO_3^- + MAPACOO^-_{(s)} + MAPACOO^-_{(p)} \rightleftharpoons 2\,H_2O + 2\,MAPA(COO^-)_2 \tag{1i}$$

Figure 1: The molecular structures of (a) DEEA and (b) MAPA.

3. Important properties for CO_2-absorbents

In this work, several properties for DEEA and MAPA were fitted to experimental data. These properties can be divided in three categories, namely: Pure properties, binary properties with water, and loaded properties upon CO_2 loading. The fitting was performed in steps: The pure component properties were fitted to form the boundaries of the binary properties at infinite dilution of either component, which again gave initial values for the loaded properties at a certain concentration of the solvent. Process simulations require detailed sub-models that can describe the absorption kinetics and physical properties like vapor-liquid equilibria and viscosity, describing the absorption capacity and solvent volatility as well as the equilibrium partial pressure of CO_2 at different solvent loadings. Furthermore, heat capacity and heat of absorption have an important role in correctly estimating the energy requirement of a process. Finally, equilibrium constants for the reactions have to be defined to determine the speciation of ions in the liquid phase. The equilibrium constants for the DEEA dissociation reaction were regressed against pKa data from Hamborg and Versteeg (2009) and the constants for the hydration reaction of CO$_2$ were taken from Edwards et al. (1978). Unfortunately, no equilibrium constants are known for the (bi)carbamate formation reactions in the MAPA reaction scheme. AspenPlus$^®$ (Version 8.6) has built in (thermodynamic) models that can be used to represent all the properties described above. The thermodynamic model used in this work was the Electrolyte Non-Random Two Liquid (ELECNRTL) model (Chen et al., 1982). This extended NRTL model takes the activity coefficients of ions in the liquid phase into account. For the vapor phase, the Redlich-Kwong equation of state was used. Additional property models used in this work can be found in Table 1 below.

Table 1: Property models used in this work as defined in AspenPlus$^®$.

	Pure	**Binary**	**Loaded**
VLE	PLXANT	NRTL	GMELCC/GMELCD
Density	DNLDIP	VLQKIJ	VLCLK
Viscosity	MULDIP	MUKIJ/MULIJ	IONMOB/IONMUB
Heat capacity	CPLDIP	No model available*	CPAQ0

*Calculated from the liquid enthalpy at constant pressure

4. Available experimental data

DEEA and MAPA have been researched extensively the past years, and data is widely available in literature. The pure vapor pressure data for DEEA and MAPA, the binary VLE data for DEEA-H$_2$O and the binary VLE data for DEEA-MAPA were taken from Hartono et al. (2013). The binary VLE data for MAPA-H$_2$O was taken from Kim et al. (2008). The loaded VLE data for the DEEA system was taken from Monteiro (2014) and Xu et al. (2014) and all viscosity and density data were taken from Pinto (2014a). Unfortunately only pure component heat capacities are available in literature and no binary or loaded heat capacities were found. The pure heat capacity for DEEA and MAPA was taken from Maham et al. (1997) and Lin et al. (2014) respectively. AspenPlus$^®$ has default values for all H$_2$O pure component parameters discussed in this work. Furthermore, the default CO$_2$ Henry coefficients were used.

5. Fitting procedure

The regressed parameters in this work regard the Antoine equation, NRTL, ELECNRTL, density, viscosity and heat capacity parameters. Experimental data is added to the model and the regression tool performs the iterative regression. For the models with typically three parameters to fit the regression tool performs well. However, when the number of parameters to fit increases, the use of the regression tool becomes more challenging. Using this tool is still possible, however it requires substantial amount of trial-and error and understanding of how the different parameters influence the fit. This is the case in fitting the ELECNRTL model which is based on the local composition of molecules and ions. For example in case of the DEEA system, 8 components can be distinguished resulting in 72 parameters whereas, in the MAPA system, 14 components can be distinguished resulting in 360 parameters. Additionally, for the MAPA system, the equilibrium constants of the reactions are regressed together with the molecule-ion parameters. To lower the amount of parameters to fit, the default ELECNRTL parameter values for the sub-system H$_2$O-CO$_2$ are typically fixed to the values estimated by the program. This lowered the amount of parameters in the DEEA and MAPA system to 36 and 300 respectively. Still this is too high for the regression tool, resulting in many regression steps, where only few selected parameters would be regressed at once and manual trial and error is necessary. Therefore in this work, an external MATLAB® code is coupled with AspenPlus®, that provides an alternative solver. This solver is based on the Particle Swarm Optimization (PSO) algorithm (Kennedy and Eberhart, 1995). With this algorithm, more parameters can be regressed simultaneously to experimental data compared to the conventional solver. The MATLAB® code generates parameter sets according to the PSO algorithm as input for the AspenPlus® model, which uses the ELECNRTL model to calculate the chemical equilibrium and phase equilibrium. This is iteratively done, until a certain threshold is reached for the accuracy of the solution. A drawback of this algorithm is that the computation time for the regression is significantly increased. However, this regression is still much faster than manual fitting by changing a few parameters at a time using the conventional regression tool.

6. Results

The accuracy of the fitted model to the experimental data was assessed using the averaged absolute relative deviation (AARD) error definition, as defined by

$$AARD = \frac{1}{N} \sum_{i=k}^{N} 100 \frac{|\eta_k - \phi_k|}{|\phi_k|}, \tag{2}$$

where N is the amount of data points, η_k is the value of the fit at a certain point and Φ_k is the experimental value at the same point. The AARD values calculated in this work are listed in Table 2. It can be seen that all pure component properties have accurate fits to the experimental data. Also the considered properties for the binary systems were fitted with an acceptable low AARD. Further, a satisfactory fit of the DEEA model was found to the loaded VLE data, whereas the MAPA model gave no satisfactory fit. It is important to note that without the ELECNRTL parameters, no concentration/activity of ions is known and loaded density, viscosity and heat capacity parameters cannot be fitted, as these parameters are dependent on these concentrations or activities. The reason for the bad fit for the MAPA system is probably due to the high amount of parameters and missing equilibrium constants. The phase envelope diagram for the DEEA-H_2O and MAPA-H_2O mixture is shown in Figure 2. It can be seen that for both mixtures, with the regressed NRTL parameters, the model gives accurate bubble and dew point curves. The DEEA-MAPA mixture data is fitted with an AARD of 3.0 %. The loaded VLE results for the regression of the molecule-ion parameters of the DEEA-H_2O-CO_2 system can be found in Figure 3. As can be seen in this figure, for 2M and 3M DEEA solutions, a satisfactory fit is found and the AARD value is 16.7 %. This is a relatively high error compared to the other component parameters, however it is comparable to other modelled data found in literature for loaded VLE data (Monteiro et al., 2013). The valid range of operation for this model is between 2M and 3M DEEA solutions, and between 40 and 120 °C. The sufficient fit for the DEEA solution proves that the regression algorithm used in this work is an effective algorithm to fit VLE data upon CO_2 loading. The focus of future research should move towards the fitting of the ELECNRTL parameters for the MAPA solution. In order to obtain a satisfactory fit, more molecule-ion pairs should be assumed constant and the equilibrium constants of all reactions should be known. Furthermore, the model results for combining the two solvents should be validated against experimental data.

Table 2: The AARD (%) values obtained in this work.

	DEEA			MAPA		
	Pure	**Binary**	**Loaded**	**Pure**	**Binary**	**Loaded**
VLE	0.29	0.71	16.7*	0.85	1.44	No fit
Density	0.01	0.59	0.78	0.20	0.51	No fit
Viscosity	0.64	6.9	9.1	0.21	5.0	No fit
Heat capacity	0.15	No data	No data	0.04	No data	No data

*Regressed with the PSO algorithm

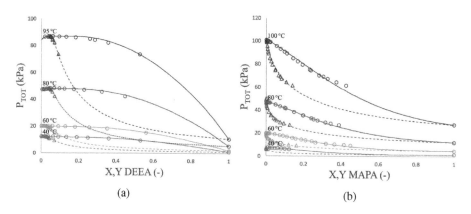

(a) (b)

Figure 2: Experimental data from Hartono et al. (2013) and Kim et al. (2008) (O/△) and model results (-) for the phase envelope diagram for the (a) DEEA-H$_2$O binary system and (b) MAPA-H$_2$O binary system at different temperatures. The continuous lines are the bubble point curves and the dashed lines are the dew point curves.

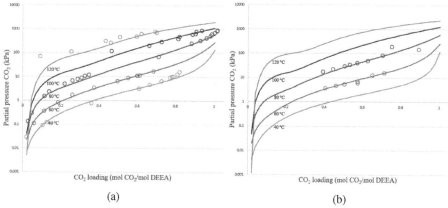

(a) (b)

Figure 3: Experimental data from Monteiro et al. (2013) and Xu et al. (2014) (o) and model results (-) for the partial pressure of CO$_2$ at a certain CO$_2$ loading for the (a) 2M and (b) 3M DEEA solution at different temperatures.

7. Conclusions

In this work, the basis for the thermodynamic model for the promising DEEA+MAPA solvent for post-combustion CO_2 capture was developed using AspenPlus®. Different pure, binary and loaded parameters for the DEEA and MAPA system were regressed with the conventional regression tool, while the PSO algorithm was coupled with AspenPlus® to regress the molecule-ion parameters of the ELECNRTL model for the DEEA solution. No good fit was obtained for MAPA, and research should focus on the regression of the ELECNRTL molecule-ion parameters of this MAPA system.

References

M. W. Arshad, N. von Solms, K. Thomsen, H. F. Svendsen, 2013. Heat of absorption of co2 in aqueous solutions of deea, mapa and their mixture. Energy Procedia 37, 1532 – 1542.

I. M. Bernhardsen, H. K. Knuutila, 2017. A review of potential amine solvents for co2 absorption process: Absorption capacity, cyclic capacity and pka. International Journal of Greenhouse Gas Control 61, 27 – 48.

C.-C. Chen, H. I. Britt, J. F. Boston, L. B. Evans, 1982. Local composition model for excess gibbs energy of electrolyte systems. part i: Single solvent, single completely dissociated electrolyte systems. AIChE Journal 28 (4), 588–596.

T. J. Edwards, G. Maurer, J. Newman, J. M. Prausnitz, 1978. Vapor-liquid equilibria in multicomponent aqueous solutions of volatile weak electrolytes. AIChE Journal 24 (6), 966–976.

E. S. Hamborg, G. F. Versteeg, 2009. Dissociation constants and thermodynamic properties of amines and alkanolamines from (293 to 353) k. Journal of Chemical & Engineering Data 54 (4), 1318–1328.

A. Hartono, F. Saleem, M. W. Arshad, M. Usman, H. F. Svendsen, 2013. Binary and ternary vle of the 2-(diethylamino)-ethanol (deea)/3-(methylamino)-propylamine (mapa)/water system. Chemical Engineering Science 101, 401 – 411.

J. Kennedy, R. Eberhart, 12 1995. Particle swarm optimization. Proceedings of IEEE International Conference on Neural Networks 4, 1942 – 1948 vol.4.

I. Kim, H. F. Svendsen, E. Børresen, 2008. Ebulliometric determination of vaporliquid equilibria for pure water, monoethanolamine, n-methyldiethanolamine, 3-(methylamino)-propylamine, and their binary and ternary solutions. Journal of Chemical & Engineering Data 53 (11), 2521–2531.

S.-Y. Lin, R. B. Leron, M.-H. Li, 2014. Molar heat capacities of diethylenetriamine and 3-(methylamino)propylamine, their aqueous binaries, and aqueous ternaries with piperazine. Thermochimica Acta 575, 34 – 39.

Y. Maham, L. G. Hepler, A. E. Mather, A. W. Hakin, R. A. Marriott, 1997. Molar heat capacities of alkanolamines from 299.1 to 397.8 k group additivity and molecular connectivity analyses. J. Chem. Soc., Faraday Trans. 93, 1747–1750.

J. Monteiro, D. Pinto, S. A.H. Zaidy, A. Hartono, H. Svendsen, 11 2013. Vle data and modelling of aqueous n,n-diethylethanolamine (deea) solutions. International Journal of Greenhouse Gas Control 19, 432440.

J.-S. Monteiro, 2014. Contributions to kinetics and equilibrium of co_2 absorption into n,n,-diethylethanolamine (deea), n-methyl-1,3-propane-diamine (mapa) and their blends. Ph.D. thesis, Norwegian university of science and technology, Norway.

D. Pinto, 2014a. Co2 capture solvents: modeling and experimental characterization. Ph.D. thesis, Norwegian university of science and technology, Norway.

D. D. Pinto, S. A. Zaidy, A. Hartono, H. F. Svendsen, 2014b. Evaluation of a phase change solvent for co2 capture: Absorption and desorption tests. International Journal of Greenhouse Gas Control 28, 318 – 327.

Z. Xu, S. Wang, G. Qi, A. A. Trollebø, H. F. Svendsen, C. Chen, 2014. Vapor liquid equilibria and heat of absorption of co2 in aqueous 2-(diethylamino)-ethanol solutions. International Journal of Greenhouse Gas Control 29, 92 – 103.

Anton A. Kiss, Edwin Zondervan, Richard Lakerveld, Leyla Özkan (Eds.)
Proceedings of the 29th European Symposium on Computer Aided Process Engineering
June 16th to 19th, 2019, Eindhoven, The Netherlands. © 2019 Elsevier B.V. All rights reserved.
http://dx.doi.org/10.1016/B978-0-128-18634-3.50183-1

Immune system modelling in case of a septic shock

Jean Tallon,[a] Francoise Couenne,[a] Claire Bordes,[a] Melaz Tayakout-Fayolle,[a,*]
Fabienne Venet,[b] Guillaume Monneret,[b] Patrice Nony,[c] François Gueyffier[c]

[a]Univ Lyon, Université Claude Bernard Lyon 1, CNRS, LAGEP UMR 5007, 43 boulevard du 11 novembre 1918, F-69100, VILLEURBANNE, France

[b]Hospices Civils de Lyon, 5 place d'Arsonval 69437 LYON Cedex 03 – France

[c]Laboratoire de Biologie et Biométrie Evolutive-Equipe Modélisation des Effets Thérapeutiques, UMR 5558 Université Claude Bernard Lyon1, Lyon, France

melaz.tayakout-fayolle@univ-lyon1.fr

Abstract

A dynamical pathophysiological model is presented in the case of septic shock. The proposed approach takes into account the environment and the different subsystems. The considered immune system is the blood, the subsystems are leukocyte cells and cytokines. The interactions between blood cells, plasma and the environment are described via mass balances. The transport phenomena between cells and blood and thermodynamic equilibrium are considered. The quantities of pro and anti-cytokines present in the body are combined to propose global information on the inflammatory state of the patient. The proposed model is strongly nonlinear. Simulations showed how the global information evolves after septic shock. In particular, the model has the ability to evolve to alternative homeostatic equilibrium in case of septic shock.

Keywords: septic shock, dynamic modelling, transport phenomena, thermodynamic equilibrium, simulation.

1. Introduction

Homeostasis refers to the ability of living organisms to maintain their internal state constant despite any change in the environment. Sepsis is the body's response to a very strong infectious attack by a pathogen. Septic shock is diagnosed when organ failure is observed with other various clinical symptoms, such as hypotension. The mortality of patients in France with sepsis was 27% in 2016. Worldwide, a person dies from sepsis complications every 4 seconds. Sepsis has been recognized as a major public health problem by World Health Organization in 2017 (WHA resolution, 2017). Alteration of immune homeostasis plays a central role in sepsis pathophysiology. Following the initial pro-inflammatory response leading to organ failure and shock, sepsis and septic shock are associated with the delayed development of immune dysfunctions (Hotchkiss et al., 2013) (Venet and Monneret, 2018). The intensity and duration of sepsis-induced immune alterations have been associated with increased risk of secondary infections and mortality.

However, a more exhaustive understanding of these alterations and of their evolution over time is mandatory and could lead to the elucidation of innovative therapeutic targets and associated companion biomarkers in a personalized medicine approach.

The immune system modelling is not new (Malek et al., 2015), but quickly limited by the number of species.

The system is closed, uniform and thermodynamic or transport phenomena between cells and blood are not considered. The objective of this paper is to improve the knowledge of the homeostasis evolution in the case of septic shock by establishment of dynamical pathophysiological model, to understand mechanisms involved in pro-inflammatory and anti-inflammatory responses and to predict the inflammation level (as shown in Figure 1). Our approach considers the environment and different subsystems. The immune system in this case is the blood, the subsystems are leukocyte cells and cytokine pairs (pro-inflammatory and anti-inflammatory). Cytokines are essential to mechanisms of inflammation and are widely described in the literature. They are released by various cells in the body, such leukocytes, and they induce responses through binding to specific receptors on the surface of target cells. The immune system is open and continuously in interaction with its surroundings. A model considering the previous assumptions has been developed for one cytokine pair, their corresponding receptors and leukocyte cells.

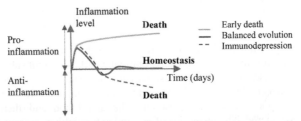

Figure 1: Different scenarios of the supposed evolution of inflammation state of patient

In section 2, assumptions of the model and different material balances are presented. In section 3 simulations of different scenarios of septic shocks are given. Finally, in section 4 we propose conclusion and future work.

2. Model

The objective is to describe the interactions between the cytokines, their receptors, and the leucocyte cells in the blood system. The interaction between the system and surrounding is introduced in the model by constant source terms: cells continually produced by the bone marrow, and cytokines continually produced by tissues and organs.

2.1. Assumptions

The blood system is described with two phases: a fluid phase, and leucocyte cells. The cells are uniformly dispersed in the fluid phase. The blood volume is assumed to be constant. The chosen pair of cytokines is IL10 and IL18 with their associated receptors. All the white blood cells are represented by average leucocyte cells. The receptors are described as being only on the surface of the cells and supposed uniformly distributed. The cytokines and receptors are produced in the cells.

Linear Driving Force model is used to represent the transfer of cytokines from the cell to the blood and the transfer of cytokines from the blood to receptors. The cytokines in the blood are adsorbed on receptors. This adsorption is already described in some existing pharmacokinetic models (Androulakis et al., 2015). Langmuir equilibrium is assumed for the adsorption. The inflammation comes from the variation of the cytokines, which can stimulate or inhibit the leucocytes production as schematically represented in Figure 3.

The adsorbed IL10 and IL18 cytokine on their receptors IL10R and IL18R respectively (see KEGG Pathway Database) can directly trigger the chemical production of the same cytokines and receptors by cells shown in Figure 4.

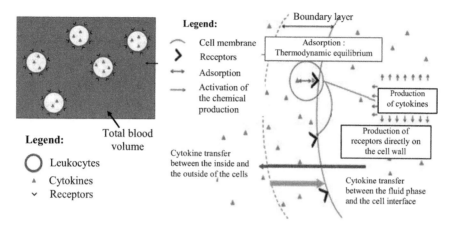

Figure 3: (left) Representation of the blood system and (right) representation of the cytokine adsorption

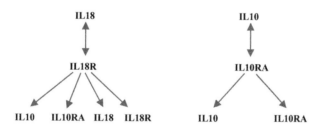

Figure 4 : Schematic representation of the mechanisms of the IL18/IL10 model

2.2. Notations

A and B notations have been chosen for IL18 and IL10 respectively. The adsorbed concentrations of A and B are denoted with index ads. The concentrations of A (mol/m^3) and B (mol/m^3) in the cell are denoted with index c and the ones at the interface with index int. The associated receptors will be denoted R_A (mol/m^3) and R_B (mol/m^3). The expressions of the adsorbed concentrations are given below:

$$A_{ads} = \frac{R_A\,K_A\,A_{int}}{1 + K_A\,A_{int}}, \quad B_{ads} = \frac{R_B\,K_B\,B_{int}}{1 + K_B\,B_{int}}$$

With K_A (m^3/mol) and K_B (m^3/mol) are the Langmuir coefficients.

2.3. Material balances of cytokines

The material balances of A and B in the fluid, at the interface of the cells and in the cells, are as follow:

$$\frac{dV_l\,A}{dt} = V_c(k_{la}^{intA}(A_{int} - A) + k_{la}^{cA}(A_c - A)) - k_d^A A\,V_l + S_A(t) \tag{1}$$

$$\frac{dV_c\,A_{ads}}{dt} = -k_{la}^{intA}\,(A_{int} - A)\,V_c \tag{2}$$

$$\frac{dV_c\,A_c}{dt} = V_c\,k_A\,A_{ads} - V_c\,k_{la}^{cA}\,(A_c - A) - V_c\,k_d^A\,A_c \tag{3}$$

$$\frac{dV_l\,B}{dt} = V_c\left(k_{la}^{intB}(B_{int} - B) + k_{la}^{cB}(B_c - B)\right) - k_d^B\,B\,V_l + S_B(t) \tag{4}$$

$$\frac{dV_cB_{ads}}{dt} = -V_c\,k_{la}^{intB}(B_{int} - B) \tag{5}$$

$$\frac{d\,V_cB_c}{dt} = V_c\,k_B B_{ads} + V_c k_{BA} A_{ads} - V_c\,k_{la}^{cB}(B_c - B) - V_c\,k_d^B B_c \tag{6}$$

Where V_l (m^3), V_c (m^3) represent the volume of the blood system cells respectively. For cytokine A: k_{la}^{intA} (m/s), k_{la}^{cA} (m/s) represent the mass transfer coefficient between blood and interface and between blood and cell, respectively), k_d^A (s^{-1}) and k_A (s^{-1}) the death and production kinetic constants of cytokine A from A_{ads}, respectively. The same stands for B. k_{BA} (s^{-1}) represents the production kinetic constant of cytokine B from A_{ads}. S_A (mol/s) and S_B (mol/s) are source terms of cytokines from environment.

2.4. Material balances of the receptors at the interface of the cell

$$\frac{d\,V_c\,R_A}{dt} = V_c\,k_{RA}\,A_{ads} + k_1\frac{d\,N_c}{dt}\,R_A \tag{7}$$

$$\frac{dV_c\,R_B}{dt} = V_c\,k_{RB}^A\,A_{ads} + V_c\,k_{RB}\,B_{ads} + k_2\frac{d\,N_c}{dt}R_B \tag{8}$$

k_{RA} (s^{-1}), k_{RB} (s^{-1}) and k_{RB}^A (s^{-1}) represent the production kinetic constants of receptor A from A_{ads}, receptor B from B_{ads} and receptor B from A_{ads}, respectively. N_c is the number of cells in the blood. $k_1(m^3)$ and $k_2(m^3)$ represent the proportion of receptors A and B, respectively, produced or destroyed induced by the variation of cells numbers.

2.5. Material balances of the cell

Finally, the variation of the number of cells in the fluid is:

$$\frac{d\,V_l\,N_c}{dt} = f\,k_c\,N_cV_l - k_d^c\,N_cV_l + S_c(t) \tag{9}$$

With f (mol/m^3) the inflammation level function defined as:

$$f(t) = A - \alpha * B \tag{10}$$

The parameter k_c $(m^3/mol/s)$ is introduced to adjust the influence of the function f. k_d^c (s^{-1}) is a death kinetic constant for cells. $S_c(t)$ (mol/s) is a source term from the bone marrow.

3. Simulations

We perform three simulations with same parameters: $K_A = 1.5\ 10^{-7}$, $K_B = 9.08\ 10^{-7}$, $k_{la}^{intA} = k_{la}^{intB} = k_{la}^{cA} = k_{la}^{cB} = 10^4$, $k_d^A = k_d^B = 3.3\ 10^{-2}$, $k_d^c = 6.94\ 10^{-4}$, $k_A = 10^7$, $k_B = 0.12\ 10^7$, $k_c = 700$, $k_{BA} = 1.1\ 10^6$, $k_{RA} = k_{RB}^A = k_{RB} = 0.066$, $k_1 = 0.4$, $k_2 = 5\ 10^{-4}$, $V_l = 5\ 10^{-4}$, $V_c = 3\ 10^{-5}$, $A_{healthy} = 3.045$, $B_{healthy} = 3.18$, $\alpha_{healthy} = A_{healthy}/B_{healthy}$, $S_A = 7\ 10^{-3}$, $S_B = \alpha_{healthy}S_A$, $S_c = 7\ 10^{-4}$, $N_{healthy} = 33\ 10^9$ cells, $R_{healthy} = 5.971$. The function f was defined to zero for the healthy patient: $f_{healthy} = 0$. Three different initial (non-stationary) states corresponding to an anti-inflammatory state ($f_0 = -10$) have been used:

IS1: ($A_0 = 3.045$, $A_{0ads} = A_0/10$, $A_{0c} = A_0/10$, $B_0 = 9.18$, $B_{0ads} = B_0/10$, $B_{0c} = B_0/10$, $R_{A0} = 5.971$, $R_{B0} = 7.401$, $N_{c0} = 88.5\ 10^9$),

IS2: ($A_0 = 3.045$, $A_{0ads} = A_0/10$, $A_{0c} = A_0/10$, $B_0 = 9.18$, $B_{0ads} = B_0/10$, $B_{0c} = B_0/10$, $R_{A0} = 5.971$, $R_{B0} = 9.401$, $N_{c0} = 35.5\ 10^9$),

IS3: ($A_0 = 3.045$, $A_{0ads} = A_0/10$, $A_{0c} = A_0/10$, $B_0 = 9.18$, $B_{0ads} = B_0/10$, $B_{0c} = B_0/10$, $R_{A0} = 5.971$, $R_{B0} = 9.401$, $N_{0c} = 82.5\ 10^9$).

A, B, R and N_c were made dimensionless by dividing by $A_{healthy}, B_{healthy}, R_{healthy}$ and $N_{healthy}$ respectively.

Figure 5 shows dynamic evolution in the case IS1. Figure 6 gives the inflammation function in the case of IS2 and IS3. With IS1 and IS3 the septic shock leads to death of the patient since the inflammation function does not tends to 0. With IS1 conditions the patient reaches a pro-inflammatory state. With IS3 conditions, the patient is initially in an anti-inflammatory state. In case of IS1 and IS2, the cell number is equivalent and high compared to the healthy patient and seems to lead to the early death and immunodepression for IS1 and IS2 respectively. The patient with IS2 initial state begins more initial receptor of anti-inflammatory cytokines that the patient with IS1 initial state. Even though its state (more anti-inflammatory cytokine receptors) seems to be first improved, it finally leads to the patient death. On the other hand, the patient with IS2 state but with a cell number corresponding to healthy state, returns to homeostasis state. It can be noticed that from three different initial conditions we obtain three different steady states. So the model is able to represent the change of homeostasis that appears after septic shock.

4. Conclusion

Very encouraging qualitative results were obtained by the model developed for homeostasis description on the basis of 2 types of cytokines indicating the interest of the proposed approach. However, many cytokines exist and have specific actions. So network modelling will be necessary and essential to better approach the behavior of the inflammation, because there is no species controlling all the others. Each molecule or cell has its role in the immune system, and none is redundant. This approach will be further investigated. Finally, the simulations have to be confronted with experimental data.

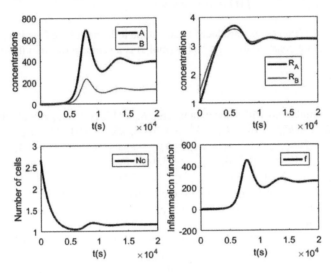

Figure 5: Simulation results with initial state IS1

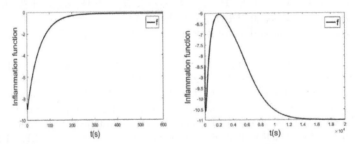

Figure 6: Inflammation function dynamic behaviour with initial state IS2 (right) and IS3 (left)

References

WHA resolution, 2017, Global Sepsis Alliance. https://www.global-sepsis-alliance.org/news/2017/5/26/wha-adopts-resolution-on-sepsis.

R.S. Hotchkiss , G. Monneret , D. Payen, 2013, Nat Rev Immunol., Vol 13, Is 12, PP 862-74

F. Venet, G. Monneret, 2018, Nat Rev Nephrol, Vol 14, Is 2, PP 121-137

H. Malek, M. M. Ebadzadeh, R. Safabakhsh, A. Razavi, J. Zaringhalam, 2015, Comput. Biol. Med. 67, PP 1–12

I.P. Androulakis, P.D. Mavroudis, S.A. Corbett and S.E. Calvano, 2015, Circadian characteristics of permissive and suppressive effects of cortisol and their role in homeostasis and the acute inflammatory response. Math. Biosci., Vol 260, PP 54–64.

KEGG Pathway Database : cytokine-cytokine receptor interaction - Homo sapiens

Anton A. Kiss, Edwin Zondervan, Richard Lakerveld, Leyla Özkan (Eds.)
Proceedings of the 29th European Symposium on Computer Aided Process Engineering
June 16th to 19th, 2019, Eindhoven, The Netherlands. © 2019 Elsevier B.V. All rights reserved.
http://dx.doi.org/10.1016/B978-0-128-18634-3.50184-3

More power to the individual modeller using ontologies

Heinz A Preisig[a*], Arne Tobias Elve[a] and Sigve Karolius[a]

[a]*Department of Chemical Engineering; NTNU; Trondheim, Norway*

Abstract

Ontology driven process simulation yields a significant improvement not only in terms of accelerating the modelling process itself, but also the quality. Time saving allows for exploring many more alternatives in a shorter time, thus the domain of design for a given process, is readily expanded and quality reduced debugging. To make the use of ontologies successful, one needs to step away from the common data-mining utilisation of ontology, but rather use them to control and guide the modelling process. The construction of the ontology itself is a stage-wise process, where the previously added knowledge is used to control the next stage. From the root definition to the structure of the multi-disciplinary domain, to adding the mathematical description, to designing the controls of the modelling-user graphical interface, the control of constructing the model interactively, to the instantiation an the numerical solution to the visualisation, the ontology is involved at every state improving the overall task equally on every stage.

Keywords: Process Modelling, Automatic Code Generation, Ontology, Graph-based Modelling

1. The Issues

1.1. The Multi-Disciplinary Challenge

Defining modelling as mapping a physical process into a digital twin, being a mathematical model that is realised on a digital device, the modelling activities of the typical chemical engineers would traditionally imply the modelling of unit operations and their combination into plants. Most of the modelling is centred around steady-state processes, with dynamic models mostly being used for control-related activities such as controller design, tuning and testing on a digital plant model. By also allowing for human-in-the-loop then this would also include the operating training with the human acting as a controller, mostly a supervisory controller.

Due to the fast development of computing, both on the hardware and the software side, the use of detailed models in the chemical engineering is rapidly increasing thereby enabling the handling of more and more complex digital twins of our physical plant object. The development affects all disciplines, and with the increasing capabilities, the demand for multi-disciplinary modelling activities is equally rapidly expanding.

Disciplines tend to live their own life generating and solving their problems. The call for interdisciplinary activities requires the integration of the respective software tools and puts high demands on the users. Many companies have been or are in the process of establishing interdisciplinary modelling groups with the objective to increase the coverage of their modelling activities.

1.2. The Customer Challenge

The software users are primarily facing the need for broader knowledge. Disciplines tend to live their own life, for various reasons, but not at least because of the sheer volume of knowledge required for an individual to become functional in the discipline-specific domains. The users want to have the models to cover a broader range of scales and application domains. A prime example is the utilisation of material models, which has the simple objective to eliminate a large portion of the experimental work required to determine the properties of components but mainly of mixtures. The problem is easy to visualise: a mixture of 2 components covering the range of their concentration range will cover the whole feasible mixing range. Assuming it to cover the full range, thus from pure A to pure B, and performing an experiment in intervals of 10 % one needs 11 experiments to cover the range. With 3 components, this results in 66 experiments, thus naturally multiplying with the number of components and the reduction of the intervals.

The potential substitute is to model the mixture with molecular modelling tools. Programs such as COSMO-RS (Klamt, 2018), LAMMPS (Plimpton, 1995) and suits like MaterialStudio ™ are increasingly used to estimate physical properties. Despite having made significant progress on the user-friendliness, these programs typically have a steep learning curve as well as demanding a level of familiarity with the underlying theory to interpret the results. This applies equally to the next upper domain of granularity, the mesoscale, thus all those scales that lie between the molecular level and the macroscopic level whereby macroscopic refers to a scale that captures the dimensions of the product being modelled. The discipline-dependency is probably strongest on both ends of the scale, and weakest in the middle.

Even in the case where one succeeds to assemble a suitable team, the next barrier is the software. The programs, when not in-house developed, need to be evaluated and purchased or licenses must be obtained and maintained. This obviously requires money for the purchase or licence, but it also requires people who administrate and operate the software and the required hardware facilities.

1.3. The Provider Challenge

The customers are asking for integrated simulation environments that make it possible to predict a product based on the complete history being based on the computational integration of all scales. Whilst feasible to link essentially all the scales into a multi-scale modelling environment as was shown in the MoDeNa EC Framework 7 project, the demand on the people is enormous. Having a specialist in the consortium and intense communications are essential. Less of a problem was the construction of a software platform that allows simulating processes including the full range from quantum mechanics for kinetics to mechanical properties of a polymerised polyurethane foam. Having an experienced senior leader of the latter development proved to yield a solution within two years.

The customer is asking for a simple-to-use environment, preferably a graphical interface that allows the definition of simulations[1] graphically. This implies that the provider is integrated into a platform, which knows about the different "programs" and which knows on how to combine the programs to generate the desired solution to a user-specified problem.

Technically, this implies that this platform knows about the different "programs" that provide solutions to specific problems, which for the time being we term *solvers*. The platform thus requires knowledge of the available solvers as well as the required data inflow and outflow. It also implies that these *solvers* can be connected by a piping mechanism, meaning that the data from one *solver* can be streamed as input to another. The mechanism is thereby not essential for the user. It may be realised as a data stream or may be passed through a file even with intermediate processing integrated. As long as the mechanism is not time limiting the specifics of the integration are of no concern to the customer. This also applies to the *solvers* being linked to the relevant databases. The dream, and thus the task, is to construct the platform such that it can provide this level of convenience and beyond – it should also advise on what to use and how to use all specific to the problem domain relevant to the customer.

2. Controlling the Modelling Processes using Ontologies

Ideally, the platform acts as an adviser and contracted builder of solutions to a domain of problems spanning over a specified set of disciplines. This can range from physics quantum mechanics to mechanical product properties to controlled unit operations, plant models, performance analysis, nearly anything that let itself capture in a mathematical model.

2.1. Simulation – the Core

Simulation is the core operation, whereby *simulation* is the task of computing the response of a mathematical representation of the plant, the mathematical model, to external excitations. For example, what is the effect of changing raw product quality on the product, what is the effect of changing the energy input into a device, the mass flow to be handled by a plant etc. Simulation is also the core of process design, where the design parameters are optimised based on the objective to meet defined production goals, like concentration and mass flow, whilst minimising waste and energy consumption.

A single-block simulation will capture the complete behaviour in a set of equations, which may be very large indeed and solve these equations using suitable methods. In contrast, a multi-scale, multi-block simulation will solve the problem by solving the blocks sequentially or more generically in a logic-controlled sequence. The MoDeNa project is an excellent example, where polyurethane foam was modelled over the full range from quantum to mechanical properties, which also lead to the definition of a standard for modelling processes (CEN workshop committee, 2018) .

Simulations are also the core of controller tuning and performance checking before implementing them on an actual plant. Operating training tests the operator as a human-in-the-loop, a concept which expands to reaction training in accidents. The latter is very much the same as the flight simulator training machinery for pilots.

---

[1]The term *simulation* is here used generically implying all operations that lead to the execution of a simulation.

2.2. Ontology – the Tool

The core of the platform provides the means to specify the problem. In accordance to the MODA (CEN workshop committee, 2018) a graphical interface could provide the means to define the problem interactively as a directed graph, where the nodes represent the computational tasks, some of which are solvers, some of which provide input convert and process output from the various solvers.

2.2.1. Base Ontology

The design philosophy has the main aspects of (i) **small is beautiful** constructing first of all the ontology from a minimal set of classes and a (ii) **context-free approach** constructing mathematical models named by the ontology in the (iii) **state space**.

The first lead to a high-level abstraction of a generic "process" or "system" , namely any process/system is represented as a directed graph in which discipline-specific tokens are "living". The nodes/vertices represent the capacities for the tokens, whilst the arcs/edges represent the transfer of tokens, thus model the interaction. The base ontology captures the multi-disciplinary domain into a tree of ontologies where each node in this tree inherits the parent nodes completely. The disciplines are thus split hierarchically into sub-disciplines. A simple example is given in Figure 1. This represents the first step in the construction of the ontology. It allows to control the definition of the *base component models* for each specified knowledge domain whilst providing the hierarchical structure of the different domains. The *base component models* are the mathematical models for the node/vertice and the arc/edge behaviour in the respective domain-specific graphs.

For example for process engineering, thus the continuous domain of physical systems, this may be a lumped system for a node giving equations for the conservation of mass, species mass and energy. For the arcs it may be the transfer of mass with the mechanism *convection* or the mechanism *diffusion*, to mention two.

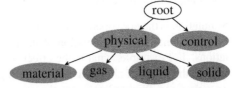

Figure 1: A two-discipline ontology tree

2.2.2. The Multi-Network Framework

A different view is given in Figure 2, which indicates the multi-network for an unspecified example showing the nature of interactions: the intrafaces transfer tokens between subdomains, whilst interfaces transmute tokens from one type into another one. For example, a physical phase interface transfer tokens (energy, mass etc.) whilst the control system observes the state of the physical system and manipulates the physical valve position.

The approach gives an apparent meaning to both types of interaction, at the same time allowing for control of the node connections inside a domain and between domains. For the *interfaces* in the control case, it is the measurement on one side, whilst it is the simplified representation of a set of physical components that convert a control output signal into a valve position. For the *interface* to a material model, it is typically the canonical variables

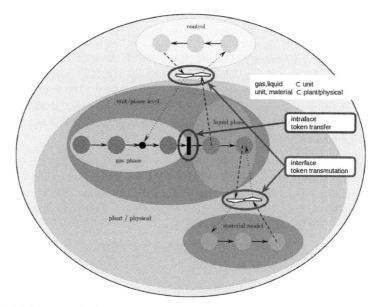

Figure 2: Multi-network view with intra- and interfaces for token transfer & transmutation

of the energy representation whilst it is a physical property that is reported back. If the *interface* connects to a molecular simulation, the one side is typically a lifting whilst on the other side is a homogenisation.

2.2.3. Equations

The equations are appended to the ontology following the rule that they are inherited into all the branches. Thus the node representing the physical systems is populated with the basic conservation principles, whilst the frame variable, time, is in the root node for dynamic systems. The spatial coordinates, being also physical frame variables, are added to the node of the physical system. The population of the ontology with variables and equations is based on the **state-space approach**. The definition starts with the state and the constants as well as the incidence matrix capturing the model's network structure. The tokens in the nodes define the states, thus state variables are defined accordingly in the base ontology. They, together with the constants, define the physical units. Derived quantities can only be defined based on already defined quantities leading to a lower-diagonal definition space, which is also always closed and complete (Preisig, 2010). This provides control not only about the units, but also the indexing for nodes, arcs and tokens. This ensures complete control over the structure of the equation definition. When combined with the ontology it also enforces completeness of the model as an index-one simulation problem with a given sequence in which the equations must be evaluated.

The definition of the equations is done using a parser, the description of which lies outside of the scope of this paper. The parser generates an abstract syntax tree (Elve and Preisig, 2018). Compilation then only requires a set of target-specific templates that implement the syntax of the target language for the basic operations and functions. This can readily be extended to accommodate user-specified functions.

2.2.4. Model Construction

A graphical editor provides the interface for the modeller, the user that builds the process models based on a given ontology. The interface controls the user's input, ensuring that it is consistent with the context provided by the ontology. It makes it impossible to make mistakes that contradict the structures defined in the ontology. The editor allows for a hierarchical definition of the model, to allow for capturing complex models essentially without any limitations than basics of computing, such as the upper limit of an integer for the counter of model elements.

The user only specifies his view on the model topology by specifying the nodes, their dynamic and distribution nature and the arcs as token transfers including their nature, namely the transfer mechanism being modelled. The remaining part is automatically added to the model via a bipartite graph analysis operating on the equation/variable graphs of the respective domain specific equation set.

3. Achievements

- Tools to define a hierarchical multi-disciplinary ontology
- Equation inclusion tool that is controlled by the ontology and constructs lower-triagonal equation systems for the discipline-specific base components describing the capacity and transfer properties for all discipline-specific properties.
- Complete control over connecting discipline-specific domains.
- Proper handling of subdomains including the transition over scales and from particulate to continuous domains
- Result is index one differential algebraic or partial differential algebraic systems of equations conserving the model structure, which can be utilised in the solvers.
- Complete separation of model structure from behaviour description.
- Latter allows the implementation of model reduction algorithms that are based on order-of-magnitude assumptions.
- Time/length-scale motivated model reduction is facilitated as an operation on the structure, thus affects only the index sets, not the behaviour equations.
- Complete documentation of the model, structure, equations and all assumptions.
- For simulation, the initialisation is clearly defined.
- Explicit implementation of global boundary conditions.
- Highly efficient modelling tool – a reactor in 5 minutes...

References

CEN workshop committee, 2018. Materials modelling - terminology, classification and metadata. URL *ftp://ftp.cencenelec.eu/CEN/Sectors/TCandWorkshops/Workshops/WS%20MODA/CWA_17284.pdf*

A. T. Elve, H. A. Preisig, 2018. From ontology to executable program code. Comp & Chem Eng. URL *http://www.sciencedirect.com/science/article/pii/S0098135418309311*

A. Klamt, 2018. The cosmo and cosmo-rs solvation models. WIREs Comput Mol Sci 8, 1–11.

S. Plimpton, 1995. Fast parallel algorithms for short-range molecular dynamics. J Comp Phys 117, 1–10.

H. A. Preisig, 2010. Constructing and maintaining proper process models. Comp & Chem Eng 34(9), 1543–1555.

Anton A. Kiss, Edwin Zondervan, Richard Lakerveld, Leyla Özkan (Eds.)
Proceedings of the 29th European Symposium on Computer Aided Process Engineering
June 16th to 19th, 2019, Eindhoven, The Netherlands. © 2019 Elsevier B.V. All rights reserved.
http://dx.doi.org/10.1016/B978-0-128-18634-3.50185-5

Relative Optimality Index for Evaluation of the Approximate Methods for Synthesis of Flexible Processes under Uncertainty

Klavdija Zirngast, Zdravko Kravanja, Zorka Novak Pintarič[*]

University of Maribor, Faculty of Chemistry and Chemical Engineering, Smetanova 17, 2000 Maribor, Slovenia

zorka.novak@um.si

Abstract

This contribution introduces a new indicator called Relative Optimality Index (ROI) which measures the extent to which the expected objective value of a flexible process flow sheet obtained by an approximate sequential approach is similar to the optimal solution obtained by more rigorous methods. MINLP flexible process syntheses were performed using various approximate robust approaches and the results were compared to the reference value obtained with the Gaussian quadrature method: a) sequential one-scenario method over randomly selected vertices, b) sequential method in which a two-scenario problem was solved in each iteration simultaneously at the nominal point and randomly selected vertex point, c) a method similar to b) but the most violated point from the previous iteration was used in the subsequent iteration instead of a randomly selected vertex, and d) a novel method which identifies a few vertices critical for flexibility, and solves a few-scenario problem simultaneously in the nominal point and these critical vertices. In this way, better trade-offs between first- and second-stage variables are established. These estimated values are then used as target values during the fine tuning of process structure and design variables that should bring both the flexibility index and the ROI as close as possible to the desired value of 1.

Keywords: uncertainty, flexibility, Relative Optimality Index

1. Introduction

Synthesis of flexible process flow sheets with large numbers of uncertain input data suffers from the problem that the exact optimal results usually cannot be obtained, because rigorous methods, such as simultaneous multi-scenario Gaussian quadrature, cannot be carried out due to uncontrolled increase in the size of the mathematical model. Several approximate approaches have been developed that are based on a large reduction of scenarios, for example, a simultaneous few-scenario method at the nominal and critical points (Novak Pintarič et al., 2013), a method based on probability distances (Zeballos et al., 2014), or sequential procedures in which one-scenario problems are solved sequentially in numbers of randomly selected points (Zirngast et al., 2018). Decomposition approaches were also proposed to facilitate the solution of large-scale problems under uncertainty; for example, an improved L-shaped method based on Benders decomposition (Li and Grossmann, 2018).

The problem with approximate approaches is that the results deviate from optimality; moreover, when dealing with large numbers of uncertainty parameters, a compromise is sought between flexibility, optimality and computational effort. It is therefore important to address challenges in the area of optimization under uncertainty, because industrial engineering problems, such as demand side management, supply chains and process planning, design and synthesis, require that the risk and uncertainties be taken into account (Grossmann et al., 2017).

In this paper, a robust approach is proposed for Mixed Integer NonLinear Programming (MINLP) process synthesis under uncertainty based on a new identification procedure of those points critical for flexibility. In addition, a new Relative Optimality Index (ROI) is proposed for evaluating the precision of the approximate methods. The developed ROI represents, on one hand, a tool to establish how close the expected value obtained by an approximate method is to the exact value. On the other hand, it provides an approach for targeting the expected values and the appropriate trade-offs between the first- and second-stage variables of those flow sheets generated by robust sequential approaches under large numbers of uncertain parameters for which exact results would be impossible to obtain.

2. Methods for synthesis of flexible processes under uncertainty

The presence of uncertain parameters during MINLP synthesis of chemical processes requires discretization of infinite mathematical models at several discrete points i.e. scenarios, and optimization of the expected objective function. The latter involves the solution of a multiple integral which is approximated in discrete scenarios weighted by the corresponding weights or probabilities as shown in Eq. (1).

$$EZ = \min\left(c^{\mathrm{T}} y + \sum_{s} p_{s} \cdot f(d, x_{s}, z_{s}, \theta_{s}) \right)$$

$$\text{s. t.} \quad h(d, x_{s}, z_{s}, \theta_{s}) = 0$$

$$g(d, x_{s}, z_{s}, \theta_{s}) + By \leq 0 \qquad\qquad s \in S \qquad\qquad (1)$$

$$d \geq g_{\mathrm{d}}(x_{s}, z_{s}, \theta_{s})$$

$$Ay \leq a$$

$$d, x_{s}, z_{s} \geq 0, \ y \in \{0,1\}, \ \theta^{\mathrm{LO}} \leq \theta \leq \theta^{\mathrm{UP}}$$

Eq. (1) presents a two-stage stochastic model with recourse in which first-stage variables (topology and sizes of process units, y and d) should fit all scenarios, while second-stage variables (operating and control variables, x and z) are specific for each scenario. S is a set of selected scenarios denoted by subscript s, EZ an expected value of scalar objective variable Z, p probability of scenarios, c and f fixed and variable costs, h equality constraints, g inequality constraints, g_{d} design expressions, θ uncertain parameters, A, B and a are the matrices and vector of constants. The above problem can be solved using various methods which differ in selection of scenarios and in the way they treat the scenarios, either simultaneously or sequentially. The number of scenarios is a crucial factor, as the accuracy of the result and the computational effort increase with it.

2.1. Gaussian quadrature

The scenarios in this method correspond to the zeros of the Legendre polynomials, while their weight coefficients represent probabilities (see Acevedo and Pistikopoulos, 1998). The most accurate results would be obtained if the model would be solved simultaneously in all combinations of quadrature points of uncertain parameters; however, the problem size grows substantially as the number of constraints and second-stage variables are multiplied by $N_Q{}^{N_P}$, where N_Q is the number of quadrature points and N^U the number of uncertain parameters.

2.2. Sequential one- and two-scenario methods with randomly selected vertex

In order to avoid a tremendous increase in model size when using the Gaussian method, more robust sequential approaches were developed, based on the decomposition of the problem into a) determination of the first-stage variables, and b) adjustment of the second-stage variables (Zirngast et al., 2018). The procedure starts with the optimal process structure obtained by one-scenario MINLP synthesis at the nominal conditions. This structure is then solved at the randomly selected vertex so that the existing process units can enlarge, and new units can be added to achieve feasibility. The procedure continues with new vertices until the first-stage variables change. The flexibility index of the obtained process structure is then determined, and stochastic Monte Carlo optimization is performed in a finite number of randomly selected points for determining second-stage variables and the expected objective value at a specific level of confidence. The two-scenario approach differs from the one-scenario method in that MINLP synthesis problem for first-stage variables is solved simultaneously at the nominal point and random vertex in order to better target the trade-offs between first- and second-stage variables.

2.3. Sequential two-scenario method with most violated vertex

This approach is like the two-scenario method described in section 2.2, except that it does not use a randomly selected vertex next to the nominal point but the most violated vertex from the previous iteration. This vertex is identified by analyzing a flexibility index for the first-stage variables obtained in each iteration, as in (Bansal et al., 2002). The vertex with the lowest flexibility is then identified and added to the nominal point in the subsequent iteration.

2.4. Simultaneous multi-scenario method in critical and nominal points

The approaches described in sections 2.2 and 2.3 start with the initial process structure obtained at the nominal point whose flexibility index is usually close to 0. A new approach is therefore developed that starts with a partly flexible initial topology, and then derives a flexible structure by handling this initial topology through one of the previously described approaches. Identification of critical points starts with a two-scenario MINLP process synthesis at a nominal point and random vertex, followed by determination of the flexibility index of the first-stage variables obtained. After processing a specific set of vertices, those few vertices that produce the lowest flexibility indexes are selected as critical ones. MINLP synthesis is then performed as a few-scenario problem simultaneously at the nominal point and identified critical vertices yielding first-stage variables with flexibility index substantially higher than 0. This topology is then tuned to flexibility index 1 by using one of the approaches described in sections 2.2 and 2.3.

2.5. Relative optimality index

From the above described methods, the simultaneous multi-scenario Gaussian quadrature is regarded as the most precise one, so the results of the other methods are compared with the Gaussian result by defining a Relative Optimality Index (*ROI*) in Eq. (2):

$$ROI = 1 - \frac{\left| EZ_{Gauss} - EZ_{appr} \right|}{EZ_{Gauss}} \qquad (2)$$

where EZ_{Gauss} and EZ_{appr} represent the expected values obtained by the Gaussian and approximate method, respectively. The closer the ROI value to one, the better the results obtained by an approximate method.

3. Case study

MINLP synthesis of a flexible Heat Exchanger Network (HEN) was selected as a case study. Data for process streams and utilities are given in Table 1, where T_s represents the supply temperatures, T_t target temperatures, *CF* heat capacity flow rates, and α individual heat transfer coefficients. Four uncertain parameters were supply temperatures of hot streams H1 and H2, supply temperature of cold stream C1, and heat capacity flow rate of hot stream H1. The number of uncertain parameters was intentionally kept low, so that the simultaneous Gaussian method could be performed as a reference. The objective function was minimum Total Annual Cost (TAC) composed of the utility costs plus annualized investment cost of heat transfer units. HEN synthesis was performed using MINLP model (Yee and Grossmann, 1990).

The numerical results obtained by different methods are presented in Table 2, and the optimal HEN structures in Figures 1, 2 and 3. MINLP synthesis at the nominal conditions produced an inflexible network with the lowest TAC. Simultaneous MINLP synthesis by Gaussian method was performed at three quadrature points for each parameter, yielding a flexible HEN with the reference expected TAC of 407,550 $/y, and flexibility index equal to 1. The model size was 6,230 equations, 8,538 continuous variables and 36 discrete variables, while the required CPU time was 9 h using an SBB optimization solver within GAMS on an average personal computer.

Table 1: Data for case study of HEN synthesis

Stream	T_s (K)	T_t (K)	*CF* (kW)	α (kW/(m^2·K))
H1	621 ± 5	350	28 ± 5	1.4
H2	583 ± 13	323	20	1.4
C1	388 ± 15	600	40	1.4
C2	313	393	60	1.4
Hot utility (HU)	620	619		3.5
Cold utility (CU)	298	315		1.4

Cost of heat exchangers and coolers ($/y) = $1846 \cdot A^{0.65}$ (*A* in m^2)
Cost of heaters ($/y) = $2350 \cdot A^{0.65}$ (*A* in m^2)
Price of hot utility = 230 $/kWy, price of cold utility = 20 $/kWy

Table 2: Results of flexible HEN synthesis by different methods

Method for MINLP synthesis	Expected TAC ($/y)	A (m^2)	Flexibility index	*ROI*
Nominal point	358,524	663	0.00	0.880
Gaussian quadrature (2.1*)	407,550	742	1.07	1.000
One-scenario method with randomly selected vertex (2.2*)	446,981	956	1.12	0.902
Two-scenario method with randomly selected vertex (2.2*)	426,424	748	1.20	0.954
Two-scenario method with most violated vertex (2.3*)	426,237	748	1.11	0.954
Multi-scenario method in critical and nominal points (2.4*)	424,082	743	1.17	0.959

* Number of section where the method is described

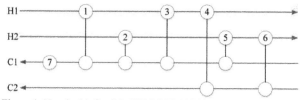

Figure 1: Nominal inflexible HEN (358,524 $/y)

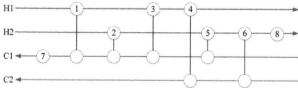

Figure 2: Flexible HEN obtained by Gaussian quadrature (407,550 $/y) and two-scenario method with most violated vertex (426,237)

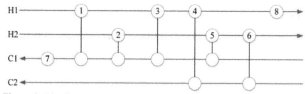

Figure 3: Flexible HEN obtained by two-scenario method with randomly selected vertex (426,424 $/y), multi-scenario method at nominal and critical points (424,082 $/y), one-scenario method with randomly s elected vertex (446,981 $/y)

Computation times for the approximate sequential methods were significantly lower than for Gaussian integration, and amounted to around 15 s. Two-scenario approaches produced lower TACs than the one-scenario method, because the presence of the nominal point besides the vertex point during determination of the first-stage variables provides at least rough information about the trade-offs with the second-stage variables.

Those approaches initiating from the nominal inflexible structure (sections 2.2 and 2.3) gave higher costs than the approach that starts from a partially flexible initial structure with flexibility index 0.55 (section 2.4). This structure was then tuned to the required flexibility by using only around 30 vertices in a two-scenario method (section 2.2) while more than 100 vertices were needed when starting the same method from the nominal inflexible structure. All two-scenario approaches achieved a Relative Optimality Index around 95 % with regard to the reference Gaussian method.

4. Conclusions

This paper demonstrates several robust approximate methods for MINLP process synthesis under uncertainty, and compares their results with a more rigorous simultaneous Gaussian quadrature method. A novel indicator, called a Relative Optimality Index, was proposed for measuring how close the results of the approximate methods are to the Gaussian one. It was established that a novel sequential two-scenario approach starting from a partially flexible initial structure produced the closest result with a ROI value of 0.96. In the future work it is intended to upgrade these approaches for determining target ratios between the first- and second-stage variables, and to use them for the approximate synthesis of large processes with many uncertain parameters for which exact optimal results cannot normally be obtained.

Acknowledgment

The authors acknowledge financial support from the Slovenian Research Agency (PhD research fellowships MR-39209, project L2-7633, and program P2-0032) and Perutnina Ptuj.

References

J. Acevedo, E. N. Pistikopoulos, 1998, Stochastic optimization based algorithms for process synthesis under uncertainty, Computers & Chemical Engineering, 22, 4, 647-671

V. Bansal, J. D. Perkins, E. N. Pistikopoulos, 2002, Flexibility analysis and design using a parametric programming framework, AIChE Journal, 48, 12, 2851-2868

I. E. Grossmann, R. M. Apap, B. A. Calfa, P. Garcia-Herreros, Q. Zhang, 2017, Mathematical Programming Techniques for Optimization under Uncertainty and Their Application in Process Systems Engineering, Theoretical Foundations of Chemical Engineering, 51, 6, 893-909

C. Li, I. E. Grossmann, 2018, An improved L-shaped method for two-stage convex 0–1 mixed integer nonlinear stochastic programs, Computers & Chemical Engineering, 112, 165-179

Z. Novak Pintarič, M. Kasaš, Z. Kravanja, 2013, Sensitivity analyses for scenario reduction in flexible flow sheet design with a large number of uncertain parameters, AIChE Journal, 59, 8, 2862-2871

T. F. Yee, I. E. Grossmann, 1990, Simultaneous optimization models for heat integration—II. Heat exchanger network synthesis, Computers & Chemical Engineering, 14, 10, 1165-1184

L. J. Zeballos, C. A. Méndez, A. P. Barbosa-Povoa, A. Q. Novais, 2014, Multi-period design and planning of closed-loop supply chains with uncertain supply and demand, Computers & Chemical Engineering, 66, 151-164

K. Zirngast, Z. Kravanja, Z. Novak Pintarič, 2018, A Robust Decomposition Methodology for Synthesis of Flexible Processes with many Uncertainty Parameters – Application to HEN Synthesis, submitted to Chemical and Biochemical Engineering Quarterly

Anton A. Kiss, Edwin Zondervan, Richard Lakerveld, Leyla Özkan (Eds.)
Proceedings of the 29th European Symposium on Computer Aided Process Engineering
June 16th to 19th, 2019, Eindhoven, The Netherlands. © 2019 Elsevier B.V. All rights reserved.
http://dx.doi.org/10.1016/B978-0-128-18634-3.50186-7

Time Resolved Sensitivity & Identifiability Analysis for Directed Parametrization of Highly Dynamic Models

Sven Daume[a,+], Julian Kager[a,b,+,*] and Christoph Herwig[a,b]

[a]*ICEBE, TU Wien, Gumpendorfer Straße 1a 166/4, 1060 Wien, Austria*
[b]*CD Laboratory on Mechanistic and Physiological Methods for Improved Bioprocesses, TU Wien, Gumpendorfer Straße 1a 166/4, 1060 Wien, Austria*
[+]*Contributed equally to the paper.*
julian.kager@tuwien.ac.at

Abstract

Biological systems can be described by ordinary differential equations of the main components with non-linear and interacting reaction kinetics. This models are helpful tools for process development and optimization. The difficulty in building a model is not to find a mathematical expression for the different kinetics but to select the ones with identifiable parameters. Besides that also the right sampling time points are important to capture the needed information for model calibration.

Within this contribution, we show how time resolved sensitivity helps to tackle this question by using the example of an *Escherichia coli* (*E. coli*) growth model. We show how the time resolved parameter sensitivities of the dynamic batch and fed-batch can be used to determine identifiable parameter sets and to schedule samples for off-line and at-line measurements.

For validation of our framework, we compared our approach with equally distributed sampling over time. The results show that our sampling approach is able to determine the best identifiable parameter sets and helps to define sample time points to finally obtain the needed parameter accuracy. Besides that with less effort (number of samples) comparable parameter accuracies could be reached.

Keywords: Sensitivity; Identifibility; Model Parametrization; Sample Timepoint Optimization

1. Introduction

Having accurate process models is of great value for all production industries, offering them to do in-silico process scheduling and optimization and to use them to monitor and control their production processes (Mears et al. (2017)). In order to obtain reliable models that can be successfully used, the model calibration stage requires carefully designed experiments with high informative content (Muñoz-Tamayo et al. (2014)).

Hereby the sampling time points are of central importance to capture the information. Especially in fermentation processes, were sampling bears a contamination risk and off-line analytics are cost and labour intense, a proper sampling strategy is important. Often equally distributed sampling or only end-points of process phases are sampled, which leads to the loss of important information.

Based on a simple *E. coli* fed-batch model, consisting of three state variables and four parameters (De Pauw and Vanrolleghem (2006)) a workflow is presented, to select identifiable parameter sets and to determine sampling time points and frequencies to obtain the aimed parameter estimation accuracy. The parameter identifiability, which considers the uniqueness of model parameters, is a prerequisite for reliable parameter estimation (Chiş et al. (2011)). Often biological models are over-parameterized, whereas only a subset of parameters are identifiable in practice. By ranking the parameters according to their influence on the model outputs, the so called parameter sensitivity, Brun et al. (2002) showed a procedure how best identifiable parameter sets can be selected for an over-parameterized model. The proposed procedure combines the collinearity, a measure of parameter uniqueness and sensitivity, a measure of parameter importance of all possible combinations.

In this contribution we extended this approach from continuous processes, were steady state conditions are reached to dynamic batch and fed-batch conditions by taking an *E. coli* growth model. The presented subset selection was based on the time resolved collinearity to determine process phases with different identifiable parameter subsets. In contrast to De Pauw and Vanrolleghem (2006) and Kutalik et al. (2004) which determined time points with highest information content, we optimized the sampling time points towards the selected parameter subset, guaranteeing reliable model parameter with preselected accuracies.

2. Materials and Methods

2.1. E. coli Fed-batch Model

For illustrating the algorithm an unstructured, unsegregated model describing an *E. coli* fed-batch process was taken from De Pauw and Vanrolleghem (2006). The model was extended by the concentration of dead cells. The model consist of three material balances: the living biomass C_X,

$$\frac{dC_X}{dt} = (\mu - k_d) \cdot C_X - \cdot C_X \frac{F_\alpha}{V}, \quad \mu = \mu_{max} \frac{C_{Glc}}{C_{Glc} + K_{Glc}} \tag{1}$$

the dead biomass C_{Xd},

$$\frac{dC_{Xd}}{dt} = k_d \cdot C_X - C_{Xd} \cdot \frac{F_\alpha}{V} \tag{2}$$

and the glucose concentration C_{Glc},

$$\frac{dC_{Glc}}{dt} = \frac{Y_{X,Glc}}{\mu} \cdot C_X + (C_{Glc,\alpha} - C_{Glc}) \cdot \frac{F_\alpha}{V} \tag{3}$$

where μ is the specific growth rate, k_d the constant death rate, $Y_{X,S}$ the yield coefficient for biomass on glucose, F_α the flow rate of the glucose feed and $C_{Glc,\alpha}$ the glucose concentration of the feed. A single substrate dependent Monod kinetic was assumed to fully describe the growth behaviour of *E. coli* in which μ_{max} is the maximum specific growth rate and K_{Glc} the saturation constant.

Normal distributed white noise, ε_{ij} was added to the model states C_j to obtain realistic data $\tilde{C}_j(t_i)$. From this noisy, data samples were taken every 5, 10, 30 and 60 min and model parameters were estimated by minimizing the profile likelihood between simulated and sampled data.

2.2. Sensitivity and Identifiability Analysis

The local sensitivity s_{jk} of the state variable C_j to parameter p_k quantifies the deflection of the state variable C_j due to small changes in p_k (DiStefano III (2015)). To identify the parameters, which influences the outputs of the described *E. coli* model most, the first-order, local sensitivity functions were simultaneously solved with the specified state equations. This local sensitivity information provides a basis for calculation of two parameter selection measures proposed by Brun et al. (2002).

$$s_{jk} = \frac{\partial C_j}{\partial p_k} * p_k \qquad \delta_k^{msqr} = \sqrt{\frac{1}{n}\sum_{j=1}^{n} s_{jk}^2} \qquad \gamma_K(t_i) = \frac{1}{\sqrt{\lambda_k(t_i)}} \qquad (4)$$

The importance index δ_k^{msqr}, which ranks the parameter according to their influence on the model states and serves as a global importance measurement. Whereas the collinearity index γ_K for a chosen parameter subset k gives the linear dependency between the selected parameters. In contrast to Brun et al. (2002) the collinearity index $\gamma_K(t_i)$ was calculated for every time point t_i. To determine the best set of parameters, the smallest eigenvalue $\lambda_k(t_i)$ of the Fisher Information Matrix $FIM(t_i)$ was used. The FIM is a measure for the information content that is stored in a measurement. It is connected to the covariance matrix of the parameters by it's inverse and is defined as follows:

$$FIM = \frac{1}{\sigma^2} \sum_{i=1}^{N} \sum_{j=1}^{n} \nabla_p C_j(t_i, p) \nabla_p C_j(t_i, p)^T \qquad (5)$$

where σ^2 is the variance of the measurements, p the parameter vector, i the number of measurements and j the number of states (Kutalik et al. (2004)).

2.3. Optimal Sampling Schedule

To determine the best sampling times a D-optimal design was chosen, maximizing the determinant of the FIM (Berger and Wong (2005)). This scalar objective function is optimized by Powell's Method analogous to the publication of Kutalik et al. (2004). This simple algorithm allows to find a suboptimal sampling time vector.

2.4. Description of General Workflow

After stating the model (step 1) the sensitivtiy analysis (step 2) the importance ranking and collinearity index are calculated (step 3). These two criterions are essential for the parameter subset selection (step 4) including only parameter subsets fulfilling both conditions (high sensitive and uncorrelated). Time optimization (step 5 and 6). Thereafter the optimization algorithm maximizes the determinant of the Fisher information and selects the most informative measurement points related to the parameter subset. Afterwards the parameter of the subset are estimated (step 7) showing acceptable errors (step 8).

3. Results and Discussion

Figure 2 shows the time series data of the simulated state variables and their corresponding in-silico samples, which were taken with a measurement frequency of 60 min. The fermentation starts in the batch mode with an initial working volume V_0 of 5 L, an initial glucose concentration $C_{Glc,0}$ of 6 g/L and an initial biomass concentration $C_{X,0}$ of 0.5 g/L. After a 6 h lasting batch phase a 4 h fed-batch followed. The fed-batch mode is characterized by a constant inflow of medium $F_\alpha =$

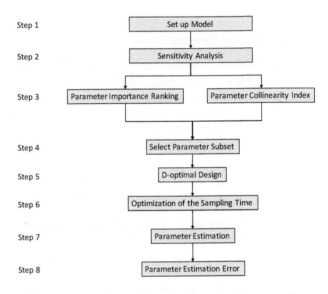

Figure 1: Overview of the workflow for improving the paramater estimation accuracy

$5*10^{-3}$ L/h with a glucose concentration of 600 g/L.

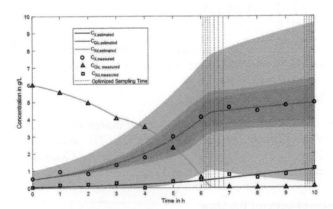

Figure 2: Overview of the optimal sampling times ($n_{sample} = 11$), the mesaured ($n_{sample} = 11$) and estimated concentration profiles of living biomass, dead biomass and glucose during an *E. coli* fed-batch process with a total process time of 10 h. Shaded areas are the 95 % confidence intervals of the biomass concentration (light grey: before subset selection, grey: after subset selection, dark grey: after sampling time optimization).

In Figure 3 the importance index of the parameters for the *E. coli* model and the time resolved collinearity index of some feasible subsets are illustrated. In total there exist 11 parameter combinations consisting of 2,3 and 4 parameters. All 4 parameters together reached high collinearities. The same goes for combinations with K_{Glc} and μ_{max}, which are not displayed in Figure 3. The parameter ranking revealed that μ_{max} is the most sensitive parameter. A change in μ_{max} leads to the largest change in the state variables. K_{Glc} is characterized by a low importance index, because it is only active in a small time window around 6 h when the glucose is nearly depleted. The subset of μ_{max}, Y_{XS} and k_d is the most linear independent and important triple combination. Within Figure 3 a time window is indicated in gray, were the selected subset shows almost no linear dependency.

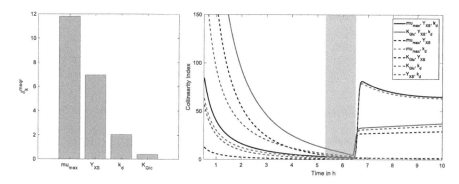

Figure 3: Selection of best identifiable Parameter set. a) Overall parameter importance, b) Time resolved identifiability of feasible parameter sets

In Table 1 the parameter estimation errors of all four parameters and the selected subset are compared for different measurement frequencies. These parameter estimation errors are based on the Cramer Rao lower bound. After parameter subset selection and exclusion

Table 1: Parameter estimation error (%) of the full parameter set with the selected parameter subset, excluding K_{Glc} at different measurement frequencies.

Data Frequency	$\Delta\mu_{max}$	ΔY_{XS}	Δk_d	ΔK_{Glc}	n Samples
(min)	(%)	(%)	(%)	(%)	
5	6.99 | 2.41	3.82 | 3.74	18.33 | 18.33	90.83 | -	121
10	9.81 | 3.41	5.47 | 5.35	23.13 | 23.13	148.10 | -	61
30	26.61|5.81	9.33 | 9.03	47.25 | 43.99	139.50 | -	21
60	29.21|7.96	12.58 | 12.27	56.62 | 56.59	1145.5 | -	11

of K_{Glc}, the parameter estimation error of μ_{max} decreases dramatically from 29 % to 8 % at a low sampling frequency. The other parameters are only slightly affected, which indicates a strong correlation between μ_{max} and K_{Glc}. The sample frequency has also an significant influence on the estimation error, showing a 3-fold increase comparing a 5 min to a hourly sampling rate. The estimation errors of the selected parameter subset with optimized sample time points are summarized in Table 2. It can be seen that by optimizing the sampling time point the estimation error can be significantly reduced. The errors are in the range of a sampling rate lower than 30 min, with only half of the samples. Compared to the same amount of equally distributed samples (60 min) the estimation error decreased by approx. 35% for μ_{max} and k_d and by 25% for Y_{XS}. The 95 % confidence interval of the biomass is shown in figure 2 before/after the subset selection and at the end of the sampling time optimization .

Table 2: Parameter estimation error (%) of the selected parmeter subsset consisting of μ_{max}, Y_{XS} and k_d after optimization of the sampling time

Measurement Frequency	$\Delta\mu_{max}$	ΔY_{XS}	Δk_d	n Samples
(min)	(%)	(%)	(%)	
60	7.96	12.27	56.59	11
optim	5.20	9.20	35.70	11

4. Conclusions and Outlook

It is shown that a combination of parameter subset selection and optimization of the sampling time points reduces the parameter estimation error drastically. The presented approach ensures that important samples are taken while at the same time overall sampling effort can be decreased. By evaluating the collinearity and parameter importance, the subsequent parameter estimation leads to more reliable models.

Although the D-optimality criterion proved to be a suitable optimization criterion for the examined fed-batch process, a further improvement might be reached when a combination of different optimality criterions for example D-optimal und E-optimal is implemented.

5. Acknowledgements

This work was supported by the Austrian research funding association (FFG) under the scope of the "AdaMo" project and by the Christian Doppler Forschungsgesellschaft (Grant No. 171).

References

M. P. Berger, W.-K. Wong, 2005. Applied optimal designs. John Wiley & Sons.

R. Brun, M. Kühni, H. Siegrist, W. Gujer, P. Reichert, 2002. Practical identifiability of asm2d parameters—systematic selection and tuning of parameter subsets. Water research 36 (16), 4113–4127.

O. Chiş, J. R. Banga, E. Balsa-Canto, 2011. Genssi: a software toolbox for structural identifiability analysis of biological models. Bioinformatics 27 (18), 2610–2611.

D. J. De Pauw, P. A. Vanrolleghem, 2006. Nesting genetic algorithms to solve a robust optimal experimental design problem.

J. DiStefano III, 2015. Dynamic systems biology modeling and simulation. Academic Press.

Z. Kutalik, K.-H. Cho, O. Wolkenhauer, 2004. Optimal sampling time selection for parameter estimation in dynamic pathway modeling. Biosystems 75 (1-3), 43–55.

L. Mears, S. M. Stocks, M. O. Albaek, G. Sin, K. V. Gernaey, 2017. Mechanistic fermentation models for process design, monitoring, and control. Trends in biotechnology 35 (10), 914–924.

R. Muñoz-Tamayo, P. Martinon, G. Bougaran, F. Mairet, O. Bernard, 2014. Getting the most out of it: optimal experiments for parameter estimation of microalgae growth models. Journal of Process Control 24 (6), 991–1001.

Anton A. Kiss, Edwin Zondervan, Richard Lakerveld, Leyla Özkan (Eds.)
Proceedings of the 29th European Symposium on Computer Aided Process Engineering
June 16th to 19th, 2019, Eindhoven, The Netherlands. © 2019 Elsevier B.V. All rights reserved.
http://dx.doi.org/10.1016/B978-0-128-18634-3.50187-9

On Robustness of Mixed-Integer reformulations of Generalized Disjunctive Programs

Miloš Bogataj[*], Zdravko Kravanja

Faculty of Chemistry and Chemical Engineering, University of Maribor, Smetanova ulica 17, SI-2000 Maribor, Slovenija

milos.bogataj@um.si

Abstract

In this work, we compare the performance of the Alternative Mixed-Integer (AMI) reformulation of GDPs against those of the Big-M and Hull Reformulation (HR) in a framework of nonconvex mixed-integer nonlinear models. The robustness and efficiency of the reformulations are tested on a synthetic example using commercially available solvers, namely SBB, DICOPT++, SCIP, and Alpha-ECP. The comparison is carried out on the following key criteria: efficiency (CPU usage, number of iterations), robustness (number of successfully solved problems), quality of the obtained solutions (comparison of the objective function values). Results obtained in this study indicate that the AMI reformulation represents a competitive alternative to Big-M and HR.

Keywords: Disjunctive Programming, Mixed-Integer Programming, Nonconvex problems, Robustness, and Efficiency.

1. Introduction

The Generalized disjunctive Programs (GDPs), be it linear or nonlinear, can be formulated as mixed-integer (non)linear problems (MI(N)LPs) in several ways (Nemhauser and Wolsey (1988), Lee and Grossmann (2003), Trespalacios and Grossmann (2015)). This, however, leads to models of different sizes (i.e. in a number of variables and constraints) and tightness – tightness being the relation of the feasible region of a problem to the feasible region of its continuous relaxation. Furthermore, when GDPs are nonlinear and nonconvex, the robustness of nonlinear subproblems becomes an important aspect. We can infer that the ability of the solvers to solve these problems strongly depends on the type of reformulation.

The AMI reformulation was originally proposed by Bogataj and Kravanja (2018). The reformulation of a GDP to a MINLP is analogous to the HR presented by Lee and Grossman (2003), as shown below. The Boolean variables are transformed into 0-1 variables y_{ik}, the continuous variables x into disaggregated variables x_{ik}^D and the logical propositions reformulated into a set of linear constraints . There is, however, an important difference between the reformulations. That is, the disaggregated variables x_{ik}^D are not required to be forced to 0 when $y_{ik} = 0$. Instead, due to mixed-integer translation of variables they are forced to arbitrary fixed values x_{ik}^F , which are usually chosen between nonzero lower and upper bounds of the disaggregated variables.

$$\min \ Z = \sum_{ik} c_{ik} + f(x)$$

$$\text{s.t.} \quad h^g(x) \le 0$$

$$\underset{i \in D_k}{\vee} \begin{bmatrix} Y_{ik} \\ g_{ik}(x) \le 0 \\ c_{ik} = \gamma_{ik} \end{bmatrix} \quad k \in K$$

$$\underset{i \in D_k}{\vee} Y_{ik} \quad k \in K$$

$$\Omega(Y) = True$$

$$x \in \mathbb{R}^n, c_{ik} \in \mathbb{R}, Y_{ik} \in \{True, False\}$$

(GDP)

$$\min \ Z = \sum_{ik} y_{ik} \gamma_{ik} + f(x)$$

$$\text{s.t.} \quad h^g(x) \le 0$$

$$x = \sum_{i \in D_k} x_{ik}^{\mathrm{D}} - (1 - y_{ik}) x_{ik}^{\mathrm{F}} \quad k \in K$$

$$g_{ik}(x_{ik}^{\mathrm{D}}) - (1 - y_{ik}) g_{ik}(x_{ik}^{\mathrm{F}}) \le 0 \quad i \in D_k, k \in K$$

$$x_{ik}^{\mathrm{D}} \ge x_{ik}^{\mathrm{D,LO}} y_{ik} + (1 - y_{ik}) x_{ik}^{\mathrm{F}} \quad i \in D_k, k \in K$$

$$x_{ik}^{\mathrm{D}} \le x_{ik}^{\mathrm{D,UP}} y_{ik} + (1 - y_{ik}) x_{ik}^{\mathrm{F}} \quad i \in D_k, k \in K$$

$$Ey \le e$$

$$\sum_{i \in D_k} y_{ik} = 1 \quad k \in K$$

$$x^{\mathrm{LO}} \le x \le x^{\mathrm{UP}}, y_{ik} \in \{0,1\}$$

(AMI)

2. Optimization Problem

The problem used in the study represents a nonconvex variation of the Circles Example by Lee and Grossmann (2000). The GDP formulation of the problem is given by (GDP-NC).

$$\min Z = (x_1 - 3)^2 - (x_2 - 2)^2 + \sum_{k \in K} c_k$$

$$s.t.$$

$$g_j(x_1, x_2) \le 0 \quad j \in J$$

$$\vee_{i \in D_k} \begin{bmatrix} Y_{ik} \\ \breve{h}_{ik}(x_1, x_2) \le 0 \\ \hat{h}_{ik}(x_1, x_2) \ge 0 \\ c_k = \gamma_{ik} \end{bmatrix} \quad k \in K \qquad \text{(GDP-NC)}$$

$$\underset{i \in D_k}{\vee} Y_{ik} \quad k \in K$$

$$\Omega(Y) = True$$

$$x_1^{\mathrm{LO}} \le x_1 \le x_1^{\mathrm{UP}}, \ x_2^{\mathrm{LO}} \le x_2 \le x_2^{\mathrm{UP}}$$

$$c_k \in R^1, Y_{ik} \in \{True, False\}, i \in D_k, k \in K, j \in J$$

It represents a minimization of a nonconvex objective function over disjoint nonconvex feasible regions. These are obtained by intersecting the feasible regions described by convex constraints $\breve{h}_{ik}(x_1, x_2) \equiv (x_1 - \breve{a}_{ik})^2 + (x_2 - \breve{b}_{ik})^2 - \breve{r}_{ik}^2 \le 0$ and their nonconvex counterparts $\hat{h}_{ik}(x_1, x_2) \equiv (x_1 - \hat{a}_{ik})^2 + (x_2 - \hat{b}_{ik})^2 - \hat{r}_{ik}^2 \ge 0$. Feasible regions of $\breve{h}_{ik}(x_1, x_2)$ correspond to the interior of circles with centers at ($x_1 = \breve{a}_{ik}, x_2 = \breve{b}_{ik}$) and radii $\breve{r}_{ik}$, whereas the feasible regions of $\hat{h}_{ik}(x_1, x_2)$ are to the exteriors of the corresponding circles.

The coefficients $\hat{a}_{ik}, \hat{b}_{ik}$ and $\hat{r}_{ik}$ are determined in such a way that the graphical representation of each of the disjoint feasible regions corresponds to either crescent or annulus. The constraints $g_j(x_1, x_2)$ are hyperbolae (i.e. $x_1^2 - x_2^2 + d \leq 0$, $x_1^2 + x_2^2 - e \geq 0$) globally constraining the disjoint feasible regions.

2.1. Numerical Studies

To provide insights into the studied properties of the reformulations, two numerical examples of different sizes with respect to the number of equations, continuous and discrete variables were considered. The GDP representation of the optimization problem was reformulated into a MINLP problem using Big-M, Hull Reformulation and AMI reformulation. The examples were solved using Branch and Bound, Outer Approximation / Equality Relaxation and Extended Cutting Plane algorithms implemented in SBB, SCIP, DICOPT++ and Alpha-ECP solvers. The models were coded in GAMS 25.1.3 and solved on a PC equipped with Intel® Core™ i7-4770 3.40 GHz processor and 16 GB RAM.

The first example is a small instance of (GDP-NC). It is comprised of 6 disjunctions, each having 6 terms. The feasible region is constrained by 2 global constraints. The second example is a larger instance of (GDP-NC), comprised of 2 disjunctions, each having 500 terms. The global constraints were omitted in the latter example. In both, only one term per disjunction can be selected as *True*. The model statistics regarding the MINLPs for the three reformulations is given in Table 1.

Table 1: Model Statistics.

Example 1	**Big - M**	**HR /AMI**
Continuous Variables	49	121
Discrete Variables	36	36
Equations	91	247
Example 2	**Big - M**	**HR /AMI**
Continuous Variables	1,005	3,005
Discrete Variables	1,000	1,000
Equations	2,003	6,007

3. Results

3.1. Example 1

The example was solved with the four solvers from 100 randomly selected starting points - identical in each run for the different solves. The globally optimal objective value for the given example is –95.98, which was determined by Baron.

By comparing the mean values of the objective functions, as shown in Fig 1, we observe that AMI reformulation produces the most compliant results. The weighted average of objective values obtained by the AMI reformulation is –79.91, the weighted average of objective values obtained by the HR –70.57, and –63.67 by the Big-M reformulation.

In terms of robustness (i.e. number of feasible solutions), Big-M reformulation dominates the three formulations, producing 100% feasible solutions. AMI reformulation averaged at 92% and HR at 51%. A more detailed statistics regarding the robustness of the reformulations are presented in Fig. 2.

In terms of efficiency, the HR is computationally the least demanding (see Fig 3). The weighted average CPU time for HR is 1.7 s, which is, however, comparable to the weighted average CPU time for AMI reformulation. The Big-M reformulation averages at slightly longer CPU time of 8.6 s.

Finally, there are a few additional results worth mentioning. In the case of the AMI reformulation, the largest standard deviations in objective function values and CPU time are observed when using AlphaECP solver. SCIP failed in each of the HR instances, however, it provided globally optimal solutions in all the instances of the Big-M formulation.

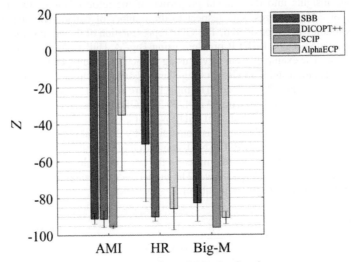

Figure 1: Mean values of objective functions.

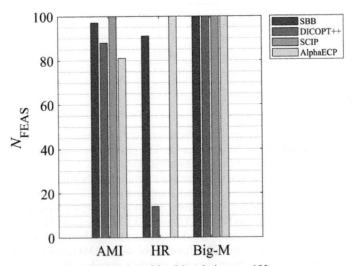

Figure 2: Number of feasible solutions per 100 runs.

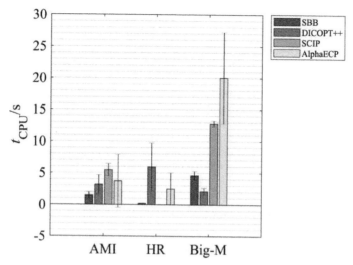

Figure 3: Average computational times.

3.2. Example 2

The example was solved from a starting point that is feasible with respect to the relaxed MINLP of a given reformulation. The CPU time limit was set to 3,000 s. The results are given in Table 2.

Table 2: Statistical results.

Reformulation	Metrics	SBB	DICOPT++	SCIP	AlphaECP
AMI	Z	−128,734	−128,734	−128,734	−95,870
AMI	t_{CPU}/s	96	62	1,632	299
AMI	Nds/Iter	517	14	1,969	274
HR	Z	/	/	−114,809	−41,577
HR	t_{CPU}/s	/	/	3,000	81.5
HR	Nds/Iter	/	/	919,662	114
Big-M	Z	−15,299	141.5	−15,296	−6,872
Big-M	t_{CPU}/s	3,000	35	499	3,000
Big-M	Nds/Iter	40,475	20	9,426	2,700

From the results presented in Table 2 we can conclude that the AMI reformulation outperformed both HR and Big-M reformulation in terms of solution quality and computational efficiency. Note that the CPU time limit was hit in 1 instance of HR (SCIP) and 2 instances of Big-M reformulation (SBB and AlphaECP).

All the solvers utilized in this study provided solutions to the AMI and Big-M reformulation, while two solvers (SBB and DICOPT++) failed to provide solution to the HR because of solver failure.

4. Conclusions

We have presented a study on the performance of the alternative mixed-integer (AMI) reformulation of GDPs against the Big-M and hull reformulation (HR) in a framework nonconvex MINLPs. The result obtained thus far indicate that AMI reformulation exhibits desirable properties that make it favorable for larger nonconvex MINLPs models. Although these results should not be generalized nor considered as conclusive, there are some theoretical indications as to why the AMI reformulation may outperform the other two. First, it tends to reduce the search space of nonlinear subproblems by bounding it to the true lower and upper bounds of continuous variables. Second, the reformulation avoids the usage of the perspective function and thus reduces the number of nonlinearities. Finally, due to the translation of continuous variables, the reformulation does not require the functions being defined at 0.

Future studies will focus on research dedicated to providing theoretical answers regarding the AMI reformulation, and testing it on different optimization/synthesis problems.

Acknowledgements

This research was financially supported by the Slovenian Research Agency (Program P2-0032).

References

G. L. Nemhauser, L. A: Wolsey, 1988, Integer and combinatorial optimization. Wiley-Interscience, Willey.

S. Lee, I. E. Grossmann, 2000, New algorithms for nonlinear generalized disjunctive programming. Computers and Chemical Engineering, 24, 2125–2141.

S. Lee, I. E. Grossmann, 2003, Generalized Convex Disjunctive Programming: Nonlinear Convex Hull Relaxation. Computational Optimization and Applications, 26 (1), 83–100.

F. Trespalacios, I. E. Grossmann, 2015, Improved Big-M reformulation for generalized disjunctive programs. Computers and Chemical Engineering. 76, 98–103.

M. Bogataj, Z. Kravanja, 2018, Alternative mixed-integer reformulation of Generalized Disjunctive Programs, Computer Aided Chemical Engineering, 43, 549–554.

Anton A. Kiss, Edwin Zondervan, Richard Lakerveld, Leyla Özkan (Eds.)
Proceedings of the 29th European Symposium on Computer Aided Process Engineering
June 16th to 19th, 2019, Eindhoven, The Netherlands. © 2019 Elsevier B.V. All rights reserved.
http://dx.doi.org/10.1016/B978-0-128-18634-3.50188-0

A Comparison of Data Reconciliation Tools for Modelling Heat Recovery

Petar Sabev Varbanov[a,*], Jun Yow Yong[b], Jiří Jaromír Klemeš[a],
Zdravko Kravanja[c]

[a]*Sustainable Process Integration Laboratory – SPIL, NETME Centre, Faculty of Mechanical Engineering, Brno University of Technology, Technická 2896/2, 616 00 Brno, Czech Republic.*

[b]*Department of Computer Science and Systems Technology, Faculty of Information Technology, University of Pannonia, Egyetem u. 10, Veszprém, Hungary.*

[c]*University of Maribor, Faculty of Chemistry and Chemical Engineering, Smetanova ulica 17, 2000 Maribor, Slovenia.*

varbanov@fme.vutbr.cz

Abstract

Data Reconciliation is an important step in extracting data from an existing plant. It is especially important for Heat Integration Analysis. In this work, the Iterative PNS Method is introduced as a new method for Heat Exchanger Network Data Reconciliation. This method uses Linear Programming to reduce the computational cost of the complex non-linear data reconciliation problem. The results from the illustrative case study indicate that it performs almost as well as the other state-of-the-art method found in the literature.

Keywords: Heat Exchanger Network, Data Reconciliation, Iterative PNS Method.

1. Introduction

Data extraction is a key activity in performing retrofit of Heat Exchanger Networks (HENs) (Klemeš et al., 2018). It is used to obtain a credible set of data from measurements for the Heat Integration. The topic was briefly mentioned in the HEN synthesis book by Shenoy (1995), providing a non-linear optimisation example. In a previous work (Yong et al., 2016a), an Iterative Method for solving the HEN data reconciliation problem has been proposed. That reduced the model complexity and computational cost required during data reconciliation. VBA tools for energy systems data reconciliation have also been presented (Mayo, 2015). There have been further works – considering rigorous and simplified HEN models (Ijaz et al., 2013), as well as parameter tuning using process-network synthesis (PNS) algorithms (Bartos and Bertok, 2018). Sufficient accuracy of the model with user-friendly data input and acceptable computational time can be key in providing process engineers with a tool for efficient and accurate data extraction.
In this work, a new Iterative PNS Method is derived from the Iterative Method. It uses linear objective functions in the sub-models to reduce the required computational effort. The performance of this method is compared with standard NLP (simultaneous method in this work) and MILP using a linear reformulation.

2. Problem Statement

Consider an existing HEN with total m number of heat exchangers (including heaters and coolers) with m ∈ M. Each hot (H) or cold (C) stream has its own inlet (I) and outlet (O).

These generate a set of streams, s ∈ {HI, HO, CI, CO}. For each stream, n measurements are taken (n ∈ N). For the purpose of heat integration analysis, temperature (T) and heat capacity flowrate (CP) are required. It is desired to obtained the reconciled value (R).

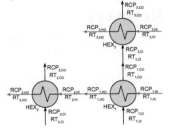

Figure 1: An example of a HEN

3. Models and Equations

3.1. Simultaneous Method

Simultaneous Solving Method

$$Min \sum_{m}^{M} \sum_{s}^{S} \sum_{n}^{N} \left(\left(RCP_{m,s} - CP_{m,s,n}\right)^2 + \left(RT_{m,s} - T_{m,s,n}\right)^2 \right) \tag{1}$$

subject to:

Mass balance constraints around each heat exchanger, for all heat exchanger

$$RCP_{m,HI} = RCP_{m,HO} \tag{2}$$
$$RCP_{m,CI} = RCP_{m,CO} \tag{3}$$

Energy balance constraints around each heat exchanger, for all heat exchanger

$$RCP_{m,HI}\left(RT_{m,HI} - RT_{m,HO}\right) = RCP_{m,CI}\left(RT_{m,CO} - RT_{m,CI}\right) \tag{4}$$

Constraints from network arising from the connections between heat exchangers

$$RCP_{m1,HO} = RCP_{m2,HI} \tag{5}$$
$$RCP_{m1,CO} = RCP_{m3,CI} \tag{6}$$
$$RT_{m1,HO} = RT_{m2,HI} \tag{7}$$
$$RT_{m1,CO} = RT_{m3,CI} \tag{8}$$

Figure 2: Data reconciliation model for solving two types of parameters simultaneously

Eq. (1) contains the objective function, combining CP and T values. Since this is only a numerical abstraction without a direct physical meaning, the mixture of the measurement units is not a problem. While in general, the difference in magnitude may cause the model to be biased on either one of the parameters, in the current model such issues have not arisen. In the future work, appropriate weighting and normalization should be introduced for obtaining more robust models. In the simultaneous method, the model shows high non-linearity from the parameters, constraints and objective function. In the case of parameters, CP is a function of T. To reduce this complexity, it is assumed that CP is independent of T. The energy balance constraints, as in Eq. (4), contain bi-linear terms of the reconciliation variables. These non-linear constraints can be reduced to linear by applying the Iterative Method (Yong et al., 2016a)

3.2. Iterative Method

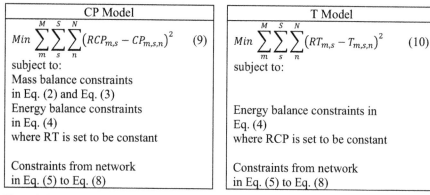

CP Model	T Model
$Min \sum\limits_{m}^{M} \sum\limits_{s}^{S} \sum\limits_{n}^{N} \left(RCP_{m,s} - CP_{m,s,n}\right)^2$ (9)	$Min \sum\limits_{m}^{M} \sum\limits_{s}^{S} \sum\limits_{n}^{N} \left(RT_{m,s} - T_{m,s,n}\right)^2$ (10)
subject to:	subject to:
Mass balance constraints in Eq. (2) and Eq. (3) Energy balance constraints in Eq. (4) where RT is set to be constant	Energy balance constraints in Eq. (4) where RCP is set to be constant
Constraints from network in Eq. (5) to Eq. (8)	Constraints from network in Eq. (5) to Eq. (8)

Figure 3: Equations used in the CP model and T model

The Iterative Method divides the model from the simultaneous method into two sub-models. In each sub-model, the instances of one parameter type are reconciled while the instances of the other type are kept constant. By only considering one type of parameter at a time, the energy balance constraints are reduced to linear. This also solves the problems arising from different magnitudes and dimensions in the Iterative Method. The method first chooses one of the sub-models are the starting model. After obtaining the reconciled parameters, they are used as constants in the other sub-model. This process iterates until the convergences or satisfactory level is met. This method is explained in details in the work of Yong et al. (2016b). However, the models used in the Iterative Method are still non-linear, due to the square operation in the objective function.

3.3. Iterative PNS Method

It should be noted that the purpose of the square operation in the objective function is to remove any negative values arising from large measured values, e.g. when $RCP_{m,s} < CP_{m,s,n}$. This is so that the negative values do not reduce any differences for other $RCP_{m,s} > CP_{m,s,n}$. To reduce this non-linearity, the absolute value is proposed i.e.

CP Model	T Model
$Min \sum\limits_{m}^{M} \sum\limits_{s}^{S} \sum\limits_{n}^{N} \left|RCP_{m,s} - CP_{m,s,n}\right|$ (11)	$Min \sum\limits_{m}^{M} \sum\limits_{s}^{S} \sum\limits_{n}^{N} \left|RT_{m,s} - T_{m,s,n}\right|$ (12)

Figure 4: Objective functions that use absolute value in sub-models.

Using these models following Iterative Method changes to mixed integer linear programming (MILP). As the models call for minimisation, $RCP_{m,s}$ are desired to be as close as to $CP_{m,s,n}$. By applying Process Network Synthesis (PNS) algorithm, these models can be further reduced to just linear programming (LP). Consider the following,

$$Y_{m,s,n} = \left|RCP_{m,s} - CP_{m,s,n}\right| \tag{13}$$

It can be interpreted as

$$Y_{m,s,n} = RCP_{m,s} - CP_{m,s,n} \qquad\qquad \text{for } RCP_{m,s} > CP_{m,s,n} \tag{14}$$
$$Y_{m,s,n} = CP_{m,s,n} - RCP_{m,s} \qquad\qquad \text{for } RCP_{m,s} \le CP_{m,s,n} \tag{15}$$

To apply the PNS algorithm in the models, let

$$RCP_{m,s} = RCP1_{m,s,n} + RCP2_{m,s,n} \tag{16}$$

$RCP_{m,s}$ is the desired product that has a unit cost of 1. Let there be existing ($Y1_{m,s,n}$) and new ($Y2_{m,s,n}$) pre-treatment units. $Y1_{m,s,n}$ is to be fed with streams $RCP1_{m,s,n}$ and vice versa for $Y2_{m,s,n}$. It is assumed that $Y1_{m,s,n}$ has fixed operating cost at $CP_{m,s,n}$ but its capacity is limited at $CP_{m,s,n}$. The $Y2_{m,s,n}$ has only the operating cost of $2 \times RCP2_{m,s,n}$. The net profit is to be

$$ZCP_{m,s,n} = RCP1_{m,s,n} - CP_{m,s,n} + RCP2_{m,s,n} - 2 \times RCP2_{m,s,n}$$
$$= RCP1_{m,s,n} - RCP2_{m,s,n} - CP_{m,s,n}$$

(17)

With the following additional constraint

e (18)

The objective is to maximise the net profit and the objective function for the CP model is

$$Max \sum_{m}^{M} \sum_{s}^{S} \sum_{n}^{N} ZCP_{m,s,n}$$

(18)

Eq. (18) has the same purpose as Eq. (9) in the CP model used in the original Iterative Method. It is to have $RCP_{m,s}$ to be as close as to $CP_{m,s,n}$. The same process is applied for the T model where all CP terms are replaced with T terms. All the equations are linear.

Table 1: Mean values for all the parameters in the illustrative case study.

m	$T_{m,HI}$ (°C)	$T_{m,HO}$ (°C)	$CP_{m,HI}$ (kW/°C)	$CP_{m,HO}$ (kW/°C)	$T_{m,CI}$ (°C)	$T_{m,CO}$ (°C)	$CP_{m,CI}$ (kW/°C)	$CP_{m,CO}$ (kW/°C)
1	184.9	62.0	400.9	399.9	28.6	129.6	498.0	498.3
2	249.6	170.5	501.5	500.9	129.7	210.6	500.1	500.1
3	569.3	369.6	301.1	301.2	210.0	330.1	499.7	500.3
4	410.3	339.3	200.1	200.2	330.9	358.4	501.4	500.5
5	467.9	367.7	299.3	300.1	358.6	418.3	499.5	500.6
6	560.2	524.6	1,000.8	1,000.6	417.8	487.2	500.0	501.1
H1	800.2	700.1	299.5	299.9	488.9	548.3	499.5	499.7
C1	60.3	19.0	299.3	400.1	4.6	9.9	3,197.6	3,199.0
C2	370.9	319.5	302.8	301.2	5.0	9.9	3,000.6	3,000.6

4. An illustrative Case Study

An illustrative case study is used to demonstrate the use of Iterative PNS Method. The HEN is shown in Figure 5. All the measurements are taken at every inlets and outlets of every heat exchangers, heaters and coolers. After sets of measurements are taken repeatedly for a fixed period of time, the outliers are discarded using statistics. Out of these sets of measurements, 10 are chosen to be used as the input data. Table 1 shows the mean value for all the parameters.

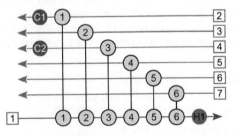

Figure 5: HEN for an illustrative case study

5. Result and Discussion

In this case study, the CP path is chosen and the CP model is to be used first for data reconciliation. Three iterations were done as the work used for comparison in Yong et al. (2016) stopped at third iterations. It should be noted that further iteration can be done to obtain a more accurate result. The percentage difference at this iteration of all the parameters is less than 2 % when compared with the result obtained in the first iteration. Table 2 shows the reconciled values obtained using Iterative PNS Method. The result is compared against mean values, as shown in the percentage difference in Table 3.

Table 2: Reconciled values for all parameters using Iterative PNS Method.

m	$T_{m,HI}$ (°C)	$T_{m,HO}$ (°C)	$CP_{m,HI}$ (kW/°C)	$CP_{m,HO}$ (kW/°C)	$T_{m,CI}$ (°C)	$T_{m,CO}$ (°C)	$CP_{m,CI}$ (kW/°C)	$CP_{m,CO}$ (kW/°C)
1	185.0	62.0	407.3	407.3	28.9	130.0	495.5	495.5
2	250.0	170.8	506.8	506.8	130.0	211.0	495.5	495.5
3	568.1	370.0	297.9	297.9	211.0	330.1	495.5	495.5
4	411.0	339.0	192.0	192.0	330.1	358.0	495.5	495.5
5	469.0	368.3	295.2	295.2	358.0	418.0	495.5	495.5
6	560.9	525.0	967.5	967.5	418.0	488.1	495.5	495.5
H1	801.0	700.0	293.9	293.9	488.1	548.0	495.5	495.5
C1	62.0	18.0	407.3	407.3	4.0	9.6	3,200.0	3,200.0
C2	370.0	319.0	297.9	297.9	5.0	9.9	3,100.6	3,100.6

Table 3: Residual differences (in %) of all reconciled parameters when compared to mean values.

m	$\Delta T_{m,HI}$	$\Delta T_{m,HO}$	$\Delta CP_{m,HI}$	$\Delta CP_{m,HO}$	$\Delta T_{m,CI}$	$\Delta T_{m,CO}$	$\Delta CP_{m,CI}$	$\Delta CP_{m,CO}$
1	0.05	0.00	1.59	1.86	1.09	0.31	-0.50	-0.56
2	0.16	0.18	1.05	1.18	0.23	0.19	-0.92	-0.92
3	-0.22	0.11	-1.06	-1.10	0.48	0.00	-0.84	-0.95
4	0.17	-0.09	-4.05	-4.09	-0.24	-0.11	-1.18	-0.99
5	0.24	0.16	-1.36	-1.61	-0.17	-0.07	-0.80	-1.02
6	0.13	0.08	-3.32	-3.30	0.05	0.18	-0.90	-1.11
H1	0.10	-0.01	-1.88	-2.01	-0.17	-0.05	-0.80	-0.83
C1	2.82	-5.26	2.00	1.79	-13.04	-2.56	0.08	0.03
C2	-0.24	-0.16	-1.62	-1.10	0.00	-0.38	3.33	3.33

From the result, most of the reconciled parameters have values of less than 5 %. Although the reconciled inlet cold stream temperature for C1 only differs by 0.6 °C from 4.6 °C, it has a difference of 13 %. Most of the parameters with high percentage differences are having low value. Another parameter, although has 3 % difference, the reconciled cold stream CP for C2 differs by 100 kW/°C from 3,000 kW/°C. This is a good level of residual errors, comparable with typical values (Romagnoli and Sánchez, 2000) and a recent refinery study (Mayo, 2015). An error level of up to 5 % is very good for the purpose of Heat Integration, where energy savings of 10 % or more would warrant credible investments, while for performing operation optimisation this level may be too high, as the expected cost improvements are of the order 2-5 %.

The results obtained are also compared with results from the simultaneous method and Iterative Method, as shown in Figure 6. From this case study, it can be seen that the Iterative PNS Method performs almost as well as the Iterative Method with less than 10 parameters having higher percentage difference. It is speculated that having a square operation in Iterative Method poses a heavier penalty on outliers. As expected, the simultaneous method performs the best out of these three methods at the cost of high computational cost.

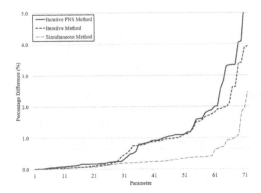

Figure 6: Comparison of three different methods.

6. Conclusions

An Iterative PNS Method is introduced in this work for HEN data reconciliation. It applies the Process Network Synthesis (PNS) Algorithm to augment the previous Iterative Method. In both of the sub-models, the objective functions are reduced from non-linear to linear, thus, it is completely solvable with Linear Programming (LP). Demonstration from an illustrative case study showed that the Iterative PNS Method is performing almost as well as the Iterative Method in terms of precision, at a reduced computational cost.

Acknowledgement

This research has been supported by the EU project "Sustainable Process Integration Laboratory – SPIL", project No. CZ.02.1.01/0.0/0.0/15_003/0000456 funded by EU "CZ Operational Programme Research, Development and Education", Priority 1: Strengthening capacity for quality research, in a collaboration with the University of Maribor, Slovenia.

References

A. Bartos, B. Bertok, 2018. Parameter tuning for a cooperative parallel implementation of process-network synthesis algorithms. Central European Journal of Operations Research. DOI: 10.1007/s10100-018-0576-1.

H. Ijaz, U.M.K. Ati, V. Mahalec, 2013. Heat exchanger network simulation, data reconciliation & optimization. Applied Thermal Engineering 52, 328–335

J.J. Klemeš, P.S. Varbanov, S.R. Wan Alwi, Z.A. Manan, 2018. Process Integration and Intensification: Saving Energy, Water and Resources, 2nd ed, de Gruyter Berlin, Germany.

C.M. Mayo, 2015. Process Stream Data Analysis: Data Reconciliation and Gross Error Detection for Process Integration Studies (MSc Dissertation). Chalmers University of Technology, Göteborg, Sweden.

J.A. Romagnoli, M.C. Sánchez, 2000, Data processing and reconciliation for chemical process operations, Process systems engineering. Academic Press, San Diego, CA, USA.

U.V. Shenoy, 1995. Heat exchanger network synthesis: Process optimization by energy and resource analysis. Gulf Pub., Houston, USA.

J.Y. Yong, A. Nemet, P.S. Varbanov, Z. Kravanja, J.J. Klemeš, 2016. Data reconciliation for Total Site Integration. Chemical Engineering Transactions 1045–1050. DOI: 10.3303/CET1652175.

J.Y. Yong, A. Nemet, M. Bogataj, Ž. Zore, P.S. Varbanov, Z. Kravanja, J.J. Klemeš, 2016b, Data reconciliation for energy system flowsheets, Computer Aided Chemical Engineering, 38, 2277–2282.

Anton A. Kiss, Edwin Zondervan, Richard Lakerveld, Leyla Özkan (Eds.)
Proceedings of the 29th European Symposium on Computer Aided Process Engineering
June 16th to 19th, 2019, Eindhoven, The Netherlands. © 2019 Elsevier B.V. All rights reserved.
http://dx.doi.org/10.1016/B978-0-128-18634-3.50189-2

Assessment of the dominant factors during hydroprocessing stabilization

Ngoc Yen Phuong Cao,[a] Benoit Celse,[a,*] Denis Guillaume,[a] Isabelle Guibard,[a] Joris W.Thybaut[b]

[a]*IFP Energies nouvelles, Rond-point de l'échangeur de Solaize, BP 3, 69360 Solaize, France*

[b]*Ghent University, Laboratory for Chemical Technology, Technologiepark 914, Ghent, B-9052, Belgium*

benoit.celse@ifp.fr

Abstract

Establishing the steady state in hydrotreating process requires several days, leading to long experimentation times in order to obtain sufficient steady-state data for kinetic modelling. However, during the evolution towards this steady state, effluent analyses are already carried out at regular time intervals to determine whether the steady state has been reached and to ensure that the reaction is under control. In this paper, the stabilization time was assessed by using experimental data during these transient conditions. The stabilization evolution is supposed to follow a first-order response. A characteristic time for stabilization τ was defined. A linear model with interaction for τ prediction was developed. It was found that a higher LHSV leads to a quicker stabilization. The extent of the impact of LHSV on τ depends on the feed resin content, i.e., the polar components with high molecule weight. A direct relationship between reactor pressure and stabilization time was found. Temperature is not a dominant factor. Stabilization of spent catalyst depends on the previous operating conditions.

Moreover, online transient data can be used in order to predict, from the first two experimental points and τ calculated by the model, the future steady-state value. By testing against new data with other feedstocks, the model has been found to provide a good prediction of the stabilization evolution and the steady-state hydrotreating performance. If this value is far from the target, operators can change the operating condition without waiting for stabilization.

Keywords: hydrocarbon, hydrotreating, kinetic modelling, reactor, stabilization, transient data.

1. Introduction

Hydrotreating is a catalytic conversion process in petroleum refining, among others for removing impurities such as nitrogen and sulphur compounds from hydrocarbon streams. A kinetic model is a significant asset in, not to say essential for the adequate design and simulation of such a process (Becker et al., 2015). It is usually developed based on experimental data acquired at steady-state conditions. One of the main challenges of hydrotreating process is that establishing this steady state typically requires several days, leading to long experimentation times in order to obtain sufficient data for kinetic modelling. However, during the transient phase towards the steady state, effluent analyses are already carried out at regular time intervals to detect the steady state and to ensure that the reaction is under control. These available transient data are currently not used for kinetic modelling because the stabilization behaviour is not well understood.

The aim of this work is, first, to get a better understanding of the stabilization behaviour during these transient conditions and secondly, to use these transient data to predict the steady-state reaction performance. If this value is far from a target, the operators can change the operating condition without waiting for stabilization and without the use of a complex model.

2. Materials & Methods

The experimental data are acquired using the IFPEN Hydrotreatment (HDT) pilot plant operating in a continuous manner. The total catalyst volume in the reactor amounts to 50 cm^3. Operating conditions are adjusted after having reached the steady state corresponding with the previous operating conditions. The acquired data cover 11 Vacuum Gas Oil (VGO) feeds over two catalysts. Operating conditions were chosen to cover a wide range for the VGO HDT process: Liquid Hourly Space Velocities (LHSV) from 0.5 to 4 h^{-1}, temperature from 350 to 410 °C and total pressure between 50 and 140 bar. The provided data are the 'liquid product nitrogen content' (N) with time on stream (TOS), totalling 920 measurements, see Figure 1. A series of points corresponding to one experimental run is called one 'episode'. Figure 1 shows 7 episodes corresponding to 42 data points during around 45 days.

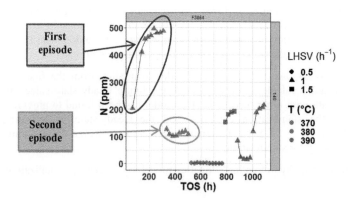

Figure 1. Data representation (P = 140 bar, point: experimental data, solid line: model fitting Equation (1))

A hydrodynamics study on the pilot plant has been carried out using a tracer technique to estimate the stabilization time purely due to hydrodynamic. The objective is to identify whether the stabilization time is determined by hydrodynamic or kinetic phenomena.

Exploratory data analysis (Tukey, 1977) is applied to our available data to assess the stabilization evolution. It resulted in a first-order transfer function as shown in Equation (1).

$$N = N_{init} + \left(N_{final} - N_{init}\right)\left(1 - \exp\left(\frac{-\left(TOS - TOS_{init}\right)}{\tau}\right)\right)$$

(1)

Where N is the liquid product nitrogen at a specific time on stream (ppm); N_{init} is the liquid product nitrogen corresponding to the first experimental point of episode (ppm); N_{final} is the last experimental point of episode (ppm); TOS is the time on stream (h); TOS_{init} is the time on stream corresponding to the first experimental point of episode (h) and τ is the characteristic time of the episode (h).

The characteristic time τ of each episode presented in the equation is estimated via nonlinear least-squares (solid line in Figure 1).

A multiple linear regression with interaction technique is then used for τ prediction to evaluate the phenomena underlying the transient data. The general linear model with interaction is illustrated in Equation (2):

$$\tau = a_1 x_1 + a_2 x_2 + a_{12} x_1 x_2 + \ldots + b$$

(2)

Where x_1, x_2 are the input variables, which can be LHSV, temperature, pressure or feed properties such as organic nitrogen content, organic sulphur content, resin content in feed, etc.; $x_1 x_2$ is the interaction term between x_1 and x_2; a_1, a_2, a_{12},... and b are the coefficients.

The most influential input variables of the model are determined via variable selection technique called 'leaps' (Furnival and Wilson, 1974). Fitting linear model and nonlinear model was done by using respectively 'lm' and 'nls' function in 'stats' package in R software. Variable selection was carried out in R by using 'leaps' package obtained from CRAN repository (Lumley, 2017).

The model is then tested against new data with other feedstocks. For each episode, τ is predicted by the model. Knowing τ and the first two points of the episode, it is possible to predict the evolution of the episode as well as the Nitrogen content at steady state calculated via Equation (3) which is developed from Equation (1). The leftover data of the episode are used to validate the model. If the predicted steady-state value is far from the target, the operating condition can be adjusted without waiting for stabilization.

$$N_{final} = \frac{N - N_{init}}{1 - \exp\left(\frac{-\left(TOS - TOS_{init}\right)}{\tau}\right)} + N_{init}$$

(3)

3. Results

The hydrodynamic response to a tracer step reached steady state significantly faster than the stabilization of the HydroDeNitrogenation (HDN) behaviour. Hence, chemical phenomena are involved in the latter.

Stabilization was found to follow a first-order model, which is similar to the observation of Sau et al. (2005) in the study of effect of organic nitrogen compounds on hydroprocessing reaction. The characteristic time τ reflects the time required to reach this steady state. First episodes take more time to stabilize than other episodes. The model was applied on two similar HDT catalysts (Catalyst A and B). Two linear models for τ were built; one for first episodes (model M1) and another for other episodes (model M2).

Model M1 was obtained with a R^2 of 0.83, as shown in the left side of Figure 2. It consists of three variables (LHSV, pressure, resin of feed) and one interaction term LHSV*resin, which are selected by the leaps algorithm. An inverse relationship between LHSV and τ was found. Temperature is not a dominant factor. These two results are coherent with Elizalde et al. (2016) who studied the dynamic behaviour of hydrocracking using the continuous kinetic lumping approach. A direct relationship between pressure and τ was observed. The interaction term shows that the impact of LHSV on τ depends on the value of feed resin, i.e., the polar components with high molecular weight. The resin in VGO can contain nitrogen.

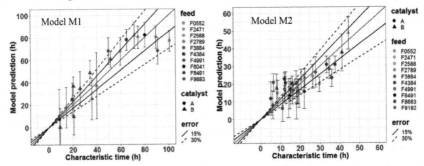

Figure 2. Parity plot with 95% confidence interval for M1 (left, $R^2 = 0.83$) and M2 (right, $R^2 = 0.66$)

However, the stabilization of other episodes seems more complex. The parity plot for model M2 is shown in the right side of Figure 2. The latter includes seven input variables (LHSV$_{exp}$, LHSV$_{pre}$, T$_{pre}$, $\dfrac{LHSV_{exp}}{LHSV_{pre}}$, $\dfrac{LHSV_{pre}}{LHSV_{exp}}$, LHSV$_{exp}$*resin, S$_{feed}$);

where LHSV$_{exp}$ is the experimental LHSV of the episode; LHSV$_{pre}$ and T$_{pre}$ are respectively LHSV and temperature of the previous episode; resin and S$_{feed}$ are respectively resin content and organic sulphur content in the feed. As can be seen, the model relies by not only on the feed and operating conditions but also on the operating conditions of the previous episode. It shows that the transient behaviour of spent catalyst is more difficult to predict than for the fresh catalyst.

Model was tested by using new data with other feedstocks. τ is predicted by the model and the steady-state value is estimated via Equation (3). Figure 3 shows two examples of such prediction for first episodes (model M1). The two first points of episode which are used to estimate the steady-state value are shown in circle shape. The remaining data in the episode are represented by triangles. The Nitrogen predicted values are very close to the experimental values. The model can predict quite well the transient behaviour and the steady-state value. This algorithm may be linked to an Advanced Process Control method to reach as fast as possible some Nitrogen targets.

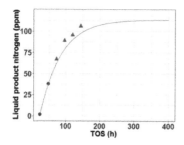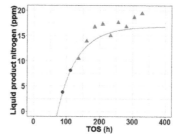

Figure 3. Two examples of the prediction of model M1 (points: experimental data, solid line: model prediction; TOS: time on stream)

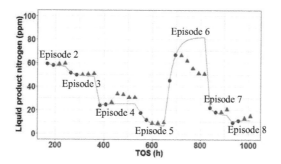

Figure 4. Prediction of model M2 (points: experimental data, solid line: model prediction; TOS: time on stream)

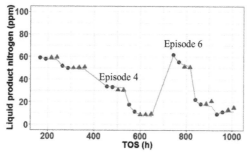

Figure 5. Prediction of model M2 for episode 4 and episode 6 while discarding the first three experimental points of both episodes

Model M2 (for other episodes) is evaluated and is shown in Figure 4. Model predicts well the evolution of episode 2, 3, 5, 7 and 8. Regarding episode 4 and 6, it seems that the transient behaviour did not follow a first-order model, which could be explained by the measurement error/experiment problem or the complex behaviour of spent catalyst. The experimentation duration is longer for these both episodes than for the others. It is possible that there was an experiment problem. If the first three points of episode 4 and 6 are discarded, the prediction is more reliable, see Figure 5. This might be investigated in another study.

4. Conclusions

Stabilization behaviour is a critical point for hydroprocessing experiments. In this work, transient data of hydrotreating process were used to assess this stabilization. It is shown that the stabilization follows the first-order model. A characteristic time for stabilization τ was defined. Two models (one for the first episodes, another for the others) were built to calculate the stabilization time and identify the most influential parameters (LHSV, resin of feed, pressure). Good prediction results were obtained, particularly for the first episodes. The stabilization of other episodes is more complicated to predict.

The model can predict the stabilization time and steady-state value from two initial measures. If the predicted steady-state value would be far from the intended target, operators can change the operating condition without waiting for stabilization. This model will be linked with an Advanced Process Control Algorithm.

This model will be also linked to design of experiment algorithm in order to be used to fit kinetic parameters (Celse et al., 2016).

References

P.J. Becker, B. Celse, D. Guillaume, H. Dulot, V. Costa, 2015, Hydrotreatment modeling for a variety of VGO feedstocks: A continuous lumping approach, Fuel, 139, 133-143.

B. Celse, J.J. Da Costa, V. Costa, 2016, Experimental Design in Nonlinear Case Applied to Hydrocracking Model: How Many Points Do We Need and Which Ones?, International Journal of Chemical Kinetics, 48, 11, 660-670.

I. Elizalde, F. Trejo, J.A.D. Muñoz, P. Torres, J. Ancheyta, Dynamic modeling and simulation of a bench-scale reactor for the hydrocracking of heavy oil by using the continuous kinetic lumping approach, Reaction Kinetics, Mechanisms and Catalysis, 2016, 118, 1, 299-311. DOI: 10.1007/s11144-016-0995-8.

J. J. Faraway, Linear Models with R, Taylor & Francis Group, New York, United States, 2014.

G. M. Furnival, R.W. Wilson, 1974, Jr, Regressions by Leaps and Bounds, Technometrics, 499-511.

T. Lumley, based on Fortran code by A. Miller, 2017, Package 'leaps': Regression subset selection, including exhaustive search, https://cran.r-project.org/web/packages/leaps/leaps.pdf.

R Core Team and contributors worldwide, Package 'stats': R statistical functions.

M. Sau, K. Basak, U. Manna, M. Santra, R. P. Verma, Effects of organic nitrogen compounds on hydrotreating and hydrocracking reactions, Catalysis Today, 2005, 109, 1-4, 112-119. DOI: 10.1016/j.cattod.2005.08.007.

J. W. Tukey, 1977, Exploratory Data Analysis, Addison-Wesley, Reading, MA.

Printed and bound by CPI Group (UK) Ltd, Croydon, CR0 4YY

03/10/2024

01040329-0006